D0406909

THE MATHEMATICS OF

PHYSICS AND CHEMISTRY

VOLUME TWO

BY

HENRY MARGENAU

Eugene Higgins Professor of Physics and Natural Philosophy
Yale University

and

GEORGE MOSELEY MURPHY

Head, Department of Chemistry
Washington Square College
New York University

D. VAN NOSTRAND COMPANY, INC.

PRINCETON, NEW JERSEY

TORONTO LONDON

NEW YORK

D. VAN NOSTRAND COMPANY, INC.
120 Alexander St., Princeton, New Jersey (*Principal office*)
24 West 40 Street, New York 18, New York

D. VAN NOSTRAND COMPANY, LTD.
358, Kensington High Street, London, W.14, England

D. VAN NOSTRAND COMPANY (Canada), LTD.
25 Hollinger Road, Toronto 16, Canada

Published simultaneously in Canada by
D. VAN NOSTRAND COMPANY (Canada), LTD.

PRINTED IN THE UNITED STATES OF AMERICA

PREFACE

This book has been conceived as a companion volume of *The Mathematics of Physics And Chemistry*. Two decades have passed since the publication of that book, and during this interval the demands for mathematical knowledge laid by the physical sciences upon their students have both shifted and increased. The early book has become incomplete in its offerings for the student of today, and we have sought to remove this fault.

Unquestionably the best way to achieve that end would have been to rewrite the book, to expand its size and its scope, along some lines which are still unconventional but hold out promise for future interest. The prospect of undertaking this frightened us. Also, we acknowledge that there already exists a monumental treatise of this elaborate sort, dedicated to the standard parts of the newer mathematics, in the work of Morse and Feshbach, whose excellence would be hard to approach. We, therefore, decided upon the less ambitious course of editing a work which offers what we regard as the most important components of today's useful mathematics in separate chapters written chiefly by experts.

We do not underestimate the difficulties inherent in this task. The heterogeneity of highly composite books, in spite of the present vogue which spawns them, always impairs their usefulness and certainly detracts from their teachability. Nor is there a way of avoiding this difficulty. One confronts here the principle of complementarity for editorial surveillance. Written in the form of an uncertainty relation, that principle reads

$$\triangle E \cdot \triangle T \geqq H$$

where $\triangle E$ is the uncertainty in the esteem an editor enjoys among his contributors, $\triangle T$ a measure of the lack of uniformity of treatment, style and symbolism in different parts of the book, and H is a great deal larger than Planck's constant. (In general H is not a constant, but a function of the contributors' prestige, ranging from small values for modest writers almost to infinity for prima donnas.) If the reader understands these facts he will have the correct perspective on the present volume.

The preparation of a collaborative work such as this requires more human understanding, generous handling and skillful strategy on the part of the publisher than any book of single authorship. We were most fortunate in having a monitor who displayed an abundance of all these qualities in Mr. W. Minrath, Vice President of the Van Nostrand Company, and we want to thank him above all for his unfailing help and his good will.

Henry Margenau
George M. Murphy

CONTENTS

CHAPTER 1

TRANSPORT THEORY OF GASES

by

DAVID MINTZER

Department of Mechanical Engineering and Astronautical Sciences, Technological Institute, Northwestern University, Evanston, Illinois

1.1. Introduction.—Statistical physics deals with the relation between the macroscopic laws that describe the internal state of a system and the dynamics of the interactions of its microscopic constituents. The derivation of the nonequilibrium macroscopic laws, such as those of hydrodynamics, from the microscopic laws has not been developed as generally as in the equilibrium case (the derivation of thermodynamic relations by equilibrium statistical mechanics). The microscopic analysis of nonequilibrium phenomena, however, has achieved a considerable degree of success for the particular case of dilute gases. In this case, the *kinetic theory*, or *transport theory*, allows one to relate the transport of matter or of energy, for example (as in diffusion, or heat flow, respectively), to the mechanics of the molecules that make up the system.

In kinetic theory, the macroscopic quantities are found as averages over the motion of many molecules; each molecular event is assumed to take place over a microscopic time interval, so that a measurement that is made over a macroscopic time interval involves many molecules. The kinetic description is, therefore, a probabilistic one in that assumptions are made about the motion of one molecule and the results of this motion are averaged over all of the molecules of the gas, giving proper weight to the probability that the various molecules of the gas can have the assumed motion.

In its most elementary aspects, kinetic theory is developed on the basis of a hard sphere model of the particles (atoms or molecules) making up the gas.[1] The assumption is made that the particles are uniformly distributed in space and that all have the same speed, but that there are equal numbers of particles moving parallel to each coordinate axis. This last assumption allows one to take averages over

[1] J. O. Hirschfelder, C. F. Curtiss, and R. B. Bird, *Molecular Theory of Gases and Liquids*, pp. 8 ff., John Wiley and Sons, Inc., New York, 1954.

the direction of motion of the particles, and thus, to obtain a statistical description of gross effects. This simple model is found to give results that are reasonable approximations to the macroscopic laws they attempt to describe. Aside from being unrealistic conceptually, however, the very simplicity of the model prevents calculation of many phenomena of interest.

In its more advanced aspects, kinetic theory is based upon a description of the gas in terms of the probability of a particle having certain values of coordinates and velocity, at a given time. Particle interactions are developed by the ordinary laws of mechanics, and the results of these are averaged over the probability distribution. The probability distribution function that is used for a given macroscopic physical situation is determined by means of an equation, the *Boltzmann transport equation*, which describes the space, velocity, and time changes of the distribution function in terms of collisions between particles. This equation is usually solved to give the distribution function in terms of certain macroscopic functions; thus, the macroscopic conditions imposed upon the gas are taken into account in the probability function description of the microscopic situation.

1.2. Distribution Function.—Let us denote a point in space, having rectangular coordinates (x,y,z), by $\mathbf{r}$; the differential volume element $dxdydz$ will be represented by $d\mathbf{r}$. Similarly, the velocity (or point in velocity space) $\mathbf{v}$ will have rectangular components (v_x,v_y,v_z); the volume element in velocity space, $dv_xdv_ydv_z$, will be represented by $d\mathbf{v}$. If dN is the number of particles which are in the differential volume $d\mathbf{r}$, at $\mathbf{r}$, and have their velocities in the range $d\mathbf{v}$, at $\mathbf{v}$, then the *distribution function* is defined by:

$$dN = f(\mathbf{r},\mathbf{v},t)d\mathbf{r}d\mathbf{v} \tag{1–1}$$

The differential lengths and velocities considered must be small compared with the macroscopic distances and velocity intervals over which there are significant changes in the gross properties of the gas. On the other hand, they must be sufficiently large so that there are a large number of particles contained in the differential space-velocity volume; this allows $f(\mathbf{r},\mathbf{v},t)$ to be a continuous function of its variables.[2]

If Eq. (1–1) is integrated over all of velocity space ($-\infty \leq v_x,v_y,v_z \leq \infty$, in general), then the number of particles in the volume $d\mathbf{r}$, at $\mathbf{r}$,

[2] The definition of the distribution function can best be made in terms of an ensemble average (see H. Margenau and G. M. Murphy, *The Mathematics of Physics and Chemistry*, 2nd Ed., p. 442, D. Van Nostrand Co., Inc., Princeton, N.J., 1956), and a connection can be made with the Liouville theorem of statistical mechanics. Cf. H. Grad, "Principles of the Kinetic Theory of Gases," *Handbuch der Physik*, Vol. XII, pp. 206 ff., Springer Verlag, Berlin, 1958.

is obtained; this gives the number of particles per unit volume, or the number density, as:

$$n(\mathbf{r},t) = \int f(\mathbf{r},\mathbf{v},t)d\mathbf{v} \tag{1-2}$$

For a gas consisting of only one constituent, of mass m, the mass density is

$$\rho(\mathbf{r},t) = mn(\mathbf{r},t) \tag{1-3}$$

1.3. Two-Particle Collisions.—One of the basic assumptions in the derivation of the Boltzmann equation is that the gas being described is sufficiently dilute so that only two-particle collisions are of importance. The mechanics of a two-body encounter will thus be described in order

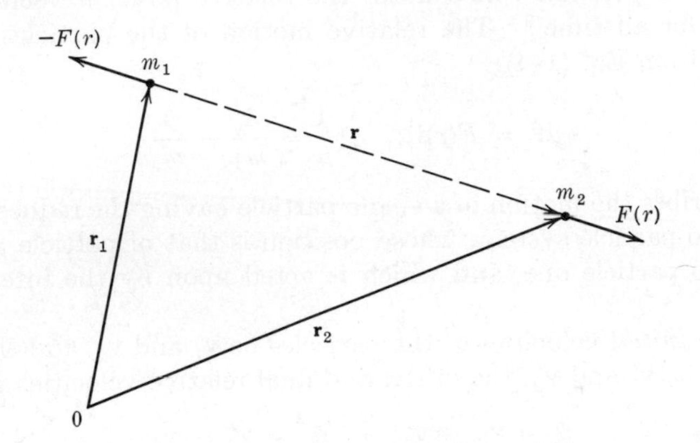

FIG. 1–1. The Two-Particle Encounter.

to derive a relation for the angle of deflection of the particles from their paths before the encounter, in terms of the relative velocity of the particles and their impact parameter, which will be defined shortly.

It is assumed that the particles, which have no internal degrees of freedom, interact through a central force field, that is, the interparticle force depends only upon the distance between the particles, and acts along the line connecting them. Since we are restricting the system to collisions between only two particles at a time, the force is assumed to have a finite range. To a good degree of approximation, this means that the force decreases with distance sufficiently rapidly so that it has negligible effect on the motion at distances of the order of the interparticle spacing ($\sim n^{-1/3}$). If the particles, of mass m_1 and m_2, are at the positions $\mathbf{r}_1$ and $\mathbf{r}_2$ with respect to some origin, the equations of motion are (see Fig. 1–1):

$$m_1\ddot{\mathbf{r}}_1 = -F(r)\mathbf{i}_r; \qquad m_2\ddot{\mathbf{r}}_2 = F(r)\mathbf{i}_r$$
$$\mathbf{r} = \mathbf{r}_2 - \mathbf{r}_1; \qquad r = |\mathbf{r}|; \qquad \mathbf{i}_r = \mathbf{r}/|\mathbf{r}| \tag{1-4}$$

where $F(r)$ is the magnitude of the force on particle two due to particle one. Any external force acting on the particles is assumed not to vary over the distances or times involved in the collision, so that the relative motion of the particles is unaffected by the external force. The effect of the external force will be assumed to be small, compared with the interaction forces during a collision, and will be neglected here; thus, the center of mass of the system moves with constant velocity. The plane formed by the relative velocity of the particles and the line joining their position will contain the relative position vector of the particles for all time.[3] The relative motion of the particles may be obtained from Eq. (1–4):

$$\mu\ddot{\mathbf{r}} = F(r)\mathbf{i}_r; \qquad \frac{1}{\mu} = \frac{1}{m_1} + \frac{1}{m_2} \tag{1-5}$$

This describes the motion of a single particle having the reduced mass[4] of the two-particle system, whose position is that of particle two with respect to particle one, and which is acted upon by the interparticle force.

Let the *initial* velocities of the particles be $\mathbf{v}_1$ and $\mathbf{v}_2$, and their *final* velocities be $\mathbf{v}_1'$ and $\mathbf{v}_2'$; the initial and final relative velocities will be

$$\mathbf{g} = \mathbf{v}_2 - \mathbf{v}_1; \qquad \mathbf{g}' = \mathbf{v}_2' - \mathbf{v}_1' \tag{1-6}$$

The velocity of the center of mass $\mathbf{G}$ is the same before and after the collision:

$$\mathbf{G} = \frac{m_1\mathbf{v}_1 + m_2\mathbf{v}_2}{m_1 + m_2} = \mathbf{G}' \tag{1-7}$$

If, as in Fig. 1–2, we describe the relative motion in the plane by means of polar coordinates (r,θ), conservation of energy requires:

$$\tfrac{1}{2}\mu(\dot{r}^2 + r^2\dot{\theta}^2) + V(r) = \tfrac{1}{2}\mu g^2 = \tfrac{1}{2}\mu g'^2;$$
$$g = |\mathbf{g}|; \qquad g' = |\mathbf{g}'| \tag{1-8}$$

[3] R. B. Lindsay, *Concepts and Methods of Theoretical Physics*, pp. 73–4, D. Van Nostrand Co., Inc., Princeton, N.J., 1951.

[4] H. Margenau and G. M. Murphy, *The Mathematics of Physics and Chemistry*, p. 413, D. Van Nostrand Co., Inc., Princeton, N.J., 1956.

where $V(r)$ is the potential associated with the interparticle force: $F(r) = -\partial V/\partial r$. Here, the total energy has been set equal to the initial kinetic energy, and to the final kinetic energy, since, by the assumption of a finite range of force, V is zero at the beginning and at the end of a collision. We see, therefore, that the relative velocity after collision is equal to the relative velocity before collision rotated through the angle χ of Fig. 1–2.

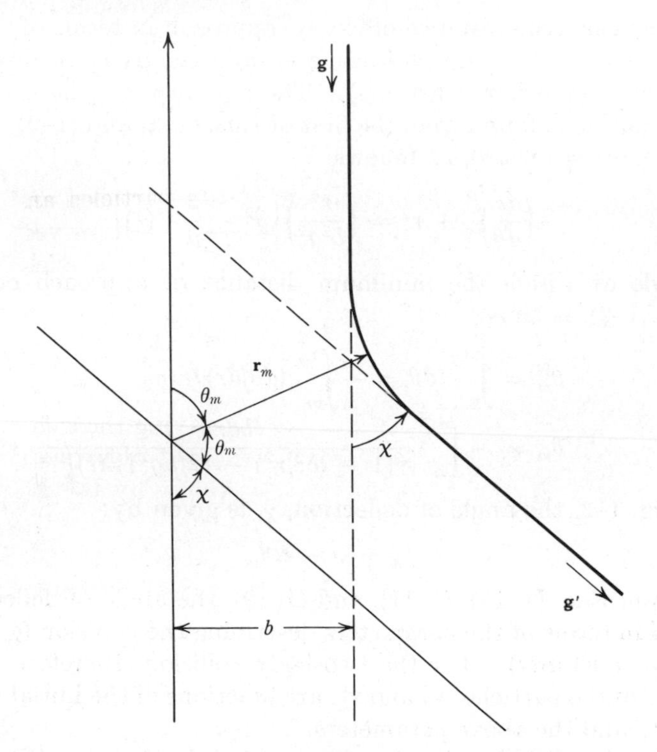

FIG. 1–2. Geometry of a Collision in a Central Force Field.

The impact parameter, b, is defined to be the perpendicular distance between the initial relative path (along $\mathbf{g}$) and the line parallel to $\mathbf{g}$ through the force center (b would be the distance of closest approach of the particles, if there were no interaction); the initial angular momentum is just μbg. Conservation of angular momentum [5] is thus:

$$\mu r^2 \dot{\theta} = \mu bg = \mu bg' \tag{1–9}$$

where $\mu bg'$ is the final angular momentum [note that $g' = g$ from

[5] R. B. Lindsay, *loc. cit.*

Eq. (1–8)]. The orbit is symmetric about a line through the force center that bisects the angle between the initial and final relative paths (the line $\mathbf{r}_m$ of Fig. 1–2).

The distance of closest approach, r_m, is obtained by using the first of Eq. (1–9) in the first of Eq. (1–8), and setting $\dot{r} = 0$. Thus we find:

$$\frac{b^2}{r_m^2} = 1 - \frac{V(r_m)}{\frac{1}{2}\mu g^2} \tag{1–10}$$

This determines the distance of closest approach in terms of the initial relative velocity, the impact parameter, and the dynamical quantities (masses and force law constants). The equation for the orbit of the relative motion is found from the first of Eqs. (1–8) and (1–9), using the identity $(\dot{r}/\dot{\theta}) = (dr/d\theta)$, as follows:

$$\left(\frac{dr}{d\theta}\right)^2 + r^2 = \left(\frac{r^4}{b^2g^2}\right)\left[g^2 - \frac{2}{\mu}V(r)\right]$$

The angle at which the minimum distance of approach occurs, θ_m (see Fig. 1–2), is thus:

$$\theta_m = \int_0^{\theta_m} d\theta = -\int_\infty^{r_m} (d\theta/dr)dr$$

$$\therefore\ \theta_m = -\int_\infty^{r_m} \frac{bdr}{r^2[1 - (b^2/r^2) - (2/\mu g^2)V(r)]^{1/2}} \tag{1–11}$$

From Fig. 1–2, the angle of deflection, χ, is given by:

$$\chi = \pi - 2\theta_m \tag{1–12}$$

Thus, from Eqs. (1–10), (1–11), and (1–12), the angle of deflection can be found in terms of the parameters describing the collision (g, b, μ, and the force constants). For the two-body collision, therefore, the final velocities of the particles, $\mathbf{v}_1'$ and $\mathbf{v}_2'$, are functions of the initial velocities $\mathbf{v}_1$ and $\mathbf{v}_2$, and the above parameters.

1.4. Angle of Deflection for Some Simple Cases.—If, as is often assumed for simplicity, the interparticle force law is given by

$$F(r) = \frac{K}{r^\nu}, \qquad \nu \geq 3 \tag{1–13}$$

the equations may be written in a simple form. Defining:

$$\beta = b/r; \quad \beta_0 = b/r_m; \quad b_0 = b(\mu g^2/K)^{1/(\nu-1)} \tag{1–14}$$

we have, from Eq. (1–10):

$$1 - \beta_0^2 - \frac{2}{\nu - 1}(\beta_0/b_0)^{\nu-1} = 0 \tag{1–15}$$

and, from Eqs. (1–11) and (1–12)

$$\chi(b_0) = \pi - 2\int_0^{\beta_0} \left[1 - \beta^2 - \frac{2}{\nu - 1}(\beta/b_0)^{\nu-1}\right]^{-1/2} d\beta \qquad (1\text{–}16)$$

One determines β_0 from Eq. (1–15), and then uses it in the integral of Eq. (1–16). For this inverse power law, the angle of deflection is thus dependent upon all of the parameters of the collision only through the single parameter b_0, and ν.

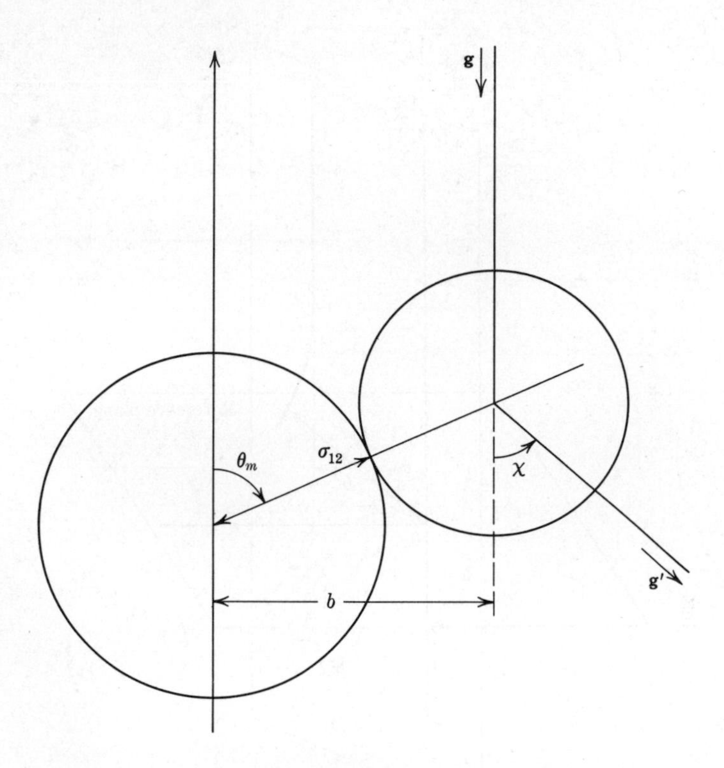

FIG. 1–3. Geometry of a Collision for Hard Spheres.

The angle of deflection for the collision of rigid elastic spheres may be obtained from Fig. 1–3. The minimum distance of approach is

$$r_m = \sigma_{12} = \tfrac{1}{2}(\sigma_1 + \sigma_2) \qquad (1\text{–}17)$$

where σ_1, σ_2 are the diameters of the two colliding particles. From the geometry, we see that

$$b = \sigma_{12} \sin \theta_m$$

so that the angle of deflection is given by:

$$\chi = \begin{cases} \pi - 2 \sin^{-1} (b/\sigma_{12}) & b \leq \sigma_{12} \\ 0 & b \geq \sigma_{12} \end{cases} \tag{1-18}$$

1.5. Some Vector Relations.—Since the relative motion takes place in a plane, one further parameter must be given in order to describe the collision in three dimensions, namely the orientation of the relative-motion plane. This may be done as in Fig. 1–4, where the collision

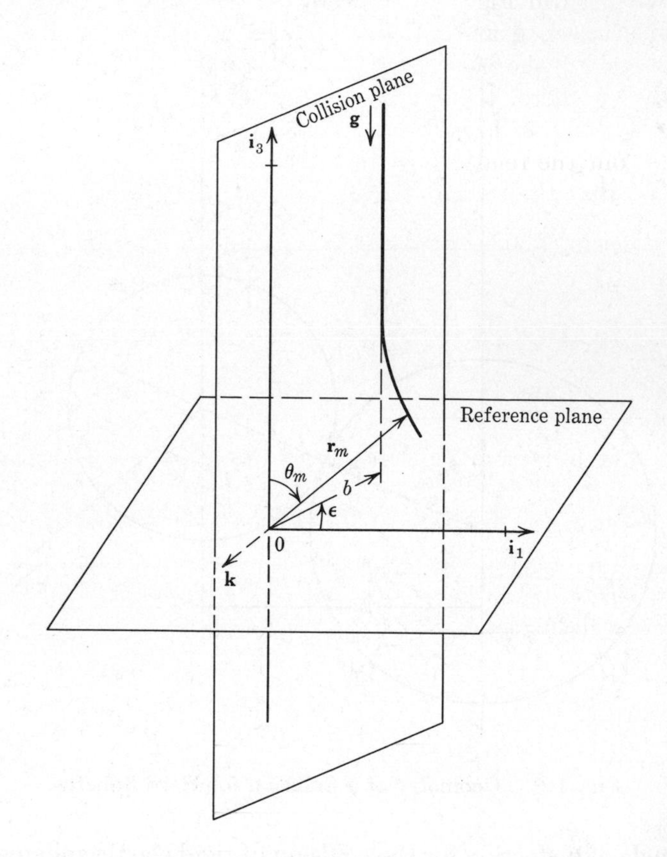

FIG. 1–4. Three-Dimensional Geometry of a Collision.

plane is shown, and a reference plane is drawn through the origin in the collision plane (the origin being the location of the force center) and perpendicular to the relative velocity vector **g**. The angle ε, measured from an arbitrary line in the reference plane to the collision plane, then defines the location of the latter. For a given value of relative velocity, the parameters b and ε specify the collision; since the angle of deflection may be found from the previous equations in terms of the geometrical factor b, the angles χ, ε may also be used to specify the collision.

If the unit vector $\mathbf{k}$ is chosen along $\mathbf{r}_m$, but directed opposite to it, $\mathbf{k}$ can be represented in terms of the angles $\pi - \theta_m$ and $\pi + \varepsilon$, or $\frac{1}{2}(\pi + \chi)$ and $\pi + \varepsilon$, where the angle θ_m is measured from the polar axis which is antiparallel to $\mathbf{g}$, as in Fig. 1–3. Noting that χ is the angle between $\mathbf{g}$ and $\mathbf{g}'$, and that $\mathbf{g}$ and $\mathbf{k}$ form an angle θ_m, the vector triangle of Fig. 1–5 can be drawn; here, the magnitude a is a size parameter, since $\mathbf{k}$ has been chosen of unit length. From the relation between χ and θ_m, it can be seen that the triangle is isosceles, so that

$$a = 2g \sin(\chi/2) = 2g \cos\theta_m \equiv 2\mathbf{g}\cdot\mathbf{k}$$

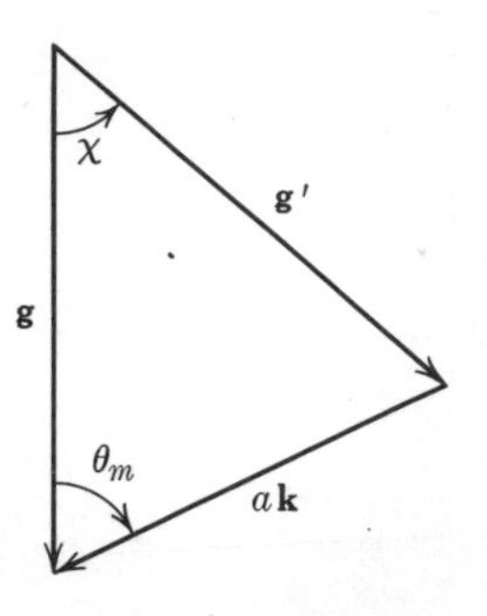

Fig. 1–5. Vector Triangle for a Collision.

Therefore

$$\mathbf{g} = \mathbf{g}' + 2(\mathbf{g}\cdot\mathbf{k})\mathbf{k} \tag{1–19}$$

From Eqs. (1–6) and (1–7), we obtain:

$$\begin{aligned} \mathbf{v}_1 &= \mathbf{G} - \left(\frac{m_2}{m_1 + m_2}\right)\mathbf{g}; \qquad \mathbf{v}_2 = \mathbf{G} + \left(\frac{m_1}{m_1 + m_2}\right)\mathbf{g} \\ \mathbf{v}_1' &= \mathbf{G} - \left(\frac{m_2}{m_1 + m_2}\right)\mathbf{g}'; \qquad \mathbf{v}_2' = \mathbf{G} + \left(\frac{m_1}{m_1 + m_2}\right)\mathbf{g}' \end{aligned} \tag{1–20}$$

If we use Eq. (1–19) in the above relations, the changes in velocity of each of the colliding particles are found to be:

$$\begin{aligned} \mathbf{v}_1' - \mathbf{v}_1 &= 2\left(\frac{m_2}{m_1 + m_2}\right)(\mathbf{g}\cdot\mathbf{k})\mathbf{k} \\ \mathbf{v}_2' - \mathbf{v}_2 &= -2\left(\frac{m_1}{m_1 + m_2}\right)(\mathbf{g}\cdot\mathbf{k})\mathbf{k} \end{aligned} \tag{1–21}$$

From these relations between the initial and final velocities of each of the particles, it follows that the jacobian of the transformation is unity, so that

$$d\mathbf{v}_1' d\mathbf{v}_2' = d\mathbf{v}_1 d\mathbf{v}_2 \tag{1–22}$$

The velocity vectors of the particles are usually represented in some stationary macroscopic coordinate system; it is this coordinate system that is used to describe the position vector $\mathbf{r}$ of the distribution function. However, the integrations involved in the integrals of the later sections are performed in terms of the relative velocity coordinate system and the center of mass coordinate system. The transformations of Eqs. (1–20) and (1–21) are used, together with the total energy of the system which can be found directly from Eq. (1–20):

$$\tfrac{1}{2}m_1v_1^2 + \tfrac{1}{2}m_2v_2^2 = \tfrac{1}{2}(m_1 + m_2)G^2 + \tfrac{1}{2}\mu g^2 \tag{1–23}$$

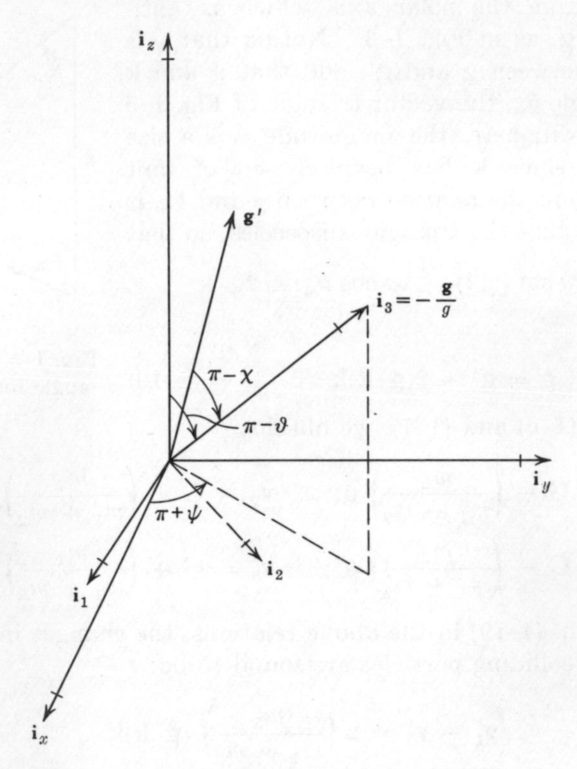

FIG. 1–6. Gas Coordinate System and Relative Velocity Coordinate System.

The transformations relating $\mathbf{v}_1$, $\mathbf{v}_2$, and $\mathbf{G}$, $\mathfrak{g}$ are Eqs. (1–20), and are such that

$$d\mathbf{v}_1 d\mathbf{v}_2 = d\mathbf{G}d\mathfrak{g} \tag{1–24}$$

In the relative velocity system of Fig. 1–4, a rectangular coordinate system is set up as follows: the $\mathbf{i}_3$ axis is the line antiparallel to $\mathfrak{g}$, through the origin; the $\mathbf{i}_1$ axis is the line in the reference plane from which ε is measured; the $\mathbf{i}_2$ axis is in the reference plane, perpendicular to $\mathbf{i}_1$ and $\mathbf{i}_3$, forming a right-handed system. The coordinates of $\mathbf{g}$ are then

$$\mathbf{g} = (0,0,-g) \tag{1-25}$$

the unit vector $\mathbf{k}$, at angles $\frac{1}{2}(\pi + \chi)$ and $\pi + \varepsilon$ has rectangular coordinates:

$$\mathbf{k} = (-\cos(\chi/2)\cos\varepsilon,\ -\cos(\chi/2)\sin\varepsilon,\ -\sin(\chi/2)) \tag{1-26}$$

the vector $\mathbf{g}'$ is found from Eq. (1–19) to be:

$$\mathbf{g}' = (g\sin\chi\cos\varepsilon,\ g\sin\chi\sin\varepsilon,\ -g\cos\chi) \tag{1-27}$$

These representations will be used to calculate collision integrals in Section 1.15.

Since the vector $\mathbf{g}'$ is represented above in terms of the $\mathbf{g}$-coordinate system $(\mathbf{i}_1,\mathbf{i}_2,\mathbf{i}_3)$ having $-\mathbf{g}$ as the $\mathbf{i}_3$ axis, it is necessary to determine the transformation to the $(\mathbf{i}_x,\mathbf{i}_y,\mathbf{i}_z)$ coordinate system in which the particle velocities are written, in order to evaluate certain integrals. If we let (ϑ,ψ) be the spherical coordinate angles of the vector $\mathbf{v}_2 - \mathbf{v}_1$, in the $\mathbf{v}$-coordinate system, then:

$$\begin{aligned}\mathbf{g} &= (v_{2x} - v_{1x})\mathbf{i}_x + (v_{2y} - v_{1y})\mathbf{i}_y + (v_{2z} - v_{1z})\mathbf{i}_z \\ &= g[\sin\vartheta\cos\psi\mathbf{i}_x + \sin\vartheta\sin\psi\mathbf{i}_y + \cos\vartheta\mathbf{i}_z]\end{aligned} \tag{1-28}$$

The unit vector $\mathbf{i}_3$ extends along $-\mathbf{g}$ as already mentioned (see Fig. 1–6); the $(\mathbf{i}_1,\mathbf{i}_2,\mathbf{i}_3)$ coordinate axes may thus be written in terms of the $(\mathbf{i}_x,\mathbf{i}_y,\mathbf{i}_z)$ axes as follows:

$$\begin{aligned}\mathbf{i}_3 &= -[\sin\vartheta\cos\psi\mathbf{i}_x + \sin\vartheta\sin\psi\mathbf{i}_y + \cos\vartheta\mathbf{i}_z] \\ \mathbf{i}_1 &= -\sin\psi\mathbf{i}_x + \cos\psi\mathbf{i}_y \\ \mathbf{i}_2 &= \cos\vartheta\cos\psi\mathbf{i}_x + \cos\vartheta\sin\psi\mathbf{i}_y - \sin\vartheta\mathbf{i}_z\end{aligned} \tag{1-29}$$

The $\mathbf{i}_1$ axis has been chosen in the $\mathbf{i}_x$-$\mathbf{i}_y$ plane; this choice is arbitrary and serves to define the axis from which the polar "scattering" angle ε is measured. Thus we have:

$$\mathbf{g} = -g\mathbf{i}_3 \tag{1-30}$$

$$\begin{aligned}\mathbf{g}' = g[&(\sin\vartheta\cos\psi\cos\chi + \cos\vartheta\cos\psi\sin\chi\sin\varepsilon - \sin\psi\sin\chi\cos\varepsilon)\mathbf{i}_x \\ &+ (\sin\vartheta\sin\psi\cos\chi + \cos\vartheta\sin\psi\sin\chi\sin\varepsilon + \cos\psi\sin\chi\cos\varepsilon)\mathbf{i}_y \\ &+ (\cos\vartheta\cos\chi - \sin\vartheta\sin\chi\sin\varepsilon)\mathbf{i}_z]\end{aligned} \tag{1-31}$$

1.6. Inverse Collisions.—The particle velocities resulting from a collision between particles of velocities $\mathbf{v}_1$ and $\mathbf{v}_2$, having collision parameters b and ε, have been denoted as $\mathbf{v}_1'$ and $\mathbf{v}_2'$; they may be found from Eqs. (1–21). Consider now the particle velocities resulting from a collision between particles of velocities $\mathbf{v}_1'$ and $\mathbf{v}_2'$, with collision parameters b and ε; let these final velocities be denoted by $\mathbf{v}_1''$ and $\mathbf{v}_2''$.

The collision that takes $(\mathbf{v}_1,\mathbf{v}_2)$ into $(\mathbf{v}_1',\mathbf{v}_2')$ will be called the direct collision; that that takes $(\mathbf{v}_1',\mathbf{v}_2')$ into $(\mathbf{v}_1'',\mathbf{v}_2'')$ will be called the inverse collision; see Fig. 1–7. Equations (1–9) and (1–10), the conservation laws for energy and for angular momentum, applied to the new system, yield $g'' = g'$; since it was found that, for the original system, $g' = g$,

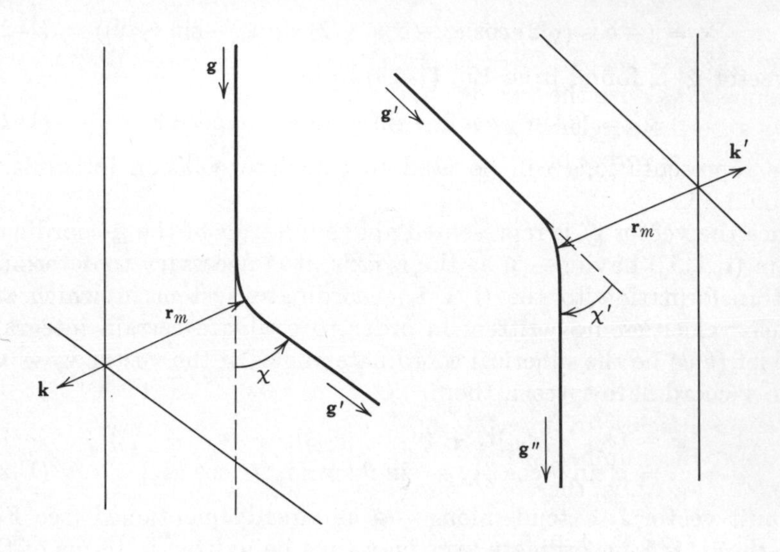

Fig. 1–7. Direct and Inverse Collisions.

we see that the final relative speed for the inverse collision is the same as the initial relative speed for the direct collision:

$$g'' = g$$

Since the orbit depends only upon g, b and the dynamical quantities (masses and force law), the angle of deflection in the inverse collision is the same as that for the direct collision (cf. Eq. (1–11)); however, the unit vector $\mathbf{k}'$ for the inverse collision is the negative of that for the direct collision. If, in Eq. (1–21), $\mathbf{v}_1$, $\mathbf{v}_2$, $\mathbf{v}_1'$, $\mathbf{v}_2'$, $\mathbf{g}$, $\mathbf{k}$ are replaced, respectively, by $\mathbf{v}_1'$, $\mathbf{v}_2'$, $\mathbf{v}_1''$, $\mathbf{v}_2''$, $\mathbf{g}'$, $-\mathbf{k}$, these equations become:

$$\mathbf{v}_1'' - \mathbf{v}_1' = +2\left(\frac{m_2}{m_1 + m_2}\right)(\mathbf{g}'\cdot\mathbf{k})\mathbf{k}$$

$$\mathbf{v}_2'' - \mathbf{v}_2' = -2\left(\frac{m_1}{m_1 + m_2}\right)(\mathbf{g}'\cdot\mathbf{k})\mathbf{k}$$

Noting, from Fig. 1–5, that $\mathbf{g}'\cdot\mathbf{k} = -(\mathbf{g}\cdot\mathbf{k})$, these equations reduce to Eq. (1–21), with

$$\mathbf{v}_1'' = \mathbf{v}_1; \qquad \mathbf{v}_2'' = \mathbf{v}_2$$

Thus, the inverse collision gives rise to the same particle velocities as those with which the corresponding direct collision is started.

1.7. Derivation of the Boltzmann Equation.—The Boltzmann equation is derived by considering the different ways in which the distribution function can change in a short time interval. Particles in the differential phase space[6] volume $d\mathbf{r}d\mathbf{v}_1$ around $(\mathbf{r},\mathbf{v}_1)$ can move to a new position by virtue of their velocity; if there is an external force acting upon the particles, their velocities can change; moreover, collisions will cause the velocity to change as well.

Let $\mathbf{a}$ be the acceleration of a particle due to any (velocity-independent) external forces on the particle:

$$\mathbf{a}(\mathbf{r},t) = \frac{1}{m}\mathbf{F}_{ext}(\mathbf{r},t) \tag{1–32}$$

Particles at $(\mathbf{r},\mathbf{v}_1)$ will move to $(\mathbf{r} + \mathbf{v}_1\Delta t, \mathbf{v}_1 + \mathbf{a}\Delta t)$ in the time interval Δt. If there were no collisions, all of the particles would move to this new volume; however, collisions will remove particles from the new volume element by "changing them" into particles of velocity $\mathbf{v}_1'$, and add particles (by inverse collisions) which had velocity $\mathbf{v}_1'$. The change in the number of particles in $d\mathbf{r}d\mathbf{v}_1$, during the time interval from t to $t + \Delta t$, is, therefore

$$f(\mathbf{r} + \mathbf{v}_1\Delta t, \mathbf{v}_1 + \mathbf{a}\Delta t, t + \Delta t)d\mathbf{r}d\mathbf{v}_1 - f(\mathbf{r},\mathbf{v}_1,t)d\mathbf{r}d\mathbf{v}_1 = \left(\frac{\partial f}{\partial t}\right)_c d\mathbf{r}d\mathbf{v}_1\Delta t$$

where $(\partial f/\partial t)_c$ represents the time rate of change in f due to collisions. Expanding the first term in a Taylor's expansion, and retaining terms linear in Δt, the equation becomes

$$\frac{\partial f}{\partial t} + \mathbf{v}_1\cdot\nabla f + \mathbf{a}\cdot\nabla_v f = \left(\frac{\partial f}{\partial t}\right)_c \tag{1–33}$$

In Eq. (1–33), ∇ is the usual del operator,[7] and ∇_v is the del operator in velocity space; in rectangular coordinates:

$$\begin{aligned} \mathbf{v}_1\cdot\nabla &= v_{1x}\frac{\partial}{\partial x} + v_{1y}\frac{\partial}{\partial y} + v_{1z}\frac{\partial}{\partial z} \\ \mathbf{a}\cdot\nabla_v &= a_x\frac{\partial}{\partial v_{1x}} + a_y\frac{\partial}{\partial v_{1y}} + a_z\frac{\partial}{\partial v_{1z}} \end{aligned} \tag{1–34}$$

[6] Ordinarily, the term phase space refers to the conjunction of configuration and momentum space. We use it here for configuration-velocity space.

[7] Cf. Margenau and Murphy, *op. cit.*, p. 155.

It is implicit in the use of the expansion, that the time for a significant change in the distribution function must be large compared with the interval Δt.

In order to determine the number of particles of velocity $\mathbf{v}_1$ that are removed from the differential volume $d\mathbf{r}d\mathbf{v}_1$ by collisions, consider a single particle of velocity $\mathbf{v}_1$. In the region of space $d\mathbf{r}$ around $\mathbf{r}$ consider particles of velocity $\mathbf{v}_2$ with collision parameters in a differential range around b and ε; after determining the effects of these collisions, all particles in this region of space, having all possible values of b and ε will be taken into account by integrating over $\mathbf{v}_2$, b, and ε. If we transform to relative velocity space, the $\mathbf{v}_1$ particle is at rest at the origin, while a "reduced-mass" particle of velocity $\mathbf{g}$ approaches it

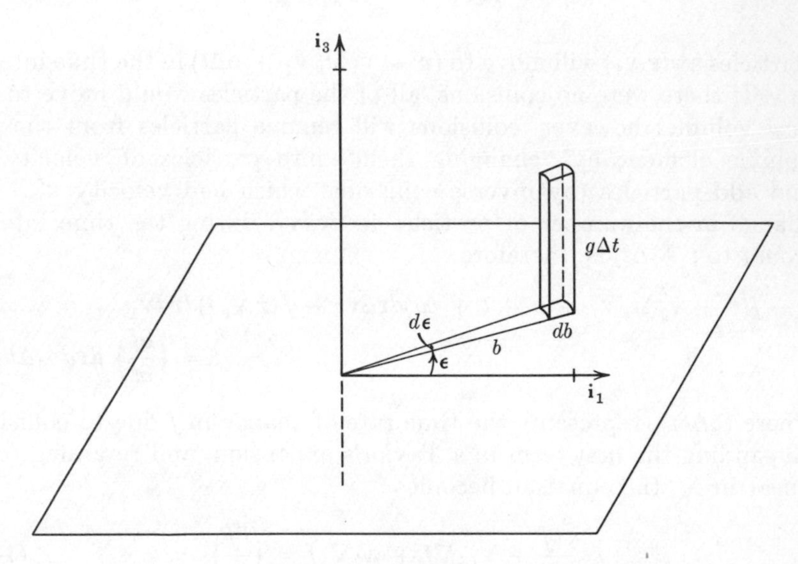

FIG. 1–8. Volume-Containing Colliding Particle.

perpendicular to the reference plane with polar coordinates (b,ε) in that plane, as shown in Fig. 1–8. During a time Δt that is large compared with the time necessary for a collision to be completed, the colliding particle is contained in the cylinder of height $g\Delta t$, and a base of sides db and $bd\varepsilon$. The colliding particle is thus in a region determined by the space volume, around $\mathbf{r}$, of $d\mathbf{r} = (g\Delta t)b\, db\, d\varepsilon$, and a velocity element $d\mathbf{v}_2$ at $\mathbf{v}_2$, *i.e.*, $d\mathbf{v}_2$ at a velocity $\mathbf{g}$ measured relative to $\mathbf{v}_1$. The number of colliding particles is thus

$$dN_c = f(\mathbf{r},\mathbf{v}_2,t)d\mathbf{v}_2\, g\Delta t\, b\, db\, d\varepsilon \tag{1–35}$$

In deriving this relation it has been assumed that the distribution function does not change significantly in a distance b, so that the distribution function describing the number of $\mathbf{v}_2$ particles is evaluated at the same point in space as that for the $\mathbf{v}_1$ particles. Since the number of $\mathbf{v}_1$ particles is $f(\mathbf{r},\mathbf{v}_1,t)d\mathbf{r}d\mathbf{v}_1$, the number of collisions between particles of velocity $\mathbf{v}_1$ and $\mathbf{v}_2$ in Δt is

$$\Delta N_- = f(\mathbf{r},\mathbf{v}_1,t)f(\mathbf{r},\mathbf{v}_2,t)gb\,db\,d\varepsilon\,d\mathbf{v}_2d\mathbf{v}_1d\mathbf{r}\Delta t \tag{1–36}$$

These collisions remove particles from the space-velocity volume around $(\mathbf{r},\mathbf{v}_1)$ and place them into the volume around $(\mathbf{r},\mathbf{v}_1')$.

To determine the collisions that bring particles into the volume around $(\mathbf{r},\mathbf{v}_1)$, the inverse collisions must be considered: it was shown previously that collisions of particles of velocities $\mathbf{v}_1'$ and $\mathbf{v}_2'$ with collision parameters b and ε give rise to a particle of velocity $\mathbf{v}_1$. As before, in the volume element $g'\Delta t\,b\,db\,d\varepsilon$, a particle of velocity $\mathbf{v}_2'$ will collide with the particle of velocity $\mathbf{v}_1'$ in the desired manner (to give a $\mathbf{v}_1$ particle); there are $f(\mathbf{r},\mathbf{v}_2',t)g'\Delta t\,b\,db\,d\varepsilon$ particles colliding with $f(\mathbf{r},\mathbf{v}_1',t)d\mathbf{r}d\mathbf{v}_1'$ particles in $d\mathbf{r}d\mathbf{v}_1'$, so that the total collisions in Δt, which produce particles of velocity $\mathbf{v}_1$ at $\mathbf{r}$, are

$$\Delta N_+ = f(\mathbf{r},\mathbf{v}_1',t)f(\mathbf{r},\mathbf{v}_2',t)g'b\,db\,d\varepsilon\,d\mathbf{v}_2'd\mathbf{v}_1'd\mathbf{r}\Delta t \tag{1–37}$$

In this expression, all values of $\mathbf{v}_1'$, $\mathbf{v}_2'$, b, and ε that lead to a particle of velocity $\mathbf{v}_1$ must be taken into account; however, since $g' = g$ and $d\mathbf{v}_1'd\mathbf{v}_2' = d\mathbf{v}_1d\mathbf{v}_2$, the expression ΔN_+ may be written entirely in terms of the variables $\mathbf{v}_1$, $\mathbf{v}_2$, b, and ε by use of Eq. (1–21).

The expressions must now be integrated over all possible values of $\mathbf{v}_2$, b, and ε to give the net change in the number of particles of velocity $\mathbf{v}_1$ due to collisions in time Δt; dividing by $d\mathbf{r}d\mathbf{v}_1\Delta t$, this gives the time rate of change in the distribution function due to collisions:

$$\left(\frac{\partial f}{\partial t}\right)_c = \int [f(\mathbf{r},\mathbf{v}_1',t)f(\mathbf{r},\mathbf{v}_2',t) - f(\mathbf{r},\mathbf{v}_1,t)f(\mathbf{r},\mathbf{v}_2,t)]gb\,db\,d\varepsilon\,d\mathbf{v}_2 \tag{1–38}$$

Since the space and time variables are the same throughout the equation, the notation

$$f(\mathbf{r},\mathbf{v}_1,t) = f_1; \qquad f(\mathbf{r},\mathbf{v}_1',t) = f_1', \quad \text{etc.}$$

is often used; the Boltzmann equation is then written as

$$\frac{\partial f_1}{\partial t} + \mathbf{v}_1\cdot\nabla f_1 + \mathbf{a}\cdot\boldsymbol{\nabla}_v f_1 = -\int [f_1f_2 - f_1'f_2']gb\,db\,d\varepsilon\,d\mathbf{v}_2 \tag{1–39}$$

1.8. Discussion of the Equation.—The Boltzmann equation describes the manner in which the distribution function for a system of particles, $f_1 = f(\mathbf{r},\mathbf{v}_1,t)$, varies in terms of its independent variables $\mathbf{r}$, the position of observation; $\mathbf{v}_1$, the velocity of the particles considered; and the time, t. The variation of the distribution function due to the external forces acting on the particles and the action of collisions are both considered. In the integral expression on the right of Eq. (1–39), the Eqs. (1–21) are used to express the velocities after collision in terms of the velocities before collision; the dynamics of the collision process are taken into account in the expression for $\chi(b,\varepsilon)$, from Eqs. (1–11) and (1–12), which enters into the $\mathbf{k}$ of Eqs. (1–21). Alternatively, as will be shown to be useful later, the velocities before and after collision may be expressed, by Eq. (1–20), in terms of $\mathbf{G}$, $\mathbf{g}$, and $\mathbf{g}'$; the dynamics of the collision comes into the relation between $\mathbf{g}$ and $\mathbf{g}'$ of Eq. (1–19).

If only one type of particle is present, $m_1 = m_2$; however, the expressions relating the velocities before and after collision do not simplify to any great extent. If several types of particles are present, then there results one Boltzmann equation for the distribution function for each type of particle; in each equation, integrals will appear for collisions with each type of particle. That is, if there are P types of particles, numbered $i = 1,2,\cdots,P$, there are P distribution functions, $f_i = f(\mathbf{r},\mathbf{v}_i,t)$, describing the system; $f_i d\mathbf{r} d\mathbf{v}_i$ is the number of particles of type i in the differential phase space volume around $(\mathbf{r},\mathbf{v}_i)$. The set of Boltzmann equations for the system would then be:

$$\frac{\partial f_i}{\partial t} + \mathbf{v}_i \cdot \nabla f_i + \mathbf{a}_i \cdot \nabla_v f_i = - \sum_{j=1}^{P} \int [f_i f_j - f_i' f_j'] g_{ij} b \, db \, d\varepsilon \, d\mathbf{v}_j, \qquad i = 1,2,\cdots,P$$

Since the solution of a system of Boltzmann equations for a many-component system is very similar to that for a simple gas, only the latter shall be discussed.

In the derivation of the Boltzmann equation, it was noted that the distribution function must not change significantly in times of the order of a collision time, nor in distances of the order of the maximum range of the interparticle force. For the usual interatomic force laws (but not the Coulomb force, which is of importance in ionized gases), this distance is less than about 10^{-7} cm; the corresponding collision times, which are of the order of the force range divided by a characteristic particle velocity (of the order of 10^5 cm/sec for hydrogen at 300° C), is about 10^{-12} seconds.

The assumption that the probability of simultaneous occurrence of two particles, of velocities $\mathbf{v}_1$ and $\mathbf{v}_2$ in a differential space volume around $\mathbf{r}$, is equal to the product of the probabilities of their occurrence individually in this volume, is known as the assumption of molecular chaos. In a dense gas, there would be collisions in rapid succession among particles in any small region of the gas; the velocity of any one particle would be expected to become closely related to the velocity of its neighboring particles. These effects of correlation are assumed to be absent in the derivation of the Boltzmann equation; since mean free paths in a rarefied gas are of the order of 10^{-5} cm, particles that interact in a collision have come from quite different regions of gas, and would be expected not to interact again with each other over a time involving many collisions.

Moreover, since the mean free path is of the order of 100 times the molecular diameter, *i.e.*, the range of force for a collision, collisions involving three or more particles are sufficiently rare to be neglected. This binary collision assumption (as well as the molecular chaos assumption) becomes better as the number density of the gas is decreased. Since these assumptions are increasingly valid as the particles spend a larger percentage of time out of the influence of another particle, one may expect that ideal gas behavior may be closely related to the consequences of the Boltzmann equation. This will be seen to be correct in the results of the approximation schemes used to solve the equation.

1.9. Boltzmann's H-Theorem.—One of the most striking features of transport theory is seen from the result that, although collisions are completely reversible phenomena (since they are based upon the reversible laws of mechanics), the solutions of the Boltzmann equation depict irreversible phenomena. This effect is most clearly seen from a consideration of Boltzmann's H-function, which will be discussed here for a gas in a uniform state (no dependence of the distribution function on position and no external forces) for simplicity.

Let us define a function of time:

$$H(t) = \int f(\mathbf{v}_1,t) \ln f(\mathbf{v}_1,t) d\mathbf{v}_1 \tag{1-40}$$

Taking the time derivative of $H(t)$, and using the Boltzmann equation, Eq. (1-39) for this case:

$$\frac{\partial H}{\partial t} = -\int [f_1 f_2 - f_1' f_2'][\ln f_1 + 1] gb\, db\, d\varepsilon\, d\mathbf{v}_1 d\mathbf{v}_2$$

As will be shown later (Section 1.11), this may be rewritten by an interchange of the integration variables:

$$\frac{\partial H}{\partial t} = -\frac{1}{4}\int [f_1 f_2 - f_1' f_2'][\ln f_1 + \ln f_2 - \ln f_1' - \ln f_2'] gb\, db\, d\varepsilon\, d\mathbf{v}_1 d\mathbf{v}_2$$

$$= \frac{1}{4}\int [f_1' f_2' - f_1 f_2] \ln (f_1 f_2 / f_1' f_2') gb\, db\, d\varepsilon\, d\mathbf{v}_1 d\mathbf{v}_2$$

When the product $f_1 f_2$ is greater than $f_1' f_2'$, the logarithm is positive, but the difference is negative; for $f_1 f_2$ less than $f_1' f_2'$, the logarithm is negative, but the difference is positive; thus, the entire integral is negative, unless the products are equal to each other.

$$\frac{\partial H}{\partial t} \begin{cases} < 0 & \text{if} \quad f_1 f_2 \lessgtr f_1' f_2' \\ = 0 & \text{if} \quad f_1 f_2 = f_1' f_2' \end{cases} \tag{1–41}$$

In those regions of velocity space where f_1 goes to zero, so that the logarithm goes to $-\infty$, the product $f_1 \ln f_1$ will go to zero; thus $H(t)$ is bounded. From Eq. (1–41), therefore, the quantity $H(t)$ starts at some value when $t = 0$, and decreases for all time, until the equilibrium condition $f_1 f_2 = f_1' f_2'$ is satisfied; $H(t)$ then remains constant.

This behavior of the H-function must be viewed in the light of the derivation of the Boltzmann equation. Since, in general, particles will be passing into and out of a differential space and velocity volume at various times, the distribution function will be a smooth function of its variables only if it represents an average behavior that suppresses fluctuations. In the same sense, the assumption about the number of collisions used in Eqs. (1–36) and (1–37) must be taken to be a statement about the average number of collisions. These averages are interpreted in the same manner as in equilibrium statistical mechanics; the Boltzmann equation expresses the average behavior of an ensemble of systems that are macroscopically identical. The H-function for any one of the members of the ensemble (defined in terms of some "exact" single particle distribution function for that member) can increase, since its particles may be performing the reverse of the motion of the particles of another ensemble member; however, since it is far more probable to have ensemble members approaching equilibrium than further deviating from equilibrium, the average behavior of the ensemble is to cause $H(t)$ to decrease.[8]

1.10. Maxwell Distribution.—From the behavior of the H-function, we may expect that a gas starting from some initial distribution func-

[8] R. C. Tolman, *The Principles of Statistical Mechanics*, pp. 146 ff., Oxford University Press, 1938.

tion will irreversibly change its state (so as to decrease $H(t)$), until it will be describable in terms of a distribution function that gives the minimum value of H for the system. This occurs when

$$f(\mathbf{r},\mathbf{v}_1,t)f(\mathbf{r},\mathbf{v}_2,t) = f(\mathbf{r},\mathbf{v}_1',t)f(\mathbf{r},\mathbf{v}_2',t) \quad (1\text{–}42)$$

or

$$\ln f_1 + \ln f_2 = \ln f_1' + \ln f_2' \quad (1\text{–}43)$$

which may be interpreted as an equation relating the velocities of two particles before and after collision; however, from the laws of mechanics, it is known that the only independent relations among these velocities are contained in the laws of conservation of number (of particles), of momentum, and of energy. Thus, the function $\ln f_1$ must be given by:

$$\ln f_1 = \alpha^{(1)}m + \boldsymbol{\alpha}^{(2)}\cdot m\mathbf{v}_1 + \alpha^{(3)}\tfrac{1}{2}mv_1^2 \quad (1\text{–}44)$$

where the α^i are constants; $\ln f_1$, when written in this way, identically satisfies Eq. (1–43); while if Eq. (1–44) were not true, Eq. (1–43) would give rise to a new conservation law. Using the definitions of number density, of the mean velocity of the particles (in a differential volume around $\mathbf{r}$), and of the temperature (for particles having no internal degrees of freedom):

$$n = \int f_1 d\mathbf{v}_1; \qquad \bar{\mathbf{v}} = \frac{1}{n}\int f_1\mathbf{v}_1 d\mathbf{v}_1; \qquad \tfrac{3}{2}kT = \frac{1}{n}\int f_1\tfrac{1}{2}m(\mathbf{v}_1 - \bar{\mathbf{v}})^2 d\mathbf{v}_1 \quad (1\text{–}45)$$

the equilibrium distribution, Eq. (1–44), becomes:

$$f(\mathbf{v}_1) = n\left(\frac{m}{2\pi kT}\right)^{3/2} e^{-m(\mathbf{v}_1-\bar{\mathbf{v}})^2/2kT} \quad (1\text{–}46)$$

The quantities n, $\bar{\mathbf{v}}$, and $(3k/m)T$ are thus the first five (velocity) moments of the distribution function. In the above equation, k is the Boltzmann constant; the definition of temperature relates the kinetic energy associated with the random motion of the particles to $\frac{1}{2}kT$ for each degree of freedom. If an equation of state is derived using this equilibrium distribution function, by determining the pressure in the gas (see Section 1.11), then this kinetic theory definition of the temperature is seen to be the absolute temperature that appears in the ideal gas law.

In the work to follow, it is convenient to define the random (or "peculiar") particle velocity as:

$$\mathbf{u} = \mathbf{v}_1 - \bar{\mathbf{v}}; \qquad \bar{\mathbf{u}} = 0 \quad (1\text{–}47)$$

1.11. Hydrodynamic Equations.—Before deriving the hydrodynamic equations, some integral theorems that are useful in the solution of the Boltzmann equation will be proved. Consider a function of velocity, $Q(\mathbf{v}_1)$, which may also be a function of position and time; let

$$\Delta_c Q = \frac{1}{n}\int Q(\mathbf{v}_1)\left(\frac{\partial f_1}{\partial t}\right)_c d\mathbf{v}_1 \tag{1–48}$$

be the rate of change of Q due to collisions; here $(\partial f/\partial t)_c$ is given by Eq. (1–38).

$$n\Delta_c Q = \int Q(\mathbf{v}_1)[f_1'f_2' - f_1f_2]gb\, db\, d\varepsilon\, d\mathbf{v}_1 d\mathbf{v}_2 \tag{1–49}$$

In the first part of the integral we may replace primed variables by unprimed ones, and vice versa:

$$\int Q(\mathbf{v}_1)f_1'f_2'\, gb\, db\, d\varepsilon\, d\mathbf{v}_1 d\mathbf{v}_2 = \int Q(\mathbf{v}_1')f_1f_2\, g'b\, db\, d\varepsilon\, d\mathbf{v}_1' d\mathbf{v}_2'$$

Using $d\mathbf{v}_1 d\mathbf{v}_2 = d\mathbf{v}_1' d\mathbf{v}_2'$ and $g' = g$ in the last equation, we may use this expression in Eq. (1–49) to obtain:

$$n\Delta_c Q = \int [Q(\mathbf{v}_1') - Q(\mathbf{v}_1)]f_1f_2\, gb\, db\, d\varepsilon\, d\mathbf{v}_1 d\mathbf{v}_2 \tag{1–50}$$

By interchanging subscripts 1 and 2, this may be rewritten; adding the result to Eq. (1–50), we find:

$$n\Delta_c Q = \tfrac{1}{2}\int [Q_1' + Q_2' - Q_1 - Q_2]f_1f_2\, gb\, db\, d\varepsilon\, d\mathbf{v}_1 d\mathbf{v}_2 \tag{1–51}$$

It may be seen from Eq. (1–51) that if Q_1 is one of the quantities conserved in a collision (the "summational invariants"), its change due to a collision is zero, as expected, by virtue of the appropriate conservation law.

Since mass, momentum, and energy are conserved in a collision, successive multiplication of the Boltzmann equation by m, $m\mathbf{v}_1$, and $\frac{1}{2}mv_1^2$, and integration over $\mathbf{v}_1$, may be expected to give rise to equations of importance in the macroscopic domain. Multiplying Eq. (1–39) by m and integrating, we have:

$$m\int \frac{\partial f_1}{\partial t}\, d\mathbf{v}_1 + m\int \mathbf{v}_1\cdot\nabla f_1 d\mathbf{v}_1 + m\mathbf{a}\cdot\int \boldsymbol{\nabla}_v f_1 d\mathbf{v}_1 = 0 \tag{1–52}$$

But

$$\int \frac{\partial f_1}{\partial t}\, d\mathbf{v}_1 = \frac{\partial}{\partial t} \int f_1 d\mathbf{v}_1 = \frac{\partial n}{\partial t}$$

$$\int \mathbf{v}_1 \cdot \nabla f_1 d\mathbf{v}_1 = \nabla \cdot \int \mathbf{v}_1 f_1 d\mathbf{v}_1 = \nabla \cdot (n\bar{\mathbf{v}})$$

$$\int \frac{\partial f_1}{\partial v_{1x}}\, d\mathbf{v}_1 = \int dv_{1y} \int dv_{1z} \left[\int \frac{\partial f_1}{\partial v_{1x}}\, dv_{1x} \right] = \int dv_{1y} \int dv_{1z} [f_1]_{v_{1x}=-\infty}^{+\infty} = 0$$

In the last equation, use has been made of the fact that $f(\mathbf{v}_1)$ goes to zero when any velocity component becomes infinitely large. Defining the mass density by:

$$\rho(\mathbf{r},t) = mn(\mathbf{r},t) \tag{1–53}$$

we obtain:

$$\frac{\partial \rho}{\partial t} + \nabla \cdot (\rho \bar{\mathbf{v}}) = 0 \tag{1–54}$$

which is the equation of continuity of hydrodynamics.

If the Boltzmann equation is multiplied by mv_{1x}, and integrated over $\mathbf{v}_1$, the first two terms become:

$$m \int v_{1x} \frac{\partial f_1}{\partial t}\, d\mathbf{v}_1 = \frac{\partial}{\partial t} \left[m \int v_{1x} f_1 d\mathbf{v}_1 \right] = \frac{\partial}{\partial t} (\rho \bar{v}_x)$$

$$m \int v_{1x} \mathbf{v}_1 \cdot \nabla f_1 d\mathbf{v}_1 = \nabla \cdot \left[m \int v_{1x} \mathbf{v}_1 f_1 d\mathbf{v}_1 \right] = \nabla \cdot [\mathbf{p}_x + \rho \bar{v}_x \bar{\mathbf{v}}]$$

provided we use the definition of the random velocity $\mathbf{u}$, Eq. (1–47), with the *pressure tensor* defined as:

$$\boldsymbol{p} = m \int \mathbf{u}\,\mathbf{u}\, f_1 d\mathbf{v}_1; \qquad p_{ij} = m \int u_i u_j f_1 d\mathbf{v}_1 \tag{1–55}$$

By Eq. (1–55), we have $\mathbf{p}_x = m \int u_x \mathbf{u} f_1 d\mathbf{v}_1$. Since mu_i is the random momentum in the i-direction (*i.e.*, the momentum associated with the i-component of the random velocity), the (i,j) component of the pressure tensor is the average of the random flow in the j-direction of the i-directed momentum. From the definition of the temperature, Eq. (1–45), the hydrostatic pressure, defined as one-third of the trace of the pressure tensor, is

$$p \equiv \tfrac{1}{3} \sum_i p_{ii} = nkT \tag{1–56}$$

The third term of the equation has parts of the form:

$$\mathbf{i}_x \int v_{1x} \frac{\partial f_1}{\partial v_{1x}} d\mathbf{v}_1 = \mathbf{i}_x \int\int dv_{1y} dv_{1z} \left\{ \Big[v_{1x} f_1 \Big]_{v_{1x}=-\infty}^{+\infty} - \int f_1 dv_{1x} \right\} = -n\mathbf{i}_x$$

$$\mathbf{i}_x \int v_{1x} \frac{\partial f_1}{\partial v_{1y}} d\mathbf{v}_1 = \mathbf{i}_x \int\int dv_{1x} dv_{1z} v_{1x} \left\{ \Big[f_1 \Big]_{v_{1y}=-\infty}^{+\infty} \right\} = 0$$

The equation that results is:

$$\frac{\partial(\rho \bar{v}_x)}{\partial t} + \nabla \cdot [\mathbf{p}_x + \rho \bar{v}_x \bar{\mathbf{v}}] - \rho a_x = 0$$

If we take Eq. (1–54) multiplied by $\bar{v}_x$, and subtract it from the above, we have

$$\rho \frac{\partial \bar{v}_x}{\partial t} + \rho(\bar{\mathbf{v}} \cdot \nabla)\bar{v}_x + \nabla \cdot \mathbf{p}_x - \rho a_x = 0 \tag{1–57}$$

Adding the equations for the y- and z-components of the mean velocity, we obtain the hydrodynamic equation of motion:

$$\rho \left[\frac{\partial \bar{\mathbf{v}}}{\partial t} + (\bar{\mathbf{v}} \cdot \nabla)\bar{\mathbf{v}} \right] + \nabla \cdot \boldsymbol{p} - \rho \mathbf{a} = 0 \tag{1–58}$$

where the vector $\nabla \cdot \boldsymbol{p}$ has components

$$(\nabla \cdot \boldsymbol{p})_i = \frac{\partial p_{xi}}{\partial x} + \frac{\partial p_{yi}}{\partial y} + \frac{\partial p_{zi}}{\partial z}, \qquad i = x,y,z \tag{1–59}$$

If we now multiply the Boltzmann equation by $\frac{1}{2}mv_1^2$, integrate over $\mathbf{v}_1$, and use the definitions of the random velocity, Eq. (1–47), and of the temperature, Eq. (1–45), the first two terms become:

$$\begin{aligned}
\tfrac{1}{2}m \int v_1^2 \frac{\partial f_1}{\partial t} d\mathbf{v}_1 &= \frac{\partial}{\partial t} \left[\tfrac{1}{2}m \int (u^2 + 2\mathbf{u} \cdot \bar{\mathbf{v}} + \bar{v}^2) f_1 d\mathbf{v}_1 \right] \\
&= \frac{\partial}{\partial t} [\tfrac{3}{2}nkT + \tfrac{1}{2}\rho \bar{v}^2] \\
\tfrac{1}{2}m \int v_1^2 \mathbf{v}_1 \cdot \nabla f_1 d\mathbf{v}_1 &= \nabla \cdot \left[\tfrac{1}{2}m \int (u^2 + 2\mathbf{u} \cdot \bar{\mathbf{v}} + \bar{v}^2)(\mathbf{u} + \bar{\mathbf{v}}) f_1 d\mathbf{v}_1 \right] \\
&= \nabla \cdot [\mathbf{q} + \tfrac{3}{2}nkT\bar{\mathbf{v}} + \boldsymbol{p} \cdot \bar{\mathbf{v}} + \tfrac{1}{2}\rho \bar{v}^2 \bar{\mathbf{v}}]
\end{aligned}$$

where the heat flow vector is defined as:

$$\mathbf{q} = \tfrac{1}{2}m \int u^2 \mathbf{u} f_1 d\mathbf{v}_1 \tag{1–60}$$

This is the random flow of the energy associated with the random velocity of the particles. The third term has parts of the form:

$$\tfrac{1}{2}m \int v_1^2 \frac{\partial f_1}{\partial v_{1x}}\, d\mathbf{v}_1 = \tfrac{1}{2}m \int\int dv_{1y}dv_{1z}\{[v_1^2 f_1]_{v_{1x}=-\infty}^{+\infty} - 2\int v_{1x} f_1 dv_{1x}\}$$
$$= -\rho\bar{v}_x$$

The equation thus becomes:

$$\frac{\partial}{\partial t}(\tfrac{3}{2}nkT + \tfrac{1}{2}\rho\bar{v}^2) + \nabla\cdot(\mathbf{q} + \tfrac{3}{2}nkT\bar{\mathbf{v}} + \boldsymbol{p}\cdot\bar{\mathbf{v}} + \tfrac{1}{2}\rho\bar{v}^2\bar{\mathbf{v}}) - \rho\mathbf{a}\cdot\bar{\mathbf{v}} = 0$$

The terms may be rewritten by breaking up the equation as follows:

$$\frac{\partial}{\partial t}(\tfrac{3}{2}nkT) + \nabla\cdot(\tfrac{3}{2}nkT\bar{\mathbf{v}}) = \tfrac{3}{2}k\left(n\frac{\partial T}{\partial t} + n\bar{\mathbf{v}}\cdot\nabla T\right)$$

where the other terms go to zero, by Eq. (1–54).

$$\frac{\partial}{\partial t}(\tfrac{1}{2}\rho\bar{v}^2) + \nabla\cdot(\boldsymbol{p}\cdot\bar{\mathbf{v}} + \tfrac{1}{2}\rho\bar{v}^2\bar{\mathbf{v}})$$
$$= \sum_i \left[\frac{\partial}{\partial t}(\tfrac{1}{2}\rho\bar{v}_i^2) + \frac{\partial}{\partial x_i}((\boldsymbol{p}\cdot\bar{\mathbf{v}})_i + \tfrac{1}{2}\rho\bar{v}^2\bar{v}_i)\right]$$
$$= \sum_i \frac{\partial}{\partial t}(\tfrac{1}{2}\rho\bar{v}_i^2) + \sum_{i,j}\left[\frac{\partial}{\partial x_i}(p_{ij}\bar{v}_j) + \frac{\partial}{\partial x_i}(\tfrac{1}{2}\rho\bar{v}_j^2\bar{v}_i)\right]$$
$$= \sum_i \left(\rho\bar{v}_i\frac{\partial\bar{v}_i}{\partial t} + \tfrac{1}{2}\bar{v}_i^2\frac{\partial\rho}{\partial t}\right)$$
$$+ \sum_{i,j}\left[p_{ij}\frac{\partial\bar{v}_j}{\partial x_i} + \bar{v}_j\frac{\partial p_{ij}}{\partial x_i} + \rho\bar{v}_i\bar{v}_j\frac{\partial\bar{v}_j}{\partial x_i} + \tfrac{1}{2}\bar{v}_j^2\frac{\partial(\rho\bar{v}_i)}{\partial x_i}\right]$$

From Eq. (1–54), multiplied by $\frac{1}{2}\bar{v}_i^2$ and summed, the sum of the second and last terms equals zero; from Eq. (1–58), scalar-multiplied from the left by $\bar{\mathbf{v}}$, the first, fourth, and fifth terms yield $\rho\bar{\mathbf{v}}\cdot\mathbf{a}$. Thus, the equation yields, upon division by $\frac{3}{2}nk$:

$$\frac{\partial T}{\partial t} + \bar{\mathbf{v}}\cdot\nabla T + \frac{2}{3nk}\nabla\cdot\mathbf{q} + \frac{2}{3nk}\boldsymbol{p}:\nabla\bar{\mathbf{v}} = 0 \qquad (1\text{–}61)$$

where the product

$$\boldsymbol{p}:\nabla\bar{\mathbf{v}} \equiv \sum_{i,j} p_{ij}\frac{\partial\bar{v}_j}{\partial x_i} \qquad (1\text{–}62)$$

Equation (1–61) is the hydrodynamic equation of energy flow.

The hydrodynamic equations are a set of five equations involving the five "simple" moments of the distribution function, n (or ρ), $\bar{v}_x$, $\bar{v}_y$, $\bar{v}_z$, and T (actually, $3kT/m$); also contained in the equations are eight other moments given by the five independent components of the pressure tensor (which is symmetric, and has its trace given in terms of the temperature, by Eq. (1–56)) and the three components of the heat flow vector. These equations become identical with the hydrodynamic equations usually derived by macroscopic consideration[9] if we write the pressure tensor and heat flow vector in the forms:

$$\begin{aligned} p_{xx} &= p + \tfrac{2}{3}\mu \nabla \cdot \bar{\mathbf{v}} - 2\mu \frac{\partial \bar{v}_x}{\partial x}, \quad p \equiv nkT \\ p_{yz} &= -\mu \left(\frac{\partial \bar{v}_z}{\partial y} + \frac{\partial \bar{v}_y}{\partial z} \right), \quad \text{etc.} \\ \mathbf{q} &= -\lambda \nabla T \end{aligned} \tag{1–63}$$

where the viscosity, μ, and the thermal conductivity, λ, are phenomenological constants (the hydrodynamic equations for $\lambda = \mu = 0$ are the Euler equations; for λ and μ nonzero, they are the Navier-Stokes equations).

From the point of view of kinetic theory, however, $\boldsymbol{p}$ and $\mathbf{q}$ are known only in terms of the distribution function, which must be determined from the Boltzmann equation. The classical technique of solving the Boltzmann equation, the Chapman-Enskog method,[10] develops a set of successive approximations to the distribution function in such a manner as to obtain the Euler equations and the Navier-Stokes equations as zeroth and first approximations, respectively, to a complete solution of the Boltzmann equation. In doing this, it is assumed that, since the equilibrium distribution function, Eq. (1–46), is a function of the first five moments (n, $\bar{\mathbf{v}}$, and T) of the distribution function (which are independent of space and time, or, actually, very restricted functions of space and time),[11] then a near-equilibrium solution can be obtained with a similar dependence upon these moments, which are taken to be functions of space and time. The Chapman-Enskog technique then develops higher approximations, by assuming that the distribution function can be expressed as a functional of $n(\mathbf{r},t)$, $\bar{\mathbf{v}}(\mathbf{r},t)$, $T(\mathbf{r},t)$, and their space derivatives (rather than allowing the distribution function to have a general space and time dependence). In developing the various Chapman-Enskog approximations, these first few moments are made to satisfy the hydrodynamic equations *to*

[9] H. Schlichting, *Boundary Layer Theory*, pp. 54 and 291, McGraw-Hill Book Co., Inc., New York, 1960.

[10] S. Chapman and T. G. Cowling, *The Mathematical Theory of Non-Uniform Gases*, Chap. 7, Cambridge University Press, 1958.

[11] Chapman and Cowling, *op. cit.*, pp. 76–81.

the approximation considered. Thus, in each order of approximation, the distribution function is obtained in terms of n, $\bar{\mathbf{v}}$, and T, and their space derivatives; these moments satisfy the hydrodynamic equations [Eqs. (1–54), (1–58), (1–61)] with $\boldsymbol{p}$ and $\mathbf{q}$ given by their definitions, Eqs. (1–55) and (1–60), using the same approximation for the distribution function.

Rather than using the Chapman-Enskog procedure directly, we shall employ the technique of Burnett,[12] which involves an expansion of the distribution function in a set of orthogonal polynomials in particle-velocity space.

1.12. Expansion Polynomials.—The techniques to be discussed here for solving the Boltzmann equation involve the use of an expansion of the distribution function in a set of orthogonal polynomials in particle velocity space. The polynomials to be used are products of Sonine polynomials and spherical harmonics; some of their properties will be discussed in this section, while the reason for their use will be left to Section 1.13.

The Sonine polynomials[13] of order n, index $l + \frac{1}{2}$, and variable ξ^2 are defined as:

$$S^{(n)}_{l+1/2}(\xi^2) = \sum_{p=0}^{n} \frac{\Gamma(n + l + \frac{3}{2})}{p!(n - p)!\Gamma(p + l + \frac{3}{2})} (-\xi^2)^p \qquad (1\text{–}64)$$

The first three of them are:

$$\begin{aligned} S^{(0)}_{l+1/2}(\xi^2) &= 1 \\ S^{(1)}_{l+1/2}(\xi^2) &= l + \tfrac{3}{2} - \xi^2 \\ S^{(2)}_{l+1/2}(\xi^2) &= \tfrac{1}{2}(l + \tfrac{5}{2})(l + \tfrac{3}{2}) - (l + \tfrac{5}{2})\xi^2 + \tfrac{1}{2}\xi^4 \end{aligned} \qquad (1\text{–}65)$$

The orthogonality and normalization condition is:

$$\int_0^\infty e^{-\xi^2} S^{(n)}_{l+1/2}(\xi^2) S^{(n')}_{l+1/2}(\xi^2) \xi^{2l+2} d\xi = \frac{1}{2} \frac{\Gamma(l + n + \frac{3}{2})}{n!} \delta_{n,n'} \qquad (1\text{–}66)$$

The following relations are also needed:

$$\begin{aligned} \xi^2 S^{(n-1)}_{l+3/2}(\xi^2) &= S^{(n-1)}_{l+1/2}(\xi^2) - n S^{(n)}_{l+1/2}(\xi^2) \\ &= (l + \tfrac{1}{2}) S^{(n)}_{l+1/2}(\xi^2) - S^{(n)}_{l-1/2}(\xi^2) \end{aligned} \qquad (1\text{–}67)$$

$$\frac{d}{d\xi} S^{(n)}_{l+1/2}(\xi^2) = -2\xi S^{(n-1)}_{l+3/2}(\xi^2)$$

[12] D. Burnett, *Proc. London Math. Soc.* (2), **39**, 385–430 (1933); **40**, 382–435 (1934).

[13] The Sonine polynomials are related to the associated Laguerre polynomials (see Margenau and Murphy, *op. cit.*, p. 128) by

$$S^n_m(x) = (-)^m L^m_{n+m}(x)/\Gamma(n + m + 1)$$

The spherical harmonics are defined in terms of the associated Legendre polynomials, of variable $\cos\theta$, and exponential functions in φ.[14]

$$Y_l^m(\theta,\varphi) = P_l^{|m|}(\cos\theta)e^{im\varphi}, \quad m = 0, \pm 1, \pm 2, \ldots, \pm l \tag{1-68}$$

where

$$P_l^0(z) = \frac{(-)^l}{2^l l!}\frac{d^l}{dz^l}(1 - z^2)^l; \qquad P_l^{|m|}(z) = (1 - z^2)^{|m|/2}\frac{d^{|m|}}{dz^{|m|}}P_1^0(z) \tag{1-69}$$

We note that $Y_l^{m*} = Y_l^{-m}$, where the asterisk denotes the complex conjugate.

1.13. The Burnett Expansion.—The Chapman-Enskog solution of the Boltzmann equation can be most easily developed through an expansion procedure due to Burnett.[15] For the distribution function of a system that is close to equilibrium, we may use as a zeroth approximation a *local equilibrium* distribution function given by the maxwellian form:

$$f_0(\mathbf{r},\mathbf{v}_1,t) = n(\mathbf{r},t)\left[\frac{m}{2\pi kT(\mathbf{r},t)}\right]^{3/2} e^{-\{m[\mathbf{v}_1 - \bar{\mathbf{v}}(\mathbf{r},t)]^2\}/2kT(\mathbf{r},t)} \tag{1-70}$$

where the number density, mean velocity, and temperature depend upon space and time. The Burnett procedure for determining the distribution function consists of an expansion in velocity space about this zero-order form.

For convenience, let us define a new velocity variable, $\boldsymbol{\xi}$, and represent this variable in spherical coordinates:

$$\boldsymbol{\xi} = \left[\frac{m}{2kT(\mathbf{r},t)}\right]^{1/2}[\mathbf{v}_1 - \bar{\mathbf{v}}(\mathbf{r},t)]; \qquad \boldsymbol{\xi} = (\xi,\theta,\varphi) \tag{1-71}$$

The expansion to be used is then:

$$f(\mathbf{r},\mathbf{v}_1,t) = f_0(\mathbf{r},\mathbf{v}_1,t)\sum_{l,m,n} a_{ln}^{(m)}(\mathbf{r},t)S_{l+1/2}^{(n)}(\xi^2)\xi^l Y_l^m(\theta,\varphi)$$

$$f_0(\mathbf{r},\mathbf{v}_1,t) = n(\mathbf{r},t)\left[\frac{m}{2\pi kT(\mathbf{r},t)}\right]^{3/2} e^{-\xi^2} \tag{1-72}$$

The expansion coefficients, $a_{ln}^{(m)}$, are functions of space and time, and will be determined from the Boltzmann equation. The product $S_{l+1/2}^{(n)}\xi^l Y_l^m$ in the expansion forms a complete orthogonal set in

[14] Cf. Margenau and Murphy, *op. cit.*, pp. 106 and 235.

[15] *Loc. cit.*

$\boldsymbol{\xi}$-space; the maxwellian form for f_0 gives the appropriate weighting factor for the orthogonality condition for the Sonine polynomials, and thus allows the coefficients $a_{ln}^{(m)}$ to be calculated.

The moments of the distribution function can be simply related to the expansion coefficients. Using the fact that $S_{1/2}^{(0)}(\xi^2)$ and $Y_0^{0*}(\theta,\varphi)$ are unity, we have for the number density:

$$\begin{aligned} n(\mathbf{r},t) &= \int f(\mathbf{r},\mathbf{v}_1,t)d\mathbf{v}_1 \\ &= \left(\frac{2kT}{m}\right)^{3/2} \int f(\mathbf{r},\mathbf{v}_1,t) S_{1/2}^{(0)}(\xi^2) Y_0^{0*}(\theta,\varphi)\xi^2 d\xi \sin\theta d\theta d\varphi \\ &= n(\mathbf{r},t)\frac{1}{\pi^{3/2}} \sum_{l,m,n} a_{ln}^{(m)}(\mathbf{r},t) \\ &\qquad \times \int e^{-\xi^2} S_{l+1/2}^{(n)}(\xi^2)\xi^l Y_l^m(\theta,\varphi) S_{1/2}^{(0)}(\xi^2) Y_0^{0*}(\theta,\varphi)\xi^2 \sin\theta d\xi d\theta d\varphi \end{aligned}$$

From the orthogonality condition, only the $l = 0$, $m = 0$, $n = 0$ term remains; the ξ-integration yields $[\Gamma(3/2)/2] = \sqrt{\pi}/4$; the angle integrations yield 4π. Thus:

$$a_{00}^{(0)}(\mathbf{r},t) = 1 \tag{1–73}$$

In a similar manner, the mean velocity can be found by using

$$\begin{aligned} \xi_z &= \xi\cos\theta = S_{3/2}^{(0)}(\xi^2)\xi Y_1^{0*}(\theta,\varphi) \\ \xi_x &= \frac{1}{2} S_{3/2}^{(0)}(\xi^2)\xi[Y_1^{(-1)*}(\theta,\varphi) + Y_1^{(1)*}(\theta,\varphi)] \\ \xi_y &= \frac{1}{2i} S_{3/2}^{(0)}(\xi^2)\xi[Y_1^{(-1)*}(\theta,\varphi) - Y_1^{(1)*}(\theta,\varphi)] \end{aligned}$$

these give the conditions

$$a_{10}^{(0)} = 0; \qquad a_{10}^{(1)} = 0; \qquad a_{10}^{(-1)} = 0 \tag{1–74}$$

Since $\xi^2 = [\frac{3}{2}S_{1/2}^{(0)}(\xi^2) - S_{1/2}^{(1)}(\xi^2)]Y_0^{0*}(\theta,\varphi)$, the definition of the temperature, Eq. (1–45), gives

$$a_{01}^{(0)} = 0 \tag{1–75}$$

These simple values for the first few coefficients are the result of our choice of number density and temperature as multiplicative factors in the zero-order distribution function, and of defining the expansion variable in terms of the mean velocity and temperature.

The components of the pressure tensor and of the heat-flow vector [see Eqs. (1–55), (1–60)] are given by (note that we take, throughout, $p \equiv nkT$)

$$\frac{p_{xx} - p}{p} = 3[a_{20}^{(2)} + a_{20}^{(-2)}] - \tfrac{1}{2}a_{20}^{(0)};$$

$$\frac{p_{yy} - p}{p} = -3[a_{20}^{(2)} + a_{20}^{(-2)}] - \tfrac{1}{2}a_{20}^{(0)}$$

$$\frac{p_{zz} - p}{p} = a_{20}^{(2)} \tag{1–76}$$

$$\frac{p_{xz}}{p} = \tfrac{3}{2}(a_{20}^{(1)} + a_{20}^{(-1)}); \qquad \frac{p_{xy}}{p} = 3i(a_{20}^{(2)} - a_{20}^{(-2)});$$

$$\frac{p_{yz}}{p} = \tfrac{3}{2}i(a_{20}^{(1)} - a_{20}^{(-1)})$$

$$q_x = -\tfrac{5}{4}p\left(\frac{2kT}{m}\right)^{1/2}(a_{11}^{(1)} + a_{11}^{(-1)})$$

$$q_y = -\tfrac{5}{4}p\left(\frac{2kT}{m}\right)^{1/2}i(a_{11}^{(1)} - a_{11}^{(-1)})$$

$$q_z = -\tfrac{5}{4}p\left(\frac{2kT}{m}\right)^{1/2}a_{11}^{(0)}$$

Thus, the unknown forms for the pressure tensor and heat flow vector, which are required in the hydrodynamic equations, can be found when the coefficients are determined.

1.14. Coefficient Equations.—To determine the coefficients of the expansion, the distribution function, Eq. (1–72), is used in the Boltzmann equation; the equation is then multiplied by any one of the polynomials, and integrated over velocity. This gives rise to an infinite set of coupled equations for the coefficients. Only a few of the coefficients appear on the left of each equation; in general, however, all coefficients (and products) appear on the right side due to the nonlinearity of the collision integral. Methods of solving these equations approximately will be discussed in later sections.

Rather than carrying out the calculation for the general case, which yields rather unwieldy expressions, only equations sufficient to obtain certain approximations will be developed. If we multiply the Boltzmann equation, Eq. (1–39), by $1 = S_{1/2}^{(0)}(\xi^2)Y_0^{(0)*}(\theta,\varphi)$, the resulting equation is simply the equation of conservation of mass, since integrating unity over the collision integral gives zero:

$$\frac{\partial n}{\partial t} + \nabla\cdot(n\bar{\mathbf{v}}) = 0 \tag{1–77}$$

This form of the first coefficient equation comes, for reasons noted below Eq. (1–75), from the simple form of the first few coefficients.

When we multiply Eq. (1–39) by $S^{(0)}_{3/2}(\xi^2)\xi Y^{(0)*}_1(\theta,\varphi)$, and integrate over the velocity, the left side of the Boltzmann equation yields three terms, as follows:

$$T^{(1)}_2 = \int S^{(0)}_{3/2}(\xi^2)\xi Y^{(0)*}_1(\theta,\varphi)\frac{\partial f}{\partial t}\,d\mathbf{v}$$
$$= \frac{\partial}{\partial t}\left[\left(\frac{2kT}{m}\right)^{3/2}\int S^{(0)}_{3/2}\xi Y^{(0)*}_1 f d\boldsymbol{\xi}\right] - \left(\frac{2kT}{m}\right)^{3/2}\int f\frac{\partial}{\partial t}[S^{(0)}_{3/2}\xi Y^{(0)*}_1]d\boldsymbol{\xi}$$

where we have changed the variable of integration by using Eq. (1–71), and noted that the factor $(2kT/m)^{3/2}$ is, in general, time (and space) dependent. Now

$$\frac{\partial}{\partial t}[S^{(0)}_{3/2}\xi Y^{(0)*}_1] = -\frac{1}{2T}\frac{\partial T}{\partial t}[S^{(0)}_{3/2}\xi Y^{(0)*}_1] - \left(\frac{m}{2kT}\right)^{1/2}\frac{\partial \bar{v}_z}{\partial t}S^{(0)}_{1/2}Y^{(0)*}_0$$

Making use of the orthonormality conditions, Eq. (1–66),[16] and the previously derived results of Eqs. (1–73), (1–74), we obtain

$$T^{(1)}_2 = n\left(\frac{m}{2kT}\right)^{1/2}\frac{\partial \bar{v}_z}{\partial t}$$

The second term on the left of the Boltzmann equation yields

$$T^{(2)}_2 = \int S^{(0)}_{3/2}(\xi^2)\xi Y^{(0)*}_1(\theta,\varphi)\mathbf{v}\cdot\boldsymbol{\nabla} f d\mathbf{v}$$
$$= \bar{\mathbf{v}}\cdot\left\{\boldsymbol{\nabla}\left[\left(\frac{2kT}{m}\right)^{3/2}\int S^{(0)}_{3/2}\xi Y^{(0)*}_1 f d\boldsymbol{\xi}\right] - \left(\frac{2kT}{m}\right)^{3/2}\int f\boldsymbol{\nabla}[S^{(0)}_{3/2}\xi Y^{(0)*}_1]d\boldsymbol{\xi}\right\}$$
$$+ \left(\frac{2kT}{m}\right)^{1/2}\left\{\boldsymbol{\nabla}\cdot\left[\left(\frac{2kT}{m}\right)^{3/2}\int S^{(0)}_{3/2}\xi Y^{(0)*}_1\boldsymbol{\xi} f d\boldsymbol{\xi}\right] - \left(\frac{2kT}{m}\right)^{3/2}\int f\boldsymbol{\nabla}\cdot[S^{(0)}_{3/2}\xi Y^{(0)*}_1\boldsymbol{\xi}]d\boldsymbol{\xi}\right\}$$

The manipulations are most simply carried out in rectangular coordinates; the result may be written as follows:

$$T^{(2)}_2 = \left(\frac{m}{2kT}\right)^{1/2}\left[n\bar{\mathbf{v}}\cdot\boldsymbol{\nabla}\bar{v}_z + \frac{1}{m}\boldsymbol{\nabla}\cdot(p\mathbf{a}^{(z)}_{20}) + \frac{1}{m}\frac{\partial p}{\partial z}\right]$$

where, as usual $p = nkT$, and we define a new vector

$$\mathbf{a}^{(z)}_{20} \equiv \tfrac{3}{2}(a^{(1)}_{20} + a^{(-1)}_{20})\mathbf{i}_x + \tfrac{3}{2}i(a^{(1)}_{20} - a^{(-1)}_{20})\mathbf{i}_y + a^{(0)}_{20}\mathbf{i}_z \qquad (1\text{–}78)$$

[16] Also, Margenau and Murphy, *op. cit.*, p. 109, Eq. (3.53a).

The third term on the left side of the Boltzmann equation yields

$$T_2^{(3)} = \mathbf{a} \cdot \int S_{3/2}^{(0)}(\xi^2)\xi Y_1^{(0)*}(\theta,\varphi)\nabla_v f d\mathbf{v}$$
$$= \left(\frac{2kT}{m}\right) \mathbf{a} \cdot \left\{ \int \nabla_\xi [S_{3/2}^{(0)}\xi Y_1^{(0)*} f] d\boldsymbol{\xi} - \int f \nabla_\xi [S_{3/2}^{(0)}\xi Y_1^{(0)*}] d\boldsymbol{\xi} \right\}$$

The first integral of this expression goes to zero because f vanishes strongly at $\boldsymbol{\xi} = \pm\infty$; the second yields:

$$T_2^{(3)} = -n\left(\frac{m}{2kT}\right)^{1/2} a_z$$

Since $S_{3/2}^{(0)}\xi Y_1^{(0)*} = \xi_z$, its integral over the collision term is zero (conservation of momentum in a collision). Thus the result of multiplying the Boltzmann equation by $S_{3/2}^{(0)}\xi Y_1^{(0)*}$ and integrating is:

$$\rho\left[\frac{\partial \bar{v}_z}{\partial t} + \bar{\mathbf{v}} \cdot \nabla \bar{v}_z\right] + \nabla \cdot (p\mathbf{a}_{20}^{(z)}) + \frac{\partial p}{\partial z} - \rho a_z = 0 \qquad (1\text{–}79)$$

where $\rho = mn$.

In a similar manner, multiplying Eq. (1–39) by

$$\tfrac{1}{2}S_{3/2}^{(0)}\xi(Y_1^{(-1)*} + Y_1^{(1)*})$$

and by

$$\frac{1}{2i}S_{3/2}^{(0)}\xi(Y_1^{(-1)*} - Y_1^{(1)*})$$

yields, respectively:

$$\rho\left[\frac{\partial \bar{v}_x}{\partial t} + \bar{\mathbf{v}} \cdot \nabla \bar{v}_x\right] + \nabla \cdot (p\mathbf{a}_{20}^{(x)}) + \frac{\partial p}{\partial x} - \rho a_x = 0 \qquad (1\text{–}80)$$

$$\rho\left[\frac{\partial \bar{v}_y}{\partial t} + \bar{\mathbf{v}} \cdot \nabla \bar{v}_y\right] + \nabla \cdot (p\mathbf{a}_{20}^{(y)}) + \frac{\partial p}{\partial y} - \rho a_y = 0 \qquad (1\text{–}81)$$

where

$$\begin{aligned} \mathbf{a}_{20}^{(x)} &= [3(a_{20}^{(2)} + a_{20}^{(-2)}) - \tfrac{1}{2}a_{20}^{(0)}]\mathbf{i}_x + 3i(a_{20}^{(2)} - a_{20}^{(-2)})\mathbf{i}_y \\ &\quad + \tfrac{3}{2}(a_{20}^{(1)} + a_{20}^{(-1)})\mathbf{i}_z \\ \mathbf{a}_{20}^{(y)} &= 3i(a_{20}^{(2)} - a_{20}^{(-2)})\mathbf{i}_x + [-3(a_{20}^{(2)} + a_{20}^{(-2)}) - \tfrac{1}{2}a_{20}^{(0)}]\mathbf{i}_y \\ &\quad + \tfrac{3}{2}i(a_{20}^{(1)} - a_{20}^{(-1)})\mathbf{i}_z \end{aligned} \qquad (1\text{–}82)$$

If we refer to the relations between the expansion coefficients and the components of the pressure tensor, Eqs. (1–76), we see that Eqs.

(1–79), (1–80), (1–81), are, respectively, the z-, x-, and y-components of the hydrodynamic equations of motion.

When we multiply Eq. (1–39) by $S_{1/2}^{(1)} Y_0^{(0)*}$, the integration again gives a collision integral term that goes to zero; the resulting equation is:

$$\frac{\partial T}{\partial t} + \bar{\mathbf{v}} \cdot \nabla T - \frac{m}{3nk} \nabla \cdot \left[n \left(\frac{2kT}{m} \right)^{3/2} \mathbf{a}_{11} \right] + \tfrac{2}{3} T (\boldsymbol{a}_{20} : \nabla \bar{\mathbf{v}}) + \tfrac{2}{3} T \nabla \cdot \bar{\mathbf{v}} = 0 \tag{1–83}$$

where:

$$\mathbf{a}_{11} = \tfrac{5}{4}(a_{11}^{(1)} + a_{11}^{(-1)})\mathbf{i}_x + \tfrac{5}{4} i (a_{11}^{(1)} - a_{11}^{(-1)})\mathbf{i}_y + \tfrac{5}{4} a_{11}^{(0)} \mathbf{i}_z \tag{1–84}$$

The tensor $\boldsymbol{a}_{20}$ may be written in dyadic[17] notation, using Eqs. (1–78) and (1–82), as

$$\boldsymbol{a}_{20} = \mathbf{a}_{20}^{(x)} \mathbf{i}_x + \mathbf{a}_{20}^{(y)} \mathbf{i}_y + \mathbf{a}_{20}^{(z)} \mathbf{i}_z \tag{1–85}$$

and the scalar product is defined in Eq. (1–62). This is the equation of energy flow written in terms of the coefficients; see Eqs. (1–61) and (1–76).

The polynomials used above led to the hydrodynamic equations since they involved only quantities that are conserved in a collision, and thus gave zero for the right side of the integrated equation. All other polynomials of the set, however, give rise to nonzero values for the contribution of the collision integral. For these cases, the evaluation of the left side of the equations is done as previously; the method of evaluation of the collision integral terms will be considered in the next section. For the case of particles with a force law proportional to r^{-5} (usually referred to as "Maxwell" molecules[18]), the evaluation of the collision integral is possible in a closed form. This case leads to only a finite number of single coefficients on the right side of the equation. Other force laws lead to an infinite number of terms, including products of coefficients. In this section we shall consider only the case of Maxwell molecules; the general case, discussed in Section 1.17, gives rise to similar results.

[17] See Margenau and Murphy, *op. cit.*, p. 163. In the dyadic notation, each term of a symmetric tensor contains two unit vectors; scalar multiplication of a dyadic ($\boldsymbol{D}$) and a vector ($\mathbf{V}$), denoted by $\mathbf{V} \cdot \boldsymbol{D}$, gives rise to a vector; scalar multiplication of two dyadics, denoted by $\boldsymbol{D}_1 : \boldsymbol{D}_2$, gives rise to a scalar. Thus, the dyadic $\boldsymbol{a}_{20}$ has terms of the form $a_{20,\beta}^{(\alpha)} \mathbf{i}_\alpha \mathbf{i}_\beta$ ($\equiv a_{20,\alpha}^{(\beta)} \mathbf{i}_\alpha \mathbf{i}_\beta$), where $\alpha, \beta \equiv x,y,z$; $\boldsymbol{a}_{20} \cdot \mathbf{i}_x = \mathbf{i}_x \cdot \boldsymbol{a}_{20} = \mathbf{a}_{20}^{(x)}$; $\boldsymbol{a}_{20} : \mathbf{i}_x \mathbf{i}_y = a_{20,y}^{(x)} = a_{20,x}^{(y)}$.

[18] While mathematically attractive, this force law is of limited interest physically; it represents only the interaction between permanent quadrupoles, and even this with neglect of angles of orientation. However, although the details of the dependence of viscosity upon temperature are affected by the force law used, the general form of the hydrodynamic equation in the Navier-Stokes approximation is not affected.

The use of $S_{5/2}^{(0)}\xi^2 Y_2^{(0)*}$, and $S_{3/2}^{(1)}\xi Y_1^{(0)*}$, to multiply Eq. (1–39), gives rise upon integration to:

$$\left(\frac{\partial}{\partial t} + \bar{\mathbf{v}}\cdot\nabla\right)[pa_{20}^{(0)}] + pa_{20}^{(0)}\nabla\cdot\bar{\mathbf{v}} + 2p\mathbf{a}_{20}^{(z)}\cdot\nabla\bar{v}_z - \tfrac{2}{3}p[\boldsymbol{a}_{20}:\nabla\bar{\mathbf{v}}]$$
$$+ \frac{4}{15}\nabla\cdot\left[p\left(\frac{2kT}{m}\right)^{1/2}(\mathbf{a}_{11} + \tfrac{45}{4}\mathbf{a}_{30}^{(z)})\right] + 2p\left[\frac{\partial\bar{v}_z}{\partial z} - \tfrac{1}{3}\nabla\cdot\bar{\mathbf{v}}\right]$$
$$= -\frac{p^2}{\mu}a_{20}^{(0)} \qquad (1\text{–}86)$$

$$\left(\frac{\partial}{\partial t} + \bar{\mathbf{v}}\cdot\nabla\right)\left[p\left(\frac{2kT}{m}\right)^{1/2}a_{11}^{(0)}\right] + \frac{7}{5}\left[p\left(\frac{2kT}{m}\right)^{1/2}a_{11}^{(0)}\right]\nabla\cdot\bar{\mathbf{v}}$$
$$+ \frac{2}{5}p\left(\frac{2kT}{m}\right)^{1/2}\left[(a_{11}^{(1)} + a_{11}^{(-1)})\left(\frac{\partial\bar{v}_z}{\partial x} + \frac{\partial\bar{v}_x}{\partial z}\right)\right.$$
$$\left. + i(a_{11}^{(1)} - a_{11}^{(-1)})\left(\frac{\partial\bar{v}_z}{\partial y} + \frac{\partial\bar{v}_y}{\partial z}\right) + 2\mathbf{a}_{11}\cdot\nabla\bar{v}_z\right]$$
$$+ \frac{14}{5}\nabla\cdot\left[\frac{p^2}{\rho}\mathbf{a}_{21}\right] - 2p\mathbf{a}_{20}^{(z)}\cdot\nabla(p/\rho) - \frac{4}{5}\frac{p}{\rho}\nabla\cdot(p\mathbf{a}_{20}^{(z)})$$
$$+ \frac{4}{5}\frac{p}{\rho}\mathbf{a}_{20}^{(z)}\cdot\nabla\cdot(p\boldsymbol{a}_{20}) - \frac{12}{5}p\left(\frac{2kT}{m}\right)^{1/2}(\boldsymbol{a}_{30}:\nabla\bar{\mathbf{v}}) - 2p\frac{\partial}{\partial z}(p/\rho)$$
$$= -\frac{5}{2}\frac{k}{m}\frac{p^2}{\lambda}\left(\frac{2kT}{m}\right)^{1/2}a_{11}^{(0)} \qquad (1\text{–}87)$$

In the above equations, we have made use of Eqs. (1–77), (1–79), and (1–83) to obtain only a single time-derivative term; the vectors and dyadics are defined in Eqs. (1–78), (1–80), (1–81), (1–84), (1–85), and by:

$$\mathbf{a}_{21} = \tfrac{3}{2}(a_{21}^{(1)} + a_{21}^{(-1)})\mathbf{i}_x + \tfrac{3}{2}i(a_{21}^{(1)} - a_{21}^{(-1)})\mathbf{i}_y + (a_{21}^{(0)} - \tfrac{5}{7}a_{02}^{(0)})\mathbf{i}_z$$
$$\mathbf{a}_{30}^{(x)} = [\tfrac{5}{2}(a_{30}^{(2)} + a_{30}^{(-2)}) - \tfrac{1}{4}a_{30}^{(0)}]\mathbf{i}_x + \tfrac{5}{2}i(a_{30}^{(2)} - a_{30}^{(-2)})\mathbf{i}_y + (a_{30}^{(1)} + a_{30}^{(-1)})\mathbf{i}_z$$
$$\mathbf{a}_{30}^{(y)} = \tfrac{5}{2}i(a_{30}^{(2)} - a_{30}^{(-2)})\mathbf{i}_x + [-\tfrac{5}{2}(a_{30}^{(2)} + a_{30}^{(-2)}) - \tfrac{1}{4}a_{30}^{(0)}]\mathbf{i}_y + i(a_{30}^{(1)} - a_{30}^{(-1)})\mathbf{i}_z \qquad (1\text{–}88)$$
$$\mathbf{a}_{30}^{(z)} = (a_{30}^{(1)} + a_{30}^{(-1)})\mathbf{i}_x + i(a_{30}^{(1)} - a_{30}^{(-1)})\mathbf{i}_y + (\tfrac{1}{2}a_{30}^{(0)} - \tfrac{1}{3}a_{11}^{(0)})\mathbf{i}_z$$
$$\boldsymbol{a}_{30} = \mathbf{a}_{30}^{(x)}\mathbf{i}_x + \mathbf{a}_{30}^{(y)}\mathbf{i}_y + \mathbf{a}_{30}^{(z)}\mathbf{i}_z$$

As noted previously, Eqs. (1–86) and (1–87) are valid for an interparticle force law of $F = K/r^5$; this gives rise to the single terms on the right side of these equations. The factors μ and λ are defined in the next section by Eqs. (1–96) and (1–98); again, we have used $p = nkT$.

This procedure of multiplication by one of the members of the orthogonal set of functions and integration can be continued. The equations developed above will be sufficient to obtain the Navier-Stokes approximation to the hydrodynamic equations; higher order approximations require more coefficient equations.

1.15. Collision Integrals.—The collision integral for Eq. (1–86) is evaluated from the right side of the Boltzmann equation, Eq. (1–39), by multiplying by $S^{(0)}_{5/2}\xi^2 Y^{(0)*}_2$ and integrating; we obtain:

$$C^0_{20} \equiv C[S^{(0)}_{1/2}\xi^2 Y^{(0)*}_2] \equiv -\int S^{(0)}_{5/2}\xi^2 Y^{(0)*}_2[f_1 f_2 - f_1' f_2']gb\,db\,d\varepsilon\,d\mathbf{v}_2 d\mathbf{v}_1$$

$$= \left(\frac{m}{2kT}\right)^3 \int [S^{(0)}_{5/2}(\xi'^2)\xi'^2 Y^{(0)*}_2(\theta',\varphi') - S^{(0)}_{5/2}(\xi^2)\xi^2 Y^{(0)*}_2(\theta,\varphi)] \\ f(\boldsymbol{\xi})f(\boldsymbol{\xi}_1)gb\,db\,d\varepsilon\,d\boldsymbol{\xi}d\boldsymbol{\xi}_1 \quad (1\text{–}89)$$

We have used the transformation of Eq. (1–62); the definition of $\boldsymbol{\xi}$ in Eq. (1–71) and $\boldsymbol{\xi}_1 = (m/2kT)^{1/2}[\mathbf{v}_2 - \bar{\mathbf{v}}]$; furthermore $\boldsymbol{\xi}'$ is the (reduced) velocity vector of the first particle after the collision. Expanding the polynomials, we find $S^0_{5/2}\xi^2 Y^{0*}_2 = \frac{3}{2}\xi^2_z - \frac{1}{2}\xi^2$; noting that the collision integral taken over the ξ^2 term gives zero (conservation of energy), we have:

$$C^0_{20} = \tfrac{3}{2}C(\xi^2_z) \quad (1\text{–}90)$$

We shall first perform the ε integration, then that over b; the $\boldsymbol{\xi}$ and $\boldsymbol{\xi}_1$ integrations will be done last.

Using Eqs. (1–71) and (1–20), the ξ'-term in the bracket of the collision integral is written in terms of $\mathbf{G}$ and $\mathbf{g}'$ (where now $\mathbf{G}$ is defined as the center of mass velocity of the colliding particles, taken with respect to the mean flow velocity, that is, we use the definition of Eq. (1–7) minus $\bar{\mathbf{v}}$). Equation (1–31) is used to obtain the ξ'-term in terms of the angles (ϑ,ψ) of the relative velocity $\mathbf{g} = \mathbf{v}_2 - \mathbf{v}_1$ in the $(\mathbf{i}_x,\mathbf{i}_y,\mathbf{i}_z)$ coordinate system, and the angles of scattering χ and ε. The ξ-term in the bracket of the collision integral may be obtained from the ξ'-term by setting $\chi = 0$; thus:

$$\xi'^2_z - \xi^2_z = \left(\frac{m}{2kT}\right)\{-gG_z[\cos\vartheta(\cos\chi - 1) - \sin\vartheta\sin\chi\sin\varepsilon] \\ + \tfrac{1}{4}g^2[\cos^2\vartheta(\cos^2\chi - 1) \\ - 2\sin\vartheta\cos\vartheta\sin\chi\cos\chi\sin\varepsilon \\ + \sin^2\vartheta\sin^2\chi\sin^2\varepsilon]\}$$

The ε-integration may now be carried out in straightforward fashion. The b-integration involves the mechanics of the collision [through the scattering angle $\chi = \chi(b)$, from Eqs. (1–10) to (1–12)], and, therefore, depends upon the interparticle force law. For the simple inverse power law the b-integration gives terms of the form:

$$\phi^l(g) \equiv \int (1 - \cos^l\chi)gb\,db = \left(\frac{2K}{m}\right)^{2/(\nu-1)} g^{(\nu-5)/(\nu-1)}A_l(\nu) \quad (1\text{–}91)$$

where K and ν are the force constants [see Eq. (1–13)] and $A_l(\nu)$ is a pure number

$$A_l(\nu) = \int_0^\infty [1 - \cos^l \chi(b_0)]b_0 db_0 \tag{1–92}$$

[see Eq. (1–16)]. Thus:

$$\begin{aligned} T(\boldsymbol{\xi},\boldsymbol{\xi}_1) &\equiv \int (\xi_z'^2 - \xi_z^2) gb\, db\, d\varepsilon \\ &= 2\pi \left(\frac{m}{2kT}\right)\left(\frac{2K}{m}\right)^{2/(\nu-1)} g^{(\nu-5)/(\nu-1)} \\ &\qquad \times [G_z g \cos\vartheta A_1(\nu) + \tfrac{1}{8} g^2(1 - 3\cos^2\vartheta)A_2(\nu)] \end{aligned} \tag{1–93}$$

Further evaluation of the integrals for the general case of a ν-power law will be discussed in Section 1.17; the calculation for $\nu = 5$, the Maxwell molecule force law, gives typical results, and will be completed here.

The components of $\mathbf{G}$ (which, as was noted above, are taken with respect to the mean flow velocity) and $\mathbf{g}$, which enter Eq. (1–93), are now rewritten in terms of $\boldsymbol{\xi}$ and $\boldsymbol{\xi}_1$:

$$\begin{aligned} T(\boldsymbol{\xi},\boldsymbol{\xi}_1) = \pi\left(\frac{2K}{m}\right)^{1/2} \{(\xi_{1z}^2 - \xi_z^2)A_1(5) + \tfrac{1}{4}[(\xi_{1x} - \xi_x)^2 \\ + (\xi_{1y} - \xi_y)^2 - 2(\xi_{1z} - \xi_z)^2]A_2(5)\} \end{aligned}$$

The $\boldsymbol{\xi}$ and $\boldsymbol{\xi}_1$ terms above are written in terms of members of the orthogonal polynomial set, and are used in the remaining integrals of Eq. (1–89) (the $\boldsymbol{\xi}$ and $\boldsymbol{\xi}_1$ integrals)

$$\begin{aligned} C_{20}^0 = \frac{3}{2}\frac{n^2}{\pi^3} \iint d\boldsymbol{\xi}\, d\boldsymbol{\xi}_1 e^{-(\xi^2+\xi_1^2)} T(\boldsymbol{\xi},\boldsymbol{\xi}_1) \\ \times \Biggl\{ \sum_{\substack{l,m,n \\ l',m',n'}} a_{ln}^{(m)} a_{l'n'}^{(m')} S_{l+1/2}^{(n)}(\xi^2)\xi^l Y_l^{(m)}(\theta,\varphi) \\ \times S_{l'+1/2}^{(n')}(\xi_1^2)\xi_1^{l'} Y_{l'}^{(m')}(\theta_1,\varphi_1)\Biggr\} \end{aligned} \tag{1–94}$$

By means of the orthonormality conditions, Eq. (1–66),[19] we obtain:

$$C_{20}^0 = -\frac{9\pi}{8} n^2 \left(\frac{2K}{m}\right)^{1/2} A_2(5) a_{20}^{(0)} \tag{1–95}$$

In Eq. (1–86), we have defined the coefficient of viscosity (for a $\nu = 5$ power law), using this value of C_{20}^0, as:

$$\mu = \frac{2}{3\pi}\left(\frac{m}{2K}\right)^{1/2} \frac{kT}{A_2(5)} \tag{1–96}$$

[19] See also Margenau and Murphy, *op. cit.*, Eq. (3–53a).

The collision integral for Eq. (1–87) may be developed in the same manner and yields for Maxwell molecules:

$$C_{11}^0 = -\frac{5\pi}{4}\left(\frac{2K}{m}\right)^{1/2} n^2 A_2(5) a_{11}^{(0)} \tag{1–97}$$

This gives a thermal conductivity

$$\lambda = \frac{5}{2\pi}\left(\frac{m}{2K}\right)^{1/2} \frac{k^2 T}{m A_2(5)} \equiv \frac{15}{4}\frac{k}{m}\mu \tag{1–98}$$

1.16. Chapman-Enskog Solution.—The solution of the Boltzmann equation obtained by Chapman and Enskog involves the assumption that the moments of the distribution function beyond the first five $[n(\mathbf{r},t), \bar{\mathbf{v}}(\mathbf{r},t), T(\mathbf{r},t)]$ can be written in terms of these first five moments. For the Burnett expansion, this method of development can be obtained by an iteration technique based upon the idea that the effects due to viscosity are small; thus, the Euler equations ($\mu = 0$) would be expected to be a zero-order, and the Navier-Stokes equations a first-order, approximation.

It was shown, in Eqs. (1–73), (1–74), (1–75), that $a_{00}^{(0)} = 1$, $a_{10}^{(0,\pm 1)} = 0$, $a_{01}^{(0)} = 0$. As the zeroth approximation we shall assume that λ and μ are zero (their effects are negligibly small); if Eqs. (1–86) and (1–87) are multiplied by μ and λ, respectively, we obtain the condition that a_{20}^0 and a_{11}^0 are zero; higher order equations would show that all the coefficients are zero. Thus, the coefficients are proportional to some power of μ (or λ). The zero-order approximation to the distribution function is just the local maxwellian distribution

$$f^{(0)}(\mathbf{r},\mathbf{v}_1,t) = n(\mathbf{r},t)\left[\frac{m}{2\pi k T(\mathbf{r},t)}\right]^{3/2} e^{-\{m[\mathbf{v}_1 - \bar{\mathbf{v}}(\mathbf{r},t)]^2\}/2kT(\mathbf{r},t)} \tag{1–99}$$

From Eqs. (1–76), the zero-order approximations to the pressure tensor and heat flow vector are:

$$\boldsymbol{p} = p\boldsymbol{I}; \qquad \mathbf{q} = 0 \tag{1–100}$$

where $\boldsymbol{I}$ is the unit tensor, and, as usual, $p \equiv nkT$. The coefficient equations, Eq. (1–79) to (1–81), and (1–83) are just the Euler equations of motion for a nonviscous fluid having zero heat conductivity:

$$\begin{aligned} \rho\left[\frac{\partial \bar{\mathbf{v}}}{\partial t} + \bar{\mathbf{v}}\cdot\nabla\bar{\mathbf{v}}\right] + \nabla p - \rho\mathbf{a} = 0, \quad p = nkT \\ \frac{\partial T}{\partial t} + \bar{\mathbf{v}}\cdot\nabla T + \tfrac{2}{3}T\nabla\cdot\bar{\mathbf{v}} = 0 \end{aligned} \tag{1–101}$$

All other coefficient equations are identically zero. The second of Eq. (1–101), combined with the equation of conservation of mass, Eq. (1–77), shows that the motion is isentropic:

$$nT^{-3/2} = \text{const.} \tag{1–102}$$

with γ, the ratio of specific heats, being equal to 5/3; this is the ratio of specific heats expected for a gas having only translational degrees of freedom, since the particles of the gas were assumed to have no internal degrees of freedom.

The first order approximation may be found by assuming μ and λ to be small, but not zero. If Eq. (1–86) is multiplied by μ, all coefficients on the left side, being proportional to some power of μ, give terms proportional to higher powers of μ than the first; only the last term on the left (which is not multiplied by one of the coefficients) will be proportional to the first power of μ. The first-order approximation to $a_{20}^{(0)}$ is therefore:

$$a_{20}^{(0)} = -\frac{2\mu}{p}\left[\frac{\partial \bar{v}_z}{\partial z} - \tfrac{1}{3}\nabla\cdot\bar{\mathbf{v}}\right] \tag{1–103}$$

Similarly, from Eq. (1–87):

$$a_{11}^{(0)} = \frac{4}{5}\frac{\lambda}{p}\left(\frac{m}{2kT}\right)^{1/2}\frac{\partial T}{\partial z} \tag{1–104}$$

Eqs. (1–76) show that these values of the coefficients produce the Navier-Stokes approximations to p_{zz} and q_z [see Eq. (1–63)]; the other components of $\boldsymbol{p}$ and $\mathbf{q}$ may be found from coefficient equations similar to Eq. (1–86) and (1–87) (or, by a rotation of coordinate axes). The first approximation to the distribution function (for this case of Maxwell molecules) is:

$$f^{(1)}(\mathbf{r},\mathbf{v}_1,t) = n\left(\frac{m}{2\pi kT}\right)^{3/2} e^{-[m(\mathbf{v}_1-\bar{\mathbf{v}})^2]/2kT}$$
$$\times\,[1 + A(\xi)\boldsymbol{\xi}\cdot\nabla T + B(\xi)(\boldsymbol{\xi}\boldsymbol{\xi} - \tfrac{1}{3}\xi^2\boldsymbol{I}):\nabla\bar{\mathbf{v}}]$$
$$A(\xi) = \frac{4}{5}\left(\frac{m}{2kT}\right)^{1/2}\frac{\lambda}{p}S_{5/2}^{(1)}(\xi^2); \qquad B(\xi) = -\frac{2\mu}{p}S_{5/2}^{(0)}(\xi^2)$$

The iteration procedure may be continued; more coefficient equations can be obtained, and then solved as previously. This would yield second approximations to $a_{20}^{(0)}$ (and the other $a_{20}^{(m)}$) and $a_{11}^{(0)}$ (and $a_{11}^{(\pm 1)}$) which are proportional to μ^2, to second derivatives and squares of first derivatives of mean velocity and temperature.

1.17. Case of General Central Force Law.—The evaluation of the collision integrals for the viscosity, Eq. (1–89), was simplified for the case of the intermolecular force law proportional to r^{-5} because the integration over the scattering angle, Eq. (1–91), was then independent of the relative velocity g. For the case of a general force law the physical picture does not change markedly, but the expression for the viscosity (and the thermal conductivity) does change. We shall carry out the calculation of the viscosity for a general central force law, $F = K/r^\nu$, to illustrate some of the differences.

Since the expression in Eq. (1–93), which must be used in Eq. (1–89), involves a nonintegral power of g, the evaluation of the $\boldsymbol{\xi}$ and $\boldsymbol{\xi}_1$ integrations is best carried out in a g-dependent coordinate system. We may form dimensionless coordinates $\mathbf{G}_0,\mathbf{g}_0$ in terms of the $\mathbf{G},\mathbf{g}$ system used in Eq. (1–93) (where, again, $\mathbf{G}$ is defined with respect to the mean flow velocity $\bar{\mathbf{v}}$):

$$\mathbf{g}_0 = \frac{1}{\sqrt{2}}\left(\frac{m}{2kT}\right)^{1/2}\mathbf{g} = \frac{1}{\sqrt{2}}(\boldsymbol{\xi}_1 - \boldsymbol{\xi}); \qquad \mathbf{g}_0 = (g_0,\vartheta,\psi)$$

$$\mathbf{G}_0 = \sqrt{2}\left(\frac{m}{2kT}\right)^{1/2}\mathbf{G} = \frac{1}{\sqrt{2}}(\boldsymbol{\xi}_1 + \boldsymbol{\xi}); \qquad \mathbf{G}_0 = (G_0,\vartheta_1,\psi_1) \tag{1–106}$$

$$d\mathbf{G}_0 d\mathbf{g}_0 = d\boldsymbol{\xi}_1 d\boldsymbol{\xi}; \qquad \xi_1^2 + \xi^2 = G_0^2 + g_0^2$$

Thus, using Eq. (1–106) in Eqs. (1–93) and (1–89), we have:

$$C_{20}^0 = 3\pi\left(\frac{2kT}{m}\right)^3\left(\frac{2K}{m}\right)^{2/(\nu-1)}\left(\frac{4kT}{m}\right)^{(\nu-5)/2(\nu-1)}$$
$$\iint d\mathbf{G}_0 d\mathbf{g}_0[G_0 g_0 \cos\vartheta_1 \cos\vartheta\, g_0^{(\nu-5)/(\nu-1)}A_1(\nu)$$
$$+ \tfrac{1}{4}(g_0^2 - 3g_0^2\cos^2\vartheta)g_0^{(\nu-5)/(\nu-1)}A_2(\nu)]f(\boldsymbol{\xi})f(\boldsymbol{\xi}_1) \tag{1–107}$$

where:

$$f(\boldsymbol{\xi})f(\boldsymbol{\xi}_1) =$$
$$n^2\left(\frac{m}{2\pi kT}\right)^3 e^{-(\xi^2+\xi_1^2)}\sum_{\substack{lmn\\l'm'n'}} a_{ln}^{(m)}a_{l'n'}^{(m')}S_{l+1/2}^{(n)}(\xi^2)\xi^l Y_l^m(\theta,\varphi)$$
$$S_{l'+1/2}^{(n')}(\xi_1^2)\xi_1^{l'}Y_{l'}^{m'}(\theta_1,\varphi_1) \tag{1–108}$$

However, $f(\boldsymbol{\xi})f(\boldsymbol{\xi}_1)$ can be written as a function of $\mathbf{g}_0$ and $\mathbf{G}_0$, and may, therefore, be expanded in terms of polynomials in (g_0,ϑ,ψ) and (G_0,ϑ_1,ψ_1):

$$f(\boldsymbol{\xi})f(\boldsymbol{\xi}_1) = n^2\left(\frac{m}{2\pi kT}\right)^3 e^{-(G_0^2+g_0^2)}$$
$$\sum_{\substack{rst\\r's't'}} b_{rst}^{r's't'}S_{s+1/2}^{(r)}(g_0^2)g_0^s Y_s^t(\vartheta,\psi)S_{s'+1/2}^{(r')}(G_0^2)G_0^{s'}Y_{s'}^{t'}(\vartheta_1,\psi_1) \tag{1–109}$$

The relationship between the $b_{rst}^{r's't'}$ of Eq. (1–109) and the a_{ln}^m of Eq.

(1–108) may be found by multiplying Eq. (1–109) by a set of polynomials in $\mathbf{g}_0$ and $\mathbf{G}_0$, and integrating, while the same set is written in terms of the polynomials in $\boldsymbol{\xi}$ and $\boldsymbol{\xi}_1$, using Eqs. (1–106), and similarly used in Eq. (1–108).

The term in brackets in Eq. (1–107) can be written in terms of the polynomial set of Eq. (1–109):

$$
\begin{aligned}
T &= G_0 g_0 \cos\vartheta \cos\vartheta_1 g_0^{(\nu-5)/(\nu-1)} A_1(\nu) \\
&\qquad\qquad + \tfrac{1}{4}(g_0^2 - 3g_0^2\cos^2\vartheta) g_0{}^{(\nu-5)/(\nu-1)} A_2(\nu) \\
&= S_{3/2}^{(0)}(g_0^2) g_0 Y_1^0(\vartheta,\psi) S_{3/2}^{(0)}(G_0^2) G_0 Y_1^0(\vartheta_1,\psi_1) g_0^{(\nu-5)/(\nu-1)} A_1(\nu) \\
&\quad - \tfrac{1}{2} S_{5/2}^{(0)}(g_0^2) g_0^2 Y_2^0(\vartheta,\psi) S_{1/2}^{(0)}(G_0^2) Y_0^0(\vartheta_1,\psi_1) g_0^{(\nu-5)/(\nu-1)} A_2(\nu)
\end{aligned}
$$

This expression is substituted in Eq. (1–107), and the product $f(\boldsymbol{\xi})f(\boldsymbol{\xi}_1)$ is replaced by the expansion Eq. (1–109); the integrations over $\mathbf{G}_0$, and over the angles ϑ and ψ of $\mathbf{g}_0$, can be performed. These integrations, by the orthogonality property of the polynomials give zero except for particular values of s, t, s', t', and r'; only the $g_0^2 dg_0$ integration remains. Since $S_{3/2}^0(g_0^2) = 1$, the result is

$$
\begin{aligned}
C_{20}^0 &= -\frac{6\sqrt{\pi}}{5} n^2 \left(\frac{2K}{m}\right)^{2/(\nu-1)} \left(\frac{4kT}{m}\right)^{(\nu-5)/2(\nu-1)} A_2(\nu) \\
&\quad \times \sum_r b_{r20}^{000} \int_0^\infty S_{5/2}^{(r)}(g_0^2) g_0^{6+(\nu-5)/(\nu-1)} e^{-g_0^2} dg_0 \\
&= -\frac{3\sqrt{\pi}}{5} n^2 \left(\frac{2K}{m}\right)^{2/(\nu-1)} \left(\frac{4kT}{m}\right)^{(\nu-5)/2(\nu-1)} A_2(\nu)\Gamma\left(4 - \frac{2}{\nu-1}\right) \\
&\quad \times \left\{ b_{020}^{000} + \frac{1}{2}\left[\frac{4}{\nu-1} - 1\right] b_{120}^{000} + \frac{1}{8}\left[\frac{16}{(\nu-1)^2} - 1\right] b_{220}^{000} + \cdots \right\}
\end{aligned}
\tag{1–110}
$$

The $A_1(\nu)$ term integrates to zero, since it is proportional to:

$$
\begin{aligned}
I_1 &= \iint dG_0 dg_0 S_{3/2}^{(0)}(g_0^2) g_0 Y_1^0(\vartheta,\psi) G_0 Y_1^0(\vartheta_1,\psi_1) g_0^{(\nu-5)/(\nu-1)} f f_1 \\
&\sim \iint d\boldsymbol{\xi} d\boldsymbol{\xi}_1 S_{3/2}^{(0)}(\tfrac{1}{2}|\boldsymbol{\xi}_1 - \boldsymbol{\xi}|^2)(\xi_{1z}^2 - \xi_z^2)|\boldsymbol{\xi}_1 - \boldsymbol{\xi}|^{(\nu-5)/(\nu-1)} f(\boldsymbol{\xi}) f(\boldsymbol{\xi}_1)
\end{aligned}
$$

Interchanging $\boldsymbol{\xi}$ and $\boldsymbol{\xi}_1$ in the latter integral, we find that $I_1 = -I_1$, so that

$$I_1 = 0 \tag{1–111}$$

By the procedures outlined below Eq. (1–109), we find

$$b_{020}^{000} = a_{20}^{(0)};\ b_{120}^{000} = \tfrac{1}{2} a_{21}^{(0)} - \tfrac{1}{14} a_{20}^{(0)} a_{20}^{(0)} - \tfrac{3}{7} a_{20}^{(1)} a_{20}^{(-1)} + \tfrac{24}{7} a_{20}^{(2)} a_{20}^{(-2)} \tag{1–112}$$

If the above results are used in the linear approximation (squares of coefficients neglected) of the Chapman-Enskog-Burnett iteration scheme, the higher order terms (such as $a_{21}^{(0)}$) no longer are equal to zero (from the higher order equations, see below), but can be expected to be small. As a first approximation, within the linear approximation, we may take these higher order terms to be zero; the value for the collision integral C_{20}^{0} is thus again proportional to $a_{20}^{(0)}$, which then has the same form, Eq. (1–103), as for the Maxwell molecule case. However, the viscosity, Eq. (1–95), for the general central field intermolecular force law has the value

$$\mu_1(\nu) = \frac{5}{8\sqrt{\pi}} (kmT)^{1/2}(2kT/K)^{2/(\nu-1)}/A_2(\nu)\Gamma\left(4 - \frac{2}{\nu - 1}\right) \tag{1–113}$$

To the same order of approximation of the equations, that is, with only terms linear in $\mu_1(\nu)$ kept, better approximations to the viscosity may be found by considering the equations of higher order than Eqs. (1–86) and (1–87). These new equations will, to this order of approximation, have zero on the left sides (since the higher order coefficients are taken equal to zero); on the right sides appears the factor (p/μ_1) multiplied by a series of terms like those in Eq. (1–110). Using these equations, and the first order terms of Eq. (1–86) for arbitrary ν,

$$2p\left[\frac{\partial \bar{v}_z}{\partial z} - \frac{1}{3}\nabla\cdot\bar{\mathbf{v}}\right] = -\frac{n^2k^2T^2}{\mu_1(\nu)}\left[a_{20}^{(0)} + \frac{1}{4}\left(\frac{4}{\nu - 1} - 1\right)a_{21}^{(0)} + \cdots\right] \tag{1–114}$$

[where μ_1 is given by Eq. (1–113)], one may obtain successive approximations to $a_{20}^{(0)}$ (and to $a_{21}^{(0)}\ldots$), which are linear in μ_1. These approximations to $a_{20}^{(0)}$ are of the same form as Eq. (1–104), with μ given by:[20]

$$\mu(\nu) = \mu_1(\nu)\left[1 + \frac{3(\nu - 5)^2}{2(\nu - 1)(101\nu - 113)} + \cdots\right] \tag{1–115}$$

A similar approximation scheme, which gives successive approximations, in first order, to $a_{11}^{(0)}$ can be developed; the thermal conductivity for the central force law is:

$$\lambda(\nu) = \lambda_1(\nu)\left[1 + \frac{(\nu - 5)^2}{4(\nu - 1)(11\nu - 13)} + \cdots\right];$$
$$\lambda_1(\nu) = \frac{15}{4}\frac{k}{m}\mu_1(\nu) \tag{1–116}$$

As noted at the end of Section 1.16, approximations to $a_{20}^{(0)}$ and $a_{11}^{(0)}$,

[20] Chapman and Cowling, *op. cit.*, p. 173.

which are of higher order in μ (and in derivatives of velocity and temperature), can be obtained by keeping coefficients of first order in μ in the equations, and iterating as before.

1.18. Grad's Solution.—Since the Chapman-Enskog method of solution develops the distribution function in terms of its first five moments, it determines only a special class of solutions of Boltzmann's equation. H. Grad[21] has investigated solutions obtained by solving the coefficient equations simultaneously, rather than by an iteration procedure. His simplest approximation, the *thirteen moment solution,* is based upon the same equations as those that lead to the Navier-Stokes approximation; however, by not basing the solution on the first five moments, as is done in the Burnett iteration, he obtains a solution that should be valid for a larger class of physical problems.

To see the type of differences that arises between an iterative solution and a simultaneous solution of the coefficient equations, we may proceed as follows. For the thirteen moment approximation, we shall allow the distribution function to have only thirteen nonzero moments, namely: n, $\bar{\mathbf{v}}$, T, $\boldsymbol{p}$, $\mathbf{q}$ [$\boldsymbol{p}$ has only five independent moments, since it is symmetric, and obeys Eq. (1–56)]. For the coefficients, we therefore keep $a_{00}^{(0)}$, $a_{10}^{(0,\pm 1)}$, $a_{01}^{(0)}$, $a_{20}^{(0,\pm 1,\pm 2)}$, $a_{11}^{(0,\pm 1)}$; the first five of these are known, through Eqs. (1–73) to (1–75), since these values come from using n, $\bar{\mathbf{v}}$, T in the definition of the zero-order distribution function. The coefficient equations, Eqs. (1–77), (1–79)–(1–81), (1–83), remain the same; in place of Eqs. (1–86) and (1–87), we use (for the r^{-5} force law case):

$$\left(\frac{\partial}{\partial t} + \bar{\mathbf{v}}\cdot\boldsymbol{\nabla}\right)[pa_{20}^{(0)}] + pa_{20}^{(0)}\boldsymbol{\nabla}\cdot\bar{\mathbf{v}} + 2p\mathbf{a}_{20}^{(z)}\cdot\boldsymbol{\nabla}\bar{v}_z - \tfrac{2}{3}p[\boldsymbol{a}_{20}:\boldsymbol{\nabla}\bar{\mathbf{v}}]$$
$$+ \tfrac{4}{15}\boldsymbol{\nabla}\cdot\left[p\left(\frac{2kT}{m}\right)^{1/2}(\mathbf{a}_{11} - \tfrac{15}{4}a_{10}^{(0)}\mathbf{i}_z)\right]$$
$$+ 2p\left[\frac{\partial\bar{v}_z}{\partial z} - \tfrac{1}{3}\boldsymbol{\nabla}\cdot\bar{\mathbf{v}}\right] = -\frac{p^2}{\mu}a_{20}^{(0)} \qquad (1\text{–}117)$$

$$\left(\frac{\partial}{\partial t} + \bar{\mathbf{v}}\cdot\nabla\right)\left[p\left(\frac{2kT}{m}\right)^{1/2}a_{11}^{(0)}\right] + \frac{7}{5}\left[p\left(\frac{2kT}{m}\right)^{1/2}a_{11}^{(0)}\right]\nabla\cdot\bar{\mathbf{v}}$$
$$+ \frac{28}{25}p\left(\frac{2kT}{m}\right)^{1/2}\mathbf{a}_{11}\cdot\nabla\bar{v}_z + \frac{8}{25}p\left(\frac{2kT}{m}\right)^{1/2}\mathbf{a}_{11}\cdot\frac{\partial\bar{\mathbf{v}}}{\partial z}$$
$$- 2p\mathbf{a}_{20}^{(z)}\cdot\nabla\left(\frac{p}{\rho}\right) - \frac{4}{5}\frac{p}{\rho}\nabla\cdot(p\mathbf{a}_{20}^{(z)}) + \frac{4}{5}\frac{p}{\rho}\mathbf{a}_{20}^{(z)}\cdot\nabla\cdot(p\boldsymbol{a}_{20})$$
$$- 2p\frac{\partial}{\partial z}(p/\rho) = -\frac{5}{2}\frac{k}{m}\frac{p^2}{\lambda}\left(\frac{2kT}{m}\right)^{1/2}a_{11}^{(0)} \qquad (1\text{–}118)$$

[21] H. Grad, "On the Kinetic Theory of Rarefied Gases," *Communs. Pure and Appl. Math.*, **2**, 331 (1949).

These equations, with six further equations for the other components of $\mathbf{a}_{20}$ and $\mathbf{a}_{11}$, when solved by the Burnett iteration procedure, yield the Navier-Stokes equations; when solved simultaneously, however, there is no longer the simple dependence of the pressure tensor upon the velocity gradients, and of the heat flow upon the temperature gradient, but, rather, an interdependence of these relations.

To illustrate, consider the case where ρ (or n), $\bar{\mathbf{v}}$, and T are constants and the coefficients are functions of time only. Equations (1–77), (1–79) to (1–81), and (1–83) are identically zero, while Eqs. (1–117) and (1–118) become

$$\frac{\partial}{\partial t}(pa_{20}^{(0)}) = -\frac{p^2}{\mu}a_{20}^{(0)};$$

$$\frac{\partial}{\partial t}\left[p\left(\frac{2kT}{m}\right)^{1/2}a_{11}^{(0)}\right] = -\frac{5}{2}\frac{k}{m}\frac{p^2}{\lambda}\left(\frac{2kT}{m}\right)^{1/2}a_{11}^{(0)} \tag{1–119}$$

Using the equations for the moments in terms of the coefficients, Eq. (1–76), we see that

$$p_{zz} - p = c_1e^{-t/\tau}; \qquad q_z = c_2e^{-2t/3\tau} \tag{1–120}$$
$$\tau = \mu/p$$

where c_1 and c_2 are constants. Since μ/p is of the order of the time between collisions, we see that, in this simple case, the pressure tensor and heat flow vector deviate from their "normal" values ($p\mathbf{I}$, and zero, respectively) for times of the order of the mean free time.

For more complicated physical situations, the results again deviate from the usual Navier-Stokes relations, and may be useful in investigating rapidly varying phenomena that cannot be explained in the usual (hydrodynamic) fashion.

1.19. Second Derivation of the Boltzmann Equation.—The derivation of the Boltzmann equation given in the first sections of this chapter suffers from the obvious defect that it is in no way connected with the fundamental law of statistical mechanics, *i.e.*, *Liouville's equation.* As discussed in Section 12.6 of *The Mathematics of Physics and Chemistry*, 2nd Ed.,[22] the behavior of all systems of particles should be compatible with this equation, and, thus, one should be able to derive the Boltzmann equation from it. This has been avoided in the previous derivation by implicitly making statistical assumptions about the behavior of colliding particles: that the number of collisions between particles of velocities $\mathbf{v}_1$ and $\mathbf{v}_2$ is taken proportional to $f(\mathbf{v}_1)f(\mathbf{v}_2)$ implies that there has been no previous relation between the particles (statistical independence) before collision. As noted previously, in a

[22] H. Margenau and G. M. Murphy, D. Van Nostrand Co., Inc., Princeton, N.J., 1956.

dense gas, particles may interact several times before separating sufficiently far so that further collisions will not take place; the distribution of pairs of particles, in this case, would be quite different from the product of single-particle distribution functions.

We may start with Liouville's equation for monatomic particles (no internal degrees of freedom):

$$\frac{\partial f^{(N)}}{\partial t} + \sum_{i=1}^{N} [\mathbf{v}_i \cdot \nabla_i f^{(N)} + (\mathbf{a}_i + \mathbf{A}_i) \cdot \nabla_{v_i} f^{(N)}] = 0 \qquad (1\text{–}121)$$

where N is the total number of particles in the system (all identical); the velocity of particle i is $\mathbf{v}_i$; the external force per unit mass is

$$\mathbf{a}_i = \frac{1}{m} \mathbf{F}_i^{(\text{ext})} \qquad (1\text{–}122)$$

and the total interparticle force per unit mass on particle i is:

$$\mathbf{A}_i = \frac{1}{m} \sum_{j=1}^{N}{}' \mathbf{F}_{ij}(|\mathbf{r}_i - \mathbf{r}_j|) \qquad (1\text{–}123)$$

$\mathbf{F}_{ij}$ is the force on particle i due to particle j, and is assumed to depend only upon the distance between the particles; the prime on the summation means that the term $j = i$ is omitted. The N-particle probability distribution function is defined as follows:

$$dP = f^{(N)}(\mathbf{r}_1,\mathbf{v}_1,\mathbf{r}_2,\mathbf{v}_2,\ldots,\mathbf{r}_N,\mathbf{v}_N,t) \prod_{i=1}^{N} d\mathbf{r}_i d\mathbf{v}_i \qquad (1\text{–}124)$$

This is the probability of finding particle 1 with coordinate $\mathbf{r}_1$ and velocity $\mathbf{v}_1$ (within $d\mathbf{r}_1$ and $d\mathbf{v}_1$), particle 2 with coordinate $\mathbf{r}_2$ and velocity $\mathbf{v}_2$ (within $d\mathbf{r}_2$ and $d\mathbf{v}_2$), etc. (Again we use here a phase space with velocity rather than momentum for convenience; since only one type of particle is being considered, this causes no difficulties in Liouville's equation.) The n-particle probability distribution function ($n < N$) is

$$f^{(n)}(\mathbf{r}_1,\mathbf{v}_1,\ldots,\mathbf{r}_n,\mathbf{v}_n,t) = \int f^{(N)} \prod_{i=n+1}^{N} d\mathbf{r}_i d\mathbf{v}_i \qquad (1\text{–}125)$$

It represents the probability of finding the particles numbered from 1 to n in the given configuration, without regard to the configuration of the particles numbered from $n + 1$ to N. In particular:

$$f^{(1)}(\mathbf{r}_1,\mathbf{v}_1,t) = \int f^{(2)}(\mathbf{r}_1,\mathbf{v}_1,\mathbf{r}_2,\mathbf{v}_2,t) d\mathbf{r}_2 d\mathbf{v}_2$$
$$= \int f^{(N)} \prod_{i=2}^{N} d\mathbf{r}_i d\mathbf{v}_i \qquad (1\text{–}126)$$

(It is to be noted that the Boltzmann equation involves the number density distribution function, so that $f(\mathbf{r},\mathbf{v}_1,t)$ is related to $Nf^{(1)}(\mathbf{r}_1,\mathbf{v}_1,t)$.)

In the derivation of the Boltzmann equation it is assumed that the distribution function changes only in consequence of completed collisions, *i.e.*, the effect of partial collisions is neglected. We shall, therefore, consider the single-particle distribution function averaged[23] over a time τ, which will (later) be taken large compared with a collision time:

$$\bar{f}^{(1)}(\mathbf{r}_1,\mathbf{v}_1,t) = \frac{1}{\tau}\int_0^\tau f^{(1)}(\mathbf{r}_1,\mathbf{v}_1,t+s)ds \tag{1-127}$$

(A similar analysis can be made in terms of a space average[24] over a region whose size is of the order of a molecular diameter.) Integrating Eq. (1–121) over all particles except the first:

$$\int \frac{\partial f^{(N)}}{\partial t}\prod_{i=2}^{N} d\mathbf{r}_i d\mathbf{v}_i = \frac{\partial}{\partial t} f^{(1)}(\mathbf{r}_1,\mathbf{v}_1,t)$$

$$\begin{aligned}\sum_{j=1}^{N}\int \mathbf{v}_j\cdot\nabla_j f^{(N)}\prod_{i=2}^{N} d\mathbf{r}_i d\mathbf{v}_i &= \int \mathbf{v}_1\cdot\nabla f^{(N)}\prod_{i=2}^{N} d\mathbf{r}_i d\mathbf{v}_i \\ &\quad + \sum_{j=2}^{N}\int \mathbf{v}_j\cdot\nabla_j f^{(N)}\prod_{i=2}^{N} d\mathbf{r}_i d\mathbf{v}_i \\ &= \mathbf{v}_1\cdot\nabla f^{(1)} + \sum_{j=2}^{N}\int \mathbf{v}_j\cdot\nabla_j f^{(N)} d\mathbf{r}_j d\mathbf{v}_j \prod_{k\neq j} d\mathbf{r}_k d\mathbf{v}_k\end{aligned}$$

where we have separated out the integration over the first particle in the sum. We may apply Gauss' theorem[25] to the j-particle space integration; assuming that there is no particle flow through the boundary surface, this integrates to zero. In a similar manner we may apply Gauss' theorem to the velocity integration of the third term of Eq. (1–121), so that the external force term gives:

$$\sum_{j=1}^{N}\int \mathbf{a}_j\cdot\nabla_{v_j} f^{(N)}\prod_{i=2}^{N} d\mathbf{r}_i d\mathbf{v}_i = \mathbf{a}_1\cdot\nabla_{v_1} f^{(1)}$$

[23] J. G. Kirkwood and J. Ross, "The Statistical Mechanical Basis of the Boltzmann Equation," in I. Prigogine, ed., *Transport Processes in Statistical Mechanics*, pp. 1–7, Interscience Publishers, Inc., New York, 1958. Also, J. G. Kirkwood, "The Statistical Mechanical Theory of Transport Processes; I. General Theory," *J. Chem. Phys.*, **14**, 180 (1946); "II. Transport in Gases," *J. Chem. Phys.*, **15**, 72 (1947).

[24] Cf. H. Grad, "Principles of the Kinetic Theory of Gases," *Handbuch der Physik*, Vol. XII, pp. 208 ff., Springer Verlag, Berlin, 1958.

[25] Margenau and Murphy, *op. cit.*, p. 159.

For the internal forces:

$$\frac{1}{m}\sum_{j=1}^{N}\sum_{k=1}^{N}{}' \int \mathbf{F}_{jk}(|\mathbf{r}_j - \mathbf{r}_k|)\cdot\nabla_{v_j} f^{(N)} \prod_{i=2}^{N} d\mathbf{r}_i d\mathbf{v}_i$$
$$= \frac{1}{m}\sum_{k=2}^{N}\int \mathbf{F}_{1k}\cdot\nabla_{v_1} f^{(N)}\prod_{i=2}^{N} d\mathbf{r}_i d\mathbf{v}_i + \frac{1}{m}\sum_{j=2}^{N}\sum_{k=1}^{N}{}'\int \mathbf{F}_{jk}\cdot\nabla_{v_j} f^{(N)}\prod_{i=2}^{N} d\mathbf{r}_i d\mathbf{v}_i$$

Again, we have separated the $j = 1$ term (and used the fact that $k \neq j$). In the second integral, Gauss' theorem applied to the v_j-integration reduces it to zero; in the first integral, there are $(N - 1)$ identical k-integrations. Thus we obtain for the internal force term:

$$\frac{1}{m}(N - 1)\int \mathbf{F}_{12}\cdot\nabla_{v_1} f^{(2)}(\mathbf{r}_1,\mathbf{v}_1,\mathbf{r}_2,\mathbf{v}_2,t)d\mathbf{r}_2 d\mathbf{v}_2$$

Since the number of particles is large, $N - 1 \simeq N$; averaging the result over a time τ, we have:

$$\frac{\partial \bar{f}^{(1)}}{\partial t} + \mathbf{v}_1\cdot\nabla_1\bar{f}^{(1)} + \mathbf{a}_1\cdot\nabla_{v_1}\bar{f}^{(1)} = \frac{N}{m\tau}\int \mathbf{F}_{12}\cdot\nabla_{v_1} f^{(2)}(\mathbf{r}_1,\mathbf{v}_1,\mathbf{r}_2,\mathbf{v}_2,t + s)ds d\mathbf{r}_2 d\mathbf{v}_2 \quad (1\text{–}128)$$

If three-body collisions are neglected, which is permitted at sufficiently low densities, all the interactions take place between pairs of particles; the two-particle distribution function will, therefore, satisfy Liouville's equation for two interacting particles. For $f^{(2)}(t + s)$ we may write Eq. (1–121):

$$\frac{\partial f^{(2)}}{\partial s} + \mathbf{v}_1\cdot\nabla_1 f^{(2)} + \mathbf{v}_2\cdot\nabla_2 f^{(2)} + \left(\mathbf{a}_1 + \frac{1}{m}\mathbf{F}_{12}\right)\cdot\nabla_{v_1} f^{(2)} + \left(\mathbf{a}_2 + \frac{1}{m}\mathbf{F}_{21}\right)\cdot\nabla_{v_2} f^{(2)} = 0 \quad (1\text{–}129)$$

If the effect of the external force on the particles during a collision is small in comparison to the interparticle forces, the solution of Eq. (1–129) is:

$$f^{(2)}(\mathbf{r}_1,\mathbf{v}_1,\mathbf{r}_2,\mathbf{v}_2,t + s) = f^{(2)}[\mathbf{r}_1 - \Delta\mathbf{r}_1(s), \mathbf{v}_1 - \Delta\mathbf{v}_1(s), \mathbf{r}_2 - \Delta\mathbf{r}_2(s), \mathbf{v}_2 - \Delta\mathbf{v}_2(s), t] \quad (1\text{–}130)$$

where:

$$\mathbf{v}_1 = \frac{\partial}{\partial s}[\Delta\mathbf{r}_1(s)] \qquad \mathbf{v}_2 = \frac{\partial}{\partial s}[\Delta\mathbf{r}_2(s)]$$
$$\frac{1}{m}\mathbf{F}_{12} = \frac{\partial}{\partial s}[\Delta\mathbf{v}_1(s)] \qquad \frac{1}{m}\mathbf{F}_{21} = \frac{\partial}{\partial s}[\Delta\mathbf{v}_2(s)] \quad (1\text{–}131)$$

This binary collision approximation thus gives rise to a two-particle distribution function whose velocities change, due to the two-body force $\mathbf{F}_{12}$ in the time interval s, according to Newton's law, and whose positions change by the appropriate increments due to the particles' velocities.

If, at the time $s = 0$, the particles were sufficiently far from each other so that their mutual interaction had not affected them, and the gas was sufficiently dilute so that the particles had not interacted previously (the "molecular chaos" assumption), then $f^{(2)} = f^{(1)}f^{(1)}$ at $s = 0$. This may be used on the right side of Eq. (1–130), and leads to:

$$f^{(2)}(\mathbf{r}_1,\mathbf{v}_1,\mathbf{r}_2,\mathbf{v}_2,t+s) \\ = f^{(1)}[\mathbf{r}_1 - \Delta\mathbf{r}_1(s), \mathbf{v}_1 - \Delta\mathbf{v}_1(s),t]f^{(1)}[\mathbf{r}_2 - \Delta\mathbf{r}_2(s), \mathbf{v}_2 - \Delta\mathbf{v}_2(s), t] \tag{1–132}$$

If the distribution function does not change rapidly with position, *i.e.*, the macroscopic distances involved are large compared with the distance over which a collision takes place, we may neglect the $\Delta\mathbf{r}_1$ and $\Delta\mathbf{r}_2$. Since $\boldsymbol{\nabla}_{v_1} = -\boldsymbol{\nabla}_{\Delta v_1}$, and $\Delta\mathbf{v}_2 = -\Delta\mathbf{v}_1$, the integrand of Eq. (1–128) becomes, using Eqs. (1–132) and (1–131):

$$-\mathbf{F}_{12}\cdot\nabla_{\Delta v_1}f^{(1)}[\mathbf{r}_1, \mathbf{v}_1 - \Delta\mathbf{v}_1(s), t]f^{(1)}[\mathbf{r}_2, \mathbf{v}_2 + \Delta\mathbf{v}_1(s), t] \\ = -m\frac{\partial}{\partial s}(\Delta\mathbf{v}_1)\cdot\nabla_{\Delta v_1}(f_1^{(1)}f_2^{(1)}) = -m\frac{\partial}{\partial s}(f_1^{(1)}f_2^{(1)})$$

where the subscripts indicate the variables involved. The integration over s, between the limits 0 to τ, may then be performed; the left side of Eq. (1–128) then becomes

$$L = -\frac{N}{\tau}\int\{f^{(1)}(\mathbf{r}_1, \mathbf{v}_1 - \Delta\mathbf{v}_1(\tau), t)f^{(1)}(\mathbf{r}_2, \mathbf{v}_2 - \Delta\mathbf{v}_2(\tau), t) \\ - f^{(1)}(\mathbf{r}_1,\mathbf{v}_1,t)f^{(1)}(\mathbf{r}_2,\mathbf{v}_2,t)\}d\mathbf{r}_2 d\mathbf{v}_2 \tag{1–133}$$

If the interval τ is large compared with the time for a collision to be completed (but small compared with macroscopic times), then the arguments of the distribution functions are those appropriate to the positions and velocities before and after a binary collision. The integration over $\mathbf{r}_2$ may be replaced by one over the relative distance variable $\mathbf{r}_2 - \mathbf{r}_1$; as noted in Section 1.7, collisions taking place during the time τ occur in the volume $g\,\tau\,b\,db\,d\varepsilon$, where g is the relative velocity, and (b,ε) are the relative collision coordinates. Incomplete collisions, or motions involving periodic orbits take place in a volume independent of τ; when $\Delta\mathbf{v}_1(\tau)$ and $\Delta\mathbf{v}_2(\tau)$ refer to motion for which a collision does not take place (or to the force-field free portion of the incomplete collisions) these quantities are zero, so that the integrand is likewise zero.

We use primes to denote the quantities after collision, while unprimed symbols label those before the collision; taking another time average of the equation, and using $\overline{f^{(1)}f^{(1)}} = \overline{f^{(1)}}\,\overline{f^{(1)}}$, which is valid for first order deviations from equilibrium, we obtain

$$\frac{\partial \bar{f}^{(1)}}{\partial t} + \mathbf{v}_1 \cdot \nabla_1 \bar{f}^{(1)} + \mathbf{a} \cdot \nabla_{v_1} \bar{f}^{(1)} = N \int [\bar{f}_1^{(1)\prime} \bar{f}_2^{(1)\prime} - \bar{f}_1^{(1)} \bar{f}_2^{(1)}] gb \, db \, d\varepsilon \, d\mathbf{v}_2$$

Remembering that $N\overline{f^{(1)}}$ is the average number of particles per unit volume of phase space, we recognize this as the Boltzmann equation.

1.20. Slightly Ionized Gases.—The coulomb interaction between the constituents of an ionized gas, *i.e.*, electrons and positive ions, influences their motion over distances much greater than that for intermolecular force fields. For this reason, the transport theory of plasmas (macroscopically neutral ionized gases) involves techniques somewhat different from those previously described in this chapter. For a gas that is slightly ionized, however, the approximation can be made that the charged particles do not interact with each other, but only with the (relatively) large number of neutral atoms. To determine the conductivity of such a gas, only the current due to the motion of the electrons is of importance, since the mean velocity of the ions is small; this allows us to consider only the interaction of the electrons with the atoms. Moreover, since the mass of an atom is several thousand times that of an electron, certain simplifying assumptions can be made about the particle velocities after collision. These effects lead to a simple form for the collision integral of the Boltzmann equation, known as the *Lorentz approximation*.

Consider electrons of mass m and velocity $\mathbf{v}$, and atoms of mass M and velocity $\mathbf{V}$; we have $m/M \ll 1$. The distribution function for the electrons will be denoted by $f(\mathbf{v},t)$ (we assume no space dependence); that for the atoms, $F(V)$, assumed Maxwellian; as usual, in the collision integral, unprimed quantities refer to values before collision, while primed quantities are the values after collision. In general, we would have three Boltzmann equations (one each for the electrons, ions, and neutrals), each containing three collision terms (one for "self-collisions," and one each for collisions with the other two species). We are interested only in the equation for the electron distribution function; by the assumption of slight ionization, we neglect the electron-electron collisions and the electron-ion collisions. The collision integral thus becomes:

$$\left(\frac{\partial f}{\partial t}\right)_c = -\int [f(\mathbf{v})F(V) - f(\mathbf{v}')F(V')]gb\,db\,d\varepsilon\,d\mathbf{V} \qquad (1\text{–}134)$$

If an electric field, sinusoidally varying in time, is imposed on the gas, the force on the electrons, per unit mass, is

$$\mathbf{a} = \mathbf{i}_z\gamma \cos \omega t \qquad \gamma = \frac{eE}{m} \qquad (1\text{–}135)$$

The field, of strength E, is assumed in the z-direction; the charge of the electron is e; no magnetic field effects are considered, since the electron velocities are assumed small compared with the velocity of light.[26] The Boltzmann equation is thus

$$\frac{\partial f}{\partial t} + \gamma \cos \omega t \frac{\partial f}{\partial v_z} = \left(\frac{\partial f}{\partial t}\right)_c \qquad (1\text{–}136)$$

We may solve for the electron distribution function by expanding it in Legendre polynomials in $\cos\theta$ (where $\mathbf{v} = (v,\theta,\varphi)$), and Fourier series in ωt; we shall use here only the first-order terms:

$$f(\mathbf{v},t) = f_0(v) + \gamma v_z[f_1(v) \cos \omega t + h_1(v) \sin \omega t] \qquad (1\text{–}137)$$

where f_0, f_1, h_1 depend only upon the magnitude $v = |\mathbf{v}|$. Other terms give contributions of the order of γ^2, which we neglect.

Equation (1–137) is used in Eqs. (1–136) and (1–134) to obtain three equations; the first, due to terms proportional to $\gamma \sin \omega t$:

$$v_z\omega f_1 = -(\partial v_z h_1/\partial t)_c \qquad (1\text{–}138)$$

the second, due to $\gamma \cos \omega t$ terms:

$$v_z\omega h_1 + \frac{\partial f_0}{\partial v_z} = (\partial v_z f_1/\partial t)_c \qquad (1\text{–}139)$$

and the last from the "d.c." component of the equations (since $\cos^2 \omega t = \frac{1}{2}(1 + \cos 2\omega t)$):

$$\frac{1}{2}\left(\gamma^2 f_1 + \gamma^2 v_z \frac{\partial f_1}{\partial v_z}\right) = (\partial f_0/\partial t)_c \qquad (1\text{–}140)$$

The collision terms may be simplified by using the condition that m/M is very small; this leads to the Lorentz approximation. If there were no electric field, the equilibrium situation would be one in which the mean kinetic energy of the electrons would be equal to that of the

[26] R. B. Lindsay, *op. cit.*, p. 396.

atoms; the electric field causes the electron energy to increase above its equilibrium value, so that $m\overline{v^2} \geq M\overline{V^2}$, or, for most collisions,

$$v \gg V, \qquad g \simeq v \tag{1–141}$$

To the lowest order of approximation, which is used to evaluate the collision integrals for the perturbation terms ($v_z f_1$ and $v_z h_1$), we take $m/M = 0$. There is, thus, no interchange of energy between the electrons and neutral atoms, so that

$$V' = V, \qquad v' = v \tag{1–142}$$

The collision integral of Eq. (1–138) becomes:

$$\begin{aligned}\left(\frac{\partial(v_z h_1)}{\partial t}\right)_c &= -\int [v_z h_1(v)F(V) - v_z' h_1(v')F(V')]gb\,db\,d\varepsilon\,d\mathbf{V} \\ &= -h_1(v)\int F(V)(v_z - v_z')vb\,db\,d\varepsilon\,d\mathbf{V}\end{aligned}$$

Now, $\int F(V)d\mathbf{V} = N$, the number of neutral atoms per unit volume; in integrating over the angle ε, the only component of v_z' that is nonzero is $v_z \cos\chi$ [see Eq. (1–31)]. We obtain

$$\left(\frac{\partial(v_z h_1)}{\partial t}\right)_c = -h_1(v)2\pi N v_z \int (1 - \cos\chi)v\,b\,db \tag{1–143}$$

The factor

$$\nu(v) = 2\pi N \int (1 - \cos\chi)v\,b\,db \tag{1–144}$$

is the collision frequency (of electrons with neutral atoms) for momentum transfer; the mean free path of the electron is:[27]

$$\lambda(v) = \frac{v}{\nu(v)} \tag{1–145}$$

Although this lowest order approximation is used in determining the first order corrections to the distribution function, it is necessary to go to a higher order of approximation in determining the collision integral of Eq. (1–140). If we keep terms to first order in the small quantity m/M, the collision integral may be evaluated to give[28]

$$\left(\frac{\partial f_0}{\partial t}\right)_c = \frac{1}{v^2}\frac{m}{M}\frac{\partial}{\partial v}\left(\frac{v^4 f_0}{\lambda}\right) + \frac{kT}{Mv^2}\frac{\partial}{\partial v}\left(\frac{v^3}{\lambda}\frac{\partial f_0}{\partial v}\right) \tag{1–146}$$

[27] For hard sphere collisions, $\nu(v)$ would be proportional to v, and the mean free path independent of v; $\lambda(v)$ is an equivalent mean free path for a general force law. Cf. S. Chapman and T. G. Cowling, *The Mathematical Theory of Non-Uniform Gases*, pp. 91 and 348, Cambridge University Press, 1958.

[28] Chapman and Cowling, *op. cit.*, p. 348, E. A. Desloge and S. Matthyse, *Am. J. Phys.*, **28**, 1 (1960).

Equations (1–138), (1–139), (1–143) to (1–145) may then be solved to give

$$f_1 = -\frac{\lambda}{v^2 + \omega^2\lambda^2}\frac{\partial f_0}{\partial v} \qquad h_1 = \frac{\omega\lambda}{v} f_1 \tag{1–147}$$

Equation (1–140), with Eqs. (1–146), (1–147) yields upon integration (after averaging over direction, so that v_z^2 is replaced by $v^2/3$):

$$\ln f_0 = -\int_0^{v^2} \frac{(m/2)d\,(v^2)}{kT + [M\gamma^2\lambda^2/6(v^2 + \omega^2\lambda^2)]} \tag{1–148}$$

For large thermal energies of the electrons (kT predominates in the denominator), the distribution is maxwellian; for large electric field strengths, we obtain the Margenau distribution[29] (assuming, for simplicity, constant mean-free path):

$$f_0 = A \exp\left[-\frac{3m(v^4 + 2\omega^2\lambda^2 v^2)}{2M\gamma^2\lambda^2}\right] \tag{1–149}$$

This is a generalization, for time-varying electric fields, of the Druyvesteyn distribution[30] for d.c. fields, to which (1–149) reduces when $\omega = 0$.

The electron current density may then be found from Eq. (1–137).

$$I = ne\bar{v}_z = -\tfrac{1}{3}e\gamma \int (v^2\lambda/(v^2 + \omega^2\lambda^2)) \left(\cos\omega t + \frac{\omega\lambda}{v}\sin\omega t\right)\frac{\partial f_0}{\partial v}\,d\mathbf{v}$$

For collision frequencies large compared with the frequency of the electric field, the current remains in phase with the electric field; in the reverse case, the current is 90° out of phase. The in-phase component of the current gives rise to an energy loss from the field (Joule heating loss); microscopically, this is seen to be due to the energy transferred from the electrons to the atoms upon collision.

[29] H. Margenau, *Phys. Rev.*, **69**, 508 (1946); Chapman and Cowling, *op. cit.*, p. 351.
[30] M. J. Druyvesteyn, *Physica*, **10**, 61 (1930).

CHAPTER 2

NUMERICAL ANALYSIS

by

ALSTON S. HOUSEHOLDER

Oak Ridge National Laboratory

2.1. The Field of Numerical Analysis.—As used here, *numerical analysis* will be taken to represent the art and science of digital computation. The art is learned mainly by experience; hence, this chapter will be concerned with explicit techniques and the mathematical principles that justify them. *Digital computation* is to be contrasted with *analog computation*, which is the use of slide rules, differential analyzers, model basins, and other devices in which such physical magnitudes as lengths, voltages, etc., represent the quantities under consideration.

In digital computation, numbers are represented by expansion in powers of a base (or radix) b, which is usually either 2 or 10, with coefficients that are non-negative integers $< b$. Thus

$$a = \pm(a_\sigma b^\sigma + a_{\sigma-1} b^{\sigma-1} + \cdots), \quad 0 \leq a_i < b$$

A digital computer is designed to utilize a fixed base; generally 2 when intended mainly for scientific uses, 10 otherwise. The base 2 has advantages in terms of hardware and in terms of precision. Since a finite machine can represent only a limited number of the digits a_i in the expansion of any number a, the machine representation will in general be inexact, which accounts for one of the sources of error in digital computation. Ordinarily a machine will be designed to carry a fixed number ν, the first ν, of the coefficients in the expansion of any given number.

There are two standard schemes for the machine representation of a number, called *fixed-point* and *floating-point*. The older electronic machines used only fixed-point. In its most usual form, every number was assumed to satisfy

$$|a| < 1$$

and the representation was made by storing the sign of the number and the ordered set of digits

$$(a_{-1}, a_{-2}, \ldots, a_{-\nu})$$

The usual floating-point representation permitted the storage also of an exponent, thus allowing a representation

$$a = b^{\rho}\alpha, \quad |\alpha| < 1$$

where α is stored as in fixed-point representation, and ρ is represented by a sign and the digits ρ_i in

$$\rho = \pm(\rho_0 + \rho_1 b + \rho_2 b^2 + \cdots)$$

up to some maximal number of terms. Some machines permit either type of representation, according to specification, and even those that do not usually have suitable interpretative programs, or algebraic languages, such as Algol or one of its dialects, that do permit it. For the casual user of an electronic computer, it is largely academic whether the floating point is built in or programmed, unless speed becomes a serious consideration.

Whatever the representation, whether by fixed point or floating, the number a^* that appears in the machine may deviate from the number a that is intended, and if a is among the initial data for the problem, the difference $a - a^*$ will be called the *initial error*. It may be remarked in passing that errors of measurement may also contribute to the initial error, if a is understood to represent a physical quantity known only approximately as the result of physical measurement.

Generally speaking, the outcome of any digital computation is a set of numbers in machine representation. Often the problem as originally formulated mathematically is to obtain a function defined over some domain, but the computation itself can give only (approximations to) a finite number of its functional values, or a finite number of coefficients in an expansion, or some other form of finite representation. At any rate, each number y in the finite set of numbers explicitly sought can be thought of, or perhaps even explicitly represented as, some function of the input data x:

$$y = f(x)$$

where x is a vector, each of whose elements is an input datum. As remarked, the vector x^* actually represented by the machine may deviate from the vector x intended, so that at best the functional value $f(x^*)$ can be computed. This gives rise to an error $f(x) - f(x^*)$ that will be called the *propagated error*.

Since the machine performs only arithmetic operations (and these only approximately), if f is anything but a rational function it must be approximated by a rational function, *e.g.*, by a finite number of terms in a Taylor expansion. If this rational approximation is denoted by f_a, this gives rise to an error $f(x^*) - f_a(x^*)$, generally called the *truncation error*. Finally, since even the arithmetic operations are carried out only approximately in the machine, not even $f_a(x^*)$ can usually be found exactly, and still a third type of error results, $f_a(x^*) - f_a^*(x^*)$, called *generated error*, where $f_a^*(x^*)$ is the number actually produced by the machine. Thus, the total error is the sum of these

$$f(x) - f_a^*(x^*) = [f(x) - f(x^*)] + [f(x^*) - f_a(x^*)] + [f_a(x^*) - f_a^*(x^*)]$$

Lanczos proposes the expression *parexic analysis* to denote the development of optimal approximations f_a (minimization of truncation errors), and restricts numerical analysis to the analysis and minimization of generated error. It may be observed that nothing can be done mathematically about truncation error, granted that f is the required function. Truncation error can be reduced only by reducing the initial error, hence, either by carrying out more accurate measurements, or by using a machine that carries more digits and permits a more adequate representation (or by multiple-precision arithmetic). In Lanczos's terms, the principal concern here will be with parexic analysis rather than with numerical analysis proper. There are few known general principles of numerical analysis in this sense, although special reference may be made to a series of papers by J. H. Wilkinson who has studied in detail the buildup of error in a variety of matrix computations (see Section 2.7).

The function $f(x)$ is, of course, given explicitly only rarely. If the mathematical formulation of the problem is that of finding a single number y, or only a finite set, then most often it is given implicitly as satisfying an equation or a finite set of equations. This will be called the algebraic problem (even though the equations may be transcendental), and this will be discussed first. If a function is required, this must be in some sense represented by a finite set of numbers, and the same is true if some functional (such as a definite integral) is required. This leads to the problem of approximation. Finally, the solution of a functional equation (differential, integral, or other), must be reduced in some way to an algebraic problem, and some techniques for doing this will be indicated. Most problems of numerical or parexic *analysis* fall into one of these three types. There are, however, important and difficult problems in which the difficulties are combinatorial, rather than analytical, in character. A well-known example of these is known as linear programming, where a linear function is to be maximized subject to constraints expressed in the form of linear inequalities. Such problems fall beyond the scope of the present discussion.

2.2. The Linear Algebraic Problem.—Familiarity with the basic theory of finite vectors and matrices—the notions of rank and linear dependence, the Cayley-Hamilton theorem, the Jordan normal form, orthogonality, and related principles—will be presupposed. In this section and the next, matrices will generally be represented by capital letters, column vectors by lower case English letters, scalars, except for indices and dimensions, by lower case Greek letters. The vectors $a, b, x, y, \ldots$, will have elements $\alpha_i, \beta_i, \xi_i, \eta_i, \ldots$; the matrices $A, B, \ldots$, will have column vectors $a_i, b_i, \ldots$, and elements $\alpha_{ij}, \beta_{ij}, \ldots$ but the identity I will have column vectors e_i, and elements δ_{ij}. It is convenient to let

$$e = \sum e_i$$

The conjugate transpose of $x, A, \ldots$, are $x^H, A^H, \ldots$. The characteristic roots (or simply the roots) of A are $\lambda_i(A)$; its spectral radius is

$$\rho(A) = \max_i |\lambda_i(A)|$$

its singular values $\sigma_i(A) \geq 0$ are defined by

$$\sigma_i^2(A) = \lambda_i(AA^H) = \lambda_i(A^HA)$$

when A is square. By $|a|$ will be meant the vector whose elements are $|\alpha_i|$; by $|A|$, the matrix whose elements are $|\alpha_{ij}|$. By $a \leq b$ will be meant that $\alpha_i \leq \beta_i$ for every i; by $a < b$ that $\alpha_i < \beta_i$ for every i. Similar interpretations will hold for matrices, and for the reverse inequalities. Generally, unless otherwise indicated, matrices will be supposed square and of order n, and vectors n-dimensional.

An important tool in the study of matrices is provided by vector norms and matrix norms. A *vector norm* $\|\ldots\|$ is any real valued function of the elements satisfying the following three conditions:

$$(V_1) \qquad x \neq 0 \Rightarrow \|x\| > 0$$
$$(V_2) \qquad \|\alpha x\| = |\alpha| \, \|x\|$$
$$(V_3) \qquad \|x + y\| \leq \|x\| + \|y\|$$

The ordinary euclidean length is such a norm, and, more generally, if G is any positive definite matrix, then the non-negative square root of

$$\|x\|_G^2 = x^HGx$$

is a norm. Other norms are defined by

$$\|x\|_e = \max |\xi_i|$$
$$\|x\|_{e'} = \sum |\xi_i|$$
$$\|x\|_g = \inf [\nu \mid |x| \le \nu g]$$

where g is any positive vector; and

$$\|x\|_{g'} = g^H |x|$$

where, again, g is any positive vector. It is easy to prove that *given any vector norm, the point set*

$$K = [x \mid \|x\| \le 1]$$

is a closed, bounded, convex body. To say that it is *convex* means that the segment joining any two points in K lies entirely in K, and to say that it is a *body* means that it possesses interior points. Moreover, K is *equilibrated*, which is to say that if $x \in K$ and $|\omega| \le 1$, then $\omega x \in K$.

For any matrix A it is convenient to let AK represent the set of all points Ax for which $x \in K$, and to define $\alpha K = (\alpha I)K$ for any scalar α. Then a converse to the above theorem, which also holds, can be stated as follows: *if K is a bounded, closed, equilibrated, convex body, then the function*

$$\|x\|_K = \inf [\nu \ge 0 \mid x \in \nu K]$$

is a vector norm. Thus, associated with every vector norm there is a unique bounded, closed, equilibrated, convex body and conversely. It can be verified that the convex body associated with $\|x\|_G$ is an ellipsoid, and if $G = I$ (the euclidean norm) it is the unit sphere. Associated with $\|x\|_e$, $\|x\|_{e'}$, $\|x\|_g$, $\|x\|_{g'}$, are certain parallelotopes.

Since only bounded, closed, and equilibrated convex bodies come into consideration, these qualifications will be assumed hereafter. Clearly the origin is interior to any such convex body. Hence it can be shown that if H and K are both such, then there exists a scalar κ such that

$$H \subset \kappa K$$

and, therefore, such that

$$\|x\|_K \le \kappa \|x\|_H$$

This may be expressed by saying that all vector norms (in finite-dimensional space) are topologically equivalent; otherwise, that if the sequence of vectors x_i is such that

$$\|x_i\|_H \to 0$$

then also

$$\|x_i\|_K \to 0$$

A square matrix of order n can be considered a vector in a space of n^2 dimensions, and if the matrix function $\|\ldots\|$ defines a vector norm in n^2-space, it will be called a generalized matrix norm. Thus a *generalized matrix norm* satisfies

$$(M_1) \qquad A \neq 0 \Rightarrow \|A\| > 0$$
$$(M_2) \qquad \|\alpha A\| = |\alpha|\,\|A\|$$
$$(M_3) \qquad \|A + B\| \leq \|A\| + \|B\|$$

A matrix function $\nu(\ldots)$ will be called a *multiplicative* (strictly, submultiplicative) *matrix norm*, or simply a *matrix norm*, if it is a generalized matrix norm, and satisfies also

$$(M_4) \qquad \nu(AB) \leq \nu(A)\nu(B)$$

Given any generalized matrix norm $\|\ldots\|$, for sufficiently large, fixed $\alpha > 0$,

$$\nu(A) = \alpha\|A\|$$

is a matrix norm.

A matrix norm is *consistent* (or compatible) with a given vector norm provided

$$\|Ax\| \leq \|x\|\nu(A)$$

for every A and x. Given any matrix norm, a vector norm with which it is consistent can be defined quite simply by

$$\|x\| = \nu(xa^H)$$

where $a \neq 0$ is arbitrary but fixed. Moreover, given any matrix norm and any vector norm, the matrix norm defined by

$$\nu'(A) = \alpha\nu(A)$$

for every A and for sufficiently large, fixed, $\alpha > 0$, is consistent with the vector norm.

Associated with every vector norm, there is a special consistent matrix norm defined as follows:

$$\sup(A) = \sup_{x \neq 0} \|Ax\|/\|x\| = \sup_{\|x\|=1} \|Ax\|$$

An alternative definition is

$$\sup(A) = \inf[\alpha \mid AK \subset \alpha K]$$

where K is the convex body associated with the vector norm. This norm is clearly unique, and, in fact, it has the property that

$$\sup(A) \leq \nu(A)$$

for every matrix A and for every matrix norm ν that is consistent with the given vector norm. In particular

$$\sup(I) = 1 \leq \nu(I)$$

whatever the underlying vector norm.

Since every matrix norm is consistent with some vector norm, the following important theorem follows immediately:

$$\rho(A) \leq \nu(A)$$

for every matrix A and every matrix norm. In fact, if

$$Ax = \lambda x$$

then by applying the consistency condition and V_2, it follows that

$$|\lambda| \, \|x\| \leq \|x\| \nu(A)$$

Since the λ can be any $\lambda_i(A)$, this holds for the greatest in modulus, hence for $\rho(A)$. In view of the minimal property of sup, this theorem is strongest when $\nu = \sup$.

Sometimes in the literature the spectral radius ρ is referred to as the spectral norm, but it is not a norm as the term is used here. Thus it is easy to construct a matrix $A \neq 0$ for which $\rho(A) = 0$, so that M_1 is violated. However, *for any given matrix A, and any $\varepsilon > 0$, there exists a norm ν such that*

$$\nu(A) \leq \varepsilon + \rho(A)$$

But note that the norm depends upon the matrix A itself, as well as upon ε.

The last theorem will not be proved, but it will be used to prove the following important theorem: *the infinite series*

$$I + B + B^2 + \cdots$$

converges if and only if $\rho(B) < 1$. In that event, its value is

$$(I - B)^{-1} = I + B + B^2 + \cdots$$

First, suppose $\rho(B) < 1$. Then there exists a matrix norm with $\nu(B) < 1$. Since the roots of $I - B$ and of B can be paired so that

$$\lambda_i(I - B) = 1 - \lambda_i(B)$$

it follows that $\lambda_i(I - B) \neq 0$ for every i, hence $I - B$ is nonsingular and $(I - B)^{-1}$ exists. Let

$$S_\sigma = I + B + \cdots + B^\sigma$$

then

$$\begin{aligned}(I - B)^{-1} - S_\sigma &= (I - B)^{-1}B^{\sigma+1} \\ \nu[(I - B)^{-1} - S_\sigma] &\le \nu[(I - B)^{-1}]\nu(B^{\sigma+1}) \\ &\le \nu[(I - B)^{-1}]\nu^{\sigma+1}(B)\end{aligned}$$

Since $\nu(B) < 1$, the right member vanishes in the limit, hence so does the left. Conversely, suppose S_σ has a limit S. Let V be a matrix such that

$$V^{-1}BV = J$$

is triangular, say in Jordan normal form. Thus

$$V^{-1}SV = I + J + J^2 + \cdots$$

is also triangular. But if β is a diagonal element of J, then the corresponding element in $V^{-1}SV$ is

$$1 + \beta + \beta^2 + \cdots$$

and the series converges if and only if $|\beta| < 1$. Moreover, β is a root of B. But all roots of B are on the diagonal of J, hence $\rho(B) < 1$. This completes the proof.

The euclidean norm of a matrix considered as a vector in n^2-space is a matrix norm that is consistent with the euclidean vector norm. This is perhaps the matrix norm that occurs most frequently in the literature. But the euclidean norm of I is $n^{1/2} > 1$ when $n > 1$, hence it is not a sup. In fact,

$$\sup_I (A) = \max_i \sigma_i(A)$$

which is to say that the sup associated with the euclidean vector norm is the largest singular value of the matrix. Associated with other vector norms are

$$\begin{aligned}\sup_e (A) &= \| |A|e \|_e \\ \sup_{e'} (A) &= \sup_e (A^H) \\ \sup_g (A) &= \inf [\alpha \mid |A|g \le \alpha g] \\ \sup_{g'} (A) &= \sup_g (A^H)\end{aligned}$$

Let D be a nonsingular diagonal matrix, and apply the theorem proved above to the matrix $D - B$. This matrix is nonsingular if and only if $I - D^{-1}B$ is nonsingular, and a sufficient condition for this is

$$\nu(D^{-1}B) < 1$$

If $\nu = \sup_e$, the interpretation is that $A = D - B$ *is nonsingular, provided every diagonal element exceeds in modulus the sum of the moduli of the off-diagonal elements in the same row.* This theorem will be referred to here as the dominant-diagonal theorem. It has been discovered and rediscovered many times, in varying forms, and goes by many names in the literature: Levy (who seems to have obtained it first, but for real matrices only), Minkowski, Hadamard, and others. An equivalent form, given later, goes by the name of Gershgorin (variously spelled). Related theorems come from the use of $\sup_{e'}$, and of $\sup_g$ for any $g > 0$.

The *linear systems* to be considered here are of the form

$$AX = H \tag{2–1}$$

where A will be assumed nonsingular. Hence the solution is

$$X = A^{-1}H$$

Ordinarily $H = h$ and $X = x$ are single columns, or else $H = I$ and $X = A^{-1}$. Cramer's rule, however important theoretically, is of little help in practical computation. A *direct method* prescribes a finite number of scalar operations, usually arithmetic, but in some cases including square roots that, if carried out exactly, would lead to the exact solution. For most methods in common use, unless the matrix A is sparse (containing many null elements) the number of multiplicative operations (*i.e.*, including divisions), runs between $n^3/3$ and $2n^3$, neglecting lower powers of n. Also, if H has more than a single column, most of the computation is involved in finding a single column of X, the other columns being available at only a relatively small amount of additional computation.

Since the prescribed operations, arithmetic or square rooting, are not, in general, carried out exactly, rounding errors (generated error) enter and propagate, perhaps becoming magnified, and methods differ markedly in the extent to which this occurs. Also they differ in the number of scalar operations required, but to some extent a method that is economical in terms of the number of operations can be expected to be reasonably efficient in terms of error buildup, simply because there are fewer stages at which error is introduced. Nevertheless, this is not a universal rule.

A method of *successive approximation* (s.a. method) is one that would provide the solution as the limit of an infinite sequence of steps if these steps were carried out exactly. These steps are usually quite simple, and nearly identical, each to the next, so that programming is a relatively easy task. Most methods operate upon a given approximation to obtain a better one, hence they are self-correcting. Because of rounding, at some stage the computed "correction" will no longer be an improvement, but if the computation required at any step is short and simple, it can be expected that when this stationary stage is reached the approximation in hand might be rather better than could be obtained by a direct method. Hence, it is fairly common to apply first a direct method, and only then to attempt to improve the result by s.a.

More often, however, s.a. methods are applied at the outset, with more or less arbitrary initial approximations, and without previous application of a direct method. Usually this is done if the matrix is extremely large and extremely sparse, which is most often true of the matrices that arise in the algebraic representation of a functional equation, especially a partial differential equation. The advantage is that storage requirements are much more modest for s.a. methods.

Since s.a. methods are generally simpler, these will be described first. Given any approximation X_σ, let

$$R_\sigma = H - AX_\sigma = A(X - X_\sigma) = AS_\sigma \tag{2-2}$$

This represents the extent to which the approximation X_σ fails to satisfy the equations, while S_σ represents the error, which is the amount by which the approximation X_σ deviates from the true solution X. Most methods depend upon the use of a sequence of matrices C_σ chosen in such a way that

$$X_{\sigma+1} = X_\sigma + C_\sigma R_\sigma \tag{2-3}$$

will be better than X_σ as an approximation. From Eq. (2-2) it follows that

$$\begin{aligned} X_{\sigma+1} &= C_\sigma H + M_\sigma X_\sigma \\ M_\sigma &= I - C_\sigma A \end{aligned} \tag{2-4}$$

hence

$$S_{\sigma+1} = M_\sigma X_\sigma \tag{2-5}$$

Thus, a sufficient condition for convergence is that

$$\nu(M_\sigma) < 1$$

in some norm for every σ. A method is called *stationary* in case

$$C_\sigma = C$$

is the same at every step, in which case

$$M_\sigma = M$$

and it is *necessary* and *sufficient* that

$$\rho(M) < 1$$

Since S_σ satisfies a system of equations identical with that satisfied by X, except that R_σ replaces H, a standard method for improving the result of a direct method is to do the replacement and solve as before for the correction. This obtained correction will not, of course, be the true S_σ, but only an approximation S_σ^*, and it will have been obtained as a result of a set of operations that is equivalent to the formation of $C_\sigma R_\sigma$, in accordance with Eq. (2–3). The $C_\sigma = C$ is not known explicitly, but is defined implicitly (see the methods of factorization below).

If $C_\sigma = A^{-1}$, then $M_\sigma = 0$ and the solution X is already at hand. However, A^{-1} is not available, or there would be no problem. Nevertheless, in order to make M_σ small, it is necessary that C_σ should be as close to A^{-1} as possible. In the special case $H = I$, where it is A^{-1} that is required, X_σ is itself the best available approximation to A^{-1}, hence it is natural to take $C_\sigma = X_\sigma$. This gives

$$X_{\sigma+1} = X_\sigma(2I - AX_\sigma) \tag{2–6}$$

or, equivalently

$$X_{\sigma+1} = (2I - X_\sigma A)X_\sigma \tag{2–7}$$

as an *iteration for the inverse.* In practice it is advantageous to form

$$M_\sigma = I - X_\sigma A, \qquad X_{\sigma+1} = (I + M_\sigma)X_\sigma$$

It can be verified that

$$M_{\sigma+1} = M_\sigma^2$$

hence

$$\nu(M_{\sigma+1}) \leq \nu^2(M_\sigma^2)$$

and the process is quadratically convergent if and only if $\rho(M_0) < 1$.

Except for finding the inverse, s.a. methods contrast with direct methods in that if H has several columns, the computations required for finding one column of X contribute nothing toward finding the next. Hence it will be assumed now that $H = h$, $X = x, \ldots,$ are single vectors. Consider stationary methods, and write Eq. (2–3) in the form

$$x_{\sigma+1} = x_\sigma + Cr_\sigma \tag{2–8}$$

which is equivalent to

$$x_{\sigma+1} = Ch + Mx_\sigma$$

or to

$$C^{-1}x_{\sigma+1} = h + (C^{-1}M)x_\sigma \tag{2–9}$$

This suggests splitting the matrix

$$A = A_1 + A_2$$

and writing

$$A_1x_{\sigma+1} = h - A_2x_\sigma$$

where A_1 is a matrix such that the solution for $x_{\sigma+1}$ is easy to carry out. Then

$$C = A_1^{-1} \qquad M = -A_1^{-1}A_2$$

Necessary and sufficient for convergence is that

$$\rho(A_1^{-1}A_2) < 1$$

In the *Jacobi method* (method of simultaneous displacements), A_1 is the diagonal of A. In the *Gauss-Seidel method* (method of successive displacements), A_1 is the matrix obtained from A by replacing every element above the diagonal by zero. In so-called *block relaxation*, square blocks are marked out along the diagonal, and A_1 is the matrix obtained from A by replacing every element above these blocks by zero. This is advantageous when each of the submatrices in these blocks is easily inverted. In most practical situations, if the methods converge, then block relaxation requires the fewest steps, and the Gauss-Seidel method comes next. However, examples can be constructed where the Gauss-Seidel iteration does not converge at all, and the Jacobi method does.

The conditions required by the dominant-diagonal theorem are sufficient to assure convergence of the Jacobi method. In certain important applications it happens that also $A_2 \geq 0$. In that event all three methods converge, Jacobi the most slowly.

In another important class of cases, the matrix A is positive definite. When this is so, both the Gauss-Seidel iteration and block relaxation converge, but the Jacobi iteration may or may not.

In the stationary methods, it is necessary that C be nonsingular and that $\rho(M) < 1$. In the *methods of projection*, however, C_σ varies from step to step and is singular, while $\rho(M_\sigma) = 1$. In these methods the vectors s_σ are projected, one after another, upon subspaces, each time taking the projection as a correction to be added to x_σ to produce $x_{\sigma+1}$. At each step the subspace, usually a single vector, must be different from the one before, and the subspaces must periodically span the entire space. Analytically, the method is to make each new residual smaller in some norm than the previous one. Such methods can be constructed yielding convergence for an arbitrary matrix, but they are most useful when the matrix A is positive definite and the norm is $\|s_\sigma\|_A$. This will be sketched briefly.

For an arbitrary y_σ let

$$C_\sigma = (y_\sigma^H A y_\sigma)^{-1} y_\sigma y_\sigma^H$$

Then

$$x_{\sigma+1} = x_\sigma + \gamma_\sigma y_\sigma$$
$$\gamma_\sigma = y_\sigma^H r_\sigma / y_\sigma^H A y_\sigma$$

and it can be verified that

$$\|s_\sigma\|_A^2 - \|s_{\sigma+1}\|_A^2 = \gamma_\sigma r_\sigma^H y_\sigma \geq 0 \tag{2–10}$$

The choice $y_\sigma = r_\sigma$ is the *method of steepest descent*. If the y_σ are taken to be the vectors e_i in rotation the method turns out to be the Gauss-Seidel iteration. If each y_σ is taken to be that e_i for which $e_i^H r_\sigma$ is greatest, the method is the *method of relaxation* (often attributed to Southwell but actually known to Gauss). An alternative choice is the e_i for which the reduction Eq. (2–10) in norm is greatest.

Most *direct methods* proceed by applying to A a sequence of transformations in such a way that there results a matrix that is easily inverted. Each transformation is itself representable as the multiplication of A by a matrix that is simple in form. It may be observed that if C is any matrix such that CA has the inverse B,

$$B(CA) = I$$

then certainly $BC = A^{-1}$. Hence if any matrix C can be found such that CA can be inverted more readily than A, then progress will have been made toward inverting A, or, toward solving the system

$$Ax = h$$

since clearly

$$CAx = Ch$$

On the other hand, one should not lose sight of the rather paradoxical fact that if C and A are both full (*i.e.*, possessing few or no null elements), then *more* arithmetic operations are required to form the product CA than to find A^{-1}. Hence the matrix C, which is ordinarily constructed in practice, is by no means full, and, moreover, it is easily inverted. Indeed, quite often it is C^{-1} that is formed explicitly and C by inverting C^{-1}.

The method that is oldest, most commonly used, and generally most efficient is the method known as *gaussian elimination*. It can be described as follows: if $\alpha_{11} \neq 0$, replace the second row by the result of subtracting α_{21}/α_{11} times the first row; replace the third row by the result of subtracting α_{31}/α_{11} times the first; $\cdots$. When each succeeding row has been similarly treated there will result a matrix in which α_{11} is the only non-null element appearing in the first column. It can be seen that the effect of performing these operations upon A is equivalent to multiplying A by a matrix that differs from I only in the first column. The submatrix obtained from removing the first row and the first column from this transformed matrix is now treated in the same way. There were $n - 1$ steps in the first transformation, and there will be $n - 2$ in this. Now remove the new first row and first column and continue. The final result will be an upper triangular matrix (with only zeros below the diagonal), and the product of all of the transforming matrices is a lower triangular matrix, in fact, a *unit* lower triangular matrix since only ones occur on the diagonal.

In case $X = A^{-1}H$ is required but not A^{-1} explicitly, however many columns there may be in H, all operations should be performed upon the augmented matrix (A,H), and not on A alone. But then the elements of the transforming matrices need not be recorded and retained unless they are to be used later for any reason.

It could happen that $\alpha_{11} = 0$, in which case the division is impossible. But since A is assumed nonsingular, $\alpha_{i1} \neq 0$ for some i, and by a permutation of rows, the ith row can be put into the first position. If α_{11} is small, even if nonzero, excessive rounding errors can be introduced at the outset. The general rule is as follows: scale the elements of A so that the numerically largest element in each row is approximately the same for all rows, and the numerically largest element in each column is approximately the same for all columns. This can be done easily by multiplying A on the left (to scale the rows) and on the right (to scale the columns) by suitable diagonal matrices. If these diagonal matrices are D_1 and D_2, then in place of the system $Ax = h$, one has the system $D_1AD_2y = D_1h$, where $D_2y = x$. Now search the first column of A for the largest element and move its row to first place, thereafter proceeding as before. When the transformation on the first column is complete, search the first column of the submatrix for the largest element, and continue. Each interchange of rows is equivalent to the multiplication of the matrix by a permutation matrix (the matrix I with its columns permuted). But if P is a permutation matrix, P^H is its inverse, and in the final inversion of A the effects of the permutation are easily accounted for.

The net result of all these operations is that in place of the system $Ax = h$, the system $CAx = Ch$ is obtained, where CA is an upper triangular matrix. Such a matrix is easily inverted (the inverse will be exhibited below), and the triangular system is even more easily solved. With this explanation of the gaussian method, the basic theory of this and related methods will now be developed.

Only the inversion problem will be described, since the application to finding a single vector x will be obvious. The method is equivalent to the factorization

$$A = LR$$

where L is a unit lower triangular matrix, and R is upper triangular.

Note that an upper triangular matrix can be partitioned and inverted as follows:

$$\begin{pmatrix} R_{11} & R_{12} \\ 0 & R_{22} \end{pmatrix}^{-1} = \begin{pmatrix} R_{11}^{-1} & -R_{11}^{-1}R_{12}R_{22}^{-1} \\ 0 & R_{22}^{-1} \end{pmatrix}$$

where R_{11} and R_{22} are square. This inversion can be verified directly. If R_{22} is a scalar and R_{12} a column vector, this formula gives a recursive procedure for inverting a triangular matrix by starting with the upper left-hand element and proceeding to adjoin a row below and a column to the right. If R_{11} is a scalar, a recursion is defined in the other direction, up and to the left. Corresponding formulas hold for lower triangular matrices.

Now let A be partitioned:

$$A = \begin{pmatrix} A_{11} & A_{12} \\ A_{21} & A_{22} \end{pmatrix}$$

where A_{11} and A_{22} are square. Assuming it has been found possible to perform the factorization

$$A_{11} = L_{11}R_{11}$$

where L_{11} is unit lower triangular and R_{11} upper triangular, the possibility of the factorization

$$\begin{pmatrix} A_{11} & A_{12} \\ A_{21} & A_{22} \end{pmatrix} = \begin{pmatrix} L_{11} & 0 \\ L_{21} & I \end{pmatrix} \begin{pmatrix} R_{11} & R_{12} \\ 0 & \Delta_{22} \end{pmatrix}$$

is to be investigated. Evidently

$$R_{12} = L_{11}^{-1}A_{12} \qquad L_{21} = A_{21}R_{11}^{-1}$$
$$\Delta_{22} = A_{22} - A_{21}A_{11}^{-1}A_{12}$$

This provides an inductive, and a constructive, proof of the possibility of a triangular factorization of the specified form, provided only certain submatrices are nonsingular. For suppose first, that A_{11} is a scalar, A_{12} a row vector, and A_{21} a column vector, and let $L_{11} = 1$. Then $R_{11} = A_{11}$, $R_{12} = A_{12}$, and L_{21} and Δ_{22} are uniquely defined, provided only $A_{11} \neq 0$. But A_{11} can be made $\neq 0$, at least after certain row permutations have been made. Hence the problem of factoring the matrix A of order n, has been reduced to the factorization of the matrix Δ_{22} of order $n - 1$.

The formula has also other interpretations. If the inverse of a certain submatrix of A is known in advance, advantage can be taken of the fact to reduce the work. For suppose A_{11}^{-1} is known. Then by taking $L_{11} = I$, $R_{11} = A$, and if A_{11} is of order r, then the problem is immediately reduced to that of factoring the matrix Δ_{22} of order $n - r$.

Still another interpretation can be made by taking A_{22} to be a scalar, hence A_{21} a row vector and A_{12} a column vector. Suppose A_{11} has been inverted or factored as before. Then L_{21}, R_{12}, and Δ_{22} are obtainable, the two triangular matrices are easily inverted, and their product is the inverse of the complete matrix A. This is the basis for the *method of enlargement.* The method is to start with α_{11} which is easily inverted; apply the formulas to

$$\begin{pmatrix} \alpha_{11} & \alpha_{12} \\ \alpha_{21} & \alpha_{22} \end{pmatrix}$$

to factor and invert; then border this to a third order submatrix and apply again, and continue. This method is indicated in a situation where analytically an infinite system is being considered and approximated by retaining only a finite number of equations and unknowns, the finite number being undecided in advance.

Since

$$A^{-1} = R^{-1}L^{-1}$$

the inverse can be found, if required, when the factorization is complete. Alternatively, it is possible to build up L^{-1}, and, if desired, R^{-1}, as the factorization proceeds. In doing this the inversion of L, and that of R, must start at the upper left, whereas it is perhaps more natural to start the inversion of R at the lower right. Hence, there is this possible disadvantage in inverting and factoring simultaneously. Otherwise the only difference between inverting while factoring or afterward lies in the sequencing of quite independent operations.

Generally speaking elimination (triangular factorization) with interchange is the simplest and most accurate method known for either solving a linear system or for inverting a matrix. It may be remarked that the value of the determinant is an almost immediate byproduct, since it is simply the product of the diagonal elements of R. However, another type of factorization is advantageous in some special cases. According to the method used, the first factor can be made orthogonal and the second upper triangular (alternatively, the first could be lower triangular and the second orthogonal), or else the first can be merely orthogonal by columns and the second unit upper triangular. The results differ only in that a certain diagonal matrix is, in the one case, incorporated into the triangular matrix, in the other into the orthogonal matrix.

The classical method is known as *Schmidt orthogonalization.* In the general step, the ith column of A has added to it a linear combination of the preceding columns so that the result is orthogonal to each of the preceding columns. To obtain a constructive proof of the possibility and to exhibit the algorithm, suppose each of the first i columns of A has been so treated (the first column, of course, is unchanged). Let A_i represent the matrix of these i columns. It is the hypothesis of the induction that a unit upper triangular matrix R_i of order i has been found such that

$$A_i = V_i R_i$$

where V_i satisfies

$$V_i^H V_i = D^2$$

a diagonal matrix. It is now required to find a vector r_{i+1} (of i elements) so that if

$$V_i r_{i+1} + v_{i+1} = a_{i+1}$$

the next column of A, then v_{i+1} is orthogonal to all columns of V_i (hence to all columns of A_i). But on multiplying through by V_i^H the result is

$$D_i^2 r_{i+1} = V_i^H a_{i+1}$$

since the requirement is that $V_i^H v_{i+1} = 0$, hence

$$r_{i+1} = D_i^{-2} V_i^H a_{i+1}$$

By making the substitution it is verified that with r_{i+1} so determined, v_{i+1} is, indeed, orthogonal to each column of V_i. Evidently

$$\delta_{i+1}^2 = v_{i+1}^H v_{i+1}$$

is the next diagonal element required to form D_{i+1}^2, and R_{i+1} is formed by bordering R_i:

$$R_{i+1} = \begin{pmatrix} R_i & r_{i+1} \\ 0 & 1 \end{pmatrix}$$

An obvious possible modification of this procedure is that the vectors v_i could be normalized, in which case the normalizing factors, δ_i, will occur in the diagonal of R.

A second method for achieving the same result will be mentioned briefly. If w is a unit vector, $w^H w = 1$, then the matrix $I - 2ww^H$ is unitary and its own inverse (it is also hermitian). For any vector a, it is always possible to choose a unit vector w such that

$$(I - 2ww^H)a = \alpha e_1$$

where the scalar α is the euclidean length of a. In particular, if $a = a_1$, the first column of A, and w is chosen accordingly, then

$(I - 2ww^H)A$ is a matrix whose first column has only its first element nonzero. The same principle can now be applied to the submatrix that remains after removing the first row and first column of the transformed matrix, and so on until there results, finally, an upper triangular matrix. Notice that interchange of rows is not necessary.

For a positive definite matrix the use of a unitary factor should be emphatically ruled out. For triangular factorization, if

$$A = LR$$

is positive definite, with L unit lower triangular, and if D^2 is the diagonal matrix of diagonal elements of R, then

$$D^{-2}R = L^H$$

so that the factorization has the form

$$A = LD^2L^H$$

Since this can be written

$$A = (LD)(LD)^H$$

the algorithm can be set up as to give LD. This is the method of Cholesky, or of Banachiewicz, sometimes called the "square-root method."

One method that is not a method of factorization deserves mention. This is the *method of modification*. It can be verified directly that

$$(B - \sigma uv^H)^{-1} = B^{-1} - \tau B^{-1}uv^HB^{-1}$$
$$\tau^{-1} + \sigma^{-1} = v^HB^{-1}u$$

Thus, if the inverse of a matrix B is known, that of a matrix $B - \sigma uv^H$, differing from it only by a matrix of rank 1, can be found directly. The matrix of rank 1 could be a single element, or a single row or column. It is possible, for example, to start with the inverse of any matrix (*e.g.*, the identity I), and modify it column by column, each time applying the above formula, until the inverse of A is obtained after at most n steps. In a similar way and with less work, it is possible to build up to $A^{-1}h$.

2.3. Characteristic Roots and Vectors.—The characteristic roots of a matrix of order n satisfy an algebraic equation of degree n, and, given any algebraic equation of degree n, it is possible to construct a matrix for which this is the characteristic equation. It is known that an algebraic equation of degree $n \geq 5$ cannot, in general, be solved by radicals, and for $n \geq 2$ the solutions are not, in general, expressible in terms of arithmetic operations alone. Consequently, it is necessary to devise processes leading to infinite sequences whose limits are the required roots. But then a choice presents itself, which lies between operating upon the unmodified, original matrix, at the one extreme, and, at the other extreme, obtaining the characteristic equation and applying any of the standard methods for solving algebraic equations (*e.g.*, methods described in Section 2.4). In between these extremes lie certain possibilities for simplifying the matrix somewhat but without actually forming the characteristic equation explicitly. Thus two distinct topics require discussion. One has to do with operations that can be applied to a matrix, either arbitrary or belonging to some sufficiently wide class, to produce sequences that will approach the roots in the limit. The other has to do with simplifying transformations that can be applied in advance to facilitate application of these operations. Some of the commonly used methods for obtaining these sequences will be described first.

Before this is done, however, a certain paradox needs to be discussed briefly. Given a matrix A, and a nonsingular matrix V, it is known that A, and $V^{-1}AV$, have the same characteristic polynomial, and the two matrices are said to be *similar*. Among all matrices similar to a given matrix A, there are matrices of the form

$$\operatorname{diag}(\lambda_1 I_1 + J_1, \lambda_2 I_2 + J_2, \cdots, \lambda_m, \lambda_{m+1}, \cdots)$$

where the λ_i are the roots of A, the I_i are identity matrices, and the J_i are matrices with ones just above the diagonal and zeros elsewhere. Such a matrix is in the *Jordan normal form*. However, blocks of the form $\lambda_i I_i + J_i$ may not occur, in which case the normal form is an ordinary diagonal matrix each of whose elements is a characteristic root of A. This is the case for any matrix A whose roots are distinct, and it is the case for any *normal matrix*, which is defined to be a matrix A satisfying $AA^H = A^H A$. The class of normal matrices includes hermitian, skew-hermitian, and unitary matrices, but there are also others. It is much easier to find the roots of a matrix that is similar to a diagonal matrix than to find the roots of one that is not.

But in order for a matrix to have a multiple root, it is necessary that its elements satisfy a certain algebraic relation; to have a triple root they must satisfy two relations, and so forth for roots of higher order. Thus, if a matrix is considered as a point in n^2-space, only those matrices that lie on a certain algebraic variety have multiple roots. Clearly, if the elements of a matrix are selected at random from any reasonable distribution, the probability that the matrix selected will have multiple roots is zero. Moreover, even if the matrix itself should have, the occurrence of any rounding errors would almost certainly throw the matrix off the variety and displace the roots away from one another. Hence, although it may be known *a priori* of a given matrix that it has multiple roots, unless the elements are given exactly and all computations carried out exactly, it is impossible to determine computationally that a matrix has multiple roots. This is the paradox, and because of it, the subtleties introduced by multiple roots will not be considered here.

It can be assumed, then, that the matrix A has roots $\lambda_i = \lambda_i(A)$, and that they are ordered

$$|\lambda_1| \geq |\lambda_2| \geq \cdots$$

If A is real, the occurrence of conjugate complex roots is, of course, quite possible. The simplest of all methods is to take an arbitrary initial vector v_0 and to form the sequence of iterates

$$v_{\sigma+1} = Av_\sigma$$

This can be modified, if desirable, by the introduction of a convenient scale factor from time to time. If $|\lambda_1| > |\lambda_2|$, then for sufficiently large σ, the vectors approach the direction of the characteristic vector belonging to λ_1, and

$$v_{\sigma+1} \approx \lambda_1 v_\sigma$$

approximately. The ratio of any two corresponding elements of $v_{\sigma+1}$ and v_σ gives an approximation to λ_1, but a better approximation is given by the *Rayleigh quotient*, defined as

$$v_\sigma^H v_{\sigma+1}/v_\sigma^H v_\sigma = v_\sigma^H A v_\sigma / v_\sigma^H v_\sigma \approx \lambda_1$$

The reason for this phenomenon is easy to see. Evidently

$$v_\sigma = A^\sigma v_0$$

Suppose

$$A = S\Lambda S^{-1} \qquad \Lambda = \operatorname{diag}(\lambda_1, \lambda_2, \cdots)$$

Then the first column of S is the characteristic vector belonging to λ_1. But

$$A^\sigma v_0 = S\Lambda^\sigma S^{\ 1} v_0$$

and each element of this vector has the form

$$\mu_1\lambda_1^\sigma s_1 + \mu_2\lambda_2^\sigma s_2 + \cdots = \lambda_1^\sigma[\mu_1 s_1 + \mu_2(\lambda_2^\sigma/\lambda_1^\sigma)s_2 + \cdots] \approx \lambda_1^\sigma \mu_1 s_1$$

because of the fact that $\lambda_i^\sigma/\lambda_1^\sigma$ for $i > 1$ has the limit zero as σ increases. Here the s_i are the columns of S, and the μ_i are elements of $S^{-1}v_0$.

If $|\lambda_1| = |\lambda_2|$ the case is a bit less simple. If $|\lambda_2| > |\lambda_3|$, then the vectors v_σ do not approach linear dependence in pairs, but they do in triples. Otherwise stated, the v_σ approach the space of s_1 and s_2, the characteristic vectors belonging to λ_1 and λ_2. Hence, in the limit, any three consecutive iterates, v_σ, $v_{\sigma+1}$, $v_{\sigma+2}$ approach linear dependence, and in the limit if

$$\alpha_0 v_\sigma + \alpha_1 v_{\sigma+1} + v_{\sigma+2} = 0$$

then λ_1 and λ_2 satisfy the equation

$$\lambda^2 + \alpha_1\lambda + \alpha_0 = 0$$

Again, instead of selecting the coefficients α in this way, it is better to define

$$\mu_{\sigma,\rho} = v_\sigma^H v\rho$$

and form the equation

$$\det\begin{pmatrix} \mu_{\sigma,\sigma} & \mu_{\sigma,\sigma+1} & \mu_{\sigma,\sigma+2} \\ \mu_{\sigma+1,\sigma} & \mu_{\sigma+1,\sigma+1} & \mu_{\sigma+1,\sigma+2} \\ 1 & \lambda & \lambda^2 \end{pmatrix} = 0$$

In the limit, λ_1 and λ_2 are roots of this equation. It is easy to see how this is generalized in case more of the λ's coincide in modulus, but the most important case is that of a complex conjugate pair.

Before considering how to proceed to find the remaining roots, another, closely related method will be described. The method has several variants, but basically it is due to Wielandt. Suppose μ_0 is closer (in the complex plane) to some particular root λ than to any other. Then, for a given initial v_0, form the iterates $v_1, v_2, \cdots$ by solving the equations

$$(A - \mu I)v_{\sigma+1} = v_\sigma$$

This is equivalent to the iteration

$$v_{\sigma+1} = (A - \mu I)^{-1} v_\sigma$$

where the iterating matrix has $(\lambda - \mu)^{-1}$ as its root of largest modulus. Hence in the limit the vectors v_σ approach the vector belonging to λ. Convergence can be accelerated if, from time to time, the previously used μ is replaced by the Rayleigh quotient

$$v_\sigma^H A v_\sigma / v_\sigma^H v_\sigma$$

It is sometimes argued that this method is inherently unstable and not to be depended upon because the closer μ is to λ, and hence, the more rapid the theoretical convergence, the more nearly singular (the more poorly conditioned) is the matrix $A - \mu I$. It is entirely true that when $A - \mu I$ is nearly singular the vector $v_{\sigma+1}$, considered as a solution of the system of equations, cannot be determined with any degree of accuracy. But it can be shown that the errors tend to be in the right direction, which is in the direction of s, the vector belonging to λ, and hence the real objective of the computation. Thus what appears on the surface to be a serious drawback in the method turns out to be in fact one of its strong points, a situation that has few parallels.

Just as a known root of an algebraic equation can be "divided out," and the equation reduced to one of lower order, so a known root and the vector belonging to it can be used to reduce the matrix to one of lower order whose roots are the yet unknown roots. In principle this can be continued until the matrix reduces to a scalar, which is the last remaining root. The process is known as *deflation*. Quite generally, in fact, let P be a matrix of, say, p linearly independent columns such that each column of AP is a linear combination of columns of P itself. In particular, this will be true if the columns of P are characteristic vectors. Then

$$AP = PM$$

where M is some square matrix of order p, diagonal if the columns of P are characteristic vectors. Let V be a matrix also of p columns such that

$$V^H P = I$$

This is possible since P has maximal rank p. Now all roots of M are roots of A. Assume A to be nonsingular, and suppose that if A has any multiple roots occurring among the roots of M, then it has the same multiplicity as a root of M. Then it can be shown that

$$B = A(I - PV^H)$$

has p null roots, and that the remaining roots of B are identical with the roots of A that are not also roots of M. Suppose, further, that W is a matrix of P distinct columns of I such that $W^H P$ is nonsingular. Then if V is chosen to satisfy

$$W^H A = W^H PMV^H$$

which can be done uniquely, it follows that $W^H B = 0$, which is to say that p of the rows of B are null. Hence the nonnull roots of B are those of a principal submatrix of order $n - p$.

The *method of Jacobi* applies not only to hermitian matrices, but, with some modification, to all normal matrices. It is not to be recommended, but it has some historical interest and is often mentioned in the literature. Hence, it will be described briefly as it is applied to the hermitian case. If A is hermitian, then there exists a unitary matrix V such that

$$V^H A V = \Lambda$$

is diagonal, the columns of V being the characteristic vectors. Now the sum of the squares of the moduli of the elements of a matrix is not changed when the matrix is multiplied by a unitary matrix. Hence the sum of the squares of the moduli of the elements of A is the same as that of Λ. But the nonnull elements of Λ are only on the diagonal and these are the roots of A. Hence the sum of the squares of the moduli of the elements of A is equal to the sum of the squares of its roots.

Now consider any principal submatrix of A. This is hermitian, and if a unitary transformation is applied to A so as to diagonalize this submatrix, then the sum of the squares of the diagonal elements of A is increased in the amount of the sum of the squares of the off-diagonal elements of the submatrix. In practice, the submatrices selected are of order 2. If the submatrix

$$\begin{pmatrix} \alpha_{ii} & \alpha_{ij} \\ \alpha_{ji} & \alpha_{jj} \end{pmatrix}$$

is chosen, then a rotation can be performed so that in the transformed matrix the (i,j) elements are annihilated. If a largest off-diagonal element is annihilated at each stage, it can be shown easily that the process always converges. In practice, to avoid the search, the elements are annihilated in a fixed cyclic order, and special precautions have to be taken to make sure of convergence. The process is an infinite process since elements once annihilated are later restored, though not, in general, to their original magnitude. The method is not self-correcting.

The methods of simple and of inverse iteration apply to arbitrary matrices, but many steps may be required to obtain sufficiently good convergence. It is, therefore, desirable to replace A, if possible, by a matrix that is similar (having the same roots) but having as many zeros as are reasonably obtainable in order that each step of the iteration require as few computations as possible. At the extreme, the characteristic polynomial itself could be obtained, but this is not necessarily advisable. The nature of the disadvantage can perhaps be made understandable from the following observation: in the case of a full matrix, having no null elements, the n roots are functions of the n^2 elements. They are also functions of the n coefficients of the characteristic equation, and cannot be expressed as functions of a smaller number of variables. It is to be expected, therefore, that they will be less sensitive to variations (errors) in one of the n^2 elements than to variations in a coefficient of the equation. Generally speaking this is so. Moreover, there are two intermediate forms, the Hessenberg form with $(n-1)(n-2)/2$ zeros, and the Lanczos (or tridiagonal) form with only $3n-2$ possibly nonnull elements, for each of which the sensitivity is somewhat greater than in the full matrix but considerably less than in the characteristic polynomial. The derivation of these will be described.

First, with an arbitrary initial vector $v = v_i$, consider the sequence of iterates

$$v_{i+1} = A^i v_1$$

In n-space any $n+1$ of these are linearly dependent. But unless the matrix is rather special in form (derogatory), there exist vectors v_1 for which any n consecutive vectors are linearly independent (in possible contrast to the behavior in the limit). In fact, this is true of "almost every" vector v_1. Hence, if

$$V = (v_1, v_2, \cdots, v_n)$$

then for some vector f,

$$Vf + v_{n+1} = 0 \tag{2–11}$$

which is to say that, in view of the definition of the vectors v_i, for some polynomial $\phi(\lambda)$ of degree n,

$$\phi(A)v = 0$$

But then $\phi(\lambda)$ is the characteristic polynomial of A, and its coefficients are the elements of f and can be found by solving Eq. (2–11). This is essentially the *method of Krylov*, who chose, in particular, a vector e_i (usually e_1) for v_1. Several methods of reduction of the matrix A can be derived from applying particular methods of inverting or factoring V at the same time that the successive columns of V are being developed.

Note first that if

$$F = J - fe_n^H \qquad J = (e_2, e_3, \cdots, e_n, 0)$$

then

$$AV = VF$$

and if F is known, then

$$\phi(\lambda) = \det(\lambda I - F)$$

is obtainable by a simple direct expansion.

The method of Danilevskiĭ proceeds as follows: if

$$A = A_1$$

let

$$M_2 = I - m_2 e_2^H$$

where the vector m_2 is selected so that if

$$M_2 A_1 = A_2 M_2$$

then the first column of the matrix A_2 is e_2. Since the first column of M_2 is e_1, the requirement is that the first column of $A_2 M_2$ be e_2. But if a_1 is the first column of $A = A_1$, the first column on the left is

$$a_1 - m_2(e_2^H a_1) = e_2$$
$$m_2 = (a_1 - e_2)/(e_2^H a_1)$$

This is possible, therefore, if and only if the element α_{21} in A is non-null. It can be verified directly that

$$(I - m_2 e_2^H)^{-1} = I + (e_2^H a_1) m_2 e_2^H$$

whence

$$A_2 = M_2 A_1 M_2^{-1}$$

can be computed. Next, with

$$M_3 = I - m_3 e_3^H$$

A_3 is formed from

$$M_3 A_2 = A_3 M_3$$

to have e_3 for its second column. This transformation retains the e_2 in the first column. The formation of m_3, thence of M_3^{-1}, and the entire matrix A_3 is analogous to the first step. At the final step A_n has e_n for its penultimate column, and this is the required matrix F.

Although no matrix V occurs explicitly in this sequence of transformations, it can be verified that for a V formed from $v_1 = e_1$, the matrices M_i are such that

$$M_n M_{n-1} \cdots M_2 V = I$$

hence their product is V^{-1}, and the effect is to have formed

$$V^{-1} A = F V^{-1}$$

As a practical matter, for keeping rounding errors as small as possible, it is to be observed that since the elements just below the diagonal serve as pivots, an interchange should be made when necessary in order to make the pivotal element as large as possible. Here an interchange of rows must always be accompanied by an interchange of corresponding columns.

The *method of Hessenberg*, which reduces the matrix to Hessenberg form, replaces the matrix A by

$$L^{-1}AL = H \tag{2–12}$$

where L is a unit lower triangular matrix such that

$$L^{-1}V = R$$

is upper triangular. Suppose again that $v_1 = e_1$; interchange rows and columns in $A = A_1$ so that the element α_{21} is as large as possible, and choose a vector l_2 such that

$$e_1^H l_2 = e_2^H l_2 = 0, \qquad L_2 = I - l_2 e_2^H$$
$$L_2 A_1 = A_2 L_2$$

and the first column of A_2 is null except in its first two elements. If a_1 is the first column of A_1, the first column of L_2A_1 is $a_1 - l_2(e_2^H a_1)$, and l_2, which is zero in its first two elements, has its remaining elements equal to the corresponding elements of $(e_2^H a_1)^{-1}a_1 = \alpha_{21}^{-1}a_1$. Given l_2, since

$$(I - l_2 e_2^H)^{-1} = I + l_2 e_2^H$$

(this is verified directly), A_2 can be formed. Now remove the first row and first column and repeat with the resulting matrix of order $n - 1$. By continuing the process, a sequence of unit lower triangular matrices is obtained whose product is the unit lower triangular matrix L satisfying Eq. (2–12).

A Hessenberg form H (the same form but not the same matrix) can also be obtained by a sequence of orthogonal transformations, either by plane rotations (*the method of Givens*), each rotation annihilating an individual element, or by using unitary hermitians, $I - 2w_i w_i^H$, $w_i^H w_i = 1$ (*the method of Householder*), each of which annihilates all possible elements in a column. Thus, at the first step, if $A = A_i$, and

$$W_2 = I - 2w_2 w_2^H$$

then w_2 is chosen so that $e_1^H w_2 = 0$, and in

$$W_2 A_1 = A_2 W_2$$

the first column of A_2 is zero except possibly in the first two elements.

Now remove the first row and first column and repeat with the submatrix of order $n - 1$. After continuing the process until the reduced matrix is of third order, restore the rows and columns that had been dropped, and border the transforming matrices with ones on the diagonal and zeros elsewhere. There results, then, a unitary matrix W, the product of the W_i, such that

$$WAW^H = H \tag{2–13}$$

where H is in Hessenberg form. It can be verified that either the matrix L or the matrix W, when multiplied by the matrix V formed with $v_1 = e_1$, gives an upper triangular matrix as the product.

For general matrices the reduction by triangular matrices requires less computation and is probably to be preferred. But *if A is hermitian*, observe that *the use of the unitary reduction produces a matrix H that is again hermitian*, hence, that is *tridiagonal* in form, having zeros everywhere except along, just above, and just below the main diagonal.

The reduction of a real symmetric matrix to tridiagonal form by means of orthogonal transformations was first analyzed in detail and tested by Givens, who made the reduction an element at a time with the use of plane rotations. The method bears a superficial resemblance to the Jacobi method, which also uses plane rotations, but there is an essential difference. The Jacobi method is an infinite process that leads to the diagonal form of the matrix in the limit. The method of Givens, however, aims only to reduce to tridiagonal form, and this can be achieved in a finite number, $(n - 1)(n - 2)/2$, steps. The roots themselves are still to be found, but Givens exhibited a very efficient method for doing this, and one that takes advantage of certain special properties of a tridiagonal symmetric (or hermitian) matrix. As a general-purpose method for real symmetric or complex hermitian matrices the method is by far to be preferred over all others now known. The work of reduction can be somewhat shortened in most cases by using the matrices $W_i = I - 2w_iw_i^H$ instead of plane rotations.

Once the tridiagonal form has been obtained, the method recommended for finding the roots depends, as remarked, upon a special property of such a matrix. Let the matrix be written

$$H = \begin{pmatrix} \alpha_1 & \beta_1 & 0 & 0 & \cdots \\ \beta_1 & \alpha_2 & \beta_2 & 0 & \cdots \\ 0 & \beta_2 & \alpha_3 & \beta_3 & \cdots \\ 0 & 0 & \beta_3 & \alpha_4 & \cdots \\ \cdot & \cdot & \cdot & \cdot & \cdot \end{pmatrix}$$

and define the polynomials

$$\begin{aligned}
\phi_0 &= 1 \\
\phi_1 &= \lambda - \alpha_1 \\
\phi_2 &= (\lambda - \alpha_2)\phi_1 - \beta_1^2\phi_0 \\
\phi_3 &= (\lambda - \alpha_3)\phi_2 - \beta_2^2\phi_1 \\
&\cdot \quad \cdot \quad \cdot \quad \cdot \quad \cdot \quad \cdot \quad \cdot \quad \cdot
\end{aligned}$$

It can be verified that the polynomial ϕ_i is equal to the *leading principal minor of order i of the determinant of* $\lambda I - H$, and as such the sequence of polynomials is a *Sturm sequence*. This means that if they are evaluated for any fixed number λ_0 and the signs recorded in sequence, then the number of variations (*i.e.*, pairs $+\ -$ or $-\ +$) in the sequence is exactly equal to the number of characteristic roots greater than λ_0. Hence, if an upper bound and a lower bound can be found for all the roots, then by successively bisecting this interval any root can be obtained to as high a degree of accuracy as is permitted by the number of digits to which the computations are carried out. But upper and lower bounds are easily obtained by application of the principle of the dominant-diagonal theorem. This implies that if μ' is such that

$$\begin{aligned}
\mu' - \alpha_1 &> |\beta_1| \\
\mu' - \alpha_2 &> |\beta_1| + |\beta_2| \\
\mu' - \alpha_3 &> |\beta_2| + |\beta_3| \\
&\cdot \quad \cdot \quad \cdot \quad \cdot \quad \cdot \quad \cdot \quad \cdot \quad \cdot
\end{aligned}$$

then μ' is an upper bound, and if μ'' is such that

$$\begin{aligned}
\alpha_1 - \mu'' &> |\beta_1| \\
\alpha_2 - \mu'' &> |\beta_1| + |\beta_2| \\
\alpha_3 - \mu'' &> |\beta_2| + |\beta_3| \\
&\cdot \quad \cdot \quad \cdot \quad \cdot \quad \cdot \quad \cdot \quad \cdot \quad \cdot
\end{aligned}$$

then μ'' is a lower bound.

To return to the general case, it will now be shown that *any* matrix can be reduced to tridiagonal form, but by triangular rather than orthogonal or unitary transformations. Unfortunately, since there will be, in general, some complex roots, the Givens method of solution cannot be applied. But suppose the matrix is in lower Hessenberg form, which is to say that every element two places or more above the diagonal is zero. This could be the conjugate transpose of the matrix (2–12) resulting from the transformation by lower triangular matrices. Then if the lower triangular matrices are generated for reducing this to (upper) Hessenberg form (but without interchanges of rows and of columns) none of the zeros at the upper right will be disturbed in the process of producing zeros at the lower left, and the result will be a tridiagonal matrix. The possibility of such a reduction was first shown by Lanczos. His method of achieving it produced the zeros simultaneously above and below the diagonal, but it can be shown to be mathematically equivalent to the method just described.

The characteristic polynomial can be obtained explicitly, if desired, from the tridiagonal form of the matrix, or even from the Hessenberg form, but this is not necessarily to be recommended, for reasons suggested above. Other methods are to be found in the literature, due to Leverrier, to Samuelson, to Bryan, and the escalator method of Morris and Head. In general, however, the recommended method is to reduce to tridiagonal form, then to use the Givens method of solution when the matrix is symmetric, and the iterative method otherwise. In either event, when an approximate root has been found, it may be desirable to improve it by using inverse iteration, possibly on the original, untransformed, matrix. In particular, this is the method to use for finding characteristic vectors.

A final word may be said about appraising the accuracy of a computed root. No usable rigorous bound to the errors is known that does not require approximations to all roots and vectors. Suppose, then, that X is a matrix whose columns are approximations to the characteristic vectors, and form

$$X^{-1}AX = \Lambda + R$$

where Λ is a diagonal matrix and R is a matrix with a null diagonal. If the columns of X are good approximations to the vectors, then all elements of R will be small. Let ρ_i be the sum of the moduli of the elements in the ith row of R. Then, by the principle of the dominant-diagonal theorem, if $|\lambda - \lambda_i| > \rho_i$ for every i, the matrix $\lambda I - \Lambda - R$ cannot be singular, hence every root λ of $\Lambda + R$, hence of A, must lie in a region where one of these inequalities fails, hence in one of the circular disks

$$|\lambda - \lambda_i| \leq \rho_i \tag{2–14}$$

This is Gershgorin's theorem. Moreover, if any λ_i is separated from the others, and the ρ's small enough so that the particular disk (2–14) is disjoint from all the others, then that disk contains exactly one root. By applying the theorem to the matrix $D(\Lambda + R)D^{-1}$, for a suitable matrix D, it is sometimes possible to obtain even better bounds.

2.4. Nonlinear Equations and Systems.—For solving a single nonlinear equation in a single unknown, methods may be classified as *local* and *global*. A local method aims at the evaluation of a single root. Typically it proceeds from a given approximation to an improved approximation; hence, it is a method of successive approximation and is self-correcting. Best known examples are Horner's method, Newton's method, and the method of false position. Bernoulli's method, in its simplest form, is the method that results from applying simple iteration to the comparison matrix (Section 2.3), hence may be considered a local method. But Aitken showed how to obtain from it all the roots, and the method has been further developed by Rutishauser as the QD algorithm. It will, therefore, be considered a global method. The other classical global method is the method that is variously attributed to Dandelin, to Lobachevskii, and to Graeffe, and seems, in fact, to have been developed independently by all three with minor variations. The method of Bairstow is a local method, which is applied to a real equation to produce the quadratic satisfied by a pair of conjugate complex roots.

Local methods usually take the following form: if the equation to be solved is

$$f(x) = 0 \tag{2–15}$$

and solutions are required in some region of the complex plane, an equivalent equation

$$x = \phi(x) \tag{2–16}$$

is obtained, and starting with a suitable initial approximation x_0, the sequence of terms

$$x_{i+1} = \phi(x_i) \tag{2–17}$$

is developed. If the sequence has a limit, it necessarily satisfies Eq. (2–16) and hence (2–15). In order that (2–15) and (2–16) be equivalent, it is necessary that

$$\phi(x) \equiv x + f(x)/g(x) \tag{2–18}$$

where f and g have no common zeros, and g has no poles, in the region under consideration. It is assumed that x_0 is chosen within the region, and that all subsequent terms in the sequence remain in it. If x is any zero, then a sufficient condition for convergence to x, starting with some x_0 in a neighborhood of α, is that for some positive $k < 1$, the inequality

$$|\phi(x') - \phi(x'')| \leq k|x' - x''|$$

whenever x' and x'' are both in the neighborhood. A sufficient condition for the existence of such a neighborhood is that ϕ have a derivative and

$$|\phi'(\alpha)| < 1$$

The existence of derivatives of sufficiently high order will be tacitly assumed throughout.

If

$$\phi'(\alpha) = \cdots = \phi^{(k-1)}(\alpha) = 0 \neq \phi^{(k)}(\alpha)$$

the iteration is said to be of order k, and it can be seen that

$$x_{i+1} - \alpha = (x_i - \alpha)^k \phi^{(k)}(\alpha)/k!$$

Thus, in principle, higher-order iterations converge more rapidly. In the case of *Newton's method*,

$$g(x) = -f'(x)$$

and the iteration is of second order.

Several methods are known for constructing iterations of arbitrarily high order, but most of these are of theoretical interest only. For any nonlinear equation and any iteration, the initial approximation x_0 must be in some sufficiently small neighborhood of a root α in order for convergence to that root to occur. As the order of the iteration increases, the region itself tends to decrease. This is one disadvantage of iterations of higher order. Another is that the function ϕ becomes increasingly complicated, which not only increases the computational labor per step, but also tends to increase the rounding error per step.

There is one method, however, of increasing the order of convergence, that is often extremely useful. In fact, it can be applied to an arbitrary sequence, however the sequence may have been derived; it will often produce a sequence that converges more rapidly than the original, and will even, in many cases, produce a converging sequence out of one that diverges. It is due to *Aitken*, who called it the *δ^2-process.* Beginning with x_0, let x_1 and x_2 be computed in the normal manner by Eq. (2–17), but then form x_3 by

$$x_3 = (x_0 x_2 - x_1^2)/(x_0 - 2x_1 + x_2)$$

Regarding $x_3 = x_0'$ as a new starting value, repeat to form $x_3' = x_0''$ and continue. It can be shown that if the initial iteration is of order k, that of the iteration that produces $x_0, x_0', x_0'', \cdots$ is of the order $2k - 1$. Evidently the transformation could be applied again, using the terms x_0, x_0', and x_0'' of the derived sequence to produce the initial term of a new derived sequence. However, new sources of rounding error are introduced in this process, and the finally accepted approximation should be a result $\phi(\xi)$ of substituting a ξ into the basic iteration formula (2–17).

The simplest and best known iteration is *regula falsi*. Geometrically, given any two values x_0 and x_1 such that $f(x_0)f(x_1) < 0$, and that a single root only is known to lie between x_0 and x_1, let

$$x_2 = [x_0 f(x_1) - x_1 f(x_0)]/[f(x_1) - f(x_0)]$$

This amounts to drawing the chord joining the points $[x_0, f(x_0)]$ and $[x_1, f(x_1)]$, and finding its intersection with the x-axis. Suppose that $f(x_0)f(x_2) < 0$. Then if

$$\phi(x) = [x_0 f(x) - x f(x_0)]/[f(x) - f(x_0)]$$

the iteration is linear and $f(x_0)f(x_i) < 0$ for all i. Thus the true solution is guaranteed to lie between x_0 and any iterate. But if the iteration is defined by

$$x_{i+1} = [x_{i-1} f(x_i) - x_i f(x_{i-1})]/[f(x_i) - f(x_{i-1})]$$

the convergence is actually higher than linear but lower than quadratic. This is an example of a form of iteration somewhat more general than (2–17),

$$x_{i+1} = \phi(x_i, x_{i-1}, \cdots)$$

making use of an arbitrary number of previous iterates.

These methods may be called *analytical*, by contrast with another class of iterations that might be called *arithmetic*, since they exploit the fact that the number representation is finite and digital. The familiar *Horner's method* is an example. The first step is to establish that a root lies between a certain pair of consecutive integers. Next, if the representation is decimal, $f(x)$ is evaluated at consecutive tenths to determine the pair of consecutive tenths between which the root lies. This is repeated for the hundredths, thousandths, etc., to as many places as may be desired and justified.

This method has very little other than its simplicity to recommend it in the form just described. But when a binary base is used, the corresponding procedure is to bisect the interval successively. Each bisection determines one additional binary digit to the approximation, it requires only the evaluation of the function, and the method is often efficient and accurate. The principle is used by Givens (Section 2.3) in finding the roots of a tridiagonal symmetric matrix.

Turning now to global methods, the more recent developments of the *method of Bernoulli* are based upon a theorem of König, and generalizations by Hadamard. The essential theorem is sufficiently well illustrated by the following special case: let $f(x)$ be analytic (not necessarily a polynomial) over some circular disk centered at the origin, and in this disk let it possess exactly two simple zeros, α and β. Let $g(x)$ be analytic over the same disk, and let

$$g(\alpha)g(\beta) \neq 0$$

Let

$$\begin{aligned} f(x) &= f_0 + f_1 x + f_2 x^2 + \cdots \\ g(x) &= g_0 + g_1 x + g_2 x^2 + \cdots \\ h(x) &= g(x)/f(x) = h_0 + h_1 x + h_2 x^2 + \cdots \end{aligned}$$

and set

$$P(x) = b_0(1 - x/\alpha)(1 - x/\beta) = b_0 + b_1 x + b_2 x^2 \qquad (2\text{–}19)$$

Thus $P(x) = 0$ is a quadratic whose roots are α and β, and

$$P(x)h(x) = k(x) = k_0 + k_1 x + k_2 x^2 + \cdots$$

is analytic over the disk. On introducing power series on the left, multiplying, and comparing coefficients the result is

$$\begin{aligned} b_0 h_0 &= k_0 \\ b_1 h_0 + b_0 h_1 &= k_1 \\ b_2 h_0 + b_1 h_1 + b_0 h_2 &= k_2 \\ b_2 h_1 + b_1 h_2 + b_0 h_3 &= k_3 \\ \cdot \quad \cdot \quad \cdot \quad \cdot \quad \cdot & \quad \cdot \quad \cdot \\ \cdot \quad \cdot \quad \cdot \quad \cdot \quad \cdot & \quad \cdot \quad \cdot \end{aligned}$$

Multiply these equations by $1, \alpha, \alpha^2, \cdots, \alpha^{\nu+1}$, add, making use of Eq. (2–19), and obtain

$$\alpha^\nu(b_0 + \alpha b_1)h_\nu + \alpha^{\nu+1} b_0 h_{\nu+1} = k_{\nu+1}(\alpha)$$

where

$$k_\nu(x) = k_0 + k_1 x + \cdots + k_\nu x^\nu$$

The relation just derived, along with two others involving higher powers of α, implies that

$$\det \begin{pmatrix} h_\nu & h_{\nu+1} & \alpha^2 k_{\nu+1}(\alpha) \\ h_{\nu+1} & h_{\nu+2} & \alpha k_{\nu+2}(\alpha) \\ h_{\nu+2} & h_{\nu+3} & k_{\nu+3}(\alpha) \end{pmatrix} = 0$$

and in the limit, $k_{\nu+1}(\alpha) \to k(\alpha)$. Hence, in the limit the equation

$$\det \begin{pmatrix} h_\nu & h_{\nu+1} & x^2 \\ h_{\nu+1} & h_{\nu+2} & x \\ h_{\nu+2} & h_{\nu+3} & 1 \end{pmatrix} = 0 \qquad (2\text{–}20)$$

has α as one of its roots. But the same argument, with β replacing α, shows that β is also one of the roots. Hence if α_ν and β_ν are the roots of (2–20), then as ν becomes infinite, $\alpha_\nu \to \alpha$ and $\beta_\nu \to \beta$. The generalization to n roots is obvious.

It is easy to obtain the coefficients h_i of the expansion $h(x)$. In fact,

$$g_0 + g_1x + g_2x^2 + \cdots = (f_0 + f_1x + f_2x^2 + \cdots)(h_0 + h_1x + h_2x^2 + \cdots)$$

whence, by comparing coefficients,

$$\begin{aligned} f_0h_0 &= g_0 \\ f_0h_1 + f_1h_0 &= g_1 \\ f_0h_2 + f_1h_1 + f_2h_0 &= g_2 \\ \cdots & \\ \cdots & \end{aligned}$$

and subject to the trivial restriction that $f_0 = f(0) \neq 0$, the h_i can be obtained sequentially. If $f_0 \neq 0$, there would be no restriction in replacing f by f/f_0 and assuming $f_0 = 1$, but this will not be done.

Consider an algebraic equation of degree n written in the form

$$f_0z^n + f_1z^{n-1} + \cdots + f_n = 0 \tag{2–21}$$

This is equivalent to

$$f_0 + f_1x + f_2x^2 + \cdots + f_nx^n = 0 \tag{2–22}$$

with $x = 1/z$. In its original and simplest form, the Bernoulli method takes $g_0, g_1, \cdots, g_{n-1}$ arbitrary, hence $h_0, h_1, \cdots, h_{n-1}$ arbitrary, and forms

$$\begin{aligned} f_0h_n + f_1h_{n-1} + \cdots + f_nh_0 &= 0 \\ f_0h_{n+1} + f_1h_n + \cdots + f_nh_1 &= 0 \\ \cdots & \\ \cdots & \end{aligned}$$

Then if $h_{\nu+1}/h_\nu$ has a limit, it is the smallest root of (2–22), and hence the limit of $h_\nu/h_{\nu+1}$ is the largest root of (2–21). If the roots of the sequence of quadratics (2–20) have limits, these limits are the two roots of (2–22) whose moduli are smallest (possibly complex conjugates), and the limits do exist if there are two roots smaller in moduli than any others. Note that the product of the two roots of (2–20) is equal to

$$\det \begin{pmatrix} h_{\nu+1} & h_{\nu+2} \\ h_{\nu+2} & h_{\nu+3} \end{pmatrix} \Big/ \det \begin{pmatrix} h_\nu & h_{\nu+1} \\ h_{\nu+1} & h_{\nu+2} \end{pmatrix}$$

Therefore, if there is a complex conjugate pair with minimal modulus, the square of this modulus is the limit of these ratios. But if (2–22) has roots x_i with

$$|x_1| < |x_2| < |x_3| \leq \cdots$$

then the limit of these ratios is x_1x_2, that of $h_{\nu+1}/h_\nu$ is x_1; hence, x_2 is the quotient of these limits. If all n roots are distinct in modulus, then the product

$$x_1x_2\cdots x_i$$

is the limit of ratios of ith order determinants formed from the h_ν, and the individual x_i are quotients of these limits.

These considerations throw further light on the simple iteration for finding roots of a matrix A. For

$$F(\lambda) = x^H(\lambda I - A)^{-1}y$$

is expressible as a quotient of two polynomials in λ, of which the denominator is the characteristic polynomial of A. But formally,

$$(\lambda I - A)^{-1} = \lambda^{-1}(I - \lambda^{-1}A)^{-1} = \lambda^{-1}(I + \lambda^{-1}A + \lambda^{-2}A^2 + \cdots)$$

and, therefore

$$F(\lambda) = \lambda^{-1}(\mu_0 + \lambda^{-1}\mu_1 + \lambda^{-2}\mu_2 + \cdots)$$

where

$$\mu_i = x^H A^i y$$

Therefore, $\lambda F(\lambda) = h(\lambda)$ provided the μ_i are identified with the h_i.

To return to the determinants in the h_i, those of higher order are of little practical utility unless some convenient and stable scheme can be devised for their evaluation, and this is provided by the *quotient-difference* (*QD*) *algorithm of Rutishauser and Stiefel.*

Schematically, the algorithm fills out a two-dimensional array of numbers:

$$\begin{array}{cccccc}
q_1^{(0)} & & q_2^{(-1)} & & q_3^{(-2)} & \\
 & e_1^{(0)} & & e_2^{(-1)} & & e_3^{(-2)} \\
q_1^{(1)} & & q_2^{(0)} & & q_3^{(-1)} & \\
 & e_1^{(1)} & & e_2^{(0)} & & e_3^{(-1)} \\
q_1^{(2)} & & q_2^{(1)} & & q_3^{(0)} & \\
 & e_1^{(2)} & & e_2^{(1)} & & e_3^{(0)} \\
q_1^{(3)} & & q_2^{(2)} & & q_3^{(1)} & \\
 & e_1^{(3)} & & e_2^{(2)} & & e_3^{(1)} \\
\cdot\ \cdot & \cdot\ \cdot & \cdot\ \cdot & \cdot\ \cdot & \cdot\ \cdot & \\
 & \cdot\ \cdot & \cdot\ \cdot & \cdot\ \cdot & \cdot\ \cdot & \cdot
\end{array}$$

by means of the following "rhombus rules":

$$q_{k+1}^{(i)} + e_k^{(i)} = q_k^{(i+1)} \quad e_k^{(i+1)}$$
$$q_k^{(i)} + e_k^{(i)} = q_k^{(i+1)} + e_{k-1}^{(i+1)}$$
$$e_0^{(i)} = 0$$

By means of the rhombus rules, if values are given for the elements occurring along the broken line at the top, then all other elements can be computed. The numbers to be taken are

$$\begin{aligned} q_1^{(0)} &= -f_1/f_0, \qquad & q_2^{(-1)} &= q_3^{(-2)} = \cdots = 0 \\ e_i^{(1-i)} &= f_{i+1}/f_i, & i &= 1,2,\cdots,n-1 \\ e_i^{(1-i)} &= 0, & i &= n,n+1,\cdots \end{aligned}$$

The effect of this is that each q-column is a column of quotients of determinants in the h_i, and if the roots of (2–22) are distinct in modulus, then the elements in each of these columns approaches one of the roots as a limit. In the case of a complex conjugate pair of roots, whose moduli differ from all others, the roots of the pair are limits of the roots of quadratic

$$x^2 - (q_{k+1}^{(i+1)} + q_{k+2}^{(i)})x + q_{k+1}^{(i)}q_{k+2}^{(i)} = 0$$

The other global method in common use is generally called the *method of Graeffe* in western Europe and in the United States, and the method of Lobachevskii in the USSR. The first to state the principle was Dandelin, but Graeffe devised the algorithm, simple enough in itself, that is normally used. The method is widely known, and is described in many places. Hence, it will not be described here. But it is not widely known that the method is applicable, with rather trivial modifications, to solving transcendental equations.

As usually described, it is applied to an algebraic equation (2–21) with $f_0 = 1$. With obvious changes, it can be applied equally well to the equation (2–22), with the understanding that the roots appear in the order of increasing moduli instead of in the order of decreasing moduli. But with these changes in phraseology in describing the method, it applies to any transcendental equation

$$1 + f_1z + f_2z^2 + \cdots = 0$$

where the infinite series on the left converges in some circular disk centered at the origin, and all roots lying in that disk are obtained.

The method is, of course, not self-correcting, and errors can accumulate. However, the local methods require initial approximations, and the approximations provided by this method may be improved if necessary, by applying a local method.

For solving *systems of equations*, only local methods are available. Let the equations be given in the form

$$f(x) = 0 \tag{2–23}$$

where x represents the vector whose elements are ξ_i, and f the vector whose elements are ϕ_i. The natural analogue of the local methods for a single equation would be the replacement of (2–23) by an equivalent system

$$x = h(x) \tag{2–24}$$

from which to form the iteration

$$x_{i+1} = h(x_i)$$

If $f(x)$ is expanded in a Taylor series,

$$f(x) = f(x_0) + f_x(x_0)(x - x_0) + \cdots$$

where f_x represents the jacobian, then this suggests immediately that

$$x_1 = x_0 - f_x^{-1}(x_0)f(x_0)$$

should be an improved approximation, and this amounts to taking

$$\phi(x) \equiv x - f_x^{-1}(x)f(x)$$

This is the *Newton-Raphson method*. It may be advantageous to take, however,

$$\phi(x) \equiv x - f_x^{-1}(x_0)f(x)$$

in order to avoid having to repeat at each step the treatment of the matrix f_x.

Another commonly used method is the *method of steepest descent*. If A is any positive definite matrix, ordinarily the identity I, form

$$\phi(x) = f^H(x)Af(x)$$

Evidently this function is non-negative, and it assumes a local minimum of zero at any point x satisfying (2–23). If x_0 is any approximation, and u is any vector, the function

$$\phi_0(\lambda) = \phi(x_0 + \lambda u)$$

considered as a function of the scalar λ, can be minimized, and $x_1 = x_0 + \lambda u$ at the minimum should provide an improved approximation. The vectors u could be the vectors e_i taken in rotation, by analogy with the Gauss-Seidel method for linear equations. In the method of steepest descent strictly so called, $u = \phi_x(x_0)$, the gradient vector.

To return briefly to the problem of solving a single equation in one unknown, the factorization of the polynomial does not in itself yield a solution unless one of the factors is either linear or quadratic. It does, of course, reduce the problem, in any event. The *Bairstow method* for a real algebraic equation seeks a quadratic factor whose zeros are presumably conjugate complex. If

$$\begin{aligned} p(x) &= x^2 + p_1x + p_0 \\ f(x) &\equiv q(x)p(x) + r(x) \\ r(x) &\equiv r_1x + r_0 \end{aligned}$$

and if p_1 and p_0 are considered variables, then r_1 and r_0 are functions of p_1 and p_0 that vanish when $p(x)$ is an exact divisor of $f(x)$. Thus the problem of finding a quadratic factor is that of solving the system of equations

$$r_1(p_1,p_0) = r_0(p_1,p_0) = 0$$

where the particular form of the polynomials r_1 and r_0 is obtained by carrying out the division. In practical application, initial numerical approximations are taken for p_1 and p_0 (commonly $p_1 = p_0 = 0$), the division is carried out numerically twice, first to obtain the remainder $r(x)$, and then $p(x)$ is divided into the quotient $q(x)$ to give a remainder $s(x)$ according to

$$\begin{aligned} q(x) &= p(x)t(x) + s(x) \\ s(x) &= s_1x + s_0 \end{aligned}$$

Then corrections δ_1 and δ_0 are obtained from

$$\begin{aligned} (p_1s_1 - s_0)\delta_1 - s_1\delta_0 &= -r_1 \\ p_0s_1\delta_1 - s_0\delta_0 &= -r_0 \end{aligned}$$

and added to p_1 and p_0, and the entire step repeated. The process leads to the quadratic factor whose zeros are the two zeros of $f(x)$ of smallest modulus if such two exist.

2.5. Approximation and Remainders.—In the preceding sections we have assumed that the problem to be solved is explicitly algebraic in character, which is to say that only a finite set of numbers that satisfies a finite set of essentially algebraic conditions is required. By "essentially" is meant that the equations may include expressions given explicitly by convergent Taylor series, but if the convergence has been established, then the techniques are formally the same as in the strictly algebraic case. If the problem is not explicitly algebraic, then it must be implicitly or explicitly replaced by one that is, and other branches of mathematics, notably functional analysis, must be invoked. At the threshold of this area stands the problem of approximation.

In Taylor expansions, Fourier expansions, lagrangean or newtonian interpolation, least-square fitting of polynomials, and many other approximations, one is given a set of functions

$$\phi_0, \phi_1, \cdots, \phi_n$$

and endeavors to apply linear criteria to the determination of constants r_i such that the linear combination

$$P[f|x] = \sum r_i \phi_i \tag{2–25}$$

will in some sense approximate a particular function f. To say that the criteria are linear means that if the same criteria are applied to two functions f and g, and again to any linear combination $\alpha f + \beta g$, the results will satisfy

$$P[\alpha f + \beta g|x] = \alpha P[f|x] + \beta P[g|x] \tag{2–26}$$

Moreover, when the criteria are applied to any function ϕ_i of the set, it is required that the result be that function itself:

$$P[\phi_i|x] = \phi_i \tag{2–27}$$

Otherwise stated, if

$$f(x) = P[f|x] + R[f|x] \tag{2–28}$$

where R is the *remainder* term, which represents the departure of the approximating function P from f, then

$$R[\alpha f + \beta g|x] = \alpha R[f|x] + \beta R[g|x] \tag{2–29}$$

$$R[\phi_i|x] = 0 \tag{2–30}$$

Thus, the remainder operator, R, is a linear operator that annihilates every function ϕ_i of the basic set to be used in the approximation.

The criteria themselves are expressible in the form

$$L_i f = L_i P = \mu_i \tag{2–31}$$

where the L_i are linear functional operators and the μ_i are known constants. Apart from certain general information, such as continuity, these μ_i constitute the data for the problem. Examples of such linear functional operators are the definite integral of the function, or of the product of the function by some preassigned, fixed function, the value of the function, or of one of its derivatives at a given point, some linear combination of values at several fixed points, and there are many others.

Along with the μ_i, which are associated with the function f itself, the quantities

$$L_i \phi_j = \alpha_{ij} \tag{2–32}$$

are supposed known, and it will be assumed that they form a nonsingular matrix

$$\Delta = \det(\alpha_{ij}) \neq 0 \tag{2-33}$$

Thus, the number of operators L_i must equal the number of ϕ_i. This being the case, the equations

$$\sum \alpha_{ij} r_j = \mu_i \tag{2-34}$$

which result from applying the functionals L_i to both sides of (2–25), and making the substitutions (2–31) and (2–32), can be solved for the r_i. In fact, P can be seen to satisfy the determinantal equation

$$\det \begin{pmatrix} \alpha_{00} & \cdots & \alpha_{0n} & \mu_0 \\ \cdot & \cdot & \cdot & \cdot \\ \cdot & \cdot & \cdot & \cdot \\ \alpha_{n0} & \cdots & \alpha_{nn} & \mu_n \\ \phi_0 & \cdots & \phi_n & P \end{pmatrix} \equiv 0 \tag{2-35}$$

Explicitly

$$P[f\,|x] = -\Delta^{-1} \det \begin{pmatrix} L_0\phi_0 & \cdots & L_0\phi_n & L_0 f \\ \cdot & \cdot & \cdot & \cdot \\ \cdot & \cdot & \cdot & \cdot \\ L_n\phi_0 & \cdots & L_n\phi_n & L_n f \\ \phi_0 & \cdots & \phi_n & 0 \end{pmatrix} \tag{2-36}$$

Moreover, an explicit expression for $R[f\,|x]$ is available:

$$R[f\,|x] = \Delta^{-1} \det \begin{pmatrix} L_0\phi_0 & \cdots & L_0\phi_n & L_0 f \\ \cdot & \cdot & \cdot & \cdot \\ \cdot & \cdot & \cdot & \cdot \\ L_n\phi_n & \cdots & L_n\phi_n & L_n f \\ \phi_0 & \cdots & \phi_n & f \end{pmatrix} \tag{2-37}$$

If the determinant on the right of (2–36) is expanded along the last row, one obtains an expansion of the form (2–25), the coefficient of the ϕ_i being the r_i required in (2–25). If the expansion is made along the last column one obtains an expansion of the form

$$P[f\,|x] = \sum \lambda_i(x) L_i f \tag{2-38}$$

where the $\lambda_i(x)$ are analogous to the coefficients in lagrangean interpolation and satisfy

$$L_i \lambda_j = \delta_{ij} \tag{2-39}$$

It will now be shown that a newtonian expansion can be obtained, with functionals that correspond to divided differences. First the set ϕ_i will be replaced by a new set ω_i, where each ω_i is a linear combination of $\phi_0, \phi_1, \cdots, \phi_i$, and where

$$L_i \omega_j = 0, \qquad i < j \tag{2-40}$$

This will be done recursively. Evidently (2-40) places no restriction on ω_0, whence take

$$\phi_0 = \omega_0$$

Next, let

$$\phi_1 = \omega_1 + \beta_{10}\omega_0$$

where β_{10} is to be determined. If

$$L_0\phi_1 = \beta_{10}L_0\omega_0$$

then (2-40) will be fulfilled for $i = 0, j = 1$, and this is possible provided

$$L_0\omega_0 \neq 0$$

as will now be assumed. Clearly this defines ω_1 as a linear combination of ϕ_0 and ϕ_1. Now that

$$\phi_2 = \omega_2 + \beta_{21}\omega_1 + \beta_{20}\omega_0$$

choose β_{20} to satisfy

$$L_0\phi_2 = \beta_{20}L_0\omega_0$$

after which choose β_{21} to satisfy

$$L_1\phi_2 = \beta_{21}L_1\omega_1 + \beta_{20}L_1\omega_0$$

The process can be continued so long as every

$$L_i\omega_i \neq 0$$

as will be assumed.

Next, the functionals L_i will be replaced by new ones W_i to be obtained recursively from

$$L_i = (L_i\omega_0)W_0 + (L_i\omega_1)W_1 + \cdots + (L_i\omega_i)W_i \tag{2-41}$$

It can be verified inductively that

$$W_i\omega_j = \delta_{ij} \tag{2-42}$$

With the operators W_i and functions ω_i, there results the newtonian expansion

$$P[f\,|\,x] = \omega_0 W_0 f + \omega_1 W_1 f + \cdots + \omega_n W_n f \tag{2-43}$$

This can be verified by applying each W_i to the two sides of (2–43), bearing in mind that since the W_i are linear combinations of the L_i, therefore

$$W_i f = W_i P$$

In the newtonian expansion, the W_i are the divided differences:

$$\begin{aligned} W_0 f &= f(x_0) \\ W_1 f &= f(x_0,x_1) \\ W_2 f &= f(x_0,x_1,x_2) \\ &\cdots \\ &\cdots \end{aligned}$$

and the ω_i are

$$\begin{aligned} \omega_0 &= 1 \\ \omega_1 &= x - x_0 \\ \omega_2 &= (x - x_0)(x - x_1) \\ &\cdots \\ &\cdots \end{aligned}$$

In the completely confluent case where each $x_i = x_0$, the result is the Taylor expansion up to the nth power.

No assumption has been made as to continuity, in general, but it will now be assumed that all functions have continuous derivatives of order $n + 1$. Then the ϕ_i satisfy a linear ordinary differential equation of order $n + 1$, which can be written in the form

$$\Omega y \equiv W^{-1}(x) \det \begin{pmatrix} \phi_0 & \cdots & \phi_n & y \\ \cdot & \cdot & \cdot & \cdot \\ \cdot & \cdot & \cdot & \cdot \\ \phi_0^{(n+1)} & \cdots & \phi_n^{(n+1)} & y^{(n+1)} \end{pmatrix} = 0 \qquad (2\text{–}44)$$

where

$$W(x) \equiv \det \begin{pmatrix} \phi_0 & \cdots & \phi_n \\ \cdot & \cdot & \cdot \\ \cdot & \cdot & \cdot \\ \phi_0^{(n)} & \cdots & \phi_n^{(n)} \end{pmatrix} \qquad (2\text{–}45)$$

is the wronskian, and Ω is the differential operator as defined, having the form

$$\Omega y \equiv y^{(n+1)} + \cdots$$

with leading coefficient unity and others functions of x. Any solution of (2–44) is a linear combination with constant coefficients of the ϕ_i, and any linearly independent set of $n + 1$ solutions of (2–44) would define the same operator Ω. Moreover, any linearly independent set of $n + 1$ solutions of (2–44) could be used in place of the ϕ_i in expressing $P[f|x]$, and, in fact, P itself is a particular solution. Hence $f - R$ is a solution of (2–44), and, therefore, f and R are both solutions of the nonhomogeneous equation

$$\Omega y = \psi \tag{2–46}$$

with $\psi = \Omega f$.

Now define

$$g(x,s) \equiv W^{-1}(s) \det \begin{pmatrix} \phi_0(s) & \cdots & \phi_n(s) \\ \cdot & \cdot \ \cdot \ \cdot & \cdot \\ \cdot & \cdot \ \cdot \ \cdot & \cdot \\ \phi_0^{(n-1)}(s) & \cdots & \phi_n^{(n-1)}(s) \\ \phi_0(x) & \cdots & \phi_n(x) \end{pmatrix} \equiv \sum g_i(s)\phi_i(x) \tag{2–47}$$

where s is to be regarded as a parameter. Evidently $g(x,s)$, as a function of x, satisfies (2–44), with the initial conditions

$$\left.\frac{\partial^\nu g}{\partial x^\nu}\right|^{x=s} = \begin{matrix} 0, & \nu < n \\ 1, & \nu = n \end{matrix} \tag{2–48}$$

But the initial conditions (2–48) fix $g(x,s)$ uniquely as a solution of (2–44), independently of the ϕ_i. Hence, any complete set of solutions could replace the ϕ_i in (2–47) for expressing g, although the $g_i(s)$ will be different for different sets ϕ_j. It is verified directly that any solution of (2–46) is given by

$$y(x) = \sum \alpha_i\phi_i + \int_a^x g(x,s)\psi(s)ds \tag{2–49}$$

Hence f is expressible in the form

$$f(x) = \sum \alpha_i\phi_i + \int_a^x f(x,s)\Omega f(s)ds \tag{2–50}$$

If one defines

$$G(x,s) = \begin{matrix} g(x,s), & x \geq s \\ 0, & x < s \end{matrix} \tag{2–51}$$

then G is continuous, and the variable upper limit on the integral in (2–50) can be replaced by a fixed upper limit:

$$f(x) = \sum \alpha_i\phi_i + \int_a^b G(x,s)\Omega f(s)ds \tag{2–52}$$

It has been assumed that the value of each of the functionals $L_i f$ is known. But the real object of the approximation is the approximate value of some other functional Lf which cannot be found directly. Hence, one evaluates LP and accepts this as the approximation to Lf. Naturally, the result will be in error by an amount $LR = L(f - P)$, which is ordinarily $\neq 0$. *The adequacy of the approximation for the purpose in hand is to be measured in terms of an upper bound on LR.* But the functional L evaluated for $R[f|x]$ is equal to a certain functional Q of f. Moreover, for any of the functions ϕ_i,

$$Q\phi_i = 0$$

since the approximating process applied to any of the base functions is exact. Hence, Q is a functional whose value is zero for any of the base functions. Hence, if Q is applied to both sides of (2–52), and if Q is permutable with the integral, then

$$Qf = \int_a^b QG(x,s)\Omega f(s)ds \tag{2–53}$$

Note that Q operates upon G as a function of x, not of s. The conditions under which permutability is assured will not be discussed here, but in the examples to follow, as in most others of practical importance, it will be easy to recognize that they are fulfilled.

This is the *fundamental remainder formula* sought. It expresses Qf in terms of a product, one factor, QG, being independent of the function being approximated, while the other is independent of the criteria. Some examples will now be considered.

For any approximation by polynomials of degree n,

$$\Omega = d^n/dx^n$$

Hence

$$g(x,s) = (x - s)^n/n!$$

satisfies (2–44) with initial conditions (2–48). Therefore

$$G(x,s) = \begin{cases} (x - s)^n/n!, & x \geq s \\ 0, & x < s \end{cases}$$

For simple interpolation, if one is interested in the value of $f(x)$ at a particular point x, then Qf is simply the value of $R[f|x]$ at x. Hence, for linear interpolation on the interval from 0 to 1,

$$Qf = f(x) - f(0) - x[f(1) - f(0)]$$

Hence

$$QG = \begin{cases} 0, & s \leq 0 \\ -s(1-x), & 0 < s \leq x \\ -x(1-s), & x < s \leq 1 \\ 0, & 1 < s \end{cases}$$

Therefore

$$Qf = -\int_0^x s(1-x)f''(s)ds - \int_x^1 x(1-s)f''(s)ds$$

$$= -(1-x)\int_0^x sf''(s)ds - x\int_x^1 (1-s)f''(s)ds$$

The function QG occurring in the integrand is represented by two straight line segments below the axis. If the mean value theorem is applied to the separate integrals, the result is

$$Qf = x(1-x)[xf''(\xi_1) + (1-x)f''(\xi_2)]/2, \quad 0 \leq \xi_1 \leq x \leq \xi_2 \leq 1$$

if applied to the integral as a whole

$$Qf = x(1-x)f''(\xi)/2, \quad 0 \leq \xi \leq 1$$

Let

$$F'(x) = f(x)$$

Then the trapezoidal rule applied to the interval from 0 to 1 corresponds to

$$QF = F(1) - F(0) - [F'(0) + F'(1)]/2$$

Then

$$g(x,s) = (x-s)^2/2$$

Hence

$$QG = -s(1-s)/2, \quad 0 \leq s \leq 1$$

and vanishes elsewhere. Therefore

$$QF = -\int_0^1 s(1-s)f''(s)ds/2$$

The value $[f(1) - f(-1)]/2$ would be the first-order approximation to the derivative of f at any point of the interval from -1 to $+1$. This corresponds to

$$Qf = f' - [f(1) - f(-1)]/2$$

Hence

$$QG = \begin{cases} (1+s)/2, & -1 \leq s < x \\ -(1-s)/2, & x \leq s < 1 \end{cases}$$

and $QG = 0$ elsewhere. Therefore

$$\begin{aligned} Qf &= \left[\int_{-1}^{x} (1+s)f''(s)ds - \int_{x}^{1} (1-s)f''(s)ds\right]\Big/2 \\ &= [(1+x)^2 f''(\xi_1) - (1-x)^2 f''(\xi_2)]/4, \quad -1 \le \xi_1 \le x \le \xi_2 \le 1 \end{aligned}$$

when the theorem of the mean is applied. This reflects the obvious fact that if f'' is of constant sign over the interval, then the error has opposite signs at the two ends, and will vanish somewhere in between, which is, of course, one form of the mean value theorem.

The least-square straight line fit through points at -1, 0, 1 is

$$y = (f_{-1} + f_0 + f_1)/3 + x(f_1 - f_{-1})/2$$

This corresponds to

$$Qf = f(x) - (f_{-1} + f_0 + f_1)/3 - x(f_1 - f_{-1})/2$$

Hence, taking $x < 0$,

$$QG = \begin{cases} (3x-2)(s+1)/6, & -1 \le s < x \\ (2s-1)/3 + (s-1)x/2, & x \le s < 0 \\ (3x+2)(s-1)/6, & 0 \le s < 1 \end{cases}$$

Therefore

$$\begin{aligned} Qf &= (3x-2)\int_{-1}^{x} (s+1)f''(s)ds/6 + \int_{x}^{0} [2(2s-1) + 3(s-1)x] \\ &\qquad \times f''(s)ds/6 \\ &\quad + (3x+2)\int_{0}^{1} (s-1)f''(s)ds/6 \\ &= (3x-2)(x+1)^2 f''(\xi_0)/12 \\ &\quad - x(3x^2 - 2x - 4)f''(\xi_1)/12 \\ &\quad - (3x+2)f''(\xi_2)/12, \qquad -1 \le \xi_0 \le x \le \xi_1 \le 0 \le \xi_2 \le 1 \\ &= -(3x^2 - 4x + 2)f''(\xi)/6, \qquad -1 \le \xi \le 1 \end{aligned}$$

The theorem of the mean can be applied to any case for which it is known that QG does not change sign over the interval:

$$Qf = \Omega f(\xi)\int_{a}^{b} QGds$$

In fact, it is not necessary even to know QG explicitly to apply this formula. Let $w(x)$ be any function satisfying

$$\Omega w = 1$$

Then

$$Qw = \int_a^b QGds$$

which gives

$$Qf = \Omega f(\xi)Qw$$

For polynomial approximation, take

$$w = x^{n+1}/(n+1)!$$

Then

$$Qf = f^{(n+1)}(\xi)Qx^{n+1}/(n+1)!$$

In interpolation with $x_0,x_1,\cdots,x_n$,

$$Qx^{n+1} = (x - x_0)\cdots(x - x_n)$$

this leads to the standard remainder formulas.

One can verify directly the $g(x,s)$ for each of the following basic sets:

$$1, \cos x, \sin x, \cdots, \cos nx, \sin nx$$

$$g(x,s) = \left[2 \sin \frac{x-s}{2}\right]^{2n} \Big/ (2n)!$$

$$1, \cosh x, \sinh x, \cdots, \cosh nx, \sinh nx$$

$$g(x,s) = \left[2 \sinh \frac{x-s}{2}\right]^{2n} \Big/ (2n)!$$

$$e^x, e^{2x}, \cdots, e^{(n+1)x}$$

$$g(x,s) = (e^{x-s} - 1)^n/n!$$

The literature on interpolation, quadrature, and allied topics is abundant, but the general remainder theorem here developed provides both a unifying principle, and a technique to apply in making a selection from among a variety of possible formulas of approximation.

Minimax, or *Chebyshev*, *approximation* utilizes a nonlinear criterion, and hence raises problems that are much more difficult. For a given function $f(x)$, the problem is to find a function $P(x)$ in a certain class such that

$$\max_{x \in I} |f(x) - P(x)|$$

is minimized with respect to all possible functions of the class, I being a preassigned set of points, finite or infinite. Among the classes of greatest interest are the class of polynomials of fixed degree n, and the class of quotients of polynomials of fixed degree n and m. The problem has acquired special practical significance in recent years because of a certain characteristic of electronic digital computers: it is more efficient to store and use a scheme for evaluating a polynomial of limited degree, or the ratio of two such, than to store a table of numbers and search through and possibly interpolate. Consequently, polynomials and rational fractions representing particular special functions in common use are of considerable value in computing. Reference must be made to the literature, however, for methods of obtaining them.

2.6. Reduction from Functional Form to Algebraic Form is considered here to belong more properly to functional analysis rather than to numerical analysis, and neither an effective survey nor a representative sample of methods is possible in a few pages. Nevertheless, one or two general remarks may be in order.

For solving integral equations and for solving differential equations, it is natural to effect the reduction by means of formulas for numerical quadrature, interpolation, or differentiation, and this is, indeed, standard procedure. It is also natural to attempt to reduce the number of individual points (hence of algebraic unknowns) by using formulas of higher order. However, a higher-order interpolation or quadrature formula is not necessarily more exact than one of lower order. Also, in the case of differential equations, a new difficulty can arise, known as *instability*. To understand the source of the difficulty it is necessary, first, to bear in mind the occurrence of rounding errors throughout any digital computation, and the fact that errors, once generated, may propagate and perhaps grow as the computation proceeds. When difference equations are introduced for representing a differential equation, these are of order at least as high as the differential equation itself, and the use of quadrature formulas of higher order increases the order of the difference equation. The difference equation, therefore, has spurious solutions, and these enter the computation as rounding errors, after which they may grow exponentially and engulf the true solution.

2.7. References.—Listed below are some of the more recent and modern treatments, in English, of topics discussed above and of related material. For journal references see the bibliographies in the books below.

The treatment in this chapter has been theoretical. For a brief, clear, and very practical description of computational details for a number of standard problems, [10] is unsurpassed, and [12] can be recommended for programming techniques for automatic computers. For information on ordinary differential equations, the reader should consult [2], and for partial differential equations, [1]. For general methods of reduction to algebraic form as well as methods of solution, see [5], [7], and [8].

A good modern treatment of approximation, especially linear, is in [6], and reference may be made also to [3]. For a more elaborate treatment of matrix methods, see [4]. In [13] can be found an excellent collection of articles by various authors on a number of topics, including a good brief treatment of stability, and an introduction to functional analysis as it applies to computational practice. Perhaps the best treatment of the *QD* algorithm is by Henrici in [9].

Not listed are two forthcoming books by J. H. Wilkinson that, however, are to be highly recommended as treatments of the techniques for matrix computations.

REFERENCES

1. Forsythe, George E., and Wasow, Wolfgang R., *Finite-Difference Methods for Partial Differential Equations*, John Wiley and Sons, Inc., New York, 1960.
2. Henrici, Peter, *Discrete Variable Methods in Ordinary Differential Equations*, John Wiley and Sons, Inc., New York, 1962.
3. Householder, A. S., *Principles of Numerical Analysis*, McGraw-Hill Book Co., Inc., New York, 1953.
4. ——, *Theory of Matrices in Numerical Analysis*, Ginn and Co., Boston, in press.
5. Kantorovich, L. V., and Krylov, V. I., *Approximate Methods of Higher Analysis*, Benster, Curtis D., tr., Interscience Publishers, Inc., New York, 1958.
6. Kopal, Zdeněk, *Numerical Analysis*, 2nd Ed., John Wiley and Sons, Inc., New York, 1961.
7. Lanczos, Cornelius, *Applied Analysis*, Prentice-Hall, Inc., Englewood Cliffs, N.J., 1957.
8. ——, *Linear Differential Operators*, D. Van Nostrand Co., Inc., Princeton, N.J., 1961.
9. National Bureau of Standards, *Further Contributions to the Solution of Simultaneous Equations and the Determination of Eigenvalues*, U.S. Dept. of Commerce, National Bureau of Standards, Applied Mathematics Series, 49.
10. National Physical Laboratory, *Modern Computing Methods*, 2nd Ed., Her Majesty's Stationery Office, London, 1961.
11. Ostrowski, A. M., *Solution of Equations and Systems of Equations*, Academic Press, Inc., New York, 1960.
12. Ralston, Anthony, and Wilf, Herbert S., *Mathematical Methods for Digital Computers*, John Wiley and Sons, Inc., New York, 1960.
13. Todd, John, ed., *Survey of Numerical Analysis*, McGraw-Hill Book Co., Inc., New York, 1962.
14. Varga, Richard S., *Matrix Iterative Analysis*, Prentice-Hall, Inc., Englewood Cliffs, New Jersey, 1962.

CHAPTER 3

RANDOM PROCESSES

by

EDWARD M. HOFSTETTER[1]

Electrical Engineering Department and Research Laboratory of Electronics, Massachusetts Institute of Technology

3.1. Randomness.—The word *random* is used frequently to describe erratic and apparently unpredictable variations of an observed quantity. The noise voltage measured at the terminals of a hot resistor, the amplitude of a radar signal that has been reflected from the surface of the sea, and the velocity measured at some point in a turbulent air flow are all examples of random or unpredictable phenomena.

In any particular situation, it is usually possible to give a variety of reasons why the observed quantity behaves in an erratic manner. The observed quantity may be critically dependent on certain parameters and the observed fluctuations attributed to slight variations of these parameters. The implication here is that the observed fluctuations appear erratic only because we have not taken the trouble to make a sufficiently precise analysis of the situation to disclose the pattern the observations are following. It is also possible, in some situations, to adopt the viewpoint that certain aspects of the phenomenon being studied are inherently unknowable and that the best physical laws we can devise to explain the phenomenon will have some form of randomness or unpredictability built into them. Such is the case, for example, with thermal noise voltages, which are believed to be governed by the probabilistic laws of quantum physics.

The important point we wish to make here is that, regardless of the underlying cause of randomness, the result is the same—we cannot or will not take the trouble to predict the exact outcome of our observations. What we would like to do is develop some way of obtaining useful information about situations exhibiting randomness without necessarily having to inquire into the details of the mechanism producing the

[1] The author wishes to express his sincere thanks for the unflagging assistance of his colleagues W. B. Davenport and W. M. Siebert. Their valuable criticism and constant encouragement were of great help in writing this chapter.

randomness. Stating this somewhat differently, we would like to model physical situations in a way that gives us a smoothed-out picture of the phenomenon being studied—a picture that neither requires nor yields infinitely detailed information about the phenomenon, but is still adequate to study its gross behavior.

The basis for any physical theory is some kind of regularity or predictability in the observed phenomenon. In the case of noise voltages or other quantities that vary in an apparently random manner from observation to observation, it is often observed experimentally that averages of the quantities under study tend to be stable even though the quantities themselves may exhibit a high degree of variability. More precisely, if $X(t)$ denotes an observed noise voltage, then quantities such as the d.c. voltage defined by

$$\text{d.c. voltage} = \frac{1}{2T}\int_{t_0-T}^{t_0+T} X(t)dt \tag{3-1}$$

or the average power defined by

$$\text{average power} = \frac{1}{2T}\int_{t_0-T}^{t_0+T} X^2(t)dt \tag{3-2}$$

often turn out to be, more or less, independent of the time origin t_0 as long as the averaging time $2T$ is made long enough. Time averages that behave in this manner are, in a sense, invariants of the given noise source because they assume almost the same value for all possible waveforms put out by the source, even though these waveforms may look completely different from one another. This stability of averages (called statistical regularity) provides us with a set of measurable quantities that remain more or less constant with time, thus making it possible for us to construct a theory of random time functions that will establish rules for manipulating time averages, and will explore the relationships that must exist between various different time averages.

As a simple illustration of this philosophy, we analyze one aspect of the following data-smoothing device. The input to this device is a time function $X(t)$ and the output $Y(t)$ is given by the formula

$$Y(t) = \int_{t-T_0}^{t} X(\tau)d\tau = \int_{-T_0}^{0} X(t+\tau)d\tau \tag{3-3}$$

where T_0 denotes some positive constant.

Now, in order to calculate $Y(t)$ exactly, we must know $X(t)$ exactly; however, if we are interested only in certain *averages* of $Y(t)$, then only certain *averages* of the input must be known. The simplest example of this occurs when we ask what must be known about the input in order for the average (d.c. value) of $Y(t)$ to be calculable. The answer is given by the calculation [2]

$$\text{ave } Y = \lim_{T\to\infty} \frac{1}{2T} \int_{-T}^{T} Y(t)dt = \lim_{T\to\infty} \frac{1}{2T} \int_{-T}^{T} \left[\int_{-T_0}^{0} X(t+\tau)d\tau \right] dt$$
$$= \int_{-T_0}^{0} \left[\lim_{T\to\infty} \frac{1}{2T} \int_{-T}^{T} X(t+\tau)dt \right] d\tau = T_0(\text{ave } X) \qquad (3\text{–}4)$$

which shows that the average of the output depends only on the average of the input and the integration time T_0 of the smoothing device. Stated somewhat differently, this result shows that the average of the output $Y(t)$ is *independent* of the detailed shape of the input $X(t)$—it is the same for all inputs having the same average value. The reader will do well to keep this point in mind throughout the remainder of this chapter. Despite the (seemingly unavoidable) maze of detail and notation, all we are really attempting to do is establish a systematic procedure for calculating various averages of one time function in terms of averages of another, as we have done in the simple example above.

The theory we shall develop along these lines will be suitable for modeling that class of random phenomena for which stable time averages exist. It is important to realize that this prerequisite excludes many interesting situations such as the behavior of stock market prices. The "average" price of a given stock is certainly not the same today as it was in 1920 and, very likely, will not be the same in the year 2000. The "average" price of a stock depends very heavily on the period of time over which the average is taken and, consequently, is not a stable average in the sense required for our theory. Theories have been developed which are, at least potentially, capable of modeling random phenomena whose averages are critically dependent on the averaging period; however, we shall not consider these developments here.

The mathematical discussion to follow will be, by and large, nonrigorous. In many cases, the heuristic arguments given will serve as guidelines along which a rigorous proof could be constructed; the reader should be warned, however, that this is not necessarily a trivial task. Moreover, in some cases, the detailed conditions under which the stated results are valid have not yet been investigated by the author. This chapter should be viewed, therefore, as an outline of a possible theory of random processes rather than as a definitive treatment of the subject.

[2] The fact that the inner integral is independent of τ is fairly obvious on physical grounds and can be established rigorously by means of Eq. (3–104) to be proved later.

3.2. Distribution Functions.—We now turn to the problem of establishing mathematical models of random phenomena in which various time averages are the only important properties of the time functions involved. These models are usually called *random* or *stochastic processes*.[3] A random process is defined by specifying the values of all time averages of interest for the particular application at hand. This is often not done directly but, for the sake of convenience, by specifying the values of certain particular sets of time averages, called *distribution functions*, in terms of which all averages of interest can be calculated. It is important to note that studying a random phenomenon by means of a stochastic process model is tantamount to modeling the sequence of observed data, not by a single time function, but by the set of all time functions that have certain averages in common with the observed time function.

The problem of how to fit a random process model to a given physical situation, *i.e.*, what values to assign to the time averages, is not a purely mathematical problem, but one involving a skillful combination of both empirical and theoretical results, as well as a great deal of judgement based on practical experience. Because of their involved nature, we shall not consider such problems (called problems in *statistics* to distinguish them from the purely mathematical problems of the theory of random processes) in detail here, but instead, refer the reader to the literature.[4]

We begin our discussion of random processes with a study of the simplest kind of distribution function. The *first-order distribution function* F_X of the time function $X(t)$ is the real-valued function of a real-variable defined by[5]

$$F_X(x) = \lim_{T \to \infty} \frac{1}{2T} \int_{-T}^{T} C_x[X(t)]dt \tag{3-5}$$

[3] To bring our terminology into accord with that commonly used by mathematicians, the nomenclature *stationary random process* should be used here to distinguish our models from the more general models mentioned at the end of Section 3.1. This distinction is not meaningful in the context of this chapter, but should be borne in mind when consulting other treatments of the subject.

[4] H. Chernoff and L. E. Moses, *Elementary Decision Theory*, John Wiley and Sons, Inc., New York, 1959; H. Cramer, *Mathematical Methods of Statistics*, Princeton University Press, 1954.

[5] The reader already familiar with the Theory of Random Processes will no doubt be surprised at this definition. Most treatments of this subject define a distribution function by means of an ensemble average rather than a time average. The time-average approach has been chosen here because, in the author's opinion, it is much more direct and easy to visualize (at least at first contact) than the more elegant and general approach via ensemble averages. Further discussion of this point will be given later in the text.

where the function C_x is defined by

$$C_x(y) = \begin{cases} 1, & y \leq x \\ 0, & y > x \end{cases} \tag{3–6}$$

The significance of this definition can be understood most easily by reference to Fig. 3–1, which depicts a typical section of a time function $X(t)$ and the corresponding function $C_x[X(t)]$ drawn for a particular

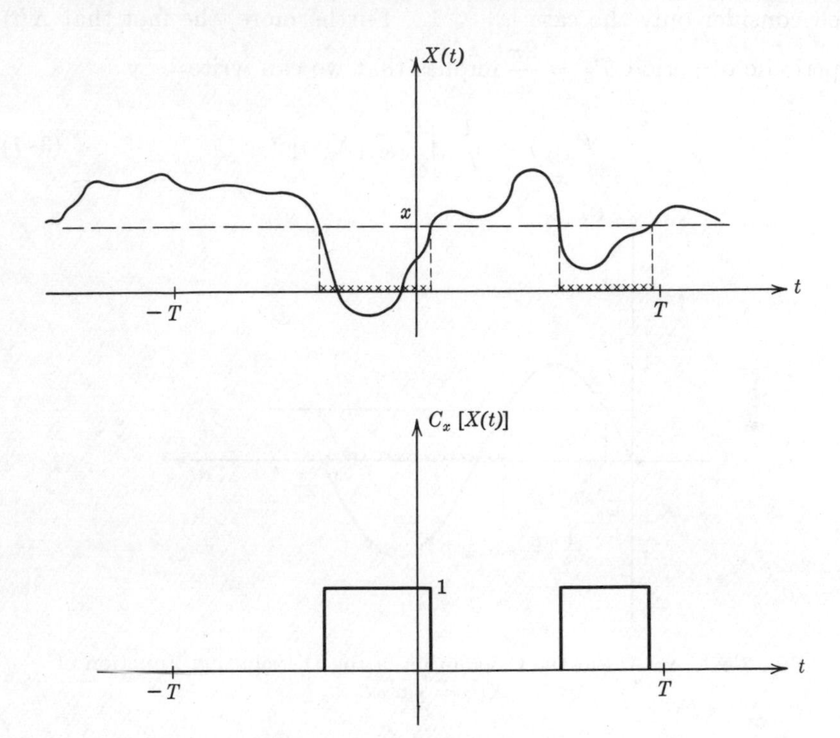

FIG. 3.1. An Aid to Understanding the Definition of the Distribution Function.

value of x. It should now be clear that the integral involved in (3–5) is equal to the total length of time $X(t)$ is less than x in the interval $[-T,T]$. This length of time is indicated by the crosshatched line segments in Fig. 3–1. Thus, the quantity $1/2T \int_{-T}^{T} C_x[X(t)]dt$ is the fraction of the time interval $[-T,T]$ during which $X(t) \leq x$ and, consequently, $F_Y(x)$ may be thought of as the fraction of time that

The author wishes to acknowledge Dr. D. Brennan whose excellent work in this area (E. J. Baghdady, *Lectures on Communication System Theory*, Chapter 2, McGraw-Hill Book Co., New York, 1961) supplied the initial form of many of the ideas used in this chapter.

$X(t) \leq x$ in the entire infinite time interval. It should be noted carefully that the function F_X gives the value, not of a single time average, but of an infinite number of time averages, one for each value of x.

In order to further clarify the definition of a distribution function, we shall now calculate the distribution function for the time function $X(t) = \sin \omega t$. First of all, it follows from the fact that $|X(t)| \leq 1$ that $F_X(x) = 0$ for $x < -1$ and $F_X(x) = 1$ for $x > 1$, so that we need consider only the case $|x| \leq 1$. Furthermore, the fact that $X(t)$ is periodic of period $T_0 = \dfrac{2\pi}{\omega}$ implies that we can write

$$F_X(x) = \frac{1}{T_0} \int_0^{T_0} C_x[X(t)]dt \tag{3–7}$$

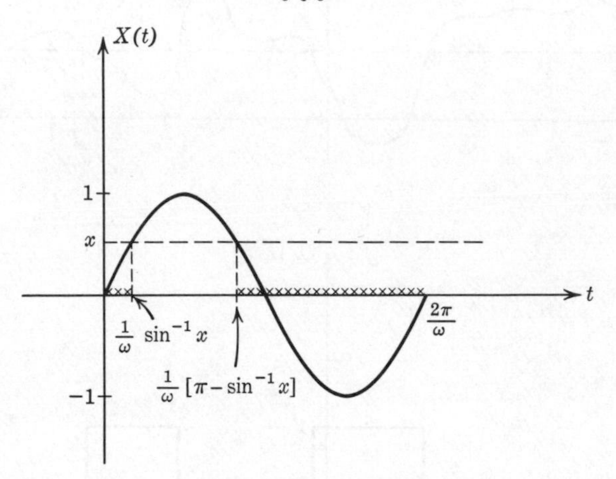

Fig. 3–2. An Aid in the Calculation of the Distribution Function of $X(t) = \sin \omega t$.

Reference to Fig. 3–2 now makes it apparent that the value of the integral in (3–7) is equal to the length of the crosshatched line segment

$$\int_0^{T_0} C_x[X(t)]dt = \frac{2\pi}{\omega} - \frac{1}{\omega}[(\pi - \sin^{-1} x) - \sin^{-1} x]$$
$$= \frac{1}{\omega}[\pi + 2 \sin^{-1} x] \tag{3–8}$$

and it follows at once that

$$F_X(x) = \begin{cases} 1, & x > 1 \\ \dfrac{1}{2} + \dfrac{1}{\pi} \sin^{-1} x, & |x| \leq 1 \\ 0, & x < -1 \end{cases} \tag{3–9}$$

This distribution is called the arcsine distribution. It is useful in certain communication problems where a desired signal is being masked by an interfering signal which, for some purposes, may be thought of as being a constant amplitude sinusoid of unknown phase. The arcsine distribution can be used, in a manner to be described shortly, to calculate certain average properties of an interfering signal of this type.

The example just given is of a rather special nature since the time function $X(t)$ is defined by means of a simple mathematical expression from which the distribution function can be easily calculated. In most cases of practical importance, the rule for generating $X(t)$ is not known (because of complexity or inherent randomness of the generation process, etc.) so that the distribution function of $X(t)$ must be determined in some other way. The techniques used for this purpose range all the way from direct measurement coupled with some kind of curve-fitting procedure to arguments that enable one to deduce the functional form of the distribution function from assumptions made about the way in which $X(t)$ is generated. Examples of the last procedure will be given in a later section.

The important point we wish to re-emphasize here is that a random process is specified or defined by giving the values of certain averages such as a distribution function. This is completely different from the way in which a time function is specified; *i.e.*, by giving the *value* the time function assumes at various instants or by giving a differential equation and boundary conditions the time function must satisfy, etc. The theory of random processes enables us to calculate certain averages in terms of other averages (known from measurements or by some indirect means), just as, for example, network theory enables us to calculate the output of a network as a function of time from a knowledge of its input as a function of time. In either case some information external to the theory must be known or at least assumed to exist before the theory can be put to use.

One further point is worth mentioning at this time. The definition of a distribution function (3–5) involves the taking of a limit and, consequently, brings up the question of the existence of this limit. The limit will not, in general, exist for all possible time functions $X(t)$, and the investigation of conditions for its existence is a legitimate mathematical problem. However, questions of this sort are quite beside the point in the present context. We are not really interested in knowing how to specify time functions in such a way that their distribution functions exist. Instead, we want to know how to specify a function F_X in such a way that it is the distribution function of *some* time function; *i.e.*, in such a way that there exists at least one $X(t)$ with the property that

$$F_X(x) = \lim_{T\to\infty} \frac{1}{2T} \int_{-T}^{T} C_x[X(t)]dt$$

Once we can answer this question (which will be done later in this section), we will have a way of specifying certain time averages of $X(t)$ without direct reference to any other analytical properties of $X(t)$.

Viewed in a somewhat different light, the point here is that we are not trying to fix, once and for all, the class of functions $X(t)$ for which all of our results will be valid but, rather, we limit our attention in any specific situation to those time functions for which certain time averages (such as a distribution function) assume specified values. This being the case, the only existence question of importance reduces to making sure that the underlying class of functions is not vacuous.

Certain time averages occur quite often and have acquired names of their own. The fraction of time that $X(t) \leq x$ will be referred to as the *probability of the event* $\{X(t) \leq x\}$. In the same vein, the fraction of time that $a < X(t) \leq b$ is called the probability of the event $\{a < X(t) \leq b\}$ and is written $P\{a < X(t) \leq b\}$. More generally, if $[a_1,b_1]$, $[a_2,b_2], \cdots$ are nonoverlapping intervals, the fraction of time that $X(t)$ satisfies any one of the inequalities $a_1 < X(t) \leq b_1$, $a_2 < X(t) \leq b_2, \cdots$, is called the probability of the event $\{a_1 < X(t) \leq b_1$ or $a_2 < X(t) \leq b_2$ or $\cdots\}$ and is written $P\{a_1 < X(t) \leq b_1$ or $a_2 < X(t) \leq b_2$ or $\cdots\}$.

Almost everybody is familiar with the notion of probability as applied to games of chance. When discussing dice games, we assign the probability 1/6 to the event "a one comes up" because there are six faces of the die that are "equally likely" to come up and the desired face is, therefore, only one possibility out of six. Operationally, the number 1/6 is taken to mean that, in a *long* sequence of N tosses of the die, approximately $1/6 \cdot N$ ones will show up. In other words, the fraction of the time that ones are showing is $\approx \frac{1/6 \cdot N}{N} = \frac{1}{6}$. Considerations of this sort are what motivated us to use the word *probability* in connection with the fraction of the time a time function satisfies certain conditions. Speaking very loosely, the probability of the event $\{X(t)$ in $A\}$ is the number of values of t for which $X(t)$ assumes a value in the set of real numbers A, divided by the total number of possible time instants in a long time interval $[-T,T]$.

It is quite easy to verify that the probabilities of all the events discussed above can be expressed in terms of the distribution function F_X. Thus, it follows at once from our definitions that

$$P\{X(t) \leq x\} = F_X(x) \tag{3-10}$$

and, noting that

$$C_b(x) - C_a(x) = \begin{cases} 1, & a < x \leq b \\ 0, & \text{otherwise} \end{cases} \tag{3-11}$$

we can write

$$\begin{aligned} P\{a < X(t) \leq b\} &= \lim_{T \to \infty} \frac{1}{2T} \int_{-T}^{T} \{C_b[X(t)] - C_a[X(t)]\} dt \\ &= F_X(b) - F_X(a) \end{aligned} \tag{3-12}$$

which expresses the probability of the event $\{a < X(t) \leq b\}$ in terms of the distribution function $F_X(x)$. Finally, an argument similar to the one just given yields the result

$$\begin{aligned} P\{a_1 < X(t) \leq b_1 \quad \text{or} \quad a_2 < X(t) \leq b_2 \quad \text{or} \quad \cdots\} \\ = \sum_k [F_X(b_k) - F_X(a_k)] \end{aligned} \tag{3-13}$$

which is valid for nonoverlapping intervals $[a_1,b_1]$, $[a_2,b_2]$, $\cdots$.

The results just obtained are special cases of a theorem that shows how a large class of time averages can be calculated in terms of the distribution function. Before demonstrating this theorem, it will be convenient for us to first discuss some useful properties of distribution functions. The most important of these are

$$\begin{aligned} &\text{(i)} && 0 \leq F_X(x) \leq 1 \\ &\text{(ii)} && \lim_{x \to -\infty} F_X(x) = 0, \qquad \lim_{x \to \infty} F_X(x) = 1 \\ &\text{(iii)} && F_X(x) \leq F_X(x') \text{ if and only if } x \leq x' \end{aligned} \tag{3-14}$$

and can be derived directly from the definition of the distribution function. It can be shown also that any real-valued function of a real variable satisfying these conditions is a distribution function; *i.e.*, given any function satisfying (i), (ii), and (iii), it is possible to construct at least one time function whose distribution function coincides with the given function. This result settles the existence question (for first-order distribution functions) discussed earlier.

We now have at our disposal the means for easily constructing examples of distribution functions. The simplest way to do this is to note that condition (iii) forces the derivative of F_X to be non-negative at all points where the derivative exists. We shall adopt the familiar convention of using Dirac delta functions to represent the derivative of F_X at points of discontinuity. It can then be shown that the derivative of F_X exists at all points either as an ordinary derivative or a Dirac delta function except in certain, highly singular situations that do not seem to have any physical significance and that we shall ignore.[6] With this understanding, all distribution functions can be written in the form,

$$F_X(x) = \int_{-\infty}^{x} p_X(\xi)d\xi \tag{3-15}$$

where

$$p_X(x) = \frac{dF_X(x)}{dx} \geq 0 \tag{3-16}$$

Conversely, if $p_X(x)$ denotes any integrable, non-negative function satisfying

$$\int_{-\infty}^{\infty} p_X(\xi)d\xi = 1 \tag{3-17}$$

then the function F_X defined by (3–15) must satisfy conditions (i), (ii), and (iii), and, therefore, be a distribution function. The reader should have no difficulty verifying this statement.

The function p_X derived from F_X is called a *first order probability density function.* The reason for this terminology can be appreciated by noting the form that Eqs. (3–10), (3–12), and (3–13) assume when they are written in terms of p_X instead of F_X

$$P\{X(t) \leq x\} = \int_{-\infty}^{x} p_X(\xi)d\xi \tag{3-18}$$

$$P\{a < X(t) \leq b\} = \int_{a}^{b} p_X(\xi)d\xi \tag{3-19}$$

$$P\{a_1 < X(t) \leq b_1 \quad \text{or} \quad a_2 < X(t) \leq b_2 \quad \text{or} \quad \cdots\} = \int_{\{a_1 < x \leq b_1 \quad \text{or} \quad a_2 < x \leq b_2 \quad \text{or} \quad \cdots\}} p_X(\xi)d\xi \tag{3-20}$$

where the notation $\int_A$ indicates the fact that the integration is to be carried out over the set of points of the real line described by A. In

[6] All difficulties of this nature could be avoided in subsequent discussions by replacing integrals of the form $\int \phi(\xi)p_X(\xi)d\xi$ by their corresponding Lebesque-Stieltjes integrals $\int \phi(\xi)dF_X(\xi)$.

other words, the probability of the event $\{X(t) \text{ is in } A\}$, where A denotes some set of points on the real line, can be obtained by integrating the probability density function over the set A

$$P\{X(t) \text{ is in } A\} = \int_A p_X(\xi)d\xi \tag{3–21}$$

The same result can be stated in looser, but somewhat more picturesque language by writing,

$$P\{x \le X(t) \le x + dx\} = p_X(x)dx \tag{3–22}$$

We conclude this section with examples of some particularly important probability density functions that will be used in later applications. In each of these examples, the reader should verify that the function p_X is a probability density function by showing that it is non-negative and has unit area. All of the integrals and sums involved are elementary except perhaps in the case of the gaussian distribution, for which the reader is referred to Cramer.[7]

The Uniform Distribution.

$$p_X(x) = \begin{cases} \dfrac{1}{2a}, & |x| \le a, \\ 0, & |x| > a, \end{cases} \quad a > 0 \tag{3–23}$$

$$F_X(x) = \begin{cases} 0, & x < -a \\ \dfrac{(x+a)}{2a}, & |x| \le a \\ 1, & x > a \end{cases} \tag{3–24}$$

The Gaussian Distribution.[8]

$$p_X(x) = \frac{1}{\sqrt{2\pi}\,\sigma} e^{-(1/2\sigma^2)(x-m)^2}, \quad \sigma > 0 \tag{3–25}$$

$$F_X(x) = \Phi\left(\frac{x-m}{\sigma}\right)$$

where

$$\Phi(x) = \frac{1}{\sqrt{2\pi}} \int_{-\infty}^{x} e^{-\xi^2/2} d\xi \tag{3–26}$$

[7] *Mathematical Methods of Statistics*, Princeton University Press, 1954.

[8] $\Phi(x)$ is related to the error function, and extensive tables of it exist. See, for example, Cramer, *op. cit.*, for a short table and references to other tables.

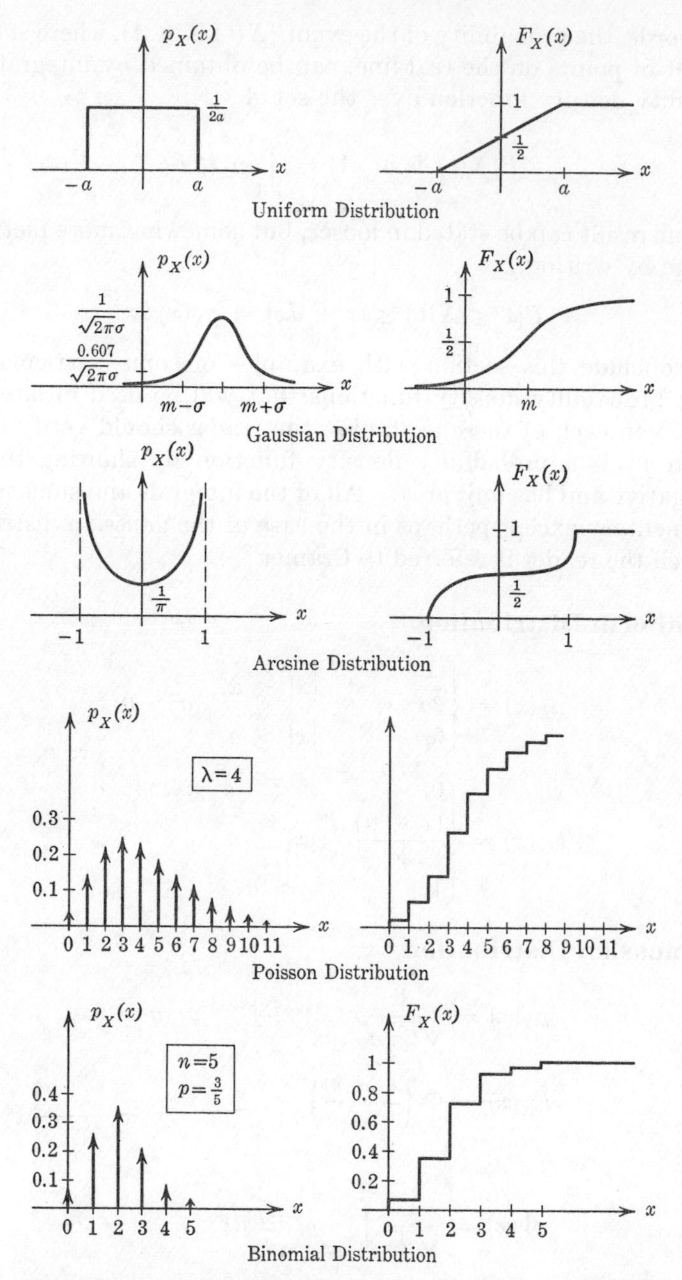

FIG. 3–3. Some Important Probability Density Functions and Their Corresponding Distribution Functions. Arrows are used to indicate Dirac delta functions with the height of the arrow indicating the area under the delta function.

The Arcsine Distribution.

$$p_X(x) = \begin{cases} \dfrac{1}{\pi\sqrt{1 - x^2}}, & |x| < 1 \\ 0, & |x| \geq 1 \end{cases} \tag{3-27}$$

$$F_X(x) = \begin{cases} 0, & x \leq -1 \\ \dfrac{1}{2} + \dfrac{1}{\pi} \sin^{-1} x, & |x| < 1 \\ 1, & x \geq 1 \end{cases} \tag{3-28}$$

The Poisson Distribution.[9]

$$p_X(x) = \sum_{k=0}^{\infty} \frac{\lambda^k}{k!} e^{-\lambda}\delta(x - k), \quad \lambda > 0 \tag{3-29}$$

$$F_X(x) = \begin{cases} 0, & x < 0 \\ \displaystyle\sum_{k=0}^{n} \frac{\lambda^k}{k!} e^{-\lambda}, & n \leq x < n + 1 \end{cases} \tag{3-30}$$

The Binomial Distribution.

$$p_X(x) = \sum_{k=0}^{n} \binom{n}{k} p^k(1 - p)^{n-k}\delta(x - k), \quad 0 < p < 1 \tag{3-31}$$

$$F_X(x) = \begin{cases} 0, & x < 0 \\ \displaystyle\sum_{k=0}^{n} \binom{n}{k} p^k(1 - p)^{n-k}, & m \leq x < m + 1 \leq n \\ 1, & x > n \end{cases} \tag{3-32}$$

These density functions and their corresponding distribution functions are sketched in Fig. 3–3.

3.3. The Theorem of Averages.—We are now in a position to discuss the fundamental theorem of averages[10] mentioned earlier. This theorem states that all time averages of the form

$$\lim_{T\to\infty} \frac{1}{2T} \int_{-T}^{T} \phi[X(t)]dt$$

where ϕ is a real-valued function of a real variable for which the limit exists, can be calculated from a knowledge of the probability density function p_X by means of the formula

$$\lim_{T\to\infty} \frac{1}{2T} \int_{-T}^{T} \phi[X(t)]dt = \int_{-\infty}^{\infty} \phi(\xi)p_X(\xi)d\xi \tag{3-33}$$

[9] $\delta(x - x_0)$ denotes a unit Dirac delta function located at $x = x_0$.

[10] A similar theorem is called the quasi-ergodic theorem by Brennan. See footnote 5.

We shall not give a rigorous proof of Eq. (3–33) because this would take us too far afield; however, the following argument should make the truth of this formula appear quite plausible.

We begin by showing that (3–33) holds for the special case where ϕ is a "staircase" function; *i.e.*

$$\phi(x) = \begin{cases} \phi_1, & a_1 < x \leq b_1 \\ \vdots & \vdots \\ \phi_n, & a_n < x \leq b_n \\ 0, & \text{otherwise} \end{cases} \tag{3–34}$$

where the intervals $\{a_k, b_k\}$ are nonoverlapping and the ϕ_k are arbitrary real numbers. A typical "staircase" function is sketched in Fig. 3–4.

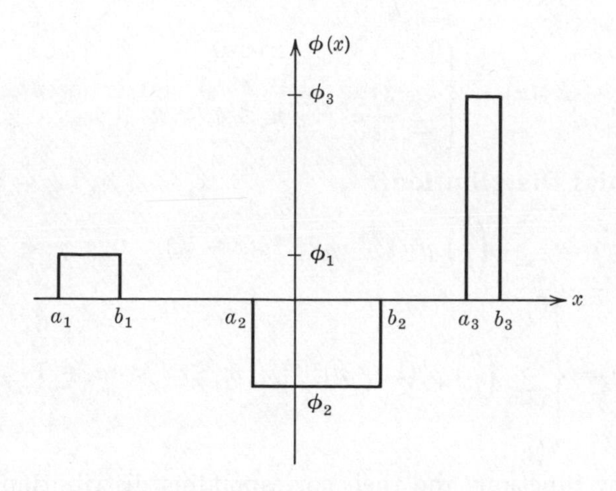

FIG. 3–4. A "Staircase" Function.

For the ϕ defined by (3–34), the right-hand side of (3–33) assumes the value

$$\int_{-\infty}^{\infty} \phi(\xi) p_X(\xi) d\xi = \sum_{k=1}^{n} \phi_k [F_X(b_k) - F_X(a_k)] \tag{3–35}$$

The left-hand side of (3–33) also may be evaluated explicitly, yielding

$$\begin{aligned} \lim_{T\to\infty} \frac{1}{2T} \int_{-T}^{T} \phi[X(t)]dt &= \lim_{T\to\infty} \frac{1}{2T} \sum_{k=1}^{n} \phi_k \begin{Bmatrix} \text{length of time that } a_k < X(t) \leq b_k \\ \text{in the time interval } [-T,T]. \end{Bmatrix} \\ &= \sum_{k=1}^{n} \phi_k [F_X(b_k) - F_X(a_k)] \end{aligned} \tag{3–36}$$

Comparison of (3–35) and (3–36) establishes the truth of (3–33) for ϕ's that are "staircase" functions.

The concluding step in the argument is to note that many ϕ can be approximated, as closely as desired, by means of a "staircase" function. This means that, given such a function ϕ, it is possible to find a sequence of "staircase" functions ϕ_n with the property

$$\phi(x) = \lim_{n \to \infty} \phi_n(x) \tag{3–37}$$

Since Eq. (3–33) holds for staircase functions, we can write

$$\lim_{T \to \infty} \frac{1}{2T} \int_{-T}^{T} \phi_n[X(t)]dt = \int_{-\infty}^{\infty} \phi_n(\xi) p_X(\xi) d\xi \tag{3–38}$$

and, taking limits on both sides of (3–38), we obtain (3–33). The major part of the argument, which has been omitted, is a justification of the change of order of limiting operations that is necessary in going from (3–38) to (3–33). Examples of specific time averages calculated by means of equation (3–33) will be given in later sections.

A specialized notation and terminology is commonly used in discussions involving averages. The right-hand side of the theorem of averages (3–33) is often abbreviated by writing

$$\int_{-\infty}^{\infty} \phi(\xi) p_X(\xi) d\xi = E[\phi(X)]$$

or, equivalently

$$= E[\phi] \tag{3–39}$$

The symbol $E[\phi(X)]$ or $E[\phi]$ is referred to as the *mathematical expectation* of the function ϕ. The use of this term stems from the early applications of the theory to games of chance, where it was used to denote the average amount a gambler could expect to win. The basic rules for manipulating the expectation symbol E are direct consequences of its definition, and are stated below for easy reference.

$$\left.\begin{aligned} E[a] &= a \\ E[a\phi_1 + b\phi_2] &= aE[\phi_1] + bE[\phi_2] \\ |E[\phi]| &\leq E[|\phi|] \end{aligned}\right\} \tag{3–40}$$

In these expressions, the symbols a and b denote constants, and the symbols ϕ, ϕ_1, and ϕ_2 functions.

The reader may have thought it odd when it was stated in the last paragraph that $E[\phi]$ is an abbreviation for the *right-hand side* of Eq. (3–33). In all our discussions, $E[\phi]$ will be an abbreviation for the left-hand side of Eq. (3–33) also, since the two sides are equal but this is *not* the case in most modern treatments of the theory of random processes. The reason for this is quite important and worth a few comments at this point.

We have chosen the notion of a time average as the starting point for the theory of random processes. Unfortunately, this seemingly innocuous and physically reasonable procedure soon runs into serious mathematical difficulties. These difficulties are of such a nature that we shall be able to continue the development along these lines either by closing one eye at appropriate places in the discussion or by adding a variety of auxiliary conditions to all our theorems. This procedure is displeasing to mathematicians, whose objective is the development of a completely rigorous theory that, at the same time, is as free as possible of clumsy, technical restrictions on the mathematical objects involved. Such a theory[11] has been developed, but at the expense of relegating the notion of time average to a secondary role. In this theory the notions of distribution function and mathematical expectation are defined in a way that makes no direct use of time averages. Of course, time averages are still the quantities that are of prime interest in most applications of the theory and, accordingly, one of the major tasks of the theory must be to show the relationship between the concepts of mathematical expectation and time average. This is done in a series of rather deep theorems, variously called laws of large numbers or ergodic theorems, which give conditions under which time averages are equal to their corresponding mathematical expectations; *i.e.*, conditions under which statements like Eq. (3–33) are true. Equation (3–33), which is a direct consequence of the definition of distribution function in terms of time averages in our discussion, becomes a major theorem that is true only when certain conditions are fulfilled in the mathematically more pleasing theory of random processes. This, at least at present, is the price one has to pay in order to have a theory that is completely acceptable to mathematicians.[12]

3.4. Random Variables.—An interesting and useful interpretation of the theorem of averages is to regard it as a means for calculating the distribution functions of certain time functions $Y(t)$ that are related to a time function $X(t)$ whose distribution function is known. More precisely, if $Y(t)$ is of the form $Y(t) = \phi[X(t)]$, then the theorem of averages enables us to calculate the distribution function of $Y(t)$

[11] The first complete statement of the theory was given by A. N. Kolmogorov, *Foundations of Probability Theory*, Chelsea Publishing Co., New York, 1956.

[12] Nonstationary problems, such as those briefly mentioned at the end of Section 3.1, do not seem to be easily amenable to this kind of an attack based on time averages, and presently must be studied by means of the more general theory just described.

in terms of the distribution function for $X(t)$. This result can be derived by starting from the definition of the distribution function for $Y(t)$ and proceeding as follows:

$$\begin{aligned} F_Y(y) &= \lim_{T\to\infty} \frac{1}{2T} \int_{-T}^{T} C_y[Y(t)]dt \\ &= \lim_{T\to\infty} \frac{1}{2T} \int_{-T}^{T} C_y[\phi\{X(t)\}]dt \\ &= \int_{-\infty}^{\infty} C_y[\phi(\xi)]\,p_X(\xi)d\xi \end{aligned} \tag{3-41}$$

where use has been made of the function C_y defined by Eq. (3–6). The relationship between p_Y and p_X implied by Eq. (3–41) can be made more explicit by writing F_Y in terms of p_Y thus obtaining

$$\int_{-\infty}^{\infty} C_y(\eta)\,p_Y(\eta)d\eta = \int_{-\infty}^{\infty} C_y[\phi(\xi)]\,p_X(\xi)d\xi \tag{3-42}$$

It should now be clear that the problem of calculating p_Y in terms of p_X is the same as that of making the change of variable $\eta = \phi(\xi)$ in the right-hand integral appearing in (3–42). This relationship can be written down explicitly if certain assumptions are made about the function ϕ. For example, if ϕ is a monotone, differentiable function (which implies that the inverse function ϕ^{-1} defined by $\phi^{-1}[\phi(\xi)] = \xi$ exists) and if $\phi(-\infty) = -\infty$ and $\phi(\infty) = \infty$, then

$$\int_{-\infty}^{\infty} C_y[\phi(\xi)]\,p_X(\xi)d\xi = \int_{-\infty}^{\infty} C_y(\eta)\,p_X[\phi^{-1}(\eta)]\,\frac{d\eta}{\phi'[\phi^{-1}(\eta)]} \tag{3-43}$$

and it follows that

$$p_Y(\eta) = \frac{p_X[\phi^{-1}(\eta)]}{\phi'[\phi^{-1}(\eta)]} \tag{3-44}$$

If the condition that $\phi(-\infty) = -\infty$ and $\phi(\infty) = \infty$ is dropped, then equation (3–44) still holds in the range $\phi(-\infty) < \eta < \phi(\infty)$ but $p_Y(\eta) = 0$ when η falls outside this range. The way in which equation (3–44) must be modified when the monotonicity condition on ϕ fails is best illustrated by means of an example.

The thermally produced noise voltage $X(t)$ appearing across the terminals of a hot resistor is often modeled by assuming that the probability density function for $X(t)$ is gaussian,

$$p_X(x) = \frac{1}{\sqrt{2\pi}\sigma}\, e^{-(1/2\sigma^2)x^2} \tag{3-45}$$

(It will be shown in Section 3.5 that this choice of the parameters of the gaussian corresponds to assuming that the d.c. noise voltage is equal to zero and that the total noise power is equal to σ^2. The reason for assuming a gaussian distribution rather than any other will be discussed in Section 3.13.) A problem of practical importance is the determination of the probability density function of the output of a nonlinear device whose input is a thermal noise voltage $X(t)$. Specifically, let us consider the case where the device is cubic; *i.e.*, the output is $Y(t) = \phi[X(t)]$ and $\phi(x) = x^3$. This function ϕ satisfies the conditions for the validity of (3–44) so we can write,

$$p_Y(\eta) = \frac{\dfrac{1}{\sqrt{2\pi}\sigma} e^{-(1/2\sigma^2)[\eta^{1/3}]^2}}{3[\eta^{1/3}]^2} = \frac{1}{3\sqrt{2\pi}\sigma} \eta^{-2/3} e^{-(1/2\sigma^2)\eta^{2/3}} \tag{3–46}$$

An example of this change-of-variable technique where ϕ is not monotonic arises when we choose a quadratic device, $\phi(x) = x^2$. Equation (3–42) is valid for any ϕ, so we can write

$$\int_{-\infty}^{\infty} C_y(\eta)\, p_Y(\eta)\, d\eta = \frac{1}{\sqrt{2\pi}\sigma} \int_{-\infty}^{\infty} C_y[\xi^2] e^{-(1/2\sigma^2)\xi^2} d\xi \tag{3–47}$$

Our objective is to make the change of variable $\eta = \xi^2$ in the right-hand integral. An easy way of accomplishing this is to first write the integral as the sum of two integrals in each of which the function ϕ is monotonic and then change variables in each integral separately. Carrying out this procedure, we obtain

$$\begin{aligned}
&\frac{1}{\sqrt{2\pi}\sigma} \int_{-\infty}^{\infty} C_y[\xi^2] e^{-(1/2\sigma^2)\xi^2} d\xi \\
&\quad = \frac{1}{\sqrt{2\pi}\sigma} \int_{-\infty}^{0} C_y[\xi^2] e^{-(1/2\sigma^2)\xi^2} d\xi + \frac{1}{\sqrt{2\pi}\sigma} \int_{0}^{\infty} C_y[\xi^2] e^{-(1/2\sigma^2)\xi^2} d\xi \\
&\quad = \frac{1}{2} \frac{1}{\sqrt{2\pi}\sigma} \int_{0}^{\infty} C_y[\eta] e^{-(1/2\sigma^2)\eta} \frac{d\eta}{\sqrt{\eta}} + \frac{1}{2} \frac{1}{\sqrt{2\pi}\sigma} \int_{0}^{\infty} C_y[\eta] e^{-(1/2\sigma^2)\eta} \frac{d\eta}{\sqrt{\eta}} \\
&\quad = \frac{1}{\sqrt{2\pi}\sigma} \int_{0}^{\infty} C_y[\eta] e^{-(1/2\sigma^2)\eta} \frac{d\eta}{\sqrt{\eta}}
\end{aligned} \tag{3–48}$$

and it follows that

$$p_Y(\eta) = \begin{cases} \dfrac{1}{\sqrt{2\pi\eta}\sigma} e^{-(1/2\sigma^2)\eta}, & \eta > 0 \\ 0, & \eta \leq 0 \end{cases} \tag{3–49}$$

The next example will illustrate a different technique for solving change of variable problems. The background of the problem is the same as in the previous examples, except that we choose ϕ as defined by

$$\phi(x) = \begin{cases} 0, & |X| \leq 1 \\ 1, & |X| > 1 \end{cases} \tag{3-50}$$

We shall calculate the distribution function of $Y(t) = \phi[X(t)]$ by returning to basic definitions

$$F_Y(y) = P\{Y(t) \leq y\} = P\{\phi[X(t)] \leq y\}$$

$$= \begin{cases} 0, & y < 0 \\ P\{|X(t)| \leq 1\}, & 0 \leq y < 1 \\ 1, & 1 \leq y \end{cases}$$

$$= \begin{cases} 0, & y < 0 \\ \dfrac{1}{\sqrt{2\pi}\sigma} \displaystyle\int_{-1}^{+1} e^{-(1/2\sigma^2)\xi^2} d\xi, & 0 \leq y < 1 \\ 1, & 1 \leq y \end{cases}$$

$$= \begin{cases} 0, & y < 0 \\ 2\Phi\left(\dfrac{1}{\sigma}\right) - 1, & 0 \leq y < 1\ ^{13} \\ 1, & 1 \leq y \end{cases} \tag{3-51}$$

The probability density function p_Y can now be obtained by differentiation with the result

$$p_Y(y) = \left[2\Phi\left(\frac{1}{\sigma}\right) - 1\right] \delta(y) + 2\left[1 - \Phi\left(\frac{1}{\sigma}\right)\right] \delta(y - 1) \tag{3-52}$$

The process of deriving new *time* functions from old ones by means of a relationship of the form $Y(t) = \phi[X(t)]$ occurs so often that the functions ϕ used for this purpose are given a special name; they are called *random variables.* In a later section we shall extend the notion of a random variable to cover more general relationships between time functions than the simple one considered above; for the time being, however, we will restrict our use of the word random variable to mean any[14] function of a real variable that is used to generate new time functions from $X(t)$ by means of the equation $Y(t) = \phi[X(t)]$. The use of the nomenclature random *variable* to denote a *function* may be somewhat confusing at first, but this terminology is traditional and so widely used that it would only promote misunderstanding to depart from it here.

[13] The function Φ was defined by Eq. 3-2.6.

[14] A rigorous theory requires some smoothness conditions on the functions.

The results derived at the beginning of this section can now be expressed by the statement: every random variable ϕ has a distribution function F_ϕ, which is given by the equation

$$F_\phi(y) = \int_{-\infty}^{\infty} C_y[\phi(\xi)]p_X(\xi)d\xi \tag{3-53}$$

Note carefully that the same random variable (function) ϕ may have many different distribution functions depending on the distribution function of the underlying function $X(t)$. We will avoid confusion on this point by adopting the convention that, in any one problem, and unless an explicit statement to the contrary is made, all random variables are to be used in conjunction with a time function $X(t)$ whose distribution function is to be the same in all expressions in which it appears. With this convention, the notation F_ϕ is just as unambiguous as the more cumbersome notation $F_{\phi(X)}$ so that we are free to make use of whichever seems more appropriate in a given situation.

The notion of the distribution function of a random variable ϕ is also useful in connection with problems where it is not possible or convenient to subject the underlying function $X(t)$ to direct measurements, but where certain derived time functions of the form $Y(t) = \phi[X(t)]$ are available for observation. The theorem of averages then tells us what averages of $X(t)$ it is possible to calculate when all that is known is the distribution function of ϕ. The answer is quite simple: if f denotes (almost) any real-valued function of a real variable, then all X averages of the form

$$\lim_{T\to\infty} \frac{1}{2T}\int_{-T}^{T} f\{\phi[X(t)]\}dt$$

can be calculated in terms of the probability density of ϕ by means of the formula

$$\lim_{T\to\infty} \frac{1}{2T}\int_{-T}^{T} f\{\phi[X(t)]\}dt = \int_{-\infty}^{\infty} f(\xi)p_\phi(\xi)d\xi \tag{3-54}$$

In other words, there are two ways of calculating the average on the left of Eq. (3–54); either in terms of p_ϕ as above, or in terms of p_X by means of the formula

$$\lim_{T\to\infty} \frac{1}{2T}\int_{-T}^{T} f\{\phi[X(t)]\}dt = \int_{-\infty}^{\infty} f[\phi(\xi)]p_X(\xi)d\xi \tag{3-55}$$

If both p_ϕ and p_X are known, then the choice between these two methods of calculation is purely one of convenience. But, if only p_ϕ is known, for whatever reason, then the first formula provides us with a way of calculating certain average properties of $X(t)$.

There is one further point that is worth mentioning in connection with the random variable concept. We have repeatedly stressed the fact that the theory of random processes is primarily concerned with averages of time functions and not with their detailed structure. The same comment applies to random variables. The distribution function of a random variable (or perhaps some other less complete information about averages) is the quantity of interest; not its functional form. The functional form of the random variable is only of interest insofar as it enables us to derive its distribution function from the known distribution function of the underlying time function $X(t)$. It is the relationship between averages of various time functions that is of interest and not the detailed relationship between the time functions themselves.

3.5. Moments.[15]—We have seen how a large class of time averages can be calculated from a knowledge of the first-order distribution function. In a later section, higher-order distribution functions will be defined and it will be shown that virtually any time average can be calculated from a knowledge of the appropriate distribution function. This means that a random process can be completely specified (values assigned to all possible time averages) by giving a complete set of higher-order distribution functions. However, in many cases where not enough is known about the random phenomenon in question to enable us to make simplifying assumptions, the task of specifying a complete set of distribution functions is so great that we are forced to model the phenomenon in a less complete but simpler way. This is, incidentally, not necessarily a disadvantage—the questions we want to ask about the random phenomenon may not require a completely specified model in order to be answered. Several examples where this occurs will be given as we proceed.

One way of avoiding the difficulty of having to measure, or in some way specify, a complete distribution function is to restrict attention to those theorems or relationships that do not depend on the detailed shape of the distribution function, but rather depend only on certain more easily measured parameters of the distribution function. A convenient and widely used set of such parameters is the *moments of the distribution function*. In the case of first order distribution

[15] For a more complete discussion of the material in this and the next section, see W. Feller, *Probability Theory and Its Applications*, John Wiley and Sons, Inc., New York, 1950, and E. Parzen, *Modern Probability Theory and Its Applications*, John Wiley and Sons, Inc., New York, 1960.

functions, *the* n^{th} *order moment* α_n of the distribution function F_ϕ is defined by the equation

$$\alpha_n = E[\phi^n] = \int_{-\infty}^{\infty} \xi^n p_\phi(\xi) d\xi \tag{3-56}$$

The quantity α_n is also often referred to as the nth moment of the random variable ϕ. We shall use these two designations interchangeably. The first order moment α_1 (often called the *mean* of ϕ and designated by the symbol m or m_ϕ) is a measure of where "most" of the area under p_X is located in much the same way (and with similar reservations!) that the center of mass of a body gives an indication of where most of the mass of the body is concentrated. In fact, m is the coordinate of the center of mass of a unit quantity of mass distributed on the ξ-axis in such a way that $p_\phi(\xi)\Delta\xi$ units of mass are located in a small interval $\Delta\xi$ centered at the point ξ.

The interpretation of the higher-order moments α_n is simplified if they are first centered about the first moment. To this end, we define the nth *central moment* μ_n of the distribution function F_ϕ or, equivalently, of the random variable ϕ as follows:

$$\mu_n = E[(\phi - m)^n] = \int_{-\infty}^{\infty} (\xi - m)^n p_\phi(\xi) d\xi \tag{3-57}$$

The second order central moment μ_2 is used so frequently that it is very often designated by a special symbol σ^2 or σ_ϕ^2 and referred to as the *variance* of the distribution. The square root of the variance, σ, is usually called the *standard deviation* of the distribution and taken as a measure of the extent to which the distribution is spread about the mean. Calculation of the variance can often be facilitated by use of the following formula, which relates the mean, the variance, and the second moment of a distribution

$$\begin{aligned} \sigma^2 &= E[(\phi - m)^2] = E[\phi^2 - 2m\phi + m^2] \\ &= E[\phi^2] - 2mE[\phi] + m^2 \\ &= \alpha_2 - 2m^2 + m^2 = \alpha_2 - m^2 \end{aligned}$$

that is,

$$\sigma^2 = \alpha_2 - m^2 \tag{3-58}$$

Formulas relating the first n central moments to the first n α_k's can be derived using the same procedure.

A few examples should serve to illustrate the technique of calculating means and variances, and to point out the need for caution when using the above-mentioned interpretations. The mean of the gaussian distribution, Eq. (3–25), is given by

$$\begin{aligned}\alpha_1 &= \int_{-\infty}^{\infty} \xi \frac{1}{\sqrt{2\pi}\sigma} e^{-(1/2\sigma^2)(\xi - m)^2} d\xi \\ &= \frac{1}{\sqrt{2\pi}} \int_{-\infty}^{\infty} (\sigma x + m) e^{-\frac{1}{2}x^2} dx \\ &= \frac{\sigma}{\sqrt{2\pi}} \int_{-\infty}^{\infty} x e^{-\frac{1}{2}x^2} dx + m \frac{1}{\sqrt{2\pi}} \int_{-\infty}^{\infty} e^{-\frac{1}{2}x^2} dx \\ &= 0 + m = m\end{aligned}$$

that is,

$$\alpha_1 = m \tag{3–59}$$

and the variance by

$$\begin{aligned}\mu_2 &= \int_{-\infty}^{\infty} (\xi - m)^2 \frac{1}{\sqrt{2\pi\sigma^2}} e^{-(1/2\sigma^2)(\xi - m)^2} d\xi \\ &= \frac{\sigma^2}{\sqrt{2\pi}} \int_{-\infty}^{\infty} x^2 e^{-\frac{1}{2}x^2} dx \\ &= \sigma^2\end{aligned}$$

that is,

$$\mu_2 = \sigma^2 \tag{3–60}$$

The last integral was evaluated by means of the following, very useful trick. Starting from the basic integral

$$\frac{1}{\sqrt{2\pi}} \int_{-\infty}^{\infty} e^{-\frac{1}{2}x^2} dx = 1 \tag{3–61}$$

we make the change of variable $x = \sqrt{\mu} y$, which yields the following identity in the parameter μ

$$\frac{1}{\sqrt{2\pi}} \int_{-\infty}^{\infty} e^{-\frac{1}{2}\mu y^2} dy = \mu^{-\frac{1}{2}} \tag{3–62}$$

Differentiation of both sides of (3–62) with respect to μ and setting $\mu = 1$, now yields the result

$$\begin{aligned}\frac{d}{d\mu} \frac{1}{\sqrt{2\pi}} \int_{-\infty}^{\infty} e^{-\frac{1}{2}\mu y^2} dy \bigg|_{\mu=1} &= -\frac{1}{2} \cdot \frac{1}{\sqrt{2\pi}} \int_{-\infty}^{\infty} y^2 e^{-\frac{1}{2}dy} \\ &= \frac{d}{d\mu} (\mu^{-\frac{1}{2}}) \bigg|_{\mu=1} = -\frac{1}{2}\end{aligned} \tag{3–63}$$

from which it follows that

$$\frac{1}{\sqrt{2\pi}} \int_{-\infty}^{\infty} y^2 e^{-\frac{1}{2}y^2} dy = 1 \tag{3–64}$$

By differentiating (3–62) n times before setting $\mu = 1$, we obtain the formula

$$\frac{1}{\sqrt{2\pi}} \int_{-\infty}^{\infty} y^{2n} e^{-\frac{1}{2}y^2} dy = 1 \cdot 3 \cdot 5 \cdots (2n - 1)$$
$$= \frac{(2n)!}{2^n n!} \tag{3–65}$$

by means of which it can be shown easily that the even central moments of the gaussian distribution are given by the formula

$$\mu_{2n} = \frac{(2n)!}{2^n n!} \sigma^{2n}, \quad n = 0,1,2,\cdots \tag{3–66}$$

All the remaining central moments μ_{2n+1} are equal to zero because the gaussian distribution is symmetric about its mean.

The next example will illustrate the technique of calculating moments when the probability density function contains Dirac delta functions. The mean of the Poisson distribution, Eq. (3–29), is given by

$$\alpha_1 = E[X] = \int_{-\infty}^{\infty} \xi \left[\sum_{k=0}^{\infty} \frac{\lambda^k}{k!} e^{-\lambda} \delta(\xi - k) \right] d\xi$$
$$= \sum_{k=0}^{\infty} \frac{\lambda^k}{k!} e^{-\lambda} \int_{-\infty}^{\infty} \xi \delta(\xi - k) d\xi$$
$$= \sum_{k=0}^{\infty} \frac{\lambda^k}{k!} e^{-\lambda} k = \lambda e^{-\lambda} \sum_{k=1}^{\infty} \frac{\lambda^{k-1}}{(k-1)!}$$
$$= \lambda e^{-\lambda} e^{\lambda} = \lambda$$

$$\alpha_1 = \lambda \tag{3–67}$$

A simple way to calculate the variance of the Poisson distribution is to first calculate α_2 and then apply Eq. (3–58)

$$\alpha_2 = E[X^2] = \int_{-\infty}^{\infty} \xi^2 \left[\sum_{k=0}^{\infty} \frac{\lambda^k}{k!} \delta(\xi - k) \right] d\xi$$
$$= \sum_{k=0}^{\infty} \frac{\lambda^k}{k!} e^{-\lambda} k^2 = \lambda e^{-\lambda} \sum_{k=1}^{\infty} \frac{\lambda^{k-1}}{(k-1)!} k$$
$$= \lambda e^{-\lambda} \sum_{k=0}^{\infty} \frac{\lambda^k}{k!} (k + 1) = \lambda e^{-\lambda} \left[\sum_{k=0}^{\infty} \frac{\lambda^k}{k!} \cdot k + \sum_{k=0}^{\infty} \frac{\lambda^k}{k!} \right]$$
$$= \lambda e^{-\lambda} [\lambda e^{\lambda} + e^{\lambda}] = \lambda^2 + \lambda \tag{3–68}$$

It now follows that

$$\mu_2 = \alpha_2 - \lambda^2 = \lambda \tag{3–69}$$

Both the mean and variance of the Poisson distribution are equal to the parameter λ.

The gaussian distribution is a good example of a case where the mean and standard derivation are good measures of the "center" of the distribution and its "spread" about the "center". This is indicated by an inspection of Fig. 3-3, which shows that the mean gives the location of the central peak of the density, and the standard deviation is the distance from the mean where the density has fallen to $e^{-1/2} = 0.607$ its peak value. Another indication that the standard deviation is a good measure of spread in this case is that 68% of the probability under the density function is located within one standard deviation of the mean. A similar discussion can be given for the Poisson distribution. The details are left as an exercise.

The arcsine distribution is a good example of a situation where the notions of "center" and "spread" of the distribution must be taken with a grain of salt. The mean of this distribution is obviously located at its center of symmetry, $m = 0$. Its variance can now be calculated as follows:

$$\begin{aligned}\sigma^2 &= \int_{-1}^{1} \xi^2 \frac{1}{\pi\sqrt{1-\xi^2}}\, d\xi \\ &= \frac{1}{\pi}\int_{-\pi/2}^{\pi/2} \sin^2 \phi \, d\phi = \tfrac{1}{2} \qquad (3\text{–}70)\end{aligned}$$

Here we have a case where *all*, not only most, of the area under the probability density function is located within $\sqrt{2}$ standard deviations of the mean, but where this fact alone gives a very misleading picture of the arcsine distribution, whose area is mainly concentrated at the edges of the distribution. Quantitatively, this is borne out by the easily verified fact that one half of the area is located outside of the interval $[-0.9, 0.9]$.

The last example brings out very clearly that knowledge of only the mean and variance of a distribution is often not sufficient to tell us much about the shape of the probability density function. In order to partially alleviate this difficulty, one sometimes tries to specify additional parameters or attributes of the distribution. One of the most important of these is the notion of the *modality* of the distribution, which is defined to be the number of distinct maxima of the probability density function. The usefulness of this concept is brought out by the observation that a unimodal distribution (such as the gaussian) will tend to have its area concentrated about the location of the maximum, thus guaranteeing that the mean and variance will be fairly reasonable measures of the center and spread of the distribution. Conversely, if it is known that a distribution is multimodal (has more than one maximum), then it is possible that the total probability is heavily concentrated in two or more distinct locations and that, consequently the customary interpretations of the mean and the variance will give a false impression of the shape of the distribution. In a multimodal situation, giving the locations of the maxima and their "widths", conveys much more precise information about the distribution than knowledge of the mean and variance.

Another useful parameter of a distribution is its median m_e defined by the equation

$$\int_{-\infty}^{m_e} p_\phi(\xi)d\xi = \tfrac{1}{2} \tag{3-71}$$

The median, like the mean, is a measure of the midpoint or center of the distribution. In some cases, such as the gaussian or uniform distribution, the median coincides with the mean, but consideration of the binomial distribution with $p \neq \frac{1}{2}$ shows that this is not generally true. The median is often a more useful measure of the center of the distribution than the mean because it is much less sensitive to the presence of a few small-probability peaks far away from the main body of the distribution. This property of the mean is illustrated by the fact that students tend to be somewhat unhappy with those few members of a class who get quiz grades much higher than their fellows and thus "raise the class average."

The preceding discussion of the variance as a measure of the spread of a distribution about its mean has been largely qualitative. One way in which the variance can be used to give quantitative information about the distribution is through use of the *Chebychev inequality*, which gives an upper bound on the amount of area contained outside an interval centered at the mean. The formal statement of the Chebychev inequality is

$$P\{|X(t) - m| \geq \varepsilon\} \leq \left(\frac{\sigma}{\varepsilon}\right)^2 \tag{3-72}$$

the inequality being valid for any choice of $\varepsilon > 0$. To prove this inequality, we first recall that the probability of the event appearing on the left-hand side can be written in terms of the probability density function p_X by means of Eq. (3–21)

$$P\{|X(t) - m| \geq \varepsilon\} = \int_{|\xi - m| \geq \varepsilon} p_X(\xi)d\xi \tag{3-73}$$

In words, Eq. (3–73) reads, the probability (fraction of the time) $X(t)$ differs from its mean m by more than ε is equal to the area under that part of the probability density function for which the variable ε lies in the set of points defined by the inequality $|\xi - m| \geq \varepsilon$. We next write the variance in terms of p_X

$$\sigma^2 = \int_{-\infty}^{\infty} (\xi - m)^2 p_X(\xi) d\xi \tag{3-74}$$

and note that, since the integrand is everywhere non-negative, the value of the integral will be decreased only if we integrate over the two tail intervals $|\xi - m| \geq \varepsilon$ instead of over the entire real line. Thus

$$\sigma^2 \geq \int_{|\xi - m| \geq \varepsilon} (\xi - m)^2 p_X(\xi) d\xi \tag{3-75}$$

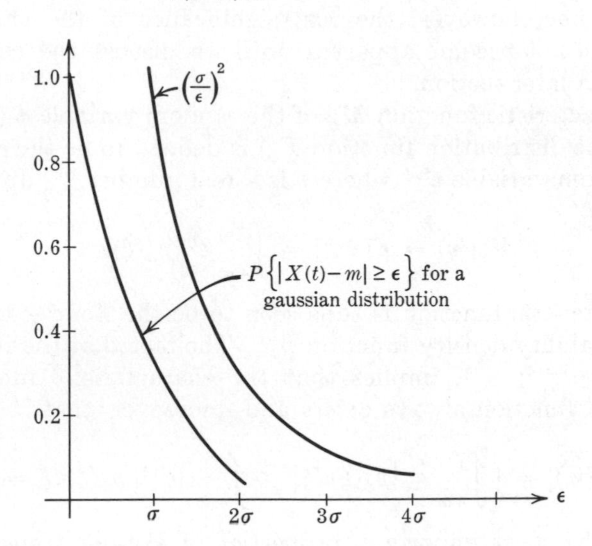

FIG. 3–5. The Chebychev Inequality.

Finally we note that the value of the integral appearing in (3–75) can be further decreased only by replacing $(\xi - m)^2$ by the smallest value it can take on in the $|\xi - m| \geq \varepsilon$; namely ε^2. Making this replacement, we obtain the inequality

$$\sigma^2 \geq \int_{|\xi - m| \geq \varepsilon} \varepsilon^2 p_X(\xi) d\xi = \varepsilon^2 P\{|X(t) - m| \geq \varepsilon\} \tag{3-76}$$

which is equivalent to the Chebychev inequality (3–72).

Fig. 3–5 compares the bound the Chebychev inequality places on the probability $P\{|X(t) - m| \geq \varepsilon\}$ with the actual value of this quantity when the underlying distribution is gaussian. The agreement between the two quantities is not particularly good; however, it should be borne in mind that the virtue of the Chebychev inequality is, not its accuracy, but the fact that it requires only a knowledge of the mean and variance. It can be shown, incidentally, that the Chebychev inequality is the best possible bound that makes use only of the mean and variance.

3.6. The Characteristic Function.—The calculation of moments is often quite tedious because of difficulties that may be encountered in evaluating the pertinent integrals or sums. This problem can be simplified quite often by calculation of the so-called characteristic function of the distribution from which, as we shall see, all moments can be derived by means of differentiation. This relationship between the characteristic function and moments is sufficient reason for studying it at this time; however, the real significance of the characteristic function will not become apparent until we discuss the central limit theorem in a later section.

The characteristic function M_ϕ of the random variable ϕ (or, equivalently, of the distribution function F_ϕ) is defined to be the expectation of the random variable $e^{iv\phi}$ where v is a real number.[16] In symbols

$$M_\phi(iv) = E[e^{iv\phi}] = \int_{-\infty}^{\infty} e^{iv\xi} p_\phi(\xi) d\xi \tag{3-77}$$

The characteristic function is thus seen to be the Fourier transform[17] of the probability density function p_ϕ. The fact that the function $e^{iv\xi}$ is bounded, $|e^{iv\xi}| = 1$, implies that the characteristic function of a distribution function always exists and, moreover, that

$$|M_\phi(iv)| = \left| \int_{-\infty}^{\infty} e^{iv\xi} p_\phi(\xi) d\xi \right| \leq \int_{-\infty}^{\infty} |e^{iv\xi}| \, p_\phi(\xi) d\xi = 1 \tag{3-78}$$

One of the most important properties of Fourier transforms and, consequently, of characteristic functions, is their invertibility. Given a characteristic function M_ϕ, one can calculate the probability density function p_ϕ by means of the inversion formula

$$p_\phi(x) = \frac{1}{2\pi} \int_{-\infty}^{\infty} M_\phi(iv) e^{-ivx} dv \tag{3-79}$$

Thus, knowledge of the characteristic function of a distribution, unlike

[16] Complex valued random variables will be discussed in Section 3.8. For the time being it is sufficient to state that the expectation of a complex function ϕ is defined by $E[\phi] = E[\phi_r] + iE[\phi_i]$ where ϕ_r and ϕ_i denote the real and imaginary parts, respectively, of ϕ.

[17] The reader is assumed to be familiar with the elementary properties of Fourier transforms.

knowledge of just a few of its moments, is equivalent to knowledge of the distribution function itself.[18]

The technique for calculating the moments of a random variable from the characteristic function of the random variable can be derived by first differentiating both sides of Eq. (3–77) n-times with respect to v

$$\frac{d^n}{dv^n} M_\phi(iv) = \int_{-\infty}^{\infty} (i\xi)^n e^{iv\xi} p_\phi(\xi) d\xi \tag{3–80}$$

Next, we note that the right-hand side of (3–80) is equal to $(i)^n$ times the nth moment of p_ϕ if v is the set equal to zero. The final formula is

$$(-i)^n \frac{d^n}{dv^n} M_\phi(iv) \bigg|_{v=0} = \alpha_n \tag{3–81}$$

A more careful derivation of (3.81) yields the additional information that this formula is valid as long as *either* side exists; in other words, finiteness of the nth moment implies existence of the nth derivative of M_ϕ and vice-versa.

The content of Eq. (3–81) is sometimes expressed in a somewhat different way by writing the (formal) Taylor series expansion of M_ϕ in the form

$$\begin{aligned} M_\phi(iv) &= \sum_{n=0}^{\infty} \frac{v^n}{n!} \left[\frac{d^n}{dv^n} M_\phi(iv) \right]_{v=0} \\ &= \sum_{n=0}^{\infty} \frac{\alpha_n}{n!} (iv)^n \end{aligned} \tag{3–82}$$

Equation (3–82) must be regarded as a purely formal expansion since, without further conditions, the various derivatives involved may not exist and, even if they do, the series may fail to converge. One of the advantages of this formula becomes apparent in those cases where it is possible to write down the Taylor series of M_ϕ without having to calculate explicitly any derivatives. Equation (3–82) then enables us to read off the desired moments from this expansion without any further calculations.

As an example of these techniques, we shall calculate the characteristic function of the gaussian distribution with zero mean and unit variance and then use it to calculate moments. Starting from the definition of the characteristic function, we obtain[18a]

[18] It can be shown, however, that, under certain conditions, knowledge of all the moments of a distribution determines the distribution uniquely.

[18a] Rigorous justification of this calculation requires the use of Cauchy's integral theorem.

$$M_\phi(iv) = \int_{-\infty}^{\infty} e^{iv\xi} \frac{1}{\sqrt{2\pi}} e^{-\frac{1}{2}\xi^2} d\xi$$
$$= \frac{1}{\sqrt{2\pi}} e^{\frac{1}{2}(iv)^2} \int_{-\infty}^{\infty} e^{-\frac{1}{2}[\xi^2 - 2iv\xi + (iv)^2]} d\xi$$
$$= \frac{1}{\sqrt{2\pi}} e^{-\frac{1}{2}v^2} \int_{-\infty}^{\infty} e^{-\frac{1}{2}(\xi - iv)^2} d\xi$$
$$= e^{-\frac{1}{2}v^2}$$

that is,

$$M_\phi(iv) = e^{-\frac{1}{2}v^2} \tag{3-83}$$

The moments of this distribution can now be obtained by making use of the known power series expansion for e^x

$$e^x = \sum_{n=0}^{\infty} \frac{x^n}{n!} \tag{3-84}$$

to write the power series for M_ϕ

$$M_\phi(iv) = e^{-\frac{1}{2}v^2} = \sum_{n=0}^{\infty} \frac{(-\frac{1}{2}v^2)^n}{n!}$$
$$= \sum_{n=0}^{\infty} \frac{(2n)!}{n!2^n} \frac{(iv)^{2n}}{(2n)!} \tag{3-85}$$

from which it follows at once that

$$\left.\begin{aligned} \alpha_{2n} &= \frac{(2n)!}{n!2^n} \\ \alpha_{2n+1} &= 0 \end{aligned}\right\} \tag{3-86}$$

This result checks with our earlier calculation of the moments of the gaussian distribution, Eq. (3-65). The characteristic function of a gaussian random variable having an arbitrary mean and variance can be calculated either directly or else by means of the method outlined in the next paragraph.

The calculation of characteristic functions is sometimes facilitated by first normalizing the random variable involved to have zero mean and unit variance. The transformation that accomplishes this is $\hat{\phi} = \dfrac{\phi - m}{\sigma}$ where m and σ denote the mean and standard deviation, respectively, of ϕ. The effect of this transformation on the characteristic function can be deduced by first noting that

$$\phi = \sigma\hat{\phi} + m \tag{3-87}$$

from which it follows that

$$\begin{aligned} M_\phi(iv) &= E[e^{iv\phi}] = E[e^{iv(\sigma\hat{\phi} + m)}] \\ &= e^{ivm}E[e^{iv\sigma\hat{\phi}}] = e^{ivm}M_{\hat{\phi}}(iv\sigma) \end{aligned}$$

that is,

$$M_\phi(iv) = e^{ivm}M_{\hat{\phi}}(iv\sigma) \tag{3–88}$$

Equation (3–88) enables us to calculate the characteristic function of the unnormalized random variable ϕ from a knowledge of the characteristic function of $\hat{\phi}$. For example, the characteristic function of a gaussian random variable ϕ having arbitrary mean and variance can be written down immediately by combining Eqs. (3–83) and (3–88)

$$M_\phi(iv) = e^{ivm - \frac{1}{2}\sigma^2 v^2} \tag{3–89}$$

We conclude this section with a derivation of the characteristic function of the Poisson distribution. Starting from the definition, Eq. (3–77), we obtain

$$\begin{aligned} M_\phi(iv) = E[e^{iv\phi}] &= \int_{-\infty}^{\infty} e^{iv\xi} \left[\sum_{k=0}^{\infty} \frac{\lambda^k}{k!} e^{-\lambda}\delta(\xi - k) \right] d\xi \\ &= \sum_{-\infty}^{\infty} \frac{\lambda^k}{k!} e^{-\lambda} e^{ivk} = e^{-\lambda} \sum_{k=0}^{\infty} \frac{(\lambda e^{iv})^k}{k!} \\ &= \exp\{-\lambda\} \exp\{\lambda e^{iv}\} \end{aligned}$$

that is,

$$M_\phi(iv) = \exp\{\lambda(e^{iv} - 1)\} \tag{3–90}$$

The first two moments of ϕ can now be calculated by writing

$$\begin{aligned} M_\phi(iv) &= \exp\left\{\lambda\left[(iv) + \frac{(iv)^2}{2!} + \cdots\right]\right\} \\ &= 1 + \lambda\left[(iv) + \frac{(iv)^2}{2} + \cdots\right] + \frac{\lambda^2}{2}\left[(iv) + \frac{(iv)^2}{2} + \cdots\right]^2 + \cdots \\ &= 1 + \lambda(iv) + (\lambda + \lambda^2)\frac{(iv)^2}{2} + \cdots \end{aligned}$$

from which it follows at once that

$$\alpha_1 = \lambda \quad \text{and} \quad \alpha_2 = \lambda + \lambda^2$$

This result checks our earlier calculations, Eq. (3–67) and Eq. (3–68).

A table giving the characteristic function, mean, and variance of some important probability distributions appears in Fig. 3–6.

Distribution	Probability Density Function	Characteristic Function	Mean	Variance
Gaussian	$\frac{1}{\sqrt{2\pi}\,\sigma} e^{-\frac{1}{2}\sigma^2(x-m)^2}$	$e^{jvm - \frac{1}{2}\sigma^2 v^2}$	m	σ^2
Poisson	$\sum_{k=0}^{\infty} \frac{\lambda^k}{k!} e^{-\lambda}\,\delta(x-k)$	$e^{\lambda[e^{jv}-1]}$	λ	λ
Binomial	$\sum_{k=0}^{n} \binom{n}{k} p^k (1-p)^{n-k}\,\delta(x-k)$	$[(1-p)+pe^{jv}]^n$	np	$np(1-p)$
Arcsine	$\frac{1}{\pi\sqrt{1-x^2}}$, $\lvert x\rvert<1$; 0, $\lvert x\rvert\geq 1$	$J_0(v)$*	0	$\frac{1}{2}$
Uniform	$\frac{1}{2a}$, $\lvert x\rvert<a$; 0, $\lvert x\rvert\geq a$	$\frac{\sin va}{va}$	0	$\frac{a^2}{3}$

FIG. 3–6. Some Typical Characteristic Functions, Means, and Variances. *J_0 denotes the zero order Bessel function of the first kind.

3.7. Joint Distribution Functions.—The purpose of this section is to extend the results obtained in previous sections to averages that are not necessarily of the form

$$\lim_{T\to\infty} \frac{1}{2T} \int_{-T}^{T} \phi[X(t)]dt$$

These more general averages arise quite naturally in a variety of problems of which the following is a simple example.

An engineer has been observing a complicated and apparently random time function $X(t)$. He notices that, although he cannot predict the value of X at a given instant with any precision, he can do a reasonable job of guessing the value of X at some future instant $t + \tau$, $\tau > 0$, once he knows the value of X at time t. In order to systematize this guessing procedure, he now poses the question: how can I choose constants a and b in such a way that the quantity $aX(t) + b$ will be a good guess of $X(t + \tau)$? As a criterion of goodness, he chooses the average of the square of the error between his estimate of $X(t + \tau)$ and the true value of that quantity. Mathematically, the problem, is to choose the constants a and b so as to minimize the average

$$\varepsilon = \lim_{T\to\infty} \frac{1}{2T} \int_{-T}^{T} [X(t + \tau) - aX(t) - b]^2 dt \qquad (3\text{–}91)$$

This problem can be solved by first making the substitution $\hat{X}(t) = X(t) - m_X$ and then expanding the integrand as follows[19]

$$\begin{aligned}
\varepsilon &= \lim_{T\to\infty} \frac{1}{2T} \int_{-T}^{T} [\hat{X}(t+\tau) - a\hat{X}(t) - b - m_X(a-1)]^2 dt \\
&= \lim_{T\to\infty} \frac{1}{2T} \int_{-T}^{T} [\hat{X}(t+\tau) - a\hat{X}(t)]^2 dt + [b + m_X(a-1)]^2 \\
&= \sigma_X^2 - 2a \lim_{T\to\infty} \frac{1}{2T} \int_{-T}^{T} \hat{X}(t)\hat{X}(t+\tau)\,dt + a^2\sigma_X^2 + [b + m_X(a-1)]^2 \\
&= \sigma_X^2 - \left[\frac{1}{\sigma_X} \lim_{T\to\infty} \frac{1}{2T} \int_{-T}^{T} \hat{X}(t)\hat{X}(t+\tau)dt\right]^2 \\
&\quad + \left[\frac{1}{\sigma_X} \lim_{T\to\infty} \frac{1}{2T} \int_{-T}^{T} \hat{X}(t)\hat{X}(t+\tau)dt - a\sigma_X\right]^2 \\
&\quad + [b + m_X(a-1)]^2
\end{aligned} \qquad (3\text{–}92)$$

This expression is obviously a minimum when the second and third terms are set equal to zero

$$\left.\begin{aligned}
a &= \frac{1}{\sigma_X^2} \lim_{T\to\infty} \frac{1}{2T} \int_{-T}^{T} \hat{X}(t)\hat{X}(t+\tau)dt \\
b &= m_X(1-a)
\end{aligned}\right\} \qquad (3\text{–}93)$$

The interesting thing about this problem is that its solution turns out to depend on an average that is not of the form considered earlier. A moment's reflection should make it obvious that something of this sort must happen because the averages we have considered previously in no way give us any information about the time scale of the phenomenon being investigated. Our ability to predict the future of a time function from a knowledge of its past is very much dependent on how rapidly future values depart (on the average) from past values. Thus, the fact that the solution to our prediction problem required a knowledge of a time average involving the values of X at two different instants of time is not mysterious but simply the result of asking a question whose answer depends on the rate-of-change of the phenomenon.

The problem just considered can be generalized in a useful way by assuming that we want to predict the value of a time function Y at time t from our knowledge of the value of a *different* time function X at time t. For example, $X(t)$ could be a noise voltage measured at some point in an electrical network and $Y(t)$ the noise voltage measured at a

[19] Use has been made of the fact that $E[X(t)] = E[X(t+\tau)]$. The proof of this is contained in the more general statement, Eq. (3–104), to be established later in this section.

different point in the same network. Making the same assumptions as we did previously, our problem becomes that of finding the values of the constants a and b that minimize the expression

$$\varepsilon = \lim_{T\to\infty} \frac{1}{2T} \int_{-T}^{T} [Y(t) - aX(t) - b]^2 dt \tag{3-94}$$

The solution to this problem can be found by the same method used earlier with the result

$$\left.\begin{aligned} a &= \frac{1}{\sigma_X^2} \lim_{T\to\infty} \int_{-T}^{T} \hat{Y}(t)\hat{X}(t)dt \\ b &= m_Y - am_X \end{aligned}\right\} \tag{3-95}$$

where σ_X and σ_Y denote the standard deviations of $X(t)$ and $Y(t)$ respectively, m_X and m_Y their means, and $\hat{X}(t) = X(t) - m_X$, $\hat{Y}(t) = Y(t) - m_Y$. As a check on our work, we see that Eq. (3–95) reduces to Eq. (3–93) when we set $Y(t) = X(t + \tau)$. The importance of this problem is that it gives us an example of a situation in which an average that depends on *two* time functions arises.

We turn now to a study of time averages that involve the values of several different time functions at several instants of time. A quite general average of this type is of the form[20]

$$\lim_{T\to\infty} \frac{1}{2T} \int_{-T}^{T} \phi[X(t + \tau_1),\cdots,X(t + \tau_n), Y(t + \tau_1'),\cdots,Y(t + \tau_m')]dt \tag{3-96}$$

where ϕ denotes a real valued function of $n + m$ real variables and $\tau_1 < \tau_2 < \cdots < \tau_n$, $\tau_1' < \tau_2' < \cdots < \tau_m'$ are real numbers.

All averages of the form (3–96) can be calculated in terms of a canonical set of averages called joint distribution functions by means of an extension of the theorem of averages proved in Section 3.3. To this end, we shall define the nth order distribution function of X for time spacings $\tau_1 < \tau_2 < \cdots < \tau_n$ by the equation,

$$F_{X,\tau_1,\cdots,\tau_n}(x_1,\cdots,x_n) = \lim_{T\to\infty} \frac{1}{2T} \int_{-T}^{T} C_{x_1,\cdots,x_n}[X(t + \tau_1),\cdots,X(t + \tau_n)]dt \tag{3-97}$$

where $C_{x_1,\cdots,x_n}$ denotes the function of n real variables defined by

$$C_{x_1,\cdots,x_n}(z_1,\cdots,z_n) = \begin{cases} 1, & z_1 \le x_1 \text{ and } z_2 \le x_2 \text{ and} \cdots z_n \le x_n \\ 0, & \text{otherwise} \end{cases} \tag{3-98}$$

[20] We shall limit ourselves to averages involving two different time functions. The extension to more than two functions is obvious.

More generally, the $n + m^{\text{th}}$ order joint distribution function of X and Y for time spacings $\tau_1 < \tau_2 < \cdots < \tau_n$ and $\tau_1' < \tau_2' < \cdots < \tau_m'$ respectively, is defined by

$$F_{\substack{X,\tau_1,\cdots,\tau_n\\ Y,\tau_1',\cdots,\tau_m'}}(x_1,\cdots,x_n,y_1,\cdots,y_m)$$
$$= \lim_{T\to\infty} \frac{1}{2T} \int_{-T}^{T} C_{\substack{x_1,\cdots,x_n\\ y_1,\cdots,y_m}}[X(t+\tau_1),\cdots,X(t+\tau_n),$$
$$Y(t+\tau_1'),\cdots,Y(t+\tau_m')]dt \qquad (3\text{–}99)$$

In order to facilitate writing, expressions such as (3–99) usually will be abbreviated by means of vector notation as follows

$$F_{X,\bar{\tau}_n;Y,\bar{\tau}_m'}(\bar{x}_n,\bar{y}_m)$$
$$= \lim_{T\to\infty} \frac{1}{2T} \int_{-T}^{T} C_{\bar{x}_n,\bar{y}_m}[X(t+\bar{\tau}_n),Y(t+\bar{\tau}_m')]dt \qquad (3\text{–}100)$$

The use of the notation $X(t + \bar{\tau}_n)$ to mean $X(t + \tau_1),\cdots,X(t + \tau_n)$ is unconventional but the intended meaning should be clear in all cases.

In order to clarify these definitions, a geometrical interpretation of $F_{X,0,\tau}(x_1,x_2)$ is given in Fig. 3–7. It should be clear from this picture that $F_{X,0,\tau}(x_1,x_2)$ is the fraction of the time that, *simultaneously*, $X(t) \leq x_1$ and $X(t + \tau) \leq x_2$. Similar interpretations hold for all the joint distribution functions defined above.

The properties of joint distribution functions can be stated most easily in terms of their associated probability density functions. The $n + m^{\text{th}}$ order joint probability density function $p_{X,\bar{\tau}_n;Y,\bar{\tau}_m'}(\bar{x}_n,\bar{y}_m)$ is defined by the equation

$$p_{X,\bar{\tau}_n;Y,\bar{\tau}_m}(\bar{x}_n,\bar{y}_m) = \frac{\partial^{n+m}}{\partial \bar{x}_n \partial \bar{y}_m} F_{X,\bar{\tau}_n;Y,\bar{\tau}_m'}(\bar{x}_n,\bar{y}_m) \qquad (3\text{–}101)[21]$$

In most cases of interest, this $n + m^{\text{th}}$ order derivative can be written as an ordinary $n + m^{\text{th}}$ order derivative and some Dirac delta functions. Situations do exist in which this is not true, but they do not seem to have any physical significance and we shall ignore them. In any event, all difficulties of this nature could be avoided by replacing integrals involving probability density functions by their corresponding Lebesque–Stieltjes integrals.

21 $\dfrac{\partial^{n+m}}{\partial \bar{x}_n \partial \bar{y}_m}$ means $\dfrac{\partial^{n+m}}{\partial x_1 \cdots \partial x_n \partial y_1 \cdots \partial y_m}$

Some of the most important properties of higher-order probability density functions are the following:[22]

$$\int_{-\infty}^{\infty}\int p_{X,\bar{\tau}_n;Y,\bar{\tau}'_m}(\bar{\xi}_n,\bar{\eta}_m)d\bar{\xi}_n d\bar{\xi}_m = 1 \tag{3–102}$$

$$p_{X,\bar{\tau}_n;Y,\bar{\tau}'_m}(\bar{x}_n,\bar{y}_m) \geq 0 \tag{3–103}$$[23]

$$p_{X,\tau+\bar{\tau}_n;Y,\tau+\bar{\tau}'_m}(\bar{x}_n,\bar{y}_m) = p_{X,\bar{\tau}_n;Y,\bar{\tau}'_m}(\bar{x}_n,\bar{y}_m) \tag{3–104}$$

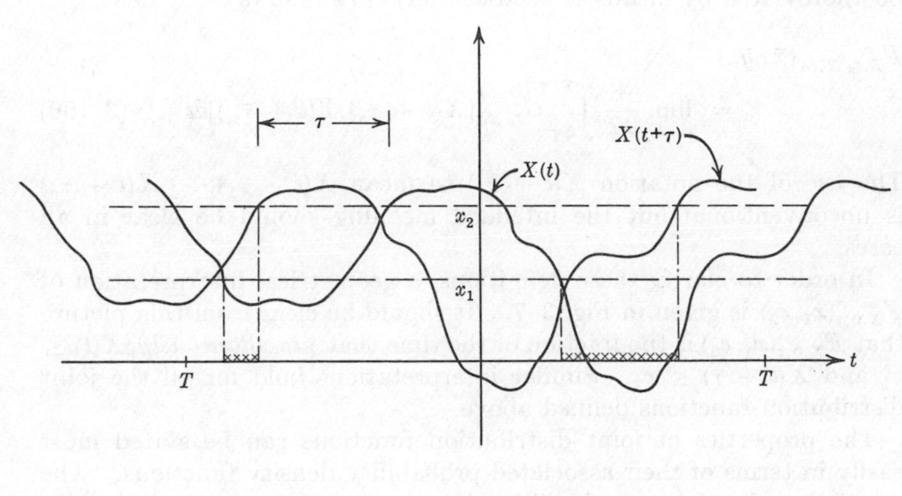

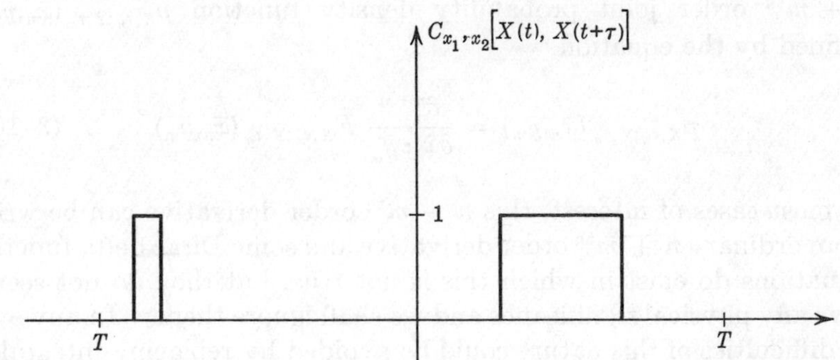

FIG. 3–7. An Aid to Visualizing a Second-Order Distribution Function.

[22] $\int_{-\infty}^{\infty} f(\bar{\xi}_n)d\bar{\xi}_n$ means $\int_{-\infty}^{\infty}\cdots\int_{-\infty}^{\infty} f(\xi_1,\cdots\xi_n)d\xi_1,\cdots,d\xi_n$

[23] $\tau + \bar{\tau}_n$ means $\tau + \tau_1, \tau + \tau_2, \ldots, \tau + \tau_n$.

The first property, Eq. (3–102), follows at once upon recognizing that the distribution function can be written in the form

$$F_{X,\tau_n;Y,\tau'_m}(\bar{x}_n,\bar{y}_m) = \int_{-\infty}^{\bar{x}_n} \int_{-\infty}^{\bar{y}_m} p_{X,\tau_n;Y,\tau'_m}(\xi_n,\bar{\eta}_m)d\xi_n d\bar{\eta}_m \qquad (3\text{–}105)$$

and that Eq. (3–100) implies that $\lim_{\substack{\bar{x}_n \to \infty \\ \bar{y}_m \to \infty}} F_{X,\tau_n;Y,\tau'_m}(\bar{x}_n,\bar{y}_m) = 1.$

The second property, Eq. (3–103), is also an immediate consequence of our definitions but notational complexity makes its derivation somewhat more involved. We shall, accordingly, limit ourselves to a derivation of (3–103) in the two-dimensional case after which the reader should have little conceptual difficulty devising his own proof for the higher dimensional cases.

We begin by recalling the definition of a derivative [24]

$$\begin{aligned}
p(x_1,x_2) &= \frac{\partial^2}{\partial x_1 \partial x_2} F(x_1,x_2) \\
&= \frac{\partial}{\partial x_1} \lim_{\Delta x_2 \to 0} \left[\frac{F(x_1,x_2 + \Delta x_2) - F(x_1,x_2)}{\Delta x_2}\right] \\
&= \lim_{\substack{\Delta x_1 \to 0 \\ \Delta x_2 \to 0}} \left[\frac{F(x_1 + \Delta x_1,x_2 + \Delta x_2) - F(x_1 + \Delta x_1,x_2)}{\Delta x_1 \Delta x_2} - \frac{F(x_1,x_2 + \Delta x_2) - F(x_1,x_2)}{\Delta x_1 \Delta x_2}\right] \\
&= \lim_{\substack{\Delta x_1 \to 0 \\ \Delta x_2 \to 0}} \left[\frac{F(x_1 + \Delta x_1,x_2 + \Delta x_2) - F(x_1 + \Delta x_1,x_2) - F(x_1,x_2 + \Delta x_2) + F(x_1,x_2)}{\Delta x_1 \Delta x_2}\right]
\end{aligned} \qquad (3\text{–}106)$$

A few moments' thought should make it clear that the numerator of equation (3–106) can be interpreted as the fraction of the time that $X(t)$ simultaneously satisfies the inequalities $x_1 < X(t) \leq x_1 + \Delta x_1$, $x_2 < X(t + \tau) \leq x_2 + \Delta x_2$. One way to do this is with the aid of pictures such as those shown in Fig. 3–8. The quantity $F(x_1 + \Delta x_1, x_2 + \Delta x_2)$ is the fraction of the time that the pair of values $[X(t), X(t + \tau)]$ falls in the crosshatched part of the (x_1,x_2) plane shown in part (a) of Fig. 3–8. Next, $F(x_1 + \Delta x_1, x_2 + \Delta x_2) - F(x_1 + \Delta x_1,x_2)$ is the fraction of the time that $[X(t), X(t + \tau)]$ falls in the crosshatched area in part (b). $F(x_1 + \Delta x_1, x_2 + \Delta x_2) - F(x_1 + \Delta x_1,x_2) - F(x_1,x_2$

[24] p means $p_{X,0,\tau}$ and F means $F_{X,0,\tau}$ in this derivation.

$+ \Delta x_2)$ is now seen to be the fraction of the time $[X(t), X(t + \tau)]$ falls in the small crosshatched rectangle shown in part (c) *minus* the fraction of the time $[X(t), X(t + \tau)]$ falls in the crosshatched quadrant. Finally, the entire numerator is seen to be equal to the fraction of the time $[X(t), X(t + \tau)]$ falls in the crosshatched rectangle shown in part (d) of Fig. 3–8.

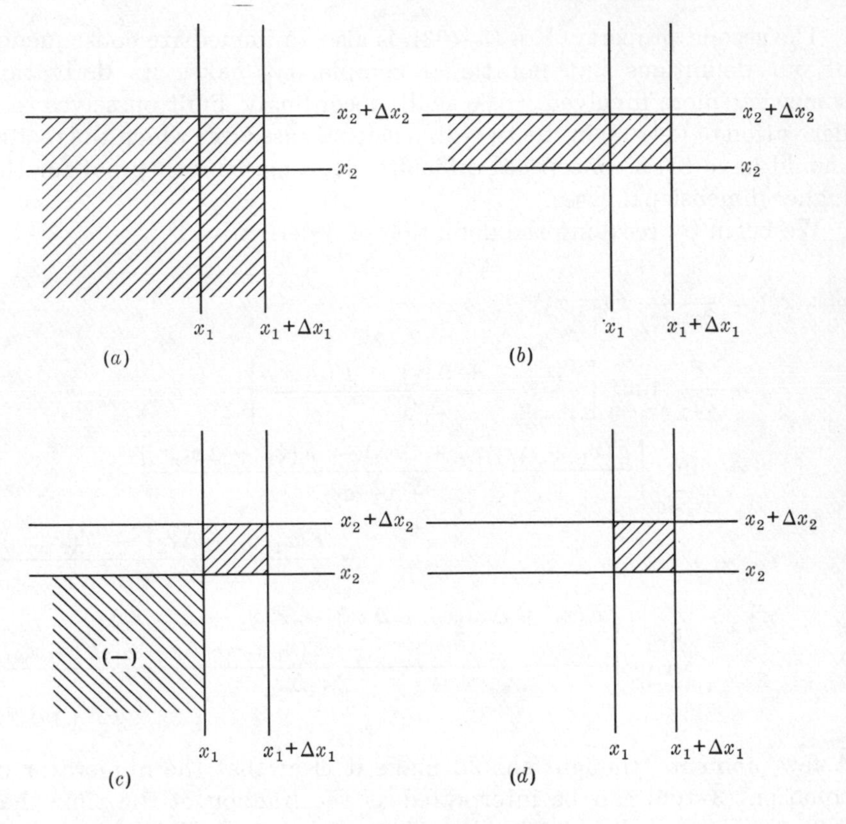

FIG. 3–8. An Aid to Understanding a Derivation in the Text.

The derivation can now be concluded by noting that since the numerator of Eq. (3–106) is the fraction of time something happens, it must always be non-negative. Consequently, the function $p(x_1,x_2)$, being the limit of non-negative quantities, must also be non-negative.

Equation (3–104) (sometimes called the stationarity property of a probability density function) follows from the definition of the joint distribution function upon making the change of variable $t' = t + \tau$

$$
\begin{aligned}
F_{X,\tau+\tau_n;\tau+\tau'_m}(\bar{x}_n,\bar{y}_m)
&= \lim_{T\to\infty} \frac{1}{2T}\int_{-T}^{T} C_{\bar{x}_n,\bar{y}_m}[X(t+\tau+\bar{\tau}_n),\,Y(t+\tau+\bar{\tau}'_m)]dt \\
&= \lim_{T\to\infty} \frac{1}{2T}\int_{-T+\tau}^{T+\tau} C_{\bar{x}_n,\bar{y}_m}[X(t'+\tau_n),\,Y(t'+\tau'_m)]dt' \\
&= \lim_{T\to\infty}\left[-\frac{1}{2T}\int_{-T}^{-T+\tau} + \frac{1}{2T}\int_{-T}^{T} + \frac{1}{2T}\int_{T}^{T+\tau}\right]
\end{aligned} \tag{3–107}
$$

[25]

The limit of the middle term of equation (3–107) is, by definition, $F_{X,\bar{\tau}_n;Y,\bar{\tau}'_m}(\bar{x}_n,\bar{y}_m)$ and the other two terms approach zero because the function $C_{\bar{x}_n,\bar{y}_m}$ is bounded; for example,

$$
\begin{aligned}
\left|\frac{1}{2T}\int_{T}^{T+\tau} C_{\bar{x}_n,\bar{y}_m}[X(t'+\bar{\tau}_n),\,Y(t'+\bar{\tau}'_m)]dt'\right|
&\le \frac{1}{2T}\int_{T}^{T+\tau}\left|C_{\bar{x}_n,\bar{y}_m}[X(t'+\bar{\tau}_n),\,Y(t'+\bar{\tau}'_m)]\right|dt' \\
&\le \frac{1}{2T}\int_{T}^{T+\tau} 1dt' = \frac{\tau}{2T}\to 0 \text{ as } T\to\infty
\end{aligned} \tag{3–108}
$$

We have thus established the equation

$$F_{X,\tau+\bar{\tau}_n;Y,\tau+\bar{\tau}'_m}(\bar{x}_n,\bar{y}_m) = F_{X,\bar{\tau}_n;Y,\bar{\tau}'_m}(\bar{x}_n,\bar{y}_m) \tag{3–109}$$

from which Eq. (3–104) follows by differentiation.

Higher-order probability functions also obey a variety of consistency conditions which are best illustrated by means of examples such as the following:

$$p_{X,\tau_1,\tau_2}(x_1,x_2) = \int_{-\infty}^{\infty} p_{X,\tau_1,\tau_2,\tau_3}(x_1,x_2,\xi_3)d\xi_3 \tag{3–110}$$

$$p_{X,\tau_2,\tau_3}(x_2,x_3) = \int_{-\infty}^{\infty} p_{X,\tau_1,\tau_2,\tau_3}(\xi_1,x_2,x_3)d\xi_1 \tag{3–111}$$

$$
\begin{aligned}
p_X(x_1) = p_{X,\tau_1}(x_1) &= \int_{-\infty}^{\infty} p_{X,\tau_1,\tau_2}(x_1,\xi_2)d\xi_2 \\
&= \iint_{-\infty}^{\infty} p_{X,\tau_1,\tau_2,\tau_3}(x_1,\xi_2,\xi_3)d\xi_2 d\xi_3
\end{aligned} \tag{3–112}
$$

$$p_X(x_1) = p_{X,\tau_1}(x_1) = \int_{-\infty}^{\infty} p_{X,\tau_1;Y,\tau'_1}(x_1,\eta_1)d\eta_1 \tag{3–113}$$

$$p_Y(y_1) = p_{Y,\tau'_1}(y_1) = \int_{-\infty}^{\infty} p_{X,\tau_1;Y,\tau'_1}(\xi_1,y_1)d\xi_1 \tag{3–114}$$

[25] This assumes that $\tau > 0$. The changes necessary for the case $\tau < 0$ are obvious.

The reader should also note carefully that if $\tau_2 - \tau_1 = \tau_3 - \tau_2$, Eqs. (3–104), (3–110), and (3–111) imply that the third-order probability density $p_{X,\tau_1,\tau_2,\tau_3}$ must satisfy the condition

$$p_{X,\tau_1,\tau_2}(x_1,x_2) = \int_{-\infty}^{\infty} p_{X,\tau_1,\tau_2,\tau_3}(x_1,x_2,\xi_3)d\xi_3$$
$$= \int_{-\infty}^{\infty} p_{X,\tau_1,\tau_2,\tau_3}(\xi_1,x_1,x_2)d\xi = p_{X,\tau_2,\tau_3}(x_1,x_2) \qquad (3\text{–}115)$$

In other words, if it is possible to derive a particular lower-order probability density in two (or more) ways from a given higher-order probability density, the result must be the same in all cases.

As a concrete illustration of these ideas, let us investigate whether the function defined by $(a > 0,\ b > 0)$

$$p(x,y) = \begin{cases} \dfrac{1}{ab}, & |x| \leq \dfrac{a}{2} \text{ and } |y| \leq \dfrac{b}{2} \\ 0, & \text{otherwise} \end{cases} \qquad (3\text{–}116)$$

satisfies the *necessary* conditions for being the second-order probability density function of a time function X for two prescribed time increments τ_1 and τ_2. We begin by noting that $p(x,y) \geq 0$ and that

$$\iint_{-\infty}^{\infty} p(\xi,\eta)d\xi d\eta = \frac{1}{ab}\cdot a \cdot b = 1$$

Next, we calculate the derived first-order densities (sometimes called marginal densities)

$$p_1(x) = \int_{-\infty}^{\infty} p(x,\eta)d\eta = \begin{cases} \dfrac{1}{a}, & |x| \leq \dfrac{a}{2} \\ 0, & \text{otherwise} \end{cases} \qquad (3\text{–}117)$$

$$p_2(y) = \int_{-\infty}^{\infty} p(\xi,y)d\xi = \begin{cases} \dfrac{1}{b}, & |y| \leq \dfrac{b}{2} \\ 0, & \text{otherwise} \end{cases} \qquad (3\text{–}118)$$

However, $p_1(x)$ must equal $p_2(x)$ if $p(x,y)$ is to be probability density function p_{X,τ_2,τ_2} and we conclude that this will be the case only if $a = b$. On the other hand, if $a \neq b$, $p(x,y)$ still satisfies all the *necessary* conditions for being the probability density $p_{X,\tau_1;Y,\tau_1'}$ of two *different* time functions X and Y at two prescribed time increments τ_1 and τ_1'.

At this point in the development of the theory of (stationary) random processes, we encounter what appears to be the only major difficulty with the (time-average) method of approach we have chosen. The crux of this difficulty is the fact that necessary *and sufficient* conditions to guarantee that a given collection of functions will be a set of joint probability density functions do not seem to be known. In other words, if we construct a set of joint probability density functions according to the rules set forth above, we have no way of knowing, *in general*, whether we are dealing with a vacuous situation —one in which there is no time-function having the assigned joint probability density functions.

This would be an untenable position were it not for the fact that in a number of important, special cases it is possible, using the tools of ergodic theory or some *ad hoc* technique, to establish the existence of time functions having the specified joint probability density functions. There arguments are far from simple and will not be entered into here. It should be noted, however, that the Kolmogorov theory [26] does not eliminate this existence question, but rather postpones it until a later point in the argument. In either theory, the question of whether the mathematical objects being studied are indeed time averages must be faced sooner or later.[27]

In the sequel, we shall pay no further attention to the issue just discussed and proceed, in effect, as though our necessary conditions were also sufficient. In all of our specific examples (barring certain degenerate cases) the author believes this to be the case although no attempt will be made to prove this fact. All other general theorems should be mentally prefaced with the proviso: if there exists a time function having the probability density functions or other averages required below, then it follows that...

3.8. The Multidimensional Theorem of Averages and Some of its Applications.—The multidimensional theorem of averages is a straightforward generalization of equation (3–33), and states that for "any" function ϕ of $n + m$-real variables

$$\lim_{T\to\infty} \frac{1}{2T} \int_{-T}^{T} \phi[X(t + \bar{\tau}_n), X(t + \bar{\tau}'_m)]dt$$

$$= \iint_{-\infty}^{\infty} \phi(\bar{\xi}_n, \bar{\eta}_m) p_{X,\bar{\tau}_n;Y,\bar{\tau}'_m}(\bar{\xi}_n, \bar{\eta}_m) d\bar{\xi}_n d\bar{\eta}_m \qquad (3\text{–}119)$$

[26] A. N. Kolmogorov, *Foundations of Probability Theory*, Chelsea Publishing Co., New York, 1956.

[27] There is a school of mathematicians who are willing to assign meaning to the averages appearing in the Kolmogorov theory even when they are not necessarily related to time averages. This is not the viewpoint of this chapter.

The justification of Eq. (3–119) is similar in every respect to the one presented in the one-dimensional case. One first verifies, by direct calculation, that Eq. (3–119) is valid for $n + m$ dimensional "staircase" functions—functions that are constant over $n + m$-dimensional intervals of the form $\bar{a}_n < \bar{x}_n \leq \bar{b}_n$, $\bar{c}_m < \bar{y}_m \leq \bar{d}_m$—and then argues that, since "any" function ϕ can be approximated as closely as desired by "staircase" functions, Eq. (3–119) must also hold for "all" ϕ.

One application of (3–119) is the calculation of the probabilities of events. The probability of the event $\{[X(t + \bar{\tau}_n), Y(t + \bar{\tau}'_m)] \text{ in } A\}$, where A denotes some set of points in $n + m$-dimensional space, is defined to be the fraction of the time that the $n + m$-dimensional vector $[X(t + \bar{\tau}_n), Y(t + \bar{\tau}'_m)]$ lies in the set A. If we define the function C_A as follows,

$$C_A(\bar{x}_n,\bar{y}_m) = \begin{cases} 1, & [\bar{x}_n,\bar{y}_m] \text{ in } A \\ 0, & \text{otherwise,} \end{cases} \tag{3–120}$$

we see that

$$\begin{aligned} P\{[X(t + \bar{\tau}_m), Y(t + \bar{\tau}'_m)] \text{ in } A\} \\ &= \lim_{T\to\infty} \frac{1}{2T} \int_{-T}^{T} C_A[X(t + \bar{\tau}_n), Y(t + \bar{\tau}'_m)]dt \\ &= \iint_{-\infty}^{\infty} C_A(\bar{\xi}_n,\bar{\eta}_m) p_{X,\bar{\tau}_n;Y,\bar{\tau}'_m}(\bar{\xi}_n,\bar{\eta}_m) d\bar{\xi}_n d\bar{\eta}_m \\ &= \iint_A p_{X,\bar{\tau}_n;Y,\bar{\tau}'_m}(\bar{\xi}_n,\bar{\eta}_m) d\bar{\xi}_n d\bar{\eta}_m \end{aligned} \tag{3–121}$$

where, as usual, the symbol $\int\int_A$ is used to denote integration over the set A. Equation (3–131) is the justification for calling the function $p_{X,\bar{\tau}_n;Y,\bar{\tau}'_m}$ a probability density function—the probability of the event $\{[X(t + \bar{\tau}_n), Y(t + \bar{\tau}'_m)] \text{ in } A\}$ is obtained by integrating $p_{X,\bar{\tau}_n;Y,\bar{\tau}'_m}$ over the set A.

The notions of random variable and mathematical expectation also carry over to the multidimensional case. A function ϕ of $n + m$-real variables is called a random variable when it is used to generate a new time function $Z(t)$ from the time functions $X(t)$ and $Y(t)$ by means of the equation

$$Z(t) = \phi[X(t + \tau_1),\cdots,X(t + \tau_n), Y(t + \tau'_1),\cdots,Y(t + \tau'_m)] \tag{3–122}$$

It should be carefully noted that a *random variable* ϕ is only unambiguously defined when the time increments $\bar{\tau}_n$ and $\bar{\tau}'_m$ are specified in addition to the function ϕ. Only then can we generate a unique time function $Z(t)$ from a pair of time functions $X(t)$ and $Y(t)$ by means of (3–122).

The mathematical expectation of a random variable ϕ is denoted by $E[\phi]$ and defined by

$$E[\phi] = \iint\limits_{-\infty}^{\infty} \phi(\bar{\xi}_n,\bar{\eta}_m) p_{X,\bar{\tau}_n;Y,\bar{\tau}'_m}(\bar{\xi}_n,\bar{\eta}_m) d\bar{\xi}_n d\bar{\eta}_m \tag{3–123}$$

The expectation symbol E obeys the same rules of manipulation, Eq. (3–40), as in the one-dimensional case. The only additional comment needed here is that the addition rule holds even when the two random variables concerned are defined with respect to different sets of τ's. The proof of this fact is immediate when the various expectations involved are written as time averages.

The multidimensional theorem of averages can be used to calculate the higher-order joint distribution functions of derived sets of time functions, each of which is of the form

$$Z(t) = \phi[X(t + \bar{\tau}_n), Y(t + \bar{\tau}'_m)] \tag{3–124}$$

in terms of higher-order joint distribution functions of $X(t)$ and $Y(t)$. In order to avoid notational complexities, we shall illustrate this procedure by means of some simple examples. Suppose that the function $Z(t)$ is derived from two functions $X(t)$ and $Y(t)$ by means of the formula

$$\begin{aligned} Z(t) &= X(t + \tau) + Y(t + \tau') \\ &= \phi[X(t + \tau), Y(t + \tau')] \end{aligned} \tag{3–125}$$

where

$$\phi(x,y) = x + y \tag{3–126}$$

Now by definition

$$\begin{aligned} F_Z(z) &= \lim_{T\to\infty} \frac{1}{2T} \int_{-T}^{T} C_z[Z(t)]dt \\ &= \lim_{T\to\infty} \frac{1}{2T} \int_{-T}^{T} C_z\{\phi[X(t + \tau), Y(t + \tau')]\}dt \\ &= \iint\limits_{-\infty}^{\infty} C_z[\phi(\xi,\eta)] p_{X,\tau;Y,\tau'}(\xi,\eta) d\xi d\eta \\ &= \iint\limits_{-\infty}^{\infty} C_z(\xi + \eta) p_{X,\tau;Y,\tau'}(\xi,\eta) d\xi d\eta \end{aligned} \tag{3–127}$$

We now make the change of variable $\zeta = \xi + \eta$ in the last integral to obtain the result

$$F_Z(z) = \iint_{-\infty}^{\infty} C_z(\zeta) p_{X,\tau;Y,\tau'}(\xi,\zeta - \xi) d\xi d\zeta$$
$$= \int_{-\infty}^{z} \left[\int_{-\infty}^{\infty} p_{X,\tau;Y,\tau'}(\xi,\zeta - \xi) d\xi \right] d\zeta \qquad (3\text{–}128)$$

Differentiation of both sides of Eq. (3–128) now yields the final result

$$p_Z(z) = \int_{-\infty}^{\infty} p_{X,\tau;Y,\tau'}(\xi, z - \xi) d\xi \qquad (3\text{–}129)$$

which relates the first-order distribution function of $Z(t)$ to a second-order joint distribution function of $X(t)$ and $Y(t)$. An important special case of Eq. (3–129) arises[28] when $p_{X,\tau;Y,\tau'}(x,y) = p_X(x)p_Y(y)$ and then p_Z is the convolution of p_X with p_Y

$$p_Z(z) = \int_{-\infty}^{\infty} p_X(\xi) p_Y(z - \xi) d\xi \qquad (3\text{–}130)$$

The significance of this result will be made clear in Section 3.11.

Another instructive example concerns the joint distribution function of the pair of time functions $Z_1(t)$ and $Z_2(t)$ defined by

$$\left. \begin{aligned} Z_1(t) &= aX(t + \tau) + bY(t + \tau') \\ Z_2(t) &= eX(t + \tau) + fY(t + \tau') \end{aligned} \right\} \qquad (3\text{–}131)$$

where a, b, e, f are constants.

Proceeding from the definition of $F_{Z_{1,0};Z_{2,0}}(z_1,z_2)$, we obtain[29]

$$\begin{aligned} F_{Z_1,Z_2}(z_1,z_2) &= \lim_{T\to\infty} \frac{1}{2T} \int_{-T}^{T} C_{z_1,z_2}[Z_1(t), Z_2(t)] dt \\ &= \lim_{T\to\infty} \frac{1}{2T} \int_{-T}^{T} C_{z_1,z_2}[aX(t+\tau) + bY(t+\tau'), \\ &\qquad\qquad eX(t+\tau) + fY(t+\tau')] dt \\ &= \iint_{-\infty}^{\infty} C_{z_1,z_2}(a\xi + b\eta, e\xi + f\eta) p_{X,\tau;Y,\tau'}(\xi,\eta) d\xi d\eta \end{aligned} \qquad (3\text{–}132)$$

[28] When this relationship holds, $X(t + \tau)$ and $Y(t + \tau')$ are said to be statistically independent. Statistical independence will be discussed in detail in Section 3.10.

[29] We shall use the shorthand F_{Z_1,Z_2} for $F_{Z_{1,0};Z_{2,0}}$ in this and future discussions.

We now make the two-dimensional change of variable $\zeta_1 = a\xi + b\eta$, $\zeta_2 = e\xi + f\eta$ in the double integral above. The jacobian of this transformation is

$$J = \begin{vmatrix} a & b \\ e & f \end{vmatrix} = af - be \tag{3-133}$$

and, assuming that $J \neq 0$, the double integral becomes

$$F_{Z_1,Z_2}(z_1,z_2) = |J|^{-1} \iint_{-\infty}^{\infty} C_{z_1,z_2}(\zeta_1,\zeta_2) p_{X,\tau;Y,\tau'} \left(\frac{f\zeta_1 - b\zeta_2}{J}, \frac{-e\zeta_1 + a\zeta_2}{J}\right) d\zeta_1 d\zeta_1 \tag{3-134}$$

$$= |J|^{-1} \int_{-\infty}^{z_1} \int_{-\infty}^{z_2} p_{X,\tau;Y,\tau'} \left(\frac{f\zeta_1 - b\zeta_2}{J}, \frac{-e\zeta_1 + a\zeta_2}{J}\right) d\zeta_1 d\zeta_2$$

Differentiation with respect to z_1 and z_2 now yields the final result

$$p_{Z_1,Z_2}(z_1,z_2) = |J|^{-1} p_{X,\tau;Y,\tau'} \left(\frac{fz_1 - bz_2}{J}, \frac{-ez_1 + az_2}{J}\right) \tag{3-135}$$

Equation (3–135) is valid only when $J \neq 0$; the case $J = 0$ results in the degenerate situation where $Z_2 = \frac{e}{a} Z_1$ so that the joint probability density for Z_1 and Z_2 is given by

$$p_{Z_1Z_2}(z_1,z_2) = p_{Z_1}(z_1)\delta\left(z_2 - \frac{e}{a} z_1\right) \tag{3-136}$$

where p_{Z_1} is given by a formula similar to Eq. (3–129)

$$p_{Z_1}(z_1) = \frac{1}{|b|} \int_{-\infty}^{\infty} p_{X,\tau;Y,\tau'} \left(\xi, \frac{z_1 - a\xi}{b}\right) d\xi \tag{3-137}$$

We conclude this section by introducing some notation and terminology that are quite useful in discussions involving joint distribution functions. The distribution function F_ϕ of a random variable ϕ associated with time increments $\bar{\tau}_n \bar{\tau}'_m$ is defined to be the first-order distribution function of the derived time function $Z(t) = \phi[X(t + \bar{\tau}_n), Y(t + \bar{\tau}'_m)]$; thus, $F_\phi(z) = F_Z(z)$. This definition is a straightforward generalization of our earlier definition of the distribution function of a one-dimensional random variable. More generally, given a family of random variables $\phi_1,\cdots,\phi_k$ associated with time increments $\bar{\tau}_{n_1},\bar{\tau}'_{m_1},\cdots,$ $\bar{\tau}_{n_k},\bar{\tau}'_{m_k}$ respectively, we define the joint distribution function $F_{\phi_1,\cdots,\phi_k}$ of the random variables $\phi_1,\cdots,\phi_k$ to be the joint distribution function of the derived time functions, $Z_1(t) = \phi_1[X(t + \bar{\tau}_{n_1}), Y(t + \bar{\tau}'_{m_1})],\cdots,$ $Z_k(t) = \phi_k[X(t + \bar{\tau}_{nk}), Y(t + \bar{\tau}'_{m_k})]$; in symbols

$$F_{\phi_1,\cdots,\phi_k}(z_1,\cdots,z_k) = F_{Z_1,\cdots,Z_k}(z_1,\cdots,z_k) = \lim_{T\to\infty} \frac{1}{2T}\int_{-T}^{T} C_{z_1,\cdots,z_k}[Z_1(t),\cdots,Z_k(t)]dt \quad (3\text{–}138)$$

A few minutes thought should convince the reader that all our previous results can be couched in the language of families of random variables and their joint distribution functions. Thus, the second-order distribution function F_{X,τ_1,τ_2} is the same as the joint distribution function of the random variables ϕ_1 and ϕ_2 defined by

$$\left.\begin{aligned} Z_1(t) &= \phi_1[X(t + \tau_1)];\ \phi_1(x) = x \\ Z_2(t) &= \phi_2[X(t + \tau_1)];\ \phi_2(x) = x \end{aligned}\right\} \quad (3\text{–}139)$$

because, by definition, F_{ϕ_1,ϕ_2} is the joint distribution function of

$$Z_1(t) = \phi_1[X(t + \tau_1)] = X(t + \tau_1)$$

and

$$Z_2(t) = \phi_2[X(t + \tau_2)] = X(t + \tau_2)$$

In this connection, we shall often abuse our notation somewhat by referring to F_{X,τ_1,τ_2} as the joint distribution function of the random variables $X(t + \tau_1)$ and $X(t + \tau_2)$ instead of employing the more precise but cumbersome language used at the beginning of this paragraph. In the same vein, the distribution function $F_{X,\bar{\tau}_n;Y,\bar{\tau}'_m}$ will be referred to loosely as the joint distribution function of the random variables $X(t + \tau_1),\cdots,X(t + \tau_n)$, $Y(t + \tau'_1),\cdots,Y(t + \tau'_m)$.

Once again, it should be emphasized that the functional form of a set of random variables is important only insofar as it enables us to calculate their joint distribution function in terms of other known distribution functions. Once the joint distribution function of a group of random variables is known, no further reference to their functional form is necessary in order to use the theorem of averages for the calculation of any time average of interest in connection with the given random variables.

We conclude this section with some remarks concerning complex-valued random variables. A complex-valued random variable can always be written in the form $\phi = \phi_r + i\phi_i$ where ϕ_r and ϕ_i are real-valued random variables. This means that all averages involving ϕ

can be determined once the joint distribution function F_{ϕ_r,ϕ_i} of ϕ_r and ϕ_i is known. The theory of complex-valued random variables is thus contained in the theory of families of real-valued random variables that we have already established, and requires no further comment.

3.9. Joint Moments and Characteristic Functions.—The *joint moments* $\alpha_{k_1,\cdots,k_n}$ of a family of n random variables $\phi_1,\cdots,\phi_m$ are defined by the expression

$$\begin{aligned}\alpha_{k_1,\cdots,k_n} &= E[\phi_1^{k_1}\phi_2^{k_2}\cdots\phi_n^{k_n}] \\ &= \int_{-\infty}^{\infty}\cdots\int_{-\infty}^{\infty}\xi_1^{k_1}\cdots\xi_n^{k_n}p_{\phi_1,\cdots,\phi_n}(\xi_1,\cdots,\xi_n)d\xi_1\cdots d\xi_n\end{aligned} \tag{3-140}$$

where the k_1's denote non-negative integers.

Similarly, we define *joint central moments* $\mu_{k_1,\cdots,k_n}$ by means of the expression

$$\mu_{k_1,\cdots,k_n} = E\{[\phi_1 - m_1]^{k_1}[\phi_2 - m_2]^{k_2}\cdots[\phi_n - m_n]^{k_n}\} \tag{3-141}$$

where

$$m_j = E[\phi_j] \tag{3-142}$$

The physical interpretation of these joint moments is similar in every respect to the interpretation already given for moments of the form $\alpha_k = E[\phi^k]$. Thus, $\alpha_{1,1,\cdots,1}$ provides a measure of the "center of mass" of the joint probability density function $p_{\phi_1,\cdots,\phi_n}$ and the second order central moments provide a measure of the spread of this density function about its center of mass.[30]

Perhaps the most widely studied joint moments are the second-order moments—those for which $k_1 + k_2 + \cdots + k_n = 2$. These moments are all of the form $E[\phi_i^k\phi_j^{2-k}]$; $k = 0,1,2$; $i,j = 1,\cdots,n$. The corresponding central moments are often called covariances and are of the form $E\{[\phi_i - m_i]^k[\phi_j - m_j]^{2-k}\}$.

As an example of the usefulness of second moments, recall the prediction problem discussed at the beginning of Section 3.7, in which it was found that the minimum value of the quantity

$$\varepsilon = E[X(t + \tau) - aX(t) - b]^2 \tag{3-143}$$

occurred when

$$\left.\begin{aligned}a &= \frac{E\{[X(t) - m_X][X(t + \tau) - m_X]\}}{\sigma_X^2} \\ b &= m_X(1 - a)\end{aligned}\right\} \tag{3-144}$$

[30] For further details, see H. Cramer, *Mathematical Methods of Statistics*, Princeton University Press, 1954.

In other words, the solution to our prediction is completely determined by m_X, σ_X^2 and the joint second central moment of $X(t)$ and $X(t + \tau)$.

The set of all possible joint second moments $E[X(t)X(t + \tau)]$, $-\infty < \tau < +\infty$, plays an important role in many investigations and is often referred to as the autocorrelation function $R_X(\tau)$ of the time function $X(t)$

$$R_X(\tau) = E[X(t)X(t + \tau)] \tag{3–145}$$

The set of *central* second moments is related to the autocorrelation function by means of the following simple formula,

$$E\{[X(t) - m_X][X(t + \tau) - m_X]\} = R_X(\tau) - m_X^2 \tag{3–146}$$

Since central second moments are called covariances, the function appearing on the left-hand side of Eq. (3–146) is called the autocovariance function of $X(t)$. Autocorrelation functions will be studied in more detail in Sections 3.14 and 3.15.

It is quite a simple matter to generalize the simple prediction problem just discussed to the situation where we want to obtain the best (in the sense of minimum mean square error) linear estimate of one random variable ϕ_2 given the value of another random variable ϕ_1. The quantity to be minimized is thus

$$\varepsilon = E[\phi_2 - a\phi_1 - b]^2 \tag{3–147}$$

and the solution is

$$\left.\begin{aligned} a &= \frac{E\{[\phi_1 - m_{\phi_1}][\phi_2 - m_{\phi_2}]\}}{\sigma_{\phi_1}^2} \\ b &= m_{\phi_2} - am_{\phi_1} \end{aligned}\right\} \tag{3–148}$$

The corresponding minimum ε is given by

$$\varepsilon_{min} = \sigma_{\phi_2}^2 - \left[\frac{E\{[\phi_1 - m_{\phi_1}][\phi_2 - m_{\phi_2}]\}}{\sigma_{\phi_1}}\right]^2 \tag{3–149}$$

A pair of random variables that satisfy the relation

$$E[\phi_1\phi_2] = E[\phi_1]E[\phi_2] \tag{3–150}$$

are called *uncorrelated* or *linearly independent* random variables. The reason for this terminology is that in this case, $a = 0$ which means that our prediction does not make any use of the known value of ϕ_1. In other words, as far as making a *linear* prediction of ϕ_2 is concerned, knowledge of the value of ϕ_1 is of no help. This does not mean that ϕ_1 and ϕ_2 cannot be related in a *nonlinear* way. For example, let

$\phi_2 - m_1 = [\phi_1 - m_1]^2$ ($m_1 = m_{\phi_1}$ and $m_2 = m_{\phi_2}$) and assume that the probability density function of ϕ_1 is symmetric about its mean; *i.e.*

$$p_{\phi_1 - m_1}(x) = p_{\phi_1 - m_1}(-x) \tag{3-151}$$

It then follows that

$$E\{[\phi_1 - m_1][\phi_2 - m_2]\} = E[\phi_1 - m_1]^3 = \int_{-\infty}^{\infty} \xi^3 \, p_{\phi_1 - m_1}(\xi) d\xi = 0 \tag{3-152}$$

Thus ϕ_1 and ϕ_2 are uncorrelated even though a functional relationship exists between them.

Another interesting special case occurs when $E[\phi_1 - m_1][\phi_2 - m_2] = \pm \sigma_{\phi_1}\sigma_{\phi_2}$. Such random variables are sometimes called *completely correlated* because, in this case, $\varepsilon_{min} = 0$. This means that $(\pm \sigma_{\phi_2}/\sigma_{\phi_1})(\phi_1 - m_1) = \phi_2 - \overline{m}_2$ *with probability one*, *i.e.*, the fraction of the time that $(\pm \sigma_{\phi_2}/\sigma_{\phi_1})(\phi_1[X(t), Y(t)] - m_1) \neq \phi_2[X(t), Y(t)] - m_2$ in the time interval $[-T, T]$ goes to zero as $T \to \infty$.

The joint characteristic function $M_{\phi_1 \cdots \phi_n}(jv_1, \cdots, jv_n)$ of a family of n random variables $\phi_1, \cdots, \phi_n$ is defined by the expression

$$\begin{aligned} M_{\phi_1 \cdots \phi_n}(iv_1, \cdots, iv_n) &= E[e^{i[v_1\phi_1 + \cdots + v_n\phi_n]}] \\ &= \int_{-\infty}^{\infty} \cdots \int_{-\infty}^{\infty} e^{i[v_1\xi_1 + \cdots + v_n\xi_n]} \\ &\quad \times p_{\phi_1, \cdots, \phi_m}(\xi_1, \cdots, \xi_n) d\xi_1, \cdots, d\xi_n \end{aligned} \tag{3-153}$$

The joint characteristic function is thus seen to be the n-dimensional Fourier transform of the joint probability density function $p_{\phi_1, \cdots, \phi_n}$. The n-dimensional Fourier transform, like its one-dimensional counterpart, can be inverted by means of the formula

$$\begin{aligned} &p_{\phi_1, \cdots, \phi_n}(x_1, \cdots, x_n) \\ &= \frac{1}{(2\pi)^n} \int_{-\infty}^{\infty} \cdots \int_{-\infty}^{\infty} M_{\phi_1, \cdots, \phi_n}(iv_1, \cdots, iv_n) e^{-i[v_1x_1 + \cdots + v_nx_n]} dv_1 \cdots dv_n \end{aligned} \tag{3-154}$$

In other words, knowledge of the joint characteristic function of a family of random variables is tantamount to knowledge of their joint probability density function and vice versa.

The joint characteristic function is related to the characteristic functions of the individual random variables by means of the formula

$$M_{\phi_k}(iv) = M_{\phi_1, \cdots, \phi_n}(iv_1, \cdots, iv_n) \big|_{v_j = 0, j \neq k; v_k = v} \tag{3-155}$$

One of the uses of the joint characteristic function is in the calculation of joint moments. In order to simplify the notation, we shall only illustrate how this can be accomplished in the case of a two-dimensional characteristic function

$$M_{\phi_1,\phi_2}(iv_1,iv_2) = E[e^{i[v_1\phi_1+v_2\phi_2]}] \tag{3-156}$$

It we now expand the exponential in a power series, we obtain the following expansion which places the various joint moments of ϕ_1 and ϕ_2 in evidence

$$\begin{aligned} M_{\phi_1,\phi_2}(iv_1,iv_2) &= E\left[\sum_{k=0}^{\infty} \frac{i^k[v_1\phi_1 + v_2\phi_2]^k}{k!}\right] \\ &= \sum_{k=0}^{\infty} \frac{i^k}{k!} E[v_1\phi_1 + v_2\phi_2]^k \\ &= 1 + i[v_1E(\phi_1) + v_2E(\phi_2)] \\ &\quad - \tfrac{1}{2}[v_1^2E(\phi_1^2) + 2v_1v_2E(\phi_1\phi_2) + v_2^2E(\phi_2^2)] + \cdots \end{aligned} \tag{3-157}$$

The following formulas for the joint moments of ϕ_1 and ϕ_2 now follow at once from Eq. (3–157):

$$\left.\begin{aligned} E[\phi_1] &= \frac{1}{i}\frac{\partial M_{\varphi_1\varphi_2}}{\partial v_1}\bigg|_{v_1=v_2=0} \\ E[\phi_2] &= \frac{1}{i}\frac{\partial M_{\varphi_1\varphi_2}}{\partial v_2}\bigg|_{v_1=v_2=0} \\ E[\phi_1^2] &= -\frac{\partial^2 M_{\varphi_1\varphi_2}}{\partial v_1^2}\bigg|_{v_1=v_2=0} \\ E[\phi_1\phi_2] &= -\frac{\partial^2 M_{\varphi_1\varphi_2}}{\partial v_1\partial v_2}\bigg|_{v_1=v_2=0} \\ E[\phi_2^2] &= -\frac{\partial^2 M_{\varphi_1\varphi_2}}{\partial v_2^2}\bigg|_{v_1=v_2=0} \\ E[\phi^3] &= -\frac{1}{i}\frac{\partial^3 M_{\varphi_1\varphi_2}}{\partial v_1^3}\bigg|_{v_1=v_2=0} \\ &\vdots \end{aligned}\right\} \tag{3-158}$$ [31]

Further, and considerably more important, applications of joint characteristic functions will be given in later sections.

3.10. Conditional Distribution Functions and Statistical Independence.

—The definition of a conditional distribution function is motivated by the following considerations. Suppose that we have been observing a time function X and that we want to obtain a quanti-

[31] The derivation of this equation has been purely formal. A careful argument shows that (3–158) is valid as long as either side is finite.

tative measure of the extent to which the value of X at time t influences the value X assumes at time $t + \tau$. One, quite natural, way to do this is to compare the fraction of the time $X(t + \tau)$ lies in the interval $a < X(t + \tau) \leq b$ with the fraction of the time $a < X(t + \tau) \leq b$ *in that segment of the time axis for which* $X(t)$ *lies in the interval* $c < X(t) \leq d$. In other words, we throw away that part of the time axis for which $X(t) \leq c$ or $X(t) > d$, and calculate the fraction of the *remaining* time that $a < X(t + \tau) \leq b$. If this quantity is the same as the fraction of the time that $a < X(t + \tau) \leq b$ on the entire time axis, we have a good indication that, on the average, the occurrence of a value of $X(t)$ in the interval $c < X(t) \leq d$ does not affect the chances that $X(t + \tau)$ will lie in the interval $a < X(t + \tau) \leq b$. Exactly the reverse conclusion holds if these two quantities are substantially different and the magnitude of the difference gives us a measure of how strongly the occurrence of a value of $X(t)$ in the interval $c < X(t) \leq d$ influences the occurrence of values of $X(t + \tau)$ in the interval $a < X(t + \tau) \leq b$.

The quantities mentioned above all can be calculated in terms of the probabilities of certain events. First of all, we note that, for large values of T, the quantity $2TP\{c < X(t) \leq d\}$ is asymptotically equal to the total length of time in the interval $[-T,T]$ that $X(t)$ lies in the interval $c < X(t) \leq d$. Similarly, the quantity $2TP\{c < X(t) \leq d$ and $a < X(t + \tau) \leq b\}$ is asymptotically equal to the total length of time in the interval $[-T,T]$ that $X(t)$ is in the interval $c < X(t) \leq d$ and, simultaneously, $X(t + \tau)$ is in the interval $a < X(t + \tau) \leq b$. It follows that the ratio, $2T \cdot P\{c < X(t) \leq d$ and $a < X(t + \tau) \leq b\}/2T \cdot P\{c < X(t) \leq d\}$, is asymptotically equal to the fraction of the time that $a < X(t + \tau) \leq b$ measured in that part of the time axis where, simultaneously, $c < X(t) \leq b$. This quantity is denoted $P\{a < X(t + \tau) \leq b \mid c < X(t) \leq d\}$ and is called the *conditional* probability of the event $\{a < X(t + \tau) \leq b\}$ given that the event $\{c < X(t) \leq d\}$ has occurred. The discussion above shows that this conditional probability can be calculated by means of the formula

$$P\{a < X(t + \tau) \leq b \mid c < X(t) \leq d\} = \frac{P\{a < X(t + \tau) \leq b \text{ and } c < X(t) \leq d\}}{P\{c < X(t) \leq d\}} \quad (3\text{–}159)$$

or, equivalently, in terms of the joint probability density for $X(t)$ and $X(t + \tau)$ by means of the formula [32]

[32] Unless otherwise specified, the denominator of this and similar formulas will be assumed nonzero.

$$P\{a < X(t + \tau) \leq b \,|\, c < X(t) \leq d\} = \frac{\int_c^d \int_a^b p_{X,0,\tau}(\xi_1,\xi_2) d\xi_1 d\xi_2}{\int_c^d \int_{-\infty}^{\infty} p_{X,0,\tau}(\xi_1,\xi_2) d\xi_1 d\xi_2} \quad (3\text{–}160)$$

The notion of a conditional probability can be extended to more general events than the simple intervals discussed above as follows. Let $\phi_1,\cdots,\phi_n, \phi_{n+1},\cdots,\phi_{n+m}$ denote any $n + m$ random variables and let A_n and B_m denote arbitrary sets of points in n and m-dimensional space respectively. We define the conditional probability of the event $\{[\phi_1,\cdots,\phi_n]$ in $A_n\}$[33] given that the event $\{[\phi_{n+1},\cdots,\phi_{n+m}]$ in $B_m\}$ has occurred by means of the formula

$$P\{[\phi_1,\cdots,\phi_n] \text{ in } A_n \,|\, [\phi_{n+1},\cdots,\phi_{n+m}] \text{ in } B_m\} = \frac{P\{[\phi_1,\cdots,\phi_n] \text{ in } A_n \text{ and } [\phi_{n+1},\cdots,\phi_{n+m}] \text{ in } B_m\}}{P\{[\phi_{n+1},\cdots,\phi_{n+m}] \text{ in } B_m\}} \quad (3\text{–}161)$$

This conditional probability can also be written in terms of the joint probability density function for $\phi_1,\cdots,\phi_{n+m}$ as follows:

$$P\{[\phi_1,\cdots,\phi_n] \text{ in } A_n \,|\, [\phi_{n+1},\cdots,\phi_{n+m}] \text{ in } B_m\} = \frac{\int_{A_n}\int_{B_m} p_{\phi_{n+m}}(\xi_1,\cdots,\xi_n,\xi_{n+1},\cdots,\xi_{n+m}) d\xi_1 \cdots d\xi_n d\xi_{n+1} \cdots d\xi_{n+m}}{\int_{-\infty}^{\infty}\int_{B_m} p_{\phi_{n+m}}(\xi_1,\cdots\xi_n, \xi_{n+1},\cdots\xi_{n+m}) d\xi_1 \cdots d\xi_n d\xi_{n+1} \cdots d\xi_{n+m}} \quad (3\text{–}162)$$[34]

The reader should experience little difficulty in supplying the physical interpretation of this, more general, conditional probability.

A very useful relationship, often called Bayes' rule, exists between the two conditional probabilities $P\{\bar{\phi}_n \text{ in } A_n \,|\, \bar{\phi}_m \text{ in } B_m\}$ and $P\{\bar{\phi}_m \text{ in } B_m \,|\, \bar{\phi}_n \text{ in } A_n\}$. It can be derived most easily by noting that the definition of conditional probability implies the relationships,

$$\begin{aligned} P\{\bar{\phi}_n \text{ in } A_n \,|\, \bar{\phi}_m \text{ in } B_m\} P\{\bar{\phi}_m \text{ in } B_m\} &= P\{\bar{\phi}_n \text{ in } A_n \text{ and } \bar{\phi}_m \text{ in } B_m\} \\ &= P\{\bar{\phi}_m \text{ in } B_m \,|\, \bar{\phi}_n \text{ in } A_n\} P\{\bar{\phi}_n \text{ in } A_n\} \end{aligned} \quad (3\text{–}163)$$

[33] To be precise, we should write this event as

$$\{\phi_1[X(t + \bar{\tau}_{m_1}), Y(t + \bar{\tau}'_{m_1})],\cdots, \phi_n[X(t + \bar{\tau}_{m_n}), Y(t + \bar{\tau}'_{m_n})] \text{ in } A_n\}$$

however, to simplify the notation, we will abbreviate this expression, here and elsewhere, by writing $\{[\phi_1,\ldots,\phi_n]$ in $A_n\}$.

[34] For simplicity we shall use the symbol $\bar{\phi}_n$ to denote a set of n random variables $[\phi_1\cdots,\phi_n]$ and the notation $\{\bar{\phi}_n$ in $B_n\}$ to mean the event $\{[\phi_1,\cdots,\phi_n]$ in $B_n\}$.

from which it is immediately obvious that

$$P\{\bar{\phi}_n \text{ in } A_n \mid \bar{\phi}_m \text{ in } B_m\} = \frac{P\{\bar{\phi}_m \text{ in } B_m \mid \bar{\phi}_n \text{ in } A_n\}P\{\bar{\phi}_n \text{ in } A_n\}}{P\{\bar{\phi}_m \text{ in } B_m\}} \tag{3–164}$$

Bayes' rule, Eq. (3–164), finds many applications in problems of statistical inference[35] and signal detection theory,[36] where the conditional probability on the right can be calculated directly in terms of the physical parameters of the problem, but where the quantity of real interest is the conditional probability on the left.

It is often important to be able to extend our present notion of conditional probability to the case where the conditioning event has probability zero. An example of such a situation arises when we observe a time function X and ask the question, given that the value of X at some instant is x, what is the probability that the value of X τ seconds in the future will be in the interval $[a,b]$? As long as the first order probability density of X does not have a Dirac delta function at point x, $P\{X(t) = x\} = 0$ and our present definition of conditional probability is inapplicable. (The reader should verify that the definition, Eq. (3–159), reduces to the indeterminate form $\frac{0}{0}$ in this case.)

The conditional probability distribution function of the random variables $\phi_1,\cdots,\phi_n$ given that the random variables $\phi_1,\cdots,\phi_{n+m}$ have assumed the values $x_{n+1},\cdots,x_{n+m}$ respectively, can be defined, in most cases of interest to us, by means of the following procedure. To simplify the discussion, we shall only present the details of the derivation for the case of two random variables ϕ_1 and ϕ_2. We begin by using the definition, Eq. (3–159), to write

$$\begin{aligned} P\{\phi_1 \le x_1 \mid x_2 < \phi_2 \le x_2 + \Delta x\} &= \frac{\int_{-\infty}^{x_1}\int_{x_2}^{x_2+\Delta x} p_{\phi_1,\phi_2}(\xi_1,\xi_2)\,d\xi_1 d\xi_2}{\int_{-\infty}^{\infty}\int_{x_2}^{x_2+\Delta x} p_{\phi_1,\phi_2}(\xi_1,\xi_2)\,d\xi_1 d\xi_2} \\ &= \frac{\int_{-\infty}^{x_1}\int_{x_2}^{x_2+\Delta x} p_{\phi_1,\phi_2}(\xi_1,\xi_2)\,d\xi_1 d\xi_2}{\int_{x_2}^{x_2+\Delta x} p_{\phi_2}(\xi_2)\,d\xi_2} \end{aligned} \tag{3–165}$$

[35] H. Chernoff, and L. E. Moses, *Elementary Decision Theory*, John Wiley and Sons, Inc., New York, 1959; H. Cramer, *Mathematical Methods of Statistics*, Princeton University Press, 1954.

[36] W. B. Davenport, Jr., and W. L. Root, *An Introduction to the Theory of Random Signals and Noise*, McGraw-Hill Book Co., New York, 1958; P. M. Woodward, *Probability and Information Theory with Applications to Radar*, Pergamon Press, New York, 1957.

Now, under certain smoothness conditions,[37] the denominator is asymptotically equal to $p_{\phi_2}(x_2)\Delta x$ as $\Delta x \to 0$ and the numerator is asymptotically equal to

$$\Delta x \int_{-\infty}^{x_1} p_{\phi_1,\phi_2}(\xi_1,x_2)d\xi_1$$

It follows that

$$\lim_{\Delta x \to \infty} P\{\phi_1 \le x_1 \mid x_2 < \phi_2 \le x_2 + \Delta x\} = \frac{\int_{-\infty}^{x_1} p_{\phi_1,\phi_2}(\xi_1,x_2)d\xi_1}{p_{\phi_2}(x_2)} \tag{3–166}$$

We shall now define the left-hand side of Eq. (3–166) to be the *conditional distribution* function for ϕ_1 given that ϕ_2 assumes the value x_2

$$P\{\phi_1 \le x_1 \mid \phi_2 = x_2\} = \frac{\int_{-\infty}^{x_1} p_{\phi_1,\phi_2}(\xi_1,x_2)d\xi_1}{p_{\phi_2}(x_2)} \tag{3–167}$$

The derivative of (3–167) with respect to x_1 is called the *conditional probability* density function for ϕ_1 given that $\phi_2 = x_2$ and is written

$$p_{\phi_1|\phi_2}(x_1|x_2) = \frac{\partial}{\partial x_1} P\{\phi_1 \le x_1|\phi_2 = x_2\} = \frac{p_{\phi_1,\phi_2}(x_1,x_2)}{p_{\phi_2}(x_2)} \tag{3–168}$$

Following a similar procedure, it can be shown that the conditional distribution function for $\phi_1,\cdots,\phi_n$ given that $\phi_{n+1} = x_{n+1},\cdots,$ $\phi_{n+m} = x_{n+m}$ is given by

$$F_{\phi_n|\phi_m}(\bar{x}_n|\bar{x}_m) = \frac{\int_{-\infty}^{\bar{x}_n} p_{\phi_n,\phi_m}(\bar{\xi}_n,\bar{x}_m)d\bar{\xi}_n}{p_{\phi_m}(\bar{x}_m)} \tag{3–169}$$

and the corresponding conditional probability density function by

$$p_{\phi_n|\phi_m}(\bar{x}_n|\bar{x}_m) = \frac{p_{\phi_n,\phi_m}(\bar{x}_n,\bar{x}_m)}{p_{\phi_m}(\bar{x}_m)} \tag{3–170}$$

The conditional probability density functions defined by Eq. (3–170) are joint probability density functions for fixed values of $\bar{x}_m$

$$\left.\begin{aligned} p_{\phi_n|\phi_m}(\bar{x}_n|\bar{x}_m) &\ge 0 \\ \int_{-\infty}^{\infty} p_{\phi_n|\phi_m}(\bar{\xi}_n|\bar{x}_m)d\bar{\xi}_n &= 1 \end{aligned}\right\} \tag{3–171}$$

[37] One of these conditions is, of course, that p_{ϕ_2} have no delta function at $x = x_2$.

Conditional probabilities of the form $P\{\bar{\phi}_n \text{ in } A_n \mid \bar{\phi}_m = \bar{x}_m\}$ can be calculated in terms of $p_{\phi_1|\phi_1}$ by means of the easily verified formula

$$P\{\bar{\phi}_n \text{ in } A_n \mid \bar{\phi}_m = \bar{x}_m\} = \int_{A_n} p_{\phi_n|\phi_m}(\bar{\xi}_n|\bar{x}_m)d\bar{\xi}_n \tag{3-172}$$

Finally, we note that the definition (3–170) implies that the two conditional densities $p_{\phi_n|\phi_m}$ and $p_{\phi_m|\phi_n}$ are related by the following form of Bayes' rule

$$p_{\phi_n|\phi_m}(\bar{x}_n|\bar{x}_m) = \frac{p_{\phi_m|\phi_n}(\bar{x}_m|\bar{x}_n)p_{\phi_n}(\bar{x}_n)}{p_{\phi_m}(\bar{x}_m)} \tag{3-173}$$

The discussion at the beginning of this section makes it natural for us to say that the event $\{\bar{\phi}_n \text{ in } A_n\}$ is *statistically independent* of the event $\{\bar{\phi}_m \text{ in } B_m\}$ if

$$P\{\bar{\phi}_n \text{ in } A_n \mid \bar{\phi}_m \text{ in } B_m\} = P\{\bar{\phi}_n \text{ in } A_n\} \tag{3-174}$$

When Eq. (3–174) does not hold, we shall say that the two events are *statistically dependent* and use the difference between the two sides of (3–174) as a measure of the degree to which the occurrence of the event $\{\bar{\phi}_m \text{ in } B_m\}$ affects the occurrence of the event $\{\bar{\phi}_n \text{ in } A_n\}$.

The present definition of statistical independence is somewhat inconvenient because it is asymmetric in the two events $\{\bar{\phi}_n \text{ in } A_n\}$ and $\{\bar{\phi}_m \text{ in } B_m\}$. This difficulty can be remedied by noting that, if $P\{\bar{\phi}_n \text{ in } A_n\} \neq 0$ and $P\{\bar{\phi}_m \text{ in } B_m\} \neq 0$, Eq. (3–174) is completely equivalent to the equation

$$P\{\bar{\phi}_n \text{ in } A_n \text{ and } \bar{\phi}_m \text{ in } B_m\} = P\{\bar{\phi}_n \text{ in } A_n\}\, P\{\bar{\phi}_m \text{ in } B_m\} \tag{3-175}$$

Moreover, Eq. (3–175) is automatically satisfied if either of the two events $\{\bar{\phi}_n \text{ in } A_n\}$ or $\{\bar{\phi}_m \text{ in } B_m\}$ has probability zero, which makes it convenient for us to replace our earlier definition of statistical independence, Eq. (3–174), by the new definition, Eq. (3–175).

In the light of the preceding discussion, it is tempting to extend the notion of statistical independence by calling a group of three or more events statistically independent if

$$\begin{aligned} P\{\bar{\phi}_n \text{ in } A_n \text{ and } \bar{\phi}_m \text{ in } B_m \text{ and } \bar{\phi}_p \text{ in } C_p \text{ and } \cdots\} \\ = P\{\bar{\phi}_n \text{ in } A_n\}P\{\bar{\phi}_m \text{ in } B_m\}P\{\bar{\phi}_p \text{ in } C_p\}\cdots \end{aligned} \tag{3-176}$$

However, such a definition soon leads to difficulties because it does not follow from Eq. (3–176) that, say

$$P\{\bar{\phi}_n \text{ in } A_n \text{ and } \bar{\phi}_m \text{ in } B_m\} = P\{\bar{\phi}_n \text{ in } A_n\}P\{\bar{\phi}_m \text{ in } B_m\}$$

In other words, the fact that a group of n events is statistically independent according to definition (3–176) does not necessarily imply that any smaller group of the same events is also statistically independent. This is a most embarrassing result and leads us to doubt that Eq. (3–176) is a definition of statistical independence that is in accord with our intuitive notion of independence. These considerations lead us to define a group of n events to be statistically independent if, and only if, *all* possible subgroups of these events satisfy Eq. (3–176). For example, the three events $\{\bar{\phi}_n \text{ in } A_n\}$, $\{\bar{\phi}_m \text{ in } B_m\}$, and $\{\bar{\phi}_p \text{ in } C_p\}$ are statistically independent if, and only if, all of the following equations are valid:

$$\left.\begin{aligned} P\{\bar{\phi}_n \text{ in } A_n \text{ and } \bar{\phi}_m \text{ in } B_m \text{ and } \bar{\phi}_p \text{ in } C_p\} \qquad & \\ = P\{\bar{\phi}_n \text{ in } A_n\}P\{\bar{\phi}_m \text{ in } B_m\}P\{\bar{\phi}_p \text{ in } C_p\} & \\ P\{\bar{\phi}_n \text{ in } A_n \text{ and } \bar{\phi}_m \text{ in } B_m\} = P\{\bar{\phi}_n \text{ in } A_n\}P\{\bar{\phi}_m \text{ in } B_m\} & \\ P\{\bar{\phi}_m \text{ in } B_m \text{ and } \bar{\phi}_p \text{ in } C_p\} = P\{\bar{\phi}_m \text{ in } B_m\}P\{\bar{\phi}_p \text{ in } C_p\} & \end{aligned}\right\} \qquad (3\text{–}177)$$

The same motivation that leads us to our definition of statistically independent events also leads us to call a set of n random variables $\phi_1,\cdots,\phi_n$ statistically independent if, and only if

$$p_{\phi_1,\cdots,\phi_n}(x_1,\cdots,x_n) = p_{\phi_1}(x_1)\cdots p_{\phi_n}(x_n) \qquad (3\text{–}178)$$

One important consequence of this definition is that if $\phi_1,\cdots,\phi_n$ are statistically independent random variables then *all* groups of events of the form $\{\phi_1 \text{ in } A_1\}$, $\{\phi_2 \text{ in } A_2\}$, $\cdots$, $\{\phi_n \text{ in } A_n\}$ are statistically independent.[38] This property greatly simplifies the calculation of probabilities of events associated with independent random variables.

Perhaps the most important property of statistically independent random variables is embodied in the following, easily verified, formula that is valid when $\phi_1,\cdots,\phi_n$ are statistically independent.[39]

$$E[\phi_1\phi_2\cdots\phi_n] = E[\phi_1]E[\phi_2]\cdots E[\phi_n] \qquad (3\text{–}179)$$

Equation (3–179) states the quite remarkable result that the expectation of a product of statistically independent random variables is equal to the product of their individual expectations.

In a similar fashion one can establish the following important result

$$M_{\phi_1,\cdots,\phi_n}(iv_1,\cdots,iv_n) = M_{\phi_1}(iv_1)\cdots M_{\phi_n}(iv_n) \qquad (3\text{–}180)$$

valid when $\phi_1,\cdots,\phi_n$ are statistically independent. Moreover, it is a simple matter to show that any family of random variables whose joint characteristic function factors as in Eq. (3–180) must be statistically independent. The details of this argument are

[38] The A_i's here are arbitrary sets of points on the real line.

[39] The converse of this statement is not true in general; random variables satisfying (3–179) need not be statistically independent.

$$
\begin{aligned}
p_{\phi_1,\ldots,\phi_n}(x_1,\cdots,x_n) &= \frac{1}{(2\pi)^n}\int_{-\infty}^{\infty}\cdots\int_{-\infty}^{\infty} M_{\phi_1,\ldots,\phi_n}(iv_1,\cdots,iv_n) \\
&\qquad \times e^{-i(v_1x_1+\cdots+v_nx_n)}dv_1\cdots dv_n \\
&= \frac{1}{(2\pi)^n}\int_{-\infty}^{\infty}\cdots\int_{-\infty}^{\infty} M_{\phi_1}(iv_1)\cdots M_{\phi_n}(iv_n)e^{-iv_1x_1}\cdots \\
&\qquad \times e^{-iv_nx_n}dv_1\cdots dv_n \\
&= \left[\frac{1}{2\pi}\int_{-\infty}^{\infty} M_{\phi_1}(iv_1)e^{-iv_1x_1}dv_1\right]\cdots \\
&\qquad \times \left[\frac{1}{2\pi}\int_{-\infty}^{\infty} M_{\phi_n}(iv_n)e^{-iv_nx_n}dv_n\right] \\
&= p_{\phi_1}(x_1)\cdots p_{\phi_n}(x_n) \qquad (3\text{–}181)
\end{aligned}
$$

3.11. Sums of Independent Random Variables.—Sums of statistically independent random variables play a very important role in the theory of random processes. The reason for this is twofold: sums of statistically independent random variables turn out to have some rather remarkable mathematical properties and, moreover, many physical quantities, such as thermal noise voltages or measurement fluctuations, can be usefully thought of as being sums of a large number of small, presumably independent quantities. Accordingly, this section will be devoted to a brief discussion of some of the more important properties of sums of independent random variables.

Let $\phi_1,\phi_2,\cdots$ denote an (infinite) family of statistically independent random variables[39a] and define

$$
s_n = \sum_{j=1}^{n} \phi_j \qquad (3\text{–}182)
$$

The mean and variance of the sum s_n are related to the means and variances of the summands by means of the formulas

$$
E[s_n] = E\left[\sum_{j=1}^{n}\phi_i\right] = \sum_{j=1}^{n} E[\phi_j] = \sum_{j=1}^{n} m_j\ {}^{40} \qquad (3\text{–}183)
$$

$$
\begin{aligned}
E\left[s_n - \sum_{j=1}^{m} m_j\right]^2 &= E\left[\sum_{j=1}^{n}(\phi_j - m_j)\right]^2 = \sum_{j,k=1}^{n} E[(\phi_j - m_j)(\phi_k - m_k)] \\
&= \sum_{j=1}^{n} E[(\phi_j - m_j)^2] + \sum_{\substack{j,k=1 \\ j\neq k}}^{n} E[\phi_j - m_j]E[\phi_k - m_k] \\
&= \sum_{j=1}^{n} E[(\phi_j - m_j)^2] = \sum_{j=1}^{n} \sigma_j^2 \qquad (3\text{–}184)
\end{aligned}
$$

[39a] An infinite family of random variables is said to be statistically independent if, and only if, all finite subfamilies are statistically independent.

[40] This equation is valid even if the random variables are not statistically independent.

The last equation establishes the important result that the variance of a sum of statistically independent random variables is the sum of the variances of the summands.

Another important result states that the characteristic function of a sum of statistically independent random variables is the product of the characteristic functions of the individual summands. The reader should compare this statement with the deceptively similar sounding one made on page 154, and carefully note the difference between the two. The proof of this statement is a simple calculation

$$\begin{aligned} M_{s_n}(iv) &= E\left[e^{iv\sum_{j=1}^{n}\phi_j}\right] = \int_{-\infty}^{\infty}\cdots\int_{-\infty}^{\infty} e^{iv(\xi_1+\cdots+\xi_n)} \\ &\quad\times p_{\phi_1,\cdots,\phi_n}(\xi_1,\cdots,\xi_n)d\xi_1\cdots d\xi_n \\ &= \int_{-\infty}^{\infty}\cdots\int e^{iv\xi_1}\cdots e^{iv\xi_n}p_{\phi_1}(\xi_1)\cdots p_{\phi_n}(\xi_n)d\xi_1\cdots d\xi_n \\ &= \left[\int_{-\infty}^{\infty} e^{iv\xi_1}p_{\phi_1}(\xi_1)d\xi_1\right]\cdots\left[\int_{-\infty}^{\infty} e^{iv\xi_n}p_{\phi_n}(\xi_n)d\xi_n\right] \\ &= M_{\phi_1}(iv)\cdots M_{\phi_n}(iv)\,^{41} \end{aligned} \tag{3–185}$$

One consequence of Eq. (3–185) is the important result that the sum of a family of statistically independent, gaussianly distributed random variables is again gaussianly distributed. To show this, let

$$p_{\phi_j}(x) = \frac{1}{\sqrt{2\pi}\sigma_j}\exp\left\{-\frac{1}{2\sigma_j^2}(x-m_j)^2\right\} \tag{3–186}$$

It now follows that

$$M_{\phi_j}(iv) = \exp\{ivm_j\}\exp\{-\tfrac{1}{2}\sigma_j^2v^2\} \tag{3–187}$$

and, applying Eq. (3–185), we obtain the result

$$M_{s_n}(iv) = \exp\left\{iv\sum_{j=1}^{n} m_j\right\}\exp\left\{-\tfrac{1}{2}v^2\sum_{j=1}^{n}\sigma_j^2\right\} \tag{3–188}$$

Letting $m = \sum_{j=1}^{n} m_j$ and $\sigma^2 = \sum_{j=1}^{n}\sigma_j^2$ we can now write

$$p_{s_n}(x) = \frac{1}{\sqrt{2\pi}\sigma}\exp\left\{-\frac{1}{2\sigma^2}(x-m)^2\right\} \tag{3–189}$$

which is the desired result.

[41] This result can also be established by making use of Eq. (3–130) and the well-known formula for the Fourier transform of the convolution of two functions.

Independent gaussian random variables are by no means the only ones whose distributions are preserved under addition. Another example is independent, Poisson distributed random variables, for which

$$p_{\phi_j}(x) = \sum_{k=0}^{\infty} \frac{\lambda_j^k}{k!} e^{-\lambda_j} \delta(x - k) \tag{3–190}$$

and

$$M_{\phi_j}(iv) = \exp \{\lambda_j[e^{iv} - 1]\} \tag{3–191}$$

Equation (3–185) now yields the result

$$M_{s_n}(iv) = \exp \{\lambda[e^{iv} - 1]\} \tag{3–192}$$

where

$$\lambda = \sum_{j=1}^{n} \lambda_j \tag{3–193}$$

and it follows that

$$p_{s_n}(x) = \sum_{k=0}^{\infty} \frac{\lambda^k}{k!} e^{-\lambda} \delta(x - k) \tag{3–194}$$

Our next result concerns the central limit theorem, which places in evidence the remarkable behavior of the distribution function of s_n when n is a large number. We shall now state and sketch the proof of a version of the central limit theorem that is pertinent to sums of *identically distributed* $[p_{\phi_i}(x) = p_{\phi_1}(x), i = 1,2, \cdots]$, statistically independent random variables. To simplify the statement of the theorem, we shall introduce the normalized sum s_n^* defined by

$$s_n^* = \frac{s_n - nm_1}{\sqrt{n}\sigma_1} \tag{3–195}$$

Note that s_n^* has zero mean and unit variance.

The Central Limit Theorem.—If $\phi_1,\phi_2, \cdots$ are identically distributed, statistically independent random variables having finite mean and variance, then

$$\lim_{n\to\infty} F_{s_n^*}(x) = \int_{-\infty}^{x} \frac{1}{\sqrt{2\pi}} e^{-\xi^2/2} d\xi \tag{3–196}$$

The central limit theorem thus states the remarkable fact that the distribution function of the normalized sum of identically distributed, statistically independent random variables approaches the gaussian distribution function as the number of summands approaches infinity—

regardless of what the distribution function of the individual summands is! The existence of this theorem is one of the main reasons that one very often hypothesizes that a physical quantity under study is gaussianly distributed.

The proof of the central limit theorem begins with the calculation of the characteristic function of s_n^*

$$\begin{aligned} M_{s_n^*}(iv) &= E\left[\exp\left\{iv\left(\frac{1}{\sqrt{n}\sigma_1}\sum_{j=1}^{n}(\phi_j - m_1)\right)\right\}\right] \\ &= E\left[\prod_{j=1}^{n}\exp\left\{\frac{iv}{\sqrt{n}\sigma_1}(\phi_j - m_1)\right\}\right] \\ &= \prod_{j=1}^{n} E\left[\exp\left\{\frac{iv}{\sqrt{n}\sigma_1}(\phi_j - m_1)\right\}\right] \\ &= \prod_{j=1}^{n} M_{(\phi_j - m_1)/\sigma_1}\left(\frac{iv}{\sqrt{n}}\right) \\ &= \left[M_{(\phi_1 - m_1)/\sigma_1}\left(\frac{iv}{\sqrt{n}}\right)\right]^n \end{aligned} \tag{3–197}$$

Consequently,

$$\ln M_{s_n^*}(iv) = n \ln\left[M_{(\phi_1 - m_1)/\sigma_1}\left(\frac{iv}{\sqrt{n}}\right)\right] \tag{3–198}$$

Now, since the random variable $(\phi_1 - m_1)/\sigma_1$ has finite mean $(=0)$ and variance $(=1)$, both its characteristic function and the logarithm of its characteristic function have finite first and second derivatives. It follows that $\ln M_{(\phi_1 - m_1)/\sigma_1}(iv)$ can be expanded in a Taylor series with remainder[42] as follows[43]

$$\begin{aligned} \ln M(iv) &= \ln M(0) + iv\frac{M'(0)}{M(0)} + \frac{(iv)^2}{2}\left\{\frac{M(iv\theta)M''(iv\theta) - [M'(iv\theta)]^2}{M^2(iv\theta)}\right\} \\ &= \frac{(iv)^2}{2}\left\{\frac{M''(iv\theta)}{M(iv\theta)} - \left[\frac{M'(iv\theta)}{M(iv\theta)}\right]^2\right\} \end{aligned} \tag{3–199}$$

where $0 < \theta < 1$.

Consequently,

$$\ln M_{s_n^*}(iv) = \frac{n}{2}\left(\frac{iv}{\sqrt{n}}\right)^2\left\{\frac{M''(iv\theta/\sqrt{n})}{M(iv\theta/\sqrt{n})} - \left[\frac{M'(iv\theta/\sqrt{n})}{M(iv\theta/\sqrt{n})}\right]^2\right\} \tag{3–200}$$

[42] W. Rudin, *Principles of Mathematical Analysis*, McGraw-Hill Book Co., New York, 1953.

[43] To simplify writing, $M_{(\phi_1 - m_1)/\sigma_1}$ is abbreviated M in Eqs. (3–199) through (3–203).

However,

$$\lim_{n\to\infty} M\left(\frac{iv\theta}{\sqrt{n}}\right) = M(0) = 1 \tag{3-201}$$

$$\lim_{n\to\infty} M'\left(\frac{iv\theta}{\sqrt{n}}\right) = M'(0) = E\left[\frac{\phi_1 - m_1}{\sigma_1}\right] = 0 \tag{3-202}$$

$$\lim_{n\to\infty} M''\left(\frac{iv\theta}{\sqrt{n}}\right) = M''(0) = E\left[\frac{\phi_1 - m_1}{\sigma_1}\right]^2 = 1 \tag{3-203}$$

and it follows that

$$\lim_{n\to\infty} \ln M_{s_n^*}(iv) = \tfrac{1}{2}(iv)^2 = -\tfrac{1}{2}v^2 \tag{3-204}$$

In other words

$$\lim_{n\to\infty} M_{s_n^*}(iv) = e^{-\frac{1}{2}v^2} \tag{3-205}$$

The right-hand side of Eq. (3–205) is the characteristic function of the gaussian distribution having zero mean and unit variance, and this leads us to conclude that the distribution function of s_n^* approaches

$$\int_{-\infty}^{x} \frac{1}{\sqrt{2\pi}} e^{-\xi^2/2} d\xi$$

This last step is not by far as trivial as it sounds and requires a fairly involved argument to establish it on a rigorous basis.[44] Moreover, in the absence of any additional assumptions about the distribution function of the individual summands, it is not possible to conclude that the probability density function of s_n^* approaches $(1/\sqrt{2\pi})e^{-x^2/2}$. This subtlety is not apparent in our argument but shows up when an attempt is made to give a careful discussion of the last step in the proof.

Essentially the same argument used above enables one to prove an important multidimensional version of the central limit theorem that applies to sums of independent random vectors. A k-dimensional random vector is simply a group of k random variables, $\{\phi_1,\cdots,\phi_k\}$. A set of n random vectors, $\{\phi_{11},\phi_{21},\cdots,\phi_{k1}\}$, $\{\phi_{12},\phi_{22},\cdots,\phi_{k2}\}$, $\cdots$, $\{\phi_{1n},\phi_{2n},\cdots,\phi_{kn}\}$ is said to be statistically independent if

$$p_{\phi_{11},\cdots,\phi_{kn}}(x_{11},\cdots,x_{kn}) = p_{\phi_{11},\cdots,\phi_{k1}}(x_{11},\cdots,x_{k1}) \times p_{\phi_{12},\cdots,\phi_{k2}}(x_{12},\cdots,x_{k2})\cdots p_{\phi_{1n},\cdots,\phi_{kn}}(x_{1n},\cdots,x_{kn}) \tag{3-206}$$

[44] H. Cramer, *Mathematical Methods of Statistics*, Princeton University Press, 1954; B. V. Gnedenko and A. N. Kolmogorov, *Limit Distributions for Sums of Independent Random Variables*, Addison-Wesley Publishing Co., Inc., Cambridge, Mass., 1954; M. Loève, *Probability Theory*, D. Van Nostrand Co., Inc., Princeton, N.J., 1955.

Finally, an infinite set of random vectors is defined to be statistically independent if all finite subfamilies are statistically independent. Given an infinite family of identically distributed, statistically independent random vectors having finite means and covariances, we define their normalized sum to be the vector $\{s_{1n}^*, \cdots, s_{kn}^*\}$ where

$$\left.\begin{aligned} s_{jn}^* &= \frac{1}{\sqrt{n}} \sum_{l=1}^{n} (\phi_{jl} - m_j), \quad j = 1, \cdots, k;\ n = 1, 2, \cdots \\ m_j &= E[\phi_{jl}], \qquad\qquad\qquad j = 1, \cdots, k \end{aligned}\right\} \tag{3–207}$$

The multidimensional central limit theorem now states that the multidimensional characteristic function of $s_{1n}^*, \cdots s_{kn}^*$ behaves as follows:

$$\lim_{n \to \infty} M_{s_{1n}^*, \cdots, s_{kn}^*}(iv_1, \cdots, iv_k) = e^{-\frac{1}{2}\bar{v}\Lambda\bar{v}'} \tag{3–208}$$

where $\bar{v}$ denotes the row matrix $\bar{v} = \{v_1, \cdots v_k\}$, $\bar{v}'$ is the matrix transpose of $\bar{v}$, and Λ denotes the covariance matrix of $\{\phi_{11}, \phi_{21}, \cdots, \phi_{k1}\}$; *i.e.*

$$\Lambda = \begin{bmatrix} \lambda_{11} & \lambda_{12} & \cdots & \lambda_{1k} \\ \lambda_{21} & \lambda_{22} & \cdots & \lambda_{2k} \\ \cdot & \cdot & \cdot & \cdot \\ \lambda_{k1} & \lambda_{k2} & \cdots & \lambda_{kk} \end{bmatrix} \tag{3–209}$$

where

$$\lambda_{lj} = E[(\phi_{l1} - m_l)(\phi_{j1} - m_j)] \tag{3–210}$$

It can be shown that the right-hand side of Eq. (3–208) is the k-dimensional characteristic function of a k-dimensional distribution function, and that the k-dimensional distribution function of $s_{1n}^*, \cdots, s_{kn}^*$ approaches this distribution function. Under suitable additional hypothesis, it can also be shown that the joint probability density function of $s_{1n}^*, \cdots, s_{kn}^*$ approaches the joint probability density function whose characteristic function is given by the right-hand side of Eq. (3–208). To preserve the analogy with the one-dimensional case, this distribution (density) function is called the k-dimensional, zero mean gaussian distribution (density) function. The explicit form of this density function can be obtained by taking the k-dimensional Fourier transform of $e^{-\frac{1}{2}\bar{v}\Lambda\bar{v}'}$, with the result.[45]

$$p(x_1, \cdots, x_k) = \frac{1}{(2\pi)^{k/2}|\Lambda|^{1/2}} e^{-\frac{1}{2}\bar{x}\Lambda^{-1}\bar{x}'} \tag{3–211}$$

[45] H. Cramer, *op. cit.*

where $|\Lambda|$ denotes the determinant of Λ, Λ^{-1} the matrix inverse of Λ and $\bar{x}$ the row matrix $x = \{x_1, \cdots, x_k\}$. Equation (3–211) is valid only when $|\Lambda| \neq 0$, the density function assuming a degenerate form when this is not the case.

We conclude this section by deriving an important property of jointly gaussian random variables; namely, the fact that a necessary and sufficient condition for a group of jointly gaussian random variables $\varphi_1, \cdots, \varphi_n$ to be statistically independent is that $E[\varphi_j \varphi_k] = E[\varphi_j]E[\varphi_k]$, $j \neq k$. Stated in other words, linearly independent (uncorrelated),[46] gaussian random variables are statistically independent. This statement is not necessarily true for non-gaussian random variables.

The fact that linear independence is a necessary condition for statistical independence is obvious. The sufficiency of the condition can be established by noting that the covariance matrix

$$\Lambda = \begin{bmatrix} \lambda_{11} & \lambda_{12} & \cdots & \\ \lambda_{21} & \lambda_{22} & \cdots & \\ \vdots & \vdots & & \\ \vdots & \vdots & & \lambda_{nn} \end{bmatrix}, \quad \lambda_{jk} = E[\varphi_j - m_{\varphi_j}][\varphi_k - m_{\varphi_k}] \tag{3–212}$$

is a diagonal matrix

$$\Lambda = \begin{bmatrix} \sigma_{\varphi_1}^2 & 0 & \cdots & \cdots \\ 0 & \sigma_{\varphi_2}^2 & & \\ \vdots & & \ddots & \\ \vdots & & & \sigma_{\varphi_n}^2 \end{bmatrix} \tag{3–213}$$

when the φ_j's are linearly independent. Since the φ_j are gaussian, it follows from Eq. 3–211 that their joint characteristic function can be written in the form

$$\begin{aligned} M_{\varphi_1, \cdots \varphi_n}(iv_1 \cdots iv_n) &= \exp\left\{i \sum_{j=1}^{n} m_{\varphi_j} v_j\right\} \exp\left\{-\tfrac{1}{2} \sum_{j=1}^{n} \sigma_{\varphi_j}^2 v_j^2\right\} \\ &= \prod_{j=1}^{n} \exp\{i m_{\varphi_j} v_j\} \exp\{-\tfrac{1}{2}\sigma_{\varphi_j}^2 v_j^2\} \end{aligned} \tag{3–214}$$

Statistical independence of the φ_j now follows at once from Eq. (3–181).

3.12. Random Processes in Which All Possible Time Averages are Specified.—In many problems, it is a great convenience to assume that enough information has been specified about the underlying time function(s) to enable one to calculate essentially any time average of

[46] See Section 3.9, page 146.

interest.[47] The preceding sections have made it clear that this can be accomplished by specifying all possible (for all orders and all possible time increments) joint distribution functions of the underlying time function(s). Moreover, it can be shown that the specification of all possible finite-order joint distribution functions of (say) $X(t)$ enables one to calculate, at least in principle, not only all averages of the form

$$\lim_{T\to\infty} \frac{1}{2T} \int_{-T}^{T} \phi[X(t + \tau_n)]dt$$

but also many important averages that, in a certain sense, depend on an infinite number of values of τ. A simple example of this arises when one wishes to calculate $F_Z(z)$ when $Z(t) = \int_0^1 X(t + \tau)d\tau$.

A random process can be (and often is) defined in terms of the random variable terminology introduced in Section 3.8. We include this alternate definition for completeness. Limiting ourselves to a single time function $X(t)$, it is seen that $X(t)$ is completely specified as a random process by the specification all possible finite-order *joint* distribution functions of the infinite set of random variables ϕ_τ, $-\infty < \tau < \infty$, defined by the equations

$$Z(t) = \phi_\tau[X(t)] = X(t + \tau) \tag{3–215}$$

The complete specification of a random process requires us to have some way of writing down an infinite number of distribution functions. For practical reasons, this is an impossible task unless all the distribution functions can be specified by means of a rule that enables one to calculate any distribution function of interest in terms of a finite amount of prespecified information. The following examples will illustrate these ideas by showing how some particular stochastic processes of interest can be defined.

As our first example we shall define what is known as a gaussian Markov process. This process, as we shall see later, is a good model for thermal noise or vacuum-tube-generated noise that has been passed through an RC filter with time constant α^{-1}. We begin by defining two functions f and g as follows

$$f(x) = \frac{1}{\sqrt{2\pi}} e^{-v^2/2} \tag{3–216}$$

$$g(x,y;\tau) = \frac{1}{\sqrt{2\pi}\sigma(\tau)} \exp\left\{-\frac{1}{2\sigma^2(\tau)}[x - \rho(\tau)y]^2\right\} \tag{3–217}$$

[47] Some authors use the convention that $X(t)$ is specified as a random process only when all possible time averages of $X(t)$ have been specified. In this chapter, the phrase *random process* is used in a broader sense to mean that some, but not necessarily all, time averages of $X(t)$ have been specified.

where

$$\rho(\tau) = e^{-a|\tau|},\ a > 0, \text{ and } \sigma^2(\tau) = 1 - \rho^2(\tau). \qquad (3\text{–}218)$$

In terms of these functions, we define all possible joint probability density functions for a time function $X(t)$ by writing

$$p_{X,\bar{\tau}_n}(x_1 \cdots x_n) = f(x_1)g(x_2,x_1;\ \tau_2 - \tau_1)\cdots g(x_n,x_{n-1};\ \tau_n - \tau_{n-1}) \qquad (3\text{–}219)$$

We must now verify that the definition (3–219) does indeed generate a possible set of probability density functions. First of all, $p_{X,\bar{\tau}_n}$, as defined by Eq. (3–219) is everywhere non-negative, and, moreover,

$$\begin{aligned}
\int_{-\infty}^{\infty} & p_{X,\bar{\tau}_n}(\bar{\xi}_n)d\bar{\xi}_n \\
&= \int_{-\infty}^{\infty} \cdots \int_{-\infty}^{\infty} f(\xi_1)\cdots g(\xi_n,\xi_{n-1};\ \tau_n - \tau_{n-1})d\xi_1,\cdots,d\xi_n \\
&= \int_{-\infty}^{\infty} \cdots \int_{-\infty}^{\infty} f(\xi_1)\cdots g(\xi_{n-1},\xi_{n-2};\ \tau_{n-1} - \tau_{n-2}) \\
&\quad \times \left[\frac{1}{\sqrt{2\pi}\sigma(\tau_n - \tau_{n-1})}\int_{-\infty}^{\infty} \exp\left\{-\frac{1}{2\sigma^2(\tau_n - \tau_{n-1})}\right.\right. \\
&\quad \left.\left. \times [\xi_n - \rho(\tau_n - \tau_{n-1})\xi_{n-1}]^2\right\} d\xi_n\right] d\xi_1\cdots d\xi_{n-1} \\
&= \int_{-\infty}^{\infty} \cdots \int_{-\infty}^{\infty} f(\xi_1)\cdots g(\xi_{n-1},\xi_{n-2};\ \tau_{n-1} - \tau_{n-2})d\xi_1\cdots d\xi_{n-1} \\
&= \cdots = \int_{-\infty}^{\infty} f(\xi_1)d\xi_1 = 1
\end{aligned} \qquad (3\text{–}220)$$

It now only remains for us to show that the set of functions $p_{X,\bar{\tau}_n}$ defined by Eq. (3–219) are consistent with one another in the sense discussed in Section 3.7. To do this, we note that $p_{X,\bar{\tau}_n}$ can be calculated either directly from Eq. (3–219) or by first calculating $p_{X,\bar{\tau}_m}$, where $m > n$ and the first n components of $\bar{\tau}_m$ coincide with $\bar{\tau}_n$, and then integrating out the last $m - n$ variables

$$p_{X,\bar{\tau}_n}(x_1\cdots x_n) = \int_{-\infty}^{\infty} \cdots \int_{-\infty}^{\infty} p_{X,\bar{\tau}_m}(x_1,\cdots,x_n,\xi_{n+1}\cdots\xi_m) \times d\xi_{n+1}\cdots d\xi_m \qquad (3\text{–}221)$$

The result of these two calculations must agree; in other words, we must check to see whether

$$1 = \int_{-\infty}^{\infty} \cdots \int_{-\infty}^{\infty} g(\xi_{n+1},x_n;\ \tau_{n+1} - \tau_n)\cdots \times g(\xi_m,\xi_{m-1};\ \tau_m - \tau_{m-1})d\xi_{n+1}\cdots d\xi_m \qquad (3\text{–}222)$$

The truth of this equation follows at once from the fact that

$$\int_{-\infty}^{\infty} g(\xi,x;\tau)d\xi = 1 \tag{3–223}$$

There is still one (and essentially only one) other way that $p_{X,\bar{\tau}_n}$ can be calculated; namely, by first calculating $p_{X,\bar{\tau}_m}$, where $m > n$ and the *last* n coordinates of $\bar{\tau}_m$ coincide with $\bar{\tau}_n$, and then integrating out the *first* $m - n$ variables; in symbols

$$p_{X;\bar{\tau}_n}(x_1,\cdots,x_n) = \int_{-\infty}^{\infty} \cdots \int_{-\infty}^{\infty} p_{X,\bar{\tau}_m}(\xi_1,\cdots,\xi_{m-n},x_1,\cdots,x_n) \times d\xi_1\cdots d\xi_{m-n} \tag{3–224}$$

This means that we must check the validity of the equation

$$\int_{-\infty}^{\infty} \cdots \int_{-\infty}^{\infty} f(\xi_1)g(\xi_2,\xi_1;\tau_2 - \tau_1)\cdots g(x_1,\xi_{m-n};\tau_{m-n+1} - \tau_{m-n}) \times d\xi_1\cdots d\xi_{m-n} = f(x_1) \tag{3–225}$$

The truth of Eq. (3–225) follows at once from the equation

$$\int_{-\infty}^{\infty} f(\xi)g(x,\xi;\tau)d\xi = f(x) \tag{3–226}$$

which we shall now derive.[48]

$$\begin{aligned}
\int_{-\infty}^{\infty} & f(\xi)g(x,\xi,\tau)d\xi \\
&= \frac{1}{2\pi\sigma}\int_{-\infty}^{\infty} \exp\left\{-\frac{\xi^2}{2}\right\}\exp\left\{-\frac{1}{2\sigma^2}[x - \rho\xi]^2\right\}d\xi \\
&= \frac{1}{2\pi\sigma}\exp\left\{-\frac{x^2}{2\sigma^2}\right\}\int_{-\infty}^{\infty} \exp\left\{-\frac{1}{2\sigma^2}[\xi^2 - 2\rho x\xi]\right\}d\xi \\
&= \frac{1}{2\pi\sigma}\exp\left\{-\frac{x^2}{2\sigma^2}\right\}\exp\left\{\frac{\rho^2x^2}{2\sigma^2}\right\}\int_{-\infty}^{\infty} \exp\left\{-\frac{1}{2\sigma^2}[\xi - \rho x]^2\right\}d\xi \\
&= \frac{1}{\sqrt{2\pi}}\exp\left\{-\frac{x^2}{2}\left[\frac{1-\rho^2}{\sigma^2}\right]\right\} = \frac{1}{\sqrt{2\pi}}\exp\left\{-\frac{x^2}{2}\right\} = f(x)
\end{aligned} \tag{3–227}$$

This establishes the consistency of our definitions.

Our next example concerns the Poisson process, which plays a central role in a variety of problems such as waiting lines, inventory control, electrical noise, the firing of neurons, and radioactive decay. We will discuss the application of the Poisson process to the study of certain kinds of electrical noise in a later section.

[48] In this derivation $\sigma \equiv \sigma(\tau)$ and $\rho^2 \equiv \rho^2(\tau) = 1 - \sigma^2(\tau)$.

The time functions $N(t)$ underlying the Poisson process are all of the general form shown in Fig. 3–9, where it is assumed that $N(t)$ is finite except perhaps at $t = \pm\infty$. Such functions $N(t)$ are sometimes referred to as *counting functions* because of the relations

$$N(t_0) = \begin{cases} \text{number of jumps in} \\ \text{the interval } 0 < t \le t_0, \quad t_0 > 0 \\ \text{the negative of the} \\ \text{number of jumps in} \\ \text{the interval } t_0 < t \le 0, \quad t_0 \le 0 \end{cases} \qquad (3\text{–}228)$$

and, for $t_1 < s_1$

$$N(s_1) - N(t_1) = \text{number of jumps in the interval } t_1 < t \le s_1 \qquad (3\text{–}229)$$

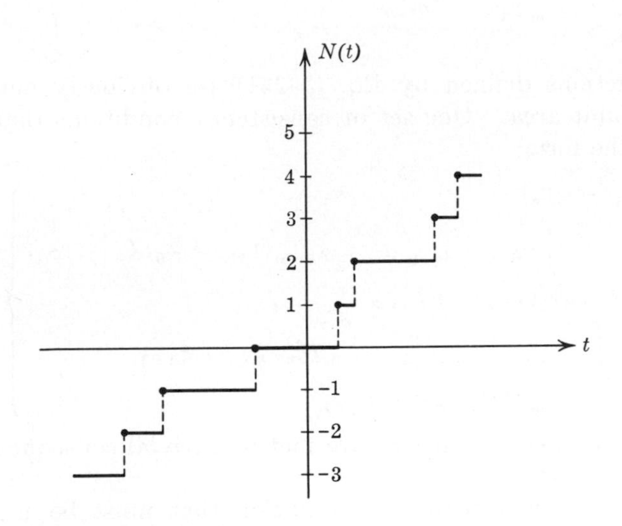

FIG. 3–9. A Typical Counting Function.

Counting functions are most often used as a convenient means of representing such phenomena as the arrival times of electrons at the plate of a vacuum tube, the times at which customers receive service in a waiting line or the times at which the atoms of a radioactive substance emit radiation.

The Poisson process is now defined by specifying a particular set of probability density functions that enable us to calculate all possible averages involving *differences* of the form $N(s_i) - N(t_i)$, $s_i \geq t_i$; *i.e.*, averages of the form

$$\lim_{T \to \infty} \frac{1}{2T} \int_{-T}^{T} \phi[N(t + s_1) - N(t + t_1), \cdots, N(t + s_n) - N(t + t_n)]dt \tag{3-230}$$

where ϕ denotes a function of n real variables. This is accomplished by defining the joint probability density function for all possible, finite families of time functions of the form $\Delta_1(t) = N(t + s_1) - N(t + t_1), \cdots, \Delta_n(t) = N(t + s_n) - N(t + t_n)$, *where the intervals* $t_1 < t \leq s_1, \cdots, t_n < t \leq s_n$ are *nonoverlapping*, as follows

$$p_{\Delta_1, \cdots, \Delta_n}(x_1, \cdots, x_n) = \prod_{k=1}^{n} p_{\Delta_k}(x_k)$$

where

$$p_{\Delta_k}(x) = \sum_{m=0}^{\infty} \frac{[\bar{n}(s_k - t_k)]^m}{m!} e^{-\bar{n}(s_k - t_k)} \delta(x - m) \tag{3-231}$$

and $\bar{n} > 0$

The functions defined by Eq. (3–231) are obviously non-negative and have unit area. One set of consistency conditions that must be met is of the form

$$\begin{aligned} p_{\Delta_1, \cdots, \Delta_n}(x_1, \cdots, x_n) &= \int_{-\infty}^{\infty} \cdots \int p_{\Delta_1, \cdots, \Delta_n, \Delta_{n+1}, \cdots, \Delta_{n+m}}(x_1, \cdots, x_n, \xi_{n+1}, \cdots, \\ &\qquad \xi_{n+m}) d\xi_{n+1} \cdots d\xi_{n+m} \\ &= \int_{-\infty}^{\infty} \int p_{\Delta_{n+m}, \cdots, \Delta_{n+1}, \Delta_1, \cdots, \Delta_n}(\xi_{n+m}, \cdots, \xi_{n+1}, \\ &\qquad x_1, \cdots, x_n) d\xi_{n+m} \cdots d\xi_{n+1} \end{aligned} \tag{3-232}$$

The fact that these conditions are met is a trivial consequence of our definition, (3–231).

The only other consistency condition that must be met is best explained by an example. Let $t_1 < t_2 < t_3$. Then, the probability density function for $\Delta(t) = N(t + t_3) - N(t + t_1)$ is defined directly by means of Eq. (3–231) and *implicitly* by means of the equation

$$\begin{aligned} \Delta(t) &= [N(t + t_3) - N(t + t_2)] + [N(t + t_2) - N(t + t_1)] \\ &\equiv \Delta_2(t) + \Delta_1(t) \end{aligned} \tag{3-233}$$

which relates p_Δ to p_{Δ_1} and p_{Δ_2}. Direct application of our definition yields

$$p_\Delta(x) = \sum_{k=0}^{\infty} \frac{[\bar{n}(t_3 - t_1)]^k}{k!} e^{-[\bar{n}(t_3 - t_1)]} \delta(x - k) \tag{3-234}$$

On the other hand, Eq. (3–233) states that Δ is the sum of two statistically independent, Poisson distributed random variables Δ_1 and Δ_2 with parameters $\bar{n}(t_2 - t_1)$ and $\bar{n}(t_1 - t_2)$ respectively. Consequently,[49] Δ must be Poisson distributed with parameter $\bar{n}(t_2 - t_1) + \bar{n}(t_3 - t_2) = \bar{n}(t_3 - t_1)$ which checks our direct calculation. The fact that the most general consistency condition of the type just considered is also met follows in a similar manner from the properties of sums of independent, Poisson distributed random variables.

Now that we have established the consistency of the definition (3–231) for *nonoverlapping* intervals $t_1 < t \leq s_1, \cdots, t_n < t \leq s_n$, we can easily verify that the joint distribution of $N(s_1) - N(t_1), \cdots, N(s_n) - N(t_n)$ is uniquely defined even if the intervals in question are overlapping. For example, let $t_1 < t \leq s_1$, $t_2 < t \leq s_2$ be two overlapping intervals—for definiteness let us assume that $t_1 < t_2 < s_1 < s_2$. The joint distribution of $N(s_1) - N(t_1)$ and $N(s_2) - N(t_2)$ is now implicitly determined by the obvious relationships

$$\left.\begin{aligned} N(s_1) - N(t_1) &= [N(t_2) - N(t_1)] + [N(s_1) - N(t_2)] \\ N(s_2) - N(t_2) &= [N(s_2) - N(s_1)] + [N(s_1) - N(t_2)] \end{aligned}\right\} \tag{3–235}$$

which express $N(s_1) - N(t_1)$ and $N(s_2) - N(t_2)$ in terms of increments of N taken over the three nonoverlapping intervals $t_1 < t \leq t_2$, $t_2 < t \leq s_1$, $s_1 < t \leq s_2$. An application of the methods of section 3.8 now yields the joint distribution of $N(s_1) - N(t_1)$ and $N(s_2) - N(t_2)$. This notion can be extended in an obvious way to show that the joint distribution of all possible families of increments $N(s_i) - N(t_i)$ is well determined.

The physical significance of the parameter $\bar{n}$ entering into the definition of the Poisson process can be established by noting that, for $s > t$,

$$E[N(s) - N(t)] = \bar{n}(s - t) \tag{3–236}$$

which means that $\bar{n}$ is the average number of jumps of $N(t)$ per unit time.

The Poisson process represents only one possible way of assigning joint distribution functions to the increments of counting functions; however, in many problems, one can argue that the Poisson process is the most reasonable choice that can be made. For example, let us consider the stream of electrons flowing from cathode to plate in a vacuum tube, and let us further assume that the plate current is low enough so that the electrons do not interact with one another in the

[49] See Eq. (3–194).

cathode-plate space. Under these conditions, it seems reasonable to assume that the number of electrons arriving at the plate in a given time interval is in no way influenced by the number of electrons that arrive in any other time interval that does not overlap the first. This assumption can be formulated mathematically by using counting functions to describe the electron arrival times and then demanding that any finite family of increments $N(t + s_i) - N(t + t_i)$, $i = 1, \cdots, n$, associated with nonoverlapping time intervals be statistically independent. In symbols

$$p_{\Delta_1, \cdots, \Delta_2}(x_1, \cdots, x_n) = \prod_{k=1}^{k} p_{\Delta_k}(x_k) \tag{3-237}$$

where

$$\Delta_k(t) = N(t + s_k) - N(t + t_k)$$

and

$$t_1 \leq s_1 \leq t_2 \leq s_2 \leq \cdots \leq t_n < s_n$$

There are many ways we could assign probability distribution functions to the increments $N(t + s_k) - N(t + t_k)$ and simultaneously satisfy the independent increment requirement expressed by Eq. (3–237); however, if we require a few additional properties, it is possible to show that the *only* possible probability density assignment is the Poisson process assignment defined by Eq. (3–231). One example of such additional requirements is the following [50]

$$\left.\begin{aligned} \lim_{h \downarrow 0} \frac{P\{N(t + h) - N(t) = 1\}}{h} &= \text{some constant } \bar{n} \\ \lim_{h \downarrow 0} \frac{P\{N(t + h) - N(t) \geq 2\}}{h} &= 0 \end{aligned}\right\} \tag{3-238}$$

In other words, if we assume that the counting function $N(t)$ has statistically independent increments (Eq. (3–237)), and has the property that the probability of a single jump occurring in a small interval of length h is approximately $\bar{n}h$ but the probability of more than one jump is zero to within terms of order h, (Eq. (3–238)), then it can be shown [51] that its probability density functions must be given by Eq. (3–231). It is the existence of theorems of this type that accounts for the great

[50] $h \downarrow 0$ means h approaches 0 through positive values of h.

[51] E. Parzen, *Stochastic Process*, p. 118, Holden-Day, Inc., San Francisco, 1962.

importance of Poisson processes. We refer the reader to the literature[52] for a complete discussion of the various other kinds of assumptions that lead to the Poisson process.

3.13. The Shot Noise Process.—In this and the next section we shall discuss two specific random processes—the shot noise process[53] and the gaussian process. These processes play a central role in many physical applications of the theory of random processes as well as being of considerable theoretical interest in themselves.

The *shot noise process* is defined in terms of the Poisson process by means of the formula

$$Y(t) = \int_{-\infty}^{\infty} h(t - \tau)dN(\tau) \tag{3-239}$$

where $N(t)$ denotes a counting function whose time averages are determined by Eq. (3–231) and $h(t)$ is a function having the properties

$$\int_{-\infty}^{\infty} |h(t)|dt < \infty, \qquad \int_{-\infty}^{\infty} |h(t)|^2 dt < \infty \tag{3-240}$$

As we shall see shortly, all possible finite order distributions of $Y(t)$ are uniquely determined in terms of the known finite order distributions of the increments of $N(t)$. Before proceeding, however, it is perhaps wise to discuss the meaning of the integral in Eq. (3–239) in more detail.

The Stieltjes integral appearing in Eq. (3–239) can be rewritten (at least formally) in the form

$$Y(t) = \int_{-\infty}^{\infty} h(t - \tau)N'(\tau)d\tau \tag{3-241}$$

which expresses $Y(t)$ as the convolution of $h(t)$ with $N'(t)$. The derivative of the counting function $N'(t)$ consists of a sequence of unit Dirac delta functions located at the jumps of $N(t)$

$$N'(t) = \sum_{\{t_k\}} \delta(t - t_k) \tag{3-242}$$

where the t_k's denote the locations of the jumps of $N(t)$ and $\sum_{\{t_k\}}$ denotes summation over all these jumps. The convolution of $N'(t)$ with $h(t)$ can now be performed explicitly with the result

$$Y(t) = \sum_{\{t_k\}} h(t - t_k) \tag{3-243}$$

The calculation of $Y(t)$ from $N(t)$ and $h(t)$ is illustrated in Fig. 3–10.

[52] A. Blanc-Lapierre and R. Fortet, *Thèorie des Fonctions Aléatoires*, Masson et Cie, Paris, 1953; J. L. Doob, *Stochastic Process*, John Wiley and Sons, Inc., New York, 1953; E. Parzen, *Stochastic Process*, Holden-Day, Inc., San Francisco, 1962.

[53] Sometimes called the generalized Poisson process.

The function $Y(t)$ also can be visualized as the result of passing the impulse train $N'(t)$ through a linear, time-invariant filter whose impulse response is $h(t)$.[54] This observation coupled with the fact that the Poisson process is often a reasonable model for the arrival times of

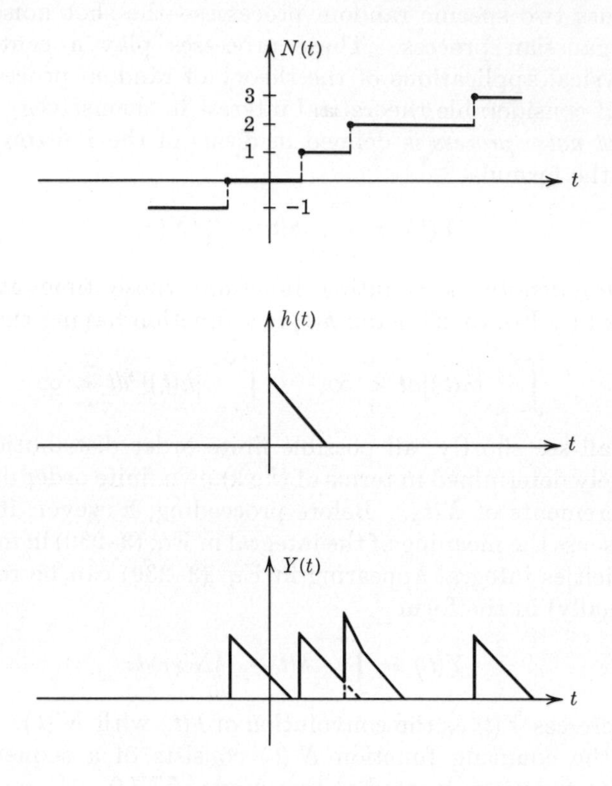

FIG. 3–10. An Aid in Understanding the Definition of the Shot Noise Process.

electrons in a vacuum tube[55] has led to widespread use of the shot noise process as a model for the vacuum tube generated noise in an electrical circuit.[56]

The only remaining issue to be discussed before we can proceed concerns the convergence of the integral in Eq. (3–239) or, equivalently,

[54] The reader unfamiliar with the notion of a linear, time-invariant filter can profit from W. M. Siebert's article in E. J. Baghdady, *Lectures on Communication System Theory*, McGraw-Hill Book Co., New York, 1961.

[55] See Section 3.12, page 167.

[56] W. B. Davenport, Jr., and W. L. Root, *An Introduction to the Theory of Random Signals and Noise*, McGraw-Hill Book Co., New York, 1958; J. L. Lawson and G. E. Uhlenbeck, *Threshold Signals*, McGraw-Hill Book Co., New York, 1950.

of the sum in Eq. (3–243). It can be shown[57] that the two conditions, Eq. (3–240), are sufficient to guarantee the convergence (in a certain sense) of the integral in Eq. (3–239). We shall not attempt to show this here, for to do so would take us too far afield. Instead, we shall adopt the procedure of limiting ourselves to $h(t)$'s that are staircase functions, *i.e.*, are of the form

$$h(t) = \begin{cases} h_1, & a_0 < t \le a_1 \\ h_2, & a_1 < t \le a_2 \\ \vdots & \vdots \qquad \vdots \\ h_n, & a_{n-1} < t \le a_n \\ 0, & \text{otherwise} \end{cases} \tag{3–244}$$

where $a_0 < a_1 < \cdots < a_n$ and the h_k's are constants. For such an $h(t)$, it is easily seen that

$$Y(t) = \sum_{k=1}^{n} h_k[N(t - a_{k-1}) - N(t - a_k)] \tag{3–245}$$

This means that the integral in Eq. (3–239) converges because all the increments of $N(t)$ are, by definition, finite. Moreover, many $h(t)$ of interest can be approximated as closely as desired by a staircase function so, at least for practical purposes, there is little loss of generality in restricting our attention to $h(t)$'s of the form (3–244).

Our first objective is going to be the determination of the finite order probability density function of $Y(t)$ in terms of the known finite order probability densities for the increments of $N(t)$. In preparation for this, we first note that, since $N(s) - N(t)$ is Poisson distributed with parameter $\bar{n}(s - t)$ for $s > t$, it follows that

$$E[N(s) - N(t)] = \bar{n}(s - t) \tag{3–246}$$

$$E[N(s) - N(t)]^2 = \bar{n}(s - t) + [\bar{n}(s - t)]^2 \tag{3–247}$$

Moreover, for two *nonoverlapping* intervals $t_1 < t \le s_1, t_2 < t \le s_2$, $N(s_1) - N(t_1)$, and $N(s_2) - N(t_2)$ are statistically independent and it follows that

$$E\{[N(s_1) - N(t_1)][N(s_2) - N(t_2)]\} = \bar{n}^2(s_1 - t_1)(s_2 - t_2) \tag{3–248}$$

Equations (3–246), (3–247), and (3–248) are often abbreviated by using the shorthand notation

$$E[dN(t)] = \bar{n}dt \tag{3–249}$$

$$E[dN(t)dN(t')] = \bar{n}\delta(t - t')dtdt' + \bar{n}^2dtdt' \tag{3–250}$$

[57] J. L. Doob, *Stochastic Process*, p. 432, John Wiley and Sons, Inc., New York, 1953.

We are now in a position to calculate the characteristic function $M_Y(iv)$ of $Y(t)$.

$$\begin{aligned} M_Y(iv) = E[e^{ivY(t)}] &= E\left[\exp\left\{iv\int_{-\infty}^{\infty} h(t-\tau)dN(\tau)\right\}\right] \\ &= E\left[\exp\left\{iv\sum_{k=1}^{n} h_k[N(t-a_{k-1}) - N(t-a_k)]\right\}\right] \\ &= E\left[\prod_{k=1}^{n} \exp\left\{ivh_k[N(t-a_{k-1}) - N(t-a_k)]\right\}\right] \end{aligned} \tag{3–251}$$

Since the increments $N(t - a_{k-1}) - N(t - a_k)$ are for nonoverlapping intervals, they are statistically independent and we can write

$$\begin{aligned} M_Y(iv) &= \prod_{k=1}^{n} E[\exp\{ivh_k[N(t-a_{k-1}) - N(t-a_k)]\}] \\ &= \prod_{k=1}^{n} \exp\{\bar{n}(a_k - a_{k-1})[e^{ivh_k} - 1]\} \end{aligned} \tag{3–252}$$

where the last step has made use of Eqs. (3–246), (3–247), and the previously derived formula for the characteristic function of the Poisson distribution. We can now write

$$\begin{aligned} M_Y(iv) &= \exp\left\{\bar{n}\sum_{k=1}^{n}(a_k - a_{k-1})[e^{ivh_k} - 1]\right\} \\ &= \exp\left\{\bar{n}\int_{-\infty}^{\infty}[e^{ivh(\tau)} - 1]d\tau\right\} \end{aligned} \tag{3–253}$$

which gives us an explicit expression for the characteristic function of $Y(t)$ in terms of $h(t)$ and $\bar{n}$. The probability density function of $Y(t)$ is the Fourier transform of Eq. (3–253); however, this can be calculated explicitly only in certain special cases.

The calculation of the higher order probability density functions of $Y(t)$ can now be effected almost at once by writing

$$\begin{aligned} M_{Y(t+\tau_1),\cdots,Y(t+\tau_m)}(iv_1,\cdots,iv_m) &\equiv M_{Y,\tau_m}(iv_1,\cdots,iv_m) \\ &= E\left[\exp\left\{i\sum_{j=1}^{m} v_j Y(t+\tau_j)\right\}\right] \end{aligned} \tag{3–254}$$

and then noting that the random variable appearing in the exponent can be written in the form

$$\begin{aligned} \sum_{j=1}^{m} v_j Y(t+\tau_j) &= \int_{-\infty}^{\infty}\left[\sum_{j=1}^{m} v_j h(t+\tau_j-\tau)\right]dN(\tau) \\ &= \int_{-\infty}^{\infty} h_0(t-\tau)dN(\tau) = Y_0(t) \end{aligned} \tag{3–255}$$

where

$$h_0(t) = \sum_{j=1}^{m} v_j h(t + \tau_j) \tag{3–256}$$

Thus, it is seen that

$$M_{Y,\bar{\tau}_m}(iv_1, \cdots iv_m) = M_{Y_0}(iv) \,|_{\,v=1} \tag{3–257}$$

where $M_{Y_0}(iv)$ is the (first order) characteristic function of the shot noise process $Y_0(t)$ defined by Eq. (3–255) in terms of the function $h_0(t)$ given by (3–256). This characteristic function has already been calculated

$$M_{Y_0}(iv) = \exp\left\{\bar{n} \int_{-\infty}^{\infty} [e^{ivh_0(\tau)} - 1] d\tau\right\} \tag{3–258}$$

Substitution of (3–256) into Eq. (3–258) now yields the desired result

$$M_{Y,\bar{\tau}_m}(iv_1, \cdots, iv_m) = \exp\left\{\bar{n} \int_{-\infty}^{\infty} \left[\exp\left(i \sum_{j=1}^{m} v_j h(\tau + \tau_j)\right) - 1\right] d\tau\right\} \tag{3–259}$$

The probability density function $p_{Y,\bar{\tau}_m}(\bar{x}_m)$ is the m-dimensional Fourier transform of Eq. (3–259) but, once again, this can only be evaluated explicitly in certain special cases.

Although we cannot easily obtain expressions for the probability density functions of $Y(t)$, it is a simple matter to calculate its various moments. We shall illustrate this technique by calculating all possible first and second moments of $Y(t)$; *i.e.*, $E[Y(t)]$ and $E[Y(t)Y(t + \tau)]$, $-\infty < \tau < \infty$. The pertinent characteristic function for this task is $M_{Y,0,\tau}$ (hereafter abbreviated $M_{Y,\tau}$) given by

$$M_{Y,\tau}(iv_1, iv_2) = \exp\left\{\bar{n} \int_{-\infty}^{\infty} [e^{iv_1 h(t) + iv_2 h(t+\tau)} - 1] dt\right\} \tag{3–260}$$

We can now calculate

$$\begin{aligned} m_Y = E[Y(t)] &= \frac{1}{i} \frac{\partial M_{Y,\tau}}{\partial v_1}\bigg|_{v_1 = v_2 = 0} \\ &= \frac{1}{i}\left[\bar{n} \int_{-\infty}^{\infty} ih(t) e^{iv_1 h(t) + iv_2 h(t+\tau)} dt\right] \\ &\quad \exp\left\{\bar{n} \int_{-\infty}^{\infty} [e^{iv_1 h(t) + iv_2 h(t+\tau)} - 1] dt\right\}\bigg|_{v_1 = v_2 = 0} \\ &= \bar{n} \int_{-\infty}^{\infty} h(t) dt \end{aligned} \tag{3–261}$$

and

$$E[Y(t)Y(t+\tau)] = -\frac{\partial^2 M_{Y,\tau}}{\partial v_1 \partial v_2}\bigg|_{v_1=v_2=0}$$

$$= \left[-\bar{n}\int_{-\infty}^{\infty} ih(t)dt\right]\bar{n}\int_{-\infty}^{\infty} ih(t+\tau)dt$$

$$-\bar{n}\int_{-\infty}^{\infty} i^2h(t)h(t+\tau)dt$$

$$= \left[\bar{n}\int_{-\infty}^{\infty} h(t)dt\right]^2 + \bar{n}\int_{-\infty}^{\infty} h(t)h(t+\tau)dt \tag{3-262}$$

The last equation, which expresses the autocorrelation function of $Y(t)$ in terms of $h(t)$, is often referred to as Campbell's[58] theorem. It is useful to note that the *autocovariance* function of $Y(t)$ is given by the simpler expression

$$E\{[Y(t) - m_Y][Y(t+\tau) - m_Y]\} = \bar{n}\int_{-\infty}^{\infty} h(t)h(t+\tau)dt \tag{3-263}$$

The function $\int_{-\infty}^{\infty} h(t)h(t+\tau)dt$ is often referred to as the autocorrelation function of the function $h(t)$; however, the reader should be careful to note the difference between the autocorrelation function of $h(t)$—an integrable function—and the autocorrelation function of $Y(t)$—a function that is *not* integrable because it does not die out in time. With this distinction in mind, Campbell's theorem can be expressed by saying that the autocovariance function of a shot noise process is $\bar{n}$ times the autocorrelation function of the function $h(t)$.

We shall conclude this section by investigating the very interesting behavior of the probability density functions of $Y(t)$ for large values of the parameter $\bar{n}$. First of all, we note that both the mean and the covariance of $Y(t)$ increase linearly with $\bar{n}$. Roughly speaking, this means that the "center" of any particular finite-order probability density function of $Y(t)$ moves further and further away from the origin as $\bar{n}$ increases and that the area under the density function is less and less concentrated at the center. For this reason, it is more convenient to study the normalized function Y^*

$$Y^*(t) = \frac{Y(t) - m_Y}{\sqrt{\bar{n}}} \tag{3-264}$$

[58] W. B. Davenport, Jr., and W. L. Root, *An Introduction to the Theory of Random Signals and Noise*, McGraw-Hill Book Co., New York, 1958; J. L. Doob, *Stochastic Process*, John Wiley and Sons, Inc., New York, 1953.

which has zero mean and covariances independent of $\bar{n}$, than it is to study Y itself. The characteristic function M_{Y^*,τ_m} is related to M_{Y,τ_m} by means of the formula

$$M_{Y^*,\tau_m}(iv_1,\cdots,iv_m) = \exp\left\{-i\frac{m_Y}{\sqrt{\bar{n}}}\sum_{j=1}^{m} v_j\right\} M_{Y,\tau_m}\left(\frac{iv_1}{\sqrt{\bar{n}}},\cdots,\frac{iv_m}{\sqrt{\bar{n}}}\right) \quad (3\text{–}265)$$

We can now write

$$M_{Y^*,\tau_m}(iv_1,\cdots,iv_m) = \exp\left\{-i\frac{m_Y}{\sqrt{\bar{n}}}\sum_{j=1}^{m} v_j\right\} \times \exp\left\{\bar{n}\int_{-\infty}^{\infty}\left[\exp\left(i\frac{1}{\sqrt{\bar{n}}}\sum_{j=1}^{m} v_j h(\tau+\tau_j)\right)-1\right]d\tau\right\} \quad (3\text{–}266)$$

Expanding the second exponential in the right-hand side of Eq. (3–266) in a power series and making use of Eq. (3–261), we obtain

$$M_{Y^*,\tau_m}(iv_1,\cdots,iv_m) = \exp\left\{-\int_{-\infty}^{\infty}\left\{\frac{1}{2}\left[\sum_{j=1}^{m} v_j h(\tau+\tau_j)\right]^2+\cdots\right\}d\tau\right\} \quad (3\text{–}267)$$

where the missing terms indicated by $\cdots$ all go to zero as $\frac{1}{\sqrt{\bar{n}}}$ or faster. It now follows[59] that

$$\lim_{\bar{n}\to\infty} M_{Y^*,\tau_m}(iv_1,\cdots,iv_m) = \exp\left\{-\frac{1}{2}\sum_{j,k=1}^{m} v_j v_k \int_{-\infty}^{\infty} h(\tau+\tau_j)h(\tau+\tau_k)d\tau\right\} \quad (3\text{–}268)$$

A comparison of Eq. (3–268) with Eq. (3–208) shows that the finite order distribution p_{Y^*,τ_m} is an m-dimensional gaussian distribution[60] with the covariance matrix

$$\Lambda = \begin{bmatrix} R_h(0) & R_h(\tau_1-\tau_2) & \cdots & R_h(\tau_1-\tau_m) \\ R_h(\tau_2-\tau_1) & \cdots & & \\ \vdots & & & \\ R_h(\tau_m-\tau_1) & & & R_h(0) \end{bmatrix} \quad (3\text{–}269)$$

where

$$R_h(\tau) = \int_{-\infty}^{\infty} h(t)h(t+\tau)dt = R_{Y^*}(\tau) \quad (3\text{–}270)$$

The last equality in 3–270 follows from Campbell's theorem.

[59] This argument tacitly assumes that $\int_{-\infty}^{\infty} |h(t)|^k dt < \infty$ for all positive integers k. A more careful argument, based on Taylor's theorem with the remainder, shows that it is sufficient that this condition be fulfilled for $k = 1,2$.

[60] Section 3.11, page 160.

A random process *all* of whose finite-order distributions are gaussian is called a gaussian random process. We have thus demonstrated the very important fact that, for large values of $\bar{n}$, a shot noise process is asymptotically a gaussian process. This is the main reason why vacuum tube generated noise in an electric circuit is usually modeled by means of a gaussian random process. The $\bar{n}$ (average number of electrons per second arriving at the plate) pertinent to such situations is enormous being on the order of 10^{18}. Moreover, many other sources of electrical noise, such as the noise generated by thermal agitation of the electrons in a resistor, can be shown[61] to be quite well modeled by a gaussian process. This is a fortunate thing because, as we shall see in the next section, gaussian processes have a number of properties that make their mathematical manipulation a relatively simple task.

3.14. The Gaussian Process.—A gaussian process was defined in the last section to be a process all of whose finite-order distributions are multi-dimensional gaussian distributions. This means that the multi-dimensional characteristic function of $p_{X,\bar{\tau}_n}$ must be of the form

$$M_{X,\bar{\tau}_n}(iv_1,\cdots,iv_n) = e^{-\frac{1}{2}\bar{v}\Lambda\bar{v}'}e^{i\bar{v}\bar{m}'} \tag{3–271}$$

where $\bar{v}$ denotes the (row) vector $v = \{v_1,\cdots,v_n\}$, Λ denotes the covariance matrix of the random variables $X(t+\tau_1)\cdots X(t+\tau_n)$, and $\bar{m}$ denotes the vector $\bar{m} = \{m_X,m_X,\cdots m_X\}$ where $m_X = E[X(t)]$. It should now be obvious that a gaussian process is completely specified once its mean $m_X = E[X(t)]$ and its autocorrelation function $R_X(\tau) = E[X(t)X(t+\tau)]$ are known because, given this information, we can determine the covariance matrix Λ for any given $\bar{\tau}_n$ as follows:

$$\Lambda = \begin{bmatrix} R_X(\tau_1-\tau_1)-m_X^2, & R_X(\tau_1-\tau_2)-m_X^2, & \cdots, & R_X(\tau_1-\tau_n)-m_X^2 \\ R_X(\tau_2-\tau_1)-m_X^2, & R_X(\tau_2-\tau_2)-m_X^2, & \cdots & \\ \vdots & & & \\ R_X(\tau_n-\tau_1)-m_X^2, & \cdots & , & R_X(\tau_n-\tau_n)-m_X^2 \end{bmatrix} \tag{3–272}$$

Among the most important properties of a gaussian process is its invariance under linear transformation. Stating the proposition in electrical engineering terminology, we shall now show that if a gaussian process $X(t)$ is passed through a linear, time-invariant filter whose impulse response is $h(t)$, then the output $Y(t)$ of this filter, given by[62]

$$Y(t) = \int_{-\infty}^{\infty} h(\tau)X(t-\tau)d\tau \tag{3–273}$$

is again a gaussian process.

[61] Davenport and Root, *op. cit.*; Lawson and Uhlenbeck, *op. cit.*

[62] We shall assume that $\int_{-\infty}^{\infty} |h(t)|dt < \infty$ and $\int_{-\infty}^{\infty} |h(t)|^2dt < \infty$.

We begin our derivation by establishing the following auxiliary result. Let $\phi_1,\phi_2,\cdots,\phi_\alpha$ denote a family of gaussian random variables

$$M_{\phi_1,\cdots,\phi_\alpha}(iv_1,\cdots,iv_\alpha) = \exp\{i\bar{v}_\alpha\bar{m}'_\phi\}\exp\{-\tfrac{1}{2}\bar{v}_\alpha\Lambda_\phi\bar{v}'_\alpha\} \quad (3\text{–}274)$$

where

$$\bar{v}_\alpha = \{v_1,\cdots,v_\alpha\}, \qquad \bar{m}_\phi = \{E[\phi_1],\cdots,E[\phi_\alpha]\}$$

and

$$\Lambda_\phi = \begin{bmatrix} \lambda_{11}\cdots & \\ \vdots & \lambda_{nn} \end{bmatrix}, \qquad \lambda_{jk} = E[(\phi_j - E[\phi_j])(\phi_k - E[\phi_k])]$$

and let A denote an arbitrary $\beta \times \alpha$ matrix. Under these conditions it follows that the random variables $\psi_1,\cdots,\psi_\beta$ defined by,

$$\bar{\psi}' = A\bar{\phi}' \quad (3\text{–}275)$$

where $\bar{\psi} = \{\psi_1,\cdots,\psi_\beta\}$ and $\bar{\phi} = \{\phi_1,\cdots,\phi_\alpha\}$, are again gaussian with covariance matrix $\Lambda_\psi = A\Lambda_\phi A'$ and with $\bar{m}'_\psi = A\bar{m}'_\phi$; *i.e.*

$$M_{\psi_1,\cdots,\psi_\beta}(iv_1,\cdots,iv_\beta) = \exp\{i\bar{v}_\beta A m'_\phi\}\exp[-\tfrac{1}{2}\bar{v}_\beta(A\Lambda_\phi A')\bar{v}'_\beta]\} \quad (3\text{–}276)$$

The proof of this assertion is quite simple

$$\begin{aligned} M_{\psi_1,\cdots,\psi_\beta}(iv_1,\cdots,iv_\beta) &= E[\exp\{i\bar{v}_\beta\bar{\psi}'\}] \\ &= E[\exp\{i\bar{v}_\beta A\bar{\phi}'\}] = E[\exp\{i\bar{u}_\beta\bar{\phi}'\}] \end{aligned} \quad (3\text{–}277)$$

where $\bar{u}_\beta = \bar{v}_\beta A$ and $\bar{v}_\beta = \{v_1,\ldots,v_\beta\}$.

However, since $\bar{\phi}$ is gaussian, we can write

$$\begin{aligned} E[\exp\{i\bar{u}_\beta\bar{\phi}'\}] &= \exp\{i\bar{u}_\beta\bar{m}'_\phi\}\exp\{-\tfrac{1}{2}\bar{u}_\beta\Lambda_\phi\bar{u}'_\beta\} \\ &= \exp\{i\bar{v}_\beta A\bar{m}'_\phi\}\exp\{-\tfrac{1}{2}\bar{v}_\beta(A\Lambda_\phi A')\bar{v}'_\beta\} \end{aligned} \quad (3\text{–}278)$$

which is the desired result.

The next step in the argument will be to make it plausible (a strict proof involves some limit arguments that would take us too far afield) that the (one-dimensional) distribution function of the random variable $Y(t)$ is gaussian. To do so, we argue that the integral in Eq. (3–273) can be approximated as closely as desired by a sum of the form

$$Y(t) = \int_{-\infty}^{\infty} h(\tau_j)X(t-\tau)d\tau \approx \sum_{j=1}^{n} h(\tau_j)X(t-\tau_j)\Delta\tau_j \quad (3\text{–}279)$$

as long as n is taken large enough and the $\Delta\tau_j$'s are taken small enough. This shows that $Y(t)$ is (approximately) a linear combination of a finite number of gaussian random variables, which means that we can apply the result just proved (using for A the $1 \times n$ matrix $[h(\tau_1),\cdots, h(\tau_n)]$) and conclude that $Y(t)$ is (at least approximately) gaussian.

A more refined argument shows that the gaussian character of the sum in Eq. (3–279) is preserved in the limit as $n \to \infty$ and $\Delta\tau_i \to 0$ so that we may conclude that $Y(t)$ is exactly gaussian. Since a (one-dimensional) gaussian distribution is completely specified by its mean and variance, we need merely calculate $E[Y(t)]$ and $E[Y^2(t)]$ to completely determine $p_Y(y)$. This is easily done as follows:

$$\begin{aligned} m_Y = E[Y(t)] = \lim_{T\to\infty} \frac{1}{2T} \int_{-T}^{T} Y(t)dt = \\ \lim_{T\to\infty} \frac{1}{2T} \int_{-T}^{T} \left[\int_{-\infty}^{\infty} h(\tau)X(t-\tau)d\tau \right] dt \\ = \int_{-\infty}^{\infty} h(\tau) \left[\lim_{T\to\infty} \frac{1}{2T} \int_{-T}^{T} X(t-\tau)dt \right] d\tau \\ = m_X \int_{-\infty}^{\infty} h(\tau)d\tau \end{aligned} \tag{3–280}$$

$$\begin{aligned} \sigma_Y^2 + m_Y^2 = E[Y^2(t)] = \\ \lim_{T\to\infty} \frac{1}{2T} \int_{-T}^{T} \left[\int_{-\infty}^{\infty} \int_{-\infty}^{\infty} h(\tau)h(\tau')X(t-\tau)X(t-\tau')d\tau d\tau' \right] dt \\ = \int_{-\infty}^{\infty} \int_{-\infty}^{\infty} h(\tau)h(\tau') \left[\lim_{T\to\infty} \frac{1}{2T} \int_{-T}^{T} X(t-\tau)X(t-\tau')dt \right] \\ = \int_{-\infty}^{\infty} \int_{-\infty}^{\infty} h(\tau)h(\tau')R_X(\tau-\tau')d\tau d\tau' \end{aligned} \tag{3–281}$$

where $R_X(\tau)$ denotes the autocorrelation function of $X(t)$.[63] Thus,

$$M_Y(iv) = \exp\{im_Y v\} \exp\{-\tfrac{1}{2}\sigma_Y^2 v^2\} \tag{3–282}$$

where m_Y and σ_Y^2 are given by Eqs. (3–280) and (3–281).

It is now a simple matter to conclude our argument by showing that *all* finite-order distribution functions of $Y(t)$ are gaussian. To accomplish this, we write

$$\begin{aligned} M_{Y,\tau_n}(iv_1,\cdots,iv_n) = E\left[\exp\left\{i \sum_{j=1}^{n} v_j Y(t+\tau_j)\right\}\right] \\ = E\left[\exp\left\{i \int_{-\infty}^{\infty} \left[\sum_{j=1}^{n} v_j h(\tau+\tau_j)\right] X(t-\tau)d\tau\right\}\right] \\ = E[\exp\{iY_0(t)\}] \end{aligned} \tag{3–283}$$

[63] The fact that

$$\lim_{T\to\infty} \frac{1}{2T} \int_{-T}^{T} X(t-\tau)X(t-\tau')dt = \lim_{T\to\infty} \frac{1}{2T} \int_{-T}^{T} X(t)X(t+\tau-\tau')dt$$

follows most easily from the fact that $p_{X,-\tau,-\tau'} = p_{X,0,\tau-\tau'}$. See Eq. (3–104).

where

$$\left.\begin{aligned} Y_0(t) &= \int_{-\infty}^{\infty} h_0(\tau)X(t-\tau)d\tau \\ h_0(t) &= \sum_{j=1}^{n} v_j h(t+\tau_j) \end{aligned}\right\} \tag{3–284}$$

and

Now, our previous result shows that $Y_0(t)$, being the result of passing $X(t)$ through the linear, time-invariant filter $h_0(t)$, must have a gaussian first-order distribution; therefore,

$$M_{Y,\tau_n}(iv_1,\cdots,iv_n) = E[\exp\{iY_0(t)\}] = \exp\{im_{Y_0}\}\exp\{-\tfrac{1}{2}\sigma_{Y_0}^2\} \tag{3–285}$$

where

$$\begin{aligned} m_{Y_0} &= m_X \int_{-\infty}^{\infty} h_0(\tau)d\tau \\ &= m_X\left[\sum_{j=1}^{n} v_j\right]\int_{-\infty}^{\infty} h(\tau)d\tau \end{aligned} \tag{3–286}$$

and

$$\begin{aligned} \sigma_{Y_0}^2 + m_{Y_0}^2 &= \int_{-\infty}^{\infty}\int_{-\infty}^{\infty} h_0(\tau)h_0(\tau')R_X(\tau-\tau')d\tau d\tau' \\ &= \sum_{j,k=1}^{n} v_j v_k \int_{-\infty}^{\infty}\int_{-\infty}^{\infty} h(\tau')h(\tau'')R_X \\ &\qquad \times (\tau'-\tau''+\tau_j-\tau_k)d\tau' d\tau'' \end{aligned} \tag{3–287}$$

We now have the final result that $Y(t)$ is a gaussian process with

$$M_{Y,\tau_n}(iv_1,\cdots,iv_n) = \exp\left\{im_Y \sum_{j=1}^{n} v_j\right\}\exp\{-\tfrac{1}{2}\bar{v}\Lambda_Y\bar{v}'\} \tag{3–288}$$

where

$$m_Y = m_X\int_{-\infty}^{\infty} h(\tau)d\tau, \tag{3–289}$$

$$\Lambda_Y = \begin{bmatrix} R_Y(\tau_1-\tau_1)-m_Y^2, & \cdots & R_Y(\tau_1-\tau_n)-m_Y^2 \\ \vdots & & \vdots \\ R_Y(\tau_n-\tau_1)-m_Y^2, & \cdots & R_Y(\tau_n-\tau_n)-m_Y^2 \end{bmatrix} \tag{3–290}$$

and

$$R_Y(\tau) = \int_{-\infty}^{\infty}\int_{-\infty}^{\infty} h(\tau')h(\tau'')R_X(\tau'-\tau''+\tau)d\tau' d\tau'' \tag{3–291}$$

We can conveniently summarize our results at this point by stating that if $X(t)$ is a gaussian process with mean m_X and autocorrelation function $R_X(\tau)$, then the output $Y(t)$ of a linear, time invariant filter with $X(t)$ as the input

$$Y(t) = \int_{-\infty}^{\infty} h(\tau)X(t - \tau)d\tau \tag{3-292}$$

is again a gaussian process with

$$m_Y = m_X \int_{-\infty}^{\infty} h(\tau)d\tau \tag{3-293}$$

and

$$R_Y(\tau) = \int_{-\infty}^{\infty} \int_{-\infty}^{\infty} h(\tau')h(\tau'')R_X(\tau' - \tau'' + \tau)d\tau'd\tau'' \tag{3-294}$$

In this connection, it should be carefully noted that, even if $X(t)$ is not a gaussian process, the mean and the autocorrelation function of the output of a linear, time-invariant filter are related to the mean and autocorrelation function of the input process according to Eqs. (3–293) and (3–294).[64] This is an important fact of which use will be made in the next section.

3.15. Harmonic Analysis of Random Processes.—The response $Y(t)$ of a linear, time-invariant electrical filter to an input $X(t)$ can be expressed in the familiar form [65]

$$Y(t) = \int_{-\infty}^{\infty} h(\tau)X(t - \tau)d\tau \tag{3-295}$$

where $h(t)$ denotes the response of the filter to a unit Dirac delta function $\delta(t)$. A great deal of insight into the action of the filter on the input can be obtained in those cases where the input is expressible as a sum of complex exponentials (harmonically analyzable) by means of a Fourier integral

$$X(t) = \int_{-\infty}^{\infty} \hat{X}(f)e^{i2\pi ft}df \tag{3-296}$$

where

$$\hat{X}(f) = \int_{-\infty}^{\infty} X(t)e^{-i2\pi ft}dt \tag{3-297}$$

[64] Y. W. Lee, *Statistical Theory of Communication*, p. 331, John Wiley and Sons, Inc., New York.

[65] The use of electrical engineering terminology here is purely for the sake of definiteness. The results obtained apply to a wide variety of problems arising in such diverse fields as mechanical vibrations, acoustics, and, with t replaced by a space parameter, optics.

In such cases, the input-output relation, Eq. (3–295), can be expressed in the form

$$\hat{Y}(f) = H(f)\hat{X}(f) \tag{3-298}$$

where $\hat{Y}(f)$ is the Fourier transform of $Y(t)$

$$\hat{Y}(f) = \int_{-\infty}^{\infty} Y(t)e^{-i2\pi ft}dt \tag{3-299}$$

and $H(f)$ is given by

$$H(f) = \int_{-\infty}^{\infty} h(t)e^{-i2\pi ft}dt \tag{3-300}$$

The Fourier transform $H(f)$ of the impulse response $h(t)$ is called the *system function.* The system function relates the Fourier transforms of the input and output time functions by means of the extremely simple Eq. (3–298), which states that the action of the filter is to modify that part of the input consisting of a complex exponential at frequency f by multiplying its amplitude (magnitude) by $|H(f)|$ and adding $\arg[H(f)]$ to its phase angle (argument).

The main assumption needed to arrive at Eq. (3–298) is that the input be expressible as a Fourier integral, Eq. (3–296). The theory of the Fourier integral shows that, with proper interpretation of the integrals involved, this will be the case when $X(t)$ satisfies an integrability condition such as

$$\int_{-\infty}^{\infty} |X(t)|dt \quad \text{finite} \tag{3-301}$$

or

$$\int_{-\infty}^{\infty} |X(t)|^2dt \quad \text{finite} \tag{3-302}$$

These conditions automatically exclude from consideration exactly those time functions $X(t)$ that we have been concerned with in this chapter; namely, functions that have nontrivial (not simply a unit jump at the origin) probability distribution functions, and, therefore, do not go to zero as $t \to \pm\infty$ as required by either Eq. (3–301) or Eq. (3–302). These integrability conditions can be waived in favor of weaker ones that do not require the functions involved to go to zero as $t \to \pm\infty$ by making use of a representation in the form of a Stieltjes-like integral[66]

$$X(t) = \int_{-\infty}^{\infty} e^{i2\pi ft}d\sigma(f) \tag{3-303}$$

[66] N. Wiener, "Generalized Harmonic Analysis," *Acta Mathematica,* **55,** 117–258 (1930).

But this theory is rather difficult, and, as we shall see shortly, is not really necessary for the development of one of the most important parts of the theory of random harmonic analysis.

Thus far, we have been exploring the possibility of using the classical techniques of harmonic analysis to analyze the effect of linear, time-invariant filters on signals that do not die out when $|t|$ is large. In this discussion, we have tacitly assumed that our ultimate objective was to give a complete description of the output in terms of a complete description of the input and the filter characteristics. But this is *not* really what we want! Our philosophy has been to describe signals as random processes—in terms of certain time averages—rather than point-by-point as functions of time. This means that our objective should be to use the ideas of harmonic analysis to facilitate the calculation of filter output *averages* in terms of filter input *averages* rather than to facilitate the exact calculation of the output from the input. A clear understanding of this point opens up a whole new avenue of approach to the problem of the harmonic analysis of random processes.

As a simple example, we recall that the expectations of the input and output of a linear, time-invariant filter are related by means of Eq. (3–293), which is reproduced below for convenience,

$$m_Y = m_X \int_{-\infty}^{\infty} h(\tau)d\tau \qquad (3\text{–}293)$$

This equation assumes a much simpler form if we express it in terms of the system function $H(f)$ instead of the impulse response $h(t)$; namely, as reference to Eq. (3–300) shows

$$m_Y = m_X H(0) \qquad (3\text{–}304)$$

we now see that Eq. (3–293) and, equivalently, Eq. (3–304) state the (not too surprising) result that the d.c. value of the output is equal to the d.c. value of the input multiplied by the d.c. (zero frequency) response of the filter.

A less trivial example arises when we inquire how the output power is related to the input signal. We have already made this calculation in Eq. (3–276),

$$E[Y^2(t)] = \int_{-\infty}^{\infty}\int_{-\infty}^{\infty} h(\tau)h(\tau')R(\tau - \tau')d\tau d\tau' \qquad (3\text{–}276)$$

which states that the output power of any linear, time-invariant filter can be calculated from a knowledge of the autocorrelation function of the input signal.

Equation (3–276) assumes a simpler form if we express it in terms of the Fourier transform[67] of $R_X(\tau)$ instead of $R_X(\tau)$ itself. Writing

$$R_X(\tau) = \int_{-\infty}^{\infty} S_X(f)e^{i2\pi f\tau}df \qquad (3\text{–}305)$$

where

$$S_X(f) = \int_{-\infty}^{\infty} R_X(\tau)e^{-i2\pi f\tau}d\tau \qquad (3\text{–}306)$$

we obtain

$$\begin{aligned} E[Y^2(t)] &= \int_{-\infty}^{\infty} \int h(\tau)h(\tau') \left[\int_{-\infty}^{\infty} S_X(f)e^{i2\pi f(\tau-\tau')}df \right] d\tau d\tau' \\ &= \int_{-\infty}^{\infty} S_X(f) \left[\int_{-\infty}^{\infty} h(\tau)e^{i2\pi f\tau}d\tau \right] \left[\int_{-\infty}^{\infty} h(\tau')e^{-i2\pi f\tau'}d\tau' \right] df \\ &= \int_{-\infty}^{\infty} S_X(f)\tilde{H}(f)H(f)df \\ &= \int_{-\infty}^{\infty} S_X(f)|H(f)|^2 df \qquad (3\text{–}307)^{68} \end{aligned}$$

In other words, the output power is the area under the product of the Fourier transform of $R_X(\tau)$ and the squared modulus of the system function $H(f)$.

Equation (3–307) also leads to a very important physical interpretation of the function $S_X(f)$; namely, that $S_X(f)$ describes the way in which the total power of $X(t)$ is distributed in frequency. This comes about if we accept the physically reasonable definition that the power in $X(t)$ contained in the frequency band $f_1 < |f| < f_2$ is equal to the total power output of the ideal band-pass filter $H(f)$ shown in Fig. 3–11, when $X(t)$ is the input. Equation (3–307) now yields the result,

power in $X(t)$ in the band $f_1 < |f| < f_2$

$$= \int_{f_1<|f|<f_2} S_X(f)df \qquad (3\text{–}308)$$

which allows us to interpret $S_X(f)$ as the *power density spectrum* of $X(t)$; *i.e.*, that function which, when integrated over the frequency band of interest, yields the power contained in $X(t)$ in that band. This result, that the Fourier transform of the autocorrelation function $R_X(\tau)$ is the power density spectrum of $X(t)$, is called the Wiener-

[67] If the Fourier transform of $R_X(\tau)$ does not exist either as an ordinary integrable function or in terms of Dirac delta functions, the following argument must be modified somewhat. We shall not concern ourselves with this case here.

[68] The notation $\tilde{H}(f)$ will be used to denote the complex conjugate of $H(f)$.

Khinchine Theorem. It tells us the very important fact that all time functions, no matter what their detailed shape, whose autocorrelation functions are equal, have their power distributed in frequency in an identical way!

A number of important properties of $S_X(f)$ are now apparent. The fact that $R_X(\tau)$ is a real, even[69] function of τ means that $S_X(f)$ must also be real and even. Moreover, since the integral of $S_X(f)$ over any band of frequencies, however narrow, is the power contained in those frequencies, this integral must be non-negative. The only way

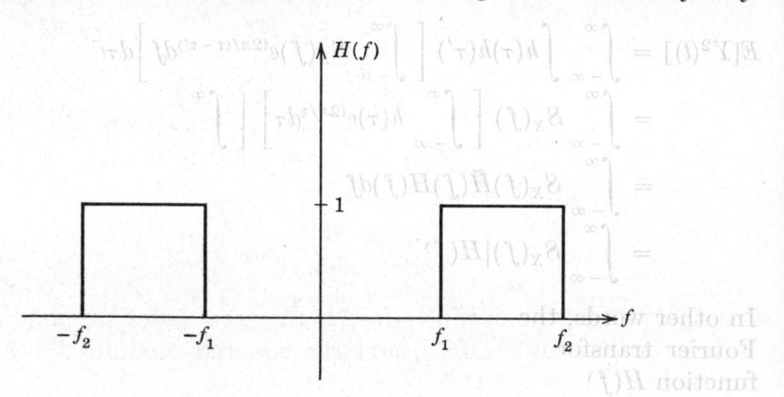

Fig. 3–11. The Power in $X(t)$ Contained in the Band $f_1 < |f| < f_2$ is the Total Power Output of $H(f)$ when $X(t)$ is the Input.

this can be so for arbitrarily narrow frequency bands is for $S_X(f)$ itself to be non-negative. We have thus demonstrated that

$$\left.\begin{aligned} &S_X(f) \text{ is real} \\ &S_X(f) = S_X(-f) \\ &S_X(f) \geq 0 \end{aligned}\right\} \tag{3–309}$$

In order to clarify these ideas, let us calculate the power density spectrum of the real, periodic function given by

$$X(t) = \sum_{k=-\infty}^{\infty} X_k e^{i2\pi(k/T_0)t} \tag{3–310}$$

where the X_k denote complex constants satisfying $X_k = \tilde{X}_{-k}$, $\sum_{k=-\infty}^{\infty} |X_k|^2 < \infty$ and T_0 denotes the period of $X(t)$. In this case, it is obvious *a priori* that the power in $X(t)$ is located only at the discrete frequencies $\pm k/T_0$, $k = 0,1,\cdots$ and that the power present

[69] The evenness follows from the fact that $p_{X0,\tau}(x) = p_{X-\tau,0}(x)$. See Eq. (3–104).

at frequency k/T_0 is $|X_k|^2$. We, therefore, know in advance that the power density spectrum of $X(t)$ must be

$$S_X(f) = \sum_{k=-\infty}^{\infty} |X_k|^2 \delta\left(f - \frac{k}{T_0}\right) \tag{3–311}$$

We shall now see how we can arrive at the same conclusion using the methods derived above, which, it should be emphasized, are applicable to a much larger class of functions than the periodic functions.

The autocorrelation function of $X(t)$ can be calculated as follows:

$$\begin{aligned} R_X(\tau) &= E[X(t)X(t+\tau)] \\ &= E\left\{\left[\sum_{j=-\infty}^{\infty} X_j e^{i2\pi(j/T_0)t}\right]\left[\sum_{k=-\infty}^{\infty} X e^{i2\pi(k/T_0)(t+\tau)}\right]\right\} \\ &= \sum_{j,k=-\infty}^{\infty} X_j X_k e^{i2\pi(k/T_0)\tau} E\left[e^{i2\pi[(j+k)/T_0]t}\right] \end{aligned} \tag{3–312}$$

A simple calculation now shows that

$$E[e^{i2\pi[(j+k)/T_0]t}] = \begin{cases} 1, & j = -k \\ 0, & j \neq -k \end{cases} \tag{3–313}$$

and it follows that

$$\begin{aligned} R_X(\tau) &= \sum_{k=-\infty}^{\infty} X_k X_{-k} e^{i2\pi(k/T_0)\tau} \\ &= \sum_{k=-\infty}^{\infty} |X_k|^2 e^{i2\pi(k/T_0)\tau} \end{aligned} \tag{3–314}$$

Since the Fourier transform of $e^{i2\pi(k/T_0)\tau}$ is $\delta(f - k/T_0)$, we have the result

$$S_X(f) = \int_{-\infty}^{\infty} R_X(\tau) e^{i2\pi f\tau} d\tau = \sum_{k=-\infty}^{\infty} |X_k|^2 \delta\left(f - \frac{k}{T_0}\right) \tag{3–315}$$

which checks with Eq. (3–311).

As a further application of the Wiener-Khinchine theorem, we shall now calculate the power density spectrum of the shot noise process. The autocorrelation function for such a process is given by Campbell's theorem, Eq. (3–262), repeated below

$$R_X(\tau) = \left[\bar{n}\int_{-\infty}^{\infty} h(t)dt\right] + \bar{n}\int_{-\infty}^{\infty} h(t)h(t+\tau)dt \tag{3–262}$$

Writing Eq. (3–262) in terms of $H(f)$, the Fourier transform of $h(t)$, we obtain

$$R_X(\tau) = [\bar{n}H(0)]^2 + \bar{n}\int_{-\infty}^{\infty} |H(f)|^2 e^{i2\pi f\tau} df \tag{3–316}$$

The Fourier transform $S_X(f)$ of $R_X(\tau)$ is now readily seen to be

$$S_X(f) = [\bar{n}H(0)]^2\delta(f) + \bar{n}|H(f)|^2 \tag{3-317}$$

Equation (3–317) shows that the power density spectrum of $X(t)$ is related in a very simple way to the Fourier transform of the individual pulses making up the shot noise process.

This last result enables us to deduce some very important facts concerning the power density spectrum of the noise produced by a vacuum tube. We shall assume that the current produced by a single electron passing from the cathode to the plate is a narrow pulse whose exact shape is unknown but whose area is equal to the electronic charge e and whose duration Δ is known. See Fig. 3–12. Setting $h(t) = i_{e(t)}$ in Eq. (3–262), we can draw the following conclusions.

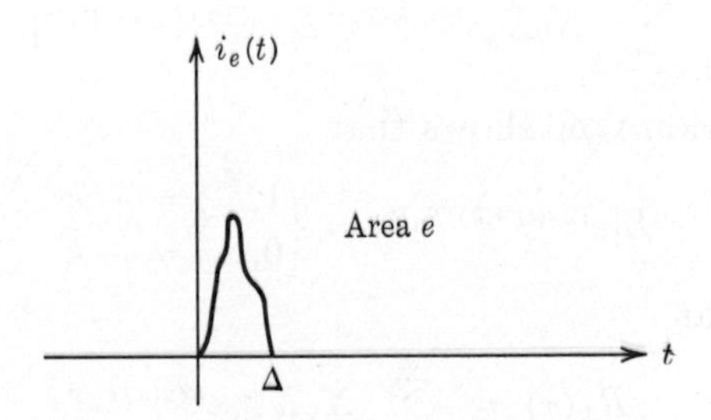

FIG. 3–12. Current Produced by a Single Electron in a Vacuum Tube. The letter e denotes the electronic charge and Δ, the transit time of the electron.

Since

$$H(0) = \int_{-\infty}^{\infty} i_{e(t)} dt = e \tag{3-318}$$

we see that the d.c. value (square root of the d.c. power) of the vacuum tube current is equal to $\bar{n}e$. Moreover, since

$$H(f) = \int_0^{\Delta} i_{e(t)} e^{-i2\pi ft} dt \approx e \quad \text{for} \quad |f| \ll \frac{1}{\Delta} \tag{3-319}$$

we see that the power density spectrum of the current is essentially flat and equal to $\bar{n}e^2$ watts per cycle for frequencies small compared with the reciprocal of the transit time. This is illustrated in Fig. 3–13. The fact that $1/\Delta$ is on the order of 10^9 for ordinary vacuum tubes now leads us to the conclusion that vacuum-tube-generated shot noise is essentially "white" noise over the band of frequencies that are usually of interest. This explains the prevalence of the "white" noise assumption in analyses of noise in vacuum tube circuits.

With the aid of the power density spectrum, we can now give a complete description of how a linear, time-invariant filter affects the frequency distribution of power of the input time function $X(t)$. To accomplish this, we must find the relationship between the power

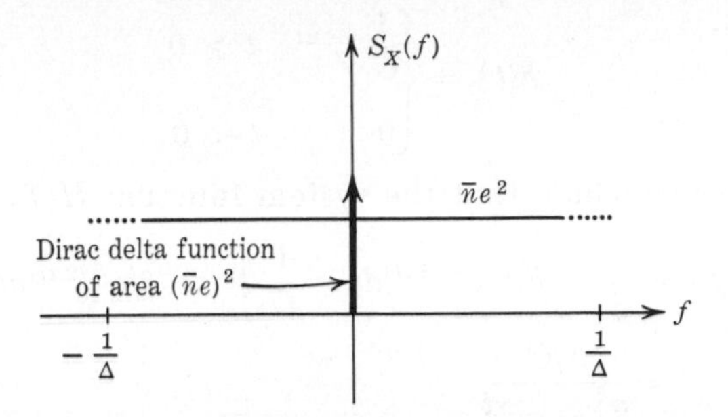

FIG. 3–13. The Power Density Spectrum of Vacuum Tube Current.

density spectra of the input $X(t)$ and the output $Y(t)$ of the filter. We have already derived the relationship between the input and output autocorrelation functions with the result

$$R_Y(\tau) = \int_{-\infty}^{\infty} h(\tau')h(\tau'')R_X(\tau' - \tau' + \tau)d\tau'd\tau'' \qquad (3\text{–}295)$$

Writing $R_X(\tau)$ as the Fourier transform of $S_X(f)$, Eq. (3–295) assumes the form

$$\begin{aligned} R_Y(\tau) &= \int_{-\infty}^{\infty}\int_{-\infty}^{\infty} h(\tau')h(\tau'')\left[\int_{-\infty}^{\infty} S_X(f)e^{i2\pi f(\tau'-\tau''+\tau)}df\right]d\tau'd\tau'' \\ &= \int_{-\infty}^{\infty} S_X(f)e^{i2\pi f\tau}\left[\int_{-\infty}^{\infty} h(\tau')e^{i2\pi f\tau'}d\tau'\right] \\ &\qquad\qquad \left[\int_{-\infty}^{\infty} h(\tau'')e^{-i2\pi f\tau''}d\tau''\right]df \\ &= \int_{-\infty}^{\infty} S_X(f)|H(f)|^2 e^{i2\pi f\tau}df \end{aligned} \qquad (3\text{–}320)$$

Equation (3–320) states that $S_X(f)|H(f)|^2$ is the Fourier transform of $R_Y(\tau)$, thus giving us the result that

$$S_Y(f) = S_X(f)|H(f)|^2 \qquad (3\text{–}321)$$

The resemblances (and differences!) between Eq. (3–321), which relates the input and output power density spectra of a linear, time-invariant filter, and Eq. (3–298), which relates the input and output Fourier transforms (when these exist) should be noted carefully.

As an example of the use of Eq. (3–321), we shall calculate the output power density spectrum of an RC filter whose input consists of "white" noise. The RC filter in question is shown in Fig. 3–14. It is a simple matter to verify that the impulse response of this filter is given by

$$h(t) = \begin{cases} \frac{1}{C} e^{-at} & t \geq 0 \\ 0 & t < 0 \end{cases} \tag{3–322}$$

from which we conclude that the system function $H(f)$ is given by

$$\begin{aligned} H(f) &= \int_{-\infty}^{\infty} h(t) e^{-i2\pi ft} dt = \frac{1}{C} \int_{0}^{\infty} e^{-at} e^{-i2\pi ft} dt \\ &= \frac{1/C}{a + i2\pi f} \end{aligned} \tag{3–323}$$

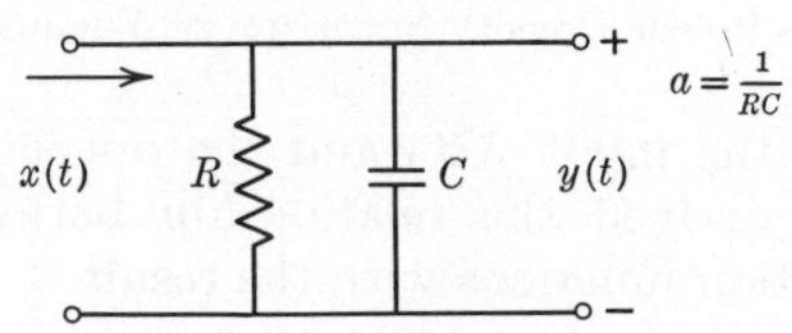

FIG. 3–14. An RC Filter Whose Input is a Current with Reference Direction Indicated by the Arrow, and Whose Output is a Voltage with Reference Polarity as Shown.

Assuming that the input noise is "white", *i.e.*, $S_X(f) = N_0$, we conclude from Eq. (3–323) that

$$S_Y(f) = \frac{N_0/C^2}{|a + i2\pi f|^2} = \frac{N_0/C^2}{a^2 + (2\pi f)^2} \tag{3–324}$$

This result can now be used to verify our earlier statement that the gaussian Markov process defined by Eq. (3–218) is a good model for RC filtered vacuum tube noise. We have already seen that vacuum tube noise is essentially gaussian (as long as $\bar{n}$ is large) and that its spectrum is essentially "white".[70] A reasonable model for RC filtered

[70] Except for the impulse at the origin representing d.c. power and arising from the fact that the vacuum tube current has a nonzero mean value. We shall neglect this mean value in the following discussion, and concentrate only on the time-varying part of the noise.

vacuum tube noise is, therefore, a gaussian process with zero mean whose spectrum is given by Eq. (3–324). The autocorrelation function of this process must be the Fourier transform of Eq. (3–324)

$$R_Y(\tau) = \int_{-\infty}^{\infty} \frac{N_0/C^2}{a^2 + (2\pi f)^2} e^{i2\pi f\tau} df = \frac{N_0}{2C^2 a} e^{-a|\tau|} \tag{3-325}$$

Equation (3–325), along with the fact that $Y(t)$ has zero mean and is gaussian, completely specifies $Y(t)$ as a random process. Detailed expressions for the characteristic function of the finite order distributions of $Y(t)$ can be calculated by means of Eq. (3–271). A straightforward, although somewhat tedious, calculation of the characteristic function of the finite-order distributions of the gaussian Markov process defined by Eq. (3–218) now shows that these two processes are in fact identical, thus proving our assertion.

CHAPTER 4

INFORMATION THEORY

by

ROBERT G. GALLAGER

Electrical Engineering Department and Research Laboratory of Electronics
Massachusetts Institute of Technology

4.1. Introduction.—This chapter will deal with that branch of communication theory growing out of C. E. Shannon's classical papers in 1948.[1] While information theory is sometimes taken to include other topics, in particular the branch of communication theory stemming from Wiener's work,[2] these topics will not be considered here. In Shannon's theory, a communication source is modeled by a random process, and a communication channel is modeled by a probability measure on the channel outputs given the input. For such models, the information rate of a source and the information being transmitted over a channel can be given mathematical definitions. Using these definitions, Shannon discovered the coding theorem, which is the central result of Information Theory.

The coding theorem states that if a source rate is less than the information capable of being transmitted by the channel, then the source output can be transmitted over the channel with as high a reliability as desired by the use of sufficiently complex data processing or coding equipment at the channel terminals. Theorem 4–11 gives a careful statement and proof of this result.

Most communication systems can be separated into the basic components shown in Fig. 4–1a. Figures 4–1b, c, d, e show some specific examples of how particular systems can be separated into these components. There is, of course, considerable flexibility in this separation: sometimes it is convenient to consider an antenna as part of the channel, and sometimes as part of the coder or decoder. Here

[1] C. E. Shannon, "A Mathematical Theory of Communication," *Bell System Technical Journal*, pp. 379 and 623 (1948). Also in book form under same title, University of Illinois Press, Urbana, Ill. For a recent treatment that is more comprehensive than this chapter, see R. M. Fano, *The Transmission of Information*, Massachusetts Institute of Technology Press, and John Wiley and Sons, Inc., New York, 1961.

[2] N. Wiener, *Cybernetics*, The Technology Press and John Wiley & Sons, Inc., New York, 1948; *Extrapolation, Interpolation, and Smoothing of Stationary Time Series*, The Technology Press and John Wiley & Sons, Inc., New York, 1948.

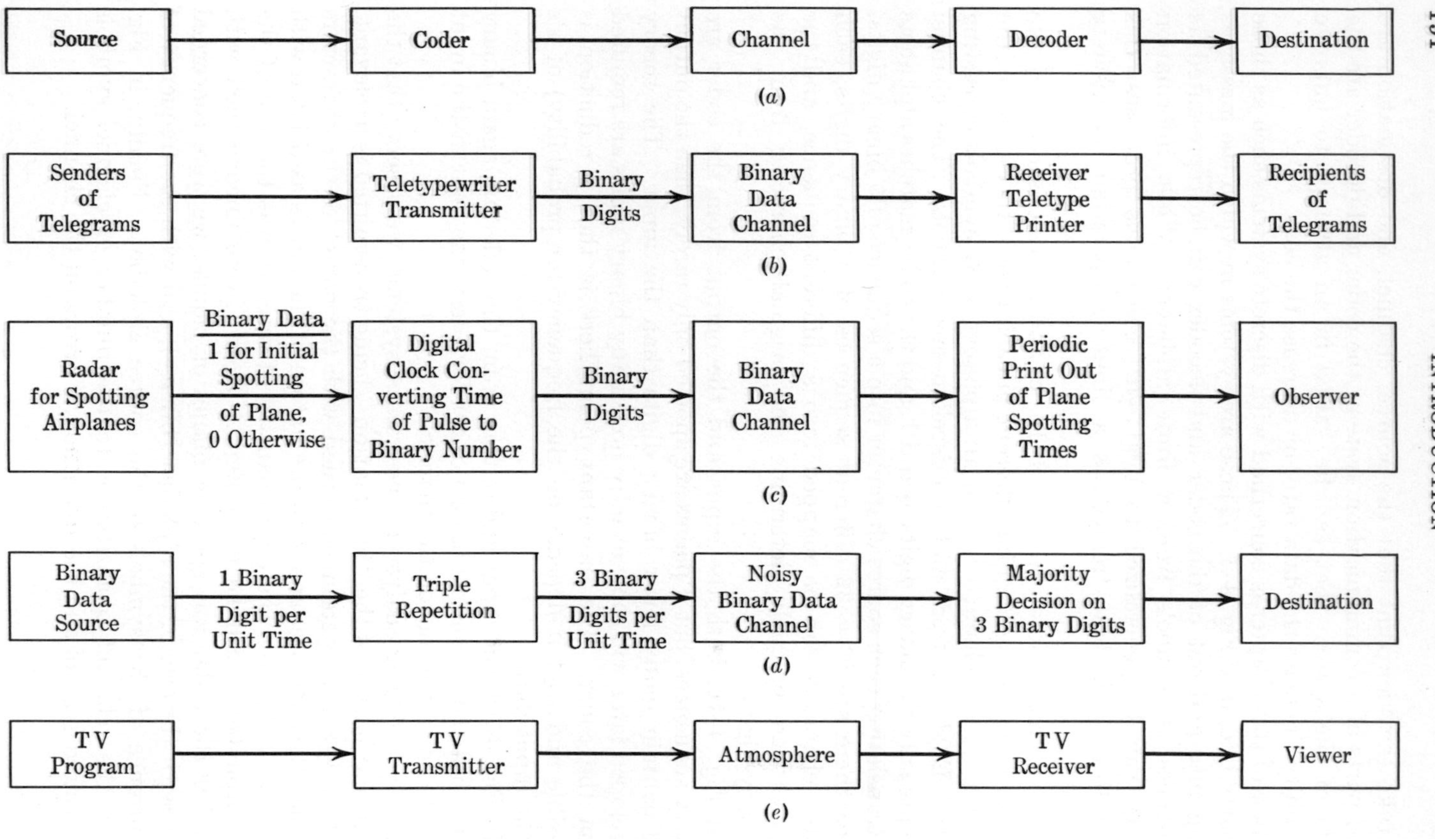

Fig. 4–1. Block Diagram of Communication System.

we take the viewpoint that the source, channel, and destination are fixed parts of a communication system; the coder and decoder are the parts of the system that can be varied in an attempt to improve reliability, increase the data rate, or decrease the cost.

Most of this chapter is concerned with discrete systems such as those in parts b, c, d of Fig. 4–1. These are systems in which the messages going into and out of the coder and decoder can be represented as sequences of symbols from a finite alphabet. While information theory can be generalized to deal with continuous processes, this generalization is best treated as a limiting operation on discrete processes.

Looking more closely at Fig. 4–1b, c, and d, we observe that the object of the coding is quite different in each case. In Fig. 4–1b, the source produces characters from an alphabet of 32 symbols consisting of the English letters and 6 miscellaneous symbols. The channel accepts only the binary digits, 0 and 1, and the coder matches alphabets by translating each source character into a sequence of 5 binary digits. Since there are $2^5 = 32$ different sequences of 5 binary digits, each source character can be mapped into a different sequence, and the decoder can uniquely determine the original character from the 5 binary digits.

In Fig. 4–1c, both the input and the output from the coder are binary sequences, but if planes are spotted only rarely, then the output will contain many fewer binary digits than the input. The theory developed later will show exactly how many binary digits are required from the coder. The important point here is that a reduction is possible and that it depends on the frequency (or probability) of 1's in the input data.

In Fig. 4–1d, the input and output from the coder are again binary digits, but the output contains 3 digits for every one digit at the input so as to correct errors on the channel.

In the foregoing analysis of these three systems, we observe that the particular nature of the "information" being transmitted is irrelevant. In Fig. 4–1b, we were unconcerned with the names of the characters on the teletypewriter and with the nature of the pulses associated with the binary digits. The only quantity of interest was the size of the two alphabets. Similarly, in Fig. 4–1c, we were unconcerned with whether the radar was spotting planes or clouds; we were concerned only with the size of the alphabet (binary), and with the frequency of occurrence of the symbols in the source alphabet. Finally, in Fig. 4–1d, the relevant quantities were the number of channel symbols per source symbol and the frequency of errors on the channel.

These examples then suggest that any general and fundamental models of communication systems (at least for digital data) should emphasize the size of the alphabets concerned and the probabilities of these letters, and should be relatively unconcerned with other characteristics of the letters. An appropriate model for this purpose consists of a random process in place of the source, a transformation on the samples of the random process for the coder, a random process at the output of the channel depending statistically on the input to the channel, and a transformation in the decoder. We are, of course, interested in knowing what transformations to use in the coder and decoder to make the decoder output as faithful a replica of the source output as possible.

The problems involved in finding random process models for particular sources and channels are, of course, very difficult. Such models can hardly ever be more than crude approximations to physical reality. Even the simplest random process model, however, makes it possible to consider a class of inputs rather than a single input and to consider the frequency with which the inputs are used.

The modeling problem can only be approached intelligently after one knows the implications of the models that can be analyzed. In the following sections, we analyze simple classes of models for sources and channels. The results of that analysis give some indication of the sensitivity of communication system performance to small changes in the model; this in turn sheds some light on the problem of choosing models. The simplified models of sources and channels that are analyzed in most of this chapter are now described in detail.

Discrete Memoryless Source.—Consider a source that produces a symbol once every T_s seconds from a finite alphabet containing M symbols. Denote the symbols in the alphabet by $u_1, u_2, \cdots, u_M$. Let $p_1 = Pr(u_1)$, $p_2 = Pr(u_2), \cdots, p_M = Pr(u_M)$ be a probability measure defined on the symbols of the alphabet. Let

$$\cdots, \mathscr{u}_{-2}, \mathscr{u}_{-1}, \mathscr{u}_0, \mathscr{u}_1, \mathscr{u}_2, \cdots$$

be the sequence of symbols coming from the source, and assume that these symbols are chosen with statistical independence by the source according to the probability measure $\boldsymbol{P} = (p_1, \cdots, p_M)$. That is

$$Pr(\mathscr{u}_n = u_m) = p_m, \quad \text{all } n, \ 1 \leq m \leq M \tag{4–1}$$

By statistical independence between terms, we mean

$$Pr(\mathscr{u}_n = u_m | \mathscr{u}_{n-1}, \mathscr{u}_{n-2}, \cdots) = Pr(\mathscr{u}_n = u_m) \tag{4–2}$$

A discrete memoryless source is a source whose statistics satisfy Eqs. (4–1) and (4–2).

Discrete Memoryless Channel.—We can define a communication channel in terms of the statistical relationship between its input and output. The channels we consider here have sequences of symbols from finite alphabets both for input and output. Let the input alphabet consist of K symbols denoted by $x_1, \cdots, x_K$, and let the output alphabet consist of J symbols denoted by $y_1, \cdots, y_J$. Each unit of time the coder can choose any one of the K input symbols for transmission, and one of the J output symbols will appear at the channel output. Due to noise in the channel, the output will not be determined uniquely from the input, but instead will be a random event satisfying a probability measure. We let $Pr(y_j|x_k)$ be the probability of receiving the jth output symbol when the kth input symbol is transmitted. These transition probabilities are assumed to be independent of time and independent of previous transmissions. More precisely, let

$$\cdots x_{-2}, x_{-1}, x_0, x_1, x_2, \cdots$$

be the sequence in time of input symbols, and let

$$\cdots, y_{-2}, y_{-1}, y_0, y_1, y_2, \cdots$$

be the corresponding output sequence. Then

$$Pr(y_n = y_j \mid x_n = x_k) = Pr(y_j \mid x_k); \quad \text{all } n, j, k \tag{4–3}$$

$$Pr(y_n \mid x_n, y_{n-1}, x_{n-1}, \cdots) = Pr(y_n \mid x_n); \quad \text{all } n \tag{4–4}$$

We refer to channel models satisfying Eqs. (4–3) and (4–4) as discrete memoryless channels.

This class of channel models appears rather restrictive at first, but it can be applied to many channels whose inputs and outputs are functions of time simply by quantizing in time and amplitude. This problem is discussed in more detail in Section 4.8 where the results that we derive for discrete memoryless channels are extended to a more general class of channels.

The major problem that we wish to consider can now be stated as follows: for a given source and channel, how reliably can the source output be transmitted to the destination, and how can one build coders and decoders that approach this ideal?

The answer to the first question is very simple, although the proof is somewhat involved. Each discrete memoryless source has a number, R, called the transmission rate, associated with it, and each discrete memoryless channel has a number, C, called the channel capacity, associated with it. If $R < C$, one can receive the source output at the destination with as few errors as desired. If $R > C$, the number of errors can not be reduced to an arbitrarily low level. This amazing result is known as the coding theorem and was discovered by Shannon.[3]

We shall prove this result in a much stronger form by considering the coder and decoder in two parts. The first part of the coder, called the source coder, will transform the source into a sequence of $R + \varepsilon$ binary digits per second, where ε can be made as small as desired. The second part of the coder, called the channel coder, will take these binary digits in sequences, say T seconds long, and transform the sequence of binary digits into a sequence of channel input symbols. Then the channel decoder will recover the binary digits from the channel output sequences. We shall show in Section 4.7 that the probability of error in this decoding can be made to satisfy

$$P_e \leq 2e^{-TE}$$

where E is a number depending on the rate, the capacity, and the channel probabilities, $Pr(y|x)$; furthermore E is positive if $R < C$. Such a result is of fundamental importance since the complexity of the coding and decoding operation is closely associated with the coder constraint time, T.

In the following sections we shall first discuss information and coding for sources, and then information and coding for channels.

4.2. Self Information and Entropy.—Let U be a discrete alphabet consisting of the symbols $u_1, u_2, \cdots, u_M$, where M is the size of the alphabet. Let $p_m = Pr(u_m)$, $1 \leq m \leq M$, be a probability measure assigned to these symbols. The set of numbers, $p_1, \cdots, p_M$, is arbitrary, except, of course, that each number is non-negative and

$$\sum_{m=1}^{M} p_m = 1$$

We will refer to the combination of alphabet and probability measure as an ensemble. The self information of the mth symbol in the ensemble is now defined as

$$I(u_m) = -\log Pr(u_m) \tag{4-5}$$

The logarithm base in Eq. (4–5) determines the units of self information. The two most common units are bits (base 2) and nats (base e); the conversion between them is given by

$$1 \text{ nat} = \frac{1}{\ln 2} \text{ bits}$$

[3] C. E. Shannon, "A Mathematical Theory of Communication," *Bell System Technical Journal*, pp. 379 and 623 (1948).

Partly for convenience and partly to achieve familiarity with both units, we will use bits in Sections 4.2 to 4.6 and nats in Sections 4.7 and 4.8.

It is important to observe that self information is a function only of the probability of a symbol and has nothing to do with the meaning or form of the symbol. Since $0 \leq p_m \leq 1$, the self information of u_m is always non-negative. Furthermore, $I(u_m)$ is a decreasing function of p_m. This is intuitively satisfying since the occurrence of something improbable is generally thought to be more informative than the occurrence of something probable.

The most important characteristic of self information is that it is a discrete random variable; that is, it is a real valued function of a symbol in a discrete ensemble. As a result, it has a distribution function, an average, a variance, and in fact moments of all orders. The average value of self information has such a fundamental importance in information theory that it is given a special symbol, H, and the name entropy. Thus

$$H(U) = \overline{I(u)} = \sum_{m=1}^{M} p_m I(u_m) = \sum_{m=1}^{M} -p_m \log_2 p_m \text{ bits} \qquad (4\text{–}6)$$

The name entropy is used here because of the similarity of Eq. (4–6) to the definition of entropy in statistical mechanics. We shall show later that $H(U)$ is the average number of binary digits per source letter required to represent the source output.

A problem arises in Eq. (4–6) if some of the probabilities are 0. We shall adopt the convention throughout the rest of this chapter that a function of probabilities, $F(p_1, p_2, \cdots, p_M)$, is defined at $p_m = 0$ by the limit of F as p_m approaches 0 from above. Thus, by convention, when $p_m = 0$, $p_m \log p_m = 0$.

Since $I(u_m) \geq 0$ for $1 \leq m \leq M$, it follows immediately that the entropy is also non-negative. We also observe that if all symbols are equiprobable, $p_m = (1/M)$ for $1 \leq m \leq M$, and

$$H(U) = \log_2 M \text{ bits} \qquad (4\text{–}7)$$

We now show that any other probability assignment yields a smaller entropy.

Theorem 4–1. Let U be an ensemble of M symbols. Then if $p_m \neq 1/M$ for one or more symbols,

$$H(U) < \log_2 M$$

Proof: It suffices to show that $H(U) - \log_2 M < 0$

$$H(U) - \log_2 M = \sum_{m=1}^{M} -p_m \log_2 p_m - \sum_{m=1}^{M} p_m \log_2 M$$
$$= \sum_{m=1}^{M} p_m \log_2 \frac{1}{p_m M}$$

Using the inequality $\ln z \leq z - 1$ for $z > 0$ with strict unequality for $z \neq 1$, we get

$$\log_2 \left(\frac{1}{p_m M}\right) < \frac{1}{\ln 2}\left(\frac{1}{p_m M} - 1\right)$$

for at least one m. Then

$$H(U) - \log_2 M < \left(\frac{1}{\ln 2}\right) \sum_{m=1}^{M} \left(\frac{p_m}{p_m M} - p_m\right) = 0$$

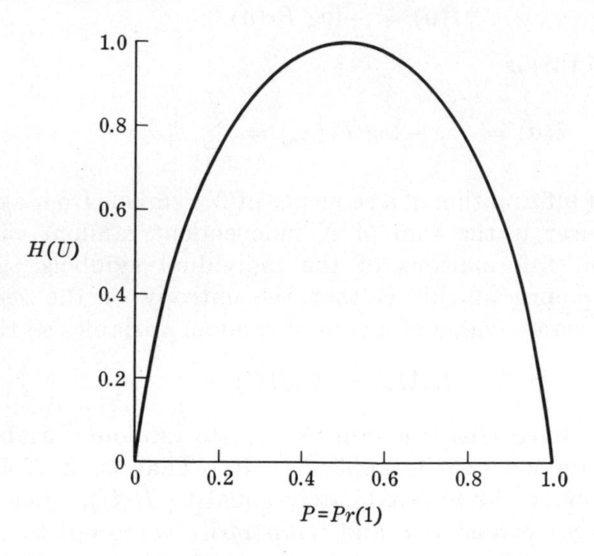

FIG. 4–2. Entropy of Binary Digit.

As an example of self information and entropy, consider the ensemble, U, consisting of the binary digits, 0, and 1. Then if we let $p = Pr(1)$,

$$I(1) = -\log p; \qquad I(0) = -\log(1 - p)$$
$$H(U) = -p \log_2 p - (1 - p) \log_2 (1 - p)$$

This entropy is sketched as a function of p in Fig. 4–2. If $p = \frac{1}{2}$, $H(U) = 1$ bit; this gives the bit additional interpretation as the maximum self information of a binary digit. If, on the other hand, $p = 10^{-5}$, then $I(1) = 16.57$ bits, $I(0) = 1.44 \times 10^{-5}$, and $H = 18.0 \times 10^{-5}$ bits. The fact that most of the contribution to the entropy comes from the improbable event fits in with Fig. 4–1c in which the coder operated by specifying when the 1's occurred.

Next consider a product ensemble, $\mathbf{U}_N$, composed of sequences of N statistically independent symbols each drawn from the ensemble U. The probability of a sequence, $\mathbf{u} = (u_1, u_2, \cdots, u_N)$ is given by

$$Pr(\mathbf{u}) = \prod_{n=1}^{N} Pr(u_n) \tag{4–8}$$

where

$$Pr(u_n = u_m) = p_m$$

The self information of a point in this product space is given, as before, by

$$I(\mathbf{u}) = -\log Pr(\mathbf{u}) \tag{4–9}$$

From Eq. (4–8) this is

$$I(\mathbf{u}) = \sum_{n=1}^{N} -\log Pr(u_n) = \sum_{n=1}^{N} I(u_n) \tag{4–10}$$

Thus, the self information of a sequence of N symbols from a discrete memoryless source is the sum of N independent random variables, namely the self informations of the individual symbols. An immediate consequence of this is that the entropy of the sequence, $H(\mathbf{U}_N)$, is the average value of a sum of random variables so that

$$H(\mathbf{U}_N) = N\,H(U) \tag{4–11}$$

Furthermore, since $I(\mathbf{u})$ is a sum of discrete random variables, the law of large numbers can be applied to it. That is, if N is large, $I(\mathbf{u})/N$ will probably be approximately equal to $H(U)$. Let us continue in this non-rigorous vein and temporarily agree not to be fussy about the meaning of approximately equal. If $I(\mathbf{u})/n \approx H(U)$, then $Pr(\mathbf{u}) \approx 2^{-N\,H(U)}$. There will be approximately $2^{N\,H(U)}$ such sequences, since there must be enough such sequences for their probabilities to add up to almost 1. We could now code these sequences into binary sequences of length $N\,H(U)$. There are $2^{N\,H(U)}$ such sequences, one for each of the "probable" sequences from the source. This indicates that $H(U)$ in bits is the number of binary digits required per source symbol to represent a source of entropy H.

These ideas will now be made precise by including the necessary

ε's and δ's. The weak law of large numbers[4] applied to $I(\mathbf{u})$ states that for any $\varepsilon > 0$ and $\delta > 0$, there exists an N_0 sufficiently large so that for sequences of length $N \geq N_0$

$$Pr\left[\left|\frac{I(\mathbf{u})}{N} - H(U)\right| \geq \delta\right] \leq \varepsilon \tag{4-12}$$

From Eqs. (4–9) and (4–12), all but at most a subset of probability ε of the N length sequences in the product ensemble have probabilities satisfying

$$2^{-N[H(U)+\delta]} \leq Pr(\mathbf{u}) \leq 2^{-N[H(U)-\delta]} \tag{4-13}$$

Similarly, since the probabilities of the sequences satisfying Eq. (4–13) must sum to between $1 - \varepsilon$ and 1, the number, L, of sequences satisfying Eq. (4–13) must lie between the following limits

$$(1 - \varepsilon)2^{N[H(X)-\delta]} \leq L \leq 2^{N[H(X)+\delta]} \tag{4-14}$$

Now let N_b be the smallest integer greater than or equal to $N[H(X) + \delta]$. Since there are 2^{N_b} binary sequences of length N_b, each of the L sequences satisfying Eq. (4–13) can be coded into a distinct binary sequence of length N_b. Since δ was arbitrary, N_b/N can be made as close to $H(U)$ as desired. Thus we have proved the following fundamental theorem.

Theorem 4–2. Given an arbitrary discrete memoryless source, U, of entropy $H(U)$, and given any $\varepsilon > 0$ and $\delta > 0$, it is possible to find an N large enough so that all but a set of probability less than ε of the N length sequences can be coded into unique binary sequences of length at most $[H(U) + \delta]N$.

We next state and prove the converse to Theorem 4–2.

Theorem 4–3. Given the same source as in Theorem 4–2, and given any $\delta_1 > 0$, $\varepsilon_1 < 1$, there exists an N_0 sufficiently large so that any code that codes sequences of $N \geq N_0$ source symbols into sequences of at most $N[H(U) - \delta_1]$ binary symbols will have an error probability greater than ε_1.

Proof: Let the δ in Eq. (4–12) be half the δ_1 of the theorem, let $\varepsilon = 1 - \varepsilon_1/2$, and let N be large enough to satisfy Eq. (4–14). Binary sequences can be provided for at most $2^{N[H(U)-2\delta]}$ of the source sequences satisfying Eq. (4–13). Thus the total probability of those sequences for which code words are provided is at most

$$2^{N[H(U)-2\delta]} \cdot 2^{-N[H(U)-\delta]} = 2^{-N\delta}$$

[4] See W. Feller, *Probability Theory and its Applications*, Chap. 10, John Wiley and Sons, Inc., New York, 1950.

Thus the probability of error (i.e. getting a source sequence for which no code word is provided) satisfies

$$P(e) \geq 1 - \varepsilon - 2^{-N\delta}$$

For N large enough, $\varepsilon \geq 2^{-N\delta}$, so that

$$P(e) \geq 1 - 2\varepsilon = \varepsilon_1$$

It is important to note in Theorem 4–2 that we could code a source into $H(U)$ binary digits per symbol only when some arbitrarily small but non-zero error was tolerable. There are M^N different N length sequences of symbols from an alphabet of M symbols and if no error is tolerable, a code word must be provided for each sequence.

Next let us consider the entropy of the coded output using a coding scheme as described in Theorem 4–2. If we agree to reserve one code word for the whole set of source sequences for which no code word was provided, then the code word corresponding to each source sequence satisfying Eq. (4–13) will have the same self information as the associated source sequence. However, the special code word provided for the set of source sequences not satisfying Eq. (4–13) will have a larger probability and a smaller self information than any of the associated source sequences. Thus the entropy of the ensemble of code words, $H(W)$, will be at most $N H(U)$, the entropy of the source sequences. Also the self information of the sequences satisfying Eq. (4–13) is at least $N[H(U) - \delta]$, so that

$$(1 - \varepsilon)N[H(U) - \delta] \leq H(W) \leq N H(U)$$

Thus the coding has reduced the entropy of the source somewhat, since it is unable to supply unique code words for all sequences; on the other hand, the redundancy per source letter in the code words, $N_b - H(W)/N$, can be made arbitrarily small.

4.3. Fixed Length to Variable Length Source Coding.—The type of coding discussed in the last section illustrated the significance of both entropy and the random variable self information. Such a coding scheme is of little practical importance, however, because of the complexity of instrumentation and the large probability of having no code word for a source sequence. A more convenient way to code is to provide variable length binary code words for sequences of some fixed length from the source. Let $\mathbf{u}_1, \mathbf{u}_2, \cdots, \mathbf{u}_J$ be all the sequences of some length N that the source can produce. J will be M^N where M is the source alphabet size. Also let the sequences $\mathbf{u}_j$ be ordered in terms of decreasing probability so that $Pr(\mathbf{u}_j) \geq Pr(\mathbf{u}_i)$ if $j < i$. Let $\mathbf{v}_1, \mathbf{v}_2, \cdots, \mathbf{v}_J$ be the binary code words assigned to the source sequences, and let $n_1, n_2, \cdots, n_J$ be the numbers of binary digits in these code words. For example, we might have the following code for $N = 2$, $M = 2$, $Pr(u_1) = .9$, $Pr(u_2) = .1$:

Sequences	Probabilities	Code Words	Length
$\mathbf{u}_1 = u_1u_1$	.81	$\mathbf{v}_1 = 0$	$n_1 = 1$
$\mathbf{u}_2 = u_1u_2$	.09	$\mathbf{v}_2 = 1\,0$	$n_2 = 2$
$\mathbf{u}_3 = u_2u_1$	.09	$\mathbf{v}_3 = 1\,1\,0$	$n_3 = 3$
$\mathbf{u}_4 = u_2u_2$	.01	$\mathbf{v}_4 = 1\,1\,1$	$n_4 = 3$

If we view a coder such as that above as a continuing process with many sequences coming from the source and being coded into code words, we see that the total length of the code word sequence is the sum of the lengths of the individual code words. Since these lengths are random variables, the number of binary digits per source sequence should approach the average length with high probability as the number of sequences from the source becomes large.

The average number of binary digits per source sequence is given by

$$\bar{N}_b = \sum_{j=1}^{J} Pr(\mathbf{u}_j) n_j \tag{4–15}$$

We shall show that $\bar{N}_b/N$ can be made as close to $H(U)$ as desired by making N sufficiently large.

An obvious restriction in selecting a set of variable length binary sequences as a code is that the sequence of source symbols must be uniquely specified by a sequence of code words. If, for example, we attempted to code the letters A, B, and C into the binary sequences 0, 1, and 00, it would be impossible to reconstruct the source letters. The binary sequence 00 could represent either AA or C.

It is possible, of course, to use some sort of blank symbol to separate code words, but this would really imply that a tertiary alphabet was available. One easy way to guarantee that the code words can be separated from each other is to use a prefix code. We define a prefix code as a code in which no code word is the same as the initial part, or prefix, of another code word. More precisely, for any i and j, if $n_i < n_j$, then $\mathbf{v}_i$ must not be equal to the first n_i digits of $\mathbf{v}_j$. The following theorem now gives necessary and sufficient conditions on the set of lengths $n_1, \cdots, n_J$ that can be used in a prefix code.

Theorem 4–4 (*Szilard, Kraft*). A necessary and sufficient condition on the lengths n_j, $1 \le j \le J$, of the J code words of a binary prefix code is that

$$\sum_{j=1}^{J} 2^{-n_j} \le 1 \tag{4–16}$$

Necessity: Let $\mathbf{v}_1, \cdots, \mathbf{v}_j$ be a set of binary sequences satisfying the prefix condition, and consider these sequences as binary fraction expansions of real numbers between 0 and 1 (*i.e.*, 1 0 1 1 corresponds to the number $1 \times 2^{-1} + 1 \times 2^{-3} + 1 \times 2^{-4}$). Then if $\mathbf{v}_j$ has length n_j, no other code word, $\mathbf{v}_i$, can fall in the interval

$$\mathbf{v}_j \leq \mathbf{v}_i < \mathbf{v}_j + 2^{-n_j}$$

without violating the prefix condition. In this sense, $\mathbf{v}_j$ occupies an interval of measure 2^{-n_j}, since no other code word can fall in that interval. But each code word occupies such an interval and these intervals, being disjoint, cannot add up to a measure greater than 1. Thus Eq. (4–16) must be satisfied.

Sufficiency: Let n_j, $1 \leq j \leq J$, be a set of numbers that satisfy Eq. (4–16), and relabel these numbers to be in order of increasing length (*i.e.*, $n_j \geq n_i$, if $j > i$). The sufficiency of Eq. (4–16) is now proved by demonstrating a code that satisfies the prefix condition. Let $\mathbf{v}_j$, as a binary expansion to n_j places, be given by:

$$\mathbf{v}_1 = 0 \quad 0 \cdots 0 \quad (n_1 \text{ places}) \tag{4–17a}$$

$$\mathbf{v}_j = \sum_{i=1}^{j-1} 2^{-n_i}, \quad 2 \leq j \leq J \tag{4–17b}$$

First we observe that each sum in Eq. (4–17a and b) can be represented by an n_j digit expansion since all the n_i, $i < j$, are less than or equal to n_j. Next, from Eq. (4–16), the sum in Eq.(4–17b) is less than 1 for all j. Finally, the prefix condition is satisfied for the set of code words specified by Eq. (4–17a and b), since for any $k < j$,

$$\mathbf{v}_j - \mathbf{v}_k = \sum_{i=k}^{j-1} 2^{-n_i} \geq 2^{-n_k} \tag{4–18}$$

This $\mathbf{v}_j$ differs from $\mathbf{v}_k$ in at least one of the first n_k digits.

Theorem 4–4 can now be used to obtain a simple relationship between the entropy of a source and the minimum average length of a set of binary code words for the source.

Theorem 4–5. Let $Pr(\mathbf{u}_1), \cdots, Pr(\mathbf{u}_J)$ be the probabilities in decreasing order of the set of sequences of length N from a discrete memoryless source of entropy $H(U)$. Then every binary prefix code for this source has an average length $\bar{N}_b$ satisfying

$$\bar{N}_b \geq N H(U) \tag{4–19}$$

and a binary prefix code exists that satisfies

$$\bar{N}_b < N H(U) + 1 \tag{4–20}$$

Proof: First we prove Eq. (4–19). Let n_j be the lengths of any set of code words for these sequences satisfying the prefix condition. Then we must show that $NH(U) - \bar{N}_b \leq 0$.

$$NH(U) - \bar{N}_b = \sum_{j=1}^{J} -Pr(\mathbf{u}_j)\log_2 Pr(\mathbf{u}_j) - \sum_{j=1}^{J} Pr(\mathbf{u}_j)n_j$$

$$= \sum_{j=1}^{J} Pr(\mathbf{u}_j)\log_2\left[\frac{2^{-n_j}}{Pr(\mathbf{u}_j)}\right] \tag{4–21}$$

Using the inequality $\ln z \leq z - 1$, we get

$$NH(U) - \bar{N}_b \leq \sum_{j=1}^{J} Pr(\mathbf{u}_j)\left(\frac{1}{\ln 2}\right)\left[\frac{2^{-n_j}}{Pr(\mathbf{u}_j)} - 1\right]$$

$$\leq \frac{1}{\ln 2}\sum_{j=1}^{J}\left[2^{-n_j} - Pr(\mathbf{u}_j)\right]$$

But from Eq. (4–16) this is at most 0, establishing Eq. (4–19). Now let n_j be the smallest integer greater than or equal to $-\log_2 Pr(\mathbf{u}_j)$.

$$-\log_2 Pr(\mathbf{u}_j) \leq n_j < -\log_2 Pr(\mathbf{u}_j) + 1 \tag{4–22}$$

We now use the left side of Eq. (4–22) to show that this set of n_j satisfies the prefix condition, and then use the right side to establish Eq. (4–20).

From the left side of Eq. (4–22)

$$Pr(\mathbf{u}_j) \geq 2^{-n_j}$$

$$1 = \sum_{j=1}^{J} Pr(\mathbf{u}_j) \geq \sum_{j=1}^{J} 2^{-n_j}$$

Thus a prefix code can be constructed. From the right side of Eq. (4–22)

$$\bar{N}_b = \sum_{j=1}^{J} Pr(\mathbf{u}_j)n_j < \sum_{j=1}^{J} Pr(\mathbf{u}_j)[-\log_2 Pr(\mathbf{u}_j) + 1]$$

$$\bar{N}_b < NH(U) + 1$$

Note that if the self information of each sequence can be made equal to the number of binary digits in its code word, then $\bar{N}_b = NH(U)$; thus the self information of a sequence in bits is the number of binary digits that should ideally be used to represent the sequence.

Dividing Eqs. (4–19) and (4–20) by N, we see that the average number of binary digits per source symbol for the best prefix condition code satisfies

$$H(U) \leq \frac{\bar{N}_b}{N} \leq H(U) + \frac{1}{N}$$

Thus, by making N large, $\bar{N}_b/N$ can be made as close to $H(U)$ as desired, which is another form of the source coding theorem proved in Theorems 4–2 and 4–3.

The preceding results, while bounding $\bar{N}_b$ for the best prefix code do not show how to find the best prefix code. The following procedure, developed by Huffman,[5] yields a minimum value of $\bar{N}_b$.

(1) Assign a 1 as the last binary digit of the code word corresponding to the least probable source sequence, and a 0 as the last binary digit of the next to least probable source sequence.

(2) Replace these two sequences by one sequence with a probability equal to the sum of the original two probabilities. The code word for this new sequence (when it is found) will be used to generate code words for the two original sequences by adding a terminal 0 or 1.

Return to step 1 with the new set of sequences; stop when only one sequence remains.

Example:

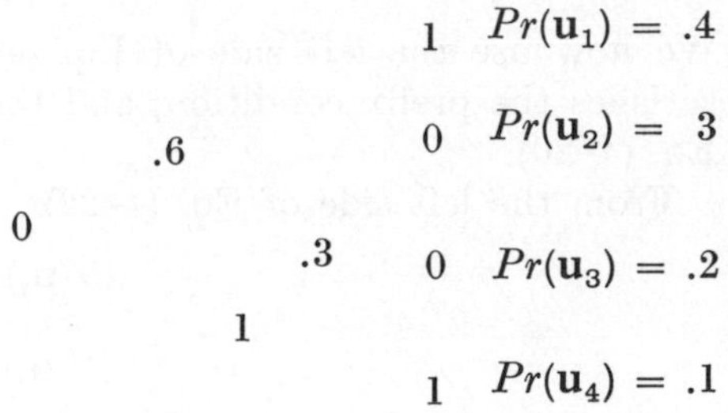

1 $Pr(\mathbf{u}_1) = .4$

.6

0 $Pr(\mathbf{u}_2) = 3$

0

.3

0 $Pr(\mathbf{u}_3) = .2$

1

1 $Pr(\mathbf{u}_4) = .1$

$\mathbf{v}_1 = 1$

$\mathbf{v}_2 = 0\,0$

$\mathbf{v}_3 = 0\,1\,0$

$\mathbf{v}_4 = 0\,1\,1$

The proof that this procedure minimizes $\bar{N}_b$ will be outlined. $\bar{N}_b$ is determined solely by the set of code word lengths, n_j. The two least probable code words, say $\mathbf{u}_J$ and $\mathbf{u}_{J-1}$, must have the longest lengths, or they could be interchanged with other code words to reduce $\bar{N}_b$. Also they must have the same length, or the last digit could be dropped from the longer word without violating the prefix condition. One realization of the optimum set of n_j can always be achieved with n_J and n_{J-1} represented by the same sequence except for the last digit, and in fact the suggested realization in Theorem 4–4 does this.

[5] D. A. Huffman, "A Method for the Construction of Minimum Redundancy Codes," *Proc. I.R.E.*, Sept. 1952.

Next observe that the average code word length for the reduced ensemble of step 2 is given by

$$\bar{N}_R = \bar{N}_b - Pr(\mathbf{u}_J) - Pr(\mathbf{u}_{J-1})$$

Thus minimization of $\bar{N}_R$ must minimize $\bar{N}_b$, since one realization of the minimum $\bar{N}_b$ can be represented in this way. By induction, the procedure minimizes $\bar{N}_b$.

4.4. Mutual Information.—In the preceding sections, self information was defined and interpreted as a fundamental quantity associated with a discrete memoryless communication source. In this section we define, and in the next section interpret, a measure of the information being transmitted over a communication system. One might at first be tempted to simply analyze the self information at each point in the system, but if the channel output is statistically independent of the input, the self information at the output of the channel bears no connection to the self information of the source. What is needed instead is a measure of the information in the channel output about the channel input.

In order to define such a quantity mathematically, consider a product ensemble, XY, consisting of the letter pairs $x_k y_j$ $(1 \leq k \leq K, 1 \leq j \leq J)$ with the probabilities $Pr(x_k y_j)$. As usual, we define

$$Pr(x_k) = \sum_{j=1}^{J} Pr(x_k y_j), \quad 1 \leq k \leq K$$

$$Pr(y_j) = \sum_{k=1}^{K} Pr(x_k y_j) \quad 1 \leq j \leq J$$

$$Pr(y_j|x_k) = Pr(x_k y_j)/p(x_k)$$

$$Pr(x_k|y_j) = Pr(x_k y_j)/p(y_j)$$

Define $I(x_k;y_j)$, the mutual information supplied by y_j about x_k as

$$I(x_k;y_j) = \log \frac{Pr(x_k|y_j)}{Pr(x_k)} \tag{4–23}$$

Mutual information is thus a random variable since it is a real valued function defined on the points of an ensemble. Consequently, it has an average, variance, distribution function, and moment generating function. It is important to note that mutual information has been defined only on product ensembles, and only as a function of two events, x and y, which are sample points in the two ensembles of which the product ensemble is formed. Mutual information is sometimes defined as a function of any two events in an ensemble, but in this case it is not a random variable. It should also be noted that the mutual information between an input x and an output y for a channel is defined only when a set of probabilities are assigned to the inputs of the channel.

In order to interpret mutual information, we can rewrite Eq. (4–23) as

$$I(x_k;y_j) = I(x_k) - I(x_k|\,y_j) \tag{4–24}$$

where $I(x_k) = -\log Pr(x_k)$ and $I(x_k|\,y_j) = -\log Pr(x_k|\,y_j)$. Thus $I(x_k;y_j)$ can be thought of as the self information of x_k less the self information still required to specify x_k after the occurrence of y_j. Note that if y_j is the same event as x_k, then $I(x_k;y_j) = I(x_k)$. Thus self information is the mutual information provided by an event about itself, and this explains the name self information. Also, if X and Y are statistically independent, then $I(x_k;y_j) = 0$ for all j and k. Finally if $Pr(x_k|\,y_j) < Pr(x_k)$, then $I(x_k;y_j) < 0$, and in channel terms, this can be thought of as an output y_j which is misleading about an input, x_k. One other peculiar aspect of mutual information is that it is symmetrical between input and output. That is

$$I(x_k;y_j) = \log \frac{Pr(x_k\,y_j)}{Pr(x_k)Pr(y_j)} = I(y_j;x_k)$$

Let us now turn our attention to the average mutual information, $\overline{I(x;y)}$.

$$\overline{I(x;y)} = \sum_{j,\,k} Pr(x_k\,y_j)I(x_k;y_j) = \sum_{j,\,k} Pr(x_k\,y_j) \log \frac{Pr(x_k|\,y_j)}{Pr(x_k)} \tag{4–25}$$

We also define the subsidiary quantities $H(X|Y)$, $H(Y|X)$, and $H(X,Y)$

$$H(X|Y) = \sum_{j,k} -Pr(y_j)Pr(x_k|\,y_j) \log Pr(x_k|\,y_j) \tag{4–26}$$

$$H(Y|X) = \sum_{j,k} -Pr(x_k)Pr(y_j|x_k) \log Pr(y_j|x_k) \tag{4–27}$$

$$H(X,Y) = \sum_{j,k} -Pr(x_k\,y_j) \log Pr(x_k\,y_j) \tag{4–28}$$

These are referred to as the entropy (or average self information) of X given Y, the entropy of Y given X, and the entropy of X and Y. It follows immediately from these definitions that

$$\overline{I(x;y)} = H(X) - H(X|Y) \tag{4–29}$$

$$= H(Y) - H(Y|X) \tag{4–30}$$

$$= H(XY) - H(X) - H(Y) \tag{4–31}$$

$$H(XY) = H(Y) + H(X|Y) \tag{4–32}$$

In a channel context, with X as the input ensemble, and Y as the output ensemble, we can interpret $H(X|Y)$ as the average additional information required at the output to specify an input when the output is given; thus $H(X|Y)$ is known as equivocation. Similarly, $H(Y|X)$ can be interpreted as the part of the entropy of Y that is not information about X, and thus $H(Y|X)$ is known as noise.

It will now be proven that the average self information is always non-negative.

$$\overline{I(x;y)} = \sum_{j,k} Pr(x_k y_j) \log \frac{Pr(x_k y_j)}{Pr(x_k)Pr(y_j)}$$

$$= \sum_{j,k} -Pr(x_k y_j) \log \frac{Pr(x_k)Pr(y_j)}{Pr(x_k y_j)}$$

Using the inequality $\ln z \leq z - 1$,

$$\overline{I(x;y)} \geq \log e \sum_{j,k} -Pr(x_k y_j) \left[\frac{Pr(x_k)Pr(y_j)}{Pr(x_k y_j)} - 1\right] = 0 \quad (4\text{–}33)$$

From Eqs. (4–29) and (4–31), we get the interesting corollaries that

$$H(X) \geq H(X|Y) \quad (4\text{–}34)$$

$$H(XY) \leq H(X) + H(Y) \quad (4\text{–}35)$$

Thus the entropy of a product ensemble, $X;Y$, can only be reduced by statistical dependence between the X and Y ensembles.

This result can also be extended to product ensembles of arbitrary order. Let $\mathbf{X}_N$ be a product ensemble for which the sample points are sequences $\mathbf{x} = (x_1,\cdots,x_N)$ of N statistically dependent letters from either the same or different alphabets. Let $Pr(\mathbf{x})$ be the probability of the sequence $\mathbf{x}$, and $Pr(x_n)$ be the probability of the nth letter, x_n. In conformity with our previous definition,

$$H(X_1,\cdots,X_N) = \overline{-\log Pr(x_1,\cdots,x_N)}$$

$$= \overline{\sum_{n=1}^{N} -\log Pr(x_n|x_{n-1},\cdots,x_1)}$$

$$= \sum_{n=1}^{N} H(X_n|X_{n-1},\cdots,X_1) \quad (4\text{–}36)$$

Considering $X_1,\cdots,X_{n-1}$ as a single ensemble, we can use Eq. (4–34) to get

$$H(X_n|X_{n-1},\cdots,X_1) \leq H(X_n) \quad (4\text{–}37)$$

Combining Eqs. (4–36) and (4–37)

$$H(X_1,\cdots,X_N) \leq \sum_{n=1}^{N} H(X_n) \tag{4–38}$$

Problem—Prove that

$$H(X_1|X_2,\cdots,X_n) \leq H(X_1|X_2,\cdots,X_{n-1}) \tag{4–39}$$

Equation (4–36) can be used to extend the results of Sections 4.2 and 4.3 to sources with statistical dependence between source letters. If the source is stationary, we can define the entropy of a discrete source with memory as

$$\lim_{N\to\infty} \frac{1}{N} H(U_1,U_2,\cdots,U_N)$$

Using Eqs. (4–36) and (4–39), it is not hard to show that this limit must exist. If the source is also ergodic, then it can be shown[6] that the source coding theorem, Theorem 4–2, still holds.

4.5. Discrete Memoryless Channels.—Recall that a discrete memoryless channel has a finite input alphabet, X, consisting of the symbols $x_1,\cdots,x_K$; a finite output alphabet Y, consisting of $y_1,\cdots,y_J$, and a set of transition probabilities $Pr(y_j|x_k)$, $1 \leq k \leq K$, $1 \leq j \leq J$. We denote a sequence of N input symbols by $\mathbf{x} = (x_1,\cdots,x_N)$ and the corresponding outputs by $\mathbf{y} = (y_1,\cdots,y_N)$. A memoryless channel is a channel satisfying

$$Pr(\mathbf{y}|\mathbf{x}) = \prod_{n=1}^{N} Pr(y_n|x_n)$$

The capacity of a discrete memoryless channel is defined as the maximum value of $\overline{I(x;y)}$ over all input probability distributions,

$$C = \underset{Pr(x_1)\cdots,Pr(x_K)}{\text{MAX}} \sum_{j,k} Pr(x_k)Pr(y_j|x_k) \log \frac{Pr(y_j|x_k)}{\sum_{i=1}^{K} Pr(y_j|x_i)Pr(x_i)} \tag{4–40}$$

where we have written out $Pr(y_j) = \sum_{i=1}^{K} Pr(y_j|x_i)Pr(x_i)$ in terms of the given transition probabilities and the input probabilities.

The significance of channel capacity, as will be shown later, is that the output from any given discrete memoryless source with an entropy per channel digit less than C can be transmitted over the channel with an arbitrarily small probability of decoding error by sufficiently

[6] B. McMillan, "The Basic Theorems of Information Theory," *Ann. Math. Stat.*, **24**, pp. 196–219 (1953).

sophisticated coding and decoding. Furthermore, if the source entropy per channel digit is greater than C, an arbitrarily small error probability cannot be achieved. These results are known as the coding theorem and its converse. Before proving these results, however, we shall discuss the calculation of capacity, and then give some additional interpretation to capacity by showing that NC is the maximum mutual information that can be transmitted over a channel by a sequence of N symbols.

Calculation of Capacity. The actual maximization of Eq. (4–40) is sometimes difficult since the maximization is over a function of K variables with the constraints that $Pr(x_k) \geq 0$, $1 \leq k \leq K$, and $\sum_{k=1}^{K} Pr(x_k) = 1$. As a result, the maximum might occur at a stationary point within the region defined by the constraints, or it might occur on the boundary of the region where some of the $Pr(x_k) = 0$. The determination of whether a stationary point or boundary point actually provides a maximum of Eq. (4–40) is greatly simplified, by a property of the average mutual information known as convexity.[7] Let $\mathbf{p}$ be a K-dimensional vector whose components are an arbitrary set of input probabilities $p_1 = Pr(x_1), \cdots, p_K = Pr(x_K)$. Then rewriting Eq. (4–40) to bring out explicitly the dependence of the mutual information on the input probabilities,

$$C = \underset{\mathbf{p}}{\text{MAX}} \, [\mathscr{I}(\mathbf{p})]$$

$$\mathscr{I}(\mathbf{p}) = \sum_{k,j} p_k Pr(y_j|x_k) \log \frac{Pr(y_j|x_k)}{\sum_i p_i Pr(y_j|x_i)} \tag{4–41}$$

$\mathscr{I}(\mathbf{p})$ is a real valued function of a K-dimensional vector defined over the region of vector space in which $p_k \geq 0$ for all k and $\sum_k p_k = 1$. A region of vector space is defined to be convex if for any two vectors, $\mathbf{p}$ and $\mathbf{q}$ in the region, and any λ, $0 \leq \lambda \leq 1$, $\lambda\mathbf{p} + (1 - \lambda)\mathbf{q}$ is also in the region. It follows immediately that the constraints $p_k \geq 0$, $\sum_k p_k = 1$ define a closed convex region of space.

A function, $f(\mathbf{p})$, is defined to be convex upward over a convex region of vector space if, for any two vectors $\mathbf{p}$ and $\mathbf{q}$ in the region, and for any λ, $0 \leq \lambda \leq 1$,

$$\lambda f(\mathbf{p}) + (1 - \lambda) f(\mathbf{q}) \leq f(\lambda\mathbf{p} + (1 - \lambda)\mathbf{q}) \tag{4–42}$$

Similarly a function is convex downward if the inequality in Eq. (4–42) is reversed. Geometrically, as a function of λ, the left side of

[7] See Blackwell and Girshick, *Theory of Games and Statistical Decisions*, Chap. 2, John Wiley & Sons, Inc., New York, 1954, for a more complete discussion of convexity.

Eq. (4–42) is the equation of a straight line between $f(\mathbf{p})$ and $f(\mathbf{q})$, whereas the right side is the curve traced out by the function as the argument varies in a straight line from $\mathbf{p}$ to $\mathbf{q}$. Thus a convex upward function is one in which all chords lie below the function.

One simple but useful way to demonstrate the convexity upward (downward) of a function is to show that it is the sum of convex upward (downward) functions. The proof of this property follows immediately from the definition of convexity. For functions of one variable convexity upward (downward) can also be demonstrated by showing that the second derivative is negative (positive) or zero over the interval of interest. Much of the usefulness of convex functions, for our purposes, stems from the following theorem:

Theorem 4–6. Let $f(\mathbf{p})$ be a convex upward (downward) function over a convex region of space, R, and let $f(\mathbf{p})$ have a stationary point at $\mathbf{q}_1$ with respect to variations in R. (That is, for any $\mathbf{p}$ in R,

$$\frac{d}{d\lambda}[f(\lambda\mathbf{p} + (1-\lambda)\mathbf{q}_1]_{\lambda=0} = 0.)$$

Then $f(\mathbf{q}_1)$ is the maximum (minimum) of $f(\mathbf{p})$ over the region R.

Proof: Let $f(\mathbf{p})$ be convex upward and suppose the theorem is not true; then for some point, $\mathbf{q}_2$ in R,

$$f(\mathbf{q}_2) - f(\mathbf{q}_1) = \varepsilon > 0 \tag{4–43}$$

By the definition of a derivative,

$$\frac{d}{d\lambda}f[\lambda\mathbf{q}_2 + (1-\lambda)\mathbf{q}_1]_{\lambda=0} = \lim_{\lambda\to 0}\frac{f[\lambda\mathbf{q}_2 + (1-\lambda)\mathbf{q}_1] - f(\mathbf{q}_1)}{\lambda} \tag{4–44}$$

$$\geq \lim_{\lambda\to 0}\frac{\lambda f(\mathbf{q}_2) + (1-\lambda)f(\mathbf{q}_1) - f(\mathbf{q}_1)}{\lambda} \tag{4–45}$$

Equation (4–45) follows from the definition of convexity, Eq. (4–42). Substituting Eq. (4–43) into (4–45), we get

$$\frac{d}{d\lambda}f[\lambda\mathbf{q}_2 + (1-\lambda)\mathbf{q}_1]_{\lambda=0} \geq \varepsilon > 0 \tag{4–46}$$

From the hypothesis of the theorem, the left side of Eq. (4–46) is 0; thus we have a contradiction and the theorem is true. For $f(\mathbf{p})$ convex downward, the proof is the same.

Note that the theorem does not rule out the possibility of a maximum persisting over a convex region on which the function is constant.

Theorem 4–8. $\mathscr{I}(\mathbf{p})$, as defined in Eq. (4–41) is a convex upward function in the convex region where $p_k \geq 0$, $1 \leq k \leq K$, $\sum_k p_k = 1$.

Proof:

$$\mathscr{I}(\mathbf{p}) = \sum_{k,j} p_k Pr(y_j|x_k) \log Pr(y_j|x_k) + \sum_j \left[\sum_k p_k Pr(y_j|x_k) \log \frac{1}{\sum_k p_k Pr(y_j|x_k)} \right] \tag{4–47}$$

The first sum in Eq. (4–47) is a linear function of $\mathbf{p}$, and therefore is convex upward, satisfying Eq. (4–42) with the equal sign. Now consider the function $f(t) = t \log 1/t$ for $t \geq 0$. Since

$$f''(t) = -\frac{\log e}{t} < 0 \quad \text{for} \quad t > 0, \tag{4–48}$$

$f(t)$ is a convex upward function of t for $t > 0$. Each bracketed term in the second sum of Eq. (4–47) can be expressed as $f[\sum_k p_k Pr(y_j|x_k)]$, and since $f(t)$ is convex upward in t, it follows immediately from Eq. (4–42) that $f[\sum_k p_k Pr(y_j|x_k)]$ is a convex upward function of $\mathbf{p}$. But the sum of convex upward functions is convex upward, so that $I(\mathbf{p})$ is convex upward, completing the proof.

From the previous two theorems, any stationary point of $\mathscr{I}(\mathbf{p})$ yields the maximum of $\mathscr{I}(\mathbf{p})$. Such a stationary point can often be found by using Lagrange multipliers or by using the symmetry of the channel. In many cases, a numerical evaluation of capacity is more convenient; in these cases, convexity is even more useful, since it guarantees that any reasonable numerical procedure that varies $\mathbf{p}$ to increase $\mathscr{I}(\mathbf{p})$ must converge to capacity.

Problem—Show that the entropy of an ensemble is a convex upward function of the probabilities of the points in the ensemble.

Problem—Show that the capacities of the two channels below are as given. The numbers on the lines between input and output are the transition probabilities, $Pr(y_j|x_k)$

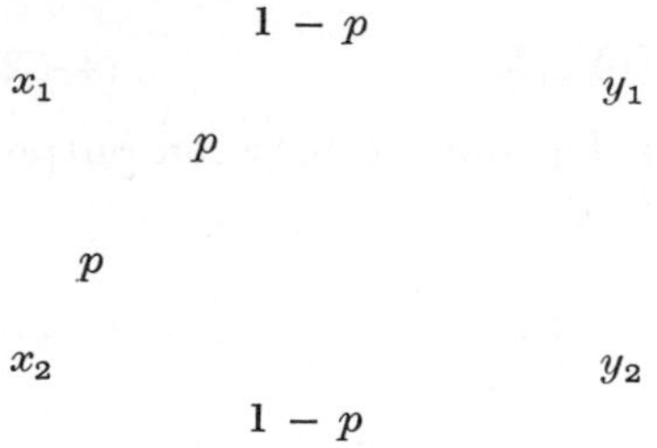

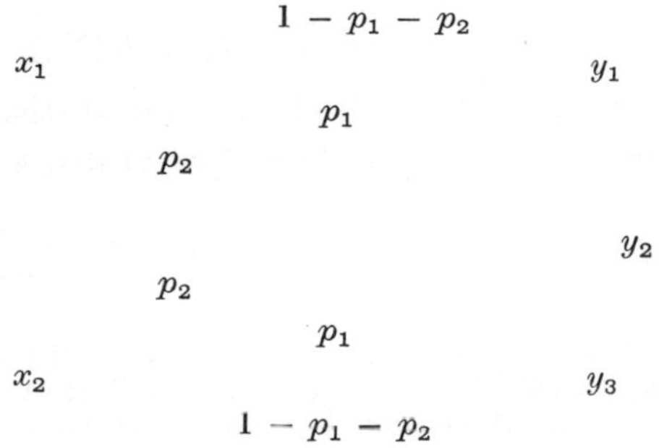

$C = \log 2 - H(p)$ $\qquad\qquad C = (1 - p_1)\left\{\log 2 - H\left(\frac{p_2}{1 - p_1}\right)\right\}$

where $H(p) = -p \log p - (1 - p) \log (1 - p)$.

The first channel above is known as a binary symmetric channel and has been extensively studied in the literature, particularly with regard to coding.[8] The probability p can be interpreted here as the probability of channel errors, and it is interesting to observe that C is the same whether p is a number p_0 or $1 - p_0$. Naturally, if p were greater than $\frac{1}{2}$, one would tend to associate each output with the opposite input, but capacity, being defined only in terms of the transition probabilities, takes account of such situations automatically.

Let $\mathbf{X}_N,\mathbf{Y}_N$ be a product ensemble of sequences of N input letters, $\mathbf{x} = (x_1,\cdots,x_N)$, and N output letters, $\mathbf{y} = (y_1,\cdots,y_N)$, from a discrete memoryless channel. The probability distribution on the input, $Pr(\mathbf{x})$ is arbitrary and does not assume statistical independence between letters. However, since the channel is memoryless, $Pr(\mathbf{y}|\mathbf{x})$ satisfies

$$Pr(\mathbf{y}|\mathbf{x}) = \prod_{n=1}^{N} Pr(y_n|x_n) \tag{4–49}$$

The average mutual information between the input and output sequences is given by

$$\overline{I(\mathbf{x};\mathbf{y})} = \sum Pr(\mathbf{x})Pr(\mathbf{y}|\mathbf{x}) \log \frac{Pr(\mathbf{y}|\mathbf{x})}{Pr(\mathbf{y})} \tag{4–50}$$

where the summation is over all input and output sequences.

Theorem 4–8. Let C be the capacity of a discrete memoryless channel, and let $\overline{I(\mathbf{x};\mathbf{y})}$ be the average mutual information between input and output sequences of length N for an arbitrary input probability measure, $Pr(\mathbf{x})$. Then

$$\overline{I(\mathbf{x};\mathbf{y})} \le NC \tag{4–51}$$

Proof: From Eq. (4–30), we have

$$\overline{I(\mathbf{x};\mathbf{y})} = H(\mathbf{Y}_N) - H(\mathbf{Y}_N|\mathbf{X}_N) \tag{4–52}$$

Equation (4–38) shows that statistical dependence between output letters can only reduce their entropy so that

$$H(\mathbf{Y}_N) \le \sum_{n=1}^{N} H(Y_n) \tag{4–53}$$

[8] W. Peterson, *Error Correcting Codes*, M.I.T. Press and John Wiley and Sons, Inc., New York, 1961. This gives an excellent discussion of a wide variety of coding techniques for this channel based on the algebraic properties of the code words. For three other equally promising approaches, see J. M. Wozencraft and B. Reiffen, *Sequential Decoding*, M.I.T. Press and John Wiley, New York, 1961; R. G. Gallager, *Low Density Parity Check Codes*, M.I.T. Press, Cambridge, Massachusetts, 1963; and J. L. Massey, *Threshold Decoding*, M.I.T. Press, Cambridge, Massachusetts, 1963.

where

$$H(Y_n) = \sum_{y_n} -Pr(y_n) \log Pr(y_n)$$

The probability measure $Pr(y_n)$ is given by

$$Pr(y_n) = \sum_{x_n} Pr(x_n)\, Pr(y_n|x_n) \tag{4-54}$$

Since $Pr(\mathbf{x})$ is completely general, the measure $Pr(x_n)$ will depend upon n, and therefore $Pr(y_n)$ and $H(Y_n)$ will depend upon n. Next, from Eq. 4-49, we have

$$\begin{aligned} H(\mathbf{Y}_N|\mathbf{X}_N) &= \overline{-\log Pr(\mathbf{y}|\mathbf{x})} \\ &= \overline{\sum_{n=1}^{N} -\log Pr(y_n|x_n)} \end{aligned}$$

But the average of a sum is the sum of the averages; thus

$$H(\mathbf{Y}_N|\mathbf{X}_N) = \sum_{n=1}^{N} \overline{-\log Pr(y_n|x_n)} = \sum_{n=1}^{N} H(Y_n|X_n) \tag{4-55}$$

Substituting Eqs. (4-54) and (4-55) into Eq. (4-52) we have

$$\overline{I(\mathbf{y};\mathbf{x})} \le \sum_{n=1}^{N} [H(Y_n) - H(Y_n|X_n)] = \sum_{n=1}^{N} \overline{I(x_n;y_n)} \tag{4-56}$$

From the definition of C,

$$\overline{I(x_n;y_n)} \le C \tag{4-57}$$

for all n, and Eq. (4-51) follows.

If the channel inputs are statistically independent, and if the individual letter probabilities are such as to give channel capacity, then the average mutual information transmitted by N letters is NC.

The previous theorem shows that the average mutual information per symbol on a channel cannot be increased over C by introducing dependence between input symbols. Next we shall show that the average mutual information per channel symbol between a source and a destination cannot be greater than C even though data processing is used at either terminal of the channel. This is intuitively satisfying since it indicates that a data processor can only process the information fed into it; it cannot generate anything new. It is results such as this that generate the connection between one's intuitive ideas about information and one's mathematical definitions.

In order to prove this result, consider the product ensemble, **XYZ**, in which **x** is the channel input sequence, **y** is the channel output sequence, and $\mathbf{v}$ is the data processor output sequence. We assume that the sequence $\mathbf{v}$ is statistically related to $\mathbf{x}$ only through $\mathbf{y}$; *i.e.*,

$$Pr(\mathbf{v}|\mathbf{y}) = Pr(\mathbf{v}|\mathbf{xy}) \tag{4–58}$$

Normally, the output $\mathbf{v}$ of a data processor would be determined completely by $\mathbf{y}$, but Eq. (4–58) also allows non-deterministic data processors for generality. We shall show that

$$\overline{I(\mathbf{x};\mathbf{v})} \leq \overline{I(\mathbf{x};\mathbf{y})} \tag{4–59}$$

First it is necessary to show that $\overline{I(\mathbf{x};\mathbf{y})} = \overline{I(\mathbf{x};\mathbf{yv})}$

$$\overline{I(\mathbf{x};\mathbf{yv})} = \overline{\log \frac{Pr(\mathbf{yv}|\mathbf{x})}{Pr(\mathbf{yv})}}$$

$$= \overline{\log \frac{Pr(\mathbf{y}|\mathbf{x})\, Pr(\mathbf{v}|\mathbf{yx})}{Pr(\mathbf{y})\, Pr(\mathbf{v}|\mathbf{y})}}$$

Equation (4–58) simplifies this to

$$\overline{I(\mathbf{x};\mathbf{yv})} = \overline{\log \frac{Pr(\mathbf{y}|\mathbf{x})}{Pr(\mathbf{y})}} = \overline{I(\mathbf{x};\mathbf{y})} \tag{4–60}$$

We can use Eq. (4–35) to bound $\overline{I(\mathbf{x};\mathbf{yv})}$, getting

$$\overline{I(\mathbf{x};\mathbf{yv})} = H(X) - H(X|YV) \geq H(X) - H(X|V) \tag{4–61}$$
$$\geq \overline{I(\mathbf{x};\mathbf{v})}$$

Combining Eqs. (4–60) and (4–61), we get Eq. (4–59); thus data processing at the output of a channel can never increase the average mutual information about the input. The symmetry of $\overline{I(\mathbf{x};\mathbf{y})}$ in $\mathbf{x}$ and $\mathbf{y}$ can now be used to extend Eq. (4–59) to data processing at the input. Let $Pr(\mathbf{u}|\mathbf{x}) = Pr(\mathbf{u}|\mathbf{xv})$. This implies that $\overline{I(\mathbf{u};\mathbf{v})} \leq \overline{I(\mathbf{x};\mathbf{v})}$. Combining this with Eq. (5–59) we get,

$$\overline{I(\mathbf{u};\mathbf{v})} \leq \overline{I(\mathbf{x};\mathbf{y})} \tag{4–62}$$

These results are sometimes interpreted as a converse to the coding theorem. That is, we have shown that the mutual information per channel symbol between a source and destination is limited by the capacity of the channel. The problem is that we have not demonstrated any relationship between error probability and source rate when the source rate is greater than the mutual information. Unfortunately, this is not as trivial to obtain as it might appear. In the next section, we find a lower bound to the probability of error when the source rate is greater than C.

4.6. Converse to Coding Theorem.—We shall show in this Section that reliable communication at rates greater than channel capacity is impossible. Although only discrete memoryless sources and channels will be considered here, it will be obvious that the results are virtually independent of the type of channel. It was shown in the last section that the average mutual information between source and destination can be no greater than channel capacity; then if the source rate is greater than capacity, some information is lost. The problem is to relate this lost information, or equivocation, to the probability of error between the source and destination.

Let a discrete memoryless source have an M letter alphabet, $u_1, \cdots, u_M$, and a probability measure, $Pr(u_1), \cdots, Pr(u_M)$. Let T_s be the time interval between successive letters of a sequence from this source. Then we define the rate of the source as the average self information per unit time,

$$R_T = \frac{H(U)}{T_s} \tag{4–63}$$

Also consider a discrete memoryless channel with an input alphabet $x_1, \cdots, x_K$, an output alphabet $y_1, \cdots, y_J$, a set of transition probabilities, $Pr(y_j|x_k)$, and a capacity C. Let T_c be the time interval between channel uses, and define the channel capacity per unit time, C_T, as

$$C_T = \frac{C}{T_c} \tag{4–64}$$

We assume that a sequence of N digits, $\mathbf{u} = (u_1, \cdots, u_N)$ from the source goes into an arbitrary coder which produces a sequence of which the length is the integer part of NT_s/T_c channel digits. There is, of course, a problem as to whether the channel should be used one more time if NT_s/T_c is not an integer. Since the results we achieve are independent of N, N can be allowed to go to infinity and the extra digit will make no difference.

At the output of the channel, the received digits are decoded by an arbitrary decoder into a sequence, $\mathbf{v} = (v_1, v_2, \cdots, v_n)$ which is supposed to be a replica of the input sequence. Define the probability of error on the nth digit, $P_{e,n}$, as the probability that $v_n \neq u_n$. We then define the probability of error for the system as

$$P_e = \frac{1}{N} \sum_{n=1}^{N} p_{e,n} \tag{4–65}$$

P_e is the overall error probability on the individual digits of the source sequence. We can now state the converse to the coding theorem.

Theorem 4–9. Let R_T be the entropy per unit time of a discrete memoryless source of alphabet size M, and let C_T be the capacity per unit time of a discrete memoryless channel. Let T_s and T_c be the intersymbol times for the source and channel, and let a sequence of N source letters be transmitted by at most

$$N \frac{T_s}{T_c}$$

channel symbols. Then the probability of error, P_e, between source digits and decoded digits must satisfy the inequality

$$(R_T - C_T)T_s \leq H(P_e) + P_e \log (M - 1) \qquad (4\text{–}66)$$

$$H(P_e) = -P_e \log P_e - (1 - P_e) \log (1 - P_e) \qquad (4\text{–}67)$$

Equation (4–66) yields an implicit lower bound to P_e that is greater than 0 when $R_T > C_T$. Observe that the bound is independent of N and depends only on the source entropy, the channel capacity per source digit ($C_T T_s$), and the source alphabet size. It would be satisfying if the dependence of Eq. (4–66) on the source alphabet size could be removed. Unfortunately the dependence of P_e on M as well as $(R_T - C_T)T_s$ is necessary, as the next theorem shows.

Theorem 4–10. Given a discrete memoryless channel of capacity per unit time, C_T, it is possible to find sources of arbitrarily large rate, R_T, and arbitrary time per source symbol, T_s, for which the error probability is arbitrarily small.

Theorem 4–10 states in effect that P_e cannot be lower bounded in terms of $(R_T - C_T)T_s$ alone, and therefore, some source parameter other than the rate is necessary in any lower bound to P_e. Theorem 4–9 is more important than 4–10, but the proof of Theorem 4–10 is simpler and more entertaining so it will be proven first.

Proof of Theorem 4–10. Choose T_s arbitrarily, and choose two arbitrary numbers, $R_0 \geq 0$, $1 > \varepsilon > 0$. We will construct a source for which the rate R_T is greater than R_0 and a coding and decoding scheme such that $P_e \leq \varepsilon$. Let $u_1, u_2, \cdots, u_M$ be the letters in the source alphabet, where M is to be determined later: Let

$$Pr(u_1) = 1 - \varepsilon$$

$$Pr(u_m) = \frac{\varepsilon}{M - 1} \quad \text{for} \quad 2 \leq m \leq M$$

Let the coder be arbitrary, and let the decoder output always be u_1. Clearly an error is made only when u_1, is not the letter from the source, but since $Pr(u_1) = 1 - \varepsilon$, $P_e = \varepsilon$. We have thus achieved the desired error probability, and now must adjust M to achieve a sufficiently large rate. The entropy of the source is given, in terms of M, by

$$H(U) = \sum_{m=1}^{M} -Pr(u_m) \log_2 Pr(u_m)$$

$$= -(1 - \varepsilon) \log_2 (1 - \varepsilon) + \varepsilon \log_2 \frac{M-1}{\varepsilon}$$

$$H(U) > \varepsilon \log_2 (M - 1) \tag{4–68}$$

Now choose M to be

$$M = 2^{R_0 T_s/\varepsilon} + 1 \tag{4–69}$$

Substituting in Eq. (4–68), $H(U) > R_0 T_s$, and consequently $R_T > R_0$, proving Theorem 4–10.

Proof of Theorem 4–9. The proof of Theorem 4–9 is somewhat lengthy, but the intuitive idea behind it is simple. We will first show that the equivocation per digit between source and output is at least $(R_T - C_T)T_s$. This average uncertainty about the input given the output can be broken into two terms; first the uncertainty about whether an error was made; and second the uncertainty about the source digit when errors are made. These are the terms on the right side of Eq. (4–66).

To prove Theorem 4–9 formally, let the sequences u, x, y, and v represent source letters, channel input symbols, channel output symbols, and decoded output letters respectively. For any given coder and decoder, a probability measure will be defined on all these sequences. Then, using Eq. (4–51)

$$\overline{I(\mathbf{x};\mathbf{y})} \le \frac{NT_s}{T_c} C = NT_s C_T$$

Since the coder and decoder cannot increase the average mutual information (see Eq. (4–62)).

$$I(\mathbf{u};\mathbf{v}) \le I(\mathbf{x};\mathbf{y}) \le NT_s C_T \tag{4–70}$$

$$H(\mathbf{U}) - H(\mathbf{U}|\mathbf{V}) \le NT_s C_T \tag{4–71}$$

$$NT_s R_T - NT_s C_T \le H(\mathbf{U}|\mathbf{V}) \tag{4–72}$$

Next we bound $H(\mathbf{U}|\mathbf{V})$ in terms of the equivocation per digit, $H(U_n|V_m)$. By definition,

$$H(\mathbf{U}|\mathbf{V}) = \overline{-\log Pr(\mathbf{u}|\mathbf{v})}$$

$$= \overline{-\log Pr(u_1|\mathbf{v}) Pr(u_2|\mathbf{v},u_1) \cdots Pr(u_N|\mathbf{v},u_1,\cdots,u_{N-1})}$$

$$= \sum_{n=1}^{N} H(u_n|\mathbf{v},u_1,\cdots,u_{n-1})$$

But from Eq. (4–39), this is bounded by

$$H(\mathbf{U}|\mathbf{V}) \leq \sum_{n=1}^{N} H(U_n|V_n) \tag{4–73}$$

Combining Eq. (4–72) with (4–73), we have

$$NT_s(R_T - C_T) \leq \sum_{n=1}^{N} H(U_n|V_n) \tag{4–74}$$

To complete the proof, we must relate the equivocation on the nth digit, $H(U_n|V_n)$, to the probability of error on the nth digit, $P_{e,n}$. It will be shown in the next few paragraphs that

$$H(U_n|V_n) \leq H(P_{e,n}) + P_{e,n} \log (M - 1) \tag{4–75}$$

This ensemble over U_n, V_n can also be considered as a triple product ensemble, $U_nV_nZ_n$, where Z_n is an ensemble consisting of the events z_e corresponding to error, and z_c corresponding to no error. The joint probabilities in this triple product ensemble are

$$\begin{aligned} Pr(u_k,v_j,z_e) &= Pr(u_kv_j); & k &\neq j \\ &= 0; & k &= j \\ Pr(u_k,v_j,z_c) &= 0; & k &\neq j \\ &= Pr(u_kv_j); & k &= j \end{aligned} \tag{4–76}$$

Since the probabilities of the elementary events are unchanged,

$$H(U_nV_n) = H(U_nV_nZ_n) \tag{4–77}$$

This can be split up into (see Eq. (4–36))

$$H(V_n) + H(U_n|V_n) = H(V_n) + H(Z_n|V_n) + H(U_n|V_nZ_n) \tag{4–78}$$

Using Eq. (4–34),

$$H(U_n|V_n) \leq H(Z_n) + H(U_n|V_nZ_n) \tag{4–79}$$

The term $H(Z_n)$ in Eq. (4–79) is the term $H(P_{e,n})$ appearing in Eq. (4–75). Also

$$\begin{aligned} H(U_n|V_nZ_n) = {} & Pr(z_e) \sum_j Pr(v_j|z_e) \sum_k -Pr(u_k|v_jz_e) \log Pr(u_k|v_jz_e) \\ & + Pr(z_c) \sum_{k,j} -Pr(u_kv_j|z_c) \log Pr(u_k|v_jz_c) \end{aligned} \tag{4–80}$$

The second term in Eq. (4–80) is 0 since $Pr(u_k|v_jz_c)$ takes on only the values 0 and 1. The first term is bounded by $Pr(z_e) \log (M - 1)$ since the sum over k is an entropy over an alphabet of size M and $Pr(u_j|v_j z_e)$ is zero. Thus

$$H(U_n|V_n) \leq H(P_{e,n}) + P_{e,n} \log (M - 1) \qquad (4\text{–}81)$$

Finally, combining Eq. (4–74) with (4–81), we have

$$(R_T - C_T)T_s \leq \sum_{n=1}^{N} \frac{H(P_{e,n})}{N} + P_e \log (M - 1) \qquad (4\text{–}82)$$

The statement of the theorem, Eq. (4–66) follows from the convexity of $H(P_{e,n})$.

Theorem 4–9 is stronger than the converse theorems that have previously appeared in the literature.[9] These other theorems deal with the probability of error on a decoded sequence. Proving that the probability of error on a sequence of length N approaches 1 as $N \to \infty$ does not prove that the error probability per source digit is bounded away from zero. If each sequence error corresponds to only one source digit error, then the source digit error rate would be $1/N$ times the sequence error rate. Thus theorems about the sequence error rate do not rule out the possibility of reliable communication for large N.

4.7. The Coding Theorem.—The preceding sections can be summarized as follows. First the entropy, $H(U)$ of a discrete memoryless source was defined. This entropy, in bits, represents the minimum average number of binary digits per source letter required to specify the source output. The capacity, C, of a discrete memoryless channel was then defined as the maximum average mutual information per digit that can be transmitted through the channel. Next we defined the source rate, R_T, as $T_s H(U)$ and the capacity per unit time, C_T, as $T_c C$ where T_s and T_c are the time intervals between successive source digits and channel symbols respectively. It was shown that if $R_T > C_T$, then reliable communication is impossible.

In this section, we shall state the final theorem necessary to give unity to the previous results; if $R_T < C_T$, then reliable communication is possible with as small an error probability as desired. This remarkable theorem was first stated and essentially proved in 1948 by C. E. Shannon.[10] The first rigorous proof of the theorem was given by Feinstein,[11] and a number of other proofs and generalizations have subsequently been given.

The theorem and proof given here will be of the random coding

[9] See, for example, J. Wolfowitz, *Coding Theorems of Information Theory*, Springer-Verlag, Berlin, and Prentice-Hall, Inc., Englewood Cliffs, N.J., 1961.

[10] C. E. Shannon, *A Mathematical Theory of Communication*, Univ. of Ill. Press, Urbana, Ill.

[11] A. Feinstein, *Foundations of Information Theory*, McGraw-Hill Book Co., Inc., New York, 1958.

type developed by Shannon,[12] Elias,[13], and Fano.[14] The major advantage of the random coding approach lies in the strong and explicit bounds that can be derived on the error probability as a function of rate and constraint length. This approach is also indispensable to a thorough understanding of some of the most promising practical coding and decoding techniques that have been developed. Finally, the random coding concept gives insight into the coding theorem and into the problem of finding good codes.

As before, we will consider a discrete memoryless channel with the K input symbols $x_1,x_2,\cdots,x_K$, the J output symbols $y_1,\cdots,y_J$, and the transition probabilities, $Pr(y_j|x_k)$, abbreviated P_{jk}, for $1 \leq k \leq K$, $1 \leq j \leq J$.

Temporarily let us assume that the source is specified by a set of M equally probable letters, $u_1,\cdots,u_M$. The coder is specified by a correspondence between these M source letters and M sequences, $\mathbf{x}_1,\mathbf{x}_2,\cdots,\mathbf{x}_M$, of N channel input symbols each. N is a positive integer known as the block length of the code. Whenever the source presents the letter u_m to the coder, the coder presents

$$\mathbf{x}_m = x_{m,1},x_{m,2},\cdots,x_{m,N}$$

to the channel. If the time interval between channel symbols is T_c, then the time interval between source symbols must be NT_c. The rate of the code, R, is defined in nats as

$$R = \frac{\ln M}{N} \tag{4–83}$$

This is the entropy of the source per channel symbol in natural units.

Suppose now that we had some other source of entropy $R' < R$ nats per channel symbol. We know from Theorem 4–2 that this source can be coded into binary digits as efficiently as desired. These binary digits can then be coded into letters of the alphabet $u_1,\cdots,u_M$. Thus, aside from the equal probability assumption for the M letter source, our results are applicable to any source.

When the source letter $u = u_m$ appears, the channel transmits the code word $\mathbf{x}_m = (x_{m,1},\cdots,x_{m,N})$ and the decoder receives the sequence $\mathbf{y} = (y_1,\cdots,y_N)$ according to the probability

$$Pr(\mathbf{y}|\mathbf{x}_m) = \prod_{n=1}^{N} Pr(y_n|x_{m,n}) \tag{4–84}$$

[12] C. E. Shannon, "Certain Results in Coding Theory for Noisy Channels," *Inf. & Cont.*, **1** (1957).

[13] P. Elias, "Coding for Noisy Channels," *IRE Convention Record*, Part 4, pp. 37–46, 1955.

[14] R. M. Fano, *The Transmission of Information*, M.I.T. Press and Wiley, 1961.

The decoder, observing the sequence, $\mathbf{y}$, guesses at which source letter was put into the coder. We call this decoded letter v, and if $v \neq u$, a decoding error has occurred.

We assume that the decoder chooses an output $v = u_m$ if

$$Pr(\mathbf{y}|\mathbf{x}_m) > Pr(\mathbf{y}|\mathbf{x}_{m'}) \quad \text{for all } m' \neq m \tag{4-85}$$

Note that

$$Pr(u = u_m|\mathbf{y}) = \frac{Pr(u = u_m)Pr(\mathbf{y}|\mathbf{x}_m)}{Pr(\mathbf{y})} \tag{4-86}$$

For equiprobable source letters, the decoding rule of Eq. (4–85) thus chooses the most likely source letter conditional on the received sequence. If no source letter is more probable than all others, we assume that a decoding error is made.

Given a particular set of code words, and given the decoding rule of Eq. (4–85), the probability of decoding error can in principle be calculated. Let Y_m be the set of channel output sequences that satisfy Eq. (4–85) for each m, $1 \leq m \leq M$. Then the probability of decoding error for the source letter u_m is

$$P_{e,m} = 1 - \sum_{\mathbf{y} \in Ym} Pr(\mathbf{y}|\mathbf{x}_m) \tag{4-87}$$

The overall probability of decoding error, P_e, is

$$P_e = \frac{1}{M} \sum_{m=1}^{M} P_{e,m} \tag{4-88}$$

Conceptually, at least, the minimum probability of decoding error on a given channel for given N and M can be found by minimizing Eq. (4–88) over all choices of code words. Even for the simplest channels, however, this problem appears to be intractable except for very small N and M.

Rather than attempting to find an optimum set of code words, we will instead define an ensemble of codes and find the average error probability over this ensemble. At least one code in the ensemble must have an error probability as low as the ensemble average. It is far from obvious that such a procedure either simplifies the calculations or yields a reasonable upper bound to the error probability, but in fact both of these objectives are achieved.

The fundamental coding theorem for discrete memoryless channels will now be stated.

Theorem 4–11. Let $P_{jk} = Pr(y_j|x_k)$, $1 \leq k \leq K$; $1 \leq j \leq J$, be the transition probabilities for a discrete memoryless channel with input letters $x_1, \cdots, x_K$ and output letters $y_1, \cdots, y_J$. Let

$$\mathbf{p} = (p_1, p_2, \cdots, p_K)$$

be an arbitrary probability distribution on the input letters, and let ρ be an arbitrary number, $0 \le \rho \le 1$. Then a code of block length N and rate R (in nats) exists for which, when the source letters are equiprobable, the probability of decoding error satisfies

$$P_e \le 2 \exp(-NE) \tag{4-89}$$

$$E = -\ln \sum_{j=1}^{J} \left[\sum_{k=1}^{K} p_k P_{jk}^{1/(1+\rho)} \right]^{1+\rho} - \rho R \tag{4-90}$$

Also a code exists for which $P_{e,m}$, the error probability conditional on source letter u_m, is uniformly bounded by

$$P_{e,m} \le 8 \exp(-NE) \quad \text{all } m, \quad 1 \le m \le M \tag{4-91}$$

when E is given by Eq. (4-90).

The implications and interpretations of this theorem require considerable discussion and this will precede the proof. First observe that Eq. (4-91) yields a bound on error probability independent of the source statistics; thus it is applicable to any source of rate less than R after appropriate source coding.

The probability of error, both in Eqs. (4-89) and (4-91), depends critically upon E, necessitating an investigation of the behavior of E as a function of R. The strongest result is achieved in Theorem 4-11 when E is maximized over $\mathbf{p}$ and ρ. As we will show later, this maximization leads to a value of E that decreases with R, but is positive for $R < C$. Thus, for $R < C$, P_e can be made to approach zero exponentially with the block length.

In order to consider the behavior of E as a function of R, ρ, and $\mathbf{p}$, the following lemma is necessary. Its proof has been relegated to an appendix since it is singularly tedious and uninstructive.

Lemma 4-1. Define $E_0(\rho)$ as

$$E_0(\rho) = -\ln \sum_{j=1}^{J} \left[\sum_{k=1}^{K} p_k P_{jk}^{1/(1+\rho)} \right]^{1+\rho} \tag{4-92}$$

Let $E_0'(\rho)$ and $E_0''(\rho)$ be the first and second derivatives of Eq. (4-92) with respect to ρ. Then, for $0 \le \rho \le 1$

$$E_0(0) = 0; E_0(\rho) \ge 0; E_0'(\rho) \ge 0; E_0''(\rho) \le 0,$$

$$E_0'(0) = \overline{I(x;y)} = \sum_{k,J} p_k P_{jk} \ln \frac{P_{jk}}{\sum_k p_k P_{jk}} \tag{4-93}$$

For a given ρ and $\mathbf{p}$, Eq. (4–90) expresses E as a linear function of R with a slope $-\rho$ and an E intercept of $E_0(\rho)$ (see Fig. 4–3). As ρ varies from 0 to 1, a set of straight lines relating E and R is generated, and this set has an upper envelope which can be found by maximizing E with respect to ρ. Performing this maximization

$$\frac{\partial E}{\partial \rho} = E_0'(\rho) - R = 0 \qquad (4\text{–}94)$$

$$R = E_0'(\rho) \qquad (4\text{–}95)$$

Since $\partial^2 E/\partial \rho^2 = E_0''(\rho) \leq 0$, a solution of Eq. (4–95) for ρ must maximize E. Furthermore, since $E_0''(\rho) \leq 0$, $E_0'(\rho)$ decreases con-

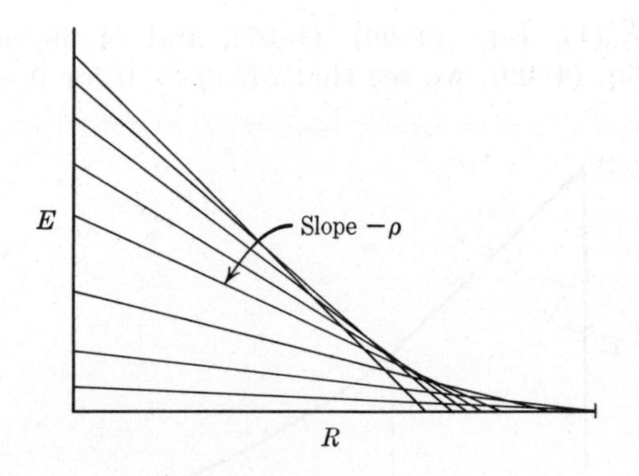

FIG. 4–3. Sketch of Eq. (4–90) with ρ as Parameter.

tinuously with ρ. Thus Eq. (4–95) must have a solution if R lies within the limits

$$E_0'(1) \leq R \leq E_0'(0) \qquad (4\text{–}96)$$

If R satisfies Eq. (4–96), then we can get a parametric solution for E maximized over ρ, $0 \leq \rho \leq 1$, by substituting Eq. (4–95) into Eq. (4–90)

$$E(\rho) = E_0(\rho) - \rho E_0'(\rho) \qquad (4\text{–}97)$$

$$R(\rho) = E_0'(\rho) \qquad 0 \leq 1 \leq \rho \qquad (4\text{–}98)$$

From Eqs. (4–97) and (4–98), the slope of this E,R curve is

$$\frac{dE(\rho)}{dR(\rho)} = \frac{\partial E(\rho)/\partial \rho}{dR(\rho)/\partial \rho} = -\rho \qquad (4\text{–}99)$$

Then since $R(\rho)$ decreases with ρ, $E(\rho)$ must increase with ρ and the E,R curve must be convex downward. Also, from lemma 4–1, $E(0) = 0$, $R(\rho) \geq 0$, and

$$R(0) = \overline{I(x;y)} \tag{4–100}$$

where $\overline{I(x;y)}$ is the average mutual information on the channel with the input probability distribution **p**. If **p** is chosen to achieve channel capacity, then $R(0) = C$. For this choice of **p**, the behavior of $E(\rho)$ as a function of $R(\rho)$ for ρ close to 0 can be derived by expanding $E(\rho)$ and $R(\rho)$ in MacLaurin series, giving the asymptotic relation

$$\lim_{R \to C} E = \frac{(C - R)^2}{2(-E_0''(0))}, \quad R < C \tag{4–101}$$

When $R < E_0'(1)$, Eqs. (4–96), (4–97), and (4–98) are no longer valid. From Eq. (4–99), we see that $\partial E/\partial\rho > 0$ for $0 \leq \rho \leq 1$; thus

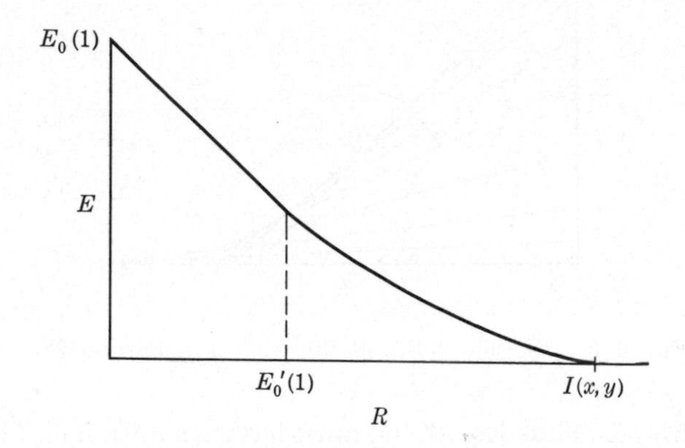

FIG. 4–4. Sketch of Eq. (4–90) Maximized Over ρ.

E is maximized by choosing $\rho = 1$. This makes E a linear function of R for $R < E_0'(1)$. Combining these results together, E, as a function of R, optimized over ρ, has the appearance given in Fig. 4–4.

Although the E,R curve derived using the input probabilities that achieve channel capacity gives a perfectly valid bound on probability of decoding error, a better bound can generally be achieved by varying **p** as R becomes less than C. For a given ρ, $0 \leq \rho \leq 1$, E can be maximized with respect to **p** by minimizing the quantity

$$\sum_j \left[\sum_k p_k P_{jk}^{1/(1+\rho)} \right]^{1+\rho}$$

with respect to $\mathbf{p} = (p_1,\cdots,p_K)$ (see Eq. (4–90)). We will show that this is a convex downward function of $\mathbf{p}$ by showing that for each j,

$$\left[\sum_k p_k P_{jk}^{1/(1+\rho)}\right]^{1+\rho}$$

is a convex downward function. Let $p_1,\cdots,p_K$ and $q_1,\cdots,q_K$ be arbitrary input probability distributions, and let λ be an arbitrary number, $0 \le \lambda \le 1$.

$$\left[\sum_k (\lambda p_k + (1-\lambda)q_k)P_{jk}^{1/(1+\rho)}\right]^{1+\rho} = \left[\lambda \sum_k p_k P_{jk}^{1/(1+\rho)} + (1-\lambda)\sum_k q_k P_{jk}^{1/(1+\rho)}\right]^{1+\rho} \tag{4–102}$$

But since $x^{1+\rho}$ is a convex downward function of x for $\rho \ge 0$,

$$\left[\sum_k (\lambda p_k + (1-\lambda)q_k)P_{jk}^{1/(1+\rho)}\right]^{1+\rho} \le \lambda\left[\sum_k p_k P_{jk}^{1/(1+\rho)}\right]^{1+\rho} + (1-\lambda)\left[\sum_k q_k P_{jk}^{1/(1+\rho)}\right]^{1+\rho} \tag{4–103}$$

Thus any stationary point of E with respect to $\mathbf{p}$ is a maximum; if no stationary point exists, the maximum occurs with $p_k = 0$ for one or more values of k.

Using a Lagrange multiplier to take care of the constraint

$$\sum_k p_k = 1$$

we get the condition for a stationary point,

$$\frac{\partial}{\partial p_k}\left\{\sum_j \left[\sum_k p_k P_{jk}^{1/(1+\rho)}\right]^{1+\rho} - \lambda \sum_k p_k\right\} = 0$$

$$\sum_j \alpha_j^\rho P_{jk}^{1/(1+\rho)} = \frac{\lambda}{1+\rho}, \qquad 1 \le k \le K \tag{4–104}$$

where

$$\alpha_j = \sum_k p_k P_{jk}^{1/(1+\rho)}, \quad 1 \le j \le J \tag{4–105}$$

These equations are usually difficult to solve. One exception to this is if $K = J$. Then Eq. (4–104) is a set of K linear equations in the K variables α_j^ρ. If a unique solution exists, then α_j can be found and Eq. (4–105) yields a set of K linear equations in the p_k; λ can then be used to set $\sum_k p_k = 1$. If the result satisfies $p_k \ge 0$ for all k, the optimum set of p_k has been found. Alternatively, if Eqs. (4–104) and

(4–105) have no solution satisfying $p_k \geq 0$ for all k, then E must be maximized by setting one or more of the $p_k = 0$. It is satisfying to observe the similarity between this maximization and the maximization to find channel capacity.

The upper envelope of E as a function of R maximized over $\mathbf{p}$ and ρ can now be found. We first maximize E over $\mathbf{p}$ for each value of ρ; numerical techniques or Eqs. (4–104) and (4–105) can be used. Then we maximize this result over ρ either by using graphical techniques to find the upper envelope or by using Eqs. (4–97) and (4–98). This optimum E,R curve is generally called the reliability curve for the given channel.

When Eqs. (4–97) and (4–98) are used to maximize over ρ, there is a variation of R with both $\mathbf{p}$ and ρ; consequently our proof that R decreases with ρ is no longer valid. However, dE/dR still equals $-\rho$ on the upper envelope. Figure 4–5 illustrates the type of reliability

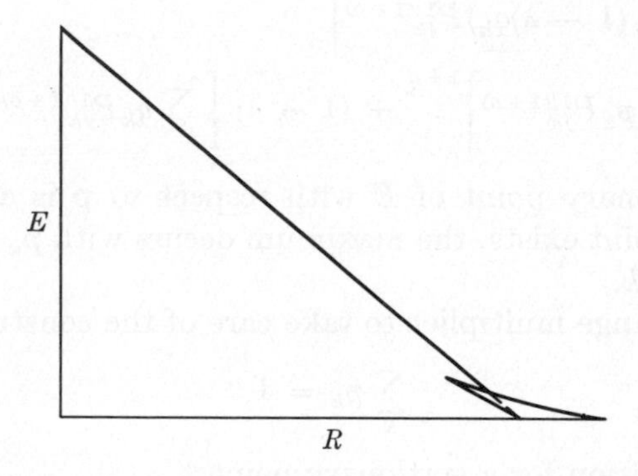

FIG. 4–5. Reliability Curve with Jump in ρ.

curve in which R increases with ρ. This simply means that some values of ρ do not yield a value of E and R on the final reliability curve. In summary, the reliability curve is convex downward and continuous, but it might have discontinuities in slope.

Although it will not be proven here, a lower bound can also be derived on the minimum achievable probability of decoding error for the same conditions as used in Theorem 4–11.[15] The result is that, for any code, and for $0 \leq \rho$,

$$P_e \geq BN^{-A} \exp -NE_L \tag{4–106}$$

$$E_L = \operatorname*{MAX}_{\mathbf{p},\rho} -\ln \sum_j \left[\sum_k p_k P_{jk}^{1/(1+\rho)} \right]^{1+\rho} - \rho R \tag{4–107}$$

[15] R. M. Fano, *The Transmission of Information*, M.I.T. Press and Wiley, 1961.

where B and A are independent of N. Note that the only difference between the upper and lower bounds is that ρ can be greater than 1 for the lower bound, and that the lower bound contains the term BN^{-A}. The maximum E for the upper bound equals E_L in the region $0 \leq \rho \leq 1$, but differs from it for rates below $E_0'(1)$ as shown in Fig. 4–6.

Random Coding. We now turn to the subsidiary developments and theorems necessary in order to prove Theorem 4–11. The first obstacle in the path of deriving an upper bound to the probability of decoding error for a particular channel is the difficulty of finding good codes. Even if we could find such codes, the problem of evaluating their error probability would be extremely tedious if M and N were large; both

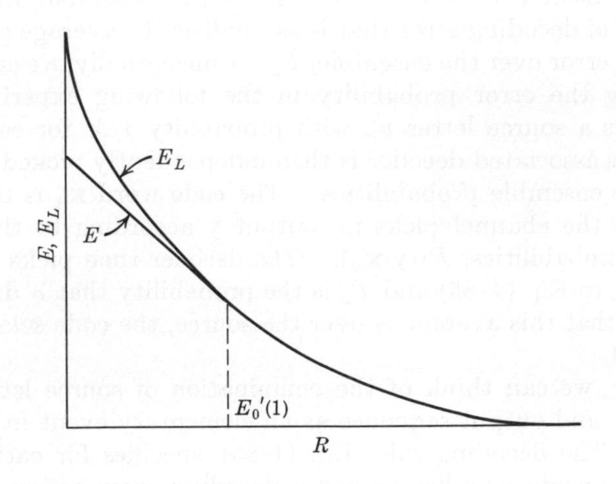

FIG. 4–6. Comparison of Upper and Lower Bound.

these problems can be avoided by defining an ensemble of codes and finding the average probability of decoding error over this ensemble. We first consider the set of all codes for a given M and N. The first code word, $\mathbf{x}_1$, can be any one of K^N different sequences of N letters, each letter being an arbitrary choice from the channel input alphabet of K letters. Similarly, every other code word can be any one of K^N sequences, so that there are $(K^N)^M$ different codes altogether. For each of these codes, we assume that there is a maximum likelihood decoder: *i.e.* a decoder that uses Eq. (4–85) for decoding. If we assign a probability measure to this set of codes, then the average probability of decoding error, $\overline{P}_e$, over the ensemble will be defined. First we choose an arbitrary set of channel input probabilities, $\mathbf{p} = p_1, \cdots, p_K$, where $p_k = Pr(x_k)$. Define the probability of a code word,

$$\mathbf{x}_m = (x_{m,1}, \cdots, x_{m,N})$$

as

$$Pr(\mathbf{x}_m) = \prod_{n=1}^{N} Pr(x_{m,n}) \tag{4–108}$$

$$Pr(x_{m,n} = x_k) = p_k \tag{4–109}$$

Finally define the probability of a code as the product of the probabilities of its code words. In other words, the probability of a code is the probability of getting that code by picking each letter of each code word independently from the ensemble X with probabilities $p_1, \cdots, p_K$. Clearly at least one code in the ensemble will have a probability of decoding error that is as small as the average probability of decoding error over the ensemble, $\overline{P}_e$. Conceptually, we can think of $\overline{P}_e$ as being the error probability in the following experiment: the source picks a source letter u_m with probability $1/M$ for each m. A code and its associated decoder is then independently picked according to the code ensemble probabilities. The code word $\mathbf{x}_m$ is then transmitted and the channel picks an output $\mathbf{y}$ according to the channel transition probabilities, $Pr(\mathbf{y}|\mathbf{x}_m)$. The decoder then picks an output v according to Eq. (4–85) and $\overline{P}_e$ is the probability that v differs from u_m. Note that this average is over the source, the code selection, and the channel.

Formally, we can think of the combination of source letter, set of code words, and output sequence as an elementary event in a product ensemble. The decoding rule, Eq. (4–85), specifies for each of these elementary events whether or not a decoding error occurs, and thus $\overline{P}_e$ is a well-defined quantity.

We next obtain a more convenient form for the decoding rule, Eq. (4–85). Define the discrepancy, $d(x_k, y_j)$, between a channel input x_k and output y_j as

$$d(x_k, y_j) = \ln \frac{f(y_j)}{Pr(y_j|x_k)} \tag{4–110}$$

where $f(y_j)$ (or f_j), $1 \leq j \leq J$, is an arbitrary set of J positive nonzero numbers whose purpose will be described later. Temporarily, we restrict our attention to channels in which

$$Pr(y_j|x_k) > 0; \quad 1 \leq j \leq J, \ 1 \leq k \leq K \tag{4–111}$$

Thus $d(x_k, y_j)$ is always finite for this class of channels.

Define the discrepancy, $D(\mathbf{x},\mathbf{y})$ between an input sequence $\mathbf{x} = (x_1,\cdots,x_N)$ and an output sequence $\mathbf{y} = (y_1,\cdots,y_N)$ as

$$D(\mathbf{x},\mathbf{y}) = \sum_{n=1}^{N} d(x_n,y_n) \tag{4–112}$$

Using Eq. (4–110) this becomes

$$D(\mathbf{x},\mathbf{y}) = \sum_{n=1}^{N} \ln f(y_n) - \ln Pr(\mathbf{y}|\mathbf{x}) \tag{4–113}$$

From Eq. (4–113), if $Pr(\mathbf{y}|\mathbf{x}_m) > Pr(\mathbf{y}|\mathbf{x}_{m'})$, then $D(\mathbf{x}_m,\mathbf{y}) < D(\mathbf{x}_{m'},\mathbf{y})$. Thus the decoding rule, Eq. (4–85), is equivalent to choosing the output that minimizes the discrepancy; *i.e.* choose $v = u_m$ if

$$D(\mathbf{x}_m,\mathbf{y}) < D(\mathbf{x}_m,\mathbf{y}) \quad \text{for all } m' \neq m,\ 1 \leq m' \leq M \tag{4–114}$$

From the manner in which the ensemble of random codes was chosen it is clear that $\overline{P}_e$ is independent of the source letter. Consequently, to reduce the notational complexity we assume that u_1 is the source letter. Then we can describe $\overline{P}_e$ as the probability (over the code ensemble and over the channel output ensemble given $\mathbf{x}_1$) of the union of events over $m = 2,3,\cdots,M$ that $D(\mathbf{x}_1,\mathbf{y}) \geq D(\mathbf{x}_m,\mathbf{y})$. We could immediately form an upper bound to $\overline{P}_e$ by bounding the probability of a union of events by the sum of the probabilities of the individual events. This does not yield a good upper bound for the following reason. When $D(\mathbf{x}_1,\mathbf{y})$ is very large, say greater than a suitable constant, Nd, it is likely to be larger than many of the $D(\mathbf{x}_m,\mathbf{y})$; this causes one decoding error to be counted many times in the bound. To avoid this difficulty, we will use separate bounding techniques on those events for which $D(\mathbf{x}_1,\mathbf{y}) \geq Nd$ and $D(\mathbf{x}_1,\mathbf{y}) < Nd$. The parameter d is arbitrary and will be optimized later. Thus,

$$\overline{P}_e \leq P_1 + P_2 \tag{4–115}$$

where

$$P_1 = Pr\left\{\bigcup_{m=2}^{M}[\text{Event that } D(\mathbf{x}_1,\mathbf{y}) > Nd; \quad D(\mathbf{x}_m,\mathbf{y}) \leq D(\mathbf{x}_1,\mathbf{y})]\right\}$$

$$P_2 = Pr\left\{\bigcup_{m=2}^{M}[\text{Event that } D(\mathbf{x}_1,\mathbf{y}) \leq Nd; \quad D(\mathbf{x}_m,\mathbf{y}) \leq D(\mathbf{x}_1,\mathbf{y})]\right\}$$

Now we can separately bound P_1 and P_2 by

$$P_1 \leq Pr[D(\mathbf{x}_1,\mathbf{y}) > Nd] \tag{4–116}$$

$$P_2 \leq \sum_{m=2}^{M} Pr[D(\mathbf{x}_1,\mathbf{y}) \leq Nd;\ D(\mathbf{x}_m,\mathbf{y}) \leq D(\mathbf{x}_1,\mathbf{y})] \tag{4–117}$$

Observe that Eq. (4–115) is an exact expression for $\overline{P}_e$ except for the bounding involved in assuming ambiguities (*i.e.* cases in which no $D(\mathbf{x}_m,\mathbf{y})$ is greater than all others) to always cause errors. Thus the arbitrary function, $f(y)$, can have no effect on Eq. (4–115) since it has no effect on which word is decoded when $\mathbf{x}_1$ is transmitted. The function $f(y)$ does have an effect on Eqs. (4–116) and (4–117) however, since it helps determine the set of output sequences for which

$$D(\mathbf{x}_1,\mathbf{y}) \geq Nd$$

Finally, observe from Eq. (4–112) that $D(\mathbf{x}_1,\mathbf{y})$ and $D(\mathbf{x}_m,\mathbf{y})$ are both defined as sums of random variables, and thus, using Eqs. (4–116) and (4–117) the problem of bounding $\overline{P}_e$ has been reduced to the problem of bounding the tails of the distributions of sums of random variables. This is best done by the Chernov bound technique, briefly described in the following paragraphs. For a more detailed exposition, see Fano,[16] Chapter 8.

Bounds on the Distribution of Sums of Random Variables. Let z be a random variable, assuming the value z_k with probability $Pr(z_k)$ for $1 \leq k \leq K$. Define the moment generating function of z as

$$g(s) = \sum_{k=1}^{K} Pr(z_k) \exp(sz_k) = \overline{\exp(sz)} \tag{4–118}$$

Let $\mathbf{z} = \sum_{n=1}^{N} z_n$ where the z_n are statistically independent and each assumes the value z_k with probability $Pr(z_k)$, $1 \leq k \leq K$. Now the moment generating function of $\mathbf{z}$ is

$$G_N(s) = \sum_{\mathbf{z}} Pr(\mathbf{z}) \exp(s\mathbf{z}) = \overline{\exp(s\mathbf{z})}$$

$$= \overline{\exp\left[\sum_{n=1}^{N} sz_n\right]} = \overline{\prod_{n=1}^{N} \exp(sz_n)}$$

This is the average of the product of the N independent random variables, $\exp(sz_n)$. For independent random variables, the average of a product is equal to the product of the averages. Thus

$$G_N(s) = \prod_{n=1}^{N} \overline{\exp(sz_n)} = g(s)^N$$

Thus, although $Pr(\mathbf{z})$ is generally quite difficult to calculate for large N, the moment generating function can be expressed quite simply as

[16] R. M. Fano, *The Transmission of Information*, M.I.T. and Wiley, 1961.

the Nth power of the moment generating function of z. Let d be an arbitrary number. Then

$$g(s)^N = \sum_{\mathbf{z}} Pr(\mathbf{z})e^{s\mathbf{z}} \geq \sum_{\mathbf{z} \geq Nd} Pr(\mathbf{z})e^{s\mathbf{z}} \tag{4–119}$$

Now, for $s \geq 0$, $\mathbf{z} \geq Nd$ implies that $e^{s\mathbf{z}} \geq e^{sNd}$. Thus the right hand summation of Eq. (4–119) can be bounded by

$$\sum_{\mathbf{z} \geq Nd} Pr(\mathbf{z})e^{s\mathbf{z}} \geq e^{sNd} \sum_{\mathbf{z} \geq Nd} Pr(\mathbf{z}) = e^{sNd} Pr(\mathbf{z} \geq Nd) \tag{4–120}$$

Combining Eq. (4–119) and (4–120), we get

$$Pr(\mathbf{z} \geq Nd) \leq g(s)^N e^{-sNd} \quad \text{for any } s \geq 0 \tag{4–121}$$

It would appear from the rather gross inequalities in Eq. (4–119) and (4–120) that the bound in Eq. (4–121) is rather poor. However, if the parameter s is correctly chosen and if d is greater than the mean value of z, this is not so. To see this, consider the product $Pr(\mathbf{z})e^{s\mathbf{z}}$. For large N, $Pr(\mathbf{z})$ falls off rather sharply on both sides of $N\bar{z}$. However, $e^{s\mathbf{z}}$ can be considered as a weighting factor that weights large $\mathbf{z}$ very heavily. Thus the product $Pr(\mathbf{z})e^{s\mathbf{z}}$ will have a peak for some $\mathbf{z}$ larger than $N\bar{z}$. The trick is to pick s so that this peak occurs at $\mathbf{z} = Nd$. Analytically, this can be done by taking the partial derivative with respect to s of the right side of Eq. (4–121) and setting it equal to 0, giving

$$d = \frac{1}{g(s)} \frac{\partial g(s)}{\partial s} \tag{4–122}$$

With the choice of s satisfying Eq. (4–122), it can be shown that the bound in Eq. (4–121), known as a Chernov bound, at least has the correct exponential dependence on N.

Equation (4–121) can now be used to bound P_1 in Eq. (4–116). From Eqs. (4–110) and (4–112), we get

$$D(\mathbf{x}_1,\mathbf{y}) = \sum_{n=1}^{N} d(x_{1n},y_n) = \sum_{n=1}^{N} \ln \frac{f(y_n)}{Pr(y_n|x_{1n})} \tag{4–123}$$

Recall now that the letters in $\mathbf{x}_1$ are chosen independently with the probability distribution $\mathbf{p} = (p_1,\cdots,p_K)$ and when $\mathbf{x}_1$ is sent the output is governed by the transition probabilities $Pr(y|x_1)$. Thus, each of the terms $d(x_{1n},y_n)$ in Eq. (4–123) is an independent random variable with the moment generating function

$$g(s) = \sum_{k=1}^{K} \sum_{j=1}^{J} p_k Pr(y_j|x_k) \exp[sd(x_k,y_j)] \tag{4–124}$$

or, from the definition of $d(x,y)$ in Eq. (4–110)

$$g(s) = \sum_k \sum_j p_k Pr(y_j|x_k)^{1-s} f(y_j)^s \qquad (4\text{–}125)$$

Now applying the Chernov bound in Eq. (4–121) to P_1 in Eq. (4–116) we get

$$P_1 \le Pr[D(\mathbf{x}_1,\mathbf{y}) \ge Nd] \le g(s)^N e^{-sNd}, \quad \text{for } s \ge 0 \qquad (4\text{–}126)$$

Notice that the right hand side of Eq. (4–126), using the definition of $g(s)$ in Eq. (4–125), is a function of s, d, $\mathbf{p}$, and $f(y)$ as well as N and $Pr(y|x)$, whereas we would like our final bound on P_e to be a function only of N, $Pr(y|x)$, and the transmission rate. These spurious parameters will be treated later after another type of Chernov bound is developed to bound P_2.

Double Chernov Bounds. Let w and z be a pair of dependent random variables, assuming the pair of values w_k,z_j with probability $Pr(w_k,z_j)$, $1 \le k \le K$; $1 \le j \le J$.

Define the joint moment generating function of w and z as

$$h(r,t) = \sum_{k=1}^{K} \sum_{j=1}^{J} Pr(w_k,z_j) \exp[w_k r + z_j t] = \overline{\exp[wr + zt]} \qquad (4\text{–}127)$$

Now consider N pairs of random variables each having the distribution above, and each pair being statistically independent of all other pairs. Define $\mathbf{w} = \sum_{n=1}^{N} w_n$; $\mathbf{z} = \sum_{n=1}^{N} z_n$ and define $H_N(r,t)$ to be the joint moment generating function of $\mathbf{w},\mathbf{z}$.

$$H_N(r,t) = \sum_{\mathbf{w},\mathbf{z}} Pr(\mathbf{w},\mathbf{z}) \exp[\mathbf{w}r + \mathbf{z}t] = \overline{\exp[\mathbf{w}r + \mathbf{z}t]}$$

$$= \overline{\exp \sum_{n=1}^{N} w_n r + z_n t} = \overline{\prod_{n=1}^{N} \exp[w_n r + z_n t]} \qquad (4\text{–}128)$$

Now since successive pairs of w and z are statistically independent, the mean of the product is equal to the product of the means.

$$H_N(r,t) = \prod_{n=1}^{N} \overline{\exp[w_n r + z_n t]} = h(r,t)^N \qquad (4\text{–}129)$$

Thus the joint generating function of $\mathbf{w},\mathbf{z}$ is simply the Nth power of the joint generating function of w,z. Now we follow a procedure similar to that of Eqs. (4–119, 4–120, 4–121) but instead of finding $Pr[\mathbf{z} \ge Nd]$, we find a bound to $Pr[\mathbf{w} \leq \alpha N; \mathbf{z} \leq \beta N]$. Using Eqs. (4–128), (4–129), we get

$$h(r,t)^N = \sum_{\mathbf{w},\mathbf{z}} Pr(\mathbf{w},\mathbf{z}) \exp[\mathbf{w}r + \mathbf{z}t]$$
$$\geq \sum_{\mathbf{w}\leq\alpha N} \sum_{\mathbf{z}\leq\beta N} Pr(\mathbf{w},\mathbf{z}) \exp[\mathbf{w}r + \mathbf{z}t] \tag{4–130}$$

Now, for $r \leq 0$, $t \leq 0$, $\mathbf{w} \leq \alpha N$, $\mathbf{z} \leq \beta N$, it follows that

$$\exp(\mathbf{w}r + \mathbf{z}t) \geq \exp(\alpha Nr + \beta Nt)$$
$$h(r,t)^N \geq \exp(\alpha Nr + \beta Nt) \sum_{\mathbf{w}\leq\alpha N} \sum_{\mathbf{z}\leq\beta N} Pr(\mathbf{w},\mathbf{z})$$
$$Pr[\mathbf{w} \leq \alpha N; \mathbf{z} \leq \beta N] \leq h(r,t)^N \exp -(\alpha Nr + \beta Nt) \qquad \text{for } r \leq 0; t \leq 0 \tag{4–131}$$

The same arguments about the closeness of this bound apply here as applied to Eq. (4–121). The quantities r and t in Eq. (4–130) can be thought of as weighting functions which, being negative, give extra weight to small values of $\mathbf{w}$ and $\mathbf{z}$ respectively. The only complication is that if $\mathbf{w}$ and $\mathbf{z}$ are negatively correlated, then decreasing r will weight both small $\mathbf{w}$ and large $\mathbf{z}$ more heavily. When optimized over r and t, Eq. (4–131) is known as a double Chernov bound.

This bound will now be applied to an arbitrary term on the right side of Eq. (4–117). Each term there can be rewritten

$$Pr[D(\mathbf{x}_1,\mathbf{y}) \leq Nd; D(\mathbf{x}_m,\mathbf{y}) \leq D(\mathbf{x}_1,\mathbf{y})]$$
$$= Pr\left[\sum_{n=1}^{N} d(x_{1,n},y_n) \leq Nd; \sum_{n=1}^{N} d(x_{m,n},y_n) - d(x_{1,n},y_n) \leq 0\right] \tag{4–132}$$

Since the channel is memoryless and the letters of the code words are independent over the ensemble of codes, the random variables in the above summations satisfy the independence condition assumed by the double Chernov bound. The random variables above are $d(x_{1,n},y_n)$ and $d(x_{m,n},y_n) - d(x_{1,n},y_n)$. These variables are defined in terms of the events $x_{1,n},y_n$ and $x_{m,n}$ with the probabilities $Pr(x_{1,n})Pr(y_n|x_{1,n})$ $Pr(x_{m,n})$. Recall that $x_{1,n}$ is the nth transmitted digit, so that y_n depends on $x_{1,n}$ but not on $x_{m,n}$. The joint moment generating function for $d(x_{1,n},y)$ and $d(x_{m,n},y_n) - d(x_{1,n},y_n)$ is thus

$$h(r,t) = \sum_{k=1}^{K} \sum_{j=1}^{J} \sum_{i=1}^{K} p_k Pr(y_j|x_k) p_i \exp\{rd(x_k,y_j) + t[d(x_i,y_j) - d(x_k,y_j)]\} \tag{4–133}$$

Substituting $\ln [f(y)/Pr(y|x)]$ for $d(x,y)$, using P_{jk} for $Pr(y_j|x_k)$, and f_j for $f(y_j)$, this becomes

$$h(r,t) = \sum_{i,j,k} p_k p_i P_{jk}^{1-r+t} P_{ji}^{-t} f_j^r \tag{4–134}$$

Applying the bound, Eq. (4–131) and (4–132), we now get

$$Pr[D(\mathbf{x}_1,\mathbf{y}) \leq Nd;\ D(\mathbf{x}_m,\mathbf{y}) \leq D(\mathbf{x}_1,\mathbf{y})] \leq h(r,t)^N \exp[-rNd] \quad \text{for any } t \leq 0;\ r \leq 0 \tag{4–135}$$

Since Eq. (4–135) is independent of m, we can sum over m by multiplying Eq. (4–135) by $M - 1$, which we overbound by M. Then Eq. (4–117) becomes

$$P_2 \leq Mh(r,t)^N \exp[-rNd] \tag{4–136}$$

Finally recalling that $R = (\ln M)/N$, and combining Eq. (4–126) for P_1 and Eq. (4–136) for P_2, we get

$$\overline{P}_e \leq g(s)^N \exp[-sNd] + h(r,t)^N \exp[-N(rd - R)] \tag{4–137}$$

for any $s \geq 0$, $t \leq 0$, $r \leq 0$, and any d, where

$$g(s) = \sum_{k,j} p_k P_{jk}^{1-s} f_j^s \tag{4–138}$$

$$h(r,t) = \sum_{k,j,i} p_k p_i P_{jk}^{1-r+t} P_{ji}^{-t} f_j^r \tag{4–139}$$

Eqs. (4–137), (4–138), and (4–139) yield an upper bound to the average probability of decoding error over an ensemble of codes involving the channel transition probabilities P_{jk}, the ensemble input probabilities, p_k, the block length N, and the code rate R. Unfortunately this expression also involves the spurious parameters s, r, t, d, and f_j; to achieve the best bound, these parameters should be eliminated by minimizing Eq. (4–137) with respect to them. The parameters will be eliminated in the order t, d and f_j. The parameters r and s will then be replaced by one parameter to yield the bound on $\overline{P}_e$ expressed in Theorem 4–11. To minimize the right side of Eq. (4–137) over t, it suffices to minimize $h(r,t)$ with respect to t.

$$\frac{\partial h(r,t)}{\partial t} = \sum_{k,j,i} p_k p_i P_{jk}^{1-r+t} P_{ji}^{-t} f_j^r \ln P_{jk} - \sum_{k,j,i} p_k p_i P_{jk}^{1-r+t} P_{ji}^{-t} f_j^r \ln P_{ji} \tag{4–140}$$

By interchanging the i and k indices of summation in the second term of Eq. (4–140), we see that the two terms are equal for $1 - r + t = -t$; thus

$$t = \frac{-1 + r}{2} \tag{4–141}$$

is a stationary point of $h(r,t)$ with respect to t. This value of t actually minimizes $h(r,t)$ as follows immediately from

$$\frac{\partial^2 h(r,t)}{\partial t^2} = \sum_{k,j,i} p_k p_i P_{jk}^{1-r+t} P_{ji}^{-t} f_j^r \left(\ln \frac{P_{jk}}{P_{ji}}\right)^2 \geq 0$$

Furthermore, for $r \leq 0$, Eq. (4–141) automatically satisfies the constraint $t \leq 0$.

Next we minimize Eq. (4–137) over d. If $s = 0$, the first term of Eq. (4–137) is 1 and minimization is pointless. If $s > 0$, then the first term of Eq. (4–137) decreases with d, and the second term is nondecreasing with d. If we choose d so as to make the two terms equal, then

$$d = \frac{1}{s - r}\left[\ln \frac{g(s)}{h(r,(r-1)/2)} - R\right] \tag{4–142}$$

This value of d must come within a factor of 2 of minimizing $\mathbf{p}_e$ since a change of d in either direction will increase one term or the other. Incorporating Eq. (4–142) into (4–137), we get

$$\overline{P}_e \leq 2e^{-NE} \tag{4–143}$$

$$E = \frac{r}{s-r} \ln g(s) - \frac{s}{s-r} \ln h(r,(r-1)/2) - \frac{s}{s-r} R \tag{4–144}$$

An exact minimization of $\overline{P}_e$ with respect to d yields instead

$$\overline{P}_e \leq \left(\frac{s}{s-r}\right)^{-s/(s-r)} \left(\frac{-r}{s-r}\right)^{r/(s-r)} e^{-NE} \tag{4–145}$$

Eq. (4–143), however, is more useful due to its simplicity. The problem has now been reduced to that of maximizing E in Eq. (4–144) over f_j $(1 \leq j \leq J)$, r, and s. First substituting Eqs. (4–138) and (4–139) into (4–144), we get

$$E = \frac{r}{s-r} \ln \sum_{j=1}^{J} \alpha_j f_j^s - \frac{s}{s-r} \ln \sum_{j=1}^{J} \beta_j^2 f_j^r - \frac{s}{s-r} R \tag{4–146}$$

where

$$\alpha_j = \sum_{k=1}^{K} p_k P_{jk}^{1-s}; \qquad \beta_j = \sum_{k=1}^{K} p_k P_{jk}^{(1-r)/2} \tag{4–147}$$

$$\frac{\partial E}{\partial f_j} = \frac{rs}{s-r}\left\{\frac{\alpha_j f_j^{s-1}}{\sum_{j=1} \alpha_j f_j^s} - \frac{\beta_j^2 f_j^{r-1}}{\sum_{j=1} \beta_j^2 f_j^r}\right\} \tag{4–148}$$

Setting this equal to 0 and multiplying by f_j, we get

$$\frac{\alpha_j f_j^s}{\sum_{j=1} \alpha_j f_j^s} = \frac{\beta_j f_j^r}{\sum_{j=1} \beta_j^2 f_j^r} \tag{4–149}$$

If we set $\alpha_j f_j^s = \beta_j^2 f_j^r$ for all j, then clearly Eq. (4–149) will be satisfied; a stationary point of E with respect to f_j, $1 \leq j \leq J$, is then given by

$$f_j = \left(\frac{\beta_j^2}{\alpha_j}\right)^{1/(s-r)}, \quad 1 \leq j \leq J \tag{4–150}$$

If each value of f_j, as given by Eq. (4–150), is multiplied by the same arbitrary scale factor, Eq. (4–149) is still satisfied; actually Eq. (4–146) is also independent of a scale factor in the f_j. Substituting Eq. (4–150) into (4–146), we note that the two sums are equal and the stationary point value of E, E_{ST} simplifies to

$$E_{ST} = -\ln\left[\sum_{j=1}^{J} \alpha_j^{-r/(s-r)} \beta_j^{2s/(s-r)}\right] - \frac{s}{s-r} R \tag{4–151}$$

To show that E_{ST} maximizes E over f_j, $1 \leq j \leq J$, we consider an arbitrary set of $f_j > 0$ and define the quantity φ_j by

$$f_j = \left[\frac{\beta_j^2}{\alpha_j}\varphi_j\right]^{1/(s-r)} \tag{4–152}$$

Substituting this into Eq. (4–146), we get

$$E_{ST} - E = -\frac{r}{s-r}\ln\frac{\sum_j \alpha_j^{-r/(s-r)}\beta_j^{2s/(s-r)}\varphi_j^{s/(s-r)}}{\sum_j \alpha_j^{-r/(s-r)}\beta_j^{2s/(s-r)}} + \frac{s}{s-r}\ln\frac{\sum_j \alpha_j^{-r/(s-r)}\beta_j^{2s/(s-r)}\varphi_j^{r/(s-r)}}{\sum_j \alpha_j^{-r/(s-r)}\beta_j^{2s/(s-r)}}$$

Finally define

$$\lambda_j = \frac{\alpha_j^{-r/(s-r)}\beta_j^{2s/(s-r)}}{\sum_j \alpha_j^{-r/(s-r)}\beta_j^{2s/(s-r)}} \tag{4–153}$$

$$E_{ST} - E = -\frac{r}{s-r}\ln\sum_j \lambda_j\varphi_j^{s/(s-r)} + \frac{s}{s-r}\ln\sum_j \lambda_j\varphi_j^{r/(s-r)} \tag{4–154}$$

Since $\sum_j \lambda_j = 1$, and since the coefficients of both logarithms are positive, we can use the convexity upward of the logarithm to give

$$E_{ST} - E \geq -\frac{r}{s-r}\sum_j \lambda_j \ln \varphi_j^{s/(s-r)} + \frac{s}{s-r}\sum_j \lambda_j \ln \varphi_j^{r/(s-r)} = 0 \tag{4–156}$$

Thus E_{ST} is the maximum of E over variation of the f_j.

Finally, we must maximize E_{ST}, which will be relabeled E, over s and r. First, transform the variables s and r into ρ and σ as follows

$$\rho = \frac{s}{s-r}; \qquad \sigma = 1 - s \tag{4–157}$$

The constraints $s \geq 0$; $r \leq 0$ constrain ρ to the interval $0 \leq \rho \leq 1$. Now define

$$\alpha_j(\sigma) = \sum_k p_k P_{jk}^{\sigma} \tag{4–158}$$

Using this definition and Eq. (4–157), the expression β_j defined in Eq. (4–147) becomes

$$\beta_j = \sum_{k=1}^{K} p_k P_{jk}^{(1-\sigma(1-\rho)/2\rho)} = \alpha_j\left(\frac{1-\sigma(1-\rho)}{2\rho}\right)$$

With these definitions, Eq. (4–151) becomes

$$E = -\ln\left\{\sum_j \alpha_j(\sigma)^{1+\rho}\left[\alpha_j\left(\frac{1-\sigma(1-\rho)}{2\rho}\right)\right]^{2\rho}\right\} - \rho R \tag{4–159}$$

In order to maximize E over σ, it is sufficient to minimize the term $F(\sigma,\rho)$ given by

$$F(\sigma,\rho) = \sum_j \alpha_j(\sigma)^{1-\rho}\left[\alpha_j\left(\frac{1-\sigma(1-\rho)}{2\rho}\right)\right]^{2\rho} \tag{4–160}$$

$$\frac{\partial F}{\partial \sigma} = \sum_j \alpha_j(\sigma)^{1-\rho}\left[\alpha_j\left(\frac{1-\sigma(1-\rho)}{2\rho}\right)\right]^{2\rho} \times \left\{\frac{(1-\rho)\alpha_j'(\sigma)}{\alpha_j(\sigma)} - \frac{(1-\rho)\alpha_j'([1-\sigma(1-\rho)]/2\rho)}{\alpha_j([1-\sigma(1-\rho)]/2\rho)}\right\} \tag{4–161}$$

The term within brackets is 0 when

$$\sigma = \frac{1-\sigma(1-\rho)}{2\rho}$$
$$\sigma = \frac{1}{1+\rho} \tag{4–162}$$

Problem—Show that $\partial^2 F/\partial\sigma^2 \geqslant 0$ so that Eq. (4–159) actually minimizes F. Hint: the Cauchy inequality can be used to show that

$$\alpha_j''(\sigma)\alpha_j(\sigma) - [\alpha_j'(\sigma)]^2 \geqslant 0$$

Substituting Eq. (4–162) into (4–159), we have

$$E = -\ln \sum_j \left[\sum_k p_k P_{jk}^{1/(1+\rho)} \right]^{1+\rho} - \rho R \tag{4–163}$$

This result is identical to Eq. (4–90) of Theorem 4–11, and we have thereby shown that this is the tightest exponential bound that can be achieved on $\overline{P}_e$ starting from Eq. (4–137). We also observe from Eq. (4–163) that the restriction $P_{jk} > 0$ for all j and k can be relaxed to $P_{jk} \geq 0$ since Eq. (4–163) is a continuous function of each P_{jk} for $P_{jk} \geq 0$. Thus if a channel has some $P_{jk} = 0$, the upper bound to $\overline{P}_e$ can be found by taking $P_{jk} > 0$, and then finding the limit of $\overline{P}_e$ as $P_{jk} \rightarrow 0$. Since Eq. (4–163) is continuous, this limit is found simply by setting $P_{jk} = 0$.

To complete the proof of Theorem 4–11, it is still necessary to show that a code exists that satisfies Eq. (4–91) for every code word. To do this, we show that a code satisfying Eq. (4–91) can be constructed from a code with twice as many code words satisfying Eq. (4–89). Let M and R be the number of code words and rate for the desired code, and let $M' = 2M$, and $R' = (\ln M')/N = R + (\ln 2)/N$. We have shown that a code exists of rate R' for which, under the circumstances of Theorem 4–11,

$$P_e \leq 2 \exp -N \left\{ -\ln \sum_j \left[\sum_k p_k P_{jk}^{1/(1-\rho)} \right]^{1+\rho} - \rho R' \right. \tag{4–164}$$

Form a new code from Eq. (4–164) by choosing those M code words for which $P_{e,m}$ is smallest. For each of these code words, $P_{e,m} \leq 2P_e$. If this were not true, then over half the code words would have an error probability greater than $2P_e$; then the average probability of error would be greater than P_e, yielding a contradiction. Using only these M code words instead of the $2M$ can only decrease the error probability on each word; thus

$$P_{e,m} \leq 4 \exp -N \left\{ -\ln \sum_j \left[\sum_k p_k P_{jk}^{1/(1+\rho)} \right]^{1+\rho} - \rho R' \right\} \tag{4–165}$$

Finally, replacing R' by $R + (\ln 2/N)$, and recognizing that $\rho \leq 1$, we get

$$P_{e,m} \leq 8 \exp(-NE) \quad \text{for all } m \tag{4–166}$$

completing the proof of Theorem 4–11.

4.8. Continuous Memoryless Channels.—The coding theorem of the last section will be extended here to the following three types of channel models; channels with discrete input and continuous output; channels with continuous input and continuous output; and channels with band limited time functions for input and output. Although these models are still somewhat crude approximations to most physical communication channels, they still provide considerable insight into the effects of the noise and the relative merits of various transmission and detection schemes.

Discrete Input, Continuous Output Channels. We consider a channel with a discrete input alphabet, $x_1,\cdots,x_K$, and an output alphabet consisting of the set of real numbers. For each input, x_k, there is a conditional probability density $Pr(y|x_k)$ determining the output y. We assume, as before, that the channel is memoryless in the sense that if $\mathbf{x} = (x_1,\cdots,x_N)$ and $\mathbf{y} = (y_1,\cdots,y_N)$ are input and output sequences, then

$$Pr(\mathbf{y}|\mathbf{x}) = \prod_{n=1}^{N} Pr(y_n|x_n)$$

where $Pr(\mathbf{y}|\mathbf{x})$ is a probability density in the N dimensional space $y_1,\cdots,y_N$.

We shall establish an upper bound on error probability for the best code of rate R and block length N on this channel by considering a decoder that quantizes the output before decoding. Theorem 4–10 already provides a bound on error probability for such a quantized channel. We then find the limit of this bound as the quantization becomes infinitely fine.

Pick $J - 1$ real numbers, $a_1 < a_2 < \cdots < a_{j-1}$. Quantize the output, y, to level y_j if $a_{j-1} < y \leq a_j$. We take a_0 to be $-\infty$ and a_J to be $+\infty$ so that y_1 and y_J correspond to intervals of infinite extent. From Theorem 4–11, using this quantization,

$$\overline{P}_e \leq 2e^{-NE} \tag{4–166}$$

$$E = -\ln \sum_{j=1}^{J} \left[\sum_{k=1}^{K} p_k \left(\int_{a_{j-1}}^{a_j} Pr(y|x_k)dy \right)^{1/(1+\rho)} \right]^{1+\rho} - \rho R \tag{4–167}$$

for any ρ, $0 \leq \rho \leq 1$, and any set of input probabilities,

$$\mathbf{p} = (p_1,p_2,\cdots,p_k)$$

Next define Δ_j as $a_j - a_{j-1}$ for each j in the range $2 \leq j \leq J - 1$.

Now we can rewrite Eq. (4–167) as

$$E = -\ln\left\{\sum_{j=2}^{J-1} \Delta_j \left[\sum_k p_k \left(\frac{\int_{a_{j-1}}^{a_j} Pr(y|x_k)dy}{\Delta_j}\right)^{1/(1+\rho)}\right]^{1+\rho} + \left[\sum_k p_k \left(\int_{a_{J-1}}^{\infty} Pr(y|x_k)dy\right)^{1/(1+\rho)}\right]^{1+\rho} + \left[\sum_k p_k \left(\int_{-\infty}^{a_1} Pr(y|x_k)dy\right)^{1/(1+\rho)}\right]^{1+\rho}\right\} - \rho R \quad (4\text{–}168)$$

Now let $J \to \infty$, and let the sequence of points $a_1, \cdots, a_{J-1}$ be chosen for each J so that

$$\lim_{J\to\infty} \Delta_j = 0, \quad \text{all } j \geq 2 \quad (4\text{–}169)$$

$$\lim_{J\to\infty} a_{J-1} = \infty \quad (4\text{–}170)$$

$$\lim_{J\to\infty} a_1 = -\infty \quad (4\text{–}171)$$

In this limit, the last two integrals in Eq. (4–168) become 0. Then we can apply the fundamental theorem of calculus to get

$$\lim_{J\to\infty} E = -\ln \int_{y=-\infty}^{\infty} dy \left[\sum_{k=1}^{K} p_k Pr(y|x_k)^{1/(1+\rho)}\right]^{1+\rho} - \rho R \quad (4\text{–}172)$$

It is easy to show that the right side of Eq. (4–172) gives the upper bound of E over all quantization choices.

Problem—Show that any addition of quantization points into Eq. (4–167) with the previous points fixed increases E for a given ρ, $\mathbf{p}$, and R.

We have shown that Theorem 4–11 also applies to continuous output channels when the sum over the output alphabet is replaced by an integral over the output values. That is,

$$P_e \leq 2e^{-NE} \quad (4\text{–}173)$$

$$E = -\ln \int_{-\infty}^{\infty} dy \left[\sum_k p_k Pr(y_j|x_k)^{1/(1+\rho)}\right]^{1+\rho} - \rho R \quad (4\text{–}174)$$

for any ρ, $0 \leq \rho \leq 1$, and any set of probabilities $p_1, \cdots, p_K$.

All of the interpretations of Theorem 4–11 given in Section 4.7 carry over immediately to the continuous output channel. The set of Eqs. (4–104) and (4–105), for finding the optimum input probabilities for a given ρ become virtually useless, but E is still a convex function of $\mathbf{p}$, so that $\mathbf{p}$ can be optimized numerically.

Channels with Continuous Input and Output. Let the channel input alphabet be the set of real numbers. Temporarily we will assume the input, x, to be bounded between two limits, $A \le x \le B$. We will also assume that a channel transition probability density, $Pr(y|x)$, exists which is a continuous function of both x and y.

Let $x_1 < x_2 < \cdots < x_K$ be a set of points in the interval $[A,B]$ and let $\mathbf{p} = (p_1,\cdots,p_k)$ be an arbitrary probability measure on these points. If the coder uses only the inputs $x_1,\cdots,x_k$, then Eqs. (4–173) and (4–174) certainly apply. Equation (4–174) can be written more suggestively if we let $F(x)$ be the distribution function for the set of points $(x_1,\cdots,x_K)$ and probabilities $(p_1,\cdots,p_K)$. That is,

$$F(x) = \sum_{k \ni x_k \le x} p_k \tag{4–175}$$

Thus, Eqs. (4–173) and (4–174) become

$$P_e \le 2e^{-NE} \tag{4–176}$$

$$E = -\ln \int_{y=-\infty}^{\infty} dy \left[\int_{X=A}^{B} Pr(y|x)^{1/(1+\rho)} dF(x) \right]^{1+\rho} - \rho R \tag{4–177}$$

On the other hand, $F(x)$ can be any step distribution function satisfying $F(A^-) = 0$, $F(B) = 1$. Consequently since $Pr(y|x)$ is a continuous function of y and x, we can pass to the limit and allow $F(x)$ to be any distribution function satisfying $F(A^-) = 0$ and $F(B) = 1$. The properties of Eq. (4–177) are the same as those of Eq. (4–90) in Theorem 4–11. We can still optimize over ρ to get the parametric relation between $E(\rho)$ and $R(\rho)$ given by Eqs. (4–97) and (4–98). The R intercept of the $E(\rho),R(\rho)$ curve is thus again

$$R = E_0'(0) = \int_{y=-\infty}^{\infty} dy \int_{x=A^-}^{B} \left[\ln \frac{Pr(y|x)}{\int_{x'-A}^{B} Pr(y|x')dF(x')} \right] Pr(y|x)dF(x) \tag{4–178}$$

Problem—Show that Eq. (4–178) is the mutual information in nats between channel input and output when $F(x)$ is the distribution function for channel inputs. Use Eq. (4–41) for quantized input and output and pass to the limit.

Problem—Let $p(x) = dF(x)/dx$ be a probability density on the channel input space. Show that if one defines $H(x)$ as

$$\lim_{\Delta \to 0} \sum_{i=1}^{(B-A)/\Delta} -p_i \log p_i; \qquad p_i = \int_{A+(i-1)\Delta}^{A+i\Delta} p(x)dx$$

then $H(x) = \infty$. Note: $H(x)$ is usually defined for continuous spaces as

$$H(x) = \int_A^B p(x) \log \frac{1}{p(x)}\, dx$$

The restriction to a bounded channel input which has been used in the preceding paragraphs corresponds to the power limitation in physical channels. For many models of physical channels, if this restriction is removed, both the rate, R, and the exponent to the probability of error, E, can be made as large as desired. Computationally, it is often more convenient to impose input power limitations by other types of constraints on $F(x)$. The most common constraint is to restrict $F(x)$ to distributions that satisfy an average energy equation such as

$$\int_{-\infty}^{\infty} x^2 dF(x) = S \tag{4-179}$$

Notice that those distribution functions that satisfy Eq. (4–179) still constitute a convex set, so that optimization of the E,R curve is still straightforward by numerical methods. It is to be observed that the choice of an $F(x)$ satisfying a constraint such as Eq. (4–179) defines an ensemble of codes; the individual codes in the ensemble will not necessarily satisfy the constraint. This is unimportant practically since each digit of each code word is chosen independently over the ensemble; thus it is most unlikely that the average power of a code will differ drastically from the average power of the ensemble. It is possible to combine the central limit theorem and the techniques used in the last two paragraphs of Section 4.7 to show that a code exists for which each code word satisfies

$$\sum_{n=1}^{N} x_{m,n}^2 \leq SN \tag{4-180}$$

and the error probability satisfies

$$P_e \leq ce^{-NE} \tag{4-181}$$

$$E = -\ln \int_{y=-\infty}^{\infty} \left[\int_{x=-\infty}^{\infty} Pr(y|x)^{1/(1+\rho)} dF(x) \right]^{1+\rho} - \rho R \tag{4-182}$$

and $F(x)$ satisfies Eq. (4–179). The constant c in Eq. (4–181) will depend upon $F(x)$ but not N.

Additive Gaussian Noise Channel.[17] An example of the use of these bounds will now be helpful. Consider a channel for which the input is an arbitrary real number and the output is the sum of the input and an independent gaussian random variable of variance σ^2. Thus,

$$Pr(y|x) = \frac{1}{\sqrt{2\pi\sigma^2}} \exp \left[-\frac{(y-x)^2}{2\sigma^2} \right] \tag{4-183}$$

[17] For stronger results, derived in a different way, see C. E. Shannon, "Probability of Error for Optimal Codes in a Gaussian Channel," *Bell System Technical Journal*, **38**, pp. 611 (1959).

An average power constraint on the input distribution will be assumed of the form,

$$\int_{y=-\infty}^{\infty} x^2 dF(x) = A\sigma^2 \tag{4–184}$$

σ^2 is called the noise energy, $A\sigma^2$ the signal energy, and A the signal to noise ratio. If we now attempt to find the optimum input probabilities to maximize Eq. (4–182) as a function of ρ, we will find that no simple analytic solution exists for $F(x)$ except in the limit as $\rho \to 0$. This $F(x)$ can be found by maximizing Eq. (4–178) subject to Eq. (4–184). First define

$$Pr(y) = \int_{-\infty}^{\infty} Pr(y|x)dF(x) \tag{4–185}$$

The random variable y with the probability density shown above is the sum of 2 independent random variables, namely the input x with variance $A\sigma^2$ and the noise with variance σ^2. Thus, $Pr(y)$ satisfies

$$\int_{-\infty}^{\infty} y^2 Pr(y)dy = (A+1)\sigma^2 \tag{4–186}$$

$$\int_{-\infty}^{\infty} Pr(y)dy = 1 \tag{4–187}$$

Rewriting Eq. (4–178) and integrating over x, we get

$$R = \int_{-\infty}^{\infty} Pr(y|x) \ln Pr(y|x)dy - \int_{-\infty}^{\infty} Pr(y) \ln Pr(y)dy \tag{4–188}$$

$$= -\tfrac{1}{2} \ln 2\pi e\sigma^2 - \int_{-\infty}^{\infty} Pr(y) \ln Pr(y)dy \tag{4–189}$$

We next find a $Pr(y)$ that maximizes Eq. (4–189) subject to the constraints of Eqs. (4–186) and (4–187). Using the method of Lagrange multipliers, we find a stationary point with respect to $Pr(y)$ of the function

$$\int_{-\infty}^{\infty} Pr(y)[-\ln Pr(y) + \lambda y^2 + \gamma]dy \tag{4–190}$$

The solution is

$$Pr(y) = \exp[\gamma - 1 + \lambda y^2] \tag{4–191}$$

Using Eqs. (4–186) and (4–187) to solve for γ and λ,

$$Pr(y) = \frac{1}{\sqrt{2\pi(A+1)\sigma^2}} \exp - \frac{y^2}{2(A+1)\sigma^2} \tag{4–192}$$

Since y is gaussian and the noise is gaussian, x must also be gaussian,

$$\frac{dF(x)}{dx} = \frac{1}{\sqrt{2\pi A\sigma^2}} \exp - \frac{x^2}{2A\sigma^2} \tag{4–193}$$

Using this probability distribution to form an ensemble of codes, we get, from Eq. (4–181),

$$P_e \leq c \exp[-NE], \quad \text{for } 0 \leq \rho \leq 1 \tag{4–194}$$

$$E = -\ln \int_{y=-\infty}^{\infty} dy \left[\int dx \frac{1}{\sqrt{2\pi A\sigma^2}} (2\pi\sigma^2)^{1/[2(1+\rho)]} \exp - \left(\frac{x^2}{2A\sigma^2} + \frac{(y-x)^2}{2\sigma^2(1+\rho)} \right) \right]^{1+\rho} - \rho R \tag{4–195}$$

$$= -\ln \int_{y=-\infty}^{\infty} dy \left[\sqrt{\frac{2\pi\sigma^2(1+\rho)}{(2\pi\sigma^2)^{1/(1+\rho)}}} \frac{\exp - [y^2/2\sigma^2(A+1+\rho)]}{\sqrt{2\pi\sigma^2(A+1+\rho)}} \right]^{1+\rho} - \rho R \tag{4–196}$$

$$E = \frac{\rho}{2} \ln \left(1 + \frac{A}{1+\rho}\right) - \rho R \tag{4–197}$$

Optimizing Eq. (4–197) over ρ, we get the parametric relationship between E and R,

$$R(\rho) = \frac{1}{2} \ln \left(1 + \frac{A}{1+\rho}\right) - \frac{1}{2} \left(\frac{\rho}{1+\rho}\right) \left(\frac{A}{A+1+\rho}\right) \tag{4–198}$$

$$E(\rho) = \frac{\rho}{2} \left(\frac{\rho}{1+\rho}\right) \left(\frac{A}{A+1+\rho}\right) \tag{4–199}$$

Eqs. (4–198) and (4–199) are valid for

$$R \geq R(1) = \tfrac{1}{2} \ln \left(1 + \frac{A}{2}\right) - \frac{A}{4(A+2)} \tag{4–200}$$

For $R \leq R(1)$,

$$E = \tfrac{1}{2} \ln \left(1 + \frac{A}{2}\right) - R \tag{4–201}$$

E could be increased somewhat for small R by optimizing $F(x)$ for each ρ, but the simplicity of Eqs. (4–198) to (4–201) make them useful despite the possibility of slight improvement. We see from setting ρ equal to 0 in Eq. (4–198) that channel capacity for this channel is given by

$$C = \tfrac{1}{2} \ln (1 + A) \tag{4–202}$$

Channels with frequency limited input and output. A function of time, $x(t)$, is said to be frequency limited to W cps (cycles per second) if it has a Fourier transform,

$$F(f) = \int_{-\infty}^{\infty} x(t) \exp -[i2\pi ft]dt \tag{4–203}$$

and if $F(f) = 0$ for $|f| \geq W$. The inverse Fourier transform for such a time function is given by

$$x(t) = \int_{-W}^{W} F(f) \exp [i2\pi ft]df \tag{4–204}$$

Since $F(f)$ is 0 outside of the interval $(-W,W)$, it can also be expanded in a Fourier series

$$F(f) = \sum_{k=-\infty}^{\infty} c_k \exp \left[\frac{i2\pi fk}{2W}\right] \tag{4–205}$$

$$c_k = \frac{1}{2W}\int_{-W}^{W} F(f) \exp - \left[\frac{i2\pi fk}{2W}\right] df \tag{4–206}$$

Comparing Eqs. (4–204) and (4–206), we see that

$$c_{-k} = \frac{1}{2W}\, x\left(\frac{k}{2W}\right) \tag{4–207}$$

$$F(f) = \sum_{k=-\infty}^{\infty} \frac{1}{2W}\, x\left(\frac{k}{2W}\right) \exp - \left[\frac{i2\pi fk}{2W}\right] \tag{4–208}$$

Substituting Eq. (4–208) into (4–204)

$$x(t) = \sum_{k=-\infty}^{\infty} \frac{1}{2W}\, x\left(\frac{k}{2W}\right) \int_{f=-W}^{W} \exp \left[i2\pi f \left(t - \frac{k}{2W}\right)\right] df \tag{4–209}$$

$$x(t) = \sum_{k=-\infty}^{\infty} x\left(\frac{k}{2W}\right) \frac{\sin 2\pi W(t - k/2W)}{2\pi W(t - k/2W)} \tag{4–210}$$

Equation (4–210) is known as the sampling theorem. It states that any time function limited to a frequency W can be uniquely determined by its values at sample points spaced $1/2W$ apart. Thus if both the input and output from a channel are limited to a frequency W, then we can represent the input and output as sequences of real numbers spaced at intervals of $1/2W$. If each output in this sequence depends on only one input, then the results for continuous input, continuous output channels can be applied. One particularly important case in which this assumption is valid is that of a channel perturbed only by additive white gaussian noise with frequencies above W filtered out.[18]

We now apply Eqs. (4–194) to (4–201) to the frequency limited, power limited, additive white gaussian noise channel. If N is the block length of a code in samples, then $T = N/2W$ is the block length in time. Furthermore if S is the available signal power and if N_0 is the noise power per unit bandwidth, then the signal to noise ratio, A, is S/N_0W. Finally we let R_T, the rate in nats per second, be $2WR$. Substituting these relations into Eqs. (4–194) and (4–197), we get

$$P_e \leq c \exp -[TE_T] \tag{4–211}$$

$$E_T = \rho W \ln\left(1 + \frac{S}{N_0W(1+\rho)}\right) - \rho R_T \quad 0 \leq \rho \leq 1 \tag{4–212}$$

Optimizing over ρ, we get the parametric relations

$$E_T(\rho) = \rho W\left(\frac{\rho}{1+\rho}\right)\left(\frac{S}{S + N_0W(1+\rho)}\right) \tag{4–213}$$

$$R_T(\rho) = W \ln\left(1 + \frac{S}{N_0W(1+\rho)}\right) - W\left(\frac{\rho}{1+\rho}\right)\left(\frac{S}{S+N_0W(1+\rho)}\right) \tag{4–214}$$

For $R_T < R_T(1)$,

$$E_T = W \ln\left(1 + \frac{S}{2N_0W}\right) - R_T \tag{4–215}$$

Channel capacity here is $R_T(0)$, which is the well-known Shannon formula

$$C = W \ln\left(1 + \frac{S}{N_0W}\right) \tag{4–216}$$

Problem—Derive the limiting forms of (4–213) through (4–216) as $W \to \infty$.

Appendix.—*Lemma:* Let $\mathbf{p} = (p_1, \cdots, p_K)$ be a probability vector, and let $P_{jk} = Pr(y_j|x_k)$; $1 \leq j \leq J$, $1 \leq k \leq K$ be a set of conditional probabilities. Then for $0 \leq \rho \leq 1$, the function

$$E_0(\rho) = -\ln \sum_{j=1}^{J}\left(\sum_{k=1}^{K} p_k P_{jk}^{1/(1+\rho)}\right)^{1+\rho} \tag{4–217}$$

[18] Davenport and Root, *Random Signals and Noise*, Chapter 6, McGraw-Hill, New York, 1958.

has the following properties:

$$E_0(0) = 0 \tag{4–218}$$

$$E_0(\rho) \geq 0 \tag{4–219}$$

$$E'_0(\rho) \geq 0 \tag{4–220}$$

$$E'_0(0) = \sum_k p_k P_{jk} \ln \frac{P_{jk}}{\sum_i p_i P_{ji}} \tag{4–221}$$

$$E''_0(\rho) \leq 0 \tag{4–222}$$

Proof:

$$E_0(\rho) = -\ln \sum_j \alpha_j^{1+\rho}, \quad \alpha_j = \sum_k p_k P_{jk}^{1/(1+\rho)} \tag{4–223}$$

$$E'_0(\rho) = \frac{-\sum_j \alpha_j^{1+\rho} [\ln \alpha_j + (1+\rho)(\alpha'_j/\alpha_j)]}{\sum_j \alpha_j^{1+\rho}} \tag{4–224}$$

$$\alpha'_j = -\sum_k \frac{1}{(1+\rho)^2} p_k P_{jk}^{1/(1+\rho)} \ln P_{jk} \tag{4–225}$$

After some manipulation, this becomes

$$E'_0(\rho) = \frac{-\sum_j \alpha_j^\rho \left[\sum_k p_k P_{jk}^{1/(1+\rho)} \ln \frac{\sum_i p_i P_{ji}^{1/(1+\rho)}}{P_{jk}^{1/(1+\rho)}}\right]}{\sum_j \alpha_j^{1+\rho}} \tag{4–226}$$

Using the inequality $-\ln z \geq 1 - z$

$$E'_0(\rho) \geq \frac{\sum_j \alpha_j^\rho \left[\sum_k p_k P_{jk}^{1/(1+\rho)} - \sum_k p_k \sum_i p_i P_{ji}^{1/(1+\rho)}\right]}{\sum_j \alpha_j^{1+\rho}} = 0 \tag{4–227}$$

This establishes Eq. (4–220) and in conjunction with Eq. (4–218), which is obvious, establishes Eq. (4–219). Setting $\rho = 0$ in Eq. (4–226) yields Eq. (4–221). It remains to establish Eq. (4–222). Taking the derivative of Eq. (4–220),

$$E_0''(\rho) = \frac{\left\{\sum_j \alpha_j^{1+\rho}\left[\ln \alpha_j + \frac{(1+\rho)\alpha_j'}{\alpha_j}\right]^2\right.}{\left[\sum_j \alpha_j^{1+\rho}\right]^2}$$

$$- \frac{\left\{\sum_j \alpha_j^{1+\rho}\left[\ln \alpha_j + \frac{(1+\rho)\alpha_j'}{\alpha_j}\right]^2\right\}\left\{\sum_j \alpha_j^{1+\rho}\right\}}{\left[\sum_j \alpha_j^{1+\rho}\right]^2}$$

$$+ \frac{\sum_j \alpha_j^{\rho-1}\{-2\alpha_j\alpha_j' - (1+\rho)[\alpha_j''\alpha_j - (\alpha_j')^2]\}}{\sum \alpha_j^{1+\rho}} \tag{4–228}$$

From the Cauchy inequality, the difference of the first two terms of Eq. (4–228) is non-positive. Writing out the part of the third term in curly brackets, we get

$$\{-2\alpha_j\alpha_j' - (1+\rho)[\alpha_j''\alpha_j - (\alpha_j')^2]\}$$

$$= -(1+\rho)\left[\sum_k \frac{1}{(1+\rho)^4} p_k P_{jk}^{1/(1+\rho)}(\ln P_{jk})^2\right]\left[\sum_k p_k P_{jk}^{1/(1+\rho)}\right]$$

$$+ (1+\rho)\left[\sum_k \frac{1}{(1+\rho)^2} p_k P_{jk}^{1/(1+\rho)} \ln P_{jk}\right]^2$$

Applying the Cauchy inequality, this term is also non-positive, giving $E_0''(\rho) \le 0$.

CHAPTER 5

OPERATIONS ANALYSIS: METHODS AND STRUCTURE OF OPERATIONS

by

THOMAS L. SAATY

Office of Naval Research

5.1. Motivation and Introduction.—Most phenomena of the physical world, as studied by the physical scientist, are, to a large extent, independent of the observer. In contrast to the physical scientist, who is more occupied with the depth of understanding of the physical world, the operations analyst is primarily occupied with the relations and interactions between various levels of complexity of the raw facts he starts with, and the ultimate effect they have on his objectives. The subject matter of operations research is operations. In referring to operations we appeal to an intuitive understanding of the reader on the subject, about which we will say more later. Man and his interests are essential aspects of the operation that is planned and set in motion by him with specific objectives in mind. The ingredients (*e.g.*, raw materials and labor) may be described simply, but the resulting structure can be complex and in time is subject to evolution. The analysis of operations is of greatest importance when it pertains to the attainment of objectives.

No matter what the objectives and operations are, neither the functioning of an operation nor the choice of objectives is always decisively perfect at the start. There are situations in which uncertainty and lack of information are factors to reckon with. Sometimes it is necessary to make extrapolations and predictions without being able to study the actual environment of the operation.

An operation may be altered to better suit the objectives when it becomes clear where additional advantage may be gained towards these objectives, and, furthermore, the latter may be modified to conform to new constraints and new events that were not clear in the initial considerations.

Thus, decision-making is an important aspect of operations research. Analysis of the existing alternatives available contributes information, and guides the authority responsible for an operation in effecting changes towards more desirable objectives. The analysis of operations is not, so far, a clear-cut process because most of it is new and much of it is very complicated.

Operations research is a scientific approach that draws on the other sciences, whether exact or applied (mathematics, physics, economics, etc.), and on known calculation procedures in order to:[1]

(1) effect a global analysis (by means of a model) of problems rendered complex by the number of interacting factors, random or fixed, independent or not, human or material, intervening simultaneously in the consideration;

(2) furnish to the authority responsible for decision the optimum amount of quantitative information on the incidence of different possible alternatives, and thus aid such authority in making an effective choice to attain a proposed objective.

Operations research has occasionally been defined as the art of giving bad answers to questions that would otherwise receive worse answers. The significance of this definition is best realized by those who have looked seriously at the world about them.

Many scientists, in connection with research in their own specialties, practice operations research as it applies to operational phenomena that interest them. Examples of operational problems vary widely in scope. They include studies of: noncongested traffic flow through the Suez Canal or the New York tunnels; optimal methods of refining crude oil according to seasonal needs; sizes of stocks to be kept in inventory to meet fluctuating demands; the allocation and rotation of crops for an entire country; the analysis and simulation of military strategy and tactics, and the effectiveness of weapons; searching for lost objects (particularly for people in the high seas); and so forth.

The pursuit of operations research consists of (a) the judgment phase (what are the problems?), (b) the research phase (how to solve these problems), and (c) the decision phase (how to act on the finding and eliminate the problems). These phases require the evaluation of objectives, analysis of an operation and the collection of evidence and resources to be committed to the study, the (mathematical) formulation of problems, the construction of theoretical models and selection of measures of effectiveness to test the models in practice, the making and testing of hypotheses as to how well a model represents the problem, prediction, refinement of the model, and the interpretation of results (usually as possible alternatives) with their respective values (payoff). The decision-maker generally combines the findings of the

[1] E. Ventura, "Comment Apprendre la Recherche Operationnelle," *Revue Française de Recherche Operationnelle*, 4e Anne, 4e Trimestre, Numero 17, 199–222 (1960).

analysis with his experience and tempers it by the dictates of statesmanship to arrive at a more rational decision than he would otherwise make. However, the fact that operations often involve people makes it difficult to follow the dictates of simplified logic. It has been neither easy nor desirable to assign worth to people or to their preferences. Note the important role that the analyst's objectivity plays in this process.

To a considerable extent, operations research as a formal discipline is occupied with the construction of *models*. This is closely related to the analysis of alternatives for decision-making. It is generally assumed that it is preferable to have a model to represent an operation, even though it is oversimplified and perhaps imperfect, than to have none. A model may be purely logical or it may be a physical analogue. A mathematical formula is an example of the former, a wind tunnel an illustration of the latter. In both cases, the model provides a coherent framework for coping with the complexities of a problem.

The literature of science is replete with models. This variety enables one to make some interesting observations. Thus, for example, one rarely regards models as unique or absolute, although, through the choice of a specific one (*e.g.*, a differential equation), unique solutions to problems may be obtained. A model is formulated to serve a specific purpose. Some models may be suitable for generalization, others may not be. These generalizations are more profitably made as extrapolations for scientific purposes, and occasionally as useful philosophical observations. A model must be flexible to absorb new information, and, hence, stochastic processes have broader and richer applicability than deterministic models.

Models are usually formed through a process of successive approximations, *i.e.*, refinements are introduced successively, based upon the worth and reliability of additional information and upon the suitability of the model for prediction. This refinement process may be described as follows:[2]

Data — Model — Prediction — Further Data — Adjustment of the Model — Further Prediction — continued as far as need be.

Among the first desirable properties of models are economy in the number of parameters that describe the essential properties of an operation, general applicability to a variety of problems, and successful prediction.

An operations research problem may be remedial in that it seeks to

[2] Thomas L. Saaty, *Mathematical Methods of Operations Research*, McGraw-Hill Book Co., New York, 1959.

correct malfunctions in an operation. It may be an optimization problem if, for example, the object is to minimize the effort used in producing outcomes that are subject to constraints. A problem may be predictive if knowledge about future behavior is sought, or if we desire to solve new problems by known techniques. Finally, a problem may be hypothetical in that it anticipates the possible occurrence of difficulties and studies a variety of solutions to be used to prevent an undesirable outcome from arising.

One observes that operations research tends to regard a problem within the operation as a whole in order to avoid overlooking significant factors that affect those parts of the operation relating to the problem.

An interesting problem solved by operations research methods is that of the flow of traffic through the New York tunnels. The presence of toll booths causes congestion of traffic at the entrances and exits of tunnels. Economical operation of the toll booths necessitates that not all booths be open at all times. By studying the statistics of the traffic, a schedule was developed indicating the number of booths to be operated at different times of the day. In this manner congestion was alleviated, and the frequency of traffic jams was reduced considerably.[3]

Another illustration of operations research is the use of linear programming techniques (Section 5.14) to obtain optimal mixtures of gasoline ingredients that will produce a result suitable for different climatic conditions and subject to demand constraints on a long-range basis.

Problems of logistics and inventory occupy the attention of many investigators because of the high cost of storage of inventory items on shelves or because of possible obsolescence of such items if one is concerned with spare parts.

Operations research has played a fundamental role in developing war gaming methods used in studying possible courses to follow in peace or in war by analyzing their outcomes. Similar methods have also been developed for business gaming. At present simulation techniques of operations research are being prepared for use in studying the economy of emergent countries. In such studies, by including information on the national product, investment in various sections of the economy, production from various sections, imports and exports, balance of payments, and so forth, it becomes possible to investigate the effect of varying these different quantities on the economy, and to recommend certain actions to the decision-makers that would improve the growth of the economy over an extended period.

An illustration of an operations research problem for which no model is yet available is the following, which occurs in queueing theory.[4] Everyone has observed, and perhaps been displeased to notice, persons in a waiting line, before a theater box-office, for example, who arrive after the observer's arrival, but who go to persons in front to solicit their cooperation in obtaining service. Thus, an

[3] Leslie C. Edie, "Traffic Delays at Toll Booths," *Operations Research*, **2**, 107–38 (1954).

[4] Thomas L. Saaty, "On the Problems of Jockeying, Collusion, Scheduling, Optimization, and Graph Theoretic Queues," *Office of Naval Research Notes*, June, 1961.

individual person must wait for this additional service obtained through collusion. How long will a person wait if he tolerates such apparently unethical practices, and what can be done to discourage collusion?

Carpools, in which several people use a single transportation conveyance, are an ethical means of collusion, in which the average waiting time may actually be shortened because fewer cars are in use. However, there is no unfair advantage taken of the limited available service. On the other hand, a long line at a box-office that has a few tickets remaining for a performance never fails to exasperate those who observe late arrivals going forward to collude with acquaintances in the front of the queue. Without such collusion, the single person has a fair chance of obtaining a ticket; with it, he has a lesser chance.

Consider for a moment the plight of a customer waiting in a single-channel, first-come first-served queue who will not seek an alliance. Collusion among customers who are all in line ahead of him may benefit him since various forms of delays, *e.g.*, dalliance, usually aggregated in the service distribution, are decreased because of the alliances. However, customers who arrive after him may ally themselves with customers ahead of him, inevitably increasing his total wait. In fact, if he were also to accommodate requests for collusion he would spend a longer time in the service facility. Such alliances, that people can see with their own eyes, are generally regarded as unethical. However, there is nothing to prevent people from collusion by telephone or other means prior to queueing.

It is interesting to note here that the delay time of a customer in the system depends also upon the number of customers arriving after him and upon the probability that they collude with him or with customers ahead of him. How to describe and relate the variables entering in the computation of this waiting time is another problem that should be considered.

The problems of operations research have stimulated new developments in several mathematical fields: various aspects of game theory, stochastic processes, the calculus of variations, graph theory, and numerical analysis, to name a few.

As already pointed out, from a theoretical standpoint, an interesting and difficult problem is the characterization of the structure of an operation with the view of developing a theory that includes all the elements of the separate theories used so far in the field. This type of coherence is not yet available. The subject of graph theory (*cf.* Section 5.2) is receiving considerable attention because of its contribution to the study of flow in networks. Both the concept of flow and the concept of network have immediate bearing on the structure problem.

There are areas in the field of management science where it has not been easy or fruitful to produce theories of use in decision making. The complexity of the concepts and structures involved have so far presented investigators with great difficulties. Some continue to attempt formalizing the structure of the field of management science but there have been no breakthroughs. Often, one is limited by the absence of the mathematical methods required in this theoretical pursuit.

Areas of advanced planning, policy planning in conflict situations, automation, space problems, psychology, and biology require fresh mathematical interest. For example, decision problems would be better understood with a fruitful, formal approach to the psychology of values and, hence, decision criteria. Today the conflicting elements cannot be resolved by existing simplified theories. Yet, with theoretical abstraction there is greater promise of achievement. It alone saves one from repetitive use of the same inadequate devices.

Attempts are being made[5] to characterize operations through the use of concepts such as partial ordering, network flow (considering its stochastic aspects), feedback, utility defined on this flow, the use of controllable and uncontrollable variables (with the possibility of prediction) in representing the flow, and the presence of competition; *i.e.*, some of the variables of the flow problem are controlled by an opponent who may have different measures of utility. Many of these ideas will occur subsequently, in this chapter, although no attempt will be made here to give a detailed characterization of the structure of an operation.

So far operations research has utilized the talents of individuals from a wide spectrum of fields ranging from chess players and physical and social scientists to mathematicians, pure and applied. Imagination and a good background in technical excellence are the basic elements in this choice of individuals. A significant consequence of all this is an opportunity for broad intellectual contacts and cross-fertilization of ideas in many diverse fields.

There are, at present, eleven operations research societies in different countries. There is also an International Federation of Operations Research Societies (IFORS). In addition to the journals published by these societies, a journal called *International Abstracts in Operations Research* has made its appearance.

Computers have come to play a significant role in solving complicated mathematical models describing operations. They are frequently used in conjunction with simulation, Monte Carlo, operational gaming, and numerical solution of various mathematical models.

Interest in developing and refining the mathematical methods of operations research has become intensified and sophisticated. Attention is generally given to *a priori* upper bounds on the number of solutions of a problem, the existence and uniqueness of solutions,

[5] Thomas L. Saaty, "On the Structure of Operations," *Office of Naval Research Notes* (1961).

characterization, construction, convergence, approximation, errors, and asymptotic behavior. We shall not dwell on all these points in our discussion, but rather shall bring out the essential features as required for each topic that we discuss. It is clear that constructing solutions is a main pursuit of operations analysis.

A word of caution is in order at this point. There is an unrealistic tendency on the part of some to think that once the mathematical solution of a problem has been found the task of the scientist is completed, and that the effort of interpreting and applying the solution is an easy one. We must emphasize the fact that the difficulty of solving an operational problem is really encountered after the mathematical solution has been obtained; *i.e.*, in the effective application of the theoretical solution to a specific, physical problem.

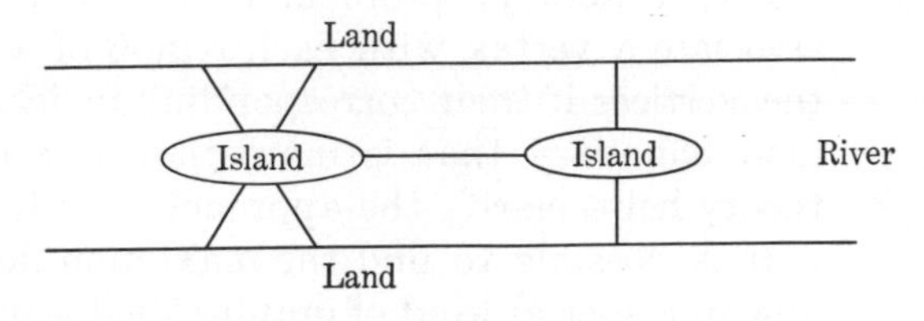

FIG. 5–1.

Whatever model is used to describe an operations research problem, be it a differential equation, a mathematical program, or a stochastic process, there is a natural tendency to seek a maximum or a minimum with a certain purpose in mind. Thus, one often finds optimization problems imbedded in the models of operations research.

Some reflection after reading the chapter would indicate that most of the subsequent models may be descriptively related to flow (this need not be conservative or continuous) that is distributed (programming), stored (inventory), delayed through bottlenecks (queues), lost through sinks and created through sources (reliability), flowing backwards (feedback), and so forth. The flow may be controlled and diverted. Illustrations of control are investment and advertising, which aim at influencing flows arising in economic problems.

We shall start out with elementary general topological considerations of flow by studying network flow. We shall follow this by a variety of models from operations research that illustrate analytical methods and problems. No illustrations of statistical methods will be given here because statistics, a fundamental tool of science, is abundantly discussed in the literature of science.

5.2. Graph Theory and Network Flow—Topological Approach to Flow. —In Königsberg, Germany, there were seven bridges connecting two islands in the Pregel River and the mainland (Fig. 5–1). People inquired whether in a single trip it was possible to start at a given point and cross all seven bridges, crossing each bridge once and only once. Euler, by assigning a vertex to each land mass (there are four in all) and connecting them by lines corresponding to the bridges that join the land masses, produced Fig. 5–2, which is known as a graph. In terms that will be explained below, vertices are joined by edges in the indicated fashion. Euler then gave a negative answer to the problem by means of a general argument on relations between edges and vertices.

The four-color problem (prove that four colors are sufficient to color any map in the plane or on a sphere so that no two adjacent regions have the same color) is another problem in which it is possible to associate a vertex with each region of a map and join the vertices if their corresponding regions have a common boundary that is more than one point. Graph theory helps clarify the approach to this problem.

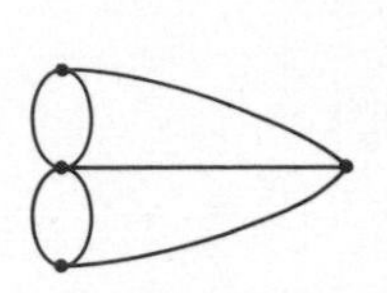

FIG. 5–2.

It is possible to find the maximum flow, *e.g.*, traffic flow in a special kind of graph called a network, which we shall discuss at some length in this section. This problem is applicable to operations research, and, hence, we give a brief outline of maximum flow through networks.

A finite set of elements $e_1, \cdots, e_m; v_1, \cdots, v_n$ is called a finite abstract graph G if to each e_i there correspond two elements v_j and v_k (which may coincide). The elements e_i are called the edges of the graph and v_j are its vertices or end points. The edge e_i is said to be incident with its corresponding vertices v_j and v_k and conversely. Two edges are parallel if they are incident with the same pair of vertices. An edge with coinciding end points is called a loop. A subset of edges and vertices of G is a subgraph if it forms a graph. A chain is a subgraph connecting two vertices v_a and v_b if it consists of distinct vertices $v_{j_1}, \cdots, v_{j_n}$ $(n \geq 1)$ and of edges $e_{i_1}, \cdots, e_{i_{n-1}}$, such that e_{i_p} is incident with the vertices v_{j_p} and $v_{j_{p+1}}$ $(1 \leq p \leq n - 1)$ where $v_{j_1} = v_a, v_{j_n} = v_b$. A circuit is a closed chain, *i.e.*, a chain whose end points coincide. A graph is connected if there is a chain between any two of its vertices. A vertex is said to be isolated if it does not form the end point of an edge. A component of a graph is the set of all vertices that are connected to a given vertex. Hence, it is a maximal connected subgraph. An isolated vertex is an example of a component. The components of a graph constitute a partition of the graph; *i.e.*, there is at least one vertex in each component, two components have no vertices in common and the union of all components yields the entire graph. It follows that a connected graph has a single component. The rank of a graph is the number of vertices minus the number of connected components (maximal connected subgraphs) of the graph.

Every abstract graph has a geometric realization. This realization is obtained by selecting m different points in space (on a surface) and designating them by $v_j, \cdots, v_k$. Then v_j is connected to v_k with as many curves (usually straight lines for convenience) as there are edges in the graph with end points v_j and v_k. The curves are drawn so as not to pass through other vertices and not to intersect one another except at

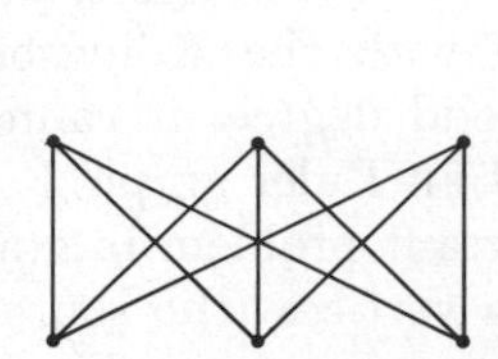
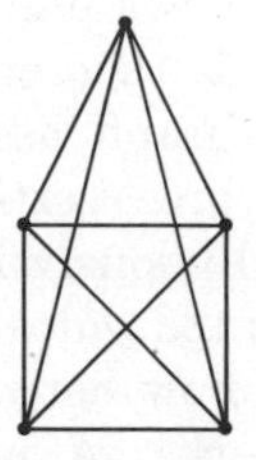

FIG. 5–3.

the end points. A planar graph has a geometric realization in two-dimensional space. Every finite graph has a geometric realization in three dimensions. Some of the foregoing notions can be extended to infinite graphs.

A well-known theorem of Kuratowski asserts that a graph is planar if, and only if, it does not contain either of the two subgraphs shown in Fig. 5–3. Note that these two subgraphs are projections in two dimensions of nonplanar graphs; *i.e.*, they can be drawn in three dimensions in such a way that no edges intersect. The foregoing theorem does not preclude the possibility that there may be intermediate vertices in these subgraphs incident with precisely two edges.

Remark: A geometric graph is directed if a direction (also called an orientation and indicated by an arrow head) is associated with each edge from one to the other of its two corresponding vertices. In this case one calls a directed edge an arc; a chain whose edges are consistently directed is called a path, and a circuit is called a cycle.

One can obtain a negative answer to the Königsberg bridge problem through the following sequence of definitions and theorems.

A finite connected graph is said to be unicursal if all its edges can be traversed (or traced) continuously. An Euler graph is one in which every vertex has even degree. The degree of a vertex is the number of edges incident with it.

Theorem: In a finite graph, there is an even number of vertices of odd degree.

Proof: If ε is the number of edges of the graph and ν_i is the number of vertices of degree i then we have $2\varepsilon = \nu_1 + 2\nu_2 + 3\nu_3 + \cdots + k\nu_k$, which on simplifying becomes

$$2\varepsilon - 2\nu_2 - 2\nu_3 - 4\nu_4 - 4\nu_5 - 6\nu_7 - \cdots = \nu_1 + \nu_3 + \nu_5 + \nu_7 + \cdots$$

The right side gives the total number of vertices of odd degree that must be even since the left side is even.

Theorem: A graph is unicursal if, and only if, it has no vertices of odd degree, or if it has precisely two such vertices.

The proof of this theorem, which is not difficult, will not be given here. Since the graph associated with the Königsberg land-bridge connections has three vertices of odd degree, it cannot be unicursal (or traceable). Obviously it is not an Euler graph.

As already pointed out an important problem in graph theory is to find a maximum flow between two vertices (the source and the sink) of a given network. A network is a connected subgraph without loops, in which each arc e has a certain flow capacity $c(e)$ assigned to it. This number is usually a positive integer. The source and the sink are known as the terminal points of the network, whereas the remaining points are known as the intermediate points. In a given network, if no arc orientation is indicated, one replaces each edge by two oppositely-oriented arcs between the vertices. At least one of the two arcs will have zero flow in the solution.

A function $f(e)$ that assumes integer values, defined on the arcs of a network, is a flow function on the network if for each arc, $c(e) \geq f(e) \geq 0$, and for each intermediate vertex we have $\sum f(e) - \sum f(e) = 0$ where the first sum is taken over the set of edges e directed to the vertex, and the second sum is taken over those edges e directed out of the vertex. In the case of the source and sink this relation holds if the first sum is taken over the edges leading to the sink and the second sum taken over those edges leading out of the source. It might be useful to think of flow as a steady state phenomenon so that an arc flow represents the constant rate of flow through the arc.

In a connected graph (or subgraph) a *cut-set* is a set of edges the deletion of all of whose elements divides (or separates) the graph (or subgraph) into two subgraphs (one of which may be a single vertex) and the deletion of no proper subset of this set of edges disconnects the graph (or subgraph). In Fig. 5–4 we have the following cut-sets

(e_1,e_2), (e_1,e_3), (e_2,e_3), and e_4. Note for example that e_1 is a subset of the first two cut-sets but is not itself a cut-set because it does not separate its subgraph into two subgraphs.

We assume that in a network there is at least one directed path from source to sink. A directed cut-set of a network is a set of directed edges such that every path from source to sink contains at least one

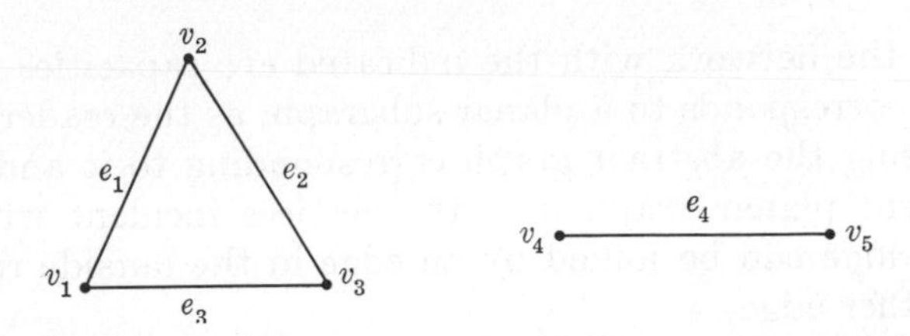

FIG. 5–4.

arc of this set. With each such cut-set is associated its capacity, which is the sum of the capacities of its arcs. In a finite network there is a cut-set whose capacity is minimum.

Theorem (*Max-Flow, Min-Cut*): The maximum flow between the source and the sink of a given network is equal to the minimum capacity of the cut-sets that separate the source from the sink.[6]

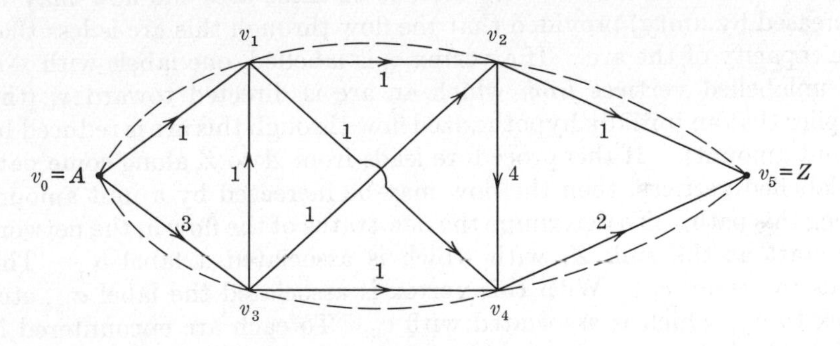

FIG. 5–5.

Proof: We shall give the main parts of the proof, which is elaborate, leaving the reader to fill in the detail.

We first note that the flow can be resolved into flow through paths leading to the sink, each of which contains one element of a cut-set, and into residual flow, which remains in some arcs of the network.

[6] L. R. Ford and D. R. Fulkerson, "Maximal Flow Through a Network," *Can. J. Math.*, **8**, 399 (1956).

Obviously, the total flow in the paths from source to sink cannot exceed the flow through the capacity of the cut-set. Hence, max (flow) $\leq$ min (cut-set capacity). To prove the equality we note that if no cut-set exists all of whose arcs are filled to capacity, then we can produce by a constructive procedure, an unsaturated path in which one or more units of flow can be introduced, ultimately obtaining saturation of a set of arcs that contains a cut-set. This cut-set has minimum total capacity.

Consider the network with the indicated arc capacities in Fig. 5–5. It actually corresponds to a planar subgraph, as the reader may verify by considering the abstract graph corresponding to it and generating an equivalent planar graph (*i.e.*, the vertices incident with the edge having a bridge can be joined by an edge in the outside region which meets no other edge).

Suppose that a flow (indicated by the dotted lines) that carries one unit of flow through each of the two dotted paths is conjectured as maximum. Thus the total flow is 2. To see whether it is possible to increase this flow (note that we could have started with the assumption that the total flow is zero) we use a certain labelling procedure. We assign a label to v_0 which we denote by a_0 and then continue to label the remaining vertices in the following manner. We consider a labelled vertex v_i and assign the label $+a_i$ to every unlabelled vertex *to* which an arc is directed from v_i (*i.e.*, for one of these arcs the flow may be increased by unity) provided that the flow through this arc is less than the capacity of the arc. If a vertex v_i is labelled, one labels with $-a_i$ all unlabelled vertices *from* which an arc is directed toward v_i (this implies that an initially hypothesized flow through this arc is reduced by a unit amount). If this procedure leads from A to Z along some path of labelled vertices, then the flow may be increased by a unit amount along this path. To determine the new status of the flow in the network we start at the sink Z, with which is associated a label a_{i_1}. This leads to vertex v_{i_1}. With this vertex is associated the label a_{i_2}, etc., back to a_{i_k}, which is associated with v_0. To each arc encountered in this backward retracing one adds or subtracts a unit of flow depending on whether the associated a is plus or minus. In any case the net effect increases the value of the flow in the network by unity. The procedure is then repeated until no path exists in which the flow can be increased. In that case the maximum flow is attained. In practice, the process is accelerated considerably by assigning to each new path not one unit of flow, but an appropriately-chosen larger value.

Note, for example, in Fig. 5–5 that since the arc incident with A and v_3 is unsaturated we label v_3 by $+a_0$. We then label both v_1 and v_2

by $+a_3$, the index of the vertex v_3 which has been labelled with $+a_0$. The vertex v_4 can now be labelled with either $+a_1$ or $+a_2$ depending on whether one considers v_1 or v_2 first, and Z can be labelled with $+a_4$. This yields a path in which a unit of additional flow may be introduced increasing the flow to 3 units. This is obviously the maximum but the procedure may be repeated to verify this fact.

If, for simplicity, we denote the capacity of the arc joining vertex i with vertex j by c_{ij}, and let x_{ij} be the flow in the arc, and if $C_{ij} \geq 0$ is the cost per unit of flow in this arc, we have a linear programming problem (to be discussed later): Minimize $\sum_{ij} C_{ij}\, x_{ij}$ for a given amount of flow c from source $A = v_0$ to sink $Z = v_n$, subject to the constraints:

$$\sum_j (x_{0j} - x_{j0}) = c$$

$$\sum_j (x_{ij} - x_{ji}) = 0 \quad \text{for each } i$$

$$\sum_j (x_{nj} - x_{jn}) = c$$

$$0 \leq x_{ij} \leq c_{ij}$$

The last formulation yields an analytical method for treating optimal flow. There are special types of linear programming problems (*e.g.*,

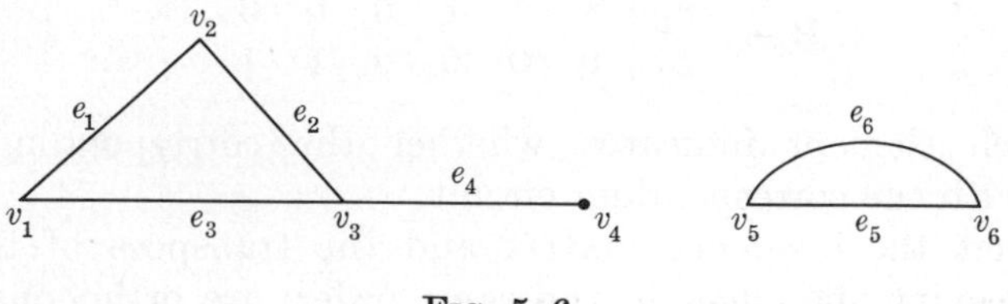

FIG. 5–6.

transportation problems) that are more conveniently solved through the network flow algorithm than through the usual methods (*e.g.*, the simplex process discussed in Section 5.14).

We now turn to another interesting subject that gives an isomorphism between graph theory and a special class of matrices. One can then study graphs through their corresponding matrices.[7] It is possible to associate with a graph, whether directed or not, several kinds of matrices of which the *incidence matrix* is best known. The elements of such a matrix of an undirected graph indicate whether an edge is incident with a vertex. Consider the two component graph in Fig. 5–6.

[7] S. Seshu and M. B. Reed, *Linear Graphs and Electrical Networks*, Addison-Wesley Publishing Co., Inc., Reading, Mass., 1961.

Its incidence matrix A is given by

$A =$ (Edges across, Vertices down)

Vertices	e_1	e_2	e_3	e_4	e_5	e_6
v_1	1	0	1	0	0	0
v_2	1	1	0	0	0	0
v_3	0	1	1	1	0	0
v_4	0	0	0	1	0	0
v_5	0	0	0	0	1	1
v_6	0	0	0	0	1	1

Note that the sum of the elements in each column is 2. For a directed graph the elements will consist of 0, 1, and -1. Also, note that the two components of the graph give rise to a partition of the incidence matrix. It is possible to generate matrices for the circuits (closed paths, *i.e.*, initial vertex coincides with the terminal vertex) and cut-sets of a graph. There are two circuits in the foregoing graph, and its circuit matrix is given by

$B =$

	e_1	e_2	e_3	e_4	e_5	e_6
c_1	1	1	1	0	0	0
c_2	0	0	0	0	1	1

where each element indicates whether the corresponding edge is incident with the corresponding circuit.

Note that the incidence matrix and the transpose of the circuit matrix (keeping the edges in the same order) are orthogonal modulo two; *i.e.*, $A\tilde{B} = 0$.[8]

Exercise: Prove this simple theorem.

Exercise: By analogy with the above, obtain the cut-set matrix and show that a similar relation holds between the circuit matrix and the cut-set matrix. Note that the cut-sets that correspond to the rows of this matrix are:

$$K_1 = (e_1,e_2), \quad K_2 = (e_2,e_3), \quad K_3 = (e_1,e_3), \quad K_4 = e_4, \quad K_5 = (e_5,e_6)$$

There is an appropriate way of generating the cut-set matrix from the incidence matrix that requires considerable detail and involves the additional idea of a tree and of fundamental circuits and cut-sets.

It is clear that an incidence matrix is associated with each graph.

[8] We have used here the notation of H. Margenau and G. M. Murphy, *The Mathematics of Physics and Chemistry*, 2nd Ed., D. Van Nostrand Co., Inc., Princeton, N.J., 1956.

An interesting and complicated problem is to characterize the properties of matrices that are actually incidence matrices of graphs. This question has been resolved and leads to several interesting ideas.

The vertices and edges of a graph may be used to represent hierarchy in an organization. A graph may also serve as an abstraction of a flow chart in an industrial process.

What is needed for operations research purposes is an extension of the theory of network flow to stochastic flow in edges that, in turn, have capacities, lengths, etc. that assume values stochastically.

We now illustrate another analytical method that uses known methods of physics to treat a concrete flow problem; *i.e.*, traffic flow. In recent years much effort has been devoted to this problem, which occupies the attention of many experts. The reader may wish to pursue the subject at greater length in the literature.

5.3. Traffic Dynamics: An Analytical Formulation of Flow.— The following theory describes the simplest situation of identical car following, such as might occur on long stretches of highway in dense traffic when no passing is possible. An approximate description of the way in which a car follows a leader is given by the relative velocity control in which acceleration at time t of the following car is proportional to the relative velocity of the two cars at a retarded time $t - \Delta$ and inversely proportional to their relative distance. The model has been tested in practice and found satisfactory under the assumptions made.[9]

The following equation describes the interaction between two vehicles in a line of cars where the traffic is dense (no passing allowed) when one car is following the other at a close enough distance to be affected by the velocity changes of the leader. They have the form of the dynamic equations of motion (or stimulus-response):

$$M\ddot{x}_{n+1}(t) = \lambda_1[\dot{x}_n(t-\Delta) - \dot{x}_{n+1}(t-\Delta)]/[x_n(t-\Delta) - x_{n+1}(t-\Delta)]$$

Here M is the mass of a car, λ_1 is a driver-car sensitivity coefficient, $\ddot{x}_{n+1}(t)$ is the acceleration of the $(n+1)$st car at time t, $(\dot{x}_n - \dot{x}_{n+1})$ is the relative velocity, $(x_n - x_{n+1})$ is the spacing from bumper to bumper at time $(t - \Delta)$, and Δ is the lag time of the driver-car system.

Integrating the above equation once, we have:

$$M\dot{x}_{n+1}(t) = \lambda_1 \log\left[\frac{x_n(t-\Delta) - x_{n+1}(t-\Delta)}{L}\right]$$

where L is the length of each car.

[9] Leslie C. Edie, "Car-following and Steady-state Theory for Non-congested Traffic," *Operations Research*, **9**, No. 1, 66–76 (1961).

It has been possible to study the asymptotic stability of the system, *i.e.*, the manner in which the fluctuations of motion of the lead car are propagated down the line of cars. The steady state behavior is easily derived. Because of velocity control between the following cars, a steady state is eventually reached in which each car moves with speed u, and, hence, $\Delta = 0$; *i.e.*, the study of the system involves no time lag.

Thus, the last equation is given by

$$u = c \log k_j / k$$

where $c = \lambda_1 / M$, $k_j = 1/L$, and $k = (x_n - x_{n-1})^{-1}$. The same result is obtained in the following interesting formulation of the problem using fluid dynamics.

The equation of motion of a one-dimensional fluid is [10]

$$\frac{du}{dt} = -\frac{c^2}{k}\frac{\partial k}{\partial x}$$

where u is the fluid, *i.e.*, traffic velocity, in miles per hour, k is the traffic density in vehicles per mile, x is the distance along the road, t is time, and c is a parameter determined from the state of the fluid. The above equation can also be written as:

$$\frac{\partial u}{\partial t} + u\frac{\partial u}{\partial x} + \frac{c^2}{k}\frac{\partial k}{\partial x} = 0 \qquad (5\text{–}1)$$

since u depends both on x and t.

Fluid flow is additionally described by a conservation of flow equation, *i.e.*, the equation of continuity

$$\frac{\partial k}{\partial t} + \frac{\partial q}{\partial x} = 0$$

where q is traffic flow in vehicles per hour.

This becomes

$$\frac{\partial k}{\partial t} + u\frac{\partial k}{\partial x} + k\frac{\partial u}{\partial x} = 0 \qquad (5\text{–}2)$$

since $q = ku$. If u is only a function of the density k then

$$\frac{\partial u}{\partial t} = \frac{du}{dk}\frac{\partial k}{\partial t}$$

$$\frac{\partial u}{\partial x} = \frac{du}{dk}\frac{\partial k}{\partial x}$$

[10] Harold Greenberg, "An Analysis of Traffic Flow," *Operations Research*, **7**, No. 1, 1–144 (1959).

which, when substituted in (5–1) and (5–2), yield

$$\frac{\partial k}{\partial t} + \left[u + \frac{c^2}{k du/dk}\right] \frac{\partial k}{\partial x} = 0$$

$$\frac{\partial k}{\partial t} + \left[u + \frac{k}{\partial u/\partial k}\right] \frac{\partial k}{\partial x} = 0$$

The coefficient determinant must vanish if this system is to have a nontrivial solution. This condition gives

$$\frac{du}{dk} = -\frac{c}{k}$$

or

$$u = c \log k_j / k$$

where k_j is the density for a traffic jam $u = 0$. We also have

$$q = ck \log (k_j / k)$$

5.4. Sales Response to Advertising: [11] **A Method of Controlling Flow.**—Experimental observations have shown that the following model may be used to compute the effect of advertising on sales. Suppose that the rate of expenditure for advertising a commodity at time t is given by $\lambda(t)$, and suppose that r is a constant response rate to this advertising. Let m be the total population reached by the advertising campaign. Let the rate of sale of the commodity at time t be $S(t)$. Assume that sales decay exponentially in time according to $1 - e^{-\mu t}$. Thus during a small time interval $(t, t + \Delta t)$, the sales rate decreases from $S(t)$ to $\mu \Delta t S(t)$.

The following equation describes the change in the sales rate with respect to time:

$$\frac{dS}{dt} = r\lambda(t) \frac{m - S(t)}{m} - \mu S(t)$$

Here $(m - S)/m$ is the fraction of potential customers.

Exercise: Obtain this equation by using Δt in the argument and passing to the limit. Assuming that the advertising rate is constant, *i.e.*, $\lambda(t) = \lambda$ and that S_0 is the sales rate at $t = 0$, the start of the campaign, solve this equation if the advertising is maintained for time T. Show that for $t > T$, *i.e.*, after advertising, the sales rate decreases exponentially, *i.e.*

$$S(t) = S(T) \exp[-\mu(t - T)]$$

[11] M. L. Vidale and H. B. Wolfe, "An Operations-Research Study of Sales Response to Advertising," *Operations Research*, **5**, No. 3, 311–456 (1957).

5.5. Probability Theory.—To pursue our study of methods of operations research, a brief, although incomplete, and somewhat abstract, presentation of ideas from probability theory will be given. In part it shows that mathematical abstraction and rigor are also in the nature of operations research. Illustrations of this topic will be given in later sections. We then give a longer discussion of maximization and minimization methods and in turn illustrate the ideas in subsequent sections. Probability and statistics and optimization methods are two major sources of operations research tools.

No special effort will henceforth be made to interpret examples as illustrations of properties in the general characterization of operations.

Probability is a real-valued function $P(a)$ of the elements of a Boolean algebra. A set of elements $O,a,b,\cdots,e$ forms a *Boolean algebra*[12] if the following hold: $a \cap a = a$, $a \cup a = a$, $a \subset a$; $a \subset b$, and $b \subset a$ imply $a = b$; $a \subset b$, $b \subset c$ imply $a \subset c$ and the three conditions $a \subset b$, $a \cap b = a$, $a \cup b = b$ are equivalent. In addition to the above relations a *σ-algebra* requires the countable additivity property (*i.e.*, if a_i $(i = 1,2,\cdots)$ is a countable sequence of sets then $\bigcup_{i=1}^{\infty} a_i$ is a member of the system). The function $P(a)$ represents the frequency of occurrence of an event. Thus, $0 \leq P(a) \leq 1$, and one must have $P(a) = 0$, for $a = 0$, $P(a) = 1$ for $a = e$ the sure event. Also $P(a \cup b) = P(a) + P(b)$ if $a \cap b = O$. The last property can be

[12] A set A is a collection of elements a. Given two sets, A and B, we define the relation $A \subset B$ (by which we mean the set A is contained in the set B) as follows: whenever an element a belongs to the set A, which we write as $a \in A$, then also $a \in B$. $A \supset B$ is the same as $B \subset A$, *i.e.*, B is contained in A. The *union* of A and B, $A \cup B$, is the set of all elements that belong to A or to B or to both. The intersection of A and B, $A \cap B$, is the set of elements that belong simultaneously to A and to B, *i.e.*, if $x \in A \cap B$ then $x \in A$ and $x \in B$. In the definition of a Boolean algebra the sets themselves are considered as the elements of the algebra. For this reason the formulas below are written in terms of small letters that designate sets and are also the elements of sets. The verbal definition of a Boolean algebra just given is equivalent to the following relations:

$$\begin{aligned} O \cap a &= O & O \cup a &= a \\ e \cap a &= a & e \cup a &= e \\ a \cap b &= b \cap a & a \cup b &= b \cup a \\ (a \cap b) \cap c &= a \cap (b \cap c) & (a \cup b) \cup c &= a \cup (b \cup c) \\ a \cap (b \cup c) &= (a \cap b) \cup (a \cap c) & a \cup (b \cap c) &= (a \cup b) \cap (a \cup c) \\ O' &= e & e' &= O \quad (a')' = a \\ (a \cap b)' &= a' \cup b' & (a \cup b)' &= a' \cap b' \\ a \cap a' &= O & a \cup a' &= e \end{aligned}$$

The complement a' of a set a contains all those elements of the algebra not in a. The element e is the set containing all elements belonging to any set of the algebra. Under the operation of intersection, it acts as the identity element. The element O is called the null or empty set.

extended to a finite number of elements, and if $\{a_n\}$ is an infinite set, then countable additivity must hold for a probability function, *i.e.*

$$P\left(\bigcup_{i=1}^{\infty} a_i\right) = \sum_{i=1}^{\infty} P(a_i)$$

where $a_i \cap a_j = 0, \quad i \neq j$

Next we define conditional probability and the independence of events as follows:

$$P(a|b) = \frac{P(a \cap b)}{P(b)}$$

where $P(a|b)$ stands for the conditional probability of the occurrence of a given that b has already occurred. If the occurrence of b does not affect the occurrence of a we have

$$P(a|b) = P(a)$$

Exercise: Verify the equivalence of the two definitions of a Boolean algebra.

Exercise: Draw diagrams to illustrate the notions of containment, union, and intersection, and the properties of a Boolean algebra.

Hence, a and b are independent if, and only if

$$P(a \cap b) = P(a)P(b)$$

The following are useful formulas:

The law of addition of probabilities:

$$P(a_1 \cup \cdots \cup a_n) = \sum_{i=1}^{n} P(a_i) - \sum_{i}\sum_{j} P(a_i \cap a_j) + \sum_{i}\sum_{j}\sum_{k} P(a_i \cap a_j \cap a_k) - \cdots \pm P(a_1 \cap a_2 \cdots \cap a_n)$$

The law of total probability:

$$P(a \cap b) = \sum_{i} P(b_i)P(a|b_i)$$

where $P(a|b_i)$ is the conditional probability of the occurrence of a, given that b_i has occurred with probability $P(b_i)$, and $b = \cup_i b_i$, where the b_i are independent.

If $b = \cup_i b_i$, *i.e.*, b is the union of a finite or countably infinite set of independent events b_i, then

$$P(b) = \sum_{i} P(b_i)$$

Let the event b be the set of causes of an event a. Now from the definition of conditional probability the probability that b_i occurs and a occurs is

$$P(a \cap b_i) = P(a|b_i)P(b_i)$$

But

$$P(a \cap b_i) = P(b_i \cap a) = P(b_i|a)P(a)$$

and

$$\begin{aligned} P(a) = P(b \cap a) &= P[(\bigcup_i b_i) \cap a] \\ &= P[\bigcup_i (a \cap b_i)] = \sum_i P(a \cap b_i) \\ &= \sum_i P(a|b_i)P(b_i) \end{aligned}$$

Thus

$$P(a|b_i)P(b_i) = P(b_i|a)P(a)$$

We now have Bayes' theorem

$$P(b_i|a) = \frac{P(a|b_i)P(b_i)}{\sum_i P(a|b_i)P(b_i)}$$

Thus, if we know *a priori* the probability of the occurrence of b_i, we can compute the *a posteriori* probability that if a occurred then b_i was the cause of it, thus going from effects to causes. The problem here is to determine $P(b_i)$, which most of the time are not known and are sometimes (inadequately) assumed to be equally likely when nothing is known about them.

A random variable is a measurable function defined on a measure space with total measure equal to unity.

We leave it to the reader to pursue the rigorous approach to probability theory in appropriate texts.

The distribution function $F(x)$ of a random variable X, is a function of a real variable, defined for each real number x to be the probability that $X \leq x$, *i.e.*, $F(x) = \text{Prob}\ (X \leq x)$. The function $F(x)$, when x is continuous, is continuous on the right, nondecreasing with

$$\lim_{x \to -\infty} F(x) = 0 \quad \text{and} \quad \lim_{x \to \infty} F(x) = 1$$

The density function $f(x)$ of a random variable X is defined by $f(x) = dF(x)/dx$; it exists whenever $F(x)$ is absolutely continuous. Thus

$$F(x) = \int_{-\infty}^{x} f(y)dy$$

The characteristic function of $F(x)$ is defined by

$$\phi(t) = E(e^{itx}) = \int_{-\infty}^{\infty} e^{itx} dF(x); \quad i = \sqrt{-1}$$

The moment generating function, when it exists, is defined by

$$M(t) = \int_{-\infty}^{\infty} e^{-tx} dF(x)$$

It is the Laplace-Stieltjes transform of $F(x)$.

The characteristic function and the moment generating function are important tools for computing moments of distributions, studying limits of sequences of distributions, and finding the distribution of sums of independent variables. If $Z = X + Y$, where X and Y are independently distributed according to the distribution functions $F(x)$ and $G(y)$ respectively, the distribution function of Z is given by

$$H(z) = \int_{-\infty}^{\infty} \int_{-\infty}^{z-y} dF(x)dG(y) = \int_{-\infty}^{\infty} F(z - y)dG(y)$$

From the characteristic function one can recover the distribution $F(x)$ as indicated by Doob:[13]

$$\tfrac{1}{2}[F(x + 0) - F(x - 0)] - \tfrac{1}{2}[F(0 + 0) - F(0 - 0)] = \frac{1}{2\pi} \int_{-\infty}^{\infty} \phi(t) \frac{1 - e^{-itx}}{it} dt$$

The nth moment μ_n about the origin is given by the nth derivative of ϕ at the origin:

$$\mu_n = E(X^n) = (-i)^n \phi^{(n)}(0) \quad (n = 0,1,\cdots)$$

The first moment μ_1 is known as the expected value of X, *i.e.*,

$$\mu_1 = E(X) = \int_{-\infty}^{\infty} x dF(x)$$

the second moment about the mean is called the variance, and is a measure of dispersion. We have

$$\sigma^2 = E[(X - \mu)^2] = \int_{-\infty}^{\infty} (x - \mu)^2 dF(x)$$

The standard deviation is σ.

A *stochastic process* is a family of random variables $\{X_t\}$ depending on a parameter t (*e.g.*, time). This definition may be extended to include

[13] J. L. Doob, *Stochastic Processes*, John Wiley and Sons, Inc., New York, 1953.

several parameters. The idea of a stochastic process will occur later in several examples of operations research.

A Compound Distribution.—We now give an illustration of computations performed on a stochastic process.

Let $S_{N_t} = X_1 + \cdots + X_{N_t}$ be a sum of random variables with random subscript N_t independently and identically distributed (according to $F(x)$). Thus N is also a random variable, and it depends on t. We wish to compute the expected value and the variance of S_{N_t}. We have

$$\text{Prob}\,(S_{N_t} \leq x) = \sum_{n=0}^{\infty} \text{Prob}\,(N_t = n)\,\text{Prob}\,(S_n \leq x)$$

and using the moment generating function $M(\theta)$, we have the series in powers of $M(\theta)$

$$P[M(\theta)] = \sum_{n=0}^{\infty} \text{Prob}\,(N_t = n)\left[\int_{-\infty}^{\infty} e^{-\theta x} dF(x)\right]^n$$

The expected value of the above series is given by

$$E(S_{N_t}) = \left.\frac{dP}{dM}\right|_{M=1} (-1)\left.\frac{dM}{d\theta}\right|_{\theta=0} = E(N_t)E(X)$$

To obtain the variance we use the characteristic function approach (of course one can also use the moment generating function).

We define

$$\Phi(\theta) = E(e^{i\theta S_{N_t}}) = \int_{-\infty}^{\infty} \sum_{n=0}^{\infty} \text{Prob}\,(N_t = n) dG(x) e^{i\theta x}$$

$$= \sum_{n=0}^{\infty} a_n(t) \int_{-\infty}^{\infty} e^{i\theta x} dG(x)$$

$$= \sum_{n=0}^{\infty} a_n(t)\phi^n(\theta) \equiv \psi\{\phi(\theta)\}$$

where $G(x) = \text{Prob}\,(S_n \leq x)$, $a_n(t) = \text{Prob}\,(N_t = n)$. By differentiating under the integral sign with respect to θ we obtain

$$\Phi'(\theta)|_{\theta=0} = iE(S_{N_t}), \qquad -\Phi''(\theta)|_{\theta=0} = \text{var}\,(S_{N_t}) + [E(S_{N_t})]^2$$

Another expression for $\Phi''(\theta)|_{\theta=0}$ is given by

$$\Phi''(\theta)|_{\theta=0} = \left.\frac{d^2\psi}{d\theta^2}\right|_{\theta=0} = \left.\frac{d\psi}{d\phi}\right|_{\phi=1} \left.\frac{d^2\phi}{d\theta^2}\right|_{\theta=0} + \left.\left(\frac{d\phi}{d\theta}\right)^2\right|_{\theta=0} \left.\frac{d^2\psi}{d\phi^2}\right|_{\phi=1}$$

From the definition of ψ we have

$$\left.\frac{d\psi}{d\phi}\right|_{\phi=1} = E(N_t) \qquad \left.\frac{d\phi}{d\theta}\right|_{\theta=0} = iE(X)$$

$$\left.\frac{d^2\phi}{d\theta^2}\right|_{\theta=0} = \{\text{var}(x) + [E(X)]^2\}$$

$$\left.\frac{d^2\psi}{d\phi^2}\right|_{\phi=0} = \sum_{n=2}^{\infty} n(n-1)a_n(t) = \text{var}(N_t) + [E(N_t)]^2 - E(N_t)$$

Note that

$$\text{var}(N_t) = \sum_{n=0}^{\infty} n^2 a_n(t) - [E(N_t)]^2$$

Substituting these expressions in the formula above, and equating the two expressions for $\Phi''(\theta)|_{\theta=0}$ yields

$$\text{var}(S_{N_t}) = E(N_t)\,\text{var}(X) + [E(X)]^2\,\text{var}(N_t)$$

Exercise: Carry out the above computations.

5.6. Queueing Theory.[14]—Queueing theory occupies a prominent position in operations research because of a wide range of applications with possible transfer of the ideas to other fields, *e.g.*, inventory, and for the use of sophisticated stochastic models.[15]

We assume that units arrive into a queueing system (consisting of a single waiting line and two service channels) at random (*i.e.*, by a Poisson distribution[16] at the instants $t_n (n = 1,2,\cdots)$ where t_n is a renewal process (*i.e.*, $T_n \equiv t_n - t_{n-1}$ with $(t_0 = o)$ are independently and identically distributed according to a common distribution which in this case is $1 - e^{-\lambda t}$). An arriving unit waits in a line following the first-come-first-served queue discipline, and is allowed into service at any one of 2 channels when the latter becomes idle. On completing service, it departs the system. Let $\{s_n\}(n = 1,2,\cdots)$ be a sequence of independent and identically distributed random variables that assume non-negative real values only. Their common distribution is assumed to be negative exponential, *i.e.*, $1 - e^{-\mu t}$. For each of the two service channels we define such a sequence. The service distributions are also

[14] Thomas L. Saaty, "Time-Dependent Solution of the Many-server Poisson Queue," *Operations Research*, **8**, No. 6 (1960).

[15] Thomas L. Saaty, *Elements of Queueing Theory*, McGraw-Hill Book Co., New York, 1961.

[16] Cf. Margenau and Murphy, *op. cit.*, p. 441.

identical for both service channels. The service process $\{s_n\}$ is independent of the input process $\{t_n\}$. The system is said to be in state E_n at time t if there are n units in line and in service at t. Because of the Poisson nature of input times, which implies an exponential distribution for the interarrival times, and because of the exponential service times, the probability of a transition from state E_n to state E_{n+1} during the interval $(t,t + dt)$ is $\lambda dt + o(dt)$ and the probability of a transition from E_n to E_{n-1} in $(t,t + dt)$ is

$n\mu dt + o(dt)$ for $n \leq 2$ (since only n channels would be occupied)

$2\mu dt + o(dt)$ for $n \geq 2$ (since two channels would be occupied)

Note for example that for small values of t,

$$1 - e^{-\lambda t} = \lambda t - \frac{(\lambda t)^2}{2!} + \cdots = \lambda t + o(t)$$

We assume that there are i units waiting in the system at $t = 0$. The differential-difference equations describing the problem are:

$$\frac{dP_0(t)}{dt} = -\lambda P_0(t) + \mu P_1(t) \qquad n = 0$$

$$\frac{dP_1(t)}{dt} = -(\lambda + \mu)P_1(t) + \lambda P_0(t) + 2\mu P_2(t) \qquad n = 1$$

$$\frac{dP_n(t)}{dt} = -(\lambda + 2\mu)P_n(t) + \lambda P_{n-1}(t) + 2\mu P_{n+1}(t) \qquad 2 \leq n \tag{5–3}$$

with initial conditions $P_n(0) = \delta_{in}$, the Kronecker symbol.[17]

The middle equation for example is derived as follows:

$$P_1(t + \Delta t) = (1 - \lambda\Delta t)(1 - \mu\Delta t)P_1(t) + \lambda\Delta t(1 - \mu\Delta t)P_0(t) + 2\mu\Delta t(1 - \lambda\Delta t)P_2(t)$$

i.e., the probability that there is one unit in the system at time $t + \Delta t$ is equal to the probability $P_1(t)$ that there was one unit in it at time t and nothing arrived [with probability $(1 - \lambda\Delta t)$] and nothing was served [with probability $(1 - \mu\Delta t)$] during Δt, or there was nothing in the system at time t, with probability $P_0(t)$ and one unit arrived during Δt (with probability $\lambda\Delta t$) with nothing served or there were two units in the system at time t with probability $P_2(t)$ and a unit was served at one of the channels during Δt (with probability $2\mu\Delta t$) and nothing

[17] Margenau and Murphy, *op. cit.*, p. 105.

arrived. Applying the law of compound probability yields the foregoing equation. Terms of higher order are negligible. Dividing by Δt and passing to the limit with respect to Δt gives the second equation of the system. Questions of the existence of unique solutions have been investigated for the more general case of the birth-death process. Our system has a unique solution that satisfies the initial conditions.

We define the generating function

$$P(z,t) \equiv \sum_{n=0}^{\infty} P_n(t)z^n; \qquad P(z,o) = z^i$$

multiply the second and third equations by z^n, and sum over the appropriate ranges of n including the first equation, yielding for $P \equiv P(z,t)$:

$$\frac{\partial P}{\partial t} = -(\lambda + 2\mu)P + \lambda z P + 2\mu \frac{P - P_0(t)}{z} + 2\mu P_0(t) - \mu(1 - z)P_1(t) \qquad (5\text{–}4)$$

on taking the Laplace transform in which typically:

$$f^*(s) \equiv \int_0^{\infty} e^{-st} f(t)dt$$

we have after grouping terms and solving for $P^*(z,s)$

$$\begin{aligned} P^*(z,s) &= \frac{z^{i+1} - \mu(1 - z)[2P_0^*(s) + zP_1^*(s)]}{sz - (1 - z)(2\mu - \lambda z)} \\ &= \frac{z^{i+1} - \mu(1 - z)[2P_0^*(s) + zP_1^*(s)]}{-\lambda(z - \alpha_1)(z - \alpha_2)} \end{aligned} \qquad (5\text{–}5)$$

On and inside the unit circle $|z| = 1$, we apply Rouché's theorem to the denominator of the expression on the right whose two zeros are

$$\alpha_k = \frac{\lambda + 2\mu + s \pm \sqrt{(\lambda + 2\mu + s)^2 - 8\mu\lambda}}{2\lambda}, \quad k = 1,2 \qquad (5\text{–}6)$$

where α_1 has the positive sign before the radical. Rouché's theorem asserts that if $f(z)$ and $g(z)$ are analytic inside and on a closed contour C, and if $|g(z)| < |f(z)|$ on C, then $f(z)$ and $f(z) + g(z)$ have the same number of zeros inside C.

Since P^* must exist inside and on $|z| = 1$, and since $|\alpha_2| < 1$ the numerator must have $(z - \alpha_2)$ as a factor, *i.e.*, vanish at α_2. We have:

$$2P_0^* + \alpha_2 P_1^* = \frac{\alpha_2^{i+1}}{\mu(1 - \alpha_2)} \tag{5-7}$$

In order to determine P_0^* and P_1^* we must solve simultaneously the foregoing equation and the first equation in (5–3) after taking the Laplace transform of the latter. We have on suppressing arguments:

$$sP_0^* = -\lambda P_0^* + \mu P_1^* \tag{5-8}$$

Thus

$$P_0^* = \frac{\alpha_2^{i+1}}{(1 - \alpha_2)[2\mu + (s + \lambda)\alpha_2]} \tag{5-9}$$

$$P_1^* = \frac{(s + \lambda)\alpha_2^{i+1}}{\mu(1 - \alpha_2)[2\mu + (s + \lambda)\alpha_2]} \tag{5-10}$$

We verify the steady state[18] results on the last two equations using the well-known fact required for the steady state, *i.e.*, $(\lambda/2\mu) < 1$ (and hence the arrival rate must not exceed the service rate) and the theorem from Laplace transforms:

$$\lim_{t \to \infty} P_n(t) = \lim_{s \to 0} sP_n^*(s)$$

Now from

$$\alpha_1\alpha_2 = \frac{2\mu}{\lambda}, \qquad s = -\lambda(1 - \alpha_1)(1 - \alpha_2), \qquad \lim_{s \to 0} \alpha_1 = \frac{2\mu}{\lambda}$$

$$\lim_{s \to 0} \alpha_2 = 1$$

we obtain:

$$\lim_{t \to 0} P_0(t) = \frac{1 - \lambda/2\mu}{1 + \lambda/2\mu}$$

$$\lim_{t \to 0} P_1(t) = \frac{\lambda}{\mu}\frac{1 - \lambda/2\mu}{1 + \lambda/2\mu}$$

which for $c = 2$ coincides with the well-known steady state results. For c channels:

$$\lim_{t \to \infty} P_n(t) \equiv p_n = \begin{cases} \dfrac{p_0}{n!}\left(\dfrac{\lambda}{\mu}\right)^n & 1 \le n \le c \\[2ex] \dfrac{p_0}{c!}\left(\dfrac{\lambda}{c\mu}\right)^c & c \le n \end{cases} \tag{5-11}$$

[18] The steady state is obtained by allowing $t \to \infty$. In this manner the initial number i should no longer appear in the result.

$$p_0 = \frac{1}{\sum_{n=0}^{c-1} \frac{(c\rho)^n}{n!} + \frac{(c\rho)^c}{c!(1-\rho)}} \tag{5–12}$$

where $\rho = \lambda/c\mu$.

Exercise: Obtain the steady state solution by writing down analogous equations to (5–3) for c channels, setting the derivatives equal to zero, suppressing time as the argument and solving the resulting difference equations.

Exercise: Compute the steady state expected number in the system

$$L = \sum_{n=1}^{\infty} np_n$$

for the 2-channel case. From this obtain the expected waiting time

$$W = \frac{L}{\lambda}$$

Justify this expression for W. Note that both L and W enable one to make decisions about the amount of waiting space needed and as to whether better and faster service is required in order to shorten the waiting time.

Substituting (5–9) and (5–10) into (5–5), and simplifying yields:

$$P^*(z,s) = \left\{ z^{i+1} - \frac{(1-z)\alpha_2^{i+1}[2\mu + (s+\lambda)z]}{(1-\alpha_2)[2\mu + (s+\lambda)\alpha_2]} \right\} \Big/ -\lambda(z-\alpha_1)(z-\alpha_2) \tag{5–13}$$

If we write:

$$2\mu + (s+\lambda)z = 2\mu + (s+\lambda)\alpha_2 + (z-\alpha_2)(s+\lambda)$$

then

$$P^*(z,s) = \frac{z^{i+1}(1-\alpha_2) - (1-z)\alpha_2^{i+1}}{-\lambda(z-\alpha_1)(z-\alpha_2)(1-\alpha_2)} - \frac{(1-z)\alpha_2^{i+1}(s+\lambda)}{\lambda\alpha_1(1-z/\alpha_1)[2\mu + (s+\lambda)\alpha_2](1-\alpha_2)} \tag{5–14}$$

The first expression on the right is the Laplace transform of the generating function of the now classical case of $c = 1$, except that μ is everywhere replaced by 2μ.

The first expression of $P^*(z,s)$ may be expanded as follows:

$$\frac{(z-\alpha_2)(z^i + \alpha_2 z^{i-1} + \cdots + \alpha_2^i) - z\alpha_2(z - \alpha_2)(z^{i-1} + \alpha_2 z^{i-2} + \cdots + \alpha_2^{i-1})}{\lambda\alpha_1(1 - z/\alpha_1)(z - \alpha_2)(1 - \alpha_2)}$$

$$= \frac{1}{\lambda\alpha_1}(z^i + \alpha_2 z^{i-1} + \cdots + \alpha_2^i)\sum_{k=0}^{\infty}\left(\frac{z}{\alpha_1}\right)^k + \frac{\alpha_2^{i+1}}{\lambda\alpha_1(1 - \alpha_2)}\sum_{k=0}^{\infty}\left(\frac{z}{\alpha_1}\right)^k \qquad (5\text{–}15)$$

The coefficient of z^n may now be obtained without difficulty. For example the second term on the right contributes:

$$\frac{\alpha_2^{i+1}}{\lambda\alpha_1^{n+1}(1 - \alpha_2)} = \frac{\alpha_2^{i+1}}{\lambda\alpha_1^{n+1}}(1 + \alpha_2 + \alpha_2^2 + \cdots)$$

$$= \frac{1}{\lambda}\left(\frac{\lambda}{2\mu}\right)^{n+1}\sum_{k=n+i+2}^{\infty}\left(\frac{2\mu}{\lambda}\right)^k \frac{1}{\alpha_1^k}$$

having used $|\alpha_2| < 1$, $\alpha_1\alpha_2 = 2\mu/\lambda$. The first term is a sum of several factors obtained from the different ways in which one can obtain z^n by multiplying the quantity in parenthesis by the series.

The second expression on the right of (5–14) may be written as:

$$-\frac{\alpha_2^{i+1}(s + \lambda)(1 - z)}{\lambda(1 - \alpha_2)[2\mu + (s + \lambda)\alpha_2]\alpha_1}\sum_{n=0}^{\infty}\left(\frac{z}{\alpha_1}\right)^n \qquad (5\text{–}16)$$

The coefficient of z^n from this expression is

$$\frac{\alpha_2^{i+1}(s + \lambda)}{\lambda(1 - \alpha_2)[2\mu + (s + \lambda)\alpha_2]}\left(\frac{1}{\alpha_1^n} - \frac{1}{\alpha_1^{n+1}}\right)$$

$$= -\frac{\alpha_2^{i+1}(s + \lambda)(1 - \alpha_1)}{(1 - \alpha_2)[2\mu + (s + \lambda)\alpha_2]\alpha_1^{n+1}} \qquad (5\text{–}17)$$

$$= -\frac{(s + \lambda)(1 - \alpha_1)}{\lambda\alpha_1^{n+1}} P_0^*$$

Again we verify the steady state property. The contribution to the steady state solution from the first expression of (5–14) on examining the inverse Laplace transform is $(1 - \lambda/2\mu)(\lambda/2\mu)^n$. To this is to be added the result obtained from multiplying (5–17) by s and taking the limit as $s \to 0$. This is $-\lambda(1 - 2\mu/\lambda)^2/(2\mu + \lambda)(2\mu/\lambda)^n$. Thus

$$\lim_{t\to\infty} P_n(t) = 2\left(\frac{\lambda}{2\mu}\right)^n \frac{1 - \lambda/2\mu}{1 + \lambda/2\mu}$$

which is also what one obtains from (5–11).

We now determine $P_0(t)$. We first note that

$$\left[1 - \left(\frac{\alpha_2}{2} - \frac{\lambda}{4\mu}\alpha_2^2\right)\right]^{-1} = \sum_{k=0}^{\infty}\left(\frac{\alpha_2}{2} - \frac{\lambda}{4\mu}\alpha_2^2\right)^k$$

$$= \sum_{k=0}^{\infty}\left(\frac{\alpha_2}{2}\right)^k \sum_{m=0}^{k}\binom{k}{m}(-1)^m\left(\frac{\lambda}{2\mu}\alpha_2\right)^m$$

Since

$$\left|\frac{\alpha_2}{2} - \frac{\lambda}{4\mu}\alpha_2^2\right| = \left|\frac{\alpha_2}{2}\right|\left|1 - \frac{\lambda}{2\mu}\alpha_2\right|$$

$$\leq \frac{|\alpha_2|}{2}\left[1 + \left|\frac{\lambda}{2\mu}\alpha_2\right|\right]$$

$$\leq \frac{|\alpha_2|}{2}[1 + 1] \leq |\alpha_2| < 1$$

and

$$\left(\frac{\alpha_2}{2} - \frac{\lambda}{4\mu}\alpha_2^2\right)^k = \left(\frac{\alpha_2}{2}\right)^k \sum_{m=0}^{k}\binom{k}{m}(-1)^m\left(\frac{\lambda}{2\mu}\alpha_2\right)^m$$

We substitute

$$s + \lambda = \frac{\lambda\alpha_2^2 + 2\mu - 2\mu\alpha_2}{\alpha_2}$$

Using decomposition in partial fractions we have

$$P_0^*(s) = \frac{\alpha_2^{i+1}}{\lambda + 2\mu}\left[\frac{1}{1 - \alpha_2} + \frac{\lambda\alpha_2 + \lambda - 2\mu}{4\mu - 2\mu\alpha_2 + \lambda\alpha_2^2}\right]$$

$$= \frac{1}{\lambda + 2\mu}\left[\sum_{k=0}^{\infty}\alpha_2^{k+i+1} + \alpha_2^{i+1}(\mu\alpha_2 + \lambda - 2\mu)\sum_{k=0}^{\infty}\left(\frac{\alpha_2}{2} - \frac{\lambda}{4\mu}\alpha_2^2\right)^k\right]$$

$$= \frac{1}{\lambda + 2\mu}\left[\sum_{k=0}^{\infty}\alpha_2^{k+i+1} + \alpha_2^{i+1}\frac{(\lambda\alpha_2 + \lambda - 2\mu)}{4\mu}\sum_{k=0}^{\infty}\left(\frac{\alpha_2}{2}\right)^k \right.$$

$$\left. \times \sum_{m=0}^{k}\binom{k}{m}(-1)^m\left(\frac{\lambda}{2\mu}\alpha_2\right)^m\right]$$

$$= \frac{1}{\lambda + 2\mu}\left[\sum_{k=0}^{\infty}\alpha_2^{k+i+1} + \frac{\lambda}{4\mu}\sum_{k=0}^{\infty}\sum_{m=0}^{k}\binom{k}{m}(-1)^m\left(\frac{\lambda}{2\mu}\right)^m \right.$$

$$\times \left(\frac{1}{2}\right)^k \alpha_2^{m+k+i+2} + \left(\frac{\lambda - 2\mu}{4\mu}\right)$$

$$\left. \times \sum_{k=0}^{\infty}\sum_{m=0}^{k}\binom{k}{m}(-1)^m\left(\frac{\lambda}{2\mu}\right)^m\left(\frac{1}{2}\right)^k\alpha_2^{m+k+i+1}\right]$$

Inversion and simplification yield:

$$P_0(t) = \frac{e^{-(\lambda+2\mu)t}}{(\lambda + 2\mu)t}\Bigg[\sum_{k=0}^{\infty} (\sqrt{\rho})^{-(k+i+1)}(k + i + 1)I_{k+i+1}(2\sqrt{2\lambda\mu t})$$

$$+\frac{\lambda}{4\mu}\sum_{k=0}^{\infty}\sum_{m=0}^{k}\binom{k}{m}(-\rho)^m(\tfrac{1}{2})^k(\sqrt{\rho})^{-(m+k+i+2)}$$

$$\times (m + k + i + 2)I_{m+k+i+2}(2\sqrt{2\lambda\mu t})$$

$$+\left(\frac{\lambda}{4\mu} - \frac{1}{2}\right)\sum_{k=0}^{\infty}\sum_{m=0}^{k}\binom{k}{m}(-1)^m(-\rho)^m(\tfrac{1}{2})^k$$

$$\times (\sqrt{\rho})^{-(m+k+i+1)}(m + k + i + 1)I_{m+k+i+1}$$

$$\times (2\sqrt{2}\lambda\mu t)\Bigg]$$

$\rho = \lambda/2\mu$ where I is the modified Bessel function of the first kind.[19] If we use $\mathscr{L}^{-1}$ to denote the inverse Laplace transform, we have[20]

$$\mathscr{L}^{-1}(s\alpha_1^{-n}) = (2\sqrt{2\lambda\mu})^{-n}[2\sqrt{2\lambda\mu}nt^{-1}I_{n-1}(2\sqrt{2\lambda\mu t}) - n(n + 1)t^{-2}I_n(2\sqrt{2\lambda\mu t})]$$

and

$$\mathscr{L}^{-1}(\alpha_1^{-n}) = (2\sqrt{2\lambda\mu})^{-n}nt^{-1}I_n(2\sqrt{2\lambda\mu t})$$

$$P_1(t) = \frac{e^{-(\lambda+2\mu)t}}{\mu(\lambda + 2\mu)}\Bigg[\sum_{k=0}^{\infty}\rho^{-(k+i+1)}\mathscr{L}^{-1}[(s + \lambda)\alpha_1^{-(k+i+1)}]$$

$$+\frac{\lambda}{4\mu}\sum_{k=0}^{\infty}\sum_{m=0}^{k}\binom{k}{m}(-1)^m\rho^m(\tfrac{1}{2})^k\rho^{-(m+k+i+2)}$$

$$\times \mathscr{L}^{-1}[(s + \lambda)\alpha_1^{-(m+k+i+2)}]$$

$$+\frac{\lambda - 2\mu}{4\mu}\sum_{k=0}^{\infty}\sum_{m=0}^{k}\binom{k}{m}(-1)^m\rho^m(\tfrac{1}{2})^k\rho^{-(m+k+i+1)}$$

$$\times \mathscr{L}^{-1}[(s + \lambda)\alpha_1^{-(m+k+i+1)}]\Bigg]$$

If we write the second component of the Laplace transform of $P_n(t)$ in the form

$$\left[\frac{s + \lambda}{\lambda\alpha_1^n} - \frac{s + \lambda}{\lambda\alpha_1^{n+1}}\right]P_0^*(s)$$

[19] See Margenau and Murphy, *op. cit.*, p. 75. $I_n(x) = i^{-n}J_n(ix)$; $i = \sqrt{-1}$.

[20] See any standard text, such as Erdelyi, Magnus, Oberhettinger, and Tricomi, *Tables of Integral Transforms*, McGraw-Hill Book Co., New York, 1954.

We have:

$$P_n(t) = e^{-(\lambda+2\mu)t}\Bigg[(\sqrt{\rho})^{n-i}I_{n-i}(2\sqrt{2\lambda\mu}t) + (\sqrt{\rho})^{n-i-1}I_{n+i+1}(2\sqrt{2\lambda\mu}t)$$

$$+ (1-\rho)\rho^n \sum_{k=n+i+2}^{\infty} (\sqrt{\rho})^{-k}I_k(2\sqrt{2\lambda\mu}t)\Bigg] + \frac{e^{-(\lambda+2\mu)t}}{\lambda(\lambda+2\mu)}$$

$$\Bigg\{\sum_{k=0}^{\infty}(\rho)^{-(k+i+1)}\mathscr{L}^{-1}[(s+\lambda)(\alpha_1^{-(n+k+i+1)} - \alpha_1^{-(n+k+i+2)})]$$

$$+ \frac{\lambda}{4\mu}\sum_{k=0}^{\infty}\sum_{m=0}^{k}\binom{k}{m}(-1)^m(\rho)^m(\tfrac{1}{2})^k(\rho)^{-(m+k+i+2)}$$

$$\times \mathscr{L}^{-1}[(s+\lambda)(\alpha_1^{-(n+m+k+i+2)} - \alpha_1^{-(n+m+k+i+3)}]$$

$$+ \frac{\lambda-2\mu}{4\mu}\sum_{k=0}^{\infty}\sum_{m=0}^{k}\binom{k}{m}(-1)^m\left(\frac{\lambda}{2\mu}\right)^m(\tfrac{1}{2})^k$$

$$\times (\rho)^{-(m+k+i+1)}\mathscr{L}^{-1}[(s+\lambda)(\alpha_1^{-(n+m+k+i+1)} - \alpha_1^{-(n+m+k+i+2)})]\Bigg\}\Bigg]$$

We have given an analytical method of deriving a time-dependent solution to our problem that is complicated but illustrates an important method. Frequently, steady state solutions are all that is needed.

Exercise: The length of a busy period is the length of time between the arrival of a unit at the empty queue and the first subsequent moment at which the queue is again empty.

To find the distribution of a busy period, one must compute $[dP_0(t)]/dt$ from the system of equations (5–3) with $c = 2$ with an absorbing barrier at the origin, *i.e.*, the first two equations are altered for this purpose to read:

$$\frac{dP_0(t)}{dt} = \mu P_1(t)$$

$$\frac{dP_1(t)}{dt} = -(\lambda+\mu)P_1(t) + 2\mu P_2(t)$$

The remaining equations are the same as in (5–3). Derive the distribution of a busy period.

Exercise: One can also study the distribution of a busy period in the two-channel case by requiring that both channels be busy (rather than at least one). The equations describing this case are:

$$P_1'(t) = 2\mu P_2(t)$$
$$P_2'(t) = -(\lambda + 2\mu)P_2(t) + 2\mu P_3(t)$$
$$P_n'(t) = -(\lambda + 2\mu)P_n(t) + \lambda P_{n-1}(t) + 2\mu P_{n+1}(t) \quad n > 2$$

Solve these equations.

If we assume negative exponential service distribution for each of two channels with parameters μ_1 and μ_2 respectively, the general method of solution proceeds essentially as before except that one is faced with the determination of conditional probabilities $P_1(1,0,t)$ and $P_1(0,1,t)$, which respectively give the probability that one unit is in the system and it is in service in the first channel at time t and the probability that one unit is in the system and it is in service in the second channel at time t.

One may assume that an arriving unit that finds the system empty joins the first channel with probability $\mu_1/(\mu_1 + \mu_2)$ and the second channel with probability $\mu_2/(\mu_1 + \mu_2)$. If only one channel is open, the unit immediately enters it for service. The equations for this case are given by:

$$P_0'(t) = -\lambda P_0(t) + \mu_1 P_1(1,0,t) + \mu_2 P_1(0,1,t)$$
$$P_1'(1,0,t) = -(\lambda + \mu_1)P_1(1,0,t) + \mu_2 P_2(t) + \frac{\mu_1}{\mu_1 + \mu_2}\lambda P_0(t)$$
$$P_1'(0,1,t) = -(\lambda + \mu_2)P_1(0,1,t) + \mu_1 P_2(t) + \frac{\mu_2}{\mu_1 + \mu_2}\lambda P_0(t) \qquad (5\text{–}18)$$
$$P_n'(t) = -(\lambda + \mu_1 + \mu_2)P_n(t) + \lambda P_{n-1}(t) + (\mu_1 + \mu_2)P_{n+1}(t) \quad n \geq 1$$

where

$$P_1(t) = P_1(1,0,t) + P_1(0,1,t) \qquad (5\text{–}19)$$

Note that if $\mu_1 = \mu_2 = \mu$, the above system reduces to that of the two-channel case with identical exponential service.

We assume that the initial number of units in the system at time $t = 0$ is $i \geq 2$.

Defining

$$P(z,t) \equiv \sum_{n=0}^{\infty} P_n(t)z^n; \qquad P(z,0) = z^i$$

we have in the usual manner:

$$\frac{\partial P}{\partial t} = -(\lambda + \mu_1 + \mu_2)P + \lambda z P + (\mu_1 + \mu_2)\frac{P - P_0(t)}{z} + (\mu_1 + \mu_2)P_0(t) - (1 - z)[\mu_2 P_1(1,0,t) + \mu_1 P_1(0,1,t)] \tag{5–20}$$

$$P^*(z,s) = \frac{z^{i+1} - (1 - z)\{(\mu_1 + \mu_2)P_0^*(s) + z[\mu_2 P_1^*(1,0,s) + \mu_1 P_1^*(0,1,s)]\}}{-\lambda(z - \alpha_1)(z - \alpha_2)} \tag{5–21}$$

To determine the unknown probabilities in the numerator of the right hand side of (5–21) we apply Rouché's theorem to the denominator. This leads to the condition that requires the vanishing of the numerator at the zero α_2 which lies inside the unit circle, which yields:

$$(\mu_1 + \mu_2)P_0^*(s) + \alpha_2[\mu_2 P_1^*(1,0,s) + \mu_1 P_1^*(0,1,s)] = \frac{\alpha_2^{i+1}}{1 - \alpha_2} \tag{5–22}$$

and which we use together with the Laplace transform of the first equation of (5–18) and of the condition

$$\sum_{n=0}^{\infty} P_n(t) = 1$$

Hence, the remaining two equations are:

$$sP_0^*(s) = -\lambda P_0^*(s) + \mu_1 P_1^*(1,0,s) + \mu_2 P_1^*(0,1,s) \tag{5–23}$$

$$\sum_{n=0}^{\infty} P_n^*(s) = \frac{1}{s} \tag{5–24}$$

To obtain (5–24) one applies the Leibnitz differentiation theorem to (5–21) in which $P_1^*(1,0,s)$ and $P_1^*(0,1,s)$ are replaced by their expressions in terms of $P_0^*(s)$. By substituting in (5–24), one has the desired result for $P_0^*(s)$ and, hence, explicitly for $P_n^*(s)$.

5.7. Inventory Problem.—In an inventory problem one essentially has a stock of goods that is held for demand by customers. There are costs involved in carrying an inventory of the stock, in obtaining it from the manufacturer, in storing and handling it, and in shortage when the demand exceeds the supply. Under various assumptions on costs, supply and demand, and even competition, it is desired to maintain a size of inventory that optimizes profits over a period of time.

There is a large variety of inventory models and almost as many methods of formulation and solution. Here we briefly illustrate a model treated in an elegant manner, more typical of the powerful methods used in the inventory field. We assume that the reader has some familiarity with inventory concepts. None but the most elementary ones are encountered here.

R. C. Singleton, in an interesting paper,[21] derives the functional equation for the stationary probability distribution of stock level just prior to delivery of inventory items.

Assume that the maximum capacity of inventory to be kept on hand is S. At the beginning of each period this stock is replenished by deliveries of random amounts R with distribution function $H(r)$. The number of periods between deliveries is a random variable D with

$$\text{Prob}\,\{D = i\} = d_i \quad i = 1,2,\cdots \quad \text{and} \quad \sum_{i=1}^{\infty} d_i = 1$$

The amount accepted for stocking is the minimum of R and the quantity to satisfy back-logged demand bringing the level up to S. The demand in the ith period is given by a random variable ξ_i with continuous density function $\phi(\xi)$; all variables $\xi_i (i = 1,2,\cdots)$ are independently and identically distributed. The level of stock at the end of period i is represented by the random variable X_i measured before adding any delivery occurring at time i. Let the random variable η_i be the time of the ith delivery. Then Prob $(\eta_i = 0) = 1$. We can write X_{η_i} and R_{η_i} to indicate dependence on η_i. We have:

$$X_{\eta_j+1} = \begin{cases} S - \displaystyle\sum_{i=\eta_j+1}^{\eta_j+1} \xi_i & \text{for } S - R_{\eta_j} \leq X_{\eta_j} \leq S \\ X_{\eta_j} + R_{\eta_j} - \displaystyle\sum_{i=\eta_j+1}^{\eta_j+1} \xi_i & \text{for } X_{\eta_j} < S - R_{\eta_j} \end{cases}$$

The distribution function $F_{\eta_j+1}(x)$ of X_{η_j+1} may now be written as:

$$F_{\eta_j+1}(x) = \text{Prob}\,(X_{\eta_j+1} < x) = \begin{cases} \displaystyle\int_0^{\infty}\int_{S-r}^{S}\int_{S-x}^{\infty} \psi(\xi)d\xi dF_{\eta_j}(t)dH(r) \\ \quad + \displaystyle\int_0^{\infty}\int_{x-r}^{S-r}\int_{r+t-x}^{\infty} \psi(\xi)d\xi \\ \qquad \times\, dF_{\eta_j}(t)dH(r) \\ \quad + \displaystyle\int_0^{\infty}\int_{-\infty}^{x-r} dF_{\eta_j}(t)dH(r), \\ \qquad\qquad \text{for } x \leq S \\ 1 \qquad\qquad \text{for } x \geq S \end{cases}$$

[21] Richard C. Singleton, "Steady State Properties of Selected Inventory Models," *Technical Report No.* **23**, under Contract NR 047–019 with Stanford University, July 21, 1960.

with

$$\psi(\xi) = \sum_{k=1}^{\infty} d_k \phi^{(k)}(\xi)$$

where $\phi^{(k)}(\xi)$ is the density function of the sum of $k\xi$'s.

To see the foregoing equation note that if $S - R_{\eta_j} \le X_{\eta_j} < S$, the demand up to time η_{j+1} must be $\ge S - x$ in order that $X_{\eta_j+1} < x$ is satisfied. On the other hand if $x - R_{\eta_j} \le X_{\eta_j} < S - R_{\eta_j}$, then the demand up to η_{j+1} must be $\ge R_{\eta_j} + X_{\eta_j} - x$ for $X_{\eta_j+1} < x$ to be satisfied. Finally, if $X_{\eta_j} < x - R_{\eta_j}$ then regardless of demand we have $X_{\eta_j+1} < x$. By interchanging the order of summation and regrouping terms, we have

$$F_{\eta_j+1}(x) = \begin{cases} \displaystyle\int_0^{\infty}\int_0^{S-x}\int_{-\infty}^{x+\xi-r} \psi(\xi)\,dF_{\eta_j}(t)\,d\xi\,dH(r) + \int_{S-x}^{\infty} \psi(\xi)\,d\xi, & \text{for } x \le S \\ 1 & \text{for } x \ge S \end{cases}$$

It can be shown that as the number of periods increases indefinitely, and if the expected demand per period is less than the delivery capacity, one may replace both $F_{\eta_j+1}(x)$ and $F_{\eta_j}(x)$ by $F(x)$ in the foregoing expression, yielding the desired expression for the stationary stock level which is an integral equation in the unknown $F(x)$. One can derive a similar expression for the stock level at the end of an arbitrary period.

Exercise: Derive the integral equation for the stationary density function $f(x)$ by differentiating the expression in $F(x)$ with respect to x.

Exercise: Let $d_k = pq^{k-1}$, $k = 1,2,\cdots$ where $0 < p = 1 - q < 1$ and $\phi(\xi) = \lambda e^{-\lambda\xi}$ for $\xi \ge 0$. Show that $\psi(\xi) = p\lambda e^{-p\lambda\xi}$. Substitute this in the expression for $f(x)$ and, differentiating with respect to x, obtain $f'(x) - p\lambda f(x) = -p\lambda E_H[f(x - R)]$ where E_H denotes the expected value of its argument with respect to $H(r)$. Trying

$$f(x) = \begin{cases} Ke^{-k(S-x)} & \text{for } x \le S \\ 0 & \text{otherwise} \end{cases}$$

for solution over $-\infty \le x \le S$ (thus $K > 0$ must be satisfied for the integral of $f(x)$ to exist) we have

$$\frac{p\lambda - K}{p\lambda} = E_H(e^{-KR})$$

This has exactly one positive solution in K, since by the condition for stationarity

$$\frac{1}{p\lambda} < E_H(R)$$

must be satisfied. Thus, for example, if

$$h(r) = \frac{dH(r)}{dr} = \frac{k^k r^{k-1} e^{-kr/r_0}}{r_0^k (k-1)!} \qquad r > 0, k > 0, r_0 > \frac{1}{p\lambda}$$

is a gamma [22] distribution with mean r_0, then there is a unique positive solution α of

$$\frac{p\lambda - K}{p\lambda} = \left(1 + \frac{Kr_0}{r}\right)^{-k}$$

where α must replace K in the expression for $f(x)$.

5.8. Reliability.[23] —Let a mechanical or an electronic system be divided into n components that can fail independently. In addition, let the failure of a component be independent of the duration and frequency of its period of use. The probability that a component not in use at time t will be used at or before time $t + \tau$ is independent of when it was last used. Assume that the system operates continuously except for interruptions caused by failure. A component that fails is replaced by a new component having identical statistics as the original had when new. Let $F_i(t)$ be the probability that an ith type component, which is new at time zero, fails by time t. Let $P_i(t)$ be the probability that such a component is "in use" at time t and let $G_i(t)$ be the probability of periods of nonuse given that it was not in use at time zero. $G_i(t)$ is the probability that the component will be called into use by time t. A component "is in use" whenever its operation is necessary for the operation of the system. For each component there are alternate periods of use and nonuse. Let $F_i^*(t)$ be the probability that a given i^{th} type component, which is new at time zero, causes system failure by time t.

Note that a component that fails at time $\tau \leq t$ causes system failure by time t if it is in use at time τ (when it fails) or if it is not in use at time τ but is called into use after τ and at or before t. These two cases respectively give the two terms on the right side of

$$F_i^*(t) = \int_0^t P_i(\tau) dF_i(\tau) + \int_0^t [1 - P_i(\tau)] G_i(t - \tau) dF_i(\tau)$$

which simplifies to

$$F_i^*(t) - \int_0^t [1 - P_i(\tau)][1 - G_i(t - \tau)] dF_i(\tau)$$

[22] The gamma distribution is given by $(b^a y^{a-1} e^{-by})/\Gamma(a)$. Its characteristic function is $(1 - it/b)^{-a}$.

[23] Betty J. Flehinger, "System Reliability as a Function of Systems Age; Effects of Intermittent Component Usage and Periodic Maintenance," *Operations Research*, **8**, No. 1, 1–158 (1960).

Let $U_i(t)$ be the expected number of system failures caused by failures of components in the ith position by time t, where the initial component is new at time zero, then

$$U_i(t) = F_i^*(t) + \int_0^t F_i^*(t - \tau)dU_i(\tau)$$

which is Volterra's integral equation of the second kind.[24]

Let $F_i^*(t,x)$ be the probability that the ith component causes a system failure in an interval of length t, given that the age of the system at the beginning of the interval is x. Then

$$F_i^*(t,x) = F_i^*(x + t) - F_i^*(x) + \int_0^t [F_i^*(x - y + t) - F_i(x - y)]dU_i(y)$$

To see this, note that system failure can occur if the component did not cause failure before the interval but does during the interval (the probability of this event is $F_i^*(x + t) - F_i^*(x)$), or if the original component has induced failure and has been replaced (perhaps several times) and the new component was installed at time $0 \leq y \leq x$ but causes system failure during $(x,x + t]$ and hence our expression for $F_i^*(t,x)$.

By means of Laplace transforms of the foregoing three equations making use of the convolution theorem and the assumptions $P_i(t) = P_i$ a constant which is the ratio of the "in use" time (t the total operating time of the ith component), $G_i(t) \equiv 1 - \exp(-t/\theta_i)$ (note that a double transform is applied to $F_i^*(t,x)$), we obtain an expression in terms of the lifetime distribution, *i.e.*,

$$\tilde{F}_i^*(r;s) = \frac{r}{s - r} \, \frac{\tilde{F}_i(r)(P_i r + 1/\theta_i)/(r + 1/\theta_i) - \tilde{F}_i(s)(P_i s + 1/\theta_i)/(s + 1/\theta_i)}{1 - \tilde{F}_i(s)(P_i s + 1/\theta_i)/(s + 1/\theta_i)}$$

Exercise: Verify the foregoing expression.

If $R(t;x)$ is the probability of survival of the system for an interval t at age x, because of the independence assumption we have

$$R(t;x) = \prod_{i=1}^{n} [1 - F_i^*(t,x)]$$

Exercise: Let $F_i(t) = 1 - \exp(-t/t_i)$ show that

$$\lim_{x\to\infty} R(t;x) = \prod_{i=1}^{n} \{\exp(-t/t_i) + [\theta_i^2(1 - P_i)/(t_i - \theta_i)] \times [t_i + (1 - P_i)\theta_i][\exp(-t/t_i) - \exp(-t/\theta_i)]\}$$

[24] Margenau and Murphy, *op. cit.*, p. 520.

5.9. Maximization, Minimization, and Minmax.—We shall discuss three wide classes of optimization problems that illustrate the ideas of the title of this section as used in operations research. They are:

(1) programming problems;
(2) isoperimetric problems; and
(3) minmax or game theoretic problems.

Here (1) and (3) involve the determination of extrema of functions and (2) studies the optimization of functionals.

5.10. Simplified Profit Maximization: An Illustration of Non-Constrained Optimization.—Before discussing programming problems we illustrate in the next two sections two common forms of elementary optimization.

Assume that a manufacturer gains α units on sold items and loses β units for unsold items. Also assume that the demand for y items is given by a probability distribution function $f(y)$ with maximum demand y_0, *i.e.*, $\int_0^{y_0} f(y)dy = 1$.

Compute the number of items x to be manufactured that maximizes the expected profit.

Profit may be represented by

$$\text{Profit} = \begin{cases} \alpha y - \beta(x - y) & \text{for } y \leq x \\ \alpha x & \text{for } y > x \end{cases}$$

We leave it as an exercise for the reader to find the condition under which the expected value of the profit is maximum; *i.e.*, maximize:

$$E[\text{Profit}] = \int_0^x [(\alpha + \beta)y - \beta x]f(y)dy + \int_x^{y_0} \alpha x f(y)dy$$

5.11. Investment.—We give an interesting illustration of a combined optimization and probability problem given by B. Roy. It is a trivial matter to show that an amount of money $(1 + r)^{-k}$, invested at the compound interest of $r\%$ over a period of k years will become a unit amount.

Consider the following inventory problem. There are p time periods at the start of each of which an order of n items is made at a cost $A(n)$, which is an increasing function of n (*e.g.*, $A(n) = a + bn$). The length of each period is a random variable, and, hence, there are p random variables X_i $(i = 1, \cdots, p)$ that are assumed to be independently and identically distributed according to the distribution function $F_n(x)$—for each period, it is the probability that there is a demand for

n items during a time interval of length $\leq x$. We observe that this is also the distribution of the duration of an expenditure. For simplicity, assume that the items considered are free informational brochures given out on demand.

To secure these items at the beginning of any period requires that money be invested at the start of the operation at a certain interest rate r. It is then used at the beginning of a period to buy n brochures for the period. Note that according to the frequency of demand and the length of time for all n items to be depleted in each period, the amount of money needed at time zero, to buy n items at the beginning of period $q < p$ will be greater the shorter the sum $X_1 + \cdots + X_{q-1}$ of the lengths of the periods up to q. This follows from the fact that this money will accumulate less interest than it would for greater values of the sum. Thus there is an optimum value of n that minimizes the amount of money to be invested in the enterprise.

The total funds to be set aside (invested) for the p periods are

$$A(n) + A(n)(1 + r)^{-X_1} + \cdots + A(n)(1 + r)^{-(X_1 + \cdots + X_{p-1})}$$

The problem is to find the n that minimizes the expected value of this function of random variables.

If we write:

$$g_n(r) = \int_0^\infty (1 + r)^{-x} dF_n(x)$$

and recall that the expected value of a function $g(x)$ of a random variable X distributed according to $F(x)$ is $\int_0^\infty g(x)dF(x)$ and that the expected value of the sum of independently distributed functions is the sum of their expected values, the problem is to find n which minimizes the cost function

$$A(n)[1 + g_n(r) + \cdots + g_n^{p-1}(r)] = A(n) \frac{1 - g_n^p(r)}{1 - g_n(r)}$$

Note that this reduces to the case where x, the duration of a period, is a function of n.

Now from the definition of a characteristic function $\phi(t)$ of a random variable x, *i.e.*

$$\phi_n(t) = \int_0^\infty e^{itx} dF_n(x)$$

by putting $t = i \log (1 + r)$ we have $g_n(r) = \phi_n(r)$. The study of our minimization problem is simplified by making an assumption that is reasonable for many cases: that two successive expenditures, one for n

items and one for m items, have the same duration as a single expenditure for $n + m$ items. Expressed in terms of characteristic functions, this means $\phi_n(r)\phi_m(r) = \phi_{n+m}(r)$.

We may now write $\phi_n(r) = \phi_1(r) \cdots \phi_1(r) = \phi_1^n(r) \equiv \phi^n(r)$. Our problem is then to minimize

$$[1 - \phi^{np}(r)] \frac{A(n)}{1 - \phi^n(r)}$$

If we assume that np is constant or that it is sufficiently large so that $\phi^{np}(r)$ is negligible (since $\phi(r) < 1$) then in either case the total sum of money to be invested is proportional to $A(n)/[1 - \phi^n(r)]$. Minimizing this function with respect to n is achieved through its logarithm since $d/dx \log f(x) = f'(x)/f(x)$ is equal to zero if $f'(x)$ vanishes, which is precisely the desired condition. Applying these ideas leads to the equation

$$\frac{\phi^{-n}(r) - 1}{-\log \phi(r)} = \frac{A(n)}{A'(n)}$$

For a given problem r is fixed, and $\phi(r)$ is known, the left side, which together with its derivative is monotonic increasing, gives rise to a curve (as a function of n) that passes through the origin where its derivative is equal to unity. The right side gives rise to a curve that intersects the ordinate axis at a positive value. The intersection of the two curves gives rise to a unique value of n, which is the solution to our problem. Note that the geometric solution leads to an approximate value of n that can be improved through the use of an iterative numerical technique. Also note that n is a discrete variable that assumes integer values, and, consequently, the appropriate integer value must be construed from the analysis. It is clear that this kind of minimization procedure would not apply if the cost function were not well behaved in n (*e.g.*, having illplaced ripples).

Exercise: Show that the density function of the sum of n independent, identical random variables with the common density function $\lambda e^{-\lambda x}$ is given by $\lambda(\lambda x)^{n-1}e^{-\lambda x}/(n - 1)!$. Note that the time intervals between events that occur by a Poisson process are exponentially distributed.

Exercise: Using the foregoing density function of the sum of n variables for the density function of demand, all the above simplifying assumptions are satisfied. Hence, show that

$$\phi(r) = [1 + \log (1 + r)^{1/\lambda}]^{-1}$$

Let $A(n) = a + bn$ and find n that minimizes the total expenditure.

5.12. Programming Problems.[25]—Let x be a vector whose components are n variables $x_1,\cdots,x_n$. The general programming problem is concerned with finding the extremum values of a function $f(x)$ subject to the constraints $x_j \geq 0$ $(j = 1,\cdots,n)$ and $g_i(x) \leq 0$ $(i = 1,\cdots,m)$. A simple but important example of this type of problem is the linear programming problem, which we shall treat in some detail later.

A point $(x_1^0,\cdots,x_n^0)$ is a global minimum of $f(x)$ if $f(x_1^0,\cdots,x_n^0) \leq f(x_1,\cdots,x_n)$ for all values of $x_1,\cdots,x_n$. It is a local minimum if this property holds for values of the variables in a neighborhood of the given point. A similar definition applies to a global and a local maximum. The theory of local and global extrema of a function of several variables free of constraints is well known and will not be discussed here. We point out, however, that the necessary condition for a stationary value that requires the vanishing of the first derivative gives rise to a constructive procedure of obtaining an extremum. Sufficiency conditions, which involve determining if the quadratic form of the second order partial derivatives is positive or negative definite at these points, determine a minimum or a maximum respectively.

To obtain better insight into the nature of solving a general programming problem, it is useful to discuss briefly the Lagrange multiplier method.[26] Note first that the constraints of the programming problem are given as inequalities, and, hence, in general we have a region of values that satisfies the constraints. The number of inequalities m need not be less than n. However, this restriction is needed for the case of equality constraints. To see this, suppose that the problem involves three variables, *i.e.*, $x \equiv (x_1,x_2,x_3)$. If the number of constraints $g_i(x) = 0$ is three, *i.e.*, $m = 3$, then in general the intersection of the three constraint surfaces is a point, and it would be trivial to extremize $f(x)$ subject to these constraints. On the other hand if $m = 2$ then the intersection of $g_i(x) = 0$ $(i = 1,2)$ is generally a curve, or if $m = 1$, $g_i(x) = 0$ is a surface, and it is a meaningful problem to extremize $f(x)$ subject to these constraints.

Suppose that it is desired to maximize $f(x_1,x_2,x_3)$ subject to $g_1(x_1,x_2,x_3) = 0$ and $g_2(x_1,x_2,x_3) = 0$. Note that because we have two constraints two of the variables can be expressed in terms of the third, and the latter can be made to vary arbitrarily.

[25] H. W. Kuhn and A. W. Tucker, "Non-linear Programming," in J. Neyman, ed., *Second Berkeley Symposium on Mathematical Statistics and Probability*, University of California Press, Berkeley, 1951; Thomas L. Saaty, *Mathematical Methods of Operations Research*, McGraw-Hill Book Co., New York, 1959.

[26] Margenau and Murphy, *op. cit.*, p. 209.

Now the first derivatives of f vanish at the maximum, and hence at the maximum

$$df = \frac{\partial f}{\partial x_1} dx_1 + \frac{\partial f}{\partial x_2} dx_2 + \frac{\partial f}{\partial x_3} dx_3 = 0$$

We always have

$$\frac{\partial g_i}{\partial x_1} dx_1 + \frac{\partial g_i}{\partial x_2} dx_2 + \frac{\partial g_i}{\partial x_3} dx_3 = 0 \quad (i = 1,2)$$

which is also valid at the maximum. If we let $i = 1,2$ respectively in the last equation and multiply the first equation by a constant λ_1, and the second by a constant λ_2 (both of which to be determined later), and add both equations to the first we have

$$\left(\frac{\partial f}{\partial x_1} + \lambda_1 \frac{\partial g_1}{\partial x_1} + \lambda_2 \frac{\partial g_2}{\partial x_1}\right) dx_1 + \left(\frac{\partial f}{\partial x_2} + \lambda_1 \frac{\partial g_1}{\partial x_2} + \lambda_2 \frac{\partial g_2}{\partial x_2}\right) dx_2 + \left(\frac{\partial f}{\partial x_3} + \lambda_1 \frac{\partial g_1}{\partial x_3} + \lambda_2 \frac{\partial g_2}{\partial x_3}\right) dx_3 = 0$$

The constants λ_1 and λ_2 are known as Lagrange multipliers. As we have already seen two of the variables can be expressed as functions of the third variable; hence, for example, dx_1 and dx_2 can be expressed in terms of dx_3, which is arbitrary. Thus λ_1 and λ_2 may be chosen so as to cause the vanishing of the coefficients of dx_1 and dx_2 (their values are obtained by solving the two simultaneous equations). Then since dx_3 is arbitrary, its coefficient must vanish in order that the entire expression shall vanish. This gives three equations that, together with the two constraint equations $g_i = 0$ $(i = 1,2)$, can be used to determine the five unknowns x_1, x_2, x_3, λ_1, and λ_2.

Exercise: Generalize this derivation to an arbitrary number of variables n and for $m < n$ constraints.

For the general case the foregoing necessary conditions for a constrained extremum follow from the necessary condition for an extremum of the lagrangian,

$$F(x,\lambda) \equiv f(x) + \sum_{i=1}^{m} \lambda_i g_i(x) \quad m < n$$

where

$$x = (x_1, \cdots, x_n) \quad \text{and} \quad \lambda = (\lambda_1, \cdots, \lambda_m)$$

These necessary conditions that require

$$\frac{\partial F}{\partial x_j} = 0, \quad j = 1, \cdots, n$$

$$\frac{\partial F}{\partial \lambda_i} = 0, \quad i = 1, \cdots, m$$

are a set of $(m + n)$ equations from which our $(m + n)$ unknowns are determined.

5.13. Weapon Allocation: An Application of Lagrange Multipliers.—The following problem was posed by M. M. Flood.[27] The object is to find the weapons allocation for m weapon-depots, each containing a_i weapons, to N target complexes of τ_j targets each, that minimizes the expected total target threat. The solution given here is due to Ash.[27]

Let x_{ij} be the number of weapons allocated from the ith depot to the jth target complex, and let a_i be the number of weapons in the ith depot, and p_{ij} be the conditional probability that an individual weapon from the ith depot destroys a member of the jth target complex, given that this member has survived onslaughts from all other depots, and τ_j be the number of targets contained in the jth complex, and α_j be the threat potential of the jth target complex, and $\sigma_{ij} = x_{ij}/\tau_j$ be the ratio of the ith weapon depot to the jth target complex. The expected survival probability of the jth target complex from weapons of the ith depot is $(1 - p_{ij}\sigma_{ij})$. The expected total target threat is

$$\sum_{j=1}^{N} \alpha_j \tau_j \prod_{i=1}^{m} (1 - p_{ij}\sigma_{ij})$$

The problem is to determine the σ_{ij} which minimize the foregoing expression subject to the constraint

$$\sigma_{ij} \geq 0$$

$$\sum_{j=1}^{N} \sigma_{ij}\tau_j = a_i \qquad (i = 1, \cdots, m)$$

If $p_{ij} = p_j$, *i.e.*, if the kill levels become functions of only the target complex, we have a linear programming problem. If we assume small kill levels such that $p_{ij}\sigma_{ij}$ is also small, then the expected target threat may be approximated by

$$f(\sigma_{11}, \cdots, \sigma_{1N}, \cdots, \sigma_{m1}, \cdots, \sigma_{mN}) = \exp[m/2] \sum_{j=1}^{N} \alpha_j \tau_j \exp\left[-\tfrac{1}{2} \sum_{i=1}^{m} (1 + p_{ij}\sigma_{ij})^2\right]$$

since $\log(1 + x) = x - \frac{1}{2}x^2 + \cdots$ for $|x| < 1$.

The Lagrangian of the problem is given by

$$f + \lambda_i \left[\sum_{j=1}^{N} \sigma_{ij}\tau_j - a_i\right]$$

[27] Milton Ash, "Flood's Assignment Model for Small Kill Levels," *Operations Research*, **7**, No. 2 (1959).

Equating to zero the partial derivatives with respect to σ_{ij} and λ_i ($j = 1,\cdots,N;\ i = 1,\cdots,m$) yields $m(N + 1)$ equations, which is exactly the number of unknowns. This yields the solution for small p_{ij}:

$$\sigma_{ij} = \frac{1}{p_{ij}} - \left(\sum_{j=1}^{N} \frac{\tau_j}{p_{ij}} - a_i\right) \Big/ A_j \sum_{j=1}^{N} \frac{\tau_j}{A_j}$$

where

$$A_j = \left(\alpha_j \prod_{i=1}^{m} p_{ij}\right)^{1/(m-1)}$$

Exercise: Verify that this solution satisfies the constraints.

5.14. Linear Programming.[28]—A linear programming problem as defined in matrix notation requires that a vector $x \geq 0$ (non-negativity constraints) be found that satisfies the constraints $Ax \leq b$, and maximizes the linear function $c\tilde{x}$. Here $x = (x_1,\cdots,x_n)$, $A = [a_{ij}]$ ($i = 1,\cdots,m;\ j = 1,\cdots,n$), $b = (b_1,\cdots,b_m)$, and $c = (c_1,\cdots,c_n)$ is the cost vector. With the original (the primal) problem is associated the dual problem $yA \geq c$, $y \geq 0$, $b\tilde{y} =$ minimum, where $y = (y_1,\cdots,y_m)$. A duality theorem [29] asserts that if either the primal or the dual has a solution then the values of the objective functions of both problems at the optimum are the same. It is a relatively easy matter to obtain the solution vector of one problem from that of the other.

In the original problem one usually has $m < n$. Thus, the vertices of the region of solution lie on the coordinate planes. This follows from the fact that, generally, in n dimensions, n hyperplanes each of dimension $(n - 1)$ intersect at a point. The dual problem defines a polytope in m-dimensional space. In this case not all vertices need lie on the coordinate planes.

We note that the *simplex process* is currently used to solve linear programs far more frequently than any other method. Briefly, this method of solution begins by choosing basis vectors in m-dimensions where m is the number of inequalities. (The latter are reduced to equalities by introducing slack variables.) For brevity we omit discussion of the case where it is not possible to form such a basis. The components of each vector comprise the coefficients of one of the variables, the first component being the coefficient of the variable in the first inequality, the second component is the coefficient of the same

[28] S. D. Gass, *Linear Programming.* McGraw-Hill Book Co., New York, 1958.

[29] D. Gale, W. H. Kuhn, and A. W. Tucker, *Activity Analysis of Production and Allocation,* pp. 317–29, John Wiley and Sons, Inc., New York, 1951.

variable in the second inequality, etc.; the mth component is its coefficient in the mth inequality. All other vectors are expressed as linear combinations of the basis vectors. Quantities $z_j - c_j$ are formed in which z_j is the scalar product of the weights in the linear combination of the ith vector in terms of the basis vectors (denoted by β_{ij}) and the vector of cost coefficients corresponding to the basis vectors. It can be seen from the statement of the problem that the latter coefficients are given in the objective function. The scalar c_j is the objective function coefficient of the variable whose coefficients were selected from the constraints to form the jth vector. When it is desired to maximize the objective function, a basis yields the solution (the latter is the scalar product of the above described cost vector and the weights β_{0j} in the expression of the constant terms vector b of the inequalities as a linear combination of the basis vectors) if $z_j \geq c_j$ for all j. Otherwise, one chooses the vector for which $c_j - z_j$ is maximum. This is the new vector to go into the basis replacing the vector that yields the minimum value for the ratio β_{0j}/β_{ij} for all $\beta_{ij} > 0$. In this manner one has a new basis.

The foregoing provides background material for basic ideas for the sequel. Of essence is the observation that with each iteration the value of the objective function improves towards the optimum value or, at worst, remains the same for iterations in the region that satisfies all the constraints. This region is called the feasible region.

Geometrically, the inequality constraints of the problem define a convex set (the feasible region) whose boundary is a polytope in n dimensions, and the objective function defines a hyperplane that is translated in a parallel direction towards that point of the convex region that yields the optimum (*e.g.*, if minimizing, this point yields the shortest distance of the objective hyperplane from the origin). It is intuitively obvious at least in 3 dimensions that the optimum is on the boundary and is usually a vertex of the polyhedron. Weyl[30] has proved this fact for the n-dimensional case. If all the vertices were easily obtainable, then one could evaluate the objective function at each vertex until the optimum is attained. From this it is clear that there should be a natural interest in the number of vertices of polytopes. There is, of course, the stronger interest in estimating the number of steps required to solve a linear programming problem by various procedures and particularly by the simplex process. Because

[30] H. Weyl, "The Elementary Theory of Complex Polyhedra; Contributions to the Theory of Games," *Annals of Mathematical Studies*, No. 24, pp. 3–18, Princeton University Press, 1950.

specific criteria for choosing new vectors, etc., are used, the simplex process does not require the use of all the vertices. It simply follows a network path towards the optimum.

Example 1.—A classical problem of linear programming is the *diet problem*. Given minimal needs for vitamins, iron, calcium, phosphorous etc., which are present in known proportions in a variety of possible foods with given prices, it is desired to determine a diet from these foods that meets the minimal needs for the vitamins and other ingredients at the lowest cost. To illustrate with a simple example and hypothetical figures, denote three types of food by F_1, F_2, F_3, and two types of dietary requirements, *e.g.*, vitamins by A and B. The table

	F_1	F_2	F_3	minimal requirements
A	4	1	6	8
B	3	7	2	5
cost	2	3	1	

gives the amount of substance A and B present in a unit of measurements of F_1, F_2, and F_3. Thus, for example, if F_i $(i = 1,2,3)$ are measured in pounds then there are four units of A in F_1 and seven units of B in F_2. The third row gives the cost per unit of F_i $(i = 1,2,3)$. The column on the right gives the minimal amount of the vitamin indicated in that row that must be taken at each meal. If one denotes by x_1, x_2, and x_3 the amounts of F_1, F_2, and F_3 to be taken then our problem becomes: minimize $2x_1 + 3x_2 + x_3$ or maximize $-2x_1 - 3x_2 - x_3$ subject to

$$\begin{aligned} 4x_1 + x_2 + 6x_3 &\geq 8 \\ 3x_1 + 7x_2 + 2x_3 &\geq 5 \\ x_i \geq 0, \quad i &= 1,2,3 \end{aligned}$$

This problem can readily be solved geometrically. However, we present it as an exercise and obtain the solution by the simplex process, using the maximization version. The process applies to large-scale problems, to which some of the most modern computers are applied.

Step 1.—The inequalities are reduced to equalities by introducing non-negative "slack variables."

$$\left.\begin{aligned} 4x_1 + x_2 + 6x_3 - x_4 = 8 \quad x_4 \geq 0 \\ 3x_1 + 7x_2 + 2x_3 - x_5 = 5 \quad x_5 \geq 0 \end{aligned}\right\} \text{ slack variables}$$

Step 2.—Write out the matrix of coefficients

$$[\mathbf{P}_1,\mathbf{P}_2,\mathbf{P}_3,\mathbf{P}_4,\mathbf{P}_5;\mathbf{P}_0] = \left[\begin{array}{ccccc|c} 4 & 1 & 6 & -1 & 0 & 8 \\ 3 & 7 & 2 & 0 & -1 & 5 \end{array}\right]$$

and write $c_1 = -2$, $c_2 = -3$, $c_3 = -1$, $c_4 = 0$, $c_5 = 0$.

Step 3.—Choose an arbitrary basis for this set of vectors. Let $\mathbf{P}_1$ and $\mathbf{P}_2$ form such a basis. Express all the vectors as linear combinations of $\mathbf{P}_1$ and $\mathbf{P}_2$ (this can be done in only one way).

	$\mathbf{P}_1$	$\mathbf{P}_2$
$\mathbf{P}_1$	1	0
$\mathbf{P}_2$	0	1
$\mathbf{P}_3$	8/5	−2/5
$\mathbf{P}_4$	−7/25	3/25
$\mathbf{P}_5$	1/25	−4/25
$\mathbf{P}_0$	51/25	−4/25

Note for example that the coefficients in the third row are a and b, respectively, in

$$\begin{pmatrix} 6 \\ 2 \end{pmatrix} = a \begin{pmatrix} 4 \\ 3 \end{pmatrix} + b \begin{pmatrix} 1 \\ 7 \end{pmatrix}$$

Step 4.—Write $z_j = \beta_{i1}c_1 + \beta_{i2}c_2$ $(i = 1,\cdots,5)$ where β_{ij} are the coefficients in the linear combination. Then

$$\begin{aligned}
z_1 &= c_1 &&= -2; \quad & c_1 &= -2 \\
z_2 &= c_2 &&= -3; & c_2 &= -3 \\
z_3 &= (8/5)c_1 - (2/5)c_2 &&= -2; & c_3 &= -1 \\
z_4 &= (-7/25)c_1 + (3/25)c_2 &&= 1/5; & c_4 &= 0 \\
z_5 &= (1/25)c_1 - (4/25)c_2 &&= 2/5; & c_5 &= 0
\end{aligned}$$

If $z_j \geq c_j$ (for all j) the process is finished, with the corresponding cost as $(51/25)c_1 - (4/25)c_2 = -18/5$. (The relation is not satisfied in this case.) For a new basis we choose the new vector to go into the basis. It is $\mathbf{P}_3$, since $(c_3 - z_3)$ is maximum. Which of the two vectors $\mathbf{P}_1$ and $\mathbf{P}_2$ it will replace in the basis is indicated in the next step.

Step 5.

$$\mathbf{P}_0 = \frac{51}{25}\mathbf{P}_1 - \frac{4}{25}\mathbf{P}_2$$

$$\mathbf{P}_3 = \frac{8}{5}\mathbf{P}_1 - \frac{2}{5}\mathbf{P}_2$$

Multiply the second equation by θ and subtract from the first equation, obtaining

$$\mathbf{P}_0 = \theta\mathbf{P}_3 + (51/25 - 8\theta/5)\mathbf{P}_1 - (4/25 - 2\theta/5)\mathbf{P}_2$$

Choose $\theta = \min_j (\beta_{0j}/\beta_{ij}), \beta_{ij} > 0$. Thus $\theta = 51/40$ and $\mathbf{P}_0 = 51/40\mathbf{P}_3 + 7/20\mathbf{P}_2$. The vector $\mathbf{P}_1$ has been replaced by $\mathbf{P}_3$. The corresponding cost will be $(51/40)c_3 + (7/20)c_2 = -93/40$ (an improvement over $-18/5$, since one is maximizing).

Step 6.—Again expressing the vectors as a linear combination of $\mathbf{P}_2$ and $\mathbf{P}_3$, obtain:

	$\mathbf{P}_2$	$\mathbf{P}_3$
$\mathbf{P}_1$	1/4	5/8
$\mathbf{P}_2$	1	0
$\mathbf{P}_3$	0	1
$\mathbf{P}_4$	1/20	−7/40
$\mathbf{P}_5$	−3/20	1/40
$\mathbf{P}_0$	7/20	51/40

As before

$$\begin{aligned} z_1 &= -11/8 & c_1 &= -2 \\ z_2 &= -3 & c_2 &= -3 \\ z_3 &= -1 & c_3 &= -1 \\ z_4 &= 1/40 & c_4 &= 0 \\ z_5 &= 17/40 & c_5 &= 0 \end{aligned}$$

Since $z_j \geq c_j$ for all j, the process is finished with the corresponding cost as

$$-\left(\frac{7}{20}(-3) + \frac{51}{40}(-1)\right) = \frac{93}{40}$$

(We changed the sign, remembering that we started to minimize the expression.) The solution is given by $x_1 = 0$, $x_2 = \frac{7}{20}$, $x_3 = \frac{51}{40}$.

Exercise: Dualize the problem and obtain the solution of the dual. Show that the values of the objective functions are the same.

Example 2.—A well-known special case of the linear programming problem is the transportation problem requiring an assignment of shipments of materials from sources to destinations according to total availability and total demand, that minimizes the total shipping cost. If we denote the sources by S_i $(i = 1,\cdots,m)$ and the destinations by

$D_j(j = 1,\cdots,m)$ then the problem is to find x_{ij} the quantity of material to be shipped from S_i to D_j such that

$$\sum_{i=1}^{m} x_{ij} = a_j \quad \text{(total availability at } S_i\text{)}$$

and

$$\sum_{j=1}^{n} x_{ij} = b_i \quad \text{(total demand at } D_j\text{)}$$

with

$$\sum_{j=1}^{n} a_j = \sum_{i=1}^{m} b_i$$

and which minimizes $\sum\sum c_{ij}x_{ij}$ when the c_{ij} is the cost per unit of shipment from S_i to D_j. Many other applications of linear programming exist.

Linear programming is also used in the scheduling of production over several discrete periods, in which the special methods of solving transportation problems are used. Without giving the complete formulation, we point out that in setting up such a problem[31] one may consider, for example, the inventory at the end of the ith time period, the maximum number of units that can be produced during the ith time period on regular time and a similar quantity of units produced on overtime, the number of units of finished product to be sold during the ith time period, the cost of production per unit on overtime, and the cost of storage per unit per time period. Different production and storage costs may be considered for each period.

Example 3 (*Parametric Linear Programming*).[32]—Consider the problem of allocating labor to different jobs. The labor available is a variable function of time. It may vary from day to day, as is the case in ship-unloading problems where it has been observed that there is a clustering of labor on certain weekdays. With this clustering there is associated an amount of output not necessarily in linear proportion to the available labor; in fact, the availability of too many working groups on a ship has been observed to hinder the smooth flow of the unloading operation and hence raise the total cost. The different jobs involved in unloading have different costs, which are in turn variable because of the expense of keeping the ship in port longer when

[31] Edward H. Bowman, "Production Scheduling by the Transportation Method of Linear Programming," *Operations Research*, **4**, 100–3 (1956).

[32] Thomas L. Saaty, "Coefficient Perturbation of a Constrained Extremum," *Operations Research*, **7**, No. 3 (1959).

labor is rare, because of the losses incurred in the delay of loading materials waiting to be shipped, etc.; hence the costs also vary with time. In practice, it has been observed that the fluctuation of labor occurs in relation to a few given jobs. The remaining jobs are performed regularly and require a fixed amount of labor that is always available. It is desired to develop a schedule of allocating labor to jobs in order to minimize the total cost.

This problem can be cast in linear programming form in which the coefficients are functions of time. In fact, many linear programming problems occurring in applications may be cast in this parametric form. For example, in the petroleum industry it has been found useful to parameterize the outputs as functions of time. In Leontieff models, this dependence of the coefficients on time is an essential part of the problem. Of special interest is the general case where the inputs, the outputs, and the costs all vary with time. When the variation of the coefficients with time is known, it is then desirable to obtain the solution as a function of time, avoiding repetitions for specific values. Here, we give by means of an example, a method of evaluating the extreme value of the parameterized problem based on the simplex process. We show how to set up a correspondence between intervals of parameter values and solutions. In that case the solution, which is a function of time, would apply to the values of the parameter in an interval. For each value in an interval, the solution vector and the extreme value may be evaluated as functions of the parameter.

We shall illustrate the ideas with a simple example and follow the example with a theoretical statement of the generalities involved. For many practical purposes it is sufficient to assume that the coefficients are linear functions of the parameter t, such as we use in our example:

Minimize

$$(30 + 6t)x_1 + (50 + 7t)x_2$$

subject to

$$(14 + 2t)x_1 + (4 + t)x_2 \leq 14 + t$$
$$(150 + 3t)x_1 + (200 + 4t)x_2 \geq 200 + 2t$$

and $x_1 \geq 0, x_2 \geq 0$. The operations used below are those of the simplex process.

We add a non-negative slack variable x_2 to the first of these inequalities and subtract a non-negative slack variable x_4 from the second, thus obtaining equations. We then set up the matrix of coefficients and proceed to solve the problem by the simplex process to show clearly the operations involved. We have:

$$\|\mathbf{P}_1,\mathbf{P}_2,\mathbf{P}_3,\mathbf{P}_4,\mathbf{P}_0\| = \left\| \begin{matrix} 14 + 2t & 4 + t & 1 & 0 & 14 + t \\ 150 + 3t & 200 + 4t & 0 & -1 & 200 + 2t \end{matrix} \right\|$$

$$c_1 = 30 + 6t \quad c_2 = 50 + 7t \quad c_3 = 0 \quad c_4 = 0$$

By putting $t = 0$ one has $(\frac{10}{11}, \frac{7}{22})$ as a solution, as can be easily verified geometrically. Let $\mathbf{P}_1$ and $\mathbf{P}_2$ be chosen as basis vectors. We then express every other vector as a linear combination of these. This yields:

	$\mathbf{P}_1$	$\mathbf{P}_2$
$\mathbf{P}_1$	1	0
$\mathbf{P}_2$	0	1
$\mathbf{P}_3$	$\frac{200 + 4t}{5t^2 + 294t + 2200}$	$-\frac{150 + 3t}{5t^2 + 294t + 2200}$
$\mathbf{P}_4$	$\frac{4 + t}{5t^2 + 294t + 2200}$	$-\frac{14 + 2t}{5t^2 + 294t + 2200}$

For example, the quantities beside $\mathbf{P}_3$ in this array are obtained by equating $\mathbf{P}_3 = a\mathbf{P}_1 + b\mathbf{P}_2$ and thus obtaining two simultaneous equations in a and b and then solving for the latter.

Now $z_j - c_j \leq 0$ must hold for all j in order to have obtained a solution x^{0*} whose components are given by the coefficients expressing $\mathbf{P}_0$ as a linear combination of $\mathbf{P}_1$ and $\mathbf{P}_2$. To impose the condition $z_j - c_j \leq 0$ on the parameter t, is to solve a set of simultaneous—not necessarily linear—inequalities in t. Then $\mathbf{P}_1$ and $\mathbf{P}_2$ would be an optimal basis for this interval of values of t. By fixing a value of t immediately outside the interval and in the neighborhood of a boundary point, the vector to be eliminated and that to be introduced into the basis are produced in the usual manner, and the process is then repeated. If no value of t satisfies the set of inequalities, then by fixing t at a given t_0, the usual procedure is used to eliminate a vector and introduce another into the basis.

For our problem:

$$z_1 = 30 + 6t \qquad \leq c_1 = 30 + 6t$$

$$z_2 = 50 + 7t \qquad \leq c_2 = 50 + 7t$$

$$z_3 = \frac{(200 + 4t)(30 + 6t) - (150 + 3t)(50 + 7t)}{5t^2 + 294t + 2200} \leq c_3 = 0$$

$$z_4 = \frac{(4 + t)(30 + 6t) - (14 + 2t)(50 + 7t)}{5t^2 + 294t + 2200} \leq c_4 = 0$$

Now z_1 and z_2 yield equality and are, therefore, satisfied for all t. To determine the range of values of t for which z_3 and z_4 are satisfied we simplify obtaining respectively

$$\frac{3t^2 + 120t - 1500}{5t^2 + 294t + 2200} \leq 0, \qquad -\frac{8t^2 + 144t + 580}{5t^2 + 294t + 2200} \leq 0$$

When studying these inequalities we use the fact that $a/b \leq 0$ implies that $a \leq 0$ and $b > 0$ or $a \geq 0$ and $b \leq 0$. This is a corollary to $ab \leq 0$ implies that $a \leq 0$ and $b \geq 0$ or $a \geq 0$ and $b \leq 0$. We also use $ab \geq 0$ implies that $a \geq 0$ and $b \geq 0$ or $a \leq 0$ and $b \leq 0$.

To satisfy the condition $z_3 - c_3 \leq 0$ we must have

$$3t^2 + 120t - 1500 \leq 0 \quad \text{and} \quad 5t^2 + 294t + 2200 > 0$$

$$\text{or} \quad 3t^2 + 120t - 1500 \geq 0 \quad \text{and} \quad 5t^2 + 294t + 2200 < 0$$

The first pair gives, on factoring, using approximate root values,

$$(t - 10)(t + 50) \leq 0 \quad \text{and} \quad (t + 8.9)(t + 49.9) > 0$$

$$t \leq 10 \text{ and } t \geq -50 \qquad t < -8.9 \text{ and } t < -49.9$$

$$\text{or } t \geq 10 \text{ and } t \leq -50 \text{ (absurd)} \quad \text{or} \quad t > -8.9 \text{ and } t > -49.9$$

These inequalities yield

$$-50 \leq t \leq 10 \quad \text{and} \quad t < -49.9 \text{ or } t > -8.9$$

Combining them, one has

$$-50 \leq t < -49.9 \quad \text{or} \quad -8.9 < t \leq 10$$

The second pair of inequalities is satisfied simultaneously by no value of t.

As for the condition $z_4 - c_4 \leq 0$, we have

$$8t^2 + 144t + 580 \geq 0 \quad \text{and} \quad 5t^2 + 294t + 2200 > 0$$

$$\text{or} \quad 8t^2 + 144t + 580 \leq 0 \quad \text{and} \quad 5t^2 + 294t + 2200 < 0$$

The first pair gives

$$(t + 11.9)(t + 6.1) \geq 0 \quad \text{and} \quad (t + 8.9)(t + 49.9) > 0$$

which simplify to

$$t \geq -11.9 \text{ and } t \geq -6.1 \qquad t > -8.9 \text{ and } t > -49.9$$

$$\textit{i.e.} \quad t \geq -6.1 \qquad t > -8.9$$

$$\text{or} \quad t \leq -11.9 \text{ and } t \leq -6.1 \qquad t < -8.9 \text{ and } t < -49.9$$

$$\textit{i.e.} \quad t \leq -11.9 \qquad t < -49.9$$

Together they give

$$t \geq -6.1 \quad \text{or} \quad t < -49.9$$

The second pair gives

$$t \geq -11.9 \text{ and } t \leq -6.1 \quad \text{and} \quad t > -8.9 \text{ and } t < -49.9$$

$$\text{or} \quad t \leq -11.9 \text{ and } t \geq -6.1 \text{ (absurd)} \qquad t < -8.9 \text{ and } t > -49.9$$

which together give $-11.9 \leq t < -8.9$

The set of values of t that satisfies all the $z_j - c_j \leq 0$ inequalities is given by:

$$-6.1 \leq t \leq 10, \qquad -50 \leq t < -49.9$$

To decide on a change of basis in this case we put $t = 11$ in order to determine the solution for values of $t \geq 10$. This violates $z_3 - c_3 \leq 0$, as can be seen from the above analysis. Hence $\mathbf{P}_3$ must come into the basis. The vector to be eliminated is obtained as usual by expressing $\mathbf{P}_0$ as a linear combination of $\mathbf{P}_1$ and $\mathbf{P}_2$ at $t = 11$, which gives

$$\mathbf{P}_0 = \frac{2770}{6039}\mathbf{P}_1 + \frac{3417}{6039}\mathbf{P}_2$$

$\mathbf{P}_3$ = a positive quantity times $\mathbf{P}_1$ + a negative quantity times $\mathbf{P}_2$

Multiplying the second expression by θ and subtracting from $\mathbf{P}_0$, then using the usual method of selecting θ, it is clear that $\mathbf{P}_1$ will drop out. Hence in the new basis we use $\mathbf{P}_2$ and $\mathbf{P}_3$:

	$\mathbf{P}_2$	$\mathbf{P}_3$
$\mathbf{P}_1$	$\dfrac{150+3t}{200+4t}$	$\dfrac{5t^2+294t+1200}{200+4t}$
$\mathbf{P}_2$	1	0
$\mathbf{P}_3$	0	1
$\mathbf{P}_4$	$-\dfrac{1}{200+4t}$	$\dfrac{4+t}{200+4t}$

Now
$$\begin{aligned} z_1 &= (150+3t)(50+7t)/(200+4t) && \le c_1 = 30+6t \\ z_2 &= 50+7t && \le c_2 = 50+7t \\ z_3 &= 0 && \le c_3 = 0 \\ z_4 &= -(50+7t)/(200+4t) && \le c_4 = 0 \end{aligned}$$

We must deal only with the first and last of these inequalities. The last one gives

$$50+7t \ge 0,\quad t \ge -\tfrac{50}{7} \qquad \text{and} \qquad 200+4t > 0,\quad t > -50$$
or
$$50+7t \le 0,\quad t \le -\tfrac{50}{7} \qquad\qquad 200+4t < 0,\quad t < -50$$

When combined these give

$$t \ge -\tfrac{50}{7} \qquad \text{or} \qquad t < -50$$

The first inequality simplifies to:

$$3t^2+120t+1500 \ge 0, \qquad (t+50)(t-10) \ge 0$$

Hence

$$t \ge -50 \quad \text{and} \quad t \ge 10 \quad \text{or} \quad t \le -50 \quad \text{and} \quad t \le 10$$

From the last inequalities, one has $t \ge 10$ and $t < -50$ as the range of values of t to which $\mathbf{P}_2$ and $\mathbf{P}_3$ correspond. There remain the solutions corresponding to the interval $-49.9 \le t \le -6.1$, which will obviously correspond to $\mathbf{P}_2$ and $\mathbf{P}_4$ since by putting $t = -10$ it is clear that $z_4 - c_4 \le 0$ is violated. Here $\mathbf{P}_4$ enters the basis obviously replacing $\mathbf{P}_3$ since it would be meaningless to have $\mathbf{P}_3$ and $\mathbf{P}_4$ as a basis.

Now $x^0(t)$ as given by the simplex process is extended to include the slack variables. These are of course ignored in the final answer. The correspondence for our example is as follows with x^0 given in the extended form.

The solution vector $x^0(t) = \|x_1^0(t),\cdots,x_4^0(t)\|$	The corresponding interval of values of t
$\left\|0, \dfrac{2t+200}{4t+200}, \dfrac{2t^2+48t+2000}{4t+200}, 0\right\|$	$t < -50$ and $t \ge 10$
$\left\|\dfrac{2t^2+54t+2000}{5t^2+294t+2200}, \dfrac{t^2+236t+700}{5t^2+294t+2200}, 0, 0\right\|$	$-50 \le t < -49.9$ and $-6.1 \le t \le 10$
$\left\|0, \dfrac{t+14}{t+4}, 0, \dfrac{2t^2+48t+2000}{t+4}\right\|$	$-49.9 \le t \le -6.1$

Note the slight errors in the end points of the intervals caused by decimal approximation. Delete the last two components of the solution vector.

To generalize the foregoing ideas, let $\mathbf{P}_{i_1}, \mathbf{P}_{i_2}, \cdots \mathbf{P}_{i_m}$ be the basis vectors of the ith iteration and let every vector $\mathbf{P}_j$ $(j = 1, \cdots, n + m)$ be expressed as a linear combination of these as follows:

$$\mathbf{P}_j = y_{i_1 j}(t)\mathbf{P}_{i_1} + y_{i_2 j}(t)\mathbf{P}_{i_2} + \cdots + y_{i_m j}(t)\mathbf{P}_{i_m}$$

Then let

$$z_j = y_{i_1 j}(t)c_{i_1}(t) + y_{i_2 j}(t)c_{i_2}(t) + \cdots + y_{i_m j}(t)c_{i_m}$$

where $c_{i_1}(t)$ is the cost coefficient corresponding to $\mathbf{P}_{i_1}(t)$, etc. Then for this basis to yield a minimum solution to the problem one must have $z_j(t) - c_j(t) \leq 0$ $(j = 1, \cdots, n + m)$.

If there is an interval of values of t common to these inequalities, one fixes a value of t at $t_0 + \varepsilon$ where $\varepsilon > 0$ is arbitrarily small and t_0 is a value on the boundary of the interval, and proceeds in the usual way to obtain a change of basis and then determine a neighboring interval of values of t. The solution vector in each case is given by the weights obtained in expressing $\mathbf{P}_0$—the column vector whose coefficients are the $b_i(t)$—as a linear combination of the basis. The process terminates in a finite number of steps since the number of vectors in the problem is finite.

If the inequalities are satisfied simultaneously by no value of t then the given basis is not optimal for any t and a change of basis would be required. This may be done by fixing a value of t and introducing a new vector into the basis in the usual way. Obviously t should not belong to one of the intervals to which a solution has already been determined.

How feasible is the method? It is clear that the main difficulty arising here is the solution of a set of simultaneous general inequalities $z_j - c_j \leq 0$. In its generality the method appears cumbersome. However, one is usually interested in parameterizing the coefficients of a few of the basis vectors. If linear parameterization is used throughout, the parameterizing of four basis vectors leads to the analysis of quartics that can be treated in general form by means of the theory of equations. There will be no theoretical difficulty in the analysis if specific numbers are used and more than four vectors are parameterized. It is to be noted that if homogeneous parameterization, *i.e.*, parameterization of the same degree, is used, the degree of the inequalities to be analyzed is unaffected by the number of rows present.

5.15. Further Comments on General Programming.—This section will utilize ideas developed in linear programming. The use of Lagrange multipliers provides one method for solving constrained optimization problems in which the constraints are given as equalities.

To solve an inequality-constrained optimization problem, such as the general programming problem, one frequently applies necessary conditions on the gradient of the function in terms of the gradients of the constraints on the boundary. Note that if the optimum is in the region, the method for obtaining the optimum is straightforward. One equates to zero the partial derivatives of the function to be optimized and obtains the solution, which is tested to see if it satisfies the constraints.

The gradient[33] of a function $f(x_1,\cdots,x_n)$ is the vector of partial derivatives:

$$\nabla f \equiv \left(\frac{\partial f}{\partial x_1}, \ldots, \frac{\partial f}{\partial x_n}\right)$$

It is well known from the calculus that the gradient vector points in the direction of maximum increase of the function f.[34]

There are several interesting theorems characterizing a maximum of a function on the boundary of a set defined by inequalities, as in the general programming problem. We give the classical theorem that states:

Theorem: A necessary condition that $f(x_1,\cdots,x_n)$ attains its maximum at a boundary point $x^0 = (x_1^0,\cdots,x_n^0)$ of $g_i(x_1,\cdots,x_n) \leq 0$ $(i = 1,\cdots,m)$, is that there exists $y_i \geq 0$ $(i = 1,\cdots,m)$, and $\beta_j \geq 0$ such that at the maximum we have:

$$\nabla f(x_1^0,\cdots,x_n^0) = \sum_{i=1}^{m} y_i \nabla g_i(x_1^0,\cdots,x_n^0) - \beta$$

where $\beta = (\beta_1,\cdots,\beta_n)$ and where if $x_j^0 > 0$ then $\beta_j = 0$ and if $g_i(x^0) < 0$ the $y_i = 0$.

Proof: We use the duality theorem of linear programming to prove the theorem. Let S be the set of subscripts such that $g_i(x^0) = 0$ for i in S. If $(x - x^0)$ is a vector directed from x^0 to $x \equiv (x_1,\cdots,x_n)$ in the feasible region with $x_i \geq 0$, then

$$\nabla f(x^0)\cdot(x - x^0) \leq 0$$

and for all i in S

$$\nabla g_i(x^0)\cdot(x - x^0) \leq 0$$

since $g_i(x)$ decrease away from the boundary and into the region. The problem is then to find $x^0 \geq 0$, which maximizes $\nabla f(x^0)\cdot x$ and satisfies

[33] Margenau and Murphy, *op. cit.*, p. 150.

[34] Thomas L. Saaty, *Mathematical Methods of Operations Research*, McGraw-Hill Book Co., New York, 1959.

$\nabla g_i(x^0) \cdot x \leq \nabla g_i(x^0) \cdot x^0$ for all x. This linear programming problem has the dual problem of finding $y_i \geq 0$ which minimize

$$\sum_{i \in S} y_i[\nabla g_i(x^0) \cdot x^0]$$

subject to the vector inequality:

$$\sum_{i \in S} y_i[\nabla g_i(x^0)] \geq \nabla f(x^0)$$

We also have $y_i = 0$ (for i not in S) correspond to $g_i(x^0) < 0$. The last set of inequalities may be reduced to equalities using the non-negative slack variable β and we have:

$$\nabla f(x^0) = \sum_{i=1}^{m} y_i \nabla g_i(x^0) - \beta$$

On taking the scalar product with x^0 and recalling that for a linear programming problem the values of the objective function of the original problem and of the dual coincide at the solution points, we conclude that whenever $x_j^0 > 0$ we must have $\beta_j = 0$.

The foregoing theorem applies to a local maximum or minimum. If the region of constraints is convex and the function f is concave, *i.e.*, $f(\alpha x_1) + (1 - \alpha)x_2 \geq \alpha f(x_1) + (1 - \alpha)f(x_2)$ for any two points x_1 and x_2 and for $0 \leq \alpha \leq 1$, then we have a global maximum.

Exercise: Maximize $f(x,y) = \int_0^x e^{-t^2/2}dt + \int_0^y e^{-t^2/2}dt$ subject to $x \geq 0$, $y \geq 0$, $x + y \leq c \equiv g(x,y)$, $c > 0$.

If we assume that the general programming problem is a maximization problem, and if we write

$$F(x,\lambda) = f(x) + \lambda g(x)$$

where

$$x \equiv (x_1,\cdots,x_n), \quad \lambda \equiv (\lambda_1,\cdots,\lambda_m), \quad g(x) \equiv (g_1(x),\cdots,g_m(x))$$

then Kuhn and Tucker have proved the following theorem:[35]

Theorem: In order that x^0 be a solution of the maximum problem, it is necessary that there exist some λ^0 such that x^0 and λ^0 satisfy

$$(1) \quad \left.\frac{\partial F}{\partial x_i}\right|_{x^0} \leq 0 \quad (i = 1,\cdots,n), \qquad \sum_{i=1}^{n} \left.\frac{\partial F}{\partial x_i}\right|_{x^0} x_i^0 = 0, \quad x^0 \geq 0$$

$$(2) \quad \left.\frac{\partial F}{\partial \lambda_j}\right|_{\lambda^0} \geq 0 \quad (j = 1,\cdots,m), \qquad \sum_{j=1}^{m} \left.\frac{\partial F}{\partial \lambda_j}\right|_{\lambda^0} \lambda_j^0 = 0, \quad \lambda^0 \geq 0$$

[35] H. W. Kuhn and A. W. Tucker, "Non-linear Programming," in J. Neyman, ed., *Second Berkeley Symposium on Mathematical Statistics and Probability,* University of California Press, Berkeley, 1951.

and sufficient that the following be satisfied:

$$F(x,\lambda^0) \le F(x^0,\lambda^0) + \sum_{i=1}^{n} \frac{\partial F}{\partial x_i}\bigg|_{x^0} (x - x^0) \tag{3a}$$

$$F(x^0,\lambda) \ge F(x^0,\lambda^0) + \sum_{j=1}^{m} \frac{\partial F}{\partial \lambda_j}\bigg|_{\lambda^0} (\lambda - \lambda^0) \tag{3b}$$

If $f(x)$ and $g(x)$ are concave functions, then a solution to the above maximum problem is equivalent to the solution of the saddle value problem that requires finding x^0 and λ^0, which satisfy

$$F(x,\lambda^0) \le F(x^0,\lambda^0) \le F(x^0,\lambda) \quad \text{for all } x \ge 0,\ \lambda \ge 0$$

Exercise: Prove that if $f(x_1,x_2)$ is differentiable in x_1 and x_2, and has a saddle point[36] at (x_1^0,x_2^0), *i.e.*, satisfies a condition similar to the saddle value problem, then

$$\frac{\partial F}{\partial x_1}\bigg|_{(x_1^0,x_2^0)} = 0, \qquad \frac{\partial F}{\partial x_2}\bigg|_{(x_1^0,x_2^0)} = 0$$

Another active branch of optimization in operations research is dynamic programming, which provides a variety of interesting ideas for formulating problems. Because we cannot discuss it in this chapter, the reader is referred, for an understanding of the subject, to the work of R. Bellman.[37]

5.16. Isoperimetric Problems: The Optimization of Functionals.[38]—Isoperimetric problems are treated in the calculus of variations.[39] They are constrained optimization problems that require finding a function that minimizes or maximizes an integral subject to (generally) integral constraints. The origin of this type problem goes back to the search for a curve with a given length C that encloses the largest area, *e.g.*, passes through (0,0) and (1,0), and for which the area between the curve and the x-axis is maximum. The problem then is to maximize

$$\int_0^1 y\,dx \quad \text{subject to} \quad \int_0^1 \sqrt{1 + \left(\frac{dy}{dx}\right)^2}\, dx = C$$

[36] Cf. Margenau and Murphy, *op. cit.*, p. 460.
[37] Richard Bellman, *Dynamic Programming*, Princeton University Press, 1957.
[38] F. B. Hillderbrand, *Methods of Applied Mathematics*, Prentice-Hall, Inc., Englewood Cliffs, N.J., 1961.
[39] Margenau and Murphy, *op. cit.*, Chapter 6.

A well-known form of isoperimetric problems is to find f, which minimizes

$$\int_a^b f(x,y,y')dx$$

where $y' = dy/dx$ subject to the constraints

$$\int_a^b g_i(x,y,y')dx = C_i, \quad i = 1,\cdots,m$$

where m can assume any value.

The theory for this problem is well known. The following necessary condition, which must be satisfied, is Euler's equation for isoperimetric problems (usually used to construct the solution):

$$\left[\frac{d}{dx}\frac{\partial f}{\partial y'} - \frac{\partial f}{\partial y}\right] + \sum_{i=1}^{m} \lambda_i \left[\frac{d}{dx}\frac{\partial g_i}{\partial y'} - \frac{\partial g_i}{\partial y}\right] = 0$$

where λ_i are similar to the Lagrange multipliers and are determined from the m constraints.

Note that one may consider a similar problem that requires finding a function of several independent variables and several dependent variables with derivatives of order higher than the first. In that case, one obtains a more complicated form of Euler's equation.

Exercise: Solve the problem stated at the beginning of this section to obtain the equation of a circle. Note that $f = y$ and $g = \sqrt{1 + y'^2}$.

Exercise: In information theory, entropy is defined by

$$-\int_{-\infty}^{\infty} y \log y dx$$

Find the y that minimizes this integral, subject to the constraints that y is a density function with given mean and variance, *i.e.*,

$$\int_{-\infty}^{\infty} y dx = 1, \qquad \int_{-\infty}^{\infty} xy dx = \mu$$

$$\int_{-\infty}^{\infty} (x - \mu)^2 y dx = \sigma^2$$

Thus obtain the gaussian distribution and evaluate the entropy.

The Neyman-Pearson lemma is a very useful result in optimization theory. Here we give without proof a statement of this lemma.

Let $f(t)$ and $g(t)$ be nonnegative bounded and continuous functions on $0 \leq t \leq t_1$. Let $m(t)$ be an increasing function with

$$\int_0^{t_1} g(t)\, dm(t) = 1$$

(where this can be taken as the Stieltjes integral). We consider the problem of finding a function of $x(t)$, $0 \leq x(t) \leq C$ (where C is a constant) which maximizes

$$\int_0^{t_1} x(t)\, f(t)\, dm(t)$$

subject to

$$\int_0^{t_1} x(t)\, g(t)\, dm(t) \leq \alpha$$

with $0 < \alpha < C$. If $x_0(t)$ yields the maximum, then the Neyman-Pearson lemma asserts that a necessary condition for

$$\int_0^{t_1} x_0(t)\, f(t)\, dm(t) = \max_x \int_0^{t_1} x(t)\, f(t)\, dm(t)$$

is that there exists a constant λ such that

$$f(t)/g(t) = \begin{cases} \geq \lambda \text{ for } x_0(t) = C \\ = \lambda \text{ for } 0 < x_0(t) < C \\ \leq \lambda \text{ for } x_0(t) = 0 \end{cases}$$

If $f(t) = \lambda\, g(t)$, then the constraint is

$$\int_0^{t_1} x_0(t)\, g(t)\, dm(t) = \alpha \text{ for } 0 \leq x_0(t) \leq C$$

The hypotheses on f and g can be relaxed through the use of measure theory.

5.17. A Search Problem.—An example of an operations research problem that gives rise to an isoperimetric model is a search problem, first given by B. Koopman,[40] that we only formulate here. Suppose that an object is distributed in a region of space with:

$$g(x)dx = \text{Prob}\,(x \leq X \leq x + dx)$$

The object need not be in the given space.

Because of this, and the fact that $g(x)$ is a probability density, we have

$$g(x)dx = \alpha \leq 1$$

[40] B. O. Koopman, "The Theory of Search," Parts I, II, and III, *Operations Research*, **4**, 324–46 and 503–31 (1956); **5**, 613–26 (1957).

Suppose a search effort $f(x)dx$ is devoted to locate the object between x and $x + dx$, and suppose that the total available effort is limited, *i.e.*,

$$\int_{-\infty}^{\infty} f(x)dx = C$$

Suppose that $P[f(x)]$ is the probability of detecting the object when it is in fact at x.

The probability of detecting an object between x and $x + dx$ is

$$g(x)\,p[f(x)]dx$$

Thus the overall probability of success of the search is

$$\int_{-\infty}^{\infty} g(x)\,p[f(x)]dx = P(f)$$

Find $f(x)$ which maximizes $P(f)$ subject to $f(x) > 0$, and to

$$\int_{-\infty}^{\infty} f(x)dx = C$$

An important special case of this problem is that in which

$$p[f(x)] = 1 - e^{-f(x)}$$

We refer the reader to the work of Guenin[41] for the general case, the solution of which is derived from:

Theorem: A necessary condition for $f(x)$ to be optimum is that at any point x such that $f(x) > 0$

$$\frac{g(x)}{df/dp} = \text{constant}$$

5.18. The Theory of Games: Minmax.[42]—The theory of games provides formal mathematical models for analyzing conflicts. Among the simplest types of known conflicts studied by game theory are parlor games, *e.g.*, chess, checkers, poker, bridge, and so forth.

In the development of game theory one considers the number of players involved, a listing of all possible and permissible (according to a set of rules) ways (called strategies) of playing the game from start to finish. If a player follows a given strategy then there is a payoff (either gain or loss) of some utility as this strategy is used against the

[41] Jacques de Guenin, "Optimum Distribution of Effort: An Extension of the Koopman Basic Theory," *Operations Research*, **9**, No. 1, 1–144 (1961).

[42] J. C. C. McKinsey, *Introduction to the Theory of Games*, McGraw-Hill Book Co., New York, 1952.

oppositions' (of which there may be several with different interests) strategies. A mathematical analysis of a game seeks to determine for each player (who wishes to play rationally) a set of strategies that, if followed accordingly, will leave him at least as well off as he can be in playing the game, and better if his opposition behaves irrationally in its choice of strategies. Among the simplest models used in game theory are those applied to two-person games. In a zero-sum game the winnings of one player are the losses of the other player and hence no payoff enters or leaves the system of two players. In the space we have to devote to this topic, we shall discuss ideas pertaining to zero-sum two-person games. It can be shown that, in finite form, such a game can be reduced to a linear programming problem and vice versa. Hence, finite, two-person zero-sum games are mathematically equivalent to linear programs. To formulate a two-person zero-sum game abstractly is to account for each player's strategies (*i.e.*, record them) in a matrix whose elements give numerical values of the payoff to be made for each strategy of one player when used against every strategy of his opponent. When each player has a finite number of strategies, the entire theory is developed on the basis of the foregoing "payoff matrix" and the game is called a rectangular game. If the number of strategies is uncountably infinite, then instead of a payoff matrix, a function is used to describe the payoff. The amount of information available to each player is an interesting aspect of game theory, which we will discuss later, in connection with decision theory.

We give the payoff matrix of a game whose two players are X and Y with respective strategies X_i $(i = 1,\cdots,m)$ and Y_j $(j = 1,\cdots,n)$. Here a_{ij} is the payoff that Y, using strategy Y_j, makes to X for using strategy X_i. Obviously the payoff from X to Y is $-a_{ij}$.

		Player Y			
		Y_1	Y_2	$\cdots$	Y_n
	X_1	a_{11}	a_{12}	$\cdots$	a_{1n}
Player	X_2	a_{21}	a_{22}	$\cdots$	a_{2n}
X	$\vdots$	$\vdots$	$\vdots$	$\cdots$	$\vdots$
	X_m	a_{m1}	a_{m2}	$\cdots$	a_{mn}

It is clear that whatever strategy X_i chooses, he is sure to obtain the minimum value of a_{ij} for that row for any choice of Y_j, *i.e.*, he is certain to get $\min_j a_{ij}$. He chooses his strategy X_i such that he obtains $\max_i \min_j a_{ij}$, *i.e.*, he chooses the row with the largest minimum. Since the payoff to Y is $-a_{ij}$, he in turn is assured $\max_j \min_i -a_{ij}$, which by the algebra of maxima and minima is equal to $-\min_j \min_i a_{ij}$. In terms of payoff from Y to X one omits the negative sign. If the two payoffs coincide, the game is said to have a "saddle point." If i_0 and j_0 are the row and column corresponding to such a saddle point then $a_{ij_0} \leq a_{i_0 j_0} \leq a_{i_0 j}$ $(i = 1,\cdots,m)$, $(j = 1,\cdots,m)$ is the definition of a saddle point.

Thus, a saddle point of the matrix is the largest element in its column and the smallest in its row. In this case X should settle for $a_{i_0 j_0}$ (called the value of the game) by playing X_{i_0}, and Y should resign himself to this payoff to X by playing Y_{j_0}. In this case each player has a single "pure" strategy to play over and over again in repetitions of the game. If the game has no saddle point then each player uses a mixed strategy (by playing in each total play of the game from start to finish one of the strategies, but the game is considered repeated a large number of times, and, hence, each strategy is played with a given frequency, *i.e.*, probability). A payoff function for this indefinite number of plays must be defined. The optimum mixed strategy is obtained on the basis of this expected payoff function, which is based on the coefficients of the matrix and the probabilities of playing the strategies. If p_i $(i = 1,\cdots,m)$ is the probability with which X plays his strategy X_i $(i = 1,\cdots,m)$ and q_j $(j = 1,\cdots,n)$ is the corresponding probability for Y_j $(j = 1,\cdots,n)$, we have

$$\sum_{j=1}^{n} q_j = 1 = \sum_{i=1}^{m} p_i, \quad 0 \leq p_i, q_j \leq 1$$

Then the expected payoff is

$$E(P,Q) = \sum_{i=1}^{m} \sum_{j=1}^{n} a_{ij} p_i q_j$$

where $P \equiv (p_1,\cdots,p_m)$, and $Q \equiv (q_1,\cdots,q_n)$. In this function each a_{ij} is multiplied by the frequency with which it occurs as a payoff, *i.e.*, by $p_i q_j$ and the sum is taken over all such products. The well known minmax theorem asserts that for every rectangular game

$$\max_P \min_Q E(P,Q) = \min_Q \max_P E(P,Q)$$

Two mixed strategies, P^*, which is a choice of $(x_1,\cdots,x_m)$, and Q^*, which is a choice of $(y_1,\cdots,y_n)$, are optimal for X and Y respectively if one has the saddle value property:

$$E(P,Q^*) \leq E(P^*,Q^*) \leq E(P^*,Q)$$

and (P^*,Q^*) is called a "strategic saddle" point.

In a continuous game both the choice of strategy and the payoff as a function of that choice are continuous. The latter is particularly important because a discontinuous payoff function may not yield a solution. Thus, instead of a matrix $[a_{ij}]$, a function $M(x,y)$ gives the payoff each time a strategy is chosen (*i.e.*, the value of x and y are fixed). The strategy of each player in this case is defined as a member of the class D of probability distribution functions that are defined as continuous, real-valued, monotonic functions such that

$$D(0) = 0, \qquad D(1) = 1$$

We define the strategy for X as $F(x)$ (compare it with p_i) and that for Y as $G(y)$ (compare it with q_j) where $0 \leq x \leq 1$ and $0 \leq y \leq 1$. It can be shown that no loss of generality results from restricting x and y to the unit square.

The minmax theorem asserts for this case that if M is a continuous function in x and y where $0 \leq x \leq 1$, $0 \leq y \leq 1$ then[43]

$$\max_{F \in D} \min_{G \in D} E(F,G)$$

and

$$\min_{G \in D} \max_{F \in D} E(F,G)$$

where

$$E(F,G) = \int_0^I \int_0^I M(x,y)dF(x)dG(y)$$

exist and are equal.

Special cases of continuous games have received considerable treatment. These are games whose payoff function is convex (which we have already defined) or separable, *i.e.*, can be written in the form

$$M(x,y) = \sum_{j=1}^{n} \sum_{i=1}^{m} a_{ij}\alpha_i(x)\beta_j(y)$$

Methods for solving games will not be given here.

Example 1.—Two persons X and Y jointly own an object worth \$3. Because joint ownership invites trouble, they decided to make sealed bids (each person's bid is not known to the other) for its possession. The one who bids higher gets the object, but he has to pay a compensation to the other person, equal to the latter's bid. They decide that each can bid, 0, 1, 2, 3, or 4 dollars, and if both bids are the same they will sell the object for \$3 and share the money equally. Neither knows what the other one will bid, and they both resort to game theory for advice on how much to bid.

[43] See J. C. C. McKinsey, *op. cit.*

The payoff matrix is given by

		Y: 0	1	2	3	4	row min
	0	0	−1.5	−1.5	−1.5	−1.5	−1.5
	1	1.5	0	−.5	−.5	−.5	−.5
X	2	1.5	.5	0*	.5	.5	0*
	3	1.5	.5	−.5	0	1.5	−.5
	4	1.5	.5	−.5	−1.5	0	−1.5
Column max		1.5	.5	0*	.5	1.5	

Note that essentially each person has an investment of \$1.5 when he starts. Thus the reader may forget the object and play the money game according to the rules given. For example, the element in the first row and second column shows that X who bid zero loses the object and therefore Y gets the object which is worth \$3, thereby making a profit of \$1.5. Since the matrix represents the payoff from Y to X we use -1.5 indicating that thereby X pays Y, *i.e.*, he loses his investment.

Since the zero with an asterisk is a saddle point, the decision is that they cannot decide by bidding and must sell the object to someone else and share the money equally.

Example 2.—We now consider the game of matching pennies, which is discrete and without a saddle point. It is a game between two players who show one side of a penny every time the game is played. Player X gets a penny from player Y if the faces match, otherwise player Y gets a penny from player X. The following payoff matrix describes the game:

		Player Y: heads	tails
Player X	heads	1	−1
	tails	−1	1

Unlike the other payoff matrix, this game does not have a saddle point, *i.e.*, there is no unique optimum pure strategy for each player. It is easily noticed that if any player knows what the other is going to do, he is certain to win a penny from his opponent. Hence, maintaining secrecy about one's acts is essential. This is achieved by actually randomizing the heads and tails and only a probability distribution of $\frac{1}{2}$ and $\frac{1}{2}$ for heads and tails respectively can keep down the payment to zero for either player. Since this is true for each player, zero is the appropriate value for the game. This game can be solved by formal methods developed by game theory.

Example 3.—Colonel Blotto is faced with the problem that he has one regiment under him and there are two battles to be fought simultaneously in two different battlefields.[44] General Beetle, his opponent, has the same problem, but unfortunately he has only a fraction α of a regiment under him where $0 < \alpha \leq 1$. Both of them have to deploy their regiments to battlefield 1 and battlefield 2 in such a way as to gain maximum results. The battles are fought to death. Each battle has the value of one regiment to both of them. The payoff is determined by the proportion of a regiment surviving the battle in each battlefield. The problem is how best should the opposing commanders divide their regiment.

We have three cases to consider:

Case I: $0 < \alpha \leq \frac{1}{2}$.
Case II: $\frac{1}{2} \leq \alpha < 1$.
Case III: $\alpha = 1$.

The payoff function has the following form:

$$M(x,y) = \operatorname{Sgnm}[x - \alpha y] + x - \alpha y + \operatorname{Sgnm}[1 - x - \alpha(1 - y)] + 1 - x - \alpha(1 - y)$$

where Sgnm stands for the signum function of analysis, *i.e.*,

$$\operatorname{Sgnm}(x) = \begin{cases} -1 & \text{if } x < 0 \\ 0 & \text{if } x = 0 \\ 1 & \text{if } x > 0 \end{cases}$$

Exercise.—Show that if $0 < \alpha < \frac{1}{2}$, or $\alpha = 1$, then the game has a saddle point, while if $\frac{1}{2} \leq \alpha < 1$, the game has a mixed strategy.

Example 4.—The following fighter-bomber dual illustrates a continuous game.[45] The payoff (given by the probability of hitting) when

[44] D. W. Blackett, "Some Blotto Games," *Naval Research Logistics Quarterly*, **1**, No. 1 (1954).

[45] T. E. Caywood and C. J. Thomas, "Applications of Game Theory in Fighter versus Bomber Combat," *Operations Research*, **3**, No. 4, 402 (1958).

the fighter fires at position x when the bomber is at position y is given by

$$M(x,y) = \begin{cases} x & \text{for } 0 \leq x \leq y \leq 1 \\ x(1-y) & \text{for } 0 \leq y \leq x \leq 1 \end{cases}$$

For this model the frequency function of the bomber's optimal strategy, as obtained through game theoretic analysis, is

$$\frac{1/(1+\sqrt{2})}{y^3} \quad \text{for } y \geq \frac{1}{1+\sqrt{2}} \quad \text{and} \quad 0 \quad \text{for } y < \frac{1}{1+\sqrt{2}}$$

The frequency function of the fighter's optimal strategy is

$$\frac{1/[\sqrt{2}(1+\sqrt{2})]}{x^3} \quad \text{when } x \geq \frac{1}{1+\sqrt{2}}$$

and 0 when $x \leq 1/(1+\sqrt{2})$, plus a probability of $1/[\sqrt{2}(1+\sqrt{2})]$ of firing at the point 1, which is the end of the battle. The value of the game is $1/(1+\sqrt{2})$.

It is assumed that the probability that the fighter hits the bomber is the same as that of the bomber hitting the fighter.

Exercise: Verify the optimability of these strategies.

5.19. Decision Theory: Formalism in the Behavioral Sciences.[46]—A formal method for examining decisions is developed through the use of a utility matrix $[u_{ij}]$ similar to the payoff matrix of game theory. In this matrix the rows correspond to the various possible acts of a decision-maker (*e.g.*, to invest money in enterprises $A_1, A_2, \cdots, A_m$) and the columns to various states, *i.e.*, circumstances (*e.g.*, possible levels of development of each enterprise) under which the acts are performed. The element u_{ij} gives the utility (return or value) for using act A_i when state s_j prevails.

States

		s_1	$\cdots$	s_n
	A_1	u_{11}	$\cdots$	u_{1n}
Acts	$\vdots$	$\vdots$		$\vdots$
	A_m	u_{m1}	$\cdots$	u_{mn}

If a single individual is involved in decision-making, then the states may be presented to him by Nature and the problem may be regarded

[46] R. Duncan Luce and Howard Raiffa, *Games and Decisions: Introduction and Critical Survey*, John Wiley and Sons, Inc., New York, 1957.

as a game against Nature. The main problem here is to decide what act or acts to choose. But this depends on what the probability is that a certain state of Nature should prevail. The story for individual decision-making is interesting and elaborate. Group decision-making is more difficult. The reader is referred to the book by Luce and Raiffa for a thorough treatment of the general subject of decision-making.

Decision-making may be undertaken by an individual under assumptions of certainty, risk, or uncertainty (partial or complete ignorance) on the states of Nature.

When it is certain what state is to be in effect one chooses that act that has the greatest utility under this state.

Decision under risk assumes that an *a priori* probability distribution $0 \leq p_i \leq 1, \sum_{i=1}^{n} p_i = 1$ is known on the states. One then chooses the act for which $\max_j \sum_{i=1}^{n} u_{ij} \cdot p_i$ is obtained.

When neither certainty nor risk applies to the states, then either partial ignorance or complete ignorance is assumed. (In either case we have no logically uncriticizable criteria of choice. However, we shall give the best known methods interesting for study.) When assuming partial ignorance, it is sometimes possible on the basis of personal experience to develop a subjective probability distribution, thus, reducing the problem to a risk problem with the important exception that each time such a distribution is selected it must be modified after discovering how it influences the choice of acts. This process is continued until one is satisfied that no further alteration would influence his choice, in which case he can proceed to the risk decision procedure. Games may be regarded as decision problems in which *a priori* probabilities are assigned to the opponent's pure strategies, which are, in this case, states of Nature. Advantage in the assignment process may be taken of prior experience with the opponent's behavior.

In the case of complete ignorance, several criteria for deciding on what act to choose have been proposed. We mention some well-known ones among them. Because of lack of space it is left to the reader to interpret and criticize each criterion as it may be in harmony or discord with his own thinking on the subject.

The Maxmin Rule.—For each state, this rule selects the minimum utility and that act with the maximum value among this collection of minima is chosen, *i.e.*, choose the act that gives $\max_i \min_j u_{ij}$.

Minmax Regret or Risk Rule.—In this case one forms a new matrix called the risk matrix in which the elements of each column k are defined by $r_{ik} = \max_i u_{ik} - u_{ik}$ $(k = 1, \cdots, n)$, (*i.e.*, for each column select the largest element and form the corresponding column of the risk matrix by taking the respective differences with every other element in that column). This rule gives a choice according to $\min_i \max_j r_{ij}$.

The Pessimism-Optimism Rule of Hurwicz.—Let $0 \leq \alpha \leq 1$; this rule suggests the choice of that act that yields

$$\max_i \left[\alpha \min_j u_{ij} + (1 - \alpha) \max_j u_{ij}\right]$$

Thus one selects the minimum and maximum value of each row and forms the quantity in brackets, which is a mixture of the least and most that is obtainable for the act. Then one maximizes this quantity over the acts. As for the constant α, it is suggested that it be determined from a number of simple related choice situations.

Exercise: Let $\alpha = 0,1$ and interpret the resulting rules.

Insufficient Reason.—When no preference can be assigned to the states, assume that they are equally likely, *i.e.*, each occurs with probability $1/n$ and proceed as in the risk method, choosing that act that gives

$$\max_i \frac{1}{n} \sum_{j=1}^{n} u_{ij}$$

Exercise: Criticize each of the foregoing rules. Suggest a rule you think is more reasonable to follow in the case of complete ignorance.

It has been possible to develop axiomatic theories for complete and partial ignorance that, by studying the sets of acts and states, yield a better understanding of the choice of criteria, and are in harmony with logical formalization of intuitively acceptable notions. We have treated in a rudimentary fashion a subject that is deep, novel, and promising.

In passing we remark that there are well-known statistical methods of hypothesis testing and parameter estimation used in decision-making. Sequential analysis is a method of sampling used to decide whether to accept or reject a lot with defective items, or whether to continue sampling. Also, there are various statistical methods used in quality control of a manufacturing process, to decide on how much the quality should be improved to be acceptable.

The following illustration of a decision process recently given by Gale and Shapley does not utilize the foregoing ideas on decision theory, but is both amusing and interesting in itself.[47]

A set of marriages is unstable if under it there are a man and a

[47] D. Gale and L. S. Shapley, "College Admissions and the Stability of Marriage," *American Mathematical Monthly*, **69**, 9–15 (1962).

woman who are not married to each other but who prefer each other to their actual mates. To prove that there is always a stable set of marriages requires that all men (of n men) and all women (of n women) rank their opposites according to preference, and each man proposes to his favorite woman. She keeps on a string, not yet accepting, the man she most prefers. The rejected men choose again according to their second preferences and so on. Each time the woman keeps on a string the most preferred man. There are at most $n^2 - 2n + 2$ iterations of choice.

The process terminates when every woman has been chosen (which must obviously be the case). Then the women accept the men for marriage. Thus, if a woman prefers another man, then obviously he does not prefer her, and, hence, there is no instability in the marriage.

A stable solution is optimal if every man is at least as well off under it as under any other stable assignment. It can be shown by induction that the above procedure is optimal.

The ideas are extended in the paper to college admissions; students often apply to several colleges, and, hence, a college may not get its quota of most preferred students as some of them are accepted by another college that they prefer.

5.20. Simulation, Monte Carlo, and Operational Gaming.—Thomas and Deemer, in a well-known paper,[48] have set down useful definitions and thoughts on simulation, Monte Carlo, and operational gaming methods.

They point out that at the heart of technical simulation there must be unreality; otherwise, there would not be need for simulation. The essence of the subject under study may be represented by a model of it that serves a certain purpose, *e.g.*, the use of a wind tunnel to simulate conditions to which an aircraft may be subjected. One uses the Monte Carlo method to study an artificial stochastic model of a physical or mathematical process, *e.g.*, evaluating a definite integral by probability methods (using random numbers) using the graph of the function as an aid.

The essence of operational gaming (*e.g.*, simulating a battle with appropriate choice of miniature equipment, personnel, and strategies) lies in the emphasis on the playing of a game. In the paper referred to above, the authors point out that there is playing to formulate a game, playing to solve a game, and playing to impart present knowledge of a game. Hence, they define operational gaming as the serious use of playing as a primary device to formulate a game, to solve a game, or to

[48] C. J. Thomas and W. L. Deemer, Jr., "The Role of Operational Gaming in Operations Research," *Operations Research*, **5**, 1–27 (1951).

impart something of the solution of a game. Game theory provides an excellent background for operational gaming.

Note that in a broad sense simulation includes gaming. However, even though not essential to it, both physical simulation and Monte Carlo methods are used in gaming.

Studying a problem through operational gaming provides education and a sense of realism, but excessive complication and elaboration diminish its effectiveness. Among the claims (which can be reasonably criticized) for operational gaming have been that it enables selling and teaching the solution of games, stimulating the imagination, incorporating intelligent interplay, pooling knowledge of experts, testing sensitivity, and incorporating probability distributions into a game.

As an illustration of simulation, the reader should compute the average waiting time in the line for customers arriving to the first-come first-served queueing system described in the section on queueing theory. Let $\lambda = 0.5$, $\mu = 0.3$ for both channels and plot the cumulative probability distributions $1 - e^{-0.5t}$ and $1 - e^{-0.3t}$. Then, using random numbers as decimals, enter the ordinate of each graph and read off the time t that may be the interarrival or the service time of a customer with the decimal as ordinate. Thus a customer arrives at time zero and goes into service in one of the channels. Obtain a service time for him. Then obtain the arrival time for the next customer. He enters the next channel. Obtain a service time for him. Then obtain an arrival time for the next customer, who must wait if both channels are occupied. He enters the first channel that becomes free. Record the interarrival times in one column, the service times for one channel in another column, and for the other channel in another column. Enter the waiting time in a fourth column. A sample of a hundred customers should give a fair approximation to the average waiting time obtained by totalling the waiting times and dividing by the number in the sample. Average values of λ and μ in each column may also be computed to test the adequacy of the sample.[49]

As we have previously seen the theoretical expression for the average waiting time is given by

$$W = \frac{\rho(2\rho)^2}{2(1-\rho)^2}\frac{p_0}{\lambda}, \quad \rho = \frac{\lambda}{2\mu}$$

$$p_0 = \left[2\rho + \frac{(2\rho)^2}{2(1-\rho)}\right]^{-1}$$

and hence for the above values of λ and μ we have $W = 1.155$.

[49] See Thomas L. Saaty, *Elements of Queueing Theory*, McGraw-Hill Book Co., New York, 1961.

Note the requirement for this simulation that $\lambda/2\mu < 1$ thus assuming a steady state exists.

5.21. Summary.—We have examined a wide variety of ideas in operations research. It is hoped that the material will provide incentive for further explorations. The attractiveness of operations research lies in the fact that so far it has not been easy to contain its scope and methods. One method practiced in science, not mentioned here, is less formal but most attractive, and that is the use of creative imagination in improvising solutions to problems. A discussion of this topic along with ways of encouraging creative problem solving is discussed elsewhere.[50] The reader is encouraged to look into this promising subject. It shows that operations research is more than a collection of mathematical methods with specific domains of application.

I am grateful to Mrs. Laura G. Barnhill for carefully reading and typing the manuscript. My thanks also go to the scientists without whose contributions it would be impossible to present this variety of ideas. In particular I wish to thank Dr. Leila Bram for many valuable comments.

REFERENCES

Ackoff, Russell L., ed., *Progress in Operations Research*, Vol. I, John Wiley and Sons, Inc., New York, 1961.

Arrow, Kenneth J., Karlin, Samuel, and Scarf, Herbert, *Studies in the Mathematical Theory of Inventory and Production*, Stanford University Press, Stanford, California, 1958.

Berge, Claude, *Théorie des Graphs et ses Applications*, Dunod, Paris, 1958.

Busacker, R., Saaty, T. L., and Trent, H., *Graph Theory for Engineers and Scientists*, John Wiley and Sons, Inc., New York, in press.

Charnes, A., and Cooper, W. W., *Management Models and Industrial Applications of Linear Programming*, Vols. I and II, John Wiley and Sons, Inc., New York, 1961.

Churchman, C. W., Ackoff, R. L., and Arnoff, E. L., *Introduction to Operations Research*, John Wiley and Sons, Inc., New York, 1957.

Edie, Leslie C., "Operations Research in a Public Corporation," *Operations Research*, **5**, 111–22 (1957).

Ford, L. R., Jr., and Fulkerson, D. R., *Flows in Networks*, Princeton University Press, Princeton, N.J., 1962.

Manne, Alan S., "A Target-Assignment Problem," *Operations Research*, **6**, No. 3, 307–466 (1958).

Moran, P. A. P., "The Theory of Storage," *Methuen's Monographs on Applied Probability and Statistics*, John Wiley and Sons, Inc., New York, 1959.

[50] See Thomas L. Saaty, *Mathematical Methods of Operations Research*, Chapter 12, McGraw-Hill Book Co., New York, 1959.

Morganthaler, George W., "The Theory and Application of Simulation in Operations Research," *Progress in Operations Research*, Vol. I, No. 9, John Wiley and Sons, Inc., New York, 1961.

Morse, P. M., and Kimball, G. E., *Methods of Operations Research*, John Wiley and Sons, Inc., New York, 1951.

Roy, B., "Les Calculs D'Actualisation Dans Le Cas De Durees Aleatoires," *Revue Française De Recherche Operationnelle*, 3e Anne, 4e Trimestre, 1959, Prix 6 NF No. 13.

Saaty, Thomas L., "Comments on the Structure of Operations," *Proceedings of the Second International Conference on Operations Research*, p. 790, Aix-en-Provence, 1960.

——, "Operations Research Orientation and Training," *Pi Mu Epsilon Journal*, **3**, No. 5, 244–7 (1961).

——, and Bram, J., *Nonlinear Mathematics*, McGraw-Hill Book Co., Inc., New York, in press.

Sasieni, M. W., Yaspan, A., and Friedman, L., *Operations Research: Methods and Problems*, John Wiley and Sons, Inc., New York, 1959.

Tákacs, Lajos, "Stochastic Processes, Problems and Solutions," *Methuen's Monographs on Applied Probability and Statistics*, John Wiley and Sons, Inc., New York, 1960.

Thomas, C. J., and Deemer, W. L., Jr., "Military Gaming," *Progress in Operations Research*, Vol. I, John Wiley and Sons, Inc., New York, 1961.

CHAPTER 6

NONLINEAR PROBLEMS IN PHYSICS AND ENGINEERING

by

NICHOLAS MINORSKY

6.1. Introduction.—Although the nonlinear problems appeared from the very beginning of mechanics (the end of the 18th century), very little had been accomplished throughout the 19th century, mainly because there was no general mathematical method and each individual problem had to be treated on its own merits.

Only at the end of the 19th century did the first attempt to approach this subject systematically appear. In fact, Poincaré became interested in certain problems in celestial mechanics,[1] and this resulted in the famous "small parameters method" of which we shall speak in Part II of this chapter. In another earlier work[2] Poincaré investigated also certain properties of integral curves defined by the differential equations of the "nearly-linear" class.

For nearly 50 years these two contributions of Poincaré remained without any contact with applied science and, moreover, were entirely unrelated to each other.

In its applications, science was encountering gradually-increasing difficulties in view of the impossibility of explaining numerous oscillatory phenomena, particularly those connected with the so-called self-sustained oscillations (first, the oscillating arcs and gaseous discharges and still later, the electron tube oscillators).

By a brilliant physical intuition B. van der Pol succeeded finally (1920) in establishing his equation (which is given in Section 6.11) but, not having any mathematical theory at his disposal, he determined the nature of the solution by the graphical method of isoclines. It became obvious that the problem, which was a real stumbling block for many years, had been finally solved, at least in principle.

[1] H. Poincaré, *Les methodes nouvelles de la mécanique celeste*, Gauthier-Villars, Paris, 1882.

[2] H. Poincaré, *J. des Math*, **3**, 7 (1881); also *Œuvres*, T.1, Gauthier-Villars, Paris, 1928.

A little later (1929) the Russian physicist Andronov pointed out[3] that the stationary state of self-excited oscillations discovered by van der Pol is expressible analytically in terms of the limit cycle concept of the theory of Poincaré.

Once this junction between the theory and the observed facts had been established, the subsequent work of fitting a number of known nonlinear phenomena into the framework of the theory of Poincaré proceeded with an extraordinary rapidity; in this initial stage (1929–1937) the work was done almost exclusively in the USSR. The western countries learned about this progress shortly before the beginning of the war, when two fundamental treatises on this subject, one by Andronov and Chaikin,[4] and the other by Krylov and Bogoliubov,[5] became available. After this, the work proceeded on an international scale.

In these developments there were two distinct stages: the first one, which dealt with the "nearly linear oscillations," found its perfect algorithm in the theories of Poincaré (both topological and analytical), which constitute the major part of this review; here the discoveries were most striking as well as systematic. Numerous phenomena that had remained as riddles for many years, sometimes even for centuries, were systematically explained. We indicate in Part I of this chapter the qualitative aspect of this progress and in Part II, the quantitative one.

However, serious difficulties appeared later when efforts were made to attack more general problems not necessarily of the nearly-linear character. In terms of the van der Pol equation this occurs when the parameter *is not* small. Here the progress was far more difficult and the results less definite; moreover there appeared two distinct theories, one of which was formulated by physicists along the lines of the theory of shocks in mechanics, and the other which was analytical and involved the use of the asymptotic expansions (Part IV of this chapter). The latter, however, turned out to be too complicated for practical purposes, and has not been extended sufficiently to be of general usefulness.

Finally, interest in these questions came from a new line of research, namely, the theory of automatic control systems. Here, however, contrary to the analytical theories that are summarized in this review, these new "piecewise analytic" or "piecewise linear" phenomena in control systems are nonanalytic by their very essence. They open an entirely new field, which is still in an early stage of development.

[3] A. Andronov, *C.R. Ac. Sc.*, Paris, **189** (1929).

[4] A. Andronov and S. Chaikin, *Theory of Oscillations*, Moscow, 1937.

[5] N. Krylov and N. Bogoliubov, *Introduction to Nonlinear Mechanics*, Kiev, 1937.

For that reason, the treatment of these new problems in this book is limited to a brief account in Part IV, especially from the point of view of their physical significance, since any systematic approach to this field is beyond the scope of this book.

PART I—TOPOLOGICAL METHODS

6.2. Introductory Remarks.—As a considerable amount of this material is likely to be known, we shall abridge the exposition, referring for details to the recent text of the author.[6]

As we mentioned in the introduction, the topological approach is very convenient here, as it is possible to eliminate the independent variable between the differential equations

$$\frac{dx}{dt} = P(x,y); \qquad \frac{dy}{dt} = Q(x,y) \tag{6–1}$$

and thus obtain the integral curve

$$\frac{dy}{dx} = \frac{Q(x,y)}{P(x,y)} \tag{6–2}$$

We note in passing that this simplification would not be possible in the case of a nonautonomous system

$$\frac{dx}{dt} = P(x,y,t); \qquad \frac{dy}{dt} = Q(x,y,t) \tag{6–3}$$

in which case dy/dx depends on t so that the geometrical (topological) representation is impossible.

6.3. Phase Plane: Singular Points.—We shall define the plane of the variables $(x,y = \dot{x})$ as the *phase plane* and investigate the behavior of integral curves (or characteristics) in that plane by means of Eq. (6–2). In case we wish to associate with these curves the motion of the representative point $R(x,y)$, we shall rather speak of them as trajectories and in this case one has to use Eq. (6–1).

Among integral curves (trajectories) we shall be particularly interested in those that are closed, which thus represent *periodic phenomena.*

The important property of autonomous systems (such as that of Eq. (6–1)) is that it is possible to replace t by $t + t_0$, t_0 being an arbitrary

[6] For further mathematical treatment of the topics of this chapter, the reader is referred to the author's text—N. Minorsky, *Nonlinear Oscillations*, D. Van Nostrand Co., Inc., Princeton, N.J., 1962.

constant ("the phase"), and still have the same solution but with a phase shift t_0. This property leads to the following assertion:

To a given closed integral curve C corresponds an infinity of trajectories (or motions) differing from each other by arbitrary constants t_0.

We recall the two definitions:

(1) A point (x_0, y_0) of the phase plane for which $P(x_0, y_0)$ and $Q(x_0, y_0)$ are not zero simultaneously is called an *ordinary point.*

(2) A point (x_0, y_0) for which both $P(x_0, y_0)$ and $Q(x_0, y_0)$ vanish simultaneously is called the *singular point.*

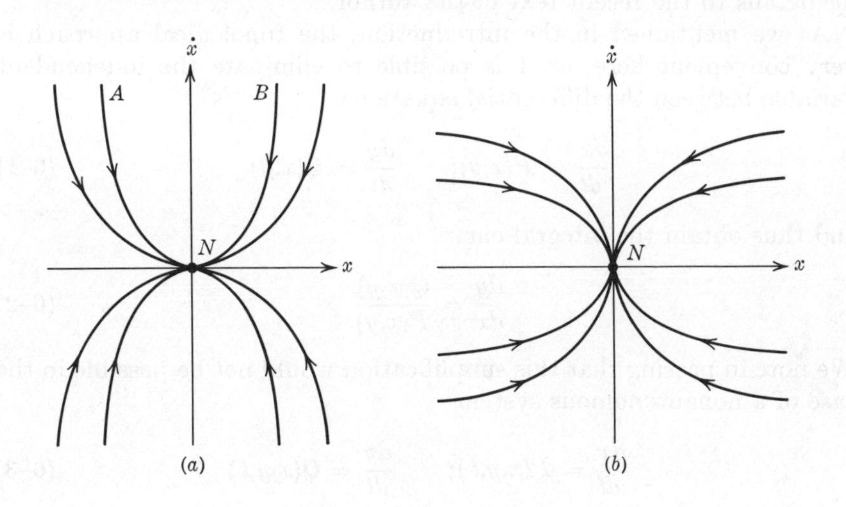

FIG. 6–1.

As dx/dt and dy/dt approach zero as R approaches the singular point, it is obvious that this approach is always asymptotic (*i.e.*, occurs either for $t \to \infty$ or for $t \to -\infty$.

Singular points represent the positions of equilibrium of dynamical systems and merit further investigation.

6.4. Elementary Singular Points.—One can start with a special case of the systems

$$\dot{x} = x; \qquad \dot{y} = ay \tag{6–4}$$

and

$$\dot{x} = -x; \qquad \dot{y} = -ay \tag{6–5}$$

whose solutions are $x = C_1 \exp(t)$; $y = C_2 \exp(at)$, and $x = C_1 \exp(-t)$; $y = C_2 \exp(-at)$, respectively. Clearly the origin is a singular point for Eqs. (6–4) and (6–5).

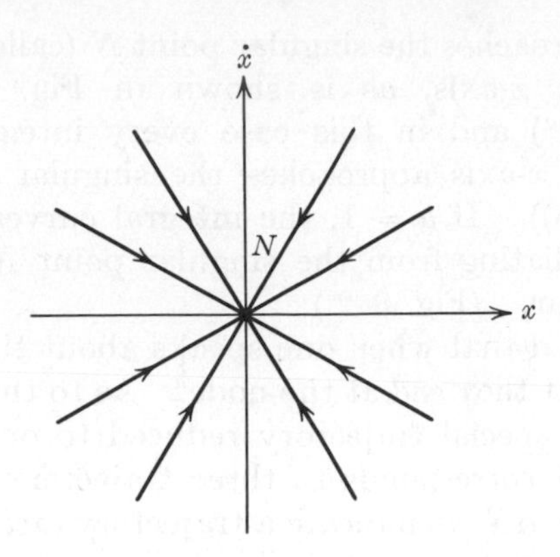

FIG. 6–2.

The integral curves on which $x \neq 0$ satisfy the differential equation

$$\frac{dy}{dx} = \frac{ay}{x} \tag{6–6}$$

which has the solution $y = C|x|^a$. Both systems have, thus, the same singular point. The sign of a determines the nature of the singular point: for $a > 0$ the integral curves are parabolic, and for $a < 0$, hyperbolic. The two cases give rise to different types of singular points. For reasons of symmetry we may restrict the discussion to positive values of x.

Consider first the case $a > 0$. If $a > 1$, as $dy/dx = Cax^{a-1}$, then $(dy/dx) \to 0$ for $x \to 0$. Hence every integral curve, with the exception

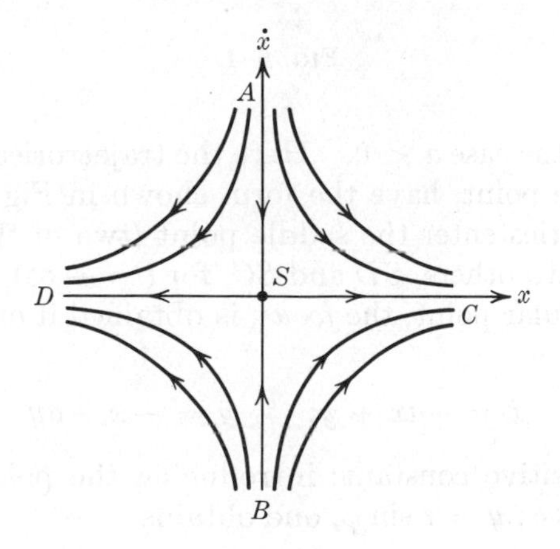

FIG. 6–3.

of the y-axis, approaches the singular point N (called the *node* or nodal point) along the x-axis, as is shown in Fig. 6–1(a). If $a < 1$, $dy/dx = Ca(1/x^{1-a})$ and in this case every integral curve with the exception of the x-axis approaches the singular point N along the y-axis (Fig. 6–1(b)). If $a = 1$, the integral curves are half-lines convergent to or radiating from the singular point N, which is called a *proper node*, or star. (Fig. 6–2.)

It must be noted that when one speaks about these trajectories one has to assume that they *end* at the node. As to the node itself, it may be regarded as a special trajectory reduced to one point. Thus, for instance, Fig. 6–1 corresponds to three trajectories: AN, BN, and N where by AN and BN we indicate a trajectory *excluding the node* N.

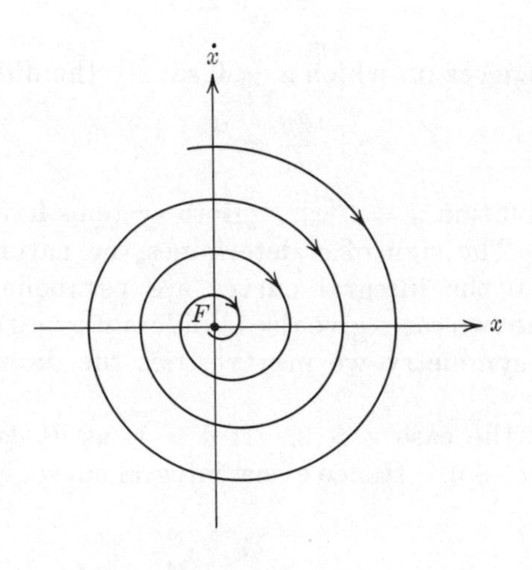

FIG. 6–4.

Consider next the case $a < 0$. Here the trajectories near the singular point, the saddle point, have the form shown in Fig. 6–3. Only four singular trajectories enter the saddle point (two of them, AS and BS, for $t \to \infty$ and two others, SD and SC, for $t \to -\infty$).

The third singular point, the *focus*, is obtained if one starts from the system

$$\dot{x} = -ax + y; \qquad \dot{y} = -x - ay \tag{6–7}$$

where a is a positive constant; introducing the polar coordinates by setting $x = r \cos \varphi$; $y = r \sin \varphi$, one obtains

$$r_1 = C_1 \exp(-at); \qquad \varphi = -t + C_2 \tag{6–8}$$

The trajectories are logarithmic spirals (Fig. 6–4). For $a > 0$, they wind on the singular point (*i.e.*, the rotation of the radius vector is clockwise); for $a < 0$, they unwind (*i.e.*, the rotation of the radius vector is counterclockwise).

It can be shown that these singular points exist also for more general linear differential equations of the form

$$\ddot{x} + 2b\dot{x} + \omega_0^2 x = 0 \tag{6–9}$$

with the only difference that the trajectories are somewhat distorted as compared to their simple form shown in Figs. 6–4 or 6–1.

Since singular points are identified with the positions of equilibria, the significance of the three principal singular points is very simple, namely: the node characterizes an aperiodically damped motion, the focus, an oscillatory damped motion, and the saddle point, an essentially unstable motion occurring, for instance, in the neighborhood of the upper (unstable) equilibrium position of the pendulum.

These conclusions are generalized for more general systems of the form

$$\dot{x} = ax + by + P_2(x, y); \qquad \dot{y} = cx + dy + Q_2(x, y) \tag{6–10}$$

in which $P_2(x, y)$ and $Q_2(x,y)$ are power series in x and y beginning with terms of second or higher degree.

It is shown that under *normal conditions* (and only these are generally of interest in applications) one can disregard the terms P_2 and Q_2 and consider only the linear terms.

The nature of equilibrium in such cases is characterized by the nature of the roots of the following characteristic equation

$$S^2 - (a + d)S + (ad - bc) = 0 \tag{6–11}$$

Summing up, the following results can be indicated:

(1) If the roots S_1 and S_2 are real and of the same sign, the singular point is a *node*; stable if S_1 and S_2 are negative, and unstable if they are positive. The condition for real unequal roots of the same sign is clearly: $0 < ad - bc < [(a + d)/2]^2$. For a stable node (*i.e.*, a node approached by its trajectories for $t \to \infty$) $a + d < 0$ and for an unstable one, $a + d > 0$.

(2) If S_1 and S_2 are real and of opposite sign, the singular point is a saddle point; the condition for this is: $ad - bc < 0$.

(3) If S_1 and S_2 are conjugate complex, the singular point is a *focus*; this requires that b and c be of opposite sign and $a + d \neq 0$; if $a + d < 0$, the focus is stable; if $a + d > 0$, it is unstable.

The argument is more complicated if one takes into account the terms $P_2(x, y)$ and $Q_2(x, y)$, but the conclusions remain the same.

In other words, in *normal cases* the nature of equilibrium is determined only by the linear terms. This is also intuitively obvious since, as the trajectory approaches the singular point (at the origin), both x and y decrease indefinitely so that ultimately only the linear terms of the first order of magnitude remain.

In applications the above properties of *simple singular points* are sufficient, and this yields very simple criteria.

The abnormal cases are far more complicated, and are not treated in this discussion. It is sufficient to say that the physical significance of these abnormal cases (reducible to singular points of high orders) has not yet been completely studied.

It must be noted that the singular point of the type *center* belongs to these "special" (or "pathological") cases. This case arises when the roots S_1 and S_2 in the above terminology become purely imaginary; the conditions are then $a + d = 0$; $|bc| > |ad|$.

Unfortunately this condition is not sufficient, and it is shown that a similar condition exists also in the case of the *weak focus*; to distinguish between the two requires the introduction of approximations of high order.

We recall that in this terminology the center is the singular point (the state of rest) for simple harmonic motion represented in the phase plane by a circle (or by an ellipse). The trajectories in this case are closed curves not having any tendency to approach the singular point (the center).

However, this simple model of a periodic motion occupied the central position in the theory of oscillations from its very beginning (Galileo) up to the time of Poincaré, when it was replaced by the new model—the *limit cycle.*

The deep philosophical significance of the new theory lies precisely at this point, and consists in replacing a somewhat metaphysical concept of the harmonic oscillator (which could never be produced experimentally) by the new concept of a physical oscillator of the *limit cycle type*, with which we are dealing in the form of electron tube circuits and similar self-excited systems.

6.5. Limit Cycles.—The new closed trajectories discovered by Poincaré[2] and which he called "*cycles limites*," constitute the essence of the nonlinear theory.

As a *closed trajectory* in the phase plane means obviously a *periodic phenomenon*, the discovery of limit cycles was fundamental for the new theory of self-excited oscillations.

In the old (Galileo) theory of oscillations the pattern of a periodic motion was assumed to be the closed trajectory around a center. As is well known a trajectory of this kind is determined by its initial conditions—a point (x_0, y_0) in the phase plane. If the initial conditions are changed, there will be another closed trajectory and so on. One has, thus, a continuous family of closed trajectories, each of which can be realized by means of proper initial conditions.

One can say, thus, that the differential equation merely prescribes the pattern of closed trajectories, but not the individual (physical) trajectories themselves; the latter are determined uniquely by the initial conditions.

In the new theory the following definition holds:

The limit cycle C is an isolated closed trajectory having the property that all other trajectories C' in its neighborhood are certain spirals winding themselves onto C either for $t \to \infty$ (in which case C is called a stable limit cycle) or for $t \to -\infty$ (an unstable limit cycle).

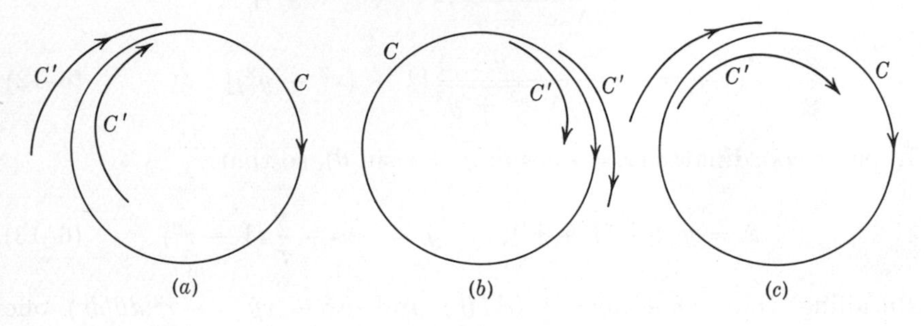

Fig. 6–5.

In some cases there also occur semistable limit cycles (in this discussion the single term *cycle* is used wherever it is unambiguous or if no confusion is to be feared) characterized by stability on one side and instability on the other side. Figure 6–5(a), (b), and (c) illustrate these definitions. Physically, only stable cycles are of interest; the unstable cycles play the role of separating the zones of attraction of stable cycles in the case when there are several cycles. It is seen from this definition that, instead of an infinity of closed trajectories, we have now only one such trajectory determined by the differential equation itself and the initial conditions do not play any part. In fact, the term "initial conditions" means just one point (x_0, y_0) of the phase plane; as a spiral trajectory C' passes through that point and ultimately winds itself onto the cycle C, it is clear that the initial conditions have nothing to do with this ultimate closed trajectory C—the stable cycle.

A difference between these two concepts can be illustrated in many ways. Consider, for example, a mathematical pendulum; in this case the old concept of trajectories around a center holds. On the other hand, in the case of a wound clock at standstill, clearly it is immaterial whether the starting impulse is small or large (as long as it is sufficient for starting, the ultimate motion will be exactly the same). Electron tube circuits and other self-excited devices exhibit similar features; their ultimate motion depends on the differential equation itself and not on the initial conditions.

Summing up, everything "which oscillates" in a stationary state in the world around us is necessarily of the "limit cycle" type; it depends only on the parameters of the system, that is, on the differential equation, and not on the initial conditions.

One can easily find differential equations having limit cycles as solutions. For example, a system:

$$\dot{x} = y + \frac{x}{\sqrt{x^2 + y^2}}[1 - (x^2 + y^2)]$$

$$\dot{y} = -x + \frac{y}{\sqrt{x^2 + y^2}}[1 - (x^2 + y^2)] \tag{6–12}$$

In polar coordinates ($x = r \cos \theta$; $y = r \sin \theta$), so that:

$$\dot{x} = y + \frac{x}{r}(1 - r^2); \qquad \dot{y} = -x + \frac{y}{r}(1 - r^2) \tag{6–13}$$

Recalling that $x\dot{x} + y\dot{y} = \frac{1}{2}(dr^2/dt)$ and $y\dot{x} - x\dot{y} = -r^2(d\theta/dt)$ one obtains:

$$\dot{r} = 1 - r^2 \tag{6–14}$$

$$\dot{\theta} = -1 \tag{6–15}$$

The second equation merely shows that the radius vector rotates with a constant angular velocity. As to (6–14) it is integrated by the standard procedure which gives:

$$r = \frac{Ae^{2t} - 1}{Ae^{2t} + 1} \tag{6–16}$$

where the constant of integration $A = (1 + r_0)/(1 - r_0)$, r_0 being the initial value of r. It is noted that $r_0 = 1$. The limit cycle in this case is a circle with radius 1. If $r_0 > 1$, the spiral winds itself onto the circle $r_1 = 1$ from the outside; if $r_0 < 1$, it winds itself onto $r_1 = 1$ from the inside.

One can give a number of similar "synthetic" examples but they are of no special interest.

What is really difficult is to ascertain whether a given differential equation has a limit cycle solution. In fact, aside from a few well-known equations (of van der Pol, Rayleigh, Liénard, etc.) we hardly know anything at all about the existence of cycles *directly*, that is, on the basis of the topological methods with which we are concerned here.

This difficulty is due to the fact that the *form of the differential equation* does not convey any information regarding the existence of cycles. However, the *form of the solution does yield this information.* Unfortunately, in entirely new problems we generally know the form of the equation and not that of its solution.

In view of this a direct search for limit cycles on the topological basis was found to be extremely difficult, as we shall see later.

On the contrary, in Part II of this chapter, which is devoted to the analytical methods, the determination of limit cycles does not present any difficulty.

6.6. Topological Configurations.—It may be noticed from the preceding that there is a certain relation between limit cycles and singular points.

More specifically, from Fig. 6–5 it is observed that the trajectories reach the limit cycle from the inside; on the other hand, in the theory of singular points we saw that when these points are unstable, trajectories leave them.

On the basis of these somewhat intuitive considerations one can assume that limit cycles and singular points form certain *topological configurations* that connect the state of rest (the singular point) with the state of a stationary motion (the limit cycle). A hydrodynamical analogy is almost obvious: *to consider a trajectory as a line of flow.* In this analogy *an unstable singular point is a source* and *a stable limit cycle is a (curvilinear) sink.* For an unstable limit cycle, on the contrary, the unstable cycle is a source and the stable singular point is a sink. The process of self-excitation from rest is thus described from $t = -\infty$ to $t = \infty$, the trajectory unrolling itself from an unstable singular point and wrapping itself on the stable cycle from the inside.

Very often instead of the complete trajectory (*i.e.*, between $t = -\infty$ and $t = \infty$) one speaks about the *half-trajectory* taking place between $t = 0$ and $t = \infty$ (or $t = -\infty$).

This analogy has been found to be very useful in investigating more complicated situations. For instance, in applications one often encounters the so-called phenomenon of a "hard self-excitation." The corresponding topological configuration is a stable singular point S surrounded by an unstable cycle U which, in turn, is surrounded by a stable cycle S; we designate it for the sake of abbreviation: SUS, the first letter referring to the singular point and the others to cycles. It is clear that a configuration of this kind is incapable of self-excitation since the singular point (state of rest) is stable.

If, however, one communicates to such a system an impulse capable of transferring the representative point R to a point A outside the unstable cycle (point A, Fig. 6–6), it is clear that from that point the self-excitation can start and R will approach the outer stable cycle.

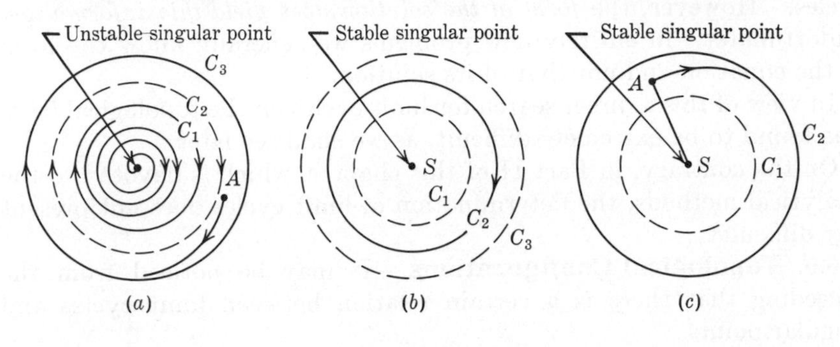

FIG. 6–6.

6.7. The Index of Poincaré.—The concept of the index was introduced by Poincaré for the purpose of establishing a necessary criterion for the existence of a closed trajectory (the limit cycle).

Consider in the phase plane of Eq. (6–1) a closed Jordan curve C not traversing any singularities. The curve may be regarded as being in the vector field V of trajectories of Eq. (6–1). Suppose that a point S moves on C in the positive direction (say, counterclockwise) and we mark for each position of S the vector V with respect to a fixed system of reference. When S has moved over an angle 2π on C, the tangent vector V resumes its initial position, having turned through an angle $2\pi I$, where I is an integer. We consider the rotation of V as positive if it turns in the same direction as S and negative in the opposite case. The integer I so defined is called the index of the curve C with respect to the vector field V.

We omit the derivation of these results[2, 6] and indicate only the conclusions.

(1) For C not containing any singular points, $I = 0$.
(2) For C containing either a focus or a node or a center, $I = +1$.
(3) For C containing a saddle point, $I = -1$.

To this we add three theorems:

(a) Index of a closed trajectory is always: $+1$.

(b) A closed trajectory contains at least one singular point.

(c) If a closed trajectory Γ contains N nodes, F focal points, C centers, and S saddle points, one has

$$I(\Gamma) = N + F + C - S = +1$$

6.8. Negative Criterion of Bendixson.—This criterion is useful when one wishes to know that no self-excited (parasitic) oscillations are possible.

Given Eq. (6–1), this criterion states: if $\partial P/\partial x + \partial Q/\partial y$ *does not change its sign* (*or vanishes identically*) *in a region* D (*of the phase plane*), *no closed trajectory can exist in* D.

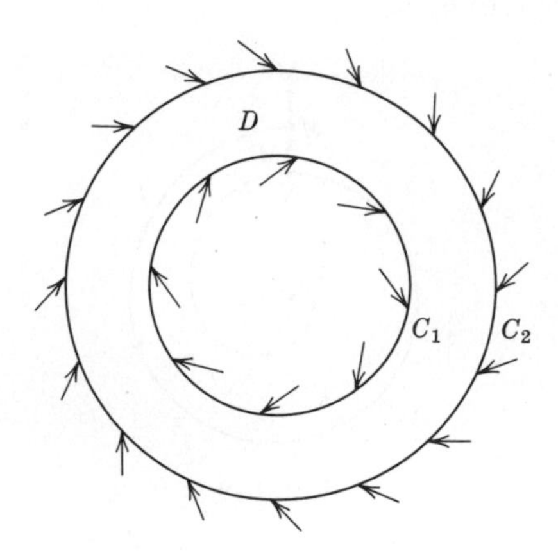

FIG. 6–7.

The proof of this theorem follows directly from Green's theorem[7] which we omit. This theorem is often useful when one wishes to be sure that an instability does not lead to the occurrence of oscillations. For examples see Minorsky.[6]

6.9. Poincaré-Bendixson (P.B.) Theorem.—This theorem gives the necessary and sufficient conditions for the existence of a cycle. Unfortunately, it requires a preliminary knowledge of the character of integral curves, which often makes its application difficult. The theorem states:

[7] I. Bendixson, *Acta Math.*, 24 (1901); also, see Minorsky, *Nonlinear Oscillations*, p. 82.

If a half-trajectory C remains in a finite domain D without approaching singular points, the C is either a closed trajectory or approaches such a trajectory.

In the case of a ring-shaped domain D (Fig. 6–7) bounded by two closed curves C_1 and C_2 (*e.g.*, circles), it is sufficient for the existence of, at least, one cycle that:

(a) trajectories enter (leave) through every point of C_1 and C_2;
(b) there are no singular points either in D or on C_1 and C_2.

The significance of this theorem is obvious on the basis of the above-mentioned hydrodynamical analogy. In fact, condition (a) requires that there must be a sink (source) in D and (b) states that this sink (source) cannot be a point; hence, it must be a curvilinear one, *i.e.*, a stable (unstable) cycle.

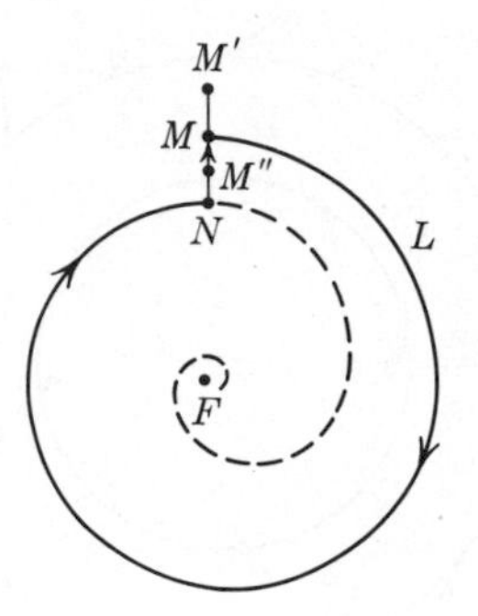

FIG. 6–8.

The above difficulty of using the P.B. theorem was obviated to some extent by Poincaré in his theory of cycles without contact, for which we refer the reader to footnote 2, as we shall have no occasion to use this theorem.

6.10. Nonanalytic Cycles.—In recent years the concept of limit cycles was enlarged so as to include cycles that have widespread application in connection with the description of oscillatory phenomena whose stationary states are not describable in the phase plane by a trajectory that is analytic.

One such case arises in the theory of clocks. As is known, a clock is a mechanism consisting of two parts: a torsional pendulum with a small damping, and an escapement mechanism replenishing the energy lost by damping in the torsional pendulum.

In the phase plane the trajectory of the torsional pendulum between the impulses delivered by the escapement mechanism is an arc MLN of a logarithmic spiral having F as its focal point (Fig. 6–8). When the representative point R reaches the point N, the mechanism (B) delivers an impact by which the initial or, rather, terminal condition is suddenly transferred to the point M, which thus appears as the initial condition for the next period. In this manner a continuous dissipation of energy on the arc MLN is compensated for in a quasi-discontinuous manner on the stretch NM, and it can be shown that a stationary state is reached when the total curve $MLNM$ becomes closed. In this way the system as a whole $(A) + (B)$ behaves in all respects as if it had a limit cycle, but in this case this cycle is not an analytic one on account of the quasi-discontinuous stretch NM.

In recent years the concept of nonanalytic cycles has found a wide application in modern automatic control systems, as is explained later in this chapter.

6.11. Differential Equations of van der Pol and Liénard.—On page 321, it was mentioned that the van der Pol equation, which is

$$\ddot{x} + \mu(x^2 - 1)\dot{x} + x = 0 \tag{6–17}$$

appeared as the first step in the modern development of nonlinear theory. We shall return to it in Part II of this chapter from the point of view of its analytical solution, but at this point a discussion of its physical significance is necessary. If one considers Eq. (6–17) as representing an oscillator, it is seen that this oscillator is characterized by a *variable damping* corresponding to the term: $\mu(x^2 - 1)\dot{x}$. In fact, near the state of rest ($x \simeq 0$) Eq. (6–17) is practically a linear differential equation with negative damping, which represents the energy input into the system. In terms of the now familiar concept of singular points, one finds easily that the singular point here is an unstable focus; the amplitudes thus begin to grow from rest, and the negative damping will thus decrease in absolute value, and will be ultimately converted into a positive damping for a sufficiently large amplitude. In this manner one can see intuitively that the stationary motion on a limit cycle will be established when the integrated work of the damping per cycle becomes zero.

Now Liénard developed a purely geometrical argument that enabled him to bypass, as it were, the analytical theory, which is discussed in Part II of this chapter. His equation is [8]

$$\ddot{x} + f(x)\dot{x} + x = 0 \tag{6–18}$$

[8] A. Liénard, *Rev. Gen. de l'Electricité*, 23 (1928); see also bibliography in footnote 6.

Although Liénard's method is purely qualitative, it has the advantage that one can carry out the argument without worrying about the smallness of the parameter μ in Eq. (6–17); as we shall see later, this is an essential limitation of the analytical theory. The work of Liénard has been continued by numerous mathematicians and, although we are unable to go into these details,[8] we shall give a few conclusions.

Instead of the ordinary $(x,\dot{x})$ phase plane, Liénard introduces the phase plane of the variables (x, y) where

$$y = \dot{x} + F(x) \tag{6–19}$$

where

$$F(x) = \int_0^x f(x)dx \tag{6–20}$$

Equation (6–18) can be written then as an equivalent system:

$$\dot{x} = v; \quad \frac{dv}{dx} + f(x) + \frac{x}{v} = 0 \tag{6–21}$$

and, in view of (6–19) and (6–20), it becomes:

$$\frac{dy}{dx} + \frac{x}{y - F(x)} = 0 \tag{6–22}$$

which can be written also as

$$xdx + (y - F(x))dy = 0 \tag{6–23}$$

If one recalls that the equation of the normal to a curve is

$$(x - X)dx + (y - Y)dy = 0$$

it is clear that (6–23) is the equation of the normal passing through the point $X = 0$, $Y = F(x)$.

This gives a simple graphical construction of integral curves. Suppose we wish to carry out this construction for the van der Pol equation for which $f(x) = x^2 - 1$; $F(x) = x^3/3 - x$.

One plots the curve $F(x)$ (Fig. 6–9) and the construction consists in tracing the direction field of lineal elements. We take, for instance $x = x_1$ to which corresponds the point M_1 on the curve $F(x)$, and transfer this point onto the y-axis by a parallel to the x-axis; we obtain thus the point N_1. From this point as a center, we trace a number of small arcs along the line P_1 (of equation $x = x_1$) and continue the construction for other points $M_2, M_3, \cdots, N_2, N_3, \cdots$.

Having constructed a field of lineal elements, one can easily trace the integral curves themselves. Among the family of these curves there is one curve that has a re-entrant path, and this corresponds to a closed trajectory and, hence, to the periodic solution.

We refer to footnotes 6 and 8 for the details of this problem, but mention only one conclusion: the fact that Liénard's argument was purely geometrical enabled him to make a fundamental discovery, the significance of which was fully understood only at a later date.

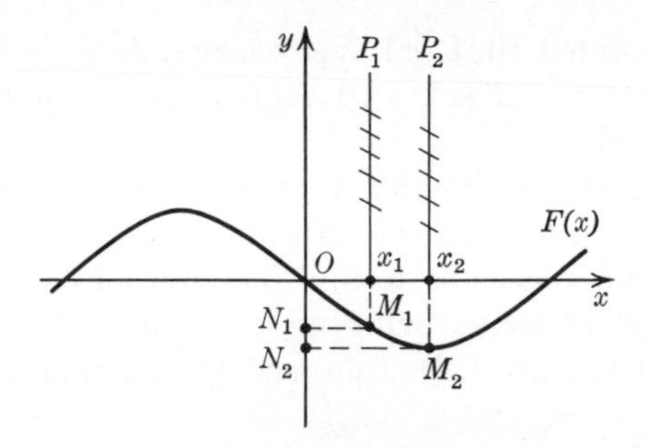

FIG. 6–9.

Suppose that, instead of writing Liénard's equation in the form (6–18) we write it as

$$\ddot{x} + \mu f(x)\dot{x} + x = 0 \tag{6–24}$$

where μ is the parameter. If one assumes that $\mu \ll 1$, Liénard finds the result which can be more fully obtained by the general theory. However, if one passes to the other asymptotic case $\mu \to \infty$, one obtains an entirely new conclusion.

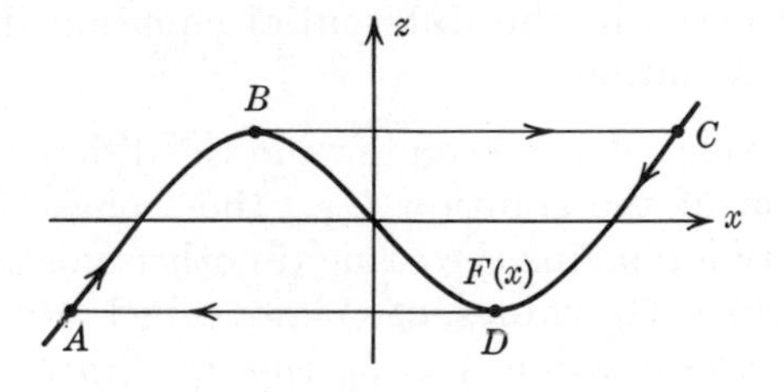

FIG. 6–10.

If one replaces $f(x)$ in (6–18) by $\mu f(x)$ as above, it can be shown that Equation (6–22) in the asymptotic case $\mu \to \infty$ reduces to

$$z - F(x)dz = 0 \tag{6–25}$$

where $z = y/\mu$. This suggests that the integral curve consists of two branches; on one of them the equation $z = F(x)$ is valid, and on the other the equation, $dz = 0$ (Fig. 6–10).

For the investigation of the velocity of R on these integral curves, it is sufficient to apply the same transformation: $y = \mu z$, which gives:

$$\frac{dx}{dt} = \mu(z - F(x)); \qquad \frac{dz}{dt} = -x/\mu \tag{6–26}$$

As we have assumed that μ is very large, dx/dt is very large everywhere except when $z = F(x)$, and dz/dt is very small when the curve $F(x)$ is not followed.

We have thus the following representation of the phenomenon (Fig. 6–10): on the arc AB the motion is slow; at the point B the representative point ceases to follow the curve $F(x)$ and its horizontal velocity becomes very large, bringing it to the point C at which a slow motion begins on the arc CD, followed by another jump DC, and so on.

Although at the time of its publication (1928) the asymptotic theory of Liénard was not given serious consideration, about 20 years later it became of importance in the development of the asymptotic theory (see Part IV).

6.12. Theory of Bifurcations.—In the preceding sections we have reviewed a few more important points of the existing topological methods in the theory of oscillation, assuming that the topological configuration or the "phase portrait" remains fixed.

In his work on the equilibrium form of a rotating fluid mass, Poincaré indicated a powerful method for dealing with transient situations by means of a parameter (not to be confused with the parameter μ previously mentioned) in the differential equation itself, which leads to the following definition:

If for certain values of a parameter λ in the differential equation, the qualitative aspect of the solution (*i.e.*, the "phase portrait") of the differential equation remains the same (in other words: the changes are only quantitative) such values of λ are called *ordinary* values. If however, for a certain value $\lambda = \lambda_0$ this qualitative aspect changes, such a special value is called a *critical* or *bifurcation value*.

Examples of such situations are very numerous; perhaps the best known example is the transition of the performance of an electronic circuit from regenerative amplification to the generation of oscillations. The parameter λ in this case is the coefficient of mutual inductance between the anode and the grid circuits. As long as $\lambda < \lambda_0$, the circuit functions as amplifier whose coefficient of amplification gradually increases as $\lambda \to \lambda_0$. When the bifurcation value $\lambda = \lambda_0$ is reached, the circuit is on the limits of regeneration and for $\lambda = \lambda_0 + \varepsilon$, where ε is as small as we please, it begins to generate oscillations of its own frequency, and its functioning as an amplifier ceases abruptly. Phenomena of this nature are of a frequent occurrence in control systems where the performance becomes more and more accurate with increasing amplification until suddenly parasitic oscillations set in and the control action becomes seriously impaired.

There are two principal types of bifurcation phenomena: those of the "first kind" and those of the "second kind."

Suppose we have a certain topological configuration, say, SUS in our previous notation; this means that the singular point is stable and the nearest cycle is unstable. The bifurcation of the first kind can be represented by the scheme:

$$SUS \to (SU)S \to U \cdot S \tag{6–27}$$

which represents the gradual approach of the unstable cycle to the stable singular point until they coalesce (which is shown by (SU)), to form a singular point of stability opposite to that which existed before. The phenomenon is reversible, that is, one can reverse the direction of the arrows and read the scheme from right to left.

This particular bifurcation exists in the example from electronics mentioned above; the regenerative amplifier has as its phase portrait SUS and after the bifurcation it becomes simply US, that is, an ordinary oscillator.

In the bifurcation of the second kind the critical coalescence for $\lambda = \lambda_0$ involves two adjoining limit cycles, one that is stable and the other, unstable. We can consider the same configuration as before, the only difference being that the coalescence is now one of two cycles that destroy each other; this gives:

$$SUS \to S(US) \to S \tag{6–28}$$

Thus, as the result of the parameter variation two adjoining cycles approach each other indefinitely and at the limit, $\lambda = \lambda_0$, they coalesce, giving rise to a semistable cycle (US) which disappears, leaving the system free from cycles.

The bifurcation of the second kind was established by Poincaré, but the bifurcation of the first kind was established more recently (1937) by A. Andronov.[4] For further discussion, see this reference, or reference 6. The direct analytical approach to the theory of bifurcation is very difficult, and the only known case in which it could be carried through is that of Andronov.

Attempts were made recently to simplify the problem by limiting it to the first approximation. The procedure can be stated briefly as follows.

Anticipating a later argument (Section 6–22) in the theory of approximations, it is possible to replace the system of Eq. (6–1) by the other one (in polar coordinates), namely

$$\frac{d\rho}{dt} = \Phi(\rho,\psi); \qquad \frac{d\psi}{dt} = \Psi(\rho,\psi) \tag{6–29}$$

where

$$\rho = x^2 + \dot{x}^2 = x^2 + y^2 = r^2; \qquad \psi = \arctan{(y/x)}$$

and $x = r\cos\psi$; $y = r\sin\psi$.

In the case of autonomous problems and in the first approximation, the system (6–29) is often reducible to the form

$$\frac{d\rho}{dt} = \Phi(\rho); \qquad \frac{d\psi}{dt} = \text{const} \tag{6–30}$$

Such results generally hold for the differential equations of van der Pol, Liénard, and some others of the same type. In view of the constant rotation $d\psi/dt$ = const., we have here, in fact, a system of concentric cycles corresponding to the real positive roots $\rho_1, \rho_2, \cdots$ of $\Phi(\rho) = 0$.

Very often the function $\Phi(\rho)$ is of the form

$$\Phi(\rho) = -k(\rho - \rho_1)(\rho - \rho_2)\cdots(\rho - \rho_n) \tag{6–31}$$

where k and ρ_i are positive constants; we assume that all roots are real and distinct; the graph of such function is shown in Fig. 6–11, where $\rho_1, \rho_2, \cdots$ are the roots. Consider one of these roots, say ρ_1, and assume that we give a little perturbation $\delta\rho > 0$ to this root. Replacing ρ by $\rho_1 + \delta\rho$ in Eq. (6–18), one has

$$\frac{d\,(\rho_1 + \delta\rho)}{dt} = \Phi\,(\rho_1 + \delta\rho) = \Phi(\rho_1) + \Phi_\rho\delta\rho + \cdots$$

We assume that we are dealing with the first approximation only; since the terms $d\rho_1/dt$ and $\Phi(\rho_1)$ cancel out in view of (6–26) we have

$$\frac{d\delta\rho}{dt} = \Phi_\rho(\rho_1)\delta\rho \tag{6–32}$$

This formula is often used in the investigation of stability by the first approximation (see Section 6.13). On the left we have the rate of change of the original perturbation, and on the right the derivative of Φ with respect to ρ at the point $\rho = \rho_1$. Clearly the motion will be stable if $d\delta\rho/dt < 0$ which requires that

$$\Phi_\rho(\rho_1) < 0 \tag{6–33}$$

The expression $\Phi_\rho(\rho_1)$ denotes the slope of the tangent to the curve at the point $\rho = \rho_1$. The inspection of Fig. 6–11 shows that at the point $\rho = \rho_1$ this slope is positive, hence the root ρ_1 is unstable; applying this argument to $\rho = \rho_2$, one finds, on the contrary, that it is stable, and so on. This is shown by the arrows in Fig. 6–11.

Since the values $\rho_1, \rho_2, \cdots$ are the equilibrium values (stable and unstable), and since there is constant rotation, clearly we have the

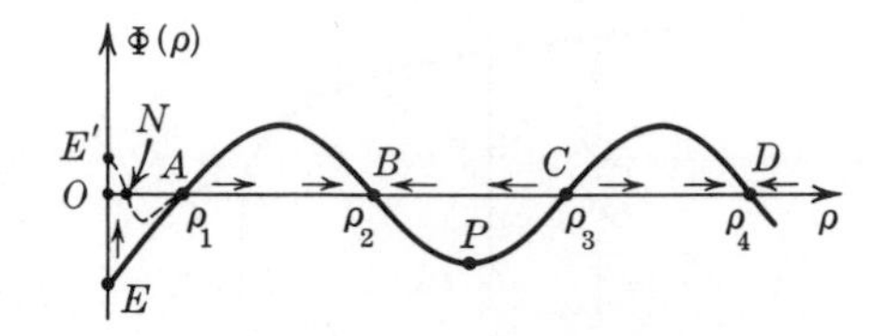

Fig. 6–11.

pattern of concentric circles, alternatively stable and unstable, which, in the first approximation, represents a concentric topological configuration (Section 6.4).

One can also gain an insight into the bifurcation; for instance, assume that we introduce a parameter λ that permits displacing the curve $\Phi(\rho)$ parallel to itself along the axis of ordinates, say upwards. It is clear that the roots ρ_2 and ρ_3 will approach each other and will coalesce into a double root ρ_{23} when the ρ-axis is tangent to $\Phi(\rho)$; if the parameter λ continues to increase, the double root (and its corresponding cycles) disappears; this is an illustration of a bifurcation of the *second kind*. One can also obtain a similar graphical interpretation for a bifurcation of the first kind.

As another example of the same nature, consider a differential equation

$$\frac{d\rho}{dt} = \sigma p(\rho^2 - p\rho - q) = \Phi(\rho) \tag{6–34}$$

where σ and p are positive constants. We can assume that there is also a second equation $d\psi/dt = \text{const.}$ which shows that the radii vectors rotate with a uniform velocity.

In this example the situation is a little more complicated. In fact, here we have three roots: the root $\rho_0 = 0$; and the roots $\rho_{1,2} = p/2 \pm \sqrt{(p^2/4) - q}$. For stability, $\Phi_\rho(\rho) = -\sigma\rho(2\rho - p)$. The first root is, clearly, the position of equilibrium; the other two roots correspond to limit cycles, and one ascertains easily that the smaller of these two roots is unstable and the larger is stable; the state of rest is also stable. We have thus the configuration SUS of the notation used previously.

Figure 6–12 is the *bifurcation diagram*, in which the quantity q is the bifurcation parameter. The ordinates of the curve represent radii of cycles, and stability and instability is indicated by • and ○, respectively. If one starts with negative values of q, the origin O is unstable, and the

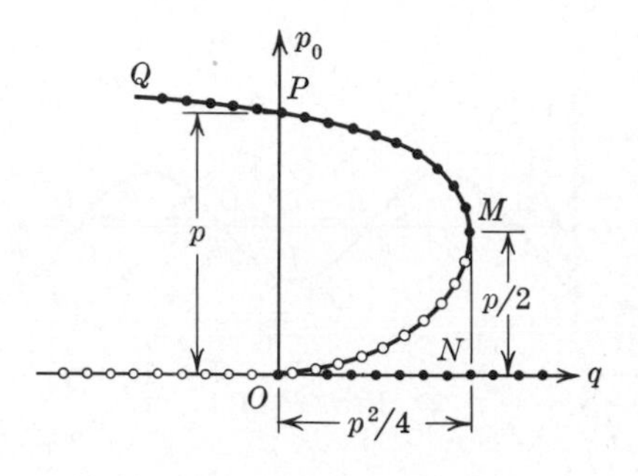

FIG. 6–12.

representative point R will jump on the stable branch. If the parameter q continues to increase, the upper (stable) branch will be traversed from Q to M. The point M is the bifurcation point of the second kind at which the two cycles (stable and unstable) coalesce and disappear. The point R will then drop onto the abscissa axis at the point N, since the abscissa axis is a locus of stable singular points. Nothing especially interesting occurs if q increases; however, if it decreases (causing the representative point to move to the left of N) the topological configuration becomes SUS on the stretch NO. In fact, in this interval the singular point is stable, the inner cycle (arc OM) is unstable, and the outer cycle (on QM) is stable.

At the point O another bifurcation point (of the first kind) is encountered: $SU \rightarrow (SU) \rightarrow U$, resulting in an unstable singular point. Thus, there will be a jump from A to B and the operation will be established on the upper stable cycle.

The two jumps at the bifurcation points form a kind of hysteresis loop, which B. van der Pol and E. Appleton, who discovered the phenomenon, call "oscillation hysteresis."

6.13. Stability (Classical Theory).—In recent years the question of stability has acquired a considerable importance in applications.[9] Here we shall discuss briefly the principal points in the two major trends in studies of stability.

(*A*) *Definition of Stability According to Liapounov.*—Given a system of differential equations of an autonomous system

$$\dot{x}_i = f_i(x_1,x_2,\cdots,x_n); \quad i = 1,\cdots,n \tag{6-35}$$

We define stability as follows:

(1) Let $u_i(t)$ be a solution of Eq. (6–35). (We note in passing that the definition holds also for nonautonomous systems.) We shall say that $u_i(t)$ is *stable* if, given $\varepsilon > 0$ and t_0, there is an $\eta = \eta(\varepsilon,t_0)$ such that any solution $v_i(t)$ for which $|u_i(t_0) - v_i(t_0)| < \eta$ satisfies $|u_i(t) - v_i(t)| < \varepsilon$ for $t \geq t_0$.

(2) If η may be chosen independently of t_0, $u_i(t)$ is said to be *uniformly stable.*

If no such η exists, $u_i(t)$ is said to be unstable.

(3) In the case when $|u_i(t) - v_i(t)| \to 0$ for $t \to \infty$, $u_i(t)$ being stable, the form of stability is called *asymptotic stability.*

One can paraphrase these definitions by saying that a solution (or motion) is stable if all solutions (or motions) which were initially close to it, continue to remain in its neighborhood; a solution (or motion) is asymptotically stable if all neighboring solutions (motions) approach it asymptotically.

These definitions concern open trajectories (or motions). One can also formulate conditions of stability for closed trajectories (or orbits).

(4) If C is an orbit, we call it *orbitally stable* if, given $\varepsilon > 0$, there is $\eta > 0$ such that if R is a representative point following a neighboring trajectory, and R is at a distance η from C at time t_0, then R remains within a distance ε from C for $t > t_0$. If no such η exists, C is orbitally unstable

(5) If C is orbitally stable and, in addition, the distance between R and C tends to zero as $t \to \infty$, this form of stability is called *asymptotic orbital stability.*

The reader can recognize that a stable limit cycle illustrates the definition (5) while a harmonic oscillator illustrates that given by (4).

[9] For a systematic account, see A. M. Liapounov, *General Problem of Stability of Motion*, Charkov, 1892; W. Hahn, *Theorie und Anwendungen der directen Methode von Liapounov*, Springer, Berlin, 1959; L. Cesari, *Asymptotic Behavior and Stability Problems*, Springer, Berlin, 1959.

(*B*) *Variational Equations.*—Consider again a dynamical system whose motion is specified by the differential equation

$$\dot{x}_i = X_i(x_1,\cdots,x_n); \quad i = 1,\cdots,n \tag{6–36}$$

We assume that X_i are continuous twice-differentiable functions of x_i and that a solution $x_{i0} = x_{i0}(t)$ may be regarded as a *nonperturbed motion.*

Consider $x_i(t)$, the neighboring solution, differing from $x_{i0}(t)$ by a function $\xi_i(t)$ so that

$$x_i(t) = x_{i0}(t) + \xi_i(t) \tag{6–37}$$

where $x_i(t)$ may be called the *perturbed solution* and $\xi_i(t)$, the perturbation. We assume that $|\xi_i(t)|$ is sufficiently small to be able to neglect higher powers of $|\xi_i|$.

If one substitutes Eq. (6–37) into (6–36), and cancels out the terms with x_{i0}, he obtains the *variational equations*

$$\dot{\xi}_i = \sum_{j=1}^{n} \left(\frac{\partial X_i}{\partial x_j}\right)_0 \xi_i \tag{6–38}$$

in which the coefficients of ξ_i are partial derivations of X_i with respect to x_j into which the nonperturbed values have been replaced after the differentiation.

Since x_{i0} is the known solution and x_i is the perturbed solution, an important case arises when $\xi_i(t) \to 0$ for $t \to \infty$. In such a case the stability is asymptotic.

It is obvious that for $x_{i0}(t)$ one can take $x_{i0}(0) = 0$, the position of equilibrium, in which case one can call $x_{i0}(0) = 0$ a *constant* or *identically zero solution.* In such a case, one can discuss the *variational equations of singular points.*

(*C*) *Variational Equations of Singular Points.*—One encounters often the differential equations of the form

$$\dot{x} = P(x,y); \qquad \dot{y} = Q(x,y) \tag{6–39}$$

where P and Q are entire series not containing constant terms so that $P(0,0) = Q(0,0) = 0$. In such a case the origin (the singular point) is precisely the identically zero solution of Eq. (6–36). If one develops P and Q about the origin one obtains the first order variational system

$$\frac{d\delta x}{dt} = P_x^0\delta x + P_y^0\delta y; \qquad \frac{d\delta y}{dt} = Q_x^0\delta x + Q_y^0\delta y \tag{6–40}$$

where δx and δy are perturbations (to the first order) and P_x^0, P_y^0, Q_x^0, and Q_y^0 are the partial derivatives of P and Q with respect to x and

y taken at the origin (0,0). It is easily shown that the characteristic Eq. (6–11) in such a case takes the form

$$S^2 - (P_x^0 + Q_y^0)S + (P_x^0 Q_y^0 - P_y^0 Q_x^0) \qquad (6\text{–}41)$$

(*D*) *Variational Equations for Systems with n Variables.*—It can be shown [10] that for differential systems of the form

$$\dot{x}_i = \sum_{j=1}^{n} a_{ij}x_j; \quad i = 1,\cdots,n \qquad (6\text{–}42)$$

where a_{ij} are real constants, the question of stability reduces to the solution of the so-called "secular" or *characteristic* equation

$$\begin{vmatrix} a_{11} - h & a_{12} & \cdots & a_{1n} \\ a_{21} & a_{22} - h & \cdots & a_{2n} \\ \cdot & \cdot & \cdot & \cdot \\ \cdot & \cdot & \cdot & \cdot \\ a_{n1} & a_{n2} & \cdots & a_{nn} - h \end{vmatrix} = 0 \qquad (6\text{–}43)$$

where the h_i are the so-called *characteristic exponents.* We have the theorems:

(1) If the characteristic exponents of (6–42) have negative real parts, the identically zero solution is asymptotically stable.

(2) If one characteristic exponent has a positive real part, it is unstable. The signs of h_i are determined by means of the Hurwitz theorem.

For differential equations with periodic coefficients, the theorems are the same but the calculation of the characteristic exponents meets with difficulty. Whereas in the preceding case (constant coefficients), the coefficients of the characteristic equation are known, in the present case the characteristic equation contains the unknown solutions. Thus, one finds oneself in a vicious circle: to be able to determine the characteristic exponents, one must know the solutions, and in order to know the latter, one must know first these exponents. The only resolution of this difficulty is to proceed by the method of successive approximations.[11]

Summing the question of the variational equations, one must say that in relatively simple systems with constant coefficients, there is no particular difficulty in carrying out these calculations. But in more

[10] See reference 6, Chapter 5, Section 6.

[11] Reference 6, Chapter 13.

complicated systems and, particularly, in those with periodic coefficients, calculations become long and tedious, especially when successive approximations are involved. Moreover, the method by its very nature concerns only the *neighborhood* of the periodic solution and this fact may be expressed by saying that it gives only the *infinitesimal stability*. If the system is perturbed to a greater degree, the method gives no information about the results.

6.14. Stability (Second Method of Liapounov).—In addition to the "first," or classical method (which was closely connected with the method of the variational equations of Poincaré, but was carried out independently and almost simultaneously with the latter) Liapounov developed the so-called second (or "direct") method. This method is extremely general and applicable to linear as well as to nonlinear systems (we recall the fact that the Hurwitz criteria hold only for linear systems). Furthermore, this second method of Liapounov gives the *stability in the large*, which is of great importance in applications, where very often the system is perturbed to a finite extent.

The only difficulty of the method is in finding a certain function V—the function of Liapounov—which permits asserting the validity of the criterion in each special case.

We give first the formulation of the theorem of Liapounov and indicate its significance later.

Definitions: Given the system of differential equations (6–36),

$$\dot{x}_i = X_i(x_1,\cdots,x_n); \quad i = 1,\cdots,n \tag{6–44}$$

in which we assume that X_i assures the existence and uniqueness of the solution, and we define as the eulerian derivative of a function V the expression:

$$\frac{dV}{dt} = \sum_{i=1}^{n} \frac{\partial V}{\partial x_i}\frac{dx_i}{dt} = \sum_{i=1}^{n} \frac{\partial V}{\partial x_i} X_i = W(x_1,\cdots,x_n) \tag{6–45}$$

we have the first theorem of Liapounov:

(*I*) *Given* (6–44) *with a singular point* $x_1 = x_2 = \cdots = x_0 = 0$, *the equilibrium is stable if it is possible to determine a function* $V = V_d$ *in a certain domain* D *whose eulerian derivative* W *is either* W_c *of the sign opposite to* V_d *or which vanishes identically in* D.

A slight modification of the preceding theorem permits establishment of the condition of asymptotic stability:

(*II*) *Given* (6–44) *with the singular point at the origin, the equilibrium is stable asymptotically if it is possible to determine a function* $V = V_d$ *whose eulerian derivative* $W = W_d$ *is of the sign opposite to that of* V_d.

There are also theorems concerning instability, one of which is:

(III) Given (6–44), *the equilibrium is unstable if it is possible to determine a function V whose eulerian derivative is* $W = W_d$, *while V assumes in every neighborhood of* 0 *values for which* $V \cdot W > 0$.

In these theorems the subscript d indicates definite. The following definitions exist: (1) The function $V = V_d$ called *definite* (positive or negative) in a certain domain D if it has values of one sign and vanishes only for $x_1 = x_2 = \cdots = x_n = 0$. Thus $V = x_1^2 + x_2^2 + x_2^3 = V_d$. (2) The function $V = V_c$ if it has the same sign or zero in D. Thus $V = (x_1 + x_2)^2 + x_3^2 = V_c$ as it vanishes for $x_3 = 0$ and $x_1 = -x_2$, otherwise it is positive. (3) The function $V = V_v$ is called indefinite (or of a variable sign) if it changes its sign in any D however small. Thus $V = x_1 = V_v$, $V = x_1^2 + x_2^2 - x_3^4 = V_v$.

Theorems (I) and (II) admit of a simple geometrical interpretation. Consider for instance, $n = 3$ and $V(x_1,x_2,x_3) = V_d > 0$, while $dV/dt = W \leq 0$.

Equations $V(x_1,x_2,x_3) = c$ determine a family of closed surfaces (at least for a sufficiently small c) which shrink to one point for $c \to 0$. For $c_1 < c_2$, the surface $V = c_1$ is enclosed inside $V = c_2$.

Consider a trajectory S of a differential system issuing for $t = t_0$ from a point close to the origin. It is clear that S will never intersect a surface $V = V_c$ from inside to outside as dV/dt is negative.

Thus, if R (the representative point) was initially inside some surface $V = c$, it will continue to remain inside that surface. With the stronger condition, $W < 0$, R will cross successively all surfaces $V = c$ from outside to inside and will thus approach the origin asymptotically. Theorems on instability can be interpreted analogously.

There have been many publications on this subject[9] in recent years, which present the theory at length. Here we mention only a few points that have a particular interest in applications.

1. *Differential Systems.*—For differential systems with constant coefficients the following theorem holds:

If the real parts of the roots of the characteristic equation are negative, there exists one and only one function $V(x_1,\cdots,x_n)$ *for any given* $U(x_1,\cdots,x_n)$; *this function* $U = U_d$ *satisfies the equation*

$$\frac{dV}{dt} = \sum_{i=1}^{n} \frac{\partial V}{\partial x_i}(p_{i1}x_1 + \cdots + p_{in}x_n) = U \tag{6–46}$$

and, moreover, $V = V_d$ of the sign opposite to that of U. For the proof of this theorem see Reference 6, p. 143.

2. *Stability on the Basis of Abridged Equations.*—The argument used in deriving the characteristic equation (3.8) was to neglect $P_2(x,y)$ and $Q_2(x,y)$, and to proceed on the basis of linear terms. It is possible to obtain more precise information regarding the validity of this assumption. Consider the system of differential equations

$$\dot{x}_i = \sum_{j=1}^{n} p_{ij}x_j + X_i(x_1,\cdots,x_n) \qquad (6\text{–}47)$$

where p_{ij} are constants and $X_i(x_1,\cdots,x_n)$ are power series beginning with terms of at least second degree.

The following theorems of Liapounov hold:

(1) *If all roots of the characteristic equation have negative real parts, the point of equilibrium* $x_i = 0$ *is asymptotically stable whatever are the terms* X_i.

(2) *If among roots of the characteristic equation there is at least one with positive real part, the point of equilibrium is unstable whatever the* X_i.

(3) *If the characteristic equation does not have any roots with positive real parts, but has some roots with zero real parts, the terms in* X_i *may influence stability. This case belongs to the so-called "critical" case that requires special investigation.*

In the case when the differential equation contains t explicitly, the formulation of Liapounov's theorems is slightly different, namely:

(1) *If the roots of the characteristic equation for the abridged system* ($X_i = 0$) *have moduli less than one, the zero solution of the system,*

$$\dot{x}_i = p_{i1}(t)x_1 + \cdots + p_{in}(t)x_n + X_i(t,x_1,\cdots,x_n) \qquad (6\text{–}48)$$

is asymptotically stable for any X_i *provided the condition*

$$|X_i(t,x_1,\cdots,x_n)| < A[|x_1| + \cdots + |x_n|]; \quad A \text{ constant} \qquad (6\text{–}49)$$

is satisfied. Moreover X_i in D is continuous and satisfies the usual condition of uniqueness for any initial conditions.

(2) *If among the roots of the characteristic equation of the abridged system there is at least one root with a modulus greater than one, the unperturbed motion is unstable for any* X_i *satisfying the stated conditions if* A *is sufficiently small.*

For proofs of these theorems and other information concerning the second method of Liapounov see references 9 and 12. Before leaving it, however, we point out its major advantages:

(1) The difficult (and often impossible) problem of integration of the variational system is replaced by a much simpler algebraic problem.

(2) The method gives directly the stability in the large instead of the "infinitesimal" stability yielded by the variational equations.

These two basic advantages of the second method make it valuable for applications, particularly the difficult ones of stability of nonlinear control systems.[13]

PART II—ANALYTICAL METHODS

6.15. Introductory Remarks.—As was mentioned in the introduction to this chapter, the quantitative part of the theory of Poincaré was first applied in celestial mechanics.[1] The two approaches; the topological,[2] and the analytical are unrelated in the original publications of Poincaré, and the connection between the two appeared nearly 50 years later when the theory of nonlinear oscillations was developed.

In celestial mechanics difficulties were experienced in connection with the so-called "secular terms," and at the end of the last century there was a tendency to get rid of these secular terms by a proper determination of the available constants (Lindstedt).

This development suggested to Poincaré the possibility of enlarging the problem by attempting to establish conditions of periodicity directly from the differential equations.[1]

In this work Poincaré made a fundamental contribution by indicating a possibility of integrating certain nonlinear differential equations of celestial mechanics by power series in terms of certain parameters. We shall not give this theorem of Poincaré[14] but will briefly mention its applications.

The use of this theory in studies of nonlinear oscillations was suggested in 1929 (by Andronov). At a later date (1937) Krylov and Bogoliubov (K.B.) simplified somewhat the method of attack by a device resembling Lagrange's method of the variation of parameters, and in this form the method became useful for solving practical problems. Most of these early applications were to autonomous systems (mainly the self-excited oscillations), but later the method was extended to

[12] L. Cesari, *Asymptotic Behavior and Stability Problems*, Springer, Berlin, 1959; I. G. Malkin, *Theory of Stability of Motion* (in Russian), Moscow, 1952.

[13] A. M. Letov, *Stability of Nonlinear Control System* (in Russian), Moscow, 1955; English translation, Princeton University Press, Princeton, N.J., 1961.

[14] See Poincaré, *Œuvres*, T. I, p. 58, Gauthier-Villars, Paris, 1928; also E. Goursat, *Cours d'Analyse*, Vol. 3, p. 20, Gauthier-Villars, Paris, 1923.

nonautonomous problems (subharmonic resonance, synchronization, etc.). However, these developments still remained within the framework of the theory of Poincaré, that is, under the assumption that the parameter (or parameters) were small, so as to assure the convergence of the series expansions. All these methods are known under the generic name, *method(s) of small parameters.*

It is important to note that in all these methods, the first term in the series solution constitutes the so-called *approximation of zero order.* This is generally the solution of a simple linear problem: *e.g.*, the harmonic oscillator; the second term appears as the *first approximation,* and so on. The amount of labor increases very rapidly with the order of approximation, but the additional information obtained from approximations of higher orders (beginning with the second) does not increase our knowledge from the *qualitative* point of view. It merely adds small quantitative corrections to the first approximation, and in most applied problems, these corrections are scarcely worth the considerable complication in calculations. For that reason the first approximation is generally sufficient in exploring a new problem, or in investigating the qualitative aspect of a phenomenon.

6.16. Autonomous (A) Versus Nonautonomous (NA) Problems. Practically all nonlinear problems of the theory of oscillations reduce to the differential equation of the form

$$\ddot{x} + x + \mu F(t,x,\dot{x}) = 0 \tag{6-50}$$

where μ is a small parameter and F is an analytic function in x and $\dot{x}$ and periodic in t with period 2π, which can always be assumed by a proper choice of the time scale.

In applications (6-50) is often of the form

$$\ddot{x} + x + \lambda \cos \omega t + \mu f(x,\dot{x}) = 0 \tag{6-51}$$

where λ and ω are constants.

There are two major classes of problems to be investigated; (NA) nonautonomous, and (A) autonomous.[15] In each of these two classes appear two subclasses: (NR) nonresonance oscillations, and (R) resonance oscillations. The treatment of these cases is slightly different.

In the first place, the difference between the (NA) systems and the (A) ones is that for the first there exists always a periodic solution with period 2π (or a rational fraction of 2π), whereas for the second, the period of oscillation (if it exists) is determined by the parameters

[15] It is recalled that a differential equation is called *autonomous* if the independent variable t (time) does not enter explicitly; otherwise it is called *nonautonomous.*

of the system (since $\lambda = 0$) and may be, in general, $2\pi - \tau$, where τ is a nonlinear correction for the period.

Another difference between the (A) and (NA) systems is that for the (A) systems (since t does not enter their equations explicitly), it is possible to replace t by $t + t_0$, t_0 being an arbitrary constant (the phase) and still have the same solution, as was mentioned earlier in this chapter.

Summing up, in the (A) systems the choice of the time origin is at our disposal but not the period; in the (NA) systems, on the contrary, the period is fixed but we cannot change the time origin.

6.17. Problem of Poincaré (Nonresonance Case).—Now consider Eqs. (6–47) or (6–48), which are sufficiently general to furnish a basis for further discussion of these systems. If $\mu = 0$, one has the differential equation of the harmonic oscillator: $\ddot{x} + x = 0$ whose solutions we know. As we assume that μ is small, Eq. (6–50) differs but little from that of the harmonic oscillator; one often says that the two differential equations are in *the neighborhood of* each other. But from this fact one cannot conclude that their solutions (trajectories) are also in the neighborhood of each other. Let us take a simple example: $F(t,x,\dot{x}) = \dot{x}$ and compare the two equations: $\ddot{x} + x = 0$ and $\ddot{x} + \mu\dot{x} + x = 0$. For the first the trajectories are circles, whereas for the second they are spirals, so that for a sufficiently large t the solutions certainly are not in the neighborhood of each other, although the differential equations are.

The establishment of conditions under which a differential equation such as

$$\ddot{x} + x + \mu F(t,x,\dot{x};\mu) = 0 \tag{6–52}$$

has a periodic solution constitutes precisely the problem of Poincaré.

Poincaré introduces two parameters β_1 and β_2 defined by the relations:

$$x(0,\beta_1,\beta_2,\mu) - \varphi(0) = \beta_1; \qquad \dot{x}(0,\beta_1,\beta_2,\mu) - \dot{\varphi}(0) = \beta_2 \tag{6–53}$$

where φ is the so-called generating solution (that is, the solution of (6–52) in which $\mu = 0$). In the case we have cited, this is merely the solution of the harmonic oscillator. The significance of β_1 and β_2 is now obvious: these parameters are the differences between the coordinates (velocities) and of a nonlinear ($\mu \neq 0$) and the corresponding linear ($\mu = 0$) oscillators for $t = t_0 = 0$ (the initial values).

But what are these initial values? This question brings out the difference between the (A) systems and the (NA) systems.

For the former we are at liberty to change the time origin as we please; we can do it so as to reduce one of the β's, say, β_2 to 0, and have only one $\beta_1 = \beta$; but we have no control over the period, which will generally acquire a certain correction τ; so that ultimately we shall have β and τ as parameters.

For the (NA) systems, on the contrary, we cannot change the time origin, so that we have both β_1 and β_2 but, as the period is that of the external periodic excitation (which can be made equal to 2π), no correction applies to it.

At this point two procedures bifurcate, one for the (NA) systems and the other for the (A) systems.

Let us consider first the (NA) case. The condition of periodicity clearly is

$$\begin{aligned} x(2\pi,\beta_1,\beta_2,\mu) - x(0,\beta_1,\beta_2,\mu) &= \psi_1(\beta_1,\beta_2,\mu) = 0 \\ \dot{x}(2\pi,\beta_1,\beta_2,\mu) - \dot{x}(0,\beta_1,\beta_2,\mu) &= \psi_2(\beta_1,\beta_2,\mu) = 0 \end{aligned} \tag{6–54}$$

which means that the coordinates x and $\dot{x}$ at the time $t = 2\pi$ have the same values as they had for $t = 0$. Hence, taking for the initial conditions of the second interval the terminal conditions of the first interval, one obtains exactly the same conclusions in the second interval and the solution x is obviously periodic in such a case, with period 2π.

The conditions of Eq. (6–53) are thus the necessary and sufficient ones for the periodicity of the solution, and it is now necessary to determine the parameters β_1 and β_2 as functions of μ so as to secure the fulfillment of Eqs. (6–53). It is noted that $\beta_1 = \beta_1(\mu)$ and $\beta_2 = \beta_2(\mu)$ such that β_1 and β_2 approach zero when $\mu \to 0$ which follows from their very definition.

On the other hand, in view of the assumed analyticity of the function, we can make use of the theorem of Poincaré, namely that the solution $x(t,\beta_1,\beta_2,\mu)$ can be represented by a series arranged according to the ascending powers of the parameters, that is

$$x(t,\beta_1,\beta_2,\mu) = \varphi(t) + A\beta_1 + B\beta_2 + C\mu + \cdots \tag{6–55}$$

where we have written only the linear terms of the series because we are seeking only the first approximation. The function $\varphi(t)$, as stated above, is the generating solution (when $\mu = 0$) and A, B, and C are the unknown functions of t. (If one wishes to go to approximations of higher order, one has to take more terms of the series of Eq. (6–55) such as $D\beta_1\beta_2 + E\beta_1\mu + F\beta_2\mu + G\mu^2 + \cdots$.)

The procedure is now obvious: if one substitutes Eq. (6–55) in Eq. (6–52) and equates the coefficients of the like powers of $\beta_1,\beta_2,\mu,\cdots$, one obtains first

$$\ddot{A} + k^2A = 0; \qquad \ddot{B} + k^2B = 0 \tag{6–56}$$

with the initial conditions

$$A(0) = 1; \quad \dot{A}(0) = 0; \quad B(0) = 0; \quad \dot{B}(0) = 1 \quad (6\text{–}57)$$

which determines: $A = \cos kt$; $B = 1/k \sin kt$, so that Eqs. (6–54) to the first order become

$$\psi_1(\beta_1,\beta_2,\mu) = [x] = (\cos 2k\pi - 1)\beta_1 + \frac{1}{k}(\sin 2k\pi)\beta_2 + [C]\mu + \cdots$$

$$\psi_2(\beta_1,\beta_2,\mu) = [\dot{x}] = -k(\sin 2k\pi)\beta_1 + (\cos 2k\pi - 1)\beta_2 + [\dot{C}]\mu + \cdots \quad (6\text{–}58)$$

where $[x] = x(2\pi) - x(0)$, etc.

Note that the conditions (6–54) are fulfilled identically for $\mu = \beta_1 = \beta_2 = 0$, in view of what was said previously. However, the jacobian of the left hand terms with β_1 and β_2 is not equal to zero for this $\mu = \beta_1 = \beta_2 = 0$, and is

$$\left[\frac{\partial(\psi_1,\psi_2)}{\partial(\beta_1,\beta_2)}\right]_{\beta_1=\beta_2=\mu=0} = (\cos 2k\pi - 1)^2 + \sin^2 2k\pi \neq 0 \quad (6\text{–}59)$$

Hence, by the implicit functions theorem, one can assert that *for a sufficiently small* μ *there exists only one solution* $\beta_1 = \beta_1(\mu)$, $\beta_2 = \beta_2(\mu)$ *which vanishes with* μ *and, besides, this solution is analytic in* μ. This means that the solution $x(t)$ is of the form:

$$x = x(t) = \varphi(t) + \mu x_1(t) + \mu^2 x_2(t) + \cdots \quad (6\text{–}60)$$

where $x_1(t),x_2(t),\cdots$ are certain periodic functions with period 2π. In order to determine these functions, one substitutes (6–60) into (6–52) and equates coefficients of equal powers of μ. It is to be noted that for this purpose the function $F(t,x,\dot{x},\mu)$ in Equation (6–52) is also developed into a power series around the point $\mu = \beta_1 = \beta_2 = 0$.

The calculations are simple but long and we indicate only the results. For the first approximation corrective terms one has the differential equation

$$\ddot{x}_1 + k^2 x_1 = F_1 = F_1(t,\varphi,\dot{\varphi},0) \quad (6\text{–}61)$$

and similarly for the other terms x_i.

If all $x_1,x_2,\cdots,x_{i-1}$ have been calculated and are periodic, F is then a known periodic function and if k is not an integer, there exists only one periodic solution of the form

$$x_0(t) = -\frac{a_0}{2k^2} - \sum_{n=1}^{\infty} \frac{a_n \cos nt + b_n \sin nt}{k^2 - n^2} = \varphi(t) \quad (6\text{–}62)$$

for all approximations, $x_0(t)$ being the generating solution (for $\mu = 0$).

6.18. Nonlinear Resonance.—The situation is more complicated if k is near to an integer n. One can assume that $n^2 - k^2 \simeq 0(\mu)$, so that $n^2 - k^2 = \mu a$, where a is finite and μ is a small quantity of the first order.

If one includes the terms μax, or $\mu(a'_n \cos nt + b'_n \sin nt)$ in the expression for $\mu F(t,x,\dot{x};\mu)$, (6–52) becomes

$$\ddot{x} + n^2 x + f'(t) = \mu F(t,x,\dot{x};\mu) \tag{6–63}$$

where

$$f'(t) = f(t) - a_n \cos nt - b_n \sin nt = \frac{a_0}{2} + \sum_{j \neq n} [a_j \cos jt + b_j \sin jt]$$

One determines first the generating solution which, in this case, has the form

$$x_0(t) = \varphi(t) + M_0 \cos nt + N_0 \sin nt \tag{6–64}$$

where M_0 and N_0 are arbitrary constants. This solution is periodic for any values of M_0 and N_0, while in the nonresonance case there was only one isolated generating periodic solution. One tries, therefore, to determine M_0 and N_0 in such a manner that Eq. (6–63) should have only one generating solution (for $\mu = 0$).

One starts again with the Poincaré series solution

$$x(t,\beta_1,\beta_2,\mu) = x_0(t) + A\beta_1 + B\beta_2 + C\mu + \cdots \tag{6–65}$$

where as before, the higher order terms have not been written. It is noted that all higher order terms vanish for $\mu = 0$, since in this case Eq. (6–65) becomes the solution of the linear generating equation in which the initial conditions enter only linearly. Thus, one obtains the conditions of periodicity in the form

$$\begin{aligned} \psi_1(\beta_1,\beta_2,\mu) &= \mu\{[C] + [D]\beta_1 + [E]\beta_2 + [F]\mu + \cdots\} \\ \psi_2(\beta_1,\beta_2,\mu) &= \mu\{[\dot{C}] + [\dot{D}]\beta_1 + [\dot{E}]\beta_2 + [\dot{F}]\mu + \cdots\} \end{aligned} \tag{6–66}$$

The problem is similar to that which we had in the preceding section. Ultimately the conditions of periodicity take the form

$$\begin{aligned} \psi_1(\beta_1,\beta_2,\mu) &= \mu\{[C] + [D]\beta_1 + [E]\beta_2 + [F]\mu + \cdots\} = 0 \\ \psi_2(\beta_1,\beta_2,\mu) &= \mu\{[\dot{C}] + [\dot{D}]\beta_1 + [\dot{E}]\beta_2 + [\dot{F}]\mu + \cdots\} = 0 \end{aligned} \tag{6–67}$$

If $\mu = 0$, these conditions are automatically fulfilled; if $\mu \neq 0$ but small, one has to adjust the variables so as to obtain zero values for the bracketed expressions in both equations. Clearly, the problem is now purely algebraic: we take an arbitrary μ under the single condition that it should be small, and we must determine functions $\beta_1(\mu)$ and

$\beta_2(\mu)$ which reduce to zero the expressions in the brackets and, besides, have the property that they vanish together with μ.

In the first place it is necessary that $[C] = 0$ and $[\dot{C}] = 0$, which results in the differential equation

$$\ddot{C} + n^2C = F(t,x_0,\dot{x}_0,0) \tag{6-68}$$

with the initial conditions: $C(0) = \dot{C}(0) = 0$. The solution is then in the form:

$$\begin{aligned} C &= \frac{1}{n}\int_0^t F[\tau,x_0(\tau),\dot{x}(\tau),0] \sin n(t - \tau)d\tau \\ \dot{C} &= \int_0^t F[\tau,x_0(\tau),\dot{x}_0(\tau),0] \cos n(t - \tau)d\tau \end{aligned} \tag{6-69}$$

Replacing x_0 and $\dot{x}_0$ by their values (6-64) one obtains two relations between the constants of integration M_0 and N_0 which fulfill the above conditions, *viz.*:

$$\begin{aligned} P(M_0,N_0) &= \int_0^{2\pi} F[\tau,M_0 \cos n\tau + N_0 \sin n\tau + \varphi(\tau) \\ &\qquad -M_0 n \sin n\tau + N_0 n \cos n\tau + \dot{\varphi}(\tau), 0] \sin n\tau d\tau = 0 \\ Q(M_0,N_0) &= \int_0^{2\pi} F(\cdots) \cos n\tau d\tau = 0 \end{aligned} \tag{6-70}$$

These equations determine the conditions under which the correspondence between the generating solution (6-64) and the original nonlinear differential equation (6-63) is assured.

This situation may be visualized as follows. There exists a family of solutions (depending on parameters M_0 and N_0) to which the actual generating solution of the nonlinear problem belongs and conditions (6-70) guarantee that out of that family one unique solution is selected which is precisely the generating solution of the nonlinear equation (6-63).

Once the constants M_0 and N_0 are determined, the rest of the problem does not present any difficulty. In fact we now have:

$$\begin{aligned} \psi_1' &= [D]\beta_1 + [E]\beta_2 + [F]\mu + \cdots = 0 \\ \psi_2' &= [\dot{D}]\beta_1 + [\dot{E}]\beta_2 + [\dot{F}]\mu + \cdots = 0 \end{aligned} \tag{6-71}$$

and those algebraic equations can be solved for $\beta_1(\mu)$ and $\beta_2(\mu)$ (for any arbitrary small μ) provided the jacobian

$$J = \left[\frac{\partial(\psi_1',\psi_2')}{\partial(\beta_1,\beta_2)}\right]_{\beta_1 = \beta_2 = \mu = 0} = \begin{bmatrix} [D][E] \\ [\dot{D}][\dot{E}] \end{bmatrix} \neq 0 \tag{6-72}$$

In fact in this case there is one and only one solution $\beta_i(\mu)$ for which $\beta_i(0) = 0$, and this is the solution analytic in μ.

If one substitutes this solution into $x(t,\beta_1,\beta_2,\mu)$ he obtains a periodic solution of Eq. (6–63) analytic in μ.

The rest of the problem reduces to the actual calculation of $[D]$, $[E]$, $\cdots$. For this purpose one substitutes for x and $\dot{x}$ the corresponding series, Eq. (6–65), develops F in Eq. (6–63) about the point $\mu = 0$ and, after this has been done, identifies the coefficients of the terms with $\beta_1\mu$ and $\beta_2\mu$.

Omitting these intermediate calculations, one obtains finally the desired expressions

$$[D] = -\frac{1}{n}\frac{\partial P}{\partial M_0}; \qquad [\dot{D}] = \frac{\partial Q}{\partial M_0}; \qquad [E] = -\frac{1}{n^2}\frac{\partial P}{\partial N_0}; \qquad [\dot{E}] = \frac{1}{n}\frac{\partial Q}{\partial N_0} \tag{6–73}$$

so that the jacobian becomes

$$\begin{bmatrix} [D][E] \\ [\dot{D}][\dot{E}] \end{bmatrix} = -\frac{1}{n^2}\frac{\partial(P,Q)}{\partial(M_0,N_0)} \tag{6–74}$$

This constitutes the essential difference from the nonresonance case in which one solution ($\mu \neq 0$) goes into the other ($\mu = 0$) without any possible multiplicity of choices. Here, in the resonance case, in view of the multiplicity (family) of periodic solutions for $\mu = 0$, one has to narrow down this choice by the conditions stated in Eqs. (6–70).

This method was applied for the first time by L. Mandelstam and N. Papalexi in connection with the theory of the subharmonic resonance (Reference 6, p. 464).

6.19. Autonomous Systems.—The preceding argument, at least in principle, holds also for the autonomous systems but, as was mentioned in Section 6–17, the parameters here are different. In fact instead of β_1 and β_2 we have here only one β but, in addition, there appears here another parameter, τ, the nonlinear period correction.

Owing to the "translation property" of autonomous systems, one can always select the time origin so that $\dot{x}(0,\beta,\mu) = 0$, in which case the conditions of periodicity (compare with Eq. 6–54) become now

$$\begin{aligned} x(T+\tau,\beta,\mu) - x(0,\beta,\mu) &= x(T+\tau,\beta,\mu) - M_0 - \beta = 0 \\ \dot{x}(T+\tau,\beta,\mu) &= 0 \end{aligned} \tag{6–75}$$

where $M_0 = x_0(0)$ and T is the "linear period." One expands these expressions in terms of τ, which gives

$$\begin{aligned} x(T,\beta,\mu) + \dot{x}(T,\beta,\mu)\tau + \tfrac{1}{2}[-k^2x(T,\beta,\mu) + \cdots]\tau^2 + \cdots - M_0 - \beta &= 0 \\ \dot{x}(T,\beta,\mu) + [-k^2x(T,\beta,\mu) + \cdots]\tau &= 0 \end{aligned} \tag{6–76}$$

The series of Poincaré in this case is:

$$x(t,\beta,\mu) = x_0(t) + A\beta + \mu[C + D\beta + E\mu + \cdots] \tag{6-77}$$

Proceeding as in Section 6–18 one obtains

$$\tau = \mu\left[\frac{1}{M_0k^2}\dot{C}\left(\frac{2\pi}{k}\right) + \cdots\right] \tag{6-78}$$

If one limits the approximation only to the first order, one obtains the equation

$$\mu\left[C\left(\frac{2\pi}{k}\right) + D\left(\frac{2\pi}{k}\right)\beta + Q\mu + \cdots\right] = 0 \tag{6-79}$$

Q being some coefficient.

We have now the same problem as in Section 6–18; we wish to determine the function $\beta(\mu)$ for any small arbitrary μ such that $\beta(\mu) \to 0$ when $\mu \to 0$. The necessary condition is $C(2\pi/k) = 0$; if $D(2\pi/k) \neq 0$, the solution for β will be unique and analytic.

One obtains again the linear differential equation for the determination of the functions C and D, namely:

$$\ddot{C} + k^2C = f(x_0,\dot{x}_0,0); \qquad \ddot{D} + k^2D = f_{x_0}\cos kt - f_{\dot{x}_0}\sin kt$$

with the initial conditions:

$$C(0) = \dot{C}(0) = D(0) = \dot{D}(0) = 0$$

where the symbols f_{x_0} and $f_{\dot{x}_0}$ designate the partial derivatives of f with respect to x and $\dot{x}$ into which the generating solutions have been substituted after the differentiation.

One obtains finally

$$\begin{aligned} C &= \frac{1}{k}\int_0^t f(x_0,\dot{x}_0,0)\sin k(t-\tau')d\tau' \\ D &= \frac{1}{k}\int_0^t [(f_{x_0}\cos k\tau' - kf_{\dot{x}_0}\sin k\tau')\sin k(t-\tau')]d\tau' \equiv \frac{\partial C}{\partial M_0} \end{aligned} \tag{6-80}$$

Therefore, the condition appears ultimately (after a change of the variable) as

$$P(M_0) = \int_0^{2\pi} f(M_0\cos u, -kM_0\sin u, 0)\sin u\,du = 0 \tag{6-81}$$

6.20. Remark.—There is one difficulty worth mentioning. In taking the solution of the form: $x(t) = x_0(t) + \mu x_1(t) + \cdots$ for autonomous systems, one encounters a complication arising from the fact that the period is not T but $T + \tau(\mu)$, μ being the nonlinear period correction.

In other words, the actual period depends on μ and, in view of this, in the condition for periodicity

$$x_0\left(t + \frac{2\pi}{k} + \tau\right) + \mu x_1\left(t + \frac{2\pi}{k} + \tau\right) + \cdots = x_0(t) + \mu x_1(t) + \cdots \tag{6–82}$$

it is impossible to assert that $x_s(t + 2\pi/k + \tau) = x_s(t)$ because the left-hand side depends on μ (through $\tau(\mu)$), whereas the right hand side is independent of μ. This can be seen from the following obvious example:

$$\sin(1 + \mu)t = \sin t + \mu t \cos t - \frac{\mu^2 t^2}{2} \sin t + \cdots \tag{6–83}$$

which shows that the function $\sin(1 + \mu)t$ has nonperiodic coefficients. This is due to the fact that the period is $2\pi/(1 + \mu)$ and thus depends on μ. This complicates the analysis as, from the form of such a solution, it is impossible to say whether the solution is periodic or not.

In order to obviate this difficulty, Krylov and Bogoliubov suggested the transformation

$$T = \frac{2\pi}{k} + \tau = \frac{2\pi}{k}(1 + h_1\mu + h_2\mu^2 + \cdots) \tag{6–84}$$

where h_i are certain unknown constants and T is the period of the solution. This amounts to replacing t in the differential equation

$$\ddot{x} + k^2 x = \mu f(x,\dot{x},\mu) \tag{6–85}$$

by

$$t = \frac{\tau}{k}(1 + h_1\mu + h_2\mu^2 + \cdots) \tag{6–86}$$

in which case the period is 2π. For further details of this transformation, see Reference 6, p. 247.

We have entered into some details of the method of Poincaré because it opened an entirely new approach to nonlinear problems encountered in applications. Moreover, the method is very general, since by taking more terms in the series solution (6–65), one can obtain approximations of higher order. However, the drawback of the method is its complexity, which resulted in efforts being directed toward a simplification of the calculating procedure.

6.21. Methods of van der Pol and of Krylov-Bogoliubov (K.B.). The two methods are closely related to each other but chronologically the van der Pol method precedes that of K.B.

The nature of these methods can be explained in the following way. Suppose we have a nearly-linear differential equation

$$\ddot{x} + x + \mu f(x,\dot{x}) = 0 \tag{6–87}$$

Instead of trying to satisfy it by a power series in terms of μ (or related parameters β_1 and β_2) as does Poincaré, we propose to satisfy it by a simple periodic solution, for instance

$$x = a \cos t + b \sin t \tag{6–88}$$

where a and b are certain unknown functions of t, as is assumed by van der Pol.

In the Krylov-Bogoliubov version, this steady state solution is assumed in the form

$$x = a \sin (t + \varphi) \tag{6–89}$$

where again a and φ are unknown functions to be determined.

As the argument is the same in both cases, the difference being in the system of coordinates used—cartesian coordinates in the van der Pol case and polar ones in the K.B. case, we shall follow the K.B. exposition, which is somewhat more convenient, as it deals directly with the amplitude a and the phase φ.[16] We comply with the K.B. notations by writing Eq. (6–87)

$$\ddot{x} + \omega^2 x + \mu f(x,\dot{x}) = 0 \tag{6–90}$$

and, accordingly, (6–89) becomes

$$x = a \sin (\omega t + \varphi); \qquad \dot{x} = a\omega \cos (\omega t + \varphi) \tag{6–91}$$

It is noted that $\dot{x}$ in (6–91) already contains a certain condition. In fact, since both a and φ are unknown functions of t, one should write:

$$x = a \sin (\omega l + \varphi) + a\omega \cos (\omega t + \varphi) + a\dot{\varphi} \cos (\omega t + \varphi) \tag{6–92}$$

In order to be able to write $\dot{x}$ in the form of (6–91), it is necessary to set:

$$\dot{a} \sin (\omega t + \varphi) + a\dot{\varphi} \cos (\omega t + \varphi) = 0 \tag{6–93}$$

If one differentiates the second equation of (6–91) one obtains

$$\ddot{x} = \dot{a}\omega \cos (\omega t + \varphi) - a\omega^2 \sin (\omega t + \varphi) - a\omega\dot{\varphi} \sin (\omega t + \varphi) \tag{6–94}$$

[16] We shall return to the van der Pol procedure in Section 6–25.

If one substitutes x, $\dot{x}$, and $\ddot{x}$ into Eq. (6–90), one has

$$\dot{a}\omega \cos(\omega t + \varphi) - a\omega\dot{\varphi} \sin(\omega t + \varphi) + \mu f[a \sin(\omega t + \varphi), a\omega \cos(\omega t + \varphi)] = 0 \tag{6–95}$$

Solving Eqs. (6–93) and (6–95) for $\dot{a}$ and $\dot{\varphi}$, one has:

$$\begin{aligned} \dot{a} &= -\frac{\mu}{\omega} f[a \sin(\omega t + \varphi), a\omega \cos(\omega t + \varphi)] \cos(\omega t + \varphi) \\ \dot{\varphi} &= \frac{\mu}{a\omega} f[a \sin(\omega t + \varphi), a\omega \cos(\omega t + \varphi)] \sin(\omega t + \varphi) \end{aligned} \tag{6–96}$$

Thus the original differential equation (6–90) of the second order has been replaced by the system (6–96) of two first order differential equations in terms of the amplitude a and the phase φ. Moreover, as Eqs. (6–96) contain the small factor μ on the right-hand side, the quantities $\dot{a}$ and $\dot{\varphi}$ are small, that is, both a and φ are *slowly varying functions of time* and one can assume that during one period $T = 2\pi/\omega$, the trigonometric functions vary but slightly.

Therefore, it is permissible, to consider a and φ as constants during the time T.

On the other hand, the functions $f(a \sin \varphi,\ a\omega \cos \varphi) \cos \varphi$ and $f(a \sin \varphi,\ a\omega \cos \varphi) \sin \varphi$ can be developed in the two trigonometric series

$$\begin{aligned} &K_0(a) + \sum_{n=1}^{\infty} [K_n(a) \cos n\varphi + L_n(a) \sin n\varphi] \\ &P_0(a) + \sum_{n=1}^{\infty} [P_n(a) \cos n\varphi + Q_n(a) \sin n\varphi] \end{aligned} \tag{6–97}$$

Where the coefficients $K_n(a), \cdots$ etc. are calculated in the usual manner. The substitution of these expressions into (6–96) results in rather complicated expressions which we do not write in full.

However, if one integrates these expressions between t and $t + T$ under the above assumption of *constancy of* a and φ during the time T, all trigonometric terms drop out and one obtains the expressions

$$\begin{aligned} \frac{a(t + T) - a(t)}{T} &= -\frac{\mu}{\omega} K_0[a(t)] \\ \frac{\varphi(t + T) - \varphi(t)}{T} &= \frac{\mu}{a\mu} P_0[a(t)] \end{aligned} \tag{6–98}$$

Since the variations Δa and $\Delta\varphi$ during T are small, one can pass from the difference equations (6–98) to the following differential equations of the first approximation [17]

$$\dot{a} = -\frac{\mu}{\omega} K_0(a); \qquad \dot{\varphi} = \frac{\mu}{a\omega} P_0(a) \tag{6–99}$$

If one replaces $K_0(a)$ and $P_0(a)$ by their Fourier expressions one obtains the differential equation of the first approximation of the K.B. theory

$$\dot{a} = -\frac{\mu}{\omega}\frac{1}{2\pi}\int_0^{2\pi} f(a \sin \varphi, a\omega \cos \varphi) \cos \varphi d\varphi = \Phi(a) \tag{6–100}$$

$$\dot{\psi} = \omega + \frac{\mu}{a\omega}\frac{1}{2\pi}\int_0^{2\pi} f(a \sin \varphi, a\omega \cos \varphi) \sin \varphi d\varphi = \Omega(a) \tag{6–101}$$

As these differential equations are well known and are used in many applied problems, we do not discuss them further.

However, there is one other point to be mentioned. In the early (1937) theory of K.B., the theory of the first approximation follows directly from the assumption of the sinusoidal solution, as explained above. In order to obtain approximations of higher order, it became necessary to use an auxiliary perturbation procedure.

From this point of view the early K.B. theory was somewhat less general than the theory of Poincaré, in which higher approximations are obtained by taking more terms in the series Eq. (6–55).

In 1958 N. N. Bogoliubov and Y. A. Mitropolsky (B.M.) published a treatise entitled *Asymptotic Methods in the Theory of Nonlinear Oscillations*,[18] which presents a considerable generalization of the early K.B. theory. Since a detailed account of this work is beyond the scope of this book, we give only a few of its salient points.

Instead of seeking a simple periodic solution of the type of Eq. (6–89), Bogoliubov and Mitropolsky seek a solution of the form

$$x = a \cos \psi + \mu u_1(a,\psi) + \mu^2 u_2(a,\psi) + \cdots \tag{6–102}$$

where $u_1(a,\psi)$, $u_2(u,\psi)$, $\cdots$ are periodic in the angular variable ψ (period 2π). Then a and ψ, considered as functions of t, are determined by the differential equations

$$\begin{aligned} \frac{da}{dt} &= \mu A_1(a) + \mu^2 A_2(a) + \cdots \\ \frac{d\psi}{dt} &= \omega + \mu B_1(a) + \mu^2 B_2(a) + \cdots \end{aligned} \tag{6–103}$$

[17] This presupposes also that T is small in comparison to the total duration of the process so that one can treat T as dt.

[18] This book will appear shortly in an English translation.

The problem now is to determine $u_1(a,\psi)$, $u_2(a,\psi)$, $A_1(a)$, $B_1(a)$, $A_2(a)$, $B_2(a)$, $\cdots$ so that Eq. (6–102), in which a and ψ are replaced by their expressions as functions of t, becomes the solution of the original equation

$$\ddot{x} + \omega^2 x = \mu f(x,\dot{x}) \tag{6–104}$$

The advantage of this procedure is that, as soon as the coefficients of the terms in Eq. (6–102) are determined, the integration of Eq. (6–104) is reduced to that of the system (6–103) in which the variables are separated.

In these calculations an additional condition is imposed:

$$\begin{aligned} &\int_0^{2\pi} u_1(a,\psi)\cos\psi d\psi = 0; \qquad \int_0^{2\pi} u_2(a,\psi)\cos\psi d\psi = 0; \cdots \\ &\int_0^{2\pi} u_1(a,\psi)\sin\psi d\psi = 0; \qquad \int_0^{2\pi} u_2(a,\psi)\sin\psi d\psi = 0; \cdots \end{aligned} \tag{6–105}$$

This means that the quantity a is determined as the full amplitude of the fundamental harmonic.

The calculations are very extensive, and are given in Reference 6, p. 329.

Their advantage is that the determination of functions $u_1, u_2, \cdots$ is reduced to the system

$$\begin{aligned} \omega^2\left(\frac{\partial^2 u_1}{\partial\psi^2} + u_1\right) &= f_0(a,\psi) + 2\omega A_1 \sin\psi + 2\omega B_1 \cos\psi \\ \omega^2\left(\frac{\partial^2 u_2}{\partial\psi^2} + u_2\right) &= f_1(a,\psi) + 2\omega A_2 \sin\psi + 2\omega B_2 \cos\psi \end{aligned} \tag{6–106}$$

which permits determining successive approximations with any desired accuracy.

In the reference cited in footnote 18, very long calculations are made by which all functions $(u_1, u_2, \cdots, A_1, A_2, \cdots, B_1, B_2, \cdots)$ are determined, and applications are developed from the general formulas so established. There are numerous applications indicated in the text illustrating the operation of this method.

In line with the general asymptotic method, Mitropolsky introduced a further generalization[19] by means of an additional independent variable τ (the "slow time"), whereby it becomes possible to investigate not only the stationary state, but also the transient one.

[19] Y. A. Mitropolsky, *Non-stationary processes in nonlinear oscillatory systems*, English translation by Air Technical Intelligence Center, Ohio.

This enlarges the scope of problems that can be treated by these asymptotic methods. For example, the important problem of nonlinear resonance could otherwise be solved only in the stationary state. With this extension it is possible to determine what happens when the zone of resonance is passed at a certain rate. Likewise, with the additional extension for the "slow time" it is possible to attack the problem of modulated oscillations, which has previously remained outside the scope of the general theory.

These *asymptotic methods*, as the name implies are not determined by the convergence of the series (6–102) and (6–103) for $m \to \infty$, but by their asymptotic properties for a fixed m and $\mu \to 0$.

6.22. Stroboscopic Method.—This method was developed a few years ago by the writer in collaboration with M. Schiffer, and is based on the transformation theory of differential equations.[20] We shall give here only the heuristic approach to this method, referring for its analytical proof to other published material.[21]

The principle is to consider a differential equation as an *operator* which after some time (which will be assumed to be 2π) transfers the representative point R from a point A of the phase plane to some other point B. This process can be written conventionally as

$$\mathscr{T}(A) = B \tag{6–107}$$

As an example, consider the differential equation: $\ddot{x} + x = 0$ of the harmonic oscillator, whose trajectories are circles. Choose one of these circles (corresponding to given initial conditions) and on this circle take a point A for $t = 0$. The transformation effected by this differential equation after the time 2π will result in a return to the same point, which can be written as

$$\mathscr{T}(A) = A \tag{6–108}$$

which means an *identical transformation.*

One can interpret this physically as follows: suppose that the trajectory of the harmonic oscillator be represented by a point on a rotating wheel. The eye observes a circle (the path of the point) if the wheel rotates rapidly; this corresponds to continuous illumination. On the other hand, if one illuminates the rotating wheel with stroboscopic flashes separated by a period 2π, a given mark on the wheel appears as a fixed point. Thus, under continuous illumination one "sees"

[20] N. Minorsky, *C.R. Ac. Sc.* (Paris), T.232 (1951); Rendiconti, *Acc. Sc*, Bologna (1952); *Cahiers de physique*, No. 119, Paris (1960).

[21] R. Gomory (Reference 6, Chapter 16); M. Urabe, *U. Science*, University of Hiroshima (1956).

a circular trajectory, and under stroboscopic illumination with period 2π one sees only one fixed point; call the first case the plane (ψ) and the second one, the plane (φ).

The two planes in reality are the same plane, but one merely *sees it* differently. In this case the matter is so simple that no further explanation is necessary, but serves to clarify further generalizations.

As the next example consider the van der Pol equation:

$$\ddot{x} + \mu(x^2 - 1)\dot{x} + x = 0$$

as operator of the transformation. As we know from the theory of the first approximation, the phase portrait of this equation is *US*, that is, an unstable singular point is surrounded by a stable limit cycle. The nonclosed trajectories are spirals (C in Fig. 6–13) winding themselves

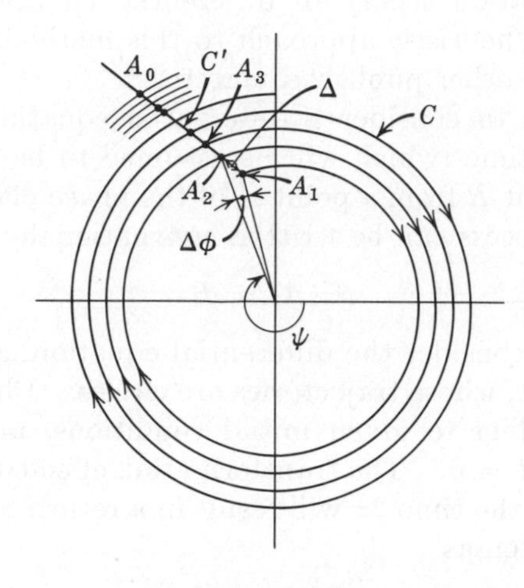

FIG. 6–13.

onto a circle of radius 2, both from inside and from outside. Moreover as the period is constant at 2π in the first approximation, the stroboscopic motion occurs along the radius, stroboscopic points approaching the fixed point A_0 both from outside $(A_1, A_2, \cdots)$ and from inside. Since the phase of the flashes is arbitrary, the above statement holds for *any radius* and one can say that the limit cycle is a locus of fixed points for stroboscopic points approaching them from all directions both from inside and from outside. One can specify this condition by writing:

$$\mathcal{T}^n_{n\to\infty}(r_0) \to 2; \qquad \mathcal{T}^n_{n\to\infty}(\varphi_0) = \varphi_0 \tag{6–109}$$

In this case we have to consider the transformation repeated n times (where $n \to \infty$) applied separately to the radius r and to the phase φ. The first tends to the asymptotic limit $r^* = 2$, but the second results in the identical transformation to the first approximation.

From this intuitive approach we can develop some further conclusions.

Suppose that we have a differential system:

$$\dot{x} = X(x,y,t); \qquad \dot{y} = Y(x,y,t) \tag{6-110}$$

We introduce the new variables defined by equations

$$\rho = r^2 = x^2 + \dot{x}^2 = x^2 + y^2; \qquad \psi = \arctan(y/x)$$
$$x = r\cos\psi; \qquad y = r\sin\psi$$

One can introduce these variables by means of the relations

$$x\dot{x} + y\dot{y} = \tfrac{1}{2}(d\rho/dt); \qquad x\dot{y} - y\dot{x} = \rho(d\psi/dt) \tag{6-111}$$

as one verifies easily. Once this change of the variables is made and x and y are replaced by $r\cos\psi$ and $r\sin\psi$ respectively, (6–110) takes the form

$$\frac{d\rho}{dt} = F(\rho,\psi,t); \qquad \frac{d\psi}{dt} = G(\rho,\psi,t) \tag{6-112}$$

where F and G are periodic functions in t with period 2π.

As we wish to consider Eqs. (6–110) as a nearly linear system (that is, in the neighborhood of the harmonic oscillator), the differential equations of the latter in the ρ,ψ variables are

$$\frac{d\rho}{dt} = 0; \qquad \frac{d\omega}{dt} = -1 \tag{6-113}$$

As $\rho = x^2 + \dot{x}^2$ is the measure of the total energy stored in the oscillator, the first equation of (6–113) merely expresses the law of conservation of energy, and the second means that the frequency is unity; the minus sign indicates that the rotation on trajectories is clockwise, whereas the angles are measured counterclockwise.

We can write Eq. (6–112) in the form:

$$\frac{d\rho}{dt} = \mu f(\rho,\psi,t) + \cdots; \qquad \frac{d\psi}{dt} = -1 + \mu g(\rho,\psi,t) + \cdots \tag{6-114}$$

as follows from the analyticity in terms of μ. These equations reduce to Eq. (6–113) for $\mu = 0$.

We can now undertake the integration by means of the series

$$\rho(t) = \rho_0(t) + \mu\rho_1(t) + \cdots; \qquad \psi(t) = \psi_0(t) + \mu\psi_1(t) + \cdots \quad (6\text{–}115)$$

where the nonwritten terms are of higher order (that is, we limit ourselves to the first approximation, since μ is small). We now replace ρ and ψ in Eqs. (6–114) by their expressions in (6–115) and identify terms of like powers of μ. We obtain thus the "zero order" approximation:

$$\rho_0(t) = \rho_0 = \text{const.}; \qquad \psi_0(t) = \varphi_0 - t \quad (6\text{–}116)$$

the constants ρ_0 and ψ_0 being clearly the initial conditions. The first order corrective terms $\rho_1(t)$ and $\psi_1(t)$ are given by the expressions

$$\rho_1(t) = \int_0^t f(\rho_0,\varphi_0 - \sigma,\sigma)d\sigma; \qquad \psi_1(t) = \int_0^t g(\rho_0,\varphi_0 - \sigma,\sigma)d\sigma \quad (6\text{–}117)$$

so that the solution in the first approximation is

$$\rho(t) = \rho_0 + \mu\rho_1(t); \qquad \psi(t) = \varphi_0 - t + \mu\psi_1(t) \quad (6\text{–}118)$$

At this point a difficulty appears; we cannot increase t indefinitely, as we have neglected higher order terms and this may impair the accuracy of the approximation in the long run. Therefore, we adopt the following procedure. Instead of letting t vary indefinitely in the expressions for $\rho_1(t)$ and $\psi_1(t)$ we vary it only during an interval from 0 to 2π. We take the terminal conditions of the first interval 2π as the initial conditions of the second interval, and so on. In such a case the error is kept small in each interval and does not accumulate, which might occur due to the higher order terms omitted in the first approximation, if we let $t \to \infty$.

In other words, we replace a continuous process by a sequence of transformations of the form

$$\rho_1(2\pi) = K'(\rho_0,\varphi_0); \qquad \psi_1(2\pi) = L'(\rho_0,\varphi_0) \quad (6\text{–}119)$$

where $K'(\rho_0,\varphi_0)$ and $L'(\rho_0,\varphi_0)$ are the integrals of (6–117) taken between 0 and 2π; we note that the variable t has disappeared in these integrations as these definite integrals are merely certain *numbers*, functions of the initial conditions.

As $\rho(t) = \rho_0 + \mu\rho_1(t)$ and $\psi(t) = \psi_0 + \mu\psi_1(t)$ and, in view of the remark just made, the result can be specified by the formulas

$$\rho(2\pi) = K(\rho_0,\varphi_0); \qquad \varphi(2\pi) = L(\rho_0,\varphi_0) \quad (6\text{–}120)$$

We have replaced ψ by φ as ψ is an angular variable and we are interested only in its variation φ (modulo 2π).

Equations (6–120) can be written also in the form (6–118)

$$\rho' = \rho + \mu\rho_1; \qquad \varphi' = \varphi + \mu\varphi_1 \tag{6–121}$$

where ρ' and φ' are the values ρ and φ at the end of the transformation and ρ and φ mean the values at the beginning of the interval 2π.

Setting $\rho' - \rho = \Delta\rho$; $\varphi' - \varphi = \Delta\varphi$ and taking out the factor 2π appearing in integrations, (6–121) becomes

$$\Delta\rho = 2\pi\mu K(\rho_0,\varphi_0); \qquad \Delta\varphi = 2\pi\mu L(\rho_0,\varphi_0) \tag{6–122}$$

So far (beginning with 6–119) we have purely numerical relations as the independent variable t (time) has disappeared in integrations (6–117). It is useful, however, to reintroduce the time element by defining

$$2\pi\mu = \Delta\tau \tag{6–123}$$

as an element of the *stroboscopic time t*. Equations (6–122) become then:

$$\frac{\Delta\rho}{\Delta\tau} = K(\rho_0,\varphi_0); \qquad \frac{\Delta\varphi}{\Delta\tau} = L(\rho_0,\varphi_0) \tag{6–124}$$

These are the difference equations that determine $\Delta\rho/\Delta\tau$ and $\Delta\varphi/\Delta\tau$ from the knowledge of the initial conditions ρ_0,φ_0 for given intervals $(0,2\pi; 2\pi,4\pi; \cdots$, etc.).

In our optical analogy, they permit calculating the stroboscopic point (ρ_1,φ_1) if one knows (ρ_0,φ_0); then (ρ_2,φ_2) after (ρ_1,φ_1) has been determined and so on.

If the process lasts long enough in comparison with the duration of the period 2π, one may consider (approximately) Δt, $\Delta\rho$, and $\Delta\varphi$ as dt, $d\rho$, and $d\varphi$ respectively and to pass thus from the difference equations (6–124) to the *stroboscopic differential equations.*

$$\frac{d\rho}{d\tau} = K(\rho,\varphi); \qquad \frac{d\varphi}{d\tau} = L(\rho,\varphi) \tag{6–125}$$

The relation between the discontinuous procedure of Eqs. (6–124) and the continuous idealization of Eq. (6–125) is the same as that which exists between the sequence of discrete stroboscopic points and the pseudocontinuous motion of the point of the wheel which appears to the eye owing to the persistence of vision.

Equations (6–125) are fundamental in what follows. The smaller the value of μ, the better the approximation becomes.

It is noted that the system is now autonomous, although the initial system is nonautonomous.

One can formulate the theorem:

(*I*) *The existence of a stable singular point of* (6–125) *is the criterion for the existence of a stable periodic solution* (*motion*) *of the original system* (6–112).

The problem (6–125) is much simpler than (6–112) particularly because to be able to ascertain the stability of the periodic solution of Equation (6–112) it is necessary to calculate the characteristic exponents (Section 6.12) which is generally a very difficult problem. In the case of Eq. (6–125) this reduces to ascertaining the stability of the singular point, which does not present any difficulty.

Finally, in the first approximation the amplitude (*i.e.*, the radius vector) ρ_0 of the singular point gives the radius of the periodic solution (which is a circle in the first approximation).

In view of this, it is generally much simpler to treat the problem in terms of the stroboscopic differential equation than to attack it directly on the basis of the original differential equation (6–112).

6.23. Examples of Application of the Stroboscopic Method.— We can consider two differential equations.

$$\ddot{x} + (1 + a \cos 2t)x = 0 \tag{6–126}$$

$$\ddot{x} + b\dot{x} + (1 + a \cos 2t)x + cx^3 = 0 \tag{6–127}$$

Both these equations are of the Mathieu type*; (6–126) is linear and (6–127) nonlinear on account of the term cx^3. It is well known that in the linear case one can eliminate the term $b\dot{x}$ by the classical transformation of the dependent variable. In the nonlinear case this is impossible and one has to keep the term $b\dot{x}$.

As we wish to stay within the scope of the small parameters method, we assume that a, b, and c are small numbers.

Let us take first the linear equation (6–126).

The equivalent system is

$$\dot{x} = y; \qquad \dot{y} = -x - ax \cos 2t \tag{6–128}$$

To introduce the polar coordinates $\rho = r^2 = x^2 + \dot{x}^2 = x^2 + y^2$; $\psi = \arctan(y/x)$ we form two combinations: $x\dot{x} + y\dot{y} = \frac{1}{2}(d\rho/dt)$; $x\dot{y} - y\dot{x} = \rho(d\psi/dt)$ which yield two differential equations

$$\frac{d\rho}{dt} = -a\rho \sin 2\psi \cos 2t; \qquad \frac{d\psi}{dt} = -1 - a \cos^2 \psi \cos 2t \tag{6–129}$$

* H. Margenau and G. Murphy, *Mathematics of Physics and Chemistry*, D. Van Nostrand Co., Inc., Princeton, N.J., 1956, p. 78.

As a is a small parameter, we can use it in the series solution

$$\rho(t) = \rho_0(t) + a\rho_1(t) + \cdots; \qquad \psi(t) = \psi_0(t) + a\psi_1(t) + \cdots \tag{6–130}$$

where the nonwritten terms are of higher order, and are not needed for the first approximation.

Substituting values of $\rho(t)$ and $\psi(t)$ of (6–130) in (6–129) and identifying terms with like powers of a, we obtain for the approximation of the zero order (*i.e.*, terms no containing a)

$$\rho_0(t) = \rho_0; \qquad \psi_0(t) = \varphi_0 - t \tag{6–131}$$

which represent the generating solution (of the harmonic oscillator: ($a = 0$) where ρ_0 and φ_0 are the initial conditions.

We substitute (6–131) into (6–130) to obtain equations for the first order corrective terms (*i.e.*, the differential equations for $d\rho_1/dt$ and $d\psi_1/dt$) and obtain

$$\frac{d\rho_1}{dt} = -\rho_0 \sin 2(\varphi_0 - t) \cos 2t; \qquad \frac{d\psi_1}{dt} = -\cos^2(\varphi_0 - t) \cos 2t \tag{6–132}$$

The integration between 0 and 2π yields

$$\rho_1(2\pi) = -\rho_0 \sin 2\varphi_0 \int_0^{2\pi} \cos^2 2t dt = -\tfrac{1}{2} 2\pi\rho_0 \sin 2\varphi_0 \tag{6–133}$$

whence

$$\rho(2\pi) = \Delta\rho = -\pi a \cdot \rho_0 \sin 2\varphi_0$$

Setting $2\pi a = \Delta\tau$, this equation becomes

$$\frac{\Delta\rho}{\Delta\tau} = -\tfrac{1}{2}\rho_0 \sin 2\varphi_0 \tag{6–134}$$

and the passage to the continuous variable yields the first stroboscopic differential equation

$$\frac{d\rho}{d\tau} = -\tfrac{1}{2}\rho \sin 2\varphi \tag{6–135}$$

Forming the second combination: $y\dot{x} - x\dot{y}$, one obtains similarly the second stroboscopic differential equation

$$\frac{d\varphi}{d\tau} = -\tfrac{1}{4} \cos 2\varphi \tag{6–136}$$

It is observed that the system (6–135) (6–136) has no singular point as $\sin 2\varphi$ and $\cos 2\varphi$ cannot vanish simultaneously.

We can conclude that (6–126) has no periodic solution.

It is observed, however, that (6–136) has a point of equilibrium when $\cos 2\varphi_0 = 0$, that is, $\sin 2\varphi_0 = \pm 1$ (as no confusion is to be feared we indicate by the subscript 0 the stationary value).

The variational equation for (6–136) is obtained if we perturb φ_0 by a small perturbation $\delta\varphi$. If one replaces φ_0 by $\varphi_0 + \delta\varphi$ in (6–136) and cancels out the equilibrium terms, one obtains

$$\frac{d\delta\varphi}{d\tau} \simeq \tfrac{1}{2} \sin 2\varphi_0 \delta\varphi \tag{6–137}$$

and one sees that the phase equilibrium is stable for $\sin 2\varphi_0 = -1$, which means that $\varphi_0 = 3\pi/4$ and unstable for $\sin 2\varphi_0 = +1$.

From any other value the phase will settle to its stable value $\varphi_0 = 3\pi/4$, but in this case Eq. (6–135) yields:

$$\frac{d\rho}{d\tau} = \tfrac{1}{2}\rho \tag{6–138}$$

This shows that ρ (energy) increases exponentially at a fixed value of the phase $\varphi_0 = 3\pi/4$. Thus in this case there is no periodic solution.

Let us now consider the nonlinear Mathieu equation (6–127).

Omitting the intermediate calculations (6–128) and (6–129), and taking instead of (6–130) the series solution in the form

$$\rho(t) = \rho_0(t) + \mu\rho_1(t) + \cdots; \qquad \psi(t) = \psi_0(t) + \mu\psi_1(t) + \cdots \tag{6–139}$$

where μ is a small parameter of the same order as a, b, and c, one finds that the zero order approximation (6–131) remains the same. As to the first order corrective terms (6–132), they are now:

$$\begin{aligned} \frac{d\rho_1}{dt} &= -\ B\rho_0 - A\rho_0 \sin 2\varphi_0 \cos^2 2t \\ \frac{d\psi_1}{dt} &= -\ \tfrac{1}{2}A \cos 2\psi_0 \cos^2 2t - \tfrac{3}{8}C\rho_0 \end{aligned} \tag{6–140}$$

where $A = a/\mu$; $B = b/\mu$, and $C = c/\mu$ are finite constants (we assume that they are positive).

Proceeding as previously (see Eq. (6–133)) and setting $2\pi\mu = \Delta\tau$, one obtains the difference equations

$$\begin{aligned} \frac{\Delta\rho}{\Delta\tau} &= -\ \tfrac{1}{2}\rho_0(2B + A \sin 2\varphi_0) = K(\rho_0,\psi_0) \\ \frac{\Delta\varphi}{\Delta\tau} &= -\ \tfrac{1}{4}[A \cos 2\varphi + \tfrac{3}{2}C\varphi_0] = L(\rho_0,\varphi_0) \end{aligned} \tag{6–141}$$

and the passage to the continuous variable yields the stroboscopic differential equation

$$\begin{aligned}\frac{d\rho}{d\tau} &= -\tfrac{1}{2}\rho[2B + A\sin 2\varphi] = K(\rho,\varphi)\\ \frac{d\varphi}{d\tau} &= -\tfrac{1}{4}[A\cos 2\varphi + \tfrac{3}{2}C\rho] = L(\rho,\varphi)\end{aligned} \tag{6–142}$$

It is seen that now the stroboscopic system has a singular point defined by the relations[22]

$$\sin 2\varphi_0 = -\frac{2B}{A}; \qquad \cos 2\varphi_0 = -\frac{3C}{2A}\rho_0 \tag{6–143}$$

We note that as $|\sin 2\varphi_0| \leq 1$ one must have

$$2B \leq A \tag{6–144}$$

From the trigonometric relationship $\sin^2 2\varphi_0 + \cos^2 2\varphi_0 = 1$, we have

$$\rho_0 = \frac{2}{3C}\sqrt{A^2 - 4B^2} \tag{6–145}$$

and the reality of ρ_0 imposes again the condition of (6–144).

It remains to be seen whether the singular point in question is stable.

By Eq. (6–41) the characteristic equation is

$$S^2 - (K_\rho + L_\varphi)S + (K_\rho L_\varphi - K_\varphi L_\rho) = 0 \tag{6–146}$$

where K_ρ, K_φ, L_ρ, and L_φ are the partial derivatives of the functions. $K(\rho,\varphi)$ and $L(\rho,\varphi)$ in Eq. (6–142) with respect to the indicated variables at the point ρ_0,φ_0. If one carries out the intermediate calculation, one obtains the characteristic equations

$$S^2 + BS + \tfrac{1}{4}(A^2 - 4B^2) = 0 \tag{6–147}$$

and one sees that the singular point is stable (since $B > 0$) if the condition (6–144) is fulfilled.

This condition is thus the necessary and sufficient condition for the existence of a stable stationary solution (oscillation) of the differential equation (6–127).

These conclusions explain the very interesting results obtained by L. Mandelstam and N. Papalexi with their "parametric generator."[23]

[22] Beginning with Eq. (6–143) the subscript 0 designates the *stationary values* of ρ and φ.

[23] L. Mandelstam and N. Papalexi, *F. Tech. Phys.* (USSR) (1934); see also Reference 6, Chapter 20.

This is merely an oscillating circuit in which one of the parameters (L or C) is made to vary at a frequency twice as great as the natural frequency of the circuit.

It was observed that with a linear circuit and in the absence of any source of energy (except probably the residual charges in condensers) the circuit becomes self-excited and builds up the voltage indefinitely until the insulation is punctured, which is in accordance with (6–138). In the second experiment these physicists inserted a nonlinear resistor in series with the circuit and obtained a stable oscillation with fixed amplitude and phase, as follows from the analysis of the differential equation (6–127).

PART III—NONLINEAR PHENOMENA

6.24. Introductory Remarks.—In the following sections we apply some of the preceding theories to the investigation of a few very important types of nonlinear oscillatory phenomena.

It would be erroneous to think that present-day mathematical methods are adequate to explain or predict all that exists in the enormous volume of experimental material that physicists and engineers have accumulated. This is due partially to the fact that we possess fairly uniform theoretical approaches only in the domain of small parameters, and also because conditions in some cases are so complicated that in spite of a knowledge of the theory, one is handicapped by computational difficulties.

Even in the well-known domain of nearly linear phenomena it would be impossible to make predictions accurately on a purely theoretical basis; historically the progress was just opposite, going from the experimental evidence to the theory and not in the opposite direction.

In order to illustrate this statement let us consider the typical differential equation that we have studied previously, that is

$$\ddot{x} + \mu f(x,\dot{x}) + x = \lambda \cos \omega t \tag{6–148}$$

If ω is an integer, say $\omega = n$ we have rather complicated manifestations of the subharmonic resonance. If it is $\omega = n + \varepsilon$, where ε is a certain small number, one has still the *subharmonic resonance*, but it is accompanied by another phenomenon of *synchronization*, which consists in the entrainment of the frequency of the *autoperiodic oscillation* (if $\lambda = 0$), by that of the *heteroperiodic oscillation* (the externally applied one).

There is still another effect to be considered. If the autoperiodic frequency exists, the application of a relatively high heteroperiodic frequency usually destroys it; this is the so-called *asynchronous quenching*.

In all these phenomena the critical factor is the parameter ω, the heteroperiodic frequency.

There is also a process called *asynchronous excitation*, in which the autoperiodic oscillation is released by means of the heteroperiodic one. It might seem that these asynchronous effects were the same; that in the quenching effect the autoperiodic oscillation is suppressed while in the excitation effect, it is released. In reality this conclusion is more apparent than real, since in the quenching effect the only requirement is that ω should be large enough, while in the excitation effect ω may have any value and what counts is the *character of the function* $f(x,\dot{x})$ in Eq. (6–148).

The foregoing discussion shows that complicated facts require a continuous readjustment of the analytical theory. Historically, the theory of nonlinear oscillations progressed precisely in this manner in the hands of the early pioneers—Lord Rayleigh, van der Pol, Appleton, and others. The following sections give a brief account of some of these investigations.

6.25. Synchronization.—This phenomenon apparently was observed for the first time by Huyghens (1629–1695) who reported the following curious observation. Two clocks fixed on a wall exhibited a certain lack of synchronization (one clock was going faster than the other). However, when the same clocks were fastened on a thin wooden board, they were found to be in synchronism.

After more than two centuries had elapsed, a similar phenomenon was discovered in electric circuits, and van der Pol was probably the first to give a theoretical explanation, which is substantially as follows:

The differential equation of an electron tube circuit with inductive coupling is:

$$L\frac{di}{dt} + Ri + \frac{1}{C}\int idt = M\frac{dI}{dt} \tag{6–149}$$

where the left-hand side represents the oscillating circuit, and the right-hand term is the action of the anode current I, exerted through an inductive coupling (M is the coefficient of mutual inductance between the anode and the grid circuits).

Suppose we add to this an external electromotive force $E_0 \sin \omega_1 t$ (for instance, through an inductive coupling in the grid circuit).

The differential equation becomes then

$$L\frac{di}{dt} + Ri + \frac{1}{C}\int idt - M\frac{dI}{dt} = E_0 \sin \omega_1 t \tag{6–150}$$

The nonlinear element here is $I = f(e_g)$, e_g being the grid voltage. If one introduces the usual approximation of the nonlinear characteristic by a polynomial, it can be shown that the differential equation takes the form

$$\ddot{v} - \alpha\dot{v} + \gamma\dot{v}^2 + \omega_0^2 v = B\omega_1^2 \sin \omega_1 t \tag{6–151}$$

where

$$v = \frac{e_g}{V_s}; \qquad \alpha = \frac{MS}{LC} - \frac{R}{L}; \qquad \gamma = \frac{MS}{3LC}; \qquad B = \frac{E_0}{V_s}; \qquad \omega_0^2 = \frac{1}{LC}$$

V_s being the saturation voltage (the voltage on the grid for which ΔV_s does not produce any appreciable variation in the anode current and S is the mutual conductance).

Van der Pol assumes the solution of the form

$$v = b_1 \sin \omega_1 t + b_2 \cos \omega_1 t \tag{6–152}$$

where b_1 and b_2 are slowly varying functions of t. If one substitutes Eq. (6–152) into (6–151), one obtains the system

$$\begin{aligned} 2\dot{b}_1 + zb_2 - \alpha b_1(1 - b^2/a_0^2) &= 0 \\ 2\dot{b}_2 - zb_1 - \alpha b_2(1 - b^2/a_0^2) &= -\ B\omega_1^2 \end{aligned} \tag{6–153}$$

where

$$z = 2(\omega_0 - \omega_1); \qquad b^2 = b_1^2 + b_2^2; \qquad a_0^2 = 4\alpha/3\gamma$$

If $b_1(t)$ and $b_2(t)$ are constant, the solution (6–152) becomes periodic with period $2\pi/\omega_1$; if $b_1(t)$ and $b_2(t)$ are slowly varying functions of time, v is almost periodic. Solving (6–153) with respect to $\dot{b}_1$ and $\dot{b}_2$, one obtains

$$\dot{b}_1 = P(b_1,b_2); \qquad \dot{b}_2 = Q(b_1,b_2) \tag{6–154}$$

and it is seen that b_1 and b_2 become constant if they correspond to the singular point of the system (6–154).

This analysis of van der Pol was continued later by Andronov and Witt,[24] who introduced additional changes of the variables

$$x = \frac{b_1}{a_0}; \qquad y = \frac{b_2}{a_0}; \qquad a = \frac{z}{\alpha}; \qquad A = -\frac{B\omega_1}{a_0\alpha};$$

$$r^2 = x^2 + y^2; \qquad \tau = \frac{\alpha t}{2}$$

[24] A. Andronov and A. Witt, *Arch. für Electroth.*, **24** (1930); also Reference 6, p. 441.

The system (6–153) becomes then

$$\frac{dx}{d\tau} = x(1 - r^2) - ay; \qquad \frac{dy}{d\tau} = ax + y(1 - r^2) + A \qquad (6\text{–}155)$$

If one sets $\rho = r^2$ this leads ultimately to the determination of ρ from the cubic equation

$$\rho[a^2 + (1 - \rho)^2] = A^2 \qquad (6\text{–}156)$$

which is treated graphically in the plane (a,ρ), considering A as the parameter of the family. We refer to Andronov and Witt for the details, and summarize them here by stating that such a diagram permits one to ascertain the possibility of synchronization for any set of parameters a and ρ.

One can also obtain the theory of synchronization by the stroboscopic method. If one starts with the differential equation

$$\ddot{x} + (cx^2 - a)\dot{x} + (1 + \gamma)x = e \sin t \qquad (6\text{–}157)$$

where a, c, γ, and e are small (it is essential to the treatment that a and c be small; however, e need not be small). In the case when e is finite, it can be shown by an asymptotic transformation* that the form of Eq. (6–157) is again obtained.

Omitting the intermediate calculations, the stroboscopic system in this case is

$$\begin{aligned} \frac{dr}{d\tau} &= -\tfrac{1}{8}C(r^3 - pr + q\cos\varphi) = R(r,\varphi) \\ \frac{d\varphi}{d\tau} &= \frac{1}{2}\left[\frac{E\sin\varphi}{r} - \Gamma\right] = \Phi(r,\varphi) \end{aligned} \qquad (6\text{–}158)$$

where $C = c/\mu$; $\Gamma = \gamma/\mu$; $p = 4A/C$; $q = 4E/C$, μ being the parameter. We shall not enter into the full discussion of (6–158) (see Reference 6, p. 444), but we shall mention that there exists a stable periodic solution (which means a state of synchronization) since the autoperiodic frequency $\omega_0^2 = 1 + \gamma$ is "entrained" by the heteroperiodic frequency $(\omega^2 = 1)$ in a certain interval $(-\Gamma_0, \Gamma_0)$ around $\Gamma = 0$ point. If this interval is exceeded, the two frequencies ω_0 and ω separate and the oscillation becomes almost periodic, as in the case of linear systems.

The synchronization phenomenon is probably the best studied nonlinear phenomenon, and it has some engineering applications. Thus, for instance, an artificial synchronization can be easily produced and used for the very accurate control of the speed of small motors synchronized with quartz oscillators; as the latter maintain their frequency very

* N. Minorsky, "Comptes Rendus" *Ac. Sc.* (*Paris*), t. **254,** 4130 (1962).

closely, they permit of a corresponding accuracy in the speed control process.

6.26. Subharmonic Resonance.—Another important nonlinear phenomenon is the so-called subharmonic resonance. In the linear theory the concept of harmonics is sufficiently well known so that it requires no further explanation other than the statement that these harmonics have frequencies higher than the fundamental wave.

In the nonlinear systems, one often encounters subharmonics that have frequencies *lower* than that of the fundamental wave. As an example, consider a nonlinear conductor of electricity such as an electron tube circuit in which there exists between the anode current i_a and the grid voltage v, a relation of the form

$$i_a = a_1 v + a_2 v^2 + a_3 v^3 \tag{6–159}$$

If v represents the two voltages of equal amplitudes but of different frequencies, say

$$v = k(\sin \omega_1 t + \sin \omega_2 t) \tag{6–160}$$

then, on replacing v in Eq. (6–159), after some simple trigonometric transformations, one finds that the system has now the following frequencies:

$$2\omega_1, 2\omega_2, 3\omega_1, 3\omega_2; \qquad \omega_1 + \omega_2; \qquad \omega_1 - \omega_2;$$
$$2\omega_1 + \omega_2, 2\omega_1 - \omega_2, 2\omega_2 + \omega_1, 2\omega_2 - \omega_1$$

The first four are the ordinary harmonics, the remaining ones are the so-called *combination tones* and those of them whose frequencies are lower than the smaller of the frequencies ω_1 and ω_2 are called *subharmonics.* By a proper choice of frequencies and nonlinearities one can obtain subharmonics of a very low order.

Once the existence of subharmonics is ascertained, one can easily conclude that if one of them is near the period of the system, a corresponding subharmonic resonance must appear. Unfortunately while the physical nature of this phenomenon is simple, its mathematical expression is not. In fact, one is generally given, not the subharmonic, but the differential equation, and the establishment of the existence of a stable subharmonic is usually not a simple matter.

The necessary condition for the subharmonic resonance occurs when the following condition is approximately fulfilled.

$$\omega_0 = m\omega_1 \pm n\omega_2 \tag{6–161}$$

where m and n are small integers. However, this is not sufficient for the actual (physical) existence of the subharmonic resonance.

L. Mandelstam and N. Papalexi were first to establish the theory of the subharmonic resonance based directly on the theory of Poincaré (Section 6.18). The derivation of this theory, together with the details of the electronic circuits, is given in[25], or in an abridged version in[6] (pages 464–473). The difficulty of the problem is due to the fact that this case is nonautonomous so that conditions of stability are determined in terms of the characteristic exponents, which always leads to rather long calculations.

As the principal aim of the stroboscopic method is to obviate this difficulty by reducing the problem to the determination of stability of singular points, we include a brief statement of this approach.

We consider the following nonautonomous differential equation

$$\ddot{x} + x + \mu f(x,\dot{x}) = \sin nt \tag{6–162}$$

in order to find a periodic solution, with period 2π, when the external periodic excitation has a period $2\pi/n$, where n is an integer.

This means that we are seeking a subharmonic resonance of order n. If $\mu = 0$ the corresponding solution is

$$x_0(t) = A \sin t + B \cos t + \frac{1}{1 - n^2} \sin nt \tag{6–163}$$

$$\dot{x}_0(t) = y_0(t) = A \cos t - B \sin t + \frac{n}{1 - n^2} \cos nt \tag{6–164}$$

Thus,

$$x_0(0) = B; \qquad y_0(0) = A + \frac{n}{1 - n^2} \tag{6–165}$$

The conditions of periodicity (of Poincaré), taking into account Eq. (6–164), are

$$\begin{aligned} x_1(t) &= -\int_0^t \sin (t - \tau) f[x_0(\tau),y_0(\tau)]d\tau \\ y_1(t) &= -\int_0^t \cos (t - \tau) f[x_0(\tau),y_0(\tau)]dt \end{aligned} \tag{6–166}$$

The problem reduces to the determination of values of the constants A and B which make the nonlinear solution periodic, with period 2π.

We limit ourselves to the first approximation. As already mentioned, the higher order approximations do not add to the qualitative character of the phenomenon, but merely add small corrections at the cost of extremely long calculations.

[25] L. Mandelstam and N. Papalexi, *Z. Physik*, **73** (1932).

There are two distinct problems: (1) the determination of the *exact* subharmonic resonance, and (2) the determination of the *zone* of that resonance. As problem (2) is more complicated than problem (1) we consider only the exact resonance (1).

In order to simplify the problem still more, we shall consider the subharmonic resonance of the order $\frac{1}{2}$ (*i.e.*, where $n = 2$) in connection with the differential equation

$$\ddot{y} - \mu(\alpha - \beta y^2)\dot{y} + y = e \sin 2t; \quad \alpha > 0, \ \beta > 0 \tag{6–167}$$

Setting $y = ex$, this differential equation becomes

$$\ddot{x} - \mu(\alpha - \beta e^2 x^2)\dot{x} + x = \sin 2t \tag{6–168}$$

the zero order solution (corresponding to $\ddot{x}_0 + x_0 = \sin 2t$) is

$$\begin{aligned} x_0(t) &= A \sin t + B \cos t - \tfrac{1}{3} \sin 2t \\ y_0(t) &= A \cos t - B \sin t - \tfrac{2}{3} \cos 2t \end{aligned} \tag{6–169}$$

the initial conditions are: $x_0(0) = B$; $y_0(0) = A - \frac{2}{3}$, and we assume also $x_1(0) = y_1(0) = 0$. We have then:

$$\begin{aligned} x_1(t) &= \int_0^t \sin(t - \tau)(\alpha - \beta e^2 x_0^2)\dot{x}_0 d\tau \\ y_1(t) &= \int_0^t \cos(t - \tau)(\alpha - \beta e^2 x_0^2)\dot{x}_0 d\tau \end{aligned} \tag{6–170}$$

To find the exact resonance, the integrations are carried out between 0 and 2π (note that this is a considerable simplification).

The conditions of periodicity then become

$$\begin{aligned} x(2\pi) - x(0) &= x_0(2\pi) - x_0(0) + \mu x_1(2\pi) = 0 \\ y(2\pi) - y(0) &= y_0(2\pi) - y_0(0) + \mu y_1(2\pi) = 0 \end{aligned} \tag{6–171}$$

but since x_0 and y_0 are periodic with period 2π, the conditions of periodicity for the stationary state are merely $x_1(2\pi) = y_1(2\pi) = 0$. As we are interested not only in the stationary state but also in its *stability*, it is useful to consider rather the *approach* to this state. It is clear that for this we must consider the stroboscopic differential equation rather than the difference equations themselves, that is:

$$\begin{aligned} \frac{d\xi}{d\tau} &= -\frac{1}{2\pi}\int_0^{2\pi} \sin \tau(\alpha - \beta e^2 x_0^2)\dot{x}_0 d\tau \\ \frac{d\eta}{d\tau} &= +\frac{1}{2\pi}\int_0^{2\pi} \cos \tau(\alpha - \beta e^2 x_0^2)\dot{x}_0 d\tau \end{aligned} \tag{6–172}$$

It is convenient to integrate by parts, observing that

$$(\alpha - \beta e^2 x_0^2)\dot{x}_0 = \frac{d}{d\tau}(\alpha x_0 - \tfrac{1}{3}\beta e^2 x_0^3)$$

As the integrated parts vanish at both limits, we have

$$\frac{d\xi}{d\tau} = \frac{1}{2\pi}\int_0^{2\pi} \cos \tau g(x_0) d\tau; \qquad \frac{d\eta}{d\tau} = \frac{1}{2\pi}\int_0^{2\pi} \sin \tau g(x_0) d\tau \tag{6-173}$$

where $g(x_0) = \alpha x_0 - \frac{1}{3}\beta e^2 x_0^3$, $x_0 = x_0(\tau)$ being given by (6–169).

It is observed that even in this simplest case the calculations are long, as $x_0(t)$ is a trigonometric trinomial.

For the first equation of (6–173), one obtains on integration and calculation

$$\pi\{\alpha B - \gamma[\tfrac{1}{4}(B^3 + A^2 B) + \tfrac{1}{18}B]\} \tag{6-174}$$

and for the second equation

$$\pi\{\alpha A - \gamma[\tfrac{1}{4}(A^3 + AB^2) + \tfrac{1}{18}A]\} \tag{6-175}$$

One can conduct the calculation either in the variables ξ,η in view of the initial conditions, or in A,B since $x(0) = B = \xi$; $y(0) = A - \frac{2}{3} = \eta$. Since A and B appear on the right, it is more convenient to use A and B throughout. This ultimately yields the stroboscopic system

$$\begin{aligned}\frac{dB}{d\tau} &= \tfrac{1}{2}B\{\alpha - \gamma[\tfrac{1}{4}(A^2 + B^2) + \tfrac{1}{18}]\}\\ \frac{dA}{d\tau} &= \tfrac{1}{2}A\{\alpha - \gamma[\tfrac{1}{4}(A^2 + B^2) + \tfrac{1}{18}]\}\end{aligned} \tag{6-176}$$

One sees at once that the polar coordinates simplify the problem.

Setting $\rho = A^2 + B^2$; $\psi = \arctan(A/B)$, and proceeding as we did previously (see Section 6.23) we obtain the first stroboscopic differential equation

$$\frac{d\rho}{d\tau} = \rho[(\alpha - \tfrac{1}{18}\beta e^2) - \tfrac{1}{4}\beta e^2 \rho] = \Phi(\rho) \tag{6-177}$$

The second stroboscopic equation is of no interest here as it reduces to $d\psi/d\tau = 0$ (this is due to the fact that the last term, y, on the left of Eq. (6–167) was taken; if, instead, we would have taken $g(y)$, the second stroboscopic differential equation would not reduce to $d\psi/d\tau = 0$).

As (6–176) is the only differential equation of interest here, one sees at once that the stationary amplitude is

$$\rho_0 = \frac{4}{\beta e^2}(\alpha - \tfrac{1}{18}\beta e^2) \tag{6-178}$$

As $\rho_0 = r_0^2$ is essentially positive, it is necessary that

$$\alpha \geq \tfrac{1}{18}\beta e^2 \tag{6-179}$$

Hence the subharmonic resonance exists as long as the amplitude e of the external periodic excitation is not too large, namely:

$$e \leq \sqrt{18\alpha/\beta} \tag{6-180}$$

This is a radical difference from the ordinary (linear) resonance, where no such restriction exists.

It is necessary to show that the subharmonic resonance whose existence we have just ascertained is stable. Here the condition of stability is very simple, since in the stroboscopic method we deal with the stability of the singular point (and not of the stationary motion). In view of this we can use the criterion (6–33), Section 6.12.

If one differentiates Eq. (6–177) with respect to ρ, and sets $\rho = \rho_0$, as given by Eq. (6–178), one finds that the condition

$$\Phi_\rho(\rho_0) \leq 0 \tag{6-181}$$

is fulfilled, which shows that the subharmonic resonance of the order $\frac{1}{2}$ is stable.

It must be noted that the above simplification (the possibility of introducing the variable ($\rho = x^2 + y^2 = r^2$)) is an exception rather than the rule, so that the computational difficulties are generally greater.

Thus, for instance, for the Duffing equation and for the resonance of the order $\frac{1}{3}$ (*i.e.*, $n = 3$) the initial differential equation is

$$\ddot{x} + x + \mu(\alpha\dot{x} + \gamma e^2 x^3) = \sin 3t$$

(compare with Eq. (6–168)).

If one carries out the analogous calculation one finds that the ultimate algebraic system for the determination of A_0 and B_0 is

$$\begin{aligned} \alpha A + \tfrac{3}{4}\gamma e^2[B(A^2 + B^2) - \tfrac{1}{4}AB + \tfrac{1}{32}B] &= 0 \\ -\alpha B + \tfrac{3}{4}\gamma e^2[(A - \tfrac{1}{8})(A^2 + B^2) + \tfrac{1}{32}A] &= 0 \end{aligned} \tag{6-182}$$

and one sees that no simplifications are possible here.

6.27. Parametric Excitation.—The so-called "parametric effects" or phenomena have been known for a long time, but it is only recently that their study has been carried out systematically.

It is well-known, for instance, that if one applies tension at properly timed intervals to pull a stretched wire or string, it begins to oscillate laterally. Lord Rayleigh performed an experiment of this kind by attaching a stretched wire to a prong of a tuning fork; when the latter vibrated, the wire also began to vibrate, laterally, at half the frequency of the tuning fork.

In general, parametric excitation (or action) may be defined as follows: if a parameter of an oscillatory system is made to vary periodically with frequency $2f$, f being the free frequency of the system, the latter begins to oscillate with its own frequency.

L. Mandelstam and N. Papalexi performed an interesting experiment of this kind with an electrical oscillatory circuit. If one of the parameters (C or L) is made to oscillate with frequency $2f$, the system becomes self-excited with frequency f; this is due to the fact that there are always small residual charges in the condenser, which are sufficient to produce the cumulative phenomenon of self-excitation. It was found that in the case of a linear oscillatory circuit the voltage builds up beyond any limit until the insulation is ultimately punctured; if, however, the system is nonlinear, the amplitude reaches a stable stationary value and oscillation acquires a periodic character. In Section 6.23 these two cases are represented by the differential equations (6–126) and (6–127) and the explanation is given in terms of their integration by the stroboscopic method.

Since that time (1934) a considerable amount of other experiments and theoretical studies has been made, so that we can write a general type of differential equation and show how it can be connected with a nonlinear effect discovered by Bethenod.[26]

Let us generalize the differential equation (6–127) by adding a nonlinear term associated with $x \cos 2t$, obtaining

$$\ddot{x} + b\dot{x} + x + (a - dx^2)x \cos 2t + cx^3 = 0 \tag{6–183}$$

The only difference from Eq. (6–127) is in the presence of the parametric term $(a - dx^2)x \cos 2t$.

If one proceeds as indicated in Section 6.23, one obtains the stroboscopic system

$$\begin{aligned} \frac{d\rho}{d\tau} &= \tfrac{1}{4}\rho[(D\rho - 2A)\sin 2\varphi - 4B] = R(\rho,\varphi) \\ \frac{d\varphi}{d\tau} &= \tfrac{1}{4}[(D\rho - A)\cos 2\varphi - \tfrac{3}{2}C\rho] = \Phi(\rho,\varphi) \end{aligned} \tag{6–184}$$

These equations are somewhat more complicated than those of (6–142) and the reader is referred for their further discussion to Reference 6 (p. 490). However, they show that it is still possible to determine a stable singular point of (6–184), which shows that (6–183) has a

[26] T. Bethenod, *C.R. Ac. Sc.* (Paris), 207 (1937).

stable periodic solution (motion), and the procedure may be developed similarly to that of Section 6.23.

It is interesting to note that this differential equation (6–183) governs the following effect (of Bethenod).

Assume that we have a pendulum (Fig. 6–14) provided with a piece of soft iron P placed coaxially with a coil C carrying an alternating current; that is, the axis of the coil coincides with the longitudinal axis OP of the pendulum at rest. If the coil is excited, one finds that the pendulum in due course begins to oscillate, and the oscillations finally reach a stationary amplitude. It is important to note that between the period of oscillation of the pendulum and the period of the alternating current there exists no rational ratio, so that the question of the subharmonic effect is ruled out.

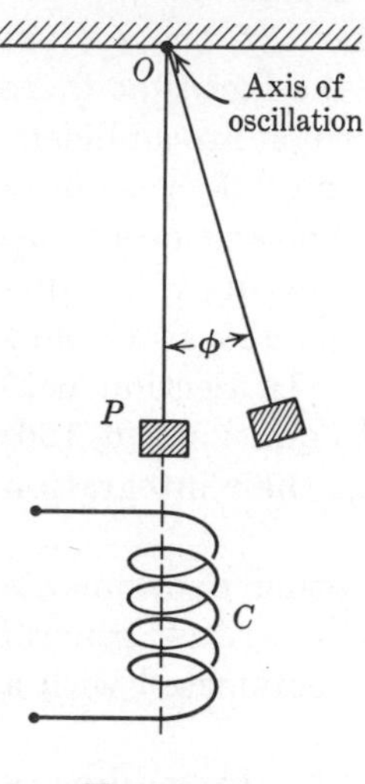

FIG. 6–14.

Y. Rocard [27] derived the differential equations of the system, but in such form that it was impossible to integrate them. These equations are

$$\frac{dL(\theta)i}{dt} + zi = E \sin \omega t;$$

$$J\ddot{\theta} + D\dot{\theta} + C\theta = \frac{d}{d\theta}\left[\tfrac{1}{2}L(\theta)i^2\right] \quad (6\text{–}185)$$

The first equation relates to the electrical part of the system and the second, to its mechanical part.

It is clear that if the pendulum oscillates, the inductance L of the circuit is a function of the angle θ, since the magnetic reluctance of the coil C varies because of the presence of the soft iron P. The first equation is the equation of an electric circuit to which is applied an e.m.f., $E \sin \omega t$, subject to the condition that the inductance of this circuit is a function of θ and has the frequency of the pendulum.

The left-hand side of the second equation of (6–185) is the pendulum equation (J being the moment of inertia, D, the coefficient of damping and C, the coefficient of the restoring moment).

The right-hand side of the second equation is the moment of the so-called ponderomotive force. As is known from Maxwell's theory, a mechanical motion tending to modify an electromagnetic configuration experiences a *mechanical reaction* opposing this change, equal numerically to the derivative of the energy stored in the system with

[27] Y. Rocard, *Dynamique générale des oscillations*, Masson, Paris, 1943.

respect to the variable that introduces this change in the configuration. In this case the stored (electromagnetic) energy is $\frac{1}{2}L(\theta)i^2$ and the variable is θ.

It is possible, however, to transform these differential equations in such a way[28] that they can be reduced to the parametric form (6–183) from which the motion of the pendulum can be ascertained. On physical grounds, it is clear that this function is maximum for $\theta = 0$, since the magnetic reluctance is maximum for this value of θ. As $|\theta|$ increases, the function $L(\theta)$ decreases, but the rate of this decrease diminishes for larger angles since the pendulum recedes into the region of the stray flux which has a tendency to become constant for larger values of θ. Thus, on physical grounds the form

$$L(\theta) = L_0 - a_2\theta^2 + a_4\theta^4 \tag{6–186}$$

answers these requirements. It will be assumed that $b_2 = a_2/L_0$; $b_4 = a_4/L_0$ are small quantities of the first order.

If one makes this assumption, one can integrate the first equation of (6–185) assuming that the periodic motion of the pendulum exists with an unknown constant period Ω, obtaining

$$\theta = \theta_0 \cos \Omega t \tag{6–187}$$

Substituting this into the second equation of (6–185), and making some intermediate calculations (and change of time scale) (Reference 6, p. 457) one obtains ultimately the differential equation:

$$\ddot{\theta} + b\dot{\theta} + \theta[1 + (a + c\theta^2) \cos 2\tau] + e\theta^3 = 0 \tag{6–188}$$

where a, b, c, and e are small coefficients that are calculated in terms of other parameters.

It is seen that Eq. (6–188) is of the form (6–183), which has a periodic solution with a stationary amplitude, and this explains the phenomenon of Bethenod.

PART IV—RELAXATION OSCILLATIONS AND NONANALYTIC NONLINEARITIES

6.28. Introductory Remarks.—Up to this point in this chapter we have given a brief survey of the wide field of *nearly linear* phenomena. If the condition of the near linearity is waived, the theory of Poincaré does not apply, and the preceding methods cease to hold. The most

[28] N. Minorsky, *C.R. Ac. Sc.* (Paris), 231 (1950); *J. Franklin Inst.*, 254 (1952).

important class of these new phenomena is usually called "relaxation oscillations."

This new field is characterized at present by a parting of the ways between physicists and engineers, on one hand, and mathematicians, on the other. The former have preferred to elaborate a purely discontinuous theory (similar to that which exists in the theory of shocks in theoretical mechanics) whereas the latter prefer an analytical attack, even upon problems in which the analyticity practically disappears, at least as some points of the cycle.

It is natural to ask which theory is "better." There is obviously no definite answer to this question and the conclusion depends on the

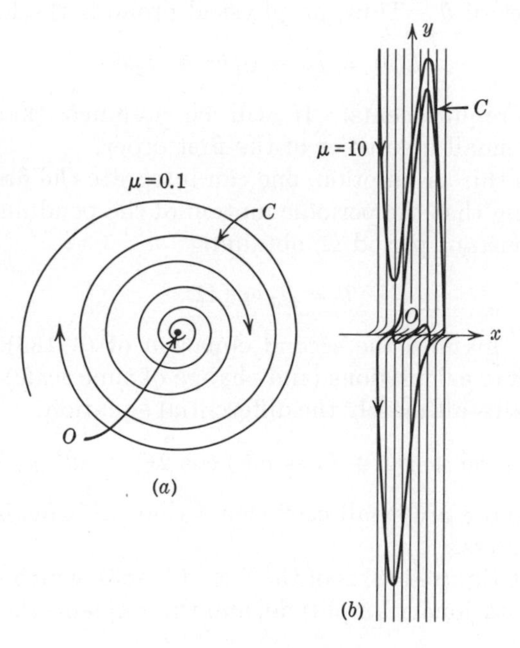

Fig. 6–15.

point of view. For physicists interested primarily in the qualitative aspects of these phenomena, the discontinuous theory is definitely preferable, as it permits ascertaining at least qualitatively what happens under given conditions; for mathematicians the so-called *asymptotic theory* offers perhaps an interesting exercise in carrying out analytically calculations in which the analyticity is practically nonexistent.

Van der Pol[29] having established his equation, and not having at the

[29] B. van der Pol, *Phil.*, May, 7th series, Vol. 2 (1926).

time (1920) any analytical theory at his disposal, attempted to determine the solution by means of the graphical construction of isoclines.

The result of this graphical analysis is shown in Fig. 6–15.

Curve C of Fig. 6–15(a) corresponds to $\mu = 0.1$, and curve C of Fig. 6–15(b) to $\mu = 10$. It is observed that in the first case the curve C is almost a circle (as in a harmonic oscillator) while in the second case it has very special features. In fact from very high velocity ($y = \dot{x}$), the solution drops very rapidly to zero (at the point where it cuts the x-axis). At this point the "relaxation" interval begins, the representative point moving near the x-axis with a very small velocity; after that its velocity increases rapidly to a considerable value, and so on.

There are two points of the cycle at which velocity decreases very rapidly from a high value to zero. To give a familiar analogy, the van der Pol oscillator for this value of μ behaves not as a "decent oscillator" but rather as a pneumatic hammer, which idles for some time while the air pressure builds up, delivers a hammer blow, losing its kinetic energy, and then begins a similar half-cycle.

In the following sections we give a brief outline of these two approaches: the discontinuous theory and the asymptotic one.

6.29. Discontinuous Theory of Relaxation Oscillations.—This theory was developed in the USSR by a number of physicists between 1930 and 1937. We give a condensed account of this work; for further details see Reference 4 or Reference 6 (pp. 610 to 630).

The essential point in this theory is the so-called *degeneration* of differential equations.

Suppose we have a simple differential equation with constant coefficients

$$a\ddot{x} + b\dot{x} + kx = 0 \tag{6–189}$$

in which the coefficient a is much smaller than b and k.

For example, (6–189) may be the differential equation of an oscillating circuit

$$L\frac{d^2i}{dt^2} + R\frac{di}{dt} + \frac{1}{C}i = 0 \tag{6–190}$$

The above condition (a much smaller than b or k) would mean that the inductance L is negligible. Such a case may be called *degenerescent.*

But if $a \equiv 0$ the differential equation (6–189), which is of the second order degenerates into one of the first order

$$b\dot{x} + kx = 0 \tag{6–191}$$

There is a difference between (6–189) and (6–191) in that the solution of (6–189) depends on two constants of integration, whereas that of (6–191) depends only on one such constant.

If one calls the solution of (6–189) $x(t)$, and that of (6–191) $\bar{x}(t)$, a simple calculation shows that

$$\begin{aligned}\alpha(t) &= x(t) - \bar{x}(t) = -x_0(ak/b^2)e^{-bt/a} + \dot{x}_0(a/b)(e^{-kt/b} - e^{-bt/a}) \\ \dot{\alpha}(t) &= \dot{x}(t) - \dot{\bar{x}}(t) = x_0(k/b)e^{-bt/a} - \dot{x}_0(ak/b^2)e^{-kt/b} + \dot{x}_0 e^{-bt/a}\end{aligned} \tag{6–192}$$

For a sufficiently large t, both $\alpha(t)$ and $\dot{\alpha}(t)$ approach zero uniformly when $a \to 0$. However, for a sufficiently small t, there is a difference between $\alpha(t)$ and $\dot{\alpha}(t)$. The former exhibits the same property of the uniform convergence, but not $\dot{\alpha}(t)$; in fact

$$\dot{\alpha}(t)_{t \approx 0} = (kx_0/b) + \dot{x}_0 \tag{6–193}$$

and this expression, being independent of a, remains finite (except perhaps for a special choice of initial conditions which is of no interest in the general case).

This property of the degenerate equation of exhibiting a nonuniform convergence of $\dot{\bar{x}}$ for $t \approx 0$ means that for the degenerate equation the velocity $\dot{\bar{x}}$ jumps quasi-discontinuously to its proper value, so that only one constant of integration is sufficient, in spite of the fact that the state of rest is specified by two initial conditions, $x_0 = \dot{x}_0 = 0$.

This somewhat subtle point shows that there are variables that are capable of exhibiting quasi-discontinuous features in the case of the degenerescent differential equation. In the above case this variable was the velocity $\dot{\bar{x}}(t)$, there are some other cases in which it may be $\bar{x}(t)$.

The next important question is of a physical nature, namely, what kind of physical variables can exhibit these quasi-discontinuous features? The answer to this question was formulated (apparently by Mandelstam) and may be regarded as a *plausible postulate.*

In a physical system only those variables that leave the energy invariant can exhibit quasi-discontinuous transitions (jumps).

Let us consider an electric system in which the inductance is negligible (we call it the L-degeneration). The energy E is then located in the condenser and is $E_C = \frac{1}{2}CV^2$ where C is capacity and V the voltage across the condenser; according to the above postulate V cannot change discontinuously. Similarly in the case of C-degeneration the energy is located in the inductance and is $E_L = \frac{1}{2}Li^2$ where i is the current in the inductance; hence i cannot vary quasi-discontinuously.[30]

[30] In the idealization we use the term "discontinuously" instead of "quasi-discontinuously."

On the other hand dy/dt can change discontinuously and as the current flowing in the condenser circuit is $i_C = C(dV/dt)$, it can change discontinuously. Likewise by the similar argument, di/dt in the inductance as well as $L(di/dt)$, the voltage across it, can change discontinuously.

This physical postulate has an obvious meaning: if energy could vary discontinuously (by a finite amount during an infinitely small time) this would mean that the power would be infinite for an infinitely short time, which is ruled out by the postulate.

We can now draw certain conclusions. Assume that we have a differential system

$$\dot{x} = X(x,y); \qquad \dot{y} = Y(x,y) \tag{6–194}$$

in which the functions X and Y are of the form

$$X(x,y) = P(x,y)/T(x,y); \qquad Y(x,y) = Q(x,y)/T(x,y) \tag{6–195}$$

Many oscillators exhibiting quasi-discontinuous features are reducible to systems like (6–195).

The essential feature of the discontinuous theory appears when a trajectory reaches a point for which $T(x_c, y_c) = 0$; we call this point (x_c, y_c) *a critical point* In such a case the differential equations (6–194) lose their meaning as x and y become infinite, exhibiting thus a discontinuous jump.

If this jump ends on some other trajectory for which $T(x,y) \neq 0$, the differential equations (6–194) again govern the motion until another jump occurs, and so on.

Thus one obtains a sequence of analytic arcs interrupted by discontinuities, the directions of which are determined by the postulate of Mandelstam. Very often this sequence of arcs and discontinuous stretches forms a closed curve, which is characteristic of a periodic phenomenon. Such phenomena are usually designated as piece-wise analytic phenomena (or oscillations).

This theory is adequate to explain practically all oscillatory phenomena in relaxation-oscillation schemes (*e.g.*, multivibrators, etc.) and, very often, to predict the cases in which the initial analytical oscillation becomes of a piece-wise analytic type if a certain parameter is changed. In fact, after the differential equations are formed, the critical lines $T(x_c,y_c) = 0$ are determined as well as the direction of Mandelstam's jumps. Thus the whole picture of the trajectories becomes manifest and one can form a general view of the whole situation. The reader can find numerous examples of these diagrams in Andronov and Chaikin's book [4] as well as in Reference 6 (pp. 618–647).

It must be noted that independently of these developments in the USSR, Th. Vogel (in France) ultimately reached similar conclusions, though starting from a somewhat different point of departure (see Reference 6, Chapter 29).

6.30. Asymptotic Theory of Relaxation Oscillations.—In the asymptotic theory no idealizations are used and a rapid transition of the representative point is not idealized by treating it as a discontinuous jump, but is studied as a continuous and analytic trajectory. Although this may seem to be a more logical procedure, the difficulties here are of a much higher order.

Since, for obvious reasons, the series of Poincaré cannot be applied here, attempts were made to use the so-called *asymptotic expansions* (this approach is to a great extent also due to Poincaré) which are not analytic and, for that reason, seem to be adequate when a trajectory has to turn around a "sharp corner," as was explained in Section 6.28.

Apparently this idea was due to Haag[31] but his writings were rather obscure and for that reason were not fully recognized. Later Dorodnitzin[32] applied this method to the van der Pol equation with large μ. His method consists in splitting the cycle into several regions, each of which is characterized by a certain definite character of motion on the integral curve. For each of these partial arcs there is set up a special asymptotic expansion, and the difficult point is to "join" these expansions. The calculations are very long (see Reference 6, pp. 676 and 685).

Another approach of a similar character was undertaken by M. L. Cartwright and J. E. Littlewood (Reference 6, p. 664); most of their papers treat of a nonhomogeneous equation of this type. The procedure is to divide the integral curve into a number of parts in which the differential equation can be simplified (forming the so-called "truncated" equations) and easily integrated. Again the difficulty of the method is to join these pieces of integral curves, while preserving the desired accuracy of approximation; no asymptotic expansions are involved, but the idea of "junctions" is the same as in the Dorodnitzin method. Taking into account the fact that these procedures are based on the *preliminary knowledge* of the integral curve, and also the fact that they relate only to the van der Pol equation, one must admit that, in spite of their great mathematical interest, they do not yet offer a convenient tool for physicists and engineers.

[31] J. Haag, *C.R. Ac. Sc.* (Paris), **202** (1936); **204** (1937); **206** (1938).

[32] A. Dorodnitzin, *Prikl. Math. i Meh* (in Russian), **2** (1947); English translation.

6.31. Nonanalytic Nonlinearities.—A somewhat different kind of nonlinearity has been recognized in recent years, as the result of observations on the behavior of control systems. It was observed long ago that control systems that appear to be reasonably linear, if considered from the point of view of their differential equations, often exhibit self-excited oscillations, a fact that is at variance with the classical theory asserting that in linear systems self-excited oscillations are impossible. Thus, for instance, in the van der Pol equation

$$\ddot{x} + \mu(x^2 - 1)\dot{x} + x = 0 \tag{6–196}$$

if the nonlinear term $\mu x^2\dot{x}$ is removed, one has a solution going to infinity without any stationary state.

On the other hand, it is also well known that a system of two linear differential equations that replace each other at the instant when $\dot{x}$ changes its sign, namely:

$$\begin{aligned} \ddot{x} + 2h\dot{x} + \omega^2 x &= 0, \qquad \text{for } \dot{x} > 0 \\ \ddot{x} + 2h\dot{x} + \omega^2 x &= \omega^2 a \quad \text{for } \dot{x} < 0 \end{aligned} \tag{6–197}$$

is capable of a "self-excitation," resulting ultimately in operation on a limit cycle.

From the standpoint of the classical (analytical) theory with which we were concerned in this review, the situation is obviously absurd since each of these two equations is linear and of a dissipative type (since $h > 0$); trajectories of both of these equations are convergent spirals tending to approach a stable focus. However, if one carries out a simple analysis (see Reference 6, p. 608), one finds that change of equations for $\dot{x} = 0$, results in the change of the focus in a quasi-discontinuous manner, so that the trajectory can still be closed owing to the existence of two nonanalytic points on the x-axis. If, however, the trajectory is closed, this means that there exists a stationary oscillation and in such a case the system (6–197) is nonlinear, although, from the standpoint of the differential equations, it is linear everywhere except at the two points at which the analyticity is lost.

These apparently paradoxical phenomena have been explained by Andronov [4] from the physical point of view, a major point being that at the two nonanalytic points impulsive inputs of energy occur which compensate for the continuous dissipation of energy on the analytic arcs of convergent spirals[33] (compare with the theory of clocks of Section 6.9).

If one takes into account the fact that in the control systems, there always exist certain "on" and "off" actions, such as "lost motion" or

[33] N. Minorsky, "Comptes Rendus," *Ac. Sc.*, t. **255**, 1374 (1962).

the action of relays or contacts, the above-mentioned changes from one differential equation to the other are inevitable, so that similar effects are to be expected. In fact, these parasitic nonlinear (and nonanalytic) oscillations constitute a serious handicap to satisfactory operation of control systems.

These phenomena are being actively studied at the present time, and constitute a new chapter in the theory of oscillations that is known as *piecewise linear oscillations*. There exists already a considerable literature on this subject in the theory of automatic control systems [11,34] but the situation is far from being definitely settled. One can expect that these studies will eventually add another body of knowledge to the theory of oscillations, that will be concerned with nonanalytic oscillatory phenomena.

[34] T. Z. Tsypkin, *Theory of relay control systems* (in Russian), Moscow, 1959; A. I. Lurje, *Einige nichtlineare Probleme aus der Theorie der Selbsttätigen Regelung* (translation from Russian), Berlin, 1957.

CHAPTER 7

ANGULAR MOMENTUM OPERATORS AND ROTATIONS IN SPACE AND TRANSFORMATION THEORY OF QUANTUM MECHANICS*

PART I—ANGULAR MOMENTUM OPERATORS AND ROTATIONS IN SPACE

by

HENRY MARGENAU

Yale University

7.1. Introduction.—The quantum mechanics of angular momenta has grown into a theory that is far more complex than its classical ancestor; yet an understanding of it is indispensable for the student of modern physics. We, therefore, expand the rudimentary indications presented formerly,[1] and present the basic techniques employed today in this useful subject.

The operator representing the angular momentum of a mass point circulating about the z-axis was given in the specific form

$$L_z = -i\hbar \left(x \frac{\partial}{\partial y} - y \frac{\partial}{\partial x} \right) \tag{7–1a}$$

or, in cylindrical coordinates,

$$L_z = -i\hbar \frac{\partial}{\partial \varphi} \tag{7–1b}$$

From Eq. (7–1a), one may construct L_x and L_y by cyclical change of coordinates, and the three operators are found to satisfy the commutation rules

$$\begin{aligned} L_xL_y - L_yL_x &= i\hbar L_z \\ L_yL_z - L_zL_y &= i\hbar L_x \\ L_zL_x - L_xL_z &= i\hbar L_y \end{aligned} \tag{7–2}$$

* This chapter deals with a few diverse matters concerning the foundations of quantum mechanics; it is intended to supplement Chapter 11 of Margenau and Murphy, *The Mathematics of Physics and Chemistry*, 2nd Ed., D. Van Nostrand Co., Inc., Princeton, N.J., 1956.

[1] H. Margenau and G. M. Murphy, *The Mathematics of Physics and Chemistry*, 2nd Ed., D. Van Nostrand Co., Inc., Princeton, N.J., 1956.

The choice of Eq. (7–1a) was postulational, justified by its success in use; an anterior reason for it was not given.

This state of affairs is in effect unchanged. But a plausibility argument that relates angular to linear momentum can be given to illuminate the meaning of L_z.

If $D(\xi)$ is a linear displacement operator that converts a function $\varphi(x)$ into $\varphi(x + \xi)$, its effect may be written in terms of a Taylor series:

$$D(\xi)\varphi(x) = \varphi(x) + \xi\varphi'(x) + \frac{\xi^2}{2}\varphi''(x) + \cdots = e^{\xi(d/dx)}\varphi(x)$$

Or, in three dimensions, if $D(\boldsymbol{\xi})$ converts $\varphi(\mathbf{r})$ into $\varphi(\mathbf{r} + \boldsymbol{\xi})$,

$$D(\boldsymbol{\xi})\varphi(\mathbf{r}) = e^{\boldsymbol{\xi}\cdot\nabla}\varphi(\mathbf{r})$$

This relation may be written with the use of the operator $P = i\hbar\nabla$, which represents the linear momentum of a particle, in the form

$$D(\xi)\varphi(r) = \exp\left(\frac{i}{\hbar}\,\boldsymbol{\xi}\cdot\mathbf{P}\right)\varphi(\mathbf{r}) \tag{7–3}$$

Here we have uncovered an interesting connection between the linear displacement operator D and the linear momentum operator P:

$$D(\boldsymbol{\xi}) = \exp\frac{i}{\hbar}\,\boldsymbol{\xi}\cdot\mathbf{P} \tag{7–4}$$

The components of the operator $\mathbf{P}$ are hermitian.[2] In general, any differential operator Q has a hermitian adjoint $Q^\dagger$, defined by the integral relation

$$\int u^*Qv\,d\tau = \int v(Q^\dagger u)^*d\tau \tag{7–5}$$

for any pair of "acceptable" functions u,v. If $Q^\dagger = Q$ the operator is said to be self-adjoint or hermitian. The matrices formed from Q are likewise adjoints[3]; they are hermitian if $Q^\dagger = Q$.

An operator U (acting on a function) is called *unitary* if

$$\int U^*u^*Uv\,d\tau = \int u^*v\,d\tau, \tag{7–6}$$

that is to say, if its application to u and v leaves their scalar product

[2] Margenau and Murphy, *op. cit.*, p. 344.

[3] These matrices are formed from Q by the rule discussed in Margenau and Murphy, *op. cit.*, p. 374, 11.17. They are adjoints in the sense of Chapter 10 of that work.

unchanged. Now there is an important theorem that states that *any operator of the form*

$$\exp\,(iH)$$

wherein H is hermitian, is necessarily unitary. The proof of this theorem is simple. If we form Eq. (7–6) with $U = e^{iH}$ we find

$$\int e^{-iH^*}u^*e^{iH}v\,d\tau \tag{7–7}$$

Imagine that e^{-iH^*} is expanded, and consider one term:

$$\int \frac{(-i)^n}{n!}\,(H^n)^*u^*e^{iH}v\,d\tau$$

If H is hermitian, H^n is likewise hermitian, and we can write this integral in the form

$$\frac{(-i)^n}{n!}\int u^*H^ne^{iH}v\,d\tau$$

Notice that the sign of i is *not* changed in this transposition of H^n. Thus, when the infinite series is restored, expression (7–7) becomes

$$\int u^*\,e^{-iH}e^{iH}v\,d\tau$$

and this is identical with (7–6).

The operator $D(\boldsymbol{\xi})$ is, therefore, unitary, since the components of $\mathbf{P}$ are hermitian (and commute, for otherwise a formula like (7–4) would have no meaning).

If H is a matrix, the operator e^{iH} is unitary in the matrix sense,[4] *i.e.*, $U^{\dagger}U = 1$. This is because

$$(e^{iH})^{\dagger} = e^{-iH^{\dagger}} = e^{-iH} = (e^{iH})^{-1}$$

Rotations are likewise unitary transformations, and we shall see that they can also be represented by an exponential operator. Let $D(\alpha)$ be a rotation about the z-axis, so that

$$D(\alpha)f(\varphi) = f(\varphi + \alpha)$$

Then, as before, $D(\alpha) = e^{\alpha(\partial/\partial\varphi)}$, and if we introduce once more the hermitian operator $L_z = -i\hbar(\partial/\partial\varphi)$,

$$D(\alpha) = e^{(i/\hbar)\alpha L_z} \tag{7–8}$$

[4] Cf. Margenau and Murphy, *op. cit.*, p. 310.

The form of L_z in Cartesian coordinates is Eq. (7–1a), and it is clear that orbital angular momentum is related to angular displacement in the same way as the linear operators are related.

In quantum mechanics, angular momenta other than orbital make their appearance. Their structure is not revealed by the simple considerations leading to (7–8). That formula, in fact, arises also from the general transformation properties of vectors under rotation, as will now be shown.

The proof takes different forms in different representations. Here we assume that quantum states are column vectors (or "spinors") ψ, with n elements, and that the scalar product has the form $\psi^\dagger\psi$. If ψ were a Schrödinger function, $\int \psi^*\psi d\tau$ would take the place of this matrix product, and in Dirac's theory of the electron, it would be replaced by $\int \psi^\dagger\psi d\tau$, ψ being a four-component spinor. But the work goes through as below with only formal changes. Use of the bra-ket notation (Chapter 8) would cover all these cases, but it obscures some of the detail we wish to exhibit here.

Consider a vector operator $\mathbf{V}$, each component of which is an n-dimensional square matrix. We demand that $\psi^\dagger\mathbf{V}\psi$ shall transform under a rotation like a proper vector.

A rotation in three dimensions is represented by a (three-square) matrix

$$R = \begin{pmatrix} R_{11} & R_{12} & R_{13} \\ R_{21} & R_{22} & R_{23} \\ R_{31} & R_{32} & R_{33} \end{pmatrix} \tag{7–9}$$

It transforms an ordinary three-dimensional vector $\mathbf{A}$ into $R\mathbf{A} = \mathbf{A}'$, *i.e.*,

$$\begin{aligned} A'_x &= R_{11}A_x + R_{12}A_y + R_{13}A_z \\ A'_y &= R_{21}A_x + R_{22}A_y + R_{23}A_z \\ A'_z &= R_{31}A_x + R_{32}A_y + R_{33}A_z \end{aligned} \tag{7–10}$$

We require that $\psi^\dagger V_x\psi$, $\psi^\dagger V_y\psi$, $\psi^\dagger V_z\psi$ transform like (7–10), whence

$$\psi'^\dagger V_x\psi' = R_{11}\psi^\dagger V_x\psi + R_{12}\psi^\dagger V_y\psi + R_{13}\psi^\dagger V_z\psi, \text{ etc.} \tag{7–11}$$

Note that we are not transforming the "vector operator" itself—its form is independent of rotation. Hence, Eq. (7–11) must be satisfied by subjecting the states ψ to a unitary transformation U:

$$\psi' = U\psi, \qquad \psi'^\dagger = \psi^\dagger U^\dagger, \qquad U^\dagger U = UU^\dagger = 1$$

Then Eq. (7–11) becomes

$$\psi^\dagger U^\dagger V_x U\psi = \psi^\dagger(R_{11}V_x + R_{12}V_y + R_{13}V_z)\psi \tag{7–12}$$

or $U^\dagger V_x U = R_{11}V_x + R_{12}V_y + R_{13}V_z$, etc.

Notice that U, V_z, V_y, V_z, are all n-dimensional matrices. To insure the unitary nature of U we introduce a vector $\mathbf{J}$, whose three components are hermitian matrices, a unit vector $\boldsymbol{\epsilon}$ in the direction of the axis of rotation, and write

$$U = e^{(i/h)\theta\boldsymbol{\epsilon}\cdot\mathbf{J}} \tag{7–13}$$

For an *infinitesimal* rotation about the z-axis

$$U = 1 + \frac{i}{\hbar}J_z d\theta \tag{7–14}$$

In this special case

$$R = \begin{pmatrix} 1 & d\theta & 0 \\ -d\theta & 1 & 0 \\ 0 & 0 & 1 \end{pmatrix} \tag{7–15}$$

On putting Eqs. (7–14) and (7–15) into (7–12), we find

$$\left(1 - \frac{i}{\hbar}J_z d\theta\right) V_x \left(1 + \frac{i}{\hbar}J_z d\theta\right) = V_x + d\theta V_y$$

so that, to within first order in $d\theta$,

$$J_z V_x - V_x J_z = i\hbar V_y \tag{7–16}$$

This equation must hold for *every* vector operator. We now show that J_x,J_y,J_z form a vector operator, $\mathbf{J}$.

From

$$\psi' = U\psi = (1 + \frac{i}{\hbar}\boldsymbol{\epsilon}\cdot\mathbf{J}d\theta)\psi$$

we find, on multiplying by $\psi^\dagger$ from the left,

$$\psi^\dagger\psi' = \psi^\dagger\psi + \frac{i}{\hbar}d\theta\boldsymbol{\epsilon}\cdot\psi^\dagger\mathbf{J}\psi \tag{7–17}$$

In this equation we transform both ψ and ψ' by a unitary operator U, which represents a rotation whose matrix is R (R acts on $\boldsymbol{\epsilon}$), obtaining

$$\psi^\dagger U^\dagger U\psi' = \psi^\dagger U^\dagger U\psi + \frac{i}{\hbar}d\theta\boldsymbol{\epsilon}'\cdot\psi^\dagger U^\dagger\mathbf{J}U\psi$$

Comparison with (7–17) shows that

$$\boldsymbol{\epsilon}\cdot\psi^\dagger\mathbf{J}\psi = \boldsymbol{\epsilon}'\cdot\psi^\dagger U^\dagger\mathbf{J}U\psi$$

This means: the scalar product of $\boldsymbol{\epsilon}$ and $\psi^\dagger\mathbf{J}\psi$ is invariant with respect to the rotation; hence, since $\boldsymbol{\epsilon}$ is a true vector, $\psi^\dagger\mathbf{J}\psi$ must likewise be a true vector.

According to Eq. (7–16), J_x therefore obeys the relation

$$J_zJ_x - J_xJ_z = i\hbar J_y \tag{7–18a}$$

Others follow by cyclic permutations; all of them can be symbolized conveniently by the vector relation

$$\mathbf{J}\times\mathbf{J} = i\hbar\mathbf{J} \tag{7–18}$$

We conclude that, when a rotation, R, transforms a vector, $\mathbf{A}$, into $R\mathbf{A}$ in accordance with Eq. (7–10) it induces in ψ a corresponding transformation from ψ to ψ' such that

$$\psi' = e^{-(i/\hbar)\boldsymbol{\epsilon}\cdot\mathbf{J}\theta}\psi \tag{7–19}$$

While the matrix R does not explicitly involve the axis of rotation along which $\boldsymbol{\epsilon}$ extends, nor the angle of rotation θ, it is known (from a theorem of Euler's) that every R is equivalent to a single rotation definable geometrically by an $\boldsymbol{\epsilon}$ and a θ.

Equation (7–19) has only formal significance; it can be used in calculations only if the dot product in the exponent need not be expanded. Otherwise, the equation would read

$$\psi' = e^{-(i/\hbar)\varepsilon_xJ_x}\cdot e^{-(i/\hbar)\varepsilon_yJ_y}\cdot e^{-(i/\hbar)\varepsilon_zJ_z}$$

and this expression is ambiguous because it depends on the order of the three factors, since the components of $\mathbf{J}$ do not commute. This is connected with the fact that finite rotations do not commute.

Any operator $\mathbf{J}$, which satisfies the commutation rule Eq. (7–18), represents quantum mechanical angular momentum. Orbital angular momentum, $\mathbf{L}$, with components explicitly given by Eq. (7–1), is a special example[5] of $\mathbf{J}$.

7.2. Eigenvalues of $\mathbf{J}_z$ and $\mathbf{J}^2$.—From the defining relations (7–18), certain very general properties of all angular momenta can be derived; in particular, it is possible to obtain a catalogue and a classification of all possible eigenvalues of J_z and of J^2.

Let us note first that, since the components of $\mathbf{J}$ do not commute, they do not have simultaneous eigenstates. But the eigenvalues of

[5] The Pauli spin operators, $\mathbf{S}$, encountered in Margenau and Murphy, p. 402, are another example.

J_x, J_y and J_z must be the same set of numbers because space is isotropic. Although **J** does not commute with its own components, J^2 does commute, as will now be shown.

To save writing the symbol $\hbar$, it is desirable to replace $\mathbf{J}/\hbar$ by $\mathscr{J}$, a vector with components X, Y, and Z, thus introducing dimensionless angular momenta X, Y, and Z. In view of Eq. (7–18) they satisfy

$$\begin{aligned} XY - YX &= iZ \qquad &\text{(a)} \\ YZ - ZY &= iX \qquad &\text{(b)} \\ ZX - XZ &= iY \qquad &\text{(c)} \end{aligned} \tag{7–20}$$

Now

$$\mathscr{J}^2X - X\mathscr{J}^2 = (Y^2X - XY^2 + Z^2X - XZ^2) \tag{7–21}$$

From (7–20a): $Y^2X = YXY - iYZ$, while

$$XY^2 = YXY + iZY$$

Similar relations are obtained for Z^2X and XZ^2 from Eq. (7–20c). When they are substituted in Eq. (7–21), it is found that

$$\mathscr{J}^2X - X\mathscr{J}^2 = 0$$

Clearly, Y and Z must also commute with J^2 if X does; hence we conclude

$$J^2\mathbf{J} - \mathbf{J}J^2 = 0 \tag{7–22}$$

A useful relation results when Eq. (7–20b) is multiplied by i and then subtracted from Eq. (7–20c). One finds

$$(X + iY)Z = (Z - 1)(X + iY) \tag{7–23a}$$

The same operations, performed with $-i$ instead of i, yield

$$(X - iY)Z = (Z + 1)(X - iY) \tag{7–23b}$$

Let ψ be a simultaneous eigenstate of Z and of J^2, so that

$$\begin{aligned} Z\psi &= a\psi \qquad &\text{(a)} \\ \mathscr{J}^2\psi &= b^2\psi \qquad &\text{(b)} \end{aligned} \tag{7–24}$$

Here a and b^2 are real because their operators are hermitian. We wish to show that

$$b^2 \geq a^2 \tag{7–25}$$

That relation follows from the fact that the operator $X^2 + Y^2$ has positive eigenvalues. To see this, write the eigenvalue equations for X, Y, and $X^2 + Y^2$:

$$X\varphi_i = x_i\varphi_i$$
$$Y\psi_i = y_i\psi_i$$
$$(X^2 + Y^2)\chi_i = k_i\chi_i$$

From the last of these,

$$k_i = \chi_i^\dagger(X^2 + Y^2)\chi_i$$

Now χ_i may be expanded either in terms of the φ_i or the ψ_i,

$$\chi_i = \sum_\lambda c_\lambda\varphi_\lambda = \sum_\mu d_\mu\psi_\mu$$

If, therefore, one uses the first expansion in the evaluation of $\chi_i^\dagger X^2\chi_i$, and the second in computing $\chi_i^\dagger Y^2\chi_i$, one obtains

$$k_i = \sum_\alpha |c_\alpha|^2 x_\alpha^2 + \sum_\mu |d_\mu|^2 y_\mu^2$$

a sum that is evidently ≥ 0. But

$$X^2 + Y^2 = \mathscr{J}^2 - Z^2$$

hence, in accordance with (24), $k_i = b^2 - a^2 \geq 0$. The inequality (7–25) is thus established.

We are now ready to find the eigenvalues a and b^2. Multiplication of Eq. (7–24a) by $X + iY$ yields

$$(X + iY)Z\psi = a(X + iY)\psi$$

and this, with the use of (7–23a) followed by rearrangement, becomes

$$Z[(X + iY)\psi] = (a + 1)[(X + iY)\psi] \tag{7–26}$$

The contents of the brackets represent a state, different from ψ, but evidently belonging to the eigenvalue $a + 1$ of Z. If ψ is an eigenfunction of Z belonging to a, then the application of $X + iY$ to ψ generates another eigenfunction of Z, namely one belonging to $a + 1$. There is, of course, the alternative possibility that it might produce 0, which also satisfies Eq. (7–26). The operator $X + iY$ is called the "upward displacement operator" for angular momenta, and it will here be denoted by $\mathscr{J}_+$. In a simple notation,

$$\mathscr{J}_+\psi(a) = \text{const.}\ \psi(a + 1) \tag{7–27}$$

The constant must be introduced because Eq. (7–26) does not guarantee normalization of both $\psi(a)$ and $\psi(a + 1)$: the normalization factors may be functions of a (and b^2). We need to know this constant later, and, hence, defer its calculation to the next section.

Repeated application of $\mathscr{J}_+$ to ψ yields the following sequence of eigenstates and eigenvalues:

Eigenstates	ψ	$(X + iY)\psi$	$(X + iY)^2\psi$	...
Eigenvalues	a	$a + 1$	$a + 2$	...

Each of these states is also an eigenstate of J^2 because J^2 and $\mathscr{J}_+$, and, therefore, $\mathscr{J}^2$ and $(\mathscr{J}_+)^n$, commute. Furthermore, each of these states belongs to the single eigenvalue b^2 of $\mathscr{J}^2$. The various $(X + iY)^n\psi$ are degenerate eigenstates of $\mathscr{J}^2$.

When Eq. (7–24a) is multiplied by $X - iY$ and rearranged in accordance with (7–23b), there results

$$Z[(X - iY)\psi] = (a - 1)[(X - iY)\psi]$$

The function $(X - iY)\psi$ is, therefore, also an eigenfunction of Z, belonging to the eigenvalue $a - 1$, $X - iY = \mathscr{J}_-$ and is, therefore, the "downward displacement operator" for angular momenta;

$$\mathscr{J}_-\psi(a) = \text{const. } \psi(a - 1) \tag{7–28}$$

Repeated application of it produces a sequence similar to the foregoing:

Eigenstates	...	$(X - iY)^2\psi$	$(X - iY)\psi$	ψ
Eigenvalues	...	$a - 2$	$a - 1$	a

All these states also belong to the eigenvalue b^2 of $\mathscr{J}^2$.

If there is a largest eigenvalue of Z, say A, then the first sequence must terminate, and this can happen only if

$$(X + iY)\psi(A) = 0 \tag{7–29}$$

while $Z\psi(A) = A\psi(A)$, $\psi(A) \neq 0$.

And if there exists a lowest eigenvalue of Z, say B, then

$$(X - iY)\psi(B) = 0 \tag{7–30}$$

while $Z\psi(B) = B\psi(B)$, $\psi(B) \neq 0$.

From these results we obtain the actual A and B, and thence, all possible a. When Eq. (7–29) is multiplied by $X - iY$ from the left, and the operator product is expanded, one finds that

$$\begin{aligned}[X^2 + Y^2 + i(XY - YX)]\psi(A) &= (X^2 + Y^2 - Z)\psi(A)\\ &= (b^2 - A^2 - A)\psi(A) = 0\end{aligned}$$

This is true if the contents of the last parenthesis vanish, *i.e.*, if

$$A = -\tfrac{1}{2} + \sqrt{b^2 + \tfrac{1}{4}} \tag{7–31}$$

The + sign of the radical is chosen to ensure that A is indeed the largest eigenvalue. Similar reasoning, starting with Eq. (7–30), which in this instance is multiplied by $X + iY$ from the left, leads to

$$B = \tfrac{1}{2} - \sqrt{b^2 + \tfrac{1}{4}}$$

Thus $B = -A$; the sequence of eigenvalues is symmetric about 0 and extends from $-A$ to A, over a numerical interval $2A$. This interval contains an integral number, let us say $N + 1$, of eigenvalues differing by 1, and

$$N = 2A$$

(Observe that N is the number of subintervals between successive values of a). But N may be even or odd. If it is even, $N = 2l$ (l is an integer) and $A = l$. The series of possible a's is then

$$-l, -l + 1, \cdots, -1, 0, 1, 2, \cdots, l \tag{7–I}$$

It includes the value 0. On the other hand, if N is odd and equals $2n + 1$, where n is an integer, $A = n + \frac{1}{2}$ and the sequence runs:

$$-(n + \tfrac{1}{2}), -(n - \tfrac{1}{2}), \cdots, -\tfrac{1}{2}, \tfrac{1}{2}, \tfrac{3}{2}, \cdots, n - \tfrac{1}{2}, n + \tfrac{1}{2} \tag{7–II}$$

It does not contain the value 0.

These two sequences exhaust all possibilities. Hence, there are two types of angular momenta, one with eigenvalues that are multiples of $\hbar$ (remember that $\mathbf{J} = \mathcal{J} h$) and one with eigenvalues that are half-odd multiples of $\hbar$. Orbital angular momentum belongs to the former type, the spin of a single electron to the latter (with $n = 0$). Since n can also be any integer greater than 0, the present results suggest that there must be many other examples. This suggestion is borne out by the fact that the addition of two angular momenta, $\mathbf{J}_1$ and $\mathbf{J}_2$, yields an operator $\mathbf{J}_3$, which is also an angular momentum in the quantum sense. Specifically, if $\mathbf{J}_1$ and $\mathbf{J}_2$ satisfy Eq. (7–18) individually, so will $\mathbf{J}_3 \equiv \mathbf{J}_1 + \mathbf{J}_2$. Hence, by addition of angular momenta from classes I and II, we get angular momenta of class (7–II) with larger values of n.

The proof of the theorem affirming that $\mathbf{J}_3$ is a proper quantum mechanical angular momentum involves only an expansion of $(\mathbf{J}_1 + \mathbf{J}_2) \times (\mathbf{J}_1 + \mathbf{J}_2)$ with subsequent use of the commutation rules for $\mathbf{J}_1$ and $\mathbf{J}_2$, and the fact that $\mathbf{J}_1$ and $\mathbf{J}_2$ commute because they act in different spaces—*i.e.*, the states of $\mathbf{J}_1$ and $\mathbf{J}_2$ are functions of different coordinates.

The maximum value of a, our A, is usually called j; the eigenvalues of Z, our a, are called m. We have seen that j is either an integer or a half-integer, and that m ranges from $-j$ to $+j$ in unit steps. The eigenvalue of $\mathscr{J}^2$, the quantity b^2, is related to j by Eq. (7–31), which, when solved for b^2, gives

$$b^2 = A(A + 1) = j(j + 1)$$

In sum, then, the eigenvalues of J_z are $m\hbar$, $-j \leq m \leq j$; the eigenvalues of J^2 are $j(j + 1)\hbar^2$.

7.3. Quantum Mechanical Addition of Angular Momenta.—To proceed further it is necessary to compute the constants in Eqs. (7–27) and (7–28). Let us write (7–27) in the form

$$\mathscr{J}_+\psi_{j,m} = G_+(j,m)\psi_{j,m+1} \tag{7–32}$$

The states $\psi_{j,m}$ and $\psi_{j,m+1}$ are understood to be normalized, so that $\psi^\dagger\psi$ is always 1. Hence,

$$\psi^\dagger_{j,m}\mathscr{J}^\dagger_+\mathscr{J}_+\psi_{j,m} = |G_+|^2\psi^\dagger_{j,m+1}\psi_{j,m+1} = |G_+|^2$$

When

$$\begin{aligned}\mathscr{J}^\dagger_+\mathscr{J}_+ &= (X^\dagger - iY^\dagger)(X + iY) = (X - iY)(X + iY)\\ &= X^2 + Y^2 + i(XY - YX)\\ &= \mathscr{J}^2 - Z^2 - Z\end{aligned}$$

is introduced in the equation for $|G_+|^2$, and these operators are allowed to act on $\psi_{j,m}$, one finds

$$\begin{aligned}|G_+|^2 = \psi^\dagger_{j,m}[j(j + 1) - m^2 - m]\psi_{j,m} &= j(j + 1) - m(m + 1)\\ &= (j - m)(j + m + 1)\end{aligned}$$

If we write Eq. (7–28) in the form

$$\mathscr{J}_-\psi_{j,m} = G_-(j,m)\psi_{j,m-1} \tag{7–33}$$

and proceed in the same way, we arrive at

$$|G_-|^2 = j(j + 1) - m^2 + m = (j + m)(j - m + 1)$$

Hence, aside from a phase factor $e^{i\varphi}$, which the present analysis leaves open and which can be chosen at will, we conclude:

$$G_+(j,m) = G_-(j,-m) = [(j - m)(j + m + 1)]^{1/2} \tag{7–34}$$

The problem of adding two angular momenta arises at many points in quantum physics. An electron has a spin and an orbital angular momentum that combine to give a resultant. The nuclear spin is compounded with the electronic angular momentum to form the total angular momentum of an atom. The spins of two electrons can be added into a resultant spin. In all such instances, states belonging to an operator $\mathbf{J}_1 \equiv \mathcal{J}_1\hbar$ are compounded with states belonging to $\mathbf{J}_2 \equiv \mathcal{J}_2\hbar$ to form eigenstates of $\mathbf{J} = \mathbf{J}_1 + \mathbf{J}_2 \equiv \mathcal{J}\hbar$, and the operators $\mathbf{J}_1$ and $\mathbf{J}_2$ are foreign to each other; they act on different coordinates or spaces and, therefore, commute.

We know that the operators $\mathcal{J}_1^2$, $\mathcal{J}_2^2$, $\mathcal{J}^2$, $\mathcal{J}_z$, which have eigenvalues $j_1(j_1 + 1)$, $j_2(j_2 + 1)$, $j(j + 1)$, and m, commute with one another. It is, therefore, possible to construct states that are sharp

TABLE 7–1

m	Possible Values of m_1	and m_2	Possible Values of j
$j_1 + j_2$	j_1	j_2	$j_1 + j_2$
$j_1 + j_2 - 1$	j_1 $j_1 - 1$	$j_2 - 1$ j_2	$j_1 + j_2$ $j_1 + j_2 - 1$
$j_1 + j_2 - 2$	j_1 $j_1 - 1$ $j_1 - 2$	$j_2 - 2$ $j_2 - 1$ j_2	$j_1 + j_2$ $j_1 + j_2 - 1$ $j_1 + j_2 - 2$
$j_1 + j_2 - 3$	j_1 $j_1 - 1$ $j_1 - 2$ $j_1 - 3$	$j_2 - 3$ $j_2 - 2$ $j_2 - 1$ j_2	$j_1 + j_2$ $j_1 + j_2 - 1$ $j_1 + j_2 - 2$ $j_1 + j_2 - 3$
....	......	......	....

with respect to all of them (*i.e.*, the four named operators are diagonal in these states, or, in still another common version, j_1, j_2, j, and m are good quantum numbers). These states might be called $\psi_{j_1 j_2 jm}$; the subscripts designate good quantum numbers. For convenience, however, the labels j_1 and j_2 will be omitted, because they are usually uninteresting.

Next, note that $J_{1z} \equiv \mathcal{J}_{1z}\hbar$ and $J_{2z} \equiv \mathcal{J}_{2}\hbar$ do *not* commute with $\mathcal{J}^2$, since the latter contains the product $\mathcal{J}_1 \cdot \mathcal{J}_2$. Hence, m_1, the eigenvalue of $\mathcal{J}_{1z}$, and m_2, the eigenvalue of $\mathcal{J}_{2z}$, cannot be good quantum numbers when a state is sharp with respect to j and m. States for which $\mathscr{J}_1^2$ and $\mathscr{J}_{1z}$ are diagonal will be written $\psi_{j_1 m_1}$; states for which $\mathscr{J}_2$ and $\mathscr{J}_{2z}$ are diagonal are $\psi_{j_2 m_2}$. Each set is complete in its own space. It is expected, therefore, that $\psi_{j,m}$ can be expanded in terms of $\psi_{j_1 m_1} \cdot \psi_{j_2 m_2}$ as basic functions. If such an expansion is possible, it has the form

$$\psi_{j,m} = \sum_{m_1 m_2} C(j_1 j_2 jm;\, m_1 m_2)\psi_{j_1 m_1}\psi_{j_2 m_2} \tag{7-35}$$

A simple bookkeeping argument that counts the states on the left and right of this equation affirms this possibility. For a given j, there are $2j_1 + 1$ possible values of m_1, for j_2 there are $2j_2 + 1$ possible m_2's. Hence, there are $(2j_1 + 1)(2j_2 + 1)$ terms on the right. An exhaustive representation of $\psi_{j,m}$ is possible if its multiplicity is also equal to $(2j_1 + 1)(2j_2 + 1)$. Let us, therefore, count the available number of m-values compatible with fixed j_1 and j_2. Table 7–1 facilitates this procedure. We first note that in the expansion (7–35), $m_1 + m_2$ must equal m. To see this, apply $\mathscr{J}_z = \mathscr{J}_{1z} + \mathscr{J}_{2z}$ to both sides of it; this multiplies the left side by m, each term on the right by $(m_1 + m_2)$. On rearranging, the equation reads

$$\sum_{m_1 m_2} (m - m_1 - m_2)C\psi_{j_1 m_1}\psi_{j_2 m_2} = 0$$

Because of the independence of the functions $\psi_{j_1 m_1}\psi_{j_2 m_2}$ this equation can be satisfied only if either $m - m_1 - m_2 = 0$ or $C = 0$. Hence, we conclude that

$$C(j_1 j_2 jm;\, m_1 m_2) = C(j_1 j_2 jm;\, m_1, m - m_1)\delta_{m_2, m-m_1}$$

The sum in (7–35) is, therefore, really a single one over m_1. Nevertheless, we shall write both indices for the sake of symmetry.

The first column of Table 7–1 lists all values of m. Since $m = m_1 + m_2$, and the maximum of this sum is $j_1 + j_2$, this is the largest permitted m. To each choice of m (between $j_1 + j_2$ and $-j_1 - j_2$) correspond several $\psi_{j_1 m_1}\psi_{j_2 m_2}$ functions and an equal number of $\psi_{j,m}$ functions. The values of m_1 and m_2 in terms of j_1 and j_2 are given in the second column, those of j and m in the third. How many functions will there be altogether? This depends on how far the table can be carried downward. Now the second column terminates when either m_1 reaches the value $-j_1$, or when m_2 reaches the value $-j_2$, whichever happens first. Hence the third column ends when j reaches the value $j_1 + j_2 - 2 \min (j_1 \text{ or } j_2) = |j_1 - j_2|$. For every j there are $2j + 1$

different functions (which appear in different boxes of the third column of the table). The total number of $\psi_{j,m}$ is, therefore

$$\sum_{j=|j_1-j_2|}^{j_1+j_2} (2j+1)$$

$$= 2\left[\frac{(j_1+j_2)(j_1+j_2+1)}{2} - \frac{(|j_1-j_2|+1)(|j_1-j_2|)}{2}\right]$$

$$+ j_1 + j_2 - |j_1 - j_2| + 1$$

$$= (2j_1+1)(2j_2+1)$$

The manifold of functions ψ_{jm} agrees with the manifold of product functions $\psi_{j_1 m_1}\psi_{j_2 m_2}$; the expansion (7–35) is safe.

The coefficients C are variously called "angular momentum addition coefficients," or Wigner coefficients, or Clebsch-Gordan coefficients. Their importance for quantum mechanics was first recognized by Wigner,[6] who also provided a formula and a complete theory of them. The notation varies among different authors who deal with them[7]; ours follows most closely that of Rose.

Some relations between different C-coefficients follow at once from the unitary nature of the transformation (7–35). Suppose we collect the quantum numbers into more compact sets, writing α for a (j,m)-combination, β for an (m_1,m_2)-combination. Also, to distinguish $\psi_{j,m}$ from $\psi_{j_1 m_1}\cdot\psi_{j_2 m_2}$, we use the letters φ and ψ. Equation (7–35) then reads

$$\varphi_\alpha = \sum_\beta C_{\alpha\beta}\psi_\beta, \quad \text{or} \quad \varphi = C\psi$$

if we regard φ and ψ as column vectors and C as a matrix. Then, because $1 = \varphi^\dagger\varphi = \psi^\dagger C^\dagger C\psi = \psi^\dagger\psi$,

$$C^\dagger C = CC^\dagger = 1$$

the unit matrix, and this means

$$\sum_\alpha C^*_{\alpha\beta}C_{\alpha\beta'} = \delta_{\beta\beta'} \tag{7–36}$$

$$\sum_\beta C_{\alpha\beta}C^*_{\alpha'\beta} = \delta_{\alpha\alpha'} \tag{7–37}$$

[6] E. P. Wigner, *Group Theory*, J. J. Griffin, trans., Academic Press, New York, 1959.

[7] E. U. Condon and G. H. Shortley, *Theory of Atomic Spectra*, Cambridge University Press, 1935; M. E. Rose, *Elementary Theory of Angular Momentum*, John Wiley and Sons, Inc., New York, 1957; A. Edmonds, *Angular Momentum in Quantum Mechanics*, Princeton University Press, 1957.

The C's, it will turn out, can be chosen as real quantities, and the star on C can be dropped.[8]

Equation (7–35) can also be written the other way around:

$$\psi = C^\dagger \varphi, \quad \text{or} \quad \psi_\beta = \sum_\alpha C^\dagger_{\beta\alpha}\varphi_\alpha = \sum_\alpha C_{\alpha\beta}\varphi_\alpha \tag{7–38}$$

We now expand Eq. (7–36), obtaining

$$\sum_{jm} C(j_1 j_2 jm;\, m_1 m_2) C(j_1 j_2 jm;\, m_1' m_2') = \delta_{m_1 m_1'}\delta_{m_2 m_2'}$$

But m_1 and m_2 fix the value of $m = m_1 + m_2$; C vanishes unless this condition is satisfied. Hence, there really is no summation over m, and we might as well write

$$\sum_j C(j_1 j_2 jm;\, m_1 m_2) C(j_1 j_2 jm;\, m_1' m_2') = \delta_{m_1 m_1'}\delta_{m_2 m_2'} \tag{7–39}$$

Equation (7–37) reads on expansion

$$\sum_{m_1 m_2} C(j_1 j_2 jm;\, m_1 m_2) C(j_1 j_2 j'm';\, m_1 m_2) = \delta_{jj'}\delta_{mm'}$$

and here again the summation over m_2 can be omitted because m_2 must be $m - m_1 = m' - m_1$. Hence, we may also write

$$\sum_{m_1} C(j{,}m;\, m_1{,}m - m_1) C(j'm;\, m_1{,}m - m_1) = \delta_{jj'} \tag{7–40}$$

In this form, we have even suppressed the unnecessary labels j_1 and j_2.

Finally, Eq. (7–38) becomes the inverse of (7–35):

$$\psi_{j_1 m_1}\psi_{j_2 m_2} = \sum_{j,m} C(j_1 j_2 jm;\, m_1 m_2)\psi_{jm} \tag{7–41}$$

where again the summation over m can be omitted because m_1 and m_2 are given.

Our analysis is altered only slightly if φ and ψ are taken to be functions rather than column vectors. In that case, the start is again made from the relation

$$\varphi_\alpha = \sum_\beta C_{\alpha\beta}\psi_\beta$$

but now the equation

$$\varphi^\dagger\varphi = \psi^\dagger\psi = 1$$

[8] Hence the C-matrices are not only unitary but orthogonal; see Margenau and Murphy, p. 310.

is replaced by

$$\int \varphi_\alpha^* \varphi_{\alpha'} d\tau = \delta_{\alpha\alpha'}, \qquad \int \psi_\beta^* \psi_\beta d\tau = \delta_{\beta\beta'}$$

and the work results again in Eqs. (7–36) to (7–38).

In the development so far we have often made use of the condition

$$m = m_1 + m_2 \tag{7–42}$$

which must be satisfied if $C(j,m; m_1m_2)$ is to differ from zero. There is another condition, known as the *triangle condition*, to be imposed on every finite C. It is apparent in Table 7–1, and has already been used in counting functions; j must lie between $|j_1 - j_2|$ and $j_1 + j_2$. We state it again for reference:

$$|j_1 - j_2| \leq j \leq j_1 + j_2 \tag{7–43}$$

If j_1 and j_2 were vectors and j their resultant, the triangle whose sides are j_1, j_2, and j_3 would not close unless j were limited by Eq. (7–43); hence, the name triangle condition, and hence, also, the analogy between quantum mechanics and the vector model.

7.4. Formulas for C-Coefficients; Recursion Relations.—Table 7–1 suggests that there is a unique correspondence between $\psi_{j,j}$ and $\psi_{j_1j_1} \cdot \psi_{j_2j_2}$ (first row). Does this mean that the two are equal? If so, the coefficient

$$C(j_1j_2\; j_1 + j_2\; j_1 + j_2;\; j_1j_2) = 1 \tag{7–44}$$

The explicit proof of this relation begins by noting that

$$\begin{aligned} \mathscr{J}^2 = \mathscr{J}_1^2 + \mathscr{J}_2^2 + 2\mathscr{J}_1 \cdot \mathscr{J}_2 \\ = \mathscr{J}_1^2 + \mathscr{J}_2^2 + \mathscr{J}_{1+}\mathscr{J}_{2-} + \mathscr{J}_{1-}\mathscr{J}_{2+} + 2\mathscr{J}_{1z}\mathscr{J}_{2z} \end{aligned} \tag{7–45}$$

Thus, when $\mathscr{J}^2$ in its expanded form is applied to $\psi_{j_1j_1} \cdot \psi_{j_2j_2}$, the result is $[j_1(j_1 + 1) + j_2(j_2 + 1) + 0 + 0 + 2j_1j_2]\psi_{j_1j_1}\psi_{j_2j_2}$, and the bracket is simply $(j_1 + j_2)(j_1 + j_2 + 1)$ or $j(j + 1)$. That is to say, for this "stretched" configuration—in which our triangle becomes a line—the product function $\psi_{j_1j_1}\psi_{j_2j_2}$ is an eigenfunction of $\mathscr{J}^2$, and it must equal ψ_{jj} except for a constant. But that constant has absolute value[1] because all functions are normalized. We take it to be 1, and thereby establish Eq. (7–44).

Knowing one C, one can derive a host of others by certain recurrence relations, which we shall now develop. In accordance with Eqs.

(7–32) and (7–34), apply $\mathscr{J}_+$ to (7–35); remember also that $\mathscr{J}_+ = \mathscr{J}_{1+} + \mathscr{J}_{2+}$. The result will be

$$\sum_{m_1 m_2} [(j-m)(j+m+1)]^{1/2}\psi_{j_1 m_1}\psi_{j_2 m_2} C(j,m+1;m_1 m_2) - \sum_{m_1 m_2} \{[(j_1-m_1)(j_1+m_1+1)]^{1/2}\psi_{j_1 m_1+1}\psi_{j_2 m_2} + [(j_2-m_2)(j_2+m_2+1)]^{1/2}\psi_{j_1 m_1}\psi_{j_2 m_2+1}\} \times C(jm;m_1 m_2) = 0$$

When the terms from these three summations are properly assembled, and the coefficients of every $\psi_{j_1 m_1}\psi_{j_2 m_2}$ are set equal to zero, one sees that

$$[(j-m)(j+m+1)]^{1/2}C(j,m+1;m_1,m_2) = [(j_1-m_1+1)(j_1+m_1)]^{1/2}C(j,m;m_1-1,m_2) + [(j_2-m_2+1)(j_2+m_2)]^{1/2}C(j,m;m_1,m_2-1) \tag{7–46}$$

When $\mathscr{J}_-$ is applied to Eq. (7–35) and the same steps are taken one arrives at the formula

$$[(j+m)(j-m+1)]^{1/2}C(j,m-1;m_1,m_2) = [(j_1+m_1+1)(j_1-m_1)]^{1/2}C(j,m;m_1+1,m_2) + [(j_2+m_2+1)(j_2-m_2)]^{1/2}C(j,m;m_1,m_2+1) \tag{7–47}$$

Equations (7–46) and (7–47) connect coefficients with the same j but different m. Other useful recursion relations for C's with equal j and m result from application of $\mathscr{J}^2$ in the form (7–45) to Eq. (7–35), *viz.*:

$$j(j+1)\sum_{m_1 m_2} C(j,m;m_1 m_2)\psi_{j_1 m_1}\psi_{j_2 m_2} = \sum_{m_1 m_2}[j_1(j_1+1)+j_2(j_2+1)+2m_1 m_2]C(j,m;m_1 m_2)\psi_{j_1 m_1}\psi_{j_2 m_2} + \sum_{m_1 m_2} G_+(j_1 m_1)G_-(j_2 m_2)C(j,m;m_1 m_2)\psi_{j_1 m_1+1}\psi_{j_2 m_2-1} + \sum_{m_1 m_2} G_-(j_1 m_1)G_+(j_2 m_2)C(j,m;m_1 m_2)\psi_{j_1 m_1-1}\psi_{j_2 m_2+1}$$

On comparing coefficients of equal $\psi_{j_1 m_2}\psi_{j_2 m_2}$, one sees that

$$[j(j+1)-j_1(j_1+1)-j_2(j_2+1)-2m_1 m_2]C(j,m;m_1 m_2) = G_+(j_1,m_1-1)G_-(j_2,m_2+1)C(j,m;m_1-1,m_2+1) + G_-(j_1,m_1+1)G_+(j_2,m_2-1)C(j,m;m_1+1,m_2-1) \tag{7–48}$$

where G is defined in Eq. (7–34).

Equations (7–39), (7–40), (7–44), (7–46), (7–47), and (7–48) are sufficient for the calculation of many C-coefficients. General formulas, too lengthy to be derived here, have been given by Wigner[9] and Racah.[10] Wigner's formula is

$$C(j_1j_2jm; m_1m_2) = \delta_{m,m_1+m_2} \times \left[(2j+1)\frac{(j+j_1-j_2)!(j-j_1+j_2)!(j_1+j_2-j)!(j+m)!(j-m)!}{(j_1+j_2+j+1)!(j_1-m_1)!(j_1+m_1)!(j_2-m_2)!(j_2+m_2)!}\right] \times \sum_\gamma \frac{(-)^{\gamma+j_2+m_2}(j_2+j+m_1-\gamma)!(j_1-m_1+\gamma)!}{\gamma!(j-j_1+j_2-\gamma)!(j+m-\gamma)!(\gamma+j_1-j_2-m)!}$$

Careful study shows it to be identical with Racah's:

$$\begin{aligned} C(j_1j_2jm; m_1m_2) &= \delta_{m,m_1+m_2} \\ &\times \left[(2j+1)\frac{(j_1+j_2-j)!(j+j_1-j_2)!(j+j_2-j_1)!}{(j_1+j_2+j+1)!}\right. \\ &\left.\times (j_1+m_1)!(j_1-m_1)!(j_2+m_2)!(j_2-m_2)!(j+m)!(j-m)!\right]^{1/2} \\ &\times \sum_\gamma \frac{(-)^\gamma}{\gamma!}[(j_1+j_2-j-\gamma)!(j_1-m_1-\gamma)!(j_2+m_2-\gamma)! \\ &\qquad \times (j-j_2+m_1+\gamma)!(j-j_1-m_2+\gamma)!]^{-1} \end{aligned}$$

From the last expression the following symmetry relations can be deduced:

$$\begin{aligned} C(j_1j_2jm; m_1m_2) &= (-)^{j_1+j_2-j}C(j_1j_2j-m; -m_1,-m_2) \\ &= (-)^{j_1+j_2-j}C(j_2j_1jm; m_2m_1) \\ &= (-)^{j_1-m_1}\left(\frac{2j+1}{2j_2+1}\right)^{1/2} C(j_1jj_2-m; m_1,-m) \end{aligned}$$

Other coefficients, which differ only in sign from the C, have been introduced for the purpose of simplifying the symmetry relations. For these we refer the reader to Rose's monograph, cited above. Numerical tabulations of C-coefficients are now abundant.[11]

We note here in passing, and without proof, an important relation between normalized spherical harmonics[12]

$$Y_{lm}(\theta,\varphi) \equiv (2\pi)^{-1/2}N_{lm}P_l^m(\cos\theta)e^{im\varphi}$$

[9] *Loc. cit.*

[10] G. Racah, *Phys. Rev.*, **62**, 438 (1932).

[11] D. L. Falkoff, C. S. Calladay, and R. E. Sells, *Can. J. Phys.*, **30**, 253 (1952); B. J. Sears and M. G. Radtke, *Chalk River Report TPI-75*, 1954; R. Saito and M. Morita, *Progr. Theoret. Phys. (Kyoto)*, **13**, 540 (1955); A. Simon, *Oak Ridge Nat. Lab. Report 1718*.

[12] Cf. Margenau and Murphy, *op. cit.*, pp. 112 *et seq.*

and C-coefficients:

$$Y_{l_1 m_1}(\theta,\varphi) Y_{l_2 m_2}(\theta,\varphi) = \sum_l \left[\frac{(2l_1 + 1)(2l_2 + 1)}{4\pi(2l + 1)}\right] \times C(l_1,l_2,l,m_1 + m_2; m_1 m_2) C(l_1 l_2 l 0; 00) Y_{l,m_1+m_2}(\theta,\phi)$$

In atomic physics, it is sometimes necessary to calculate integrals over products of *three* spherical harmonics. These can be reduced conveniently, with the help of the foregoing expression, to integrals over the product of two spherical harmonics, which are known.[13] Thus

$$\int Y^*_{l_3 m_3} Y_{l_2 m_2} Y_{l_1 m_1} \sin\theta d\theta d\varphi = \sum_l \left[\frac{(2l_1 + 1)(2l_2 + 1)}{4\pi(2l + 1)}\right]^{1/2} C(l_1,l_2,l,m_1 + m_2; m_1 m_2) \times C(l_1 l_2 l 0; 00) \int Y^*_{l_3 m_3} Y_{l,m_1+m_2} \sin\theta d\theta d\varphi$$

$$= \left[\frac{(2l_1 + 1)(2l_2 + 1)}{4\pi(2l_3 + 1)}\right]^{1/2} C(l_1 l_2 l_3 m_3; m_1 m_2) C(l_1 l_2 l_3 0; 00)$$

The last line follows because

$$\int Y^*_{l_3 m_3} Y_{l,m_1+m_2} \sin\theta d\theta d\varphi = \delta_{l,l_3} \delta_{m_1+m_2,m_3}$$

PART II—TRANSFORMATION THEORY OF QUANTUM MECHANICS

7.5. Stationary and Moving Systems.—In quantum mechanics, states can be represented by functions, rays in Hilbert space, column vectors, and sets of column vectors (as in Dirac's or Pauli's theory); observables can be various sorts of linear operators, including square matrices. This is often bewildering. To exhibit the common rationale of all these representations, the notion of Chapter 8 has been invented, being a notation that is largely indifferent to the choice of representation. It presents the extreme in which some finer points are lost, however, and these points are often important. To bridge the gulf between bewildering detail and elegant but somewhat indiscriminate synopsis, we present in this section certain ideas and formulas that are neither detailed nor elegant, but fall in the middle range and are sometimes useful.

[13] *Loc. cit.*, Chapter 3.

States in the form of *functions* ϕ develop in time according to the Schrödinger equation

$$i\hbar\dot{\phi} = H\phi \tag{7-49}$$

where H is the hamiltonian whose form may or may not change with t (time). To pass from Schrödinger's state function to Heisenberg's state vector in the simplest possible way, one introduces a complete orthonormal set of functions $\{u\}$, called the basis set, *which are constant in time,* and expands

$$\phi = \sum_{\alpha} a_{\alpha} u_{\alpha} \tag{7-50}$$

This relation defines a time-dependent column vector $\mathbf{a}$. Because $\int \phi^*\phi d\tau = 1$, Eq. (7-50) implies $\mathbf{a}^{\dagger}\mathbf{a} = 1$; $\mathbf{a}$ is a unit vector. This is true of all state vectors that correspond to normalized state functions. Substitution of (7-50) into (7-49), subsequent multiplication by u_r^*, and integration yield the Schrödinger equation (sometimes called the "equation of motion") for the component a_r

$$i\hbar\dot{a}_r = \sum_{\alpha} H_{r\alpha} a_{\alpha}$$

where $H_{ij} = \int u_i^* H u_j d\tau$.[14] In matrix form, this reads

$$i\hbar\dot{\mathbf{a}} = \boldsymbol{H}\mathbf{a} \tag{7-51}$$

and is formally identical with (7-49). The understanding is, of course, that the vector $\mathbf{a}$ and the matrix $\boldsymbol{H}$ are both constructed in the *stationary* system $\{u\}$. When this needs to be specifically indicated we shall write such quantities in the explicit form $\mathbf{a}(u)$ and $\boldsymbol{H}(u)$. The first of these, and possibly the second, is also a function of t; hence, when necessity dictates, the symbols $\mathbf{a}(u;t)$ and $\boldsymbol{H}(u;t)$ will be used, although u is not an argument in the usual sense. A symbol like $H(0)$ shall always mean: the operator H at $t = 0$, the system $\{u\}$ being unspecified.

It is often convenient to introduce a "time development matrix" $\boldsymbol{U}$, defined by the relation

$$\mathbf{a}(t) = \boldsymbol{U}\mathbf{a}(0) \tag{7-52}$$

Substitution in Eq. (7-51) then shows that $\boldsymbol{U}$ also satisfies the Schrödinger equation,

$$i\hbar\boldsymbol{U} = \boldsymbol{H}\boldsymbol{U} \tag{7-53}$$

[14] In accordance with the rule in Margenau and Murphy, 11.17, p. 374.

The equation defines $U(u)$, of course, since H is understood to be $H(u)$. The matrix U is unitary. To see this, multiply (7–53) by $U^\dagger$ on the left; then multiply the associate (or adjunct) of (7–53), $-i\hbar\dot{U}^\dagger = U^\dagger H^\dagger$, by U on the right and note that H is hermitian: $H^\dagger = H$. Subtracting one of the resulting forms from the other gives the further result

$$i\hbar(U^\dagger\dot{U} + \dot{U}^\dagger U) = i\hbar\frac{\partial}{\partial t}(U^\dagger U) = 0$$

Hence, $U^\dagger U$ = constant. But since, from Eq. (7–52), $U(0) = 1$, $U^\dagger U = U^\dagger(0)U(0) = 1$, and this defines a unitary matrix.

We now introduce a second complete orthonormal set of functions $\{v\}$, which we shall take to be functions of t, $v_i(t)$. First, however, we merely consider the set $\{v(0)\}$. Since they are by definition constant in time, they behave like the u, and all preceding equations can be written in the $v(0)$-representation. A transformation of the functions has the form

$$v_i(0) = \sum_\alpha b^i_\alpha(0)u_\alpha$$

Let us assume further that $v_i(t)$ is the function into which $v_i(0)$ evolves at time t, in obedience to Eq. (7–49). Then

$$v_i(t) = \sum_\alpha b^i_\alpha(t)u_\alpha \tag{7–54}$$

and the vectors $\mathbf{b}^i$ (with components b^i_α) satisfy

$$i\hbar\dot{\mathbf{b}}^i = H\mathbf{b}^i \tag{7–55}$$

as substitution of Eq. (7–54) into (7–49) followed by matrix formation shows.

It is possible to form a matrix from the column vectors $\mathbf{b}^i$. If this were done by putting the matrix components b_{ij} equal to b^i_j the matrix equation resulting from (7–55) would have an unsymmetric form; but if we put

$$b^i_j = b_{ji}$$

it reads

$$i\hbar\dot{b} = Hb$$

The same convention generates a matrix equation of the form

$$b(t) = U(t)b(0) \tag{7–56}$$

with U determined by Eq. (7–53). Since both the $\{v(0)\}$ and the $\{u\}$ are orthonormal,

$$\delta_{ij} = \int v_i^*(0)v_j(0)d\tau = \sum_{\alpha\mu} \int b_{\alpha i}^*(0)u_\alpha^* b_{\mu j}(0)u_\mu d\tau$$
$$= \sum_\alpha b_{\alpha i}^*(0)b_{\alpha j}(0)$$

$b(0)$ is a unitary matrix. Therefore, $b(t)$, being related to $b(0)$ by a unitary matrix (Eq. 7–56), is also unitary.

And from this we may draw the further, important conclusion that the $v_i(t)$ remain orthonormal provided the $v_i(0)$ are orthonormal, as is seen on calculating

$$\int v_i^*(t)v_j(t)d\tau = \sum_{\alpha\mu} \int b_{\alpha i}^*(t)u_\alpha^* b_{\mu j}(t)u_\mu d\tau$$
$$= (b^\dagger b)_{ij} = \delta_{ij}$$

Henceforth we refer to the u as the stationary system of functions and to the v as the moving system, understanding that the "motion" is in accordance with the Schrödinger equation.

Matrices can be formed from operators with the use of the v as well as the u. Thus

$$P_{ij}(v) = \int v_i^* P v_j d\tau = \sum_{\alpha\mu} \int b_{\alpha i}^* u_\alpha^* P b_{\mu j} u_\mu d\tau = \sum_{\alpha\mu} b_{i\alpha}^\dagger P_{\alpha u}(u) b_{\mu j}$$

or

$$P(v) = b^\dagger P(u) b \tag{7–57}$$

Hence also

$$P(u) = bP(v)b^\dagger$$

Eq. (7–57) can be expanded in the following way.

$$P(v) = b^\dagger(0)U^\dagger P(u)Ub(0) = b^\dagger(0)U^\dagger bP(v)b^\dagger Ub(0)$$

But $P(u)$ is not a function of t if the differential operator P is not an explicit function of t, which we shall assume here. Then

$$P(u) = bP(v)b^\dagger = b(0)P(v,0)b^\dagger(0)$$

and we may write

$$P(v) = b^\dagger(0)U^\dagger b(0)P(v,0)b^\dagger(0)Ub(0)$$

Thus $\boldsymbol{P}(v)$ evolves in time according to the equation

$$\boldsymbol{P}(v) = \boldsymbol{V}^{\dagger}(t)\boldsymbol{P}(v,0)\boldsymbol{V} \tag{7-58}$$

provided

$$\boldsymbol{V}(t) = \boldsymbol{b}(0)^{\dagger}\boldsymbol{U}(t)\boldsymbol{b}(0)$$

If the moving set were the one starting from the stationary set $\{u\}$, $\boldsymbol{V}$ would be equal to $\boldsymbol{U}$.

Notice, by comparing (7–58) with (7–56), that the $\boldsymbol{P}(v)$-matrix develops in time in a manner different from that of $\boldsymbol{b}$. This is also apparent when the *differential* equation controlling $\boldsymbol{P}(v)$ is compared with (7–49), which regulates $\boldsymbol{b}$. For if we differentiate (7–57) we get

$$i\hbar\dot{\boldsymbol{P}}(v) = i\hbar(\dot{\boldsymbol{b}}^{\dagger}\boldsymbol{P}(u)\boldsymbol{b} + \boldsymbol{b}^{\dagger}\boldsymbol{P}(u)\dot{\boldsymbol{b}}) = \boldsymbol{P}(v)\boldsymbol{H}(v) - \boldsymbol{H}(v)\boldsymbol{P}(v)$$

The u and v representations are sometimes distinguished as the Schrödinger and the Heisenberg representation. For stationary operators $\boldsymbol{P}$, then, the "Heisenberg equation of motion" is

$$i\hbar\dot{\boldsymbol{P}} = \boldsymbol{P}\boldsymbol{H} - \boldsymbol{H}\boldsymbol{P} \tag{7-59}$$

If $\boldsymbol{P}$ depends explicitly on t, a term $i\hbar(\partial\boldsymbol{P}/\partial t)$ (whose elements are $i\hbar(\partial\boldsymbol{P}/\partial t)_{ij}$) is added on the right. $\boldsymbol{P}(u)$ does not change in time if the operator P is stationary; otherwise its elements are $(\partial P/\partial t)_{ij}$.

Before concluding our discussion of u and v systems, it is well to make one trivial point. Had we expanded ϕ directly in the v-set, so that Eq. (7–50) takes the form

$$\phi = \sum_{\alpha} a_{\alpha}(v)v_{\alpha}$$

the vector $\mathbf{a}(v)$ is stationary,

$$\dot{\mathbf{a}}(v) = 0 \tag{7-60}$$

because the v already satisfy Eq. (7–49).

7.6. Adiabatic Representation.—Let $\{w\}$ be any complete orthonormal set of functions, variable in time, but not necessarily in accordance with Eq. (7–49). Substitute the expansion

$$\phi = \sum_{\alpha} a_{\alpha}w_{\alpha}$$

into Eq. (7–49), obtaining

$$i\hbar\sum_{\alpha}(\dot{a}_{\alpha}w_{\alpha} + a_{\alpha}\dot{w}_{\alpha}) = \sum_{\alpha} a_{\alpha}Hw_{\alpha}$$

When this is multiplied by w_μ^* and integrated, as usual, the result is

$$i\hbar\dot{a}_\mu = \sum_\alpha (H - D)_{\mu\alpha}a_\alpha \tag{7-61}$$

provided we define the operator

$$D = i\hbar \frac{\partial}{\partial t} \tag{7-62}$$

If we put further

$$\mathbf{a}(w,t) = \boldsymbol{W}\mathbf{a}(w,0) \tag{7-63}$$

we find

$$i\hbar\dot{\boldsymbol{W}} = (\boldsymbol{H} - \boldsymbol{D})\boldsymbol{W} \tag{7-64}$$

$\boldsymbol{D}$ is hermitian because, if the w-functions are orthonormal,

$$0 = i\hbar \frac{\partial}{\partial t} \int w_l^* w_m d\tau = i\hbar \left[\int w_m \frac{\partial}{\partial t} w_l^* d\tau + \int w_l^* \frac{\partial}{\partial t} w_m d\tau \right]$$
$$= \left[-i\hbar \int w_m^* \frac{\partial}{\partial t} w_l d\tau \right]^* + i\hbar \int w_l^* \frac{\partial}{\partial t} w_m d\tau = -D_{ml}^* + D_{lm}$$

Therefore, by virtue of the argument following Eq. (7–53) the matrix $\boldsymbol{W}$, defined in (7–64), is unitary. This in turn has the consequence that $\mathbf{a}(t)$ remains a unit vector.

As an especially interesting case of w-functions we consider the *adiabatic* solutions of the Schrödinger equation, *i.e.*, the solutions of

$$Hw_l = E_l w_l \tag{7-65}$$

If the hamiltonian is truly stationary, then the w_l are the space-parts of the state function; but if H is a function of t, the w_l are not strictly state functions at all. Still, Eq. (7–65) defines a complete orthonormal set, each w_l being time-dependent, and the quasi-eigenvalues E_l will also be functions of t. It is clear on physical grounds, however, that w_l will be an approximation to the true states if H varies sufficiently slowly. Hence the name, adiabatic representation.

When both sides of Eq. (7–65) are differentiated with respect to t, and the resulting equation is multiplied by w_m^* and integrated over τ, there results

$$i\hbar(\dot{H})_{ml} + E_m D_{ml} = i\hbar\dot{E}_l\delta_{ml} + E_l D_{ml} \tag{7-66}$$

On putting $m = l$ we see that

$$(\dot{H})_{ll} = \dot{E}_l$$

otherwise

$$D_{ml} = i\hbar \frac{(\dot{H})_{ml}}{E_l - E_m}, \quad l \neq m \tag{7-67}$$

While D_{ll} escapes determination by this scheme, its value is real because D is hermitian.

We return to Eq. (7–64) and write it in component form observing that, by reason of (7–65), $\boldsymbol{H}$ is diagonal:

$$i\hbar \dot{W}_{lm} = (E_l - D_{ll})W_{lm} + i\hbar \sum_{\alpha \neq l} \frac{(\dot{H})_{l\alpha}}{E_l - E_\alpha} W_{\alpha m} \tag{7-68}$$

The first term on the right can be eliminated by a proper choice of the phases that accompany the w-function. Thus suppose we use w_l in the construction of D_{ll}, obtaining

$$D_{ll} = i\hbar \int w_l^* \dot{w}_l d\tau$$

But Eq. (7–65) is also satisfied by $w_l e^{if_l}$, f_l being a real function of t that is entirely undetermined. With this new function D_{ll} becomes

$$i\hbar \int w_l^* \dot{w}_l d\tau - \hbar \dot{f}_l$$

showing that D_{ll} is indefinite to within an arbitrary choice of a real function f_l. Therefore, if our original w_l gave a term $(E_l - D_{ll})W_{lm}$ in Eq. (7–68) we choose

$$f_l = \frac{1}{\hbar} \int_0^t \left[E_l(t') - D_{ll}(t') \right] dt$$

and reduce that term to zero. By this procedure the phases of all w_l functions have become determinate, except for a constant $e^{i\alpha_l}$.

The matrix $\boldsymbol{W}$ must then obey the equation

$$\dot{\boldsymbol{W}} = \boldsymbol{M}(t)\boldsymbol{W}$$

with

$$M_{ll} = 0, \qquad M_{lm} = \frac{(\dot{H})_{lm}}{E_l - E_m} \tag{7-69}$$

It is solved by successive approximations in which one puts

$$\boldsymbol{W} = \boldsymbol{W}_0 + \boldsymbol{W}_1 + \boldsymbol{W}_2 + \cdots \tag{7-70}$$

in the hope that the elements of $\boldsymbol{W}_{i+1}$ are much smaller than those of $\boldsymbol{W}_i$.

$\boldsymbol{W}_0$ is a constant matrix which, because of Eq. (7–63), must be the unit matrix $\boldsymbol{1}$.

The validity of this approximation can be justified only pragmatically, although some qualitative conditions for it can be stated, as will be seen. Assuming the legitimacy of Eq. (7–70), and substituting into (7–69), which is now to be solved in successive "orders of smallness" of its terms, we obtain

$$W_0 = 1 \qquad \text{(a)}$$
$$W_1 = MW_0 = \mathbf{M} \qquad \text{(b)}$$
$$W_2 = MW_1 \qquad \text{etc.} \qquad \text{(c)}$$

Eq. (b) leads to

$$W_1 = \int_0^t M(t_1)dt_1$$

while (c) gives

$$W_2 = \int_0^t dt_2 M(t_2) \int_0^{t_2} dt_1 M(t_1) \quad \text{etc.}$$

In general

$$W_n(t) = \int_0^t dt_n M(t_n) \int_0^{t_n} dt_{n-1} M(t_{n-1}) \cdots \int_0^{t_2} dt_1 M(t_1) \qquad (7\text{–}71)$$

The order in which these integrals are written is important, as the M-matrices for different t do not in general commute.

There is a compact way of writing our result. W_2 can be transformed as follows:[15]

$$W_2 = \int_0^t dt_1 \int_{t_1}^t dt_2 M(t_2)M(t_1) = \int_0^t dt_2 \int_{t_2}^t dt_1 M(t_1)M(t_2)$$

Hence

$$\begin{aligned} W_2 &= \frac{1}{2}\int_0^t dt_2 \int_0^{t_2} dt_1 M(t_2)M(t_1) + \frac{1}{2}\int_0^t dt_2 \int_{t_2}^t dt_1 M(t_1)M(t_2) \\ &= \frac{1}{2}\int_0^t dt_2 \left[\int_0^{t_2} dt_1 M(t_2)M(t_1) + \int_{t_2}^t dt_1 M(t_1)M(t_2) \right] \end{aligned}$$

Let the "time-ordering operator"[16] $\mathscr{T}$, when applied to the product

[15] Based upon a formula derived in Margenau and Murphy, 14.2, p. 525.

[16] Later, in Chapter 11, we shall again encounter this operator, but with the more customary label P, which possible confusion with the momentum prevents us from using here.

$M(t_1)M(t_2)$ arrange the order of the factors so that the one with the *smaller* t comes *last*:

$$\mathscr{T}\boldsymbol{M}(t_1)\boldsymbol{M}(t_2) = \begin{cases} \boldsymbol{M}(t_1)\boldsymbol{M}(t_2) & \text{if} \quad t_2 \leq t_1 \\ \boldsymbol{M}(t_2)\boldsymbol{M}(t_1) & \text{if} \quad t_1 \leq t_2 \end{cases}$$

Then

$$\boldsymbol{W}_2 = \frac{1}{2}\int_0^t dt_2 \int_0^t dt_1 \mathscr{T}\boldsymbol{M}(t_1)\boldsymbol{M}(t_2)$$

On generalizing this definition of $\mathscr{T}$ for any number of products $\prod_i \boldsymbol{M}(t_i)$, one sees that

$$\boldsymbol{W}_n = \frac{1}{n!}\int_0^t (n) \int_0^t dt_1 \cdots dt_n \mathscr{T}\boldsymbol{M}(t_1)\boldsymbol{M}(t_2)\cdots \boldsymbol{M}(t_n)$$

and symbolically,

$$\boldsymbol{W} = \mathscr{T} \exp \int_0^t \boldsymbol{M}(t_1)dt_1 \tag{7–72}$$

This, of course, is nothing more than shorthand for Eq. (7–70) and (7–71), to which we now return.

We find on using (7–69)

$$W_{lm} = \delta_{lm} + \int_0^t \frac{(\dot{H})_{lm}}{E_l - E_m} dt_1 + \int_0^t dt_2 \sum_\alpha \frac{[\dot{H}(t_2)]_{l\alpha}}{E_l(t_2) - E_\alpha(t_2)} \times \int_0^{t_2} dt_1 \frac{[\dot{H}(t_1)]_{\alpha m}}{E_\alpha(t_1) - E_m(t_1)} + \cdots$$

Hence Eq. (7–63) reads

$$a_l(w,t) = a_l(w,0) + \sum_{\alpha \neq l} \int_0^t \frac{(\dot{H})_{l\alpha}dt_1}{E_l - E_\alpha} a_\alpha(w,0) + \cdots \tag{7–73}$$

Suppose $a_l(w,0) = \delta_{kl}$; only the kth state of the system is present initially. The first term on the right of Eq. (7–73) can then contribute nothing to any state l that differs from k; it will induce no transitions from the initial state. Retaining it alone constitutes the adiabatic approximation. The second term contributes to $a_l(w,t)$ provided $(\dot{H})_{lk}$ is finite. It is the first *diabatic* term in the expansion.

Equation (7–73) suggests a criterion for the safe use of the adiabatic approximation. It is justified if $\int_0^t (\dot{H})_{lk}/(E_l - E_k)dt \ll 1$, and this is generally true if any or all of the following conditions are met:

(1) t is very small;
(2) H changes slowly;
(3) the energy levels E_i are far apart.

Having learned how states change in the adiabatic representation, we now turn briefly to examine the "equation of motion" of matrices. Clearly,

$$i\hbar\dot{w}_m = \sum_\alpha D_{\alpha m} w_\alpha, \qquad -i\hbar\dot{w}_l^* = \sum_\alpha D_{\alpha l}^* w_\alpha^*$$

Therefore,

$$i\hbar\dot{P}_{lm} = i\hbar\frac{\partial}{\partial t}\int w_l^* P w_m d\tau = i\hbar\int(\dot{w}_l^* P w_m + w_l^* P \dot{w}_m + w_l^* \dot{P} w_m)d\tau$$

$$= -\sum_\alpha D_{l\alpha} P_{\alpha m} + \sum_\alpha P_{l\alpha} D_{\alpha m} + i\hbar\dot{P}_{lm}$$

or

$$i\hbar\dot{\boldsymbol{P}} = \boldsymbol{PD} - \boldsymbol{DP} + i\hbar\dot{\boldsymbol{P}}(intr) \tag{7-74}$$

The last term is the intrinsic change in the operator $\boldsymbol{P}$, which is zero when $\boldsymbol{P}$ does not formally depend on t, as is the case for momentum, angular momentum, and spin operators. In deriving Eq. (7-74), no use was made of the adiabatic property of the w-functions. Therefore, it holds for all time-dependent bases. In the moving representation, $\{w\} = \{v\}$, $D = H$ by virtue of Eq. (7-49), and (7-74) reverts to Eq. (7-59).

7.7. Interaction Representation.—In many physical problems the hamiltonian of a system that is engaged in interaction with another is of the form $\boldsymbol{H} + \boldsymbol{V}$, $\boldsymbol{H}$ being the stationary normal ("unperturbed") hamiltonian and $\boldsymbol{V}$ the "interaction." Equation (7-51) then reads

$$i\hbar\dot{\mathbf{a}} = (\boldsymbol{H} + \boldsymbol{V})\mathbf{a}$$

in some basis of functions $\{u\}$. In terms of the new state vector

$$\mathbf{c} = e^{(i/\hbar)Ht}\mathbf{a} \tag{7-75}$$

it takes the form

$$i\hbar\dot{\mathbf{c}} = \boldsymbol{V}'\mathbf{c} \tag{7-76}$$

provided we put

$$\boldsymbol{V}' = e^{(i/\hbar)Ht}\boldsymbol{V}e^{-(i/\hbar)Ht}$$

The use of $\mathbf{c}$ instead of $\mathbf{a}$ is said to constitute the interaction representation; it is designed to remove $\boldsymbol{H}$ from the Schrödinger equation for $\mathbf{c}$. Passage from $\mathbf{a}$ to $\mathbf{c}$ is equivalent to a change from u_α to $e^{-(i/\hbar)Ht}u_\alpha$, and in the special case where u_α is an eigenfunction of $\boldsymbol{H}$, the latter may be written $e^{-(i/\hbar)E_\alpha t}u_\alpha$. Hence, all matrices with components $P_{lm}(u)$ in the $\{u\}$ basis are transformed to P'_{lm} by the rule

$$\boldsymbol{P}' = e^{(i/\hbar)Ht}\boldsymbol{P}e^{-(i/\hbar)Ht}$$

If P is constant, P' evolves in accordance with the equation

$$i\hbar\dot{P}' = P'H - HP' \tag{7-77}$$

which, although it looks like Eq. (7–59), differs from it because here H is only the normal part of the hamiltonian and does not include the interaction. Comparing Eqs. (7–76) and (7–77), one might say that the evolution of the state $\mathbf{c}$ is controlled by the interaction alone, whereas all operators P' are controlled by the normal part of the hamiltonian.

Equation (7–76) has the same form as (7–69) with $M = (i/\hbar)V'$ and is, in general, solvable by the method of the foregoing section. The fact that $\mathbf{c}$ is a vector and W a matrix is of no consequence, and the result can again be expressed in the symbolic form (7–72)

$$\mathbf{c}(t) = \left\{\mathscr{T} \exp - \frac{i}{\hbar}\int_0^t V'(t')dt'\right\} \mathbf{c}(0) \tag{7-78}$$

7.8. The Statistical Matrix.—In the foregoing sections quantum states were represented either by functions or by vectors. There is a third possibility that involves the use of a *statistical matrix*, $\boldsymbol{\rho}$. When a state is given, perhaps in the form $\phi = \sum_\alpha a_\alpha u_\alpha$, then, as has been seen, normalization of ϕ guarantees that the vector $\mathbf{a}$ is a unit vector satisfying $\mathbf{a}^\dagger\mathbf{a} = 1$. But from $\mathbf{a}$ we can also form a square matrix,

$$\boldsymbol{\rho} = \mathbf{a}\mathbf{a}^\dagger \tag{7-79}$$

Its usefulness results primarily from the fact that the usual postulate ("mean value postulate,"[17]) for the expectation value of an observable whose operator is P, or matrix P, namely $\bar{p} = \mathbf{a}^\dagger P\mathbf{a}$, may be replaced by

$$\bar{p} = \mathrm{Tr}(\boldsymbol{\rho}P) = \mathrm{Tr}(P\boldsymbol{\rho}) \tag{7-80}$$

Tr designating the trace of the matrix product that follows. This is seen on direct expansion. Also, if $\boldsymbol{\sigma}$ is a statistical matrix belonging to a certain sharp value of a specified observable, the probability that a system with matrix $\boldsymbol{\rho}$ shall exhibit that value upon measurement is

$$w = \mathrm{Tr}(\boldsymbol{\sigma}\boldsymbol{\rho}) \tag{7-81}$$

For in the Schrödinger representation w is $|\int \psi\phi^* d\tau|^2$; if ψ is the sharp state associated with σ, then

$$\sigma_{ij} = s_i s_j^*, \quad \psi = \sum_\alpha s_\alpha u_\alpha$$

[17] Cf. Margenau and Murphy, *op. cit.*, pp. 342, 377.

whence,

$$w = |\sum_\alpha s_\alpha a_\alpha^*|^2$$

This is precisely what is obtained from Eq. (7–81) by expansion.

Among the usual advantages of such expressions as Eq. (7–80) and (7–81), one is salient: they show forth the invariance of $\bar{p}$ and w with respect to the choice of the basis functions, u, in terms of which $\boldsymbol{\rho}$, $\boldsymbol{\sigma}$, and $\boldsymbol{P}$ are expressed. The trace, as will be recalled, is invariant against unitary transformations, and the passage from one basis to another is performed by such transformations. The trace is also indifferent to an exchange of the two matrix factors, which is convenient in calculations. Finally, the statistical matrix lends itself to a certain generalization of states from pure cases to mixtures, required in quantum statistics and the theory of measurements; we turn to this question in Section 7.9.

Here we note how $\boldsymbol{\rho}$ behaves in the transfer from a stationary description in the u-basis to one in the moving system v. By inverting Eq. (7–54), we produce

$$u_\alpha = \sum_i b_{i\alpha}^\dagger v_i$$

Therefore,

$$\phi = \sum_\alpha a_\alpha \sum_\mu b_{\mu\alpha}^\dagger v_\mu = = \sum_\mu \left(\sum_\alpha b_{\mu\alpha}^\dagger a_\alpha\right) v_\mu$$

$$= \sum_\mu (\boldsymbol{b}^\dagger \mathbf{a})_\mu v_\mu$$

Hence,

$$\boldsymbol{\rho}(v) = \boldsymbol{b}^\dagger \mathbf{a}\mathbf{a}^\dagger \boldsymbol{b} = \boldsymbol{b}^\dagger \boldsymbol{\rho}(u) \boldsymbol{b} \tag{7–82}$$

Since $\mathbf{a}$ satisfies Eq. (7–51)

$$i\hbar\dot{\boldsymbol{\rho}} = i\hbar(\dot{\mathbf{a}}\mathbf{a}^\dagger + \mathbf{a}\dot{\mathbf{a}}^\dagger) = \boldsymbol{H}\boldsymbol{\rho} - \boldsymbol{\rho}\boldsymbol{H} \tag{7–83}$$

Compare this with Eq. (7–59) and observe the order of the factors on the right! Equation (7–83) is the "equation of motion" of the statistical matrix in the Schrödinger representation; $\boldsymbol{\rho}$ is constant, of course, in the Heisenberg representation.

From Eq. (7–52) we infer

$$\boldsymbol{\rho}(t) = \boldsymbol{U}\boldsymbol{\rho}(0)\boldsymbol{U}^\dagger \tag{7–84}$$

where the order of the U-factors is again different from what it is in Eq. (7–58).

A special case of some interest is one in which the hamiltonian is stationary and the $\{u\}$ are taken to be its eigenfunctions. The matrix $\boldsymbol{H}$ is then diagonal; Eq. (7–53) results in

$$U_{lm} = U_{lm}(0)e^{-(i/\hbar)E_l t} = \delta_{lm}e^{-(i/\hbar)E_l t}$$

Unless P is an explicit function of t, P_{lm} is constant;

$$\rho_{lm} = e^{-(i/\hbar)(E_l - E_m)}\rho_{lm}(0)$$

in view of Eq. (7–84), and

$$\text{Tr}\,(\boldsymbol{\rho P}) = \sum_{\alpha\mu} e^{-(i/\hbar)(E_\alpha - E_\mu)t}\rho_{\alpha\mu}(0)P_{\mu\alpha}$$

This is a function of t which oscillates with all frequencies of the system that are connected by nonvanishing matrix elements of $\boldsymbol{P}$. Only if the initial state has a sharp energy, *i.e.*, if $\rho_{\alpha\mu}(0) = \delta_{\alpha l}\delta_{\mu l}$, will this time-dependence disappear; only sharp energy states are stationary in all observables P.

If H has a small time-dependent part, as in "Interaction Representation," Section 7–3, it is advisable to use the interaction representation

$$\boldsymbol{\rho} = \mathbf{c}\mathbf{c}^\dagger$$

The statistical matrix is then computed via Eq. (7–78). When the expectation value of the energy, Tr $(\boldsymbol{\rho H})$, is then calculated in different orders of $\boldsymbol{V}$, the successive orders of time-dependent perturbation theory emerge.

Next we consider the eigenvalues and eigenvectors of $\boldsymbol{\rho}$. For this purpose we observe that

$$\boldsymbol{\rho}^2 = \boldsymbol{\rho} \tag{7–85}$$

as is seen from expansion:

$$(\rho^2)_{lm} = \sum_\alpha a_l a_\alpha^* a_\alpha a_m^* = a_l a_m^* \sum_\alpha a_\alpha^* a_\alpha = a_l a_m^* = \rho_{lm}$$

Now a relation between matrices must also hold between the eigenvalues of the matrix (if they exist); hence the eigenvalues ρ' of $\boldsymbol{\rho}$ satisfy Eq. (7–85)

$$\rho'^2 = \rho'$$

meaning that $\rho' = 0$ or 1. No other eigenvalues are possible.

Let us denote the eigenvectors of $\boldsymbol{\rho}$ by $\mathbf{r}$, so that

$$\boldsymbol{\rho}\mathbf{r} = \rho'\mathbf{r} \tag{7–86}$$

Although the eigenvalues 0 and 1 are universal, there are many possible eigenvectors $\mathbf{r}$ that depend on the kind of states $\boldsymbol{\rho}$ is to designate. To each one of an orthonormal set of functions $\phi_1,\phi_2,\cdots$, for instance, there corresponds a statistical matrix. If

$$\phi_s = \sum_\alpha a_\alpha^s u_\alpha, \quad \text{then} \quad \rho_{\alpha\mu}^s = a_\alpha^s a_\alpha^{s*}$$

Notice, too, that the vectors $\mathbf{a}^s$ and $\mathbf{a}^t$ are orthogonal,

$$\int \phi_s^* \phi_t d\tau = \sum_\alpha a_\alpha^{s*} a_\alpha^t = 0 \tag{7-87}$$

For the sth vector Eq. (7–86) reads

$$(\boldsymbol{\rho}^s\mathbf{r})_l = \sum_\alpha a_l^s a_\alpha^{s*} r_\alpha = \rho' r_l \tag{7-88}$$

Inspection and use of Eq. (7–87) show that, if ρ' is to be zero, r_α must be a constant times a_α^t, $t \neq s$. Hence, every

$$\mathbf{r} = \mathbf{a}^t, \quad t \neq s$$

is a (degenerate) eigenvector of $\boldsymbol{\rho}^s$ belonging to $\rho' = 0$. Similarly, if ρ' is to be 1, only

$$\mathbf{r} = \mathbf{a}^s$$

satisfies Eq. (7–88).

The statistical matrix may be written in the system of functions in which the coordinate x is diagonal. In one dimension, the eigenfunction of x is the Dirac delta function. The expansion of $\phi(x)$ in terms of it is

$$\phi(x) = \int \phi(x')\delta(x,x')dx'$$

all previous summations being replaced by integrations. Consequently

$$\rho_{x'x''} = \phi(x')\phi^*(x'')$$

and this product is often called Dirac's density matrix. The matrix elements of an operator P become

$$P_{x'x''} = \int \delta(x,x')P(x)\delta(x,x'')dx = P(x')\delta(x',x'')$$

Hence,

$$\begin{aligned}\overline{p} = \operatorname{Tr}(\boldsymbol{\rho}\boldsymbol{P}) &= \iint dx'dx''\rho_{x'x''}P_{x''x'} = \int dx'\phi(x')P^*(x')\phi^*(x') \\ &= \int \phi^* P\phi dx\end{aligned}$$

which is the usual expression. In the latter transformations, use was made at one point of the hermitian property of $\boldsymbol{P}$.

In this case, the eigenvectors of $\boldsymbol{\rho}$ are *functions*; Eq. (7–86) takes the form

$$\int \phi_s(x')\phi_s^*(x'')r(x'')dx'' = \rho' r(x')$$

Hence, if

$$\rho' = 1, \quad r(x') = \phi_s(x'); \qquad \text{if} \qquad \rho' = 0, \quad r(x') = \phi_t(x'), \quad t \neq s$$

The equation $\rho^2 = \rho$ now reads

$$\int \phi(x')\phi^*(x''')\phi(x''')\phi^*(x'')dx''' = \phi(x')\phi^*(x'')$$

The last interesting feature of ρ to be considered here is its function as a *projection operator*. The meaning of that phrase will be clear from the following computation. Let $\boldsymbol{\rho}$ be compounded from the state vector $\mathbf{a}$, and let it act on any vector $\mathbf{x}$. Then

$$(\boldsymbol{\rho}\mathbf{x})_i = \sum_\alpha a_i a_\alpha^* x_\alpha = (\mathbf{a}^\dagger\mathbf{x})a_i$$

so that

$$\boldsymbol{\rho}\mathbf{x} = (\mathbf{a}^\dagger\mathbf{x})\mathbf{a} \tag{7–89}$$

But $a^\dagger x$ can be interpreted as the scalar product of $\mathbf{a}$ and $\mathbf{x}$; since $\mathbf{a}$ is a unit vector, it is the length of the projection of $\mathbf{x}$ along the direction of $\mathbf{a}$; the other factor on the right is simply the unit vector $\mathbf{a}$. Thus, when $\boldsymbol{\rho}$ acts on $\mathbf{x}$ it produces a new vector along $\mathbf{a}$, and the magnitude of the new vector is the projection of $\mathbf{x}$ along $\mathbf{a}$.

7.9. Pure Cases and Mixtures.—In quantum mechanics, optimum knowledge concerning the state of a physical system is conveyed by a state function, a state vector or by the kind of statistical matrix studied above in Section 7–8. To know any one of these is analogous to knowing the values of all variables in classical mechanics. The transition from ordinary mechanics to statistical mechanics is made by ceasing to operate with the *values* of all classical variables in favor of using probabilities for the occurrence of these values. A similar step is made in quantum mechanics when attention is directed to thermodynamic phenomena: there, exact knowledge of ϕ is sacrificed to knowledge that comprehends only the probability distribution for the existence of any member of a set of states, ϕ_i. Thus, when in classical statistical mechanics we ask: what is the probability that a given particle of a gas has a specified velocity and a specified position? we ask in quantum statistics: what is the probability that a given "particle" has a specified state, ϕ_i? When that probability is a delta function, when we know precisely which ϕ_i is present, we say we have knowledge of a *pure case*; otherwise, the state is called a mixture. This terminology was introduced by von Neumann; although it is sometimes strange, it has retained its technical meaning to this day.

Von Neumann[18] did more than coin these words. He showed how the statistical matrix can be generalized to include the description of mixtures, and he succeeded, mainly by this device, in laying the foundation for the quantum mechanical counterpart of thermodynamics.

Suppose that a given physical system can be in any one, or in any linear combination of states $\phi_1, \phi_2, \cdots, \phi_n, \cdots$. Each of them, or any linear combination of them, represents a pure case. To each of these ϕ_i we now assign a probability p^i, and, furthermore, a statistical matrix $\boldsymbol{\rho}^i$. For instance, if $\phi^i = \sum_\alpha a_\alpha^i u_\alpha$, then, $\rho_{lm}^i = a_l^i a_m^{i*}$. To the *mixture*, which affirms the presence of ϕ_1 with probability p', of ϕ_2 with probability p^2, etc., we then allot the statistical matrix.

$$\boldsymbol{\rho} = \sum_i p^i \boldsymbol{\rho}^i \tag{7-90}$$

With this definition formulas (7–80) and (7–81) remain valid. For example,

$$\mathrm{Tr}\,(\boldsymbol{\rho} \boldsymbol{G}) = \sum_i p^i \mathrm{Tr}\,(\boldsymbol{\rho}^i \boldsymbol{G}) \tag{7-91}$$

This is quite different from the situation where the state is not a mixture but a quantum mechanical *superposition* of of ϕ-states. Thus, if

$$\phi = \sum_\alpha q_\alpha \phi^\alpha = \sum_\alpha q_\alpha \sum_\mu a_\mu^\alpha u_\mu$$

we are dealing with a statistical matrix whose components are

$$\rho_{lm} = \sum_\alpha q_\alpha a_l^\alpha \cdot \sum_\mu q_\mu^* a_m^{\mu *}$$

and Tr $(\boldsymbol{\rho} \boldsymbol{G})$ will be

$$\sum_{\substack{\alpha\mu \\ lm}} q_\alpha^* a_l^{\alpha *} G_{lm} q_\mu a_m^\mu$$

The sum over α and μ may be split into two parts: one containing all

[18] J. von Neumann, *Mathematical Foundations of Quantum Mechanics*, translated from the German, Robert T. Beyer, ed., Princeton University Press, 1955.

the terms in which $\alpha = \mu$ (we shall call the common index i), and the other part being the remainder. We then find for the superposition

$$\mathrm{Tr}\,(\boldsymbol{\rho} G) = \sum_{\substack{i \\ lm}} q_i^* q_i a_l^{i*} G_{lm} a_m^i + \sum_{\substack{\alpha \neq \mu \\ lm}} q_\alpha^* a_l^{\alpha *} G_{lm} q_\mu a_m^\mu$$

The first sum on the right is precisely the same as in Eq. (7–91) provided we let $|q_i|^2 = p^i$. The remainder contains terms, sometimes called "interference" terms, that are not present in (7–91).

If we take the ϕ^i to be a complete orthonormal set, u_i, and choose them as the basis of our representation, every

$$\rho_{lm}^i = \delta_{il}\delta_{im} \quad \text{and} \quad \rho_{lm} = \sum_i p^i \delta_{il}\delta_{im} = p^l \delta_{lm} \tag{7–92}$$

A matrix $\boldsymbol{\epsilon}$, whose elements ε_{lm} are $\delta_{il}\delta_{im}$, is called an elementary matrix. It contains zeros everywhere except in one place on the diagonal, namely the ith. Moreover, $\boldsymbol{\epsilon}$ satisfies

$$\boldsymbol{\epsilon}^2 = \boldsymbol{\epsilon}, \qquad \mathrm{Tr}\,\boldsymbol{\epsilon} = 1$$

If in Eq. (7–92) only one p^i were present, ρ_{lm} would be elementary.

There is an interesting theorem that states: any matrix obeying the equations

$$\boldsymbol{\rho}^2 = \boldsymbol{\rho} \quad \text{and} \quad \mathrm{Tr}\,\boldsymbol{\rho} = 1 \tag{7–93}$$

is *equivalent* to an elementary matrix.[19] To prove it, suppose $\boldsymbol{\rho}$ is diagonalized by $\boldsymbol{S}$:

$$\boldsymbol{S}^{-1}\boldsymbol{\rho}\boldsymbol{S} = \boldsymbol{D}$$

This same $\boldsymbol{S}$ will also diagonalize $\boldsymbol{\rho}^2$, hence $\boldsymbol{S}^{-1}\boldsymbol{\rho}^2\boldsymbol{S} = \boldsymbol{S}^{-1}\boldsymbol{\rho}\boldsymbol{S}\boldsymbol{S}^{-1}\boldsymbol{\rho}\boldsymbol{S} = \boldsymbol{D}^2$. If $\boldsymbol{\rho}^2 = \boldsymbol{\rho}$, then $\boldsymbol{D}^2 = \boldsymbol{D}$. This requires that every element of $\boldsymbol{D}$ is either 0 or 1. Since $\mathrm{Tr}\,\boldsymbol{\rho} = \mathrm{Tr}\,\boldsymbol{D} = 1$, only one such element can exist.

Our theorem permits the following inference. The statistical matrix of every *pure case* in quantum mechanics is equivalent to an elementary matrix and can be transformed into it by a similarity transformation. Because $\boldsymbol{\rho}$ is hermitian, the transforming matrix is unitary. A *mixture* can, therefore, always be written in the diagonal form Eq. (7–92).

This form, however, cannot satisfy Eqs. (7–93) because $\rho_{lm}^2 = (p^l)^2\delta_{lm}$, which equals ρ_{lm} only if p^l is 1 or 0. If a statistical matrix were given in an unintelligible, scrambled form and one wanted to know whether it represented a pure case, one would need only to square it and determine if it reproduces itself.

[19] Margenau and Murphy, *op. cit.*, Section 10.11, p. 316.

CHAPTER 8

THE MATHEMATICAL FORMALISM OF QUANTUM STATISTICS

by

WILLIAM BAND

Department of Physics, Washington State University

8.1. Object.—Quantum statistics was discussed briefly in Chapter 12 of *The Mathematics of Physics and Chemistry*, and as far as elementary treatments of quantum statistics are concerned,[1] that introductory discussion remains adequate. In recent years, however, a spectacular development of quantum field theory has presented us with new mathematical tools of great power, applicable at once to the problems of quantum statistics. This chapter is devoted to an exposition of the mathematical formalism of quantum field theory as it has been adapted to the discussion of quantum statistics. The entire structure is based on the concepts of Hilbert space, and we shall devote a considerable fraction of the chapter to these concepts.

8.2. Abstract Hilbert Space.—An abstract Hilbert space is defined as a set of elements, often called vectors, having the properties partially listed below as postulates. We use the symbol $\mathscr{H}$ for Hilbert space, and the "ket" symbol $|\,\rangle$ for an arbitrary vector in $\mathscr{H}$. If for any reason we must distinguish between two or more vectors in $\mathscr{H}$, we may use one or more indicators inside the ket symbol thus: $|m\rangle$, $|n,s\rangle$, etc., the nature and number of such indicators being dictated only by convenience.

Postulate A.—$\mathscr{H}$ is linear. By this is meant: (i) the vectors of $\mathscr{H}$ are such that we can define the sum of any two of them, the result being also a vector in $\mathscr{H}$: $|a\rangle + |b\rangle = |c\rangle$; (ii) they are such that a meaning can be ascribed to multiplication of any vector in $\mathscr{H}$ by a scalar complex number, the result being also a vector in $\mathscr{H}$. In particular,

[1] D. ter Haar, *Elements of Statistical Mechanics*, Holt, Rinehart, and Winston, New York, 1954; W. Band, *Introduction to Quantum Statistics*, D. Van Nostrand Co., Inc., Princeton, N.J., 1955.

multiplication by unity has its usual meaning: $1 \cdot | \rangle = | \rangle$; (iii) there exists in $\mathscr{H}$ a null vector, written $|\text{null}\rangle$ with the properties:

$$
\begin{aligned}
|\text{null}\rangle + | \rangle &= | \rangle && \text{for any } | \rangle \text{ in } \mathscr{H} \\
a \cdot |\text{null}\rangle &= |\text{null}\rangle && \text{for any complex scalar } a \\
0 \cdot | \rangle &= |\text{null}\rangle && \text{where 0 is the zero scalar, and } | \rangle \text{ is any vector in } \mathscr{H}
\end{aligned}
$$

Definition.—The set of all vectors derivable from any one vector in $\mathscr{H}$ by multiplication by a scalar is called a *ray* in $\mathscr{H}$.

Postulate B.—There exists a set of vectors indicated by the "bra" symbol $\langle \, |$ in one-to-one correspondence with the vectors of $\mathscr{H}$, forming a dual Hilbert space $\overline{\mathscr{H}}$. As a matter of notation we use the symbol $\langle f|$ for the dual vector corresponding to $|f\rangle$, etc. This dual space must be such that a meaning can be given to the scalar product of any vector $\langle f|$ in $\overline{\mathscr{H}}$ with any vector $|g\rangle$ in $\mathscr{H}$, to be denoted by the symbol $\langle f \,|\, g\rangle$ with the following properties:

(i) $\langle f|g\rangle$ is a complex number and $\langle g|f\rangle = \overline{\langle f|g\rangle}$, the complex conjugate number,

(ii) $\langle f|g\rangle = \langle f|g_1\rangle + \langle f|g_2\rangle$ if $|g\rangle = |g_1\rangle + |g_2\rangle$

$\langle f|g\rangle = \langle f_1|g\rangle + \langle f_2|g\rangle$ if $\langle f| = \langle f_1| + \langle f_2|$

(iii) $\langle f|f\rangle \geq 0$, and $\langle f|f\rangle = 0$ only if $|f\rangle = |\text{null}\rangle$.

Definition.—The *norm* of $|f\rangle$ is the square root of $\langle f|f\rangle$ and is written

$$|f| = \sqrt{\langle f|f\rangle} \tag{8-1}$$

The norm is necessarily a real number.

Other postulates required to complete the definition of $\mathscr{H}$ will not be listed here; they are concerned with the existence of a basis set of vectors and we shall discuss that question in some detail in the next section. For the present we may summarize the above defining properties of Hilbert space by saying that it is a linear space with a complex-valued scalar product.

The fact that we are discussing an abstract space means that we know only that its elements (vectors) have the postulated properties; *e.g.*, that a scalar product *exists*, but at this level of the discussion we do not know the numerical value of the scalar product. We may choose at random some familiar collection of elements, perhaps the set of all ordered pairs of real numbers (n,m); or the set of all differentiable functions of position on a line, etc., and ask whether or not they form a Hilbert space. If they do, then we can in fact evaluate the scalar product of any pair of such elements numerically, but for much of our discussion we shall not need to particularize, and shall remain at the abstract level. Here we mention a couple of examples. The set of all ordered pairs of complex numbers, called *spinors*, form a Hilbert space, "spinor space." Thus we identify the vector $|u,v\rangle$ as a column matrix $\begin{pmatrix} u \\ v \end{pmatrix}$, where u and v are arbitrary complex numbers. The dual space is formed of the set of pairs written as a row matrix, the dual of $\begin{pmatrix} u \\ v \end{pmatrix}$ being the complex conjugate pair $(\bar{u}\bar{v})$. The scalar product is defined as the matrix product $(xy)\begin{pmatrix} u \\ v \end{pmatrix} = xu + yv$ and the norm of $|u,v\rangle$ is the square root of $(\bar{u}\bar{v})\begin{pmatrix} u \\ v \end{pmatrix} = |u|^2 + |v|^2$.

We shall in this chapter be most concerned with the following example of Hilbert space. Each element $|f\rangle$ is a complex-valued numerical function $f(x)$ of one or more continuous variables represented collectively by the symbol x, such that the integral of its square modulus exists:

$$\int_{-\infty}^{+\infty} |f(x)|^2 dx < \infty \tag{8–2}$$

The dual of $|f\rangle$, *i.e.*, $\langle f|$, is the complex conjugate $\overline{f(x)}$ of $f(x)$, and the scalar product is defined by

$$\langle f|g\rangle \equiv \int_{-\infty}^{+\infty} \overline{f(x)} g(x) dx \tag{8–3}$$

This space $\mathscr{H}$ is the set of all functions $f(x)$ satisfying Eq. (8–2), and is in fact self-dual, because the complex conjugate of any function that satisfies Eq. (8–2), itself also satisfies Eq. (8–2), and so is in $\mathscr{H}$. It is to be emphasized that the symbol $|f\rangle$ represents the function $f(x)$ with its entire range of values, not just the numerical value of the function at some arbitrary point. The variable x does not appear in the symbol $|f\rangle$ for the element of $\mathscr{H}$.

The quantum states of Schrödinger's theory constitute an example of Hilbert space, and their scalar product has a direct physical meaning. Any such example of Hilbert space, where we can actually evaluate the scalar products numerically, is called a *representation* of Hilbert space. We shall continue discussing the properties of abstract Hilbert space, so that all our conclusions will apply to any and every representation.

8.3. Linear Manifolds in Hilbert Space.—Any sequence of m vectors, $|f_1\rangle,|f_2\rangle,\cdots,|f_m\rangle$, is called a linearly dependent sequence if there exist complex scalars $a_1,a_2,\cdots,a_m$, not all zero such that

$$\sum_{j=1}^{m} a_j|f_j\rangle = |\text{null}\rangle \tag{8–4}$$

The sequence is *independent* if this equation implies that all the a's be zero. Take any sequence of k independent vectors $|f_1\rangle,|f_2\rangle,\cdots,|f_k\rangle$, and form the linear combinations

$$|F\rangle \equiv \sum_{j=1}^{k} a_j|f_j\rangle \tag{8–5}$$

The set of all such vectors $|F\rangle$, for all possible choices of scalars a_j, is called a k-dimensional manifold M_k, spanned by the set $|f_1\rangle,|f_2\rangle,\cdots$, $|f_k\rangle$. This set is called the basis of M_k, and the manifold M_k is said to be *closed* because, by definition, every element of M_k can be expressed in the form (8–5).

Another of the postulates defining Hilbert space is that $\mathscr{H}$ constitutes an infinite-dimensional manifold. In other words, there must exist in $\mathscr{H}$ a denumerably infinite sequence of independent vectors $|f_1\rangle,|f_2\rangle,\cdots$ such that

$$\sum_{j=1}^{\infty} a_j|f_j\rangle = |\text{null}\rangle \quad \text{implies} \quad a_j = 0, \text{ all } j$$

Moreover, $\mathscr{H}$ must be closed in the sense that every vector $|F\rangle$ in $\mathscr{H}$ can be expressed in the form

$$|F\rangle = \sum_{j=1}^{\infty} a_j|f_j\rangle \tag{8–6}$$

This equality between a vector and an infinite sequence of vectors is to be understood in the following sense, let

$$|g_n\rangle \equiv \sum_{j=1}^{n} a_j|f_j\rangle$$

then we say that Eq. (8–6) holds if the norm of $|F\rangle - |g_n\rangle$ is less than an arbitrary small number ε provided n is sufficiently large:

$$|\,|F\rangle - |g_n\rangle| < \varepsilon \quad \text{if } n > N(\varepsilon)$$

In any Hilbert space the basis vectors $|f_j\rangle$ can always be chosen to be orthonormal:

$$\langle f_j|f_k\rangle = \delta_{jk} \tag{8–7}$$

If a basis is found that does not satisfy this condition, an orthonormal set can be constructed from it by the Schmidt process analogous to the familiar device in three-dimensional vector analysis.[2]

In terms of the function space representation of $\mathscr{H}$ mentioned in the last section, orthogonality is expressed by

$$\int \overline{f_j(x)} f_k(x) dx = \delta_{jk} \tag{8–8}$$

Closure of this basis is expressed in the following way: let

$$F(x) = \sum_{j=1}^{\infty} a_j f_j(x) \tag{8–9}$$

then derive the coefficients a_j:

$$\int \overline{f_k(x)} F(x) dx = \sum_{j=1}^{\infty} a_j \int f_j(x) \overline{f_k(x)} dx = a_k \tag{8–10}$$

Put this result back into Eq. (8–9) and we have

$$F(x) = \sum_{j=1}^{\infty} \int \overline{f_j(x')} F(x') f_j(x) dx' = \int \left[\sum_{j=1}^{\infty} f_j(x) \overline{f_j(x')} \right] F(x') dx'$$

This must be an identity, independent of $F(x)$ if any vector in $\mathscr{H}$ is to be expressible in the form (8–9). Therefore, the closure condition is

$$\sum_{j=1}^{\infty} f_j(x) f_j(x') = \delta(x - x') \tag{8–11}$$

The right side of this is the Dirac delta function.[3]

We can go through the same argument while remaining completely in the domain of abstract Hilbert space. Thus, starting with Eq. (8–6) and using Eq. (8–7) we have

$$\langle f_k | F \rangle = \sum_{j=1}^{\infty} a_j \langle f_k | f_j \rangle = a_k$$

and using this expression for a_k in Eq. (8–6) we find

$$|F\rangle = \sum_{k=1}^{\infty} \langle f_k | F \rangle | f_k \rangle = \sum_{k=1}^{\infty} | f_k \rangle \langle f_k | F \rangle \tag{8–12}$$

[2] B. Friedman, *Principles and Techniques of Applied Mathematics*, p. 16, John Wiley and Sons, Inc., New York, 1956.

[3] See H. Margenau and G. M. Murphy, *The Mathematics of Physics and Chemistry*, 2nd Ed., p. 239, D. Van Nostrand Co., Inc., Princeton, N.J., 1956; also W. Band, *An Introduction to Mathematical Physics*, Section 3, D. Van Nostrand Co., Inc., Princeton, N.J., 1959.

The last step follows because the numerical factor $\langle f_k|F\rangle$ can be written either in front or after the vector $|f_k\rangle$ without change of meaning. Thus for Eq. (8–12) to be an identity independent of the vector $|F\rangle$ we must have

$$\sum_{k=1}^{\infty} |f_k\rangle\langle f_k| = I \tag{8–13}$$

the identity operator.

To see that Eq. (8–11) is an example of Eq. (8–13), it is useful to think of $|f\rangle\langle g|$ as analogous to the dyad product in ordinary vector analysis, just as $\langle f|g\rangle$ is analogous to the scalar product. For example, in spinor space we have a set of basis vectors $\begin{pmatrix}0\\1\end{pmatrix}$ and $\begin{pmatrix}1\\0\end{pmatrix}$, any vector in this space can be expressed in terms of this basis:

$$\begin{pmatrix}u\\v\end{pmatrix} = u\begin{pmatrix}1\\0\end{pmatrix} + v\begin{pmatrix}0\\1\end{pmatrix}$$

The operator dyads are now

$$\begin{pmatrix}0\\1\end{pmatrix}(0\ 1) = \begin{pmatrix}0 & 0\\0 & 1\end{pmatrix} \quad \text{and} \quad \begin{pmatrix}1\\0\end{pmatrix}(1\ 0) = \begin{pmatrix}1 & 0\\0 & 0\end{pmatrix}$$

and the sum of these two dyads is indeed the identity matrix, in agreement with Eq. (8–13). From this same point of view we can interpret Eq. (8–11) as the components of an identity matrix having an infinity of rows and columns indicated by x and x' respectively. Thus $f(x)$ is to be regarded as a one-column matrix with x indicating the position on the column (the row index), and $\overline{f(x')}$ as a one-row matrix with x' indicating the position on the row (column index).

8.4. Linear Operators in Hilbert Space.—An operator in $\mathscr{H}$ is analogous to a transformation or mapping in ordinary space. Given any vector $|f\rangle$ in $\mathscr{H}$, the operation may transform $|f\rangle$ into $|Lf\rangle$, some other vector in $\mathscr{H}$, where the symbol L denotes the operator:

$$L|f\rangle = |Lf\rangle \tag{8–14}$$

Note that both $|f\rangle$ and $|Lf\rangle$ are vectors in the same space $\mathscr{H}$. The operator L is said to be linear if operating on a sum equals the sum of the individual operators:

$$L[a_1|f_1\rangle + a_2|f_2\rangle] = a_1|Lf_1\rangle + a_2|Lf_2\rangle \tag{8–15}$$

Let $|f_j\rangle, j = 1,2,\cdots$ be an orthonormal basis in $\mathscr{H}$, and let both the operand $|f\rangle$ in Eq. (8–14), and the resulting vector $|Lf\rangle$ be expressed in terms of this basis:

$$|f\rangle = \sum_{j=1}^{\infty} a_j|f_j\rangle, \qquad |Lf\rangle = \sum_{j=1}^{\infty} b_j|f_j\rangle \tag{8–16}$$

Equation (8–14) now reads

$$\sum_{j=1}^{\infty} a_j|Lf_j\rangle = \sum_{j=1}^{\infty} b_j|f_j\rangle$$

Form the scalar product of this equation with $\langle f_k|$ and use Eq. (8–7), there results

$$b_k = \sum_{j=1}^{\infty} a_j\langle f_k|Lf_j\rangle = \sum_{j=1}^{\infty} \langle f_k|L|f_j\rangle a_j \tag{8–17}$$

We can here regard the quantities b_k and a_j as forming one-column matrices, and the quantities

$$L_{kj} \equiv \langle f_k|L|f_j\rangle \tag{8–18}$$

as forming a square matrix. Equation (8–17) is then an ordinary matrix form of the transformation from the vector whose components are a_j to the vector with components b_k. Starting from Eq. (8–18), we can set up the expression

$$\sum_{j,k} |f_k\rangle L_{kj}\langle f_j| = \sum_{k,j} |f_k\rangle\langle f_k|L|f_j\rangle\langle f_j| = ILI = L$$

from Eq. (8–13). Thus we have the operator L expressed in terms of the basic dyads:

$$L = \sum_{j,k} |f_k\rangle L_{kj}\langle f_j| \tag{8–19}$$

from which, incidentally we can deduce

$$L|f_j\rangle = \sum_{k=1}^{\infty} L_{kj}|f_k\rangle \tag{8–20}$$

An operator L^* is called the *adjoint* of L if they are related as follows:

$$\langle L^*f|g\rangle = \langle f|Lg\rangle \tag{8–21}$$

when $|f\rangle$ and $|g\rangle$ are any two vectors in $\mathscr{H}$. We can express the vector $|L^*f_j\rangle$ in terms of the f_k-basis by analogy with Eq. (8–20):

$$|L^*f_j\rangle = L^*|f_j\rangle = \sum_{k=1}^{\infty} L^*_{kj}|f_k\rangle \tag{8–22}$$

This may be taken as the definition of the matrix L^*_{kj}. Applying Postulate $B(i)$ to Eq. (8–22) we can show that

$$\langle \mathrm{L}^* f_j| = \sum_{k=1}^{\infty} \overline{L^*_{kj}} \langle f_k| \tag{8–23}$$

and hence

$$\langle L^* f_j | f_k \rangle = \sum_{m}^{\infty} \overline{L^*_{mj}} \langle f_m | f_k \rangle = \overline{L^*_{kj}} \tag{8–24}$$

But from Eq. (8–21) we also have

$$\langle L^* f_j | f_k \rangle = \langle f_j | L f_k \rangle = L_{jk} \tag{8–25}$$

so that finally comparing the last two equations we have

$$\overline{L^*_{kj}} = L_{jk} \tag{8–26}$$

The matrix of L is the transposed conjugate[4] of the matrix of L^*. It is a useful exercise to show that the analog of Eq. (8–19) is true for the adjoint operator:

$$L^* = \sum_{k,j} |f_k\rangle L^*_{kj} \langle f_j| \tag{8–27}$$

8.5. Transformations in Hilbert Space.—Consider any vector $|f\rangle$ in $\mathscr{H}$ with components $\langle g_k | f \rangle$ with respect to some orthonormal basis $|g_k\rangle$, and with components $\langle h_k | f \rangle$ with respect to some other orthonormal basis $|h_k\rangle$. Because of Eq. (8–13), which is true for both sets $|g_k\rangle$ and $|h_k\rangle$, we have

$$|g_k\rangle = \sum_{j=1}^{\infty} |h_j\rangle \langle h_j | g_k \rangle \tag{8–28}$$

which expresses $|g_k\rangle$ as a linear combination of the basis vectors $|h_j\rangle$. Similarly

$$|h_k\rangle = \sum_{j=1}^{\infty} [g_j\rangle \langle g_j | h_k \rangle \tag{8–29}$$

We may regard these two results as matrix relations: the left side of each equation is a row matrix, the index running along the row; the quantities $\langle h_j | g_k \rangle$ or $\langle g_j | h_k \rangle$ then form matrices, rows and columns numbered by the indices. We call these the matrices of the transformation from the g-basis to the h-basis or vice versa.

[4] See Margenau and Murphy, *op. cit.*, Chapter 10.

Again, looking at the components of $|f\rangle$, we may write

$$\left.\begin{aligned} \langle g_k|f\rangle &= \sum_j \langle g_k|h_j\rangle\langle h_j|f\rangle \\ \text{and} \qquad \langle h_k|f\rangle &= \sum_j \langle h_k|g_j\rangle\langle g_j|f\rangle \end{aligned}\right\} \tag{8-30}$$

Here we must regard $\langle g_k|f\rangle$ and $\langle h_k|f\rangle$ as forming one-column matrices. Note that the square matrices $\langle g_k|h_j\rangle$ and $\langle h_k|g_j\rangle$ are mutually reciprocal, and that their product is the identity matrix:

$$\sum_j \langle g_k|h_j\rangle\langle h_j|g_m\rangle = \langle g_k|g_m\rangle = \delta_{km} \tag{8-31}$$

We shall meet examples later where the basis is not denumerable, but has a continuous index, say $|q\rangle$, where the orthogonality and closure conditions, analogs of Eqs. (8–7) and (8–13), are respectively

$$\langle q'|q''\rangle = \delta(q' - q'') \quad \text{and} \quad \int |q\rangle dq\langle q| = I \tag{8-32}$$

The transformation relations between such a continuous basis and a discrete basis are then obtained by expanding the vector as follows:

$$|q\rangle = \sum_j |h_j\rangle\langle h_j|q\rangle \quad \text{and} \quad |h_j\rangle = \int |q\rangle dq\langle q|h_j\rangle \tag{8-33}$$

which lead to

$$\langle q|f\rangle = \sum_j \langle q|h_j\rangle\langle h_j|f\rangle \quad \text{and} \quad \langle h_j|f\rangle = \int \langle h_j|q\rangle dq\langle q|f\rangle \tag{8-34}$$

If both sets are continuous, say $|q\rangle$ and $|p\rangle$, then we shall find

$$\langle q|f\rangle = \int \langle q|p\rangle dp\langle p|f\rangle \quad \text{and} \quad \langle p|f\rangle = \int \langle p|q\rangle dq\langle q|f\rangle \tag{8-35}$$

It will be noticed that continuous basis sets, with improper Dirac delta functions as scalar products, do not strictly belong to Hilbert space as defined in Section 8.3, where the basis is specifically required by postulate to be *denumerably* infinite. The nondenumerably infinite sets $|q\rangle$ or $|p\rangle$ actually span what is known as Banach spaces,[5] but we shall here conform to the custom among theoretical physicists to call them Hilbert spaces.

[5] A. E. Taylor, *Introduction to Functional Analysis*, p. 98, John Wiley and Sons, Inc., New York, 1958; B. Friedman, *Principles and Techniques of Applied Mathematics*, p. 125, John Wiley and Sons, Inc., New York, 1956.

8.6. Hilbert Space and Quantum Mechanics.—In this section we shall express the fundamental postulates of quantum mechanics in terms of the concepts developed in the previous sections.

A.—The states of any physical system have the same properties as vectors in abstract Hilbert space, and there exists a correspondence between the states of a physical system and the elements of $\mathscr{H}$, which are in what follows to be called the state vectors of the system.

B.—The state vector of any system remains some well-defined function of time except in so far as interaction occurs with some other system, when it may change to some other state vector in $\mathscr{H}$. Laboratory measurement of any property of a system necessarily involves interaction between the system and the measuring equipment, and in general changes the state vector of the system. Now any change of vector in $\mathscr{H}$ is equivalent to a transformation in $\mathscr{H}$, or in other words to an operator in $\mathscr{H}$. This leads to the following postulate:

C.—To every measurable property of a system there corresponds a linear operator in $\mathscr{H}$. If the measurement of the property corresponding to the operator L is performed on a system always initially prepared in the normalized state $|t\rangle$ at time t, the mean value of the result of a series of such repeated measurements is

$$\langle\!\langle L \rangle\!\rangle = \langle t|L|t\rangle \tag{8-36}$$

and the mean square deviation of the series of measurements is

$$\Delta L^2 = (\langle t|L|t\rangle)^2 - \langle t|L^2|t\rangle \tag{8-37}$$

We may think of Eq. (8-36) as the scalar product of the initial state vector $|t\rangle$ and the state vector $|Lt\rangle = L|t\rangle$ produced by the measurement of L. If $|t\rangle$ happens to be an eigenvector of L:

$$L|t\rangle = L'|t\rangle$$

then (8-36) is equal to the eigenvalue L' and (8-37) is zero:

$$\langle t|L|t\rangle = L'\langle t|t\rangle = L'; \qquad (\langle t|L|t\rangle)^2 = \langle t|L^2|t\rangle = L'^2$$

The eigenstates are, therefore, states in which the operator does not disturb the system, the results of a measurement being precisely reproducible. We, therefore, regard the state $|Lt\rangle$ as physically equivalent to the state $|t\rangle$ when the latter is an eigenstate of L, and it is for this reason that we assert that all states represented by a ray of vectors in $\mathscr{H}$ are physically indistinguishable: multiplication of any state vector by a complex number does not change the state it represents. The process of normalization of $|t\rangle$ does not change the state either, and even after normalization there remains an arbitrary complex factor of modulus unity that has no immediate physical significance.

D.—There exists a set of three operators, Q_k, $k = 1,2,3$ corresponding to the measurement of position $\mathbf{q} = (x,y,z)$. There exists a continuum of eigenvectors of these operators, $|\mathbf{q}\rangle$, with the following normalization properties (cf. Eq. (8–32)):

$$\langle \mathbf{q}'|\mathbf{q}''\rangle = \delta(\mathbf{q}' - \mathbf{q}''), \qquad \int |\mathbf{q}\rangle d\mathbf{q}\langle \mathbf{q}| = I \tag{8–38}$$

where the delta function is three-dimensional and the integration is over three-dimensional space; also they have the eigenvalue relations:

$$Q_k|\mathbf{q}\rangle = q_k|\mathbf{q}\rangle, \quad k = 1,2,3 \tag{8–39}$$

There exists also a set of three operators P^k corresponding to the measurement of momentum $\mathbf{p} = (p_1,p_2,p_3)$, obeying analogous rules:

$$\langle \mathbf{p}'|\mathbf{p}''\rangle = \delta(\mathbf{p}' - \mathbf{p}''), \qquad \int |\mathbf{p}\rangle d\mathbf{p}\langle \mathbf{p}| = I \tag{8–40}$$

and

$$P^k|\mathbf{p}\rangle = p^k|\mathbf{p}\rangle \tag{8–41}$$

The sets $|\mathbf{q}\rangle$ and $|\mathbf{p}\rangle$ form alternative bases in $\mathscr{H}$. If all vectors are expressed in terms of $|\mathbf{q}\rangle$ we speak of the q-representation, and if they are expressed in terms of $|\mathbf{p}\rangle$ we speak of the p-representation.

The operators $\mathbf{Q} = (Q_1,Q_2,Q_3)$ and $\mathbf{P} = (P^1,P^2,P^3)$ are conjugate to each other in the sense that they obey the following commutation rule:

$$Q_jP^k - P^kQ_j = i\hbar\delta_{kj}I \tag{8–42}$$

which is usually regarded as the basic postulate of quantum mechanics, because from it we can derive all the distinctively quantum features of the theory.

The connection between the present formulation and the more familiar one may be seen more clearly by considering the mean position of a system in an arbitrary state $|t\rangle$, given by the definition (8–36) as

$$\begin{aligned}
\langle\!\langle Q_k\rangle\!\rangle = \langle t|Q_k|t\rangle &= \iint \langle t|\mathbf{q}'\rangle d\mathbf{q}'\langle \mathbf{q}'|Q_k|\mathbf{q}''\rangle d\mathbf{q}''\langle \mathbf{q}''|t\rangle \quad \text{from (8–38)}\\
&= \iint \langle t|\mathbf{q}'\rangle d\mathbf{q}' q_k''\langle \mathbf{q}'|\mathbf{q}''\rangle d\mathbf{q}''\langle \mathbf{q}''|t\rangle\\
&= \iint \langle t|\mathbf{q}'\rangle d\mathbf{q}' q_k''\delta(\mathbf{q}' - \mathbf{q}'')d\mathbf{q}''\langle \mathbf{q}''|t\rangle\\
&= \int \langle t|\mathbf{q}'\rangle q_k'\langle \mathbf{q}'|t\rangle d\mathbf{q}'
\end{aligned} \tag{8–43}$$

Comparing this with the more familiar expression, *viz*:[6]

$$\langle\!\langle Q_k \rangle\!\rangle = \int \overline{\psi(\mathbf{q},t)} q_k \psi(\mathbf{q},t) d\mathbf{q} \tag{8-44}$$

we see that we should interpret $\langle \mathbf{q}'|t\rangle$ as equivalent to $\psi(\mathbf{q}',t)$ and $\langle t|\mathbf{q}'\rangle$ as equivalent to the complex conjugate $\overline{\psi(\mathbf{q}',t)}$:

$$\langle \mathbf{q}|t\rangle = \psi(\mathbf{q},t); \qquad \langle t|\mathbf{q}\rangle = \overline{\psi(\mathbf{q},t)} \tag{8-45}$$

This is in fact the basis of the statement made in Section 8.2 that the Schrödinger quantum states correspond to elements of Hilbert space.

8.7. The Coordinate-Momentum Transformation.—We shall first derive the matrix expressions for the operators P^k on the q-representation, and for the operators Q_k on the p-representation. From these we shall then be able to derive the transformation matrices connecting the q- and the p-representations. We start with the evident relationships:

$$\langle \mathbf{q}''|Q_k P^j|\mathbf{q}'\rangle = \int \langle \mathbf{q}''|Q_k|\mathbf{q}\rangle d\mathbf{q} \langle \mathbf{q}|P^j|\mathbf{q}'\rangle = \int q_k \langle \mathbf{q}''|\mathbf{q}\rangle d\mathbf{q} \langle \mathbf{q}|P^j|\mathbf{q}'\rangle$$

$$= \int q_k \delta(\mathbf{q}'' - \mathbf{q}') d\mathbf{q} \langle \mathbf{q}|P^j|\mathbf{q}'\rangle = q''_k \langle \mathbf{q}''|P^j|\mathbf{q}'\rangle \tag{8-46}$$

and similarly

$$\langle \mathbf{q}''|P^j Q_k|\mathbf{q}'\rangle = q'_k \langle \mathbf{q}''|P^j|\mathbf{q}'\rangle \tag{8-47}$$

Subtract these two relations and use the commutation relation (8–42):

$$i\hbar \delta_{jk} \langle \mathbf{q}''|\mathbf{q}'\rangle = (q''_k - q'_k) \langle \mathbf{q}''|P^j|\mathbf{q}'\rangle \tag{8-48}$$

Going through the same steps using the p-representation we find

$$-i\hbar \delta_{jk} \langle \mathbf{p}''|\mathbf{p}'\rangle = (p''_j - p'_j) \langle \mathbf{p}''|Q_k|\mathbf{p}'\rangle \tag{8-49}$$

Recalling Eqs. (8–38) and (8–40) and comparing Eq. (8–49) with the familiar relation[7] $-\delta(x) = x\partial[\delta(x)]/\partial x$ we see that

$$\langle \mathbf{q}''|P^j|\mathbf{q}'\rangle = -i\hbar(\partial/\partial q''_j) \langle \mathbf{q}''|\mathbf{q}'\rangle \tag{8-50}$$

and

$$\langle \mathbf{p}''|Q_k|\mathbf{p}'\rangle = i\hbar(\partial/\partial \mathbf{p}''_k) \langle \mathbf{p}''|\mathbf{p}'\rangle \tag{8-51}$$

We can collect the three components in each of these equations into a single vector notation:

$$\left.\begin{aligned} \langle \mathbf{q}''|\mathbf{P}|\mathbf{q}'\rangle &= -i\hbar \nabla_{\mathbf{q}''} \langle \mathbf{q}''|\mathbf{q}'\rangle \\ \langle \mathbf{p}''|\mathbf{Q}|\mathbf{p}'\rangle &= i\hbar \nabla_{\mathbf{p}''} \langle \mathbf{p}''|\mathbf{p}'\rangle \end{aligned}\right\} \tag{8-52}$$

[6] See Margenau and Murphy, *op. cit.*, Eq. (11.14).

[7] L. I. Schiff, *Quantum Mechanics*, Eq. (11.13), McGraw-Hill Book Co., New York, 1949.

These expressions are the analogs of Eq. (8–18) defining the matrix of the operators **P** or **Q**. The right sides of these equations are matrices only in the sense that has a meaning in Banach space—they have nondenumerable infinite numbers of rows and columns! The term "matrix" is nevertheless a useful one.

Next we consider the following identity:

$$\langle \mathbf{q}'|\mathbf{P}|\mathbf{p}'\rangle = \int \langle \mathbf{q}'|\mathbf{P}|\mathbf{q}\rangle d\mathbf{q}\langle \mathbf{q}|\mathbf{p}'\rangle = -i\hbar \int \nabla_{\mathbf{q}'}\langle \mathbf{q}'|\mathbf{q}\rangle d\mathbf{q}\langle \mathbf{q}|\mathbf{p}'\rangle \tag{8–53}$$

where we have used Eq. (8–52). Carrying out the **P** operator on the left, we then have the following differential equation for the matrix $\langle \mathbf{q}'|\mathbf{p}'\rangle$:

$$\mathbf{p}'\langle \mathbf{q}'|\mathbf{p}'\rangle = -i\hbar\nabla_{\mathbf{q}'}\langle \mathbf{q}'|\mathbf{p}'\rangle \tag{8–54}$$

This equation integrates at once to give

$$\langle \mathbf{q}'|\mathbf{p}'\rangle = K \exp\,[i\mathbf{p}'\cdot\mathbf{q}'/\hbar] \tag{8–55}$$

where K is an arbitrary constant. Because $\langle \mathbf{p}'|\mathbf{q}'\rangle$ is the complex conjugate of $\langle \mathbf{q}'|\mathbf{p}'\rangle$, the arbitrary constant can be determined by the normalization condition:

$$\int \langle \mathbf{q}'|\mathbf{p}'\rangle d\mathbf{p}'\langle \mathbf{p}'|\mathbf{q}''\rangle = \langle \mathbf{q}'|\mathbf{q}''\rangle = \delta(\mathbf{q}' - \mathbf{q}'')$$

This requires that we take $K = (2\pi\hbar)^{-3/2}$ so we have

$$\langle \mathbf{q}|\mathbf{p}\rangle = (2\pi\hbar)^{-3/2} \exp\,[i\mathbf{p}\cdot\mathbf{q}/\hbar] \tag{8–56}$$

the matrix of the transformation from the p- to the q-representation. This is the analog of the matrices shown in Eqs. (8–28) and (8–29), and again they are matrices only in the generalized sense of Banach space. The expression on the right is a periodic function in coordinate space, with a wavelength $\hbar/|\mathbf{p}|$, and wave-number vector $\mathbf{p}/\hbar$.

8.8. The Schrödinger Wave Packet.—Let the system at time t be in a state represented by the vector $|t\rangle$ in $\mathscr{H}$. This state may be specified by giving its components with respect to every coordinate eigenvector $|\mathbf{q}\rangle$ in $\mathscr{H}$, namely $\langle \mathbf{q}|t\rangle$. This is the wave function as ordinarily understood in the Schrödinger theory, see Eq. (8–45). On the other hand we may also specify the state $|t\rangle$ by giving its components with respect to every momentum eigenvector in $\mathscr{H}$, namely

$\langle \mathbf{p}|t\rangle$. We shall see that this function is the spectral distribution of the wave function. Thus, we have the identity

$$\langle \mathbf{q}|t\rangle = \int \langle \mathbf{q}|\mathbf{p}\rangle d\mathbf{p}\langle \mathbf{p}|t\rangle \tag{8–57}$$

and using Eq. (8–56) this is equivalent to

$$\langle \mathbf{q}|t\rangle = (2\pi\hbar)^{-3/2} \int \langle \mathbf{p}|t\rangle \exp\,[i\mathbf{p}\cdot\mathbf{q}/\hbar]d\mathbf{p} \tag{8–58}$$

Interpreting $\mathbf{p}/\hbar$ as the wave number vector, we see that this is a wave packet function, and that $\langle \mathbf{p}|t\rangle$ is the amplitude of the wave at the wave number $\mathbf{p}/\hbar$. Note that $\langle \mathbf{p}|t\rangle$ and $\langle \mathbf{q}|t\rangle$ can also be regarded as the Fourier transforms of each other.[8]

8.9. The Schrödinger Equation.—We return to Eq. (8–50), the coordinate representation of the operator P^k. Multiply that equation by $\langle \mathbf{q}'|t\rangle$ and integrate over all coordinates:

$$\int \langle \mathbf{q}''|P^k|\mathbf{q}'\rangle d\mathbf{q}'\langle \mathbf{q}'|t\rangle = -i\hbar \int (\partial/\partial q_k'')\langle \mathbf{q}''|\mathbf{q}'\rangle d\mathbf{q}'\langle \mathbf{q}'|t\rangle$$

or

$$\langle \mathbf{q}''|P^k|t\rangle = -i\hbar(\partial/\partial q_k'')\langle \mathbf{q}''|t\rangle \tag{8–59}$$

In words, this states that the result of operating on $|t\rangle$ by P^k, expressed as a function of coordinates $\mathbf{q}$, is the same as differentiating $|t\rangle$, also expressed as a function of $\mathbf{q}$, with respect to q_k. In this sense we recognize that the equation can be written in conventional notation as follows:

$$P^k\psi(\mathbf{q},t) = -i\hbar(\partial/\partial q_k)\psi(\mathbf{q},t) \tag{8–60}$$

which is the familiar Schrödinger operator rule for the momentum:

$$\mathbf{P} = -i\hbar\nabla_{\mathbf{q}} \tag{8–61}$$

Each side of this rule can be completed to form a Lorentz four-vector by including the following equation:

$$H = i\hbar(\partial/\partial t) \tag{8–62}$$

which is Schrödinger's equation. In the Dirac notation, in terms of Hilbert space and matching Eq. (8–59) this equation is

$$\langle \mathbf{q}|H|t\rangle = i\hbar(\partial/\partial t)\langle \mathbf{q}|t\rangle \tag{8–63}$$

[8] Margenau and Murphy, *op. cit.*, Eq. (8–13).

Example, Free Particle. In this case the hamiltonian is $H = \mathbf{P}^2/2m$ and the state vector $|t\rangle$ satisfies the equation

$$\mathbf{P}^2|t\rangle = 2mi\hbar(\partial/\partial t)|t\rangle \tag{8-64}$$

This integrates to yield

$$|t\rangle = \exp\left[-i\mathbf{P}^2(t - t_o)/2m\hbar\right]|t_o\rangle \tag{8-65}$$

We interpret this equation as an historical development of the state $|t\rangle$ from the initial state $|t_o\rangle$ at the earlier time $t_o < t$. Taking the coordinate representation of this operator relation we have

$$\begin{aligned}\langle\mathbf{q}|t\rangle &= \int\langle\mathbf{q}|\exp\left[-i\mathbf{P}^2(t - t_o)/2m\hbar\right]|\mathbf{q}_o\rangle d\mathbf{q}_o\langle\mathbf{q}_o|t_o\rangle \\ &= \int\int\int\langle\mathbf{q}|\mathbf{p}\rangle d\mathbf{p}\langle\mathbf{p}|\exp\left[-i\mathbf{P}^2(t - t_o)/2m\hbar\right] \\ &\qquad\times|\mathbf{p}'\rangle d\mathbf{p}'\langle\mathbf{p}'|\mathbf{q}_o\rangle d\mathbf{q}_o\langle\mathbf{q}_o|t_o\rangle \\ &= \int\int\exp\left[-i\mathbf{p}^2(t - t_o)/2m\hbar\right]\langle\mathbf{q}|\mathbf{p}\rangle d\mathbf{p}\langle\mathbf{p}|\mathbf{q}_o\rangle d\mathbf{q}_o\langle\mathbf{q}_o|t_o\rangle\end{aligned}$$

and using Postulate B(i) in Eq. (8–56), this yields

$$\begin{aligned}\langle\mathbf{q}|t\rangle = (2\pi\hbar)^{-3/2}\int\int&\exp\left[-i\mathbf{p}^2(t - t_o)/2m\hbar\right] \\ &\times\exp\left[i\mathbf{p}\cdot(\mathbf{q} - \mathbf{q}_o)/\hbar\right]d\mathbf{p}\langle\mathbf{q}_o|t_o\rangle d\mathbf{q}_o\end{aligned} \tag{8-66}$$

valid for $t \geq t_o$. We may suppose that the state was actually initiated at time t_o, so that $\langle\mathbf{q}|t\rangle$ is zero for $t < t_o$. We can include this boundary condition in the expression for $\langle\mathbf{q}|t\rangle$ by writing Eq. (8–66) in the form:

$$\langle\mathbf{q}|t\rangle = \int\int G(\mathbf{q},t;\, \mathbf{q}_o,t_o)\langle\mathbf{q}_o|t_o\rangle d\mathbf{q}_o dt_o \tag{8-67}$$

where

$$\begin{aligned}G(\mathbf{q},t;\, \mathbf{q}_o,t_o) = \theta(t - t_o)(2\pi\hbar)^{-3/2}\int\int\int&\exp\left[-i\mathbf{p}^2(t - t_o)/2m\hbar\right. \\ &\left.+\, i\mathbf{p}\cdot(\mathbf{q} - \mathbf{q}_o)/\hbar\right]d\mathbf{p}\end{aligned} \tag{8-68}$$

Here $\theta(t - t_o)$ is the unit step function, zero for $t < t_o$ and unity for $t \geq t_o$, while $\partial\theta(t - t_o)/\partial t = \delta(t - t_o)$. Taking the time derivative of (8–68) we find

$$i\hbar\partial G/\partial t = i\hbar\delta(t - t_o)\delta(\mathbf{q} - \mathbf{q}_o) - (\hbar^2/2m)\nabla_{\mathbf{q}}^2 G \tag{8-69}$$

which is Schrödinger's equation, modified by a discrete unit source. Thus G is Green's function for the inhomogeneous Schrödinger equation.[9] Extensive use of this and similar results has been made in the quantum theory of scattering processes.[10]

8.10. The Schrödinger Wave Function for N Particles.—In our discussion of the application of Hilbert space to quantum mechanics of a single particle, we postulated a one-to-one correspondence between the rays of $\mathscr{H}$ and the points of ordinary three-dimensional space; the symbol $|\mathbf{q}\rangle$ meant that the vector $\mathbf{q}$ identifies a normalized vector in $\mathscr{H}$. On the other hand Schrödinger's nonrelativistic theory of N particles involves setting up a $3N$ dimensional hyperspace, three dimensions for each particle, and a single (absolute) time for the whole system. The Schrödinger wave function describing the state of such a system is a function of time and all the $3N$ space variables.

$$\psi(t,\mathbf{q}_1,\mathbf{q}_2,\cdots,\mathbf{q}_N)$$

Here the symbol $\mathbf{q}_j$ indicates the 3-dimensional vector position of the jth particle. To apply Hilbert space concepts to this theory we now postulate a one-to-one correspondence between the rays of $\mathscr{H}$ and the "points" of the Schrödinger $3N$ hyperspace. Thus there exists a continuum of normalized eigenvectors in $\mathscr{H}$ represented by the symbol $|\mathbf{q}_1,\mathbf{q}_2,\cdots,\mathbf{q}_N\rangle$.

Next we postulate the existence of $3N$ operators Q_{nk}, $n = 1,2,\cdots,N$, $k = 1,2,3$, corresponding to the measurement of the position variables q_{nk}:

$$Q_{nk}|\mathbf{q}_1,\mathbf{q}_2,\cdots,\mathbf{q}_N\rangle = q_{nk}|\mathbf{q}_1,\mathbf{q}_2,\cdots,\mathbf{q}_N\rangle \tag{8–70}$$

It will often be convenient to condense the notation, and write $\mathbf{X}$ for the $3N$ dimensional vector $(\mathbf{q}_1,\mathbf{q}_2,\cdots,\mathbf{q}_N)$ so that Eq. (8–70) takes the form

$$Q_{nk}|\mathbf{X}\rangle = q_{nk}|\mathbf{X}\rangle \tag{8–71}$$

The orthogonality and completeness of the eigenvectors $|\mathbf{X}\rangle$ are expressed by the analogs of Eq. (8–40):

$$\langle\mathbf{X}'|\mathbf{X}\rangle = \delta^{3N}(\mathbf{X}' - \mathbf{X}) \tag{8–72}$$

[9] Margenau and Murphy, *op. cit.*, Section 14.7; also W. Band, *Introduction to Mathematical Physics*, Chapter IV, D. Van Nostrand Co., Inc., Princeton, N.J., 1959; Morse and Feshbach, *Methods of Theoretical Physics*, Chapter VII, McGraw-Hill Book Co., New York, 1953.

[10] Eugen Merzbacher, *Quantum Mechanics*, Chapter 21, John Wiley and Sons, Inc., New York, 1961; Schweber, Bethe, and de Hoffmann, *Mesons and Fields*, Vol. 1, Section 8a, Harper and Row, New York, 1955.

and

$$\int \cdots \int |\mathbf{X}\rangle d\mathbf{X}\langle\mathbf{X}| = I \tag{8–73}$$

Any element $|t\rangle$ in $\mathscr{H}$ can be expressed as an integral over all its components in the "directions" of its eigenvectors:

$$|t\rangle = \int \cdots \int |\mathbf{X}\rangle d\mathbf{X}\langle\mathbf{X}|t\rangle \tag{8–74}$$

the component in the direction of $|\mathbf{X}\rangle$ being $\langle\mathbf{X}|t\rangle$, which is of course the Dirac symbol for the Schrödinger function $\psi(t,\mathbf{X})$.

Again we postulate the existence of momentum operators P^{nk} and the eigenvectors of these operators, $|\mathbf{p}_1,\mathbf{p}_2,\cdots,\mathbf{p}_N\rangle$ with the properties analogous to Eq. (8–40):

$$\langle\mathbf{p}_1',\mathbf{p}_2',\cdots,\mathbf{p}_N'|\mathbf{p}_1,\mathbf{p}_2,\cdots,\mathbf{p}_N\rangle = \delta^{3N}(\mathbf{p}' - \mathbf{p}) \tag{8–75}$$

and

$$\int \cdots \int |\mathbf{p}_1,\mathbf{p}_2,\cdots,\mathbf{p}_N\rangle \prod_j d\mathbf{p}_j\langle\mathbf{p}_1,\mathbf{p}_2,\cdots,\mathbf{p}_N| = I \tag{8–76}$$

while the eigenvalue relationship reads

$$P^{nk}|\mathbf{p}_1,\mathbf{p}_2,\cdots,\mathbf{p}_N\rangle = p^{nk}|\mathbf{p}_1,\mathbf{p}_2,\cdots,\mathbf{p}_N\rangle \tag{8–77}$$

Finally the analog of Eq. (8–42), the commutation relation, becomes

$$Q_{nk}P^{mj} - P^{mj}Q_{nk} = i\hbar\delta_{nm}\delta_{jk}I \tag{8–78}$$

It is clear that the analogy between these statements and the corresponding ones of Section 8.6 permits us at once to take over the results of Sections 8.7 and 8.8 by a mere reinterpretation of the symbols. Thus, the analogs of Eq. (8–50) can be derived by steps identical to those used in Section 8.7:

$$\langle\mathbf{X}''|P^{nk}|\mathbf{X}'\rangle = -i\hbar(\partial/\partial q_{nk}'')\langle\mathbf{X}''|\mathbf{X}'\rangle \tag{8–79}$$

The analog of Eq. (8–56) is

$$\langle\mathbf{X}|\mathbf{p}_1,\mathbf{p}_2,\cdots,\mathbf{p}_N\rangle = (2\pi\hbar)^{-3N/2}\exp\left[\mathbf{X}\cdot(\mathbf{p}_1,\mathbf{p}_2,\cdots,\mathbf{p}_N)/\hbar\right] \tag{8–80}$$

which is the transformation matrix from $3N$-momentum to $3N$-coordinate hyperspace.

The analog of Eq. (8–59), giving the coordinate representation of the momentum operator is

$$\langle\mathbf{X}|P^{nk}|t\rangle = -i\hbar(\partial/\partial q_{nk})\langle\mathbf{X}|t\rangle \tag{8–81}$$

or simply

$$\mathbf{P} = -i\hbar\nabla_{\mathbf{X}}$$

The analog of Eq. (8–63), Schrödinger's equation, is

$$\langle \mathbf{X}|H|t\rangle = i\hbar(\partial/\partial t)\langle \mathbf{X}|t\rangle \tag{8–82}$$

It is, finally, fairly obvious that the method of Green's function and the inhomogeneous Schrödinger equation can also be written down for a system of $3N$ noninteracting particles, in analogy to the last paragraph in Section 8.9.

8.11. N-Particle States as Products of 1-Particle States.—The symbol $\langle \mathbf{X}|t\rangle$ is a complex number assigned by the Hilbert space vector $|t\rangle$ at time t to the point $\mathbf{X}$ in $3N$-hyperspace; it is the Schrödinger wave function for N particles. If the particles are identical, we can imagine an identical Hilbert space assigned to each particle separately, $\mathscr{H}_j$ to the jth particle. The eigenstates of any one particle are basis vectors in its own Hilbert space, and can be indicated by a suitable symbol, $|\lambda_j,t\rangle$, where λ_j is a numerical index identifying the states of the jth particle. The symbol $\langle \mathbf{q}_j|\lambda_j,t\rangle$ is a complex number assigned to the point $\mathbf{q}_j$ in the coordinate space of the jth particle by the state λ_j at time t, and is therefore the Dirac symbol for the Schrödinger one-particle wave function for the jth particle. The index λ_j may conveniently be the eigenvalue of the state it indicates, *e.g.*, the energy eigenvalue of the jth particle.

The product

$$\prod_{j=1}^{N} \langle \mathbf{q}_j|\lambda_j,t\rangle$$

is a complex number assigned to the point $\mathbf{X} = \mathbf{q}_1,\mathbf{q}_2,\cdots,\mathbf{q}_N$ at the time t by the set of vectors $|\lambda_j,t\rangle$ in all the spaces $\mathscr{H}_j$, and we can write it, in a consistent notation as

$$\langle \mathbf{X}|\{\lambda\},t\rangle = \prod_{i=1}^{N} \langle \mathbf{q}_j|\lambda_j,t\rangle \tag{8–83}$$

For any chosen set of eigenvalues $\{\lambda\}$, $|\{\lambda\},t\rangle$ is a vector in the total Hilbert space $\mathscr{H}$ consisting of all the one-particle Hilbert spaces, or the "direct sum"[11]

$$\mathscr{H} = \mathscr{H}_1 \oplus \mathscr{H}_2 \oplus \cdots \oplus \mathscr{H}_N$$

It is now claimed that the set of vectors $|\{\lambda\},t\rangle$ obtained by choosing all possible sets of one-particle eigenstates λ_j, forms a closed orthonormal basis for $\mathscr{H}$. This claim requires that we prove the following: Assuming that the spectra are discrete, *i.e.*, that for any one j, the

[11] B. Friedman, *loc. cit.*, p. 14.

values of λ_j are denumerable, and also assuming that a suitable normalization is carried out (to be discussed later), then

$$\left.\begin{aligned} &\text{(a)} \qquad \langle\{\lambda'\},t|\{\lambda\},t\rangle = \delta(\{\lambda'\},\{\lambda\}) \\ &\text{(b)} \qquad \sum_{\{\lambda\}} |\{\lambda\},t\rangle\langle\{\lambda\},t\rangle = I \end{aligned}\right\} \tag{8–84}$$

The proof of these is equivalent to proving

$$\begin{aligned} &\text{(a)} \qquad \int \langle\{\lambda'\},t|\mathbf{X}\rangle d\mathbf{X}\langle\mathbf{X}|\{\lambda\},t\rangle = \delta(\{\lambda'\},\{\lambda\}) \\ &\text{(b)} \qquad \sum_{\{\lambda\}} \langle\mathbf{X}'|\{\lambda\},t\rangle\langle\{\lambda\},t|\mathbf{X}\rangle = \langle\mathbf{X}'|\mathbf{X}\rangle = \delta(\mathbf{X}' - \mathbf{X}) \end{aligned} \tag{8–85}$$

Direct substitution of Eq. (8–83) leads to the proof of these, when we recall that the one-particle wave functions satisfy the relation

$$\int \langle\lambda_j,t|\mathbf{q}_j\rangle d\mathbf{q}_j\langle\mathbf{q}_j|\lambda_{Pj},t\rangle = \delta_{j,Pj}$$

The details are left as an exercise.

On the strength of these results we can now express any arbitrary vector $|t\rangle$ in $\mathscr{H}$ as a linear combination of the basis vectors:

$$|t\rangle = \sum_{\{\lambda\}} |\{\lambda\},t\rangle\langle\{\lambda\},t|t\rangle \tag{8–86}$$

and the corollary

$$\langle\mathbf{X}|t\rangle = \sum_{\{\lambda\}}\langle\mathbf{X}|\{\lambda\},t\rangle\langle\{\lambda\},t|t\rangle \tag{8–87}$$

The quantities $\langle\{\lambda\},t|t\rangle$ are the components of the arbitrary state $|t\rangle$ with respect to the basis vectors $|\{\lambda\},t\rangle$.

It may serve to make these results more transparent if we write them out in terms of the familiar momentum eigenfunctions of a particle in a finite box of side L with periodic boundary conditions.[12] In this case we have

$$\langle\mathbf{q}_j|\lambda_j,t\rangle = L^{-3/2} \exp\,(i\mathbf{p}_j\cdot\mathbf{q}_j/\hbar - iE_jt/\hbar) \tag{8–88}$$

and Eq. (8–83) becomes

$$\begin{aligned} \langle\mathbf{X}|\{\lambda\},t\rangle &= L^{-3N/2} \exp \sum_j \,(i\mathbf{p}_j\cdot\mathbf{q}_j\,/\hbar - iE_jt/\hbar) \\ &= L^{-3N/2} \exp\,(i\mathbf{K}\cdot\mathbf{X} - iEt/\hbar) \end{aligned} \tag{8–89}$$

[12] L. I. Schiff, *Quantum Mechanics*, Section 11, McGraw-Hill Book Co., New York, 1949.

where $\mathbf{K} = \sum_j \mathbf{p}_j/\hbar$, $E = \sum_j E_j$. The orthogonality relation of Eq. (8–85)(a) is now

$$\int \cdots \int L^{-3N} \exp\left[i(E' - E)t/\hbar\right] \exp\left[i(\mathbf{K} - \mathbf{K}')\cdot\mathbf{X}\right]d\mathbf{X} = \delta(\mathbf{K}' - \mathbf{K}) \tag{8–90}$$

and the closure relation in Eq. (8–85)(b) is

$$L^{-3N} \sum_{\mathbf{K}} \exp i\mathbf{K}\cdot(\mathbf{X}' - \mathbf{X}) = \delta(\mathbf{X}' - \mathbf{X}) \tag{8–91}$$

8.12. Symmetrization of N-Particle States.—Let P be an arbitrary permutation[13] among the eigenvalues occurring in the set $\{\lambda\}$. By this we mean the following: start with some arbitrary set of vectors $|\lambda_1\rangle, |\lambda_2\rangle, \cdots, |\lambda_N\rangle$, one for each particle in its respective Hilbert space $\mathscr{H}_1, \mathscr{H}_2, \cdots, \mathscr{H}_N$, then carry out an arbitrary permutation of the values of λ appearing in the set, among the spaces $\mathscr{H}_j$; the result is to assign the eigenvalue λ_{Pj} to the space $\mathscr{H}_j$, Pj being the index into which j is changed by the permutation P. The expression for the component of the state of the system is taken by this operation through the following transformation:

$$\langle\mathbf{X}|\{\lambda\},t\rangle \rightarrow \langle\mathbf{X}|\{\lambda\}_P,t\rangle = \prod_{j=1}^{N} \langle\mathbf{q}_j|\lambda_{Pj},t\rangle \tag{8–92}$$

Exactly the same set of eigenvalues appears in this as before, but in a different order among the particles. There are $N!$ permutations, and if we add all the $N!$ vectors like that in Eq. (8–92) we shall have a vector that is completely symmetrical in all the particles.[14] Thus we may define the symmetrical N-particle state as

$$|\{\lambda\},t\rangle_S = (K_S/N!) \sum_P |\{\lambda\}_P,t\rangle \tag{8–93}$$

where K_S is a normalization constant to be determined—Eq. (8–96).

Taking the $\mathbf{X}$ component of this symmetrical state, we have

$$\langle\mathbf{X}|\{\lambda\},t\rangle_S = (K_S/N!) \sum_P \langle\mathbf{X}|\{\lambda\}_P,t\rangle = (K_S/N!) \sum_P \prod_{j=1}^{N} \langle\mathbf{q}_j|\lambda_{PJ},t\rangle \tag{8–94}$$

[13] See Margenau and Murphy, *op. cit.*, Sections 15.12 and 15.19.

[14] *Loc. cit.*, Section 11.2, and William Band, *Introduction to Quantum Statistics*, Section 1.4, D. Van Nostrand Co., Inc., Princeton, N.J., 1955.

The normalization of the state is achieved as follows:

$$\begin{aligned} 1 &= {}_S\langle\{\lambda\},t|\{\lambda\},t\rangle_S = \int {}_S\langle\{\lambda\},t|\mathbf{X}\rangle d\mathbf{X}\langle\mathbf{X}|\{\lambda\},t\rangle_S \\ &= (K_S/N!)^2 \int \left[\sum_P \prod_{j=1}^N \langle\lambda_{Pj},t|\mathbf{q}_j\rangle\right]\left[\sum_{P'} \prod_{j=1}^N \langle\mathbf{q}_j|\lambda_{P'j},t\rangle\right] d\mathbf{X} \\ &= (K_S^2/N!) \int \prod_{j=1}^N \langle\lambda_j,t|\mathbf{q}_j\rangle \left[\sum_{P^{-1}} \sum_{P'} \prod_{j=1}^N \langle\mathbf{q}_j|\lambda_{P'j},t\rangle\right] d\mathbf{X} \\ &= (K_S^2/N!) \int \sum_P \prod_{j=1}^N \langle\lambda_j,t|\mathbf{q}_j\rangle\langle\mathbf{q}_j|\lambda_{Pj},t\rangle d\mathbf{X} \end{aligned} \tag{8–95}$$

From this it can be shown that[15]

$$K_S^2 = N!/n_1!n_2!\cdots = N!/\,\Pi\, n_\lambda! \tag{8–96}$$

where n_λ is the number of times the value λ appears among the N levels $\lambda_1,\lambda_2,\cdots,\lambda_N$. All possible values of λ in the denumerable one-particle spectrum are formally included in the product, those values of λ that are absent in the N-particle system are accounted for by setting $n_\lambda = 0$, and $0! = 1$. The numbers satisfy the identity

$$\sum_\lambda n_\lambda = N$$

The reader is advised to write out Eq. (8–94) in terms of the box eigenstates of Eq. (8–88). We may illustrate Eq. (8–96) by considering a system of three particles, $N = 3$, distributed among two different states $u_1(q)$, $u_2(q)$. Assigning the first two particles to the state u_1 and the third to the state u_2, we can form one analog of Eq. (8–92):

$$\langle\mathbf{X}|\{\lambda\},t\rangle = u_1(1)u_1(2)u_2(3)$$

There are six permutations and so

$$\langle\mathbf{X}|\{\lambda\},t\rangle_S = (2K_S/3!)[u_1(1)u_1(2)u_2(3) + u_1(1)u_2(2)u_1(3) + u_2(1)u_1(2)u_1(3)]$$

Taking the scalar product

$$\int {}_S\langle\{\lambda\},t|\mathbf{X}\rangle d\mathbf{X}\langle\mathbf{X}|\{\lambda\},t\rangle_S = 1$$

and recalling that the states u_1 and u_2 are orthogonal and normalized, we have $1 = (2K_S/3!)^2[3]$ and hence $K_S^2 = 3!/2$ in agreement with Eq. (8–96).

A completely antisymmetrical state of N particles is obtained from

[15] See Margenau and Murphy, *op. cit.*, Section 12.9.

Eq. (8–92) by summing all even permutations and subtracting all odd permutations, or in an obvious notation:

$$|\{\lambda\},t\rangle_A = (K_A/N!)\sum_P(-1)^P|\{\lambda\}_P,t\rangle \tag{8–97}$$

The normalization constant K_A can be found from a suitable modification of Eq. (8–95), which turns out to be

$$1 = (K_A^2/N!)\sum_P(-1)^P\int\prod_{j=1}^N\langle\lambda_j,t|\mathbf{q}_j\rangle\langle\mathbf{q}_j|\lambda_{Pj}|,t\rangle d\mathbf{X} \tag{8–98}$$

Because of its antisymmetry, the sum in Eq. (8–97) vanishes if any one value of λ occurs more than once in the set $\{\lambda\}$, so the numbers n_λ are all either unity or zero, and the normalization constant is found to be[16]

$$K_A^2 = N! \tag{8–99}$$

Consider again a system of three particles, $N = 3$, and distribute them among three different states $u_1(q)$, $u_2(q)$, $u_3(q)$. The antisymmetrical state is now

$$\begin{aligned}(K_A/3!)[&u_1(1)u_2(2)u_3(3) + u_1(2)u_2(3)u_3(1) + u_1(3)u_2(1)u_3(2)\\ &- u_1(1)u_2(3)u_3(2) - u_1(2)u_2(1)u_3(3) - u_1(3)u_2(2)u_3(1)]\end{aligned}$$

The scalar product of this with itself is then obviously $6(K_A/3!)^2 = 1$, and at once yields a result in agreement with Eq. (8–99).

In general whether we are discussing symmetrical or antisymmetrical states, the numbers n_λ are usually termed the occupation numbers, and if we are given a complete spectrum of one-particle states, indicated by $\{\lambda\}$, then the set of occupation numbers assigned to the values of λ, specifies the state of the system of N identical particles just as well as the assignment of a λ-value to each particle. Thus we may use the notation $\{n\}$ just as well as $\{\lambda\}$ to specify the state, and so write

$$|\{\lambda\},t\rangle_{S,A} = |\{n\},t\rangle_{S,A} \tag{8–100}$$

for the Hilbert space vector describing the symmetrical, or antisymmetrical eigenstates of the N-particle system; we can also write for the general state of the N-particle system, the expansion

$$|t\rangle_{S,A} = \sum_{\{n\}}|\{n\},t\rangle_{S,A\ S,A}\langle\{n\},t|t\rangle_{S,A} \tag{8–101}$$

Also Eqs. (8–94) and (8–97) can be written in the form

$$\langle\mathbf{X}|\{n\},t\rangle_{S,A} = (K_{S,A}/N!)\sum_P(\pm 1)^P\prod_j\langle\mathbf{q}_j|\lambda_{Pj},t\rangle \tag{8–102}$$

[16] S. S. Schweber, *Introduction to Relativistic Quantum Field Theory*, Section 6, Harper and Row, New York, 1961.

The right side of this equation contains the determinant

$$\begin{vmatrix} \langle \mathbf{q}_1|\lambda_1\rangle & \langle \mathbf{q}_1|\lambda_2\rangle & \langle \mathbf{q}_1|\lambda_3\rangle & \cdots \\ \langle \mathbf{q}_2|\lambda_1\rangle & \langle \mathbf{q}_2|\lambda_2\rangle & \langle \mathbf{q}_2|\lambda_3\rangle & \cdots \\ & & & \text{etc.} \end{vmatrix}$$

In the antisymmetrical case the determinant is evaluated in the usual way with alternating signs; in the symmetrical case all products are added. This can be done, for example, by taking the first element of the first row and multiplying it by its co-factor in the matrix, then adding the second element in the first row multiplied by its cofactor, etc. The result of this expansion leads to the following useful theorem regarding symmetrical states:[17]

$$\begin{aligned} \langle \mathbf{X}|\{n\},t\rangle_S &= \langle \mathbf{q}_1,\mathbf{q}_2,\cdots,\mathbf{q}_N|n_1,n_2,\cdots,t\rangle_S \\ &= \sum_\lambda (n_\lambda/N)^{1/2}\langle \mathbf{q}_1|\lambda,t\rangle \\ &\qquad \times \langle \mathbf{q}_2,\mathbf{q}_3,\cdots,\mathbf{q}_N|n_1,n_2,\cdots,n_\lambda - 1,\cdots,t\rangle_S \end{aligned} \tag{8-103}$$

where the vector $\mathbf{X}$ has been written out in more detail to display the decrease in total population for the cofactors. A similar expansion can be given by going down the λth column instead of across the top row. The result is another useful theorem:[17]

$$\begin{aligned} \langle \mathbf{q}_1,\mathbf{q}_2,\cdots,\mathbf{q}_N|n_1,n_2,\cdots,t\rangle_S &= \sum_{j=1}^{N} (n_\lambda N)^{-1/2}\langle \mathbf{q}_j|\lambda,t\rangle \\ &\times \langle \mathbf{q}_1,\mathbf{q}_2,\cdots,\mathbf{q}_{j-1},\mathbf{q}_{j+1},\cdots,\mathbf{q}_N|n_1,n_2,\cdots,n_\lambda - 1,\cdots,t\rangle_S \end{aligned} \tag{8-104}$$

Except for alternating signs, the antisymmetrical case yields similar theorems.

8.13. Creation and Annihilation Operators.

—In the last section there was a hint that the theory could handle problems in which populations do not remain constant. Thus $|\langle\{n\},t|t\rangle_S|^2$ is the probability density in $3N$-coordinate space that the occupation numbers are $\{n\}$, and the general symmetrical state, Eq. (8-101), is one in which there is a distribution of probabilities over different sets of occupation numbers; the sum over sets could easily be extended to include sets $\{n\}$ corresponding to different total populations N.

To follow up this idea it is convenient now to introduce the operators b_λ and b_λ^* defined by:

$$b_\lambda|n_1,n_2,\cdots,t\rangle_S = n_\lambda^{1/2}|n_1,n_2,\cdots,n_\lambda - 1,\cdots,t\rangle_S \tag{8-105}$$

$$b_\lambda^*|n_1,n_2,\cdots,t\rangle_S = (n_\lambda + 1)^{1/2}|n_1,n_2,\cdots,n_\lambda + 1,\cdots,t\rangle_S \tag{8-106}$$

[17] S. S. Schweber, *loc. cit.* For details, see p. 129 and p. 138.

The operator b_λ annihilates a particle from the λ-state, while the operator b_λ^* creates a particle in the λ-state, leaving the other states unchanged; the total population of the system changes by unity in each case. The numerical factors are chosen so that the product of the two operators in the appropriate order is given by

$$b_\lambda^* b_\lambda \equiv N_\lambda \tag{8–107}$$

and

$$N_\lambda|n_1,n_2,\cdots,n_\lambda,\cdots,t\rangle_S = n_\lambda|n_1,n_2,\cdots,n_\lambda,\cdots,t\rangle_S$$

In other words the state $|\{n\},t\rangle_S$ is an eigenstate of the operator N_λ with eigenvalues $n_\lambda : N_\lambda$ is called the population operator for the λ state.

Neither b_λ^* nor b_λ is hermitian, but one is the hermitian conjugate of the other. For this reason their product, N_λ is hermitian and cannot have negative eigenvalues. However, we can see that for any state in which n_λ is zero, the eigenvalue of N_λ is zero. We postulate now that in $\mathscr{H}$ there exists a vector corresponding to an empty system in which all the occupation numbers are zero; this system is simply a spectrum of possible one-particle states $\{\lambda\}$, in which particles could be found if they existed. This state is called the vacuum state of the system, and the corresponding vector in $\mathscr{H}$ is represented by the symbol $|0,\{\lambda\}\rangle_S$. The component of the vacuum state with respect to the coordinate in $3N$ space, *i.e.*, $\langle \mathbf{X}|0,\{\lambda\}\rangle_S$, has the physical meaning that it is the probability amplitude corresponding to absence of particles from the system. The vector must not be confused with the null vector in $\mathscr{H}$.

If we operate on the vacuum state with any annihilation operator the result is the null vector:

$$b_\lambda|0,\{\lambda\}\rangle_S = 0|0,\{\lambda\}\rangle_S = |\text{null}\rangle \tag{8–108}$$

Operating on the vacuum state with a succession of creation operators, on the other hand, permits us to build up a system with any desired population:

$$\prod_\lambda (b_\lambda^*)^{n_\lambda}|0,\{\lambda\}\rangle_S = \prod_\lambda (n_\lambda!)^{1/2}|n_1,n_2,\cdots,t\rangle_S \tag{8–109}$$

with total population

$$N = \sum_\lambda n_\lambda$$

We can also form an operator $\mathbf{N}$ defined by

$$\mathbf{N} \equiv \sum_\lambda N_\lambda \tag{8–110}$$

that can operate on the state $|\{n\},t\rangle_S$:

$$\mathbf{N}|n_1,n_2,\cdots,t\rangle_S = \left(\sum_\lambda n_\lambda\right)|n_1,n_2,\cdots,t\rangle_S \tag{8–111}$$

The state $|\{n\},t\rangle_S$ is an eigenstate of $\mathbf{N}$ with eigenvalue N, and $\mathbf{N}$ is called the total population operator. Because the vector $|\{n\},t\rangle_S$ is a function of the time, it is necessary to specify the time at which the creation or annihilation operators are applied, and in some discussions it may be advisable to indicate the time explicitly in the symbol for the operator. For our present discussion it will be sufficient to keep this time dependence in mind. In an expression such as Eq. (8–109), all the creation operators are applied at the same time, and since they all commute, this presents no logical problem. The order of the operators in the definition Eq. (8–107) is important however; the opposite order produces a different operator:

$$b_\lambda b_\lambda^* = N_\lambda + I$$

but in no case are we to regard this ordering to be in time. The operators are to be applied with the "speed of thought," and take no time to perform their operations![18]

When dealing with systems described by antisymmetrical states, the creation and annihilation operators are defined in such a way that the occupation numbers can never be greater than unity. Thus we have a creation operator a_λ^* defined by

$$a_\lambda^*|n_1,n_2,\cdots,n_\lambda,\cdots,t\rangle_A = (-1)^{s_\lambda}(1-n_\lambda)^{1/2}|n_1,n_2,\cdots,n_\lambda+1,\cdots,t\rangle_A \tag{8–112}$$

The factor[19] $(1-n_\lambda)^{1/2}$ ensures a zero result if n_λ is already unity—we cannot add another particle to that state. The factor $(-1)^{s_\lambda}$ is the alternating sign determined by the number of particles in the system below the state λ:

$$s_\lambda \equiv \sum_{\mu=1}^{\lambda-1} n_\mu \tag{8–113}$$

[18] Whether this concept can stand up under a rigorous psychological analysis has never been discussed, at least in the literature of theoretical physics. It may even be inconsistent with quantum mechanics in that the creation of a finite mass is equivalent to the creation of energy that, by the uncertainty principle, requires a finite time: $\Delta E \Delta t \sim h$. Thus the creation of an electron would require a time of the order 10^{-20} second. Higher order operations would take more time, and the divergences found in quantum field theory due to infinite series of creation operations would spread over an infinite time, and so be quite unphysical.

[19] In much of the literature the square root is omitted from this factor. Because the numbers involved are either zero or unity, this makes no real difference. We prefer to retain the square root to make Eq. (8–112) as similar as possible to Eq. (8–106) where the square root is essential.

The destruction operator is a_λ defined by

$$a_\lambda|n_1,n_2,\cdots,n_\lambda,\cdots,t\rangle_A = (-1)^{s_\lambda} n_\lambda^{1/2}|n_1,n_2,\cdots,n_\lambda - 1,\cdots,t\rangle_A \tag{8–114}$$

Here the factor $n_\lambda^{1/2}$ ensures a zero result if the state λ is already empty.

If one operates first with a_λ and then with a_λ^* one recovers the original state with the factor $(-1)^{s_\lambda}(2 - n_\lambda)^{1/2}n^{1/2} = (2n_\lambda - n_\lambda^2)^{1/2}$; and since n_λ is either unity or zero, we have $n_\lambda^2 = n_\lambda$, and $n_\lambda^{1/2} = n_\lambda$, so the factor reduces in all cases to n_λ:

$$a_\lambda^* a_\lambda|\{n\},t\rangle_A = n_\lambda|\{n\},t\rangle_A \tag{8–115}$$

and we can define the population operator for the state λ:

$$N_\lambda \equiv a_\lambda^* a_\lambda$$

the analog of Eq. (8–107).

The following commutation relations are readily derived from the definitions of the operators:

$$\left.\begin{aligned} b_\mu^* b_\lambda^* - b_\lambda^* b_\mu^* = 0; \qquad b_\mu b_\lambda - b_\lambda b_\mu = 0 \\ b_\mu b_\lambda^* - b_\lambda^* b_\mu = \delta_{\mu\lambda} \end{aligned}\right\} \tag{8–116}$$

and

$$\left.\begin{aligned} a_\mu^* a_\lambda^* + a_\lambda^* a_\mu^* = 0; \qquad a_\mu a_\lambda + a_\lambda a_\mu = 0 \\ a_\mu a_\lambda^* + a_\lambda^* a_\mu = \delta_{\mu\lambda} \end{aligned}\right\} \tag{8–117}$$

It is to be remarked that these operators can act only on states of the system expressed in occupation number representation, as explicitly appearing in the definitions, Eqs. (8–105), (8–106), (8–112), and (8–114). We can multiply any one of these operators by a scalar factor, so that we can also define the following operators:

$$B(\mathbf{q},t) \equiv \sum_\lambda \langle \mathbf{q}|\lambda,t\rangle b_\lambda; \qquad B^*(\mathbf{q},t) \equiv \sum_\lambda \langle \lambda,t|\mathbf{q}\rangle b_\lambda^* \tag{8–118}$$

where $\langle \mathbf{q}|\lambda,t\rangle$ is the one-particle wave function of Section 8.11. Similarly, we define operators for antisymmetrical systems:

$$A(\mathbf{q},t) \equiv \sum_\lambda \langle \mathbf{q}|\lambda,t\rangle a_\lambda; \qquad A^*(\mathbf{q},t) \equiv \sum_\lambda \langle \lambda,t|\mathbf{q}\rangle a_\lambda^* \tag{8–119}$$

These operators have the following commutation properties

$$\left.\begin{aligned} B(\mathbf{q},t)B^*(\mathbf{q}',t) - B^*(\mathbf{q}',t)B(\mathbf{q},t) = \delta(\mathbf{q}' - \mathbf{q}) \\ A(\mathbf{q},t)A^*(\mathbf{q}',t) + A^*(\mathbf{q}',t)A(\mathbf{q},t) = \delta(\mathbf{q}' - \mathbf{q}) \end{aligned}\right\} \tag{8–120}$$

all other products commuting. The physical meaning of these operators is indicated by the following procedure:

$$\begin{aligned}\int B^*(\mathbf{q},t)B(\mathbf{q},t)d\mathbf{q} &= \sum_{\mu}\sum_{\lambda}\int \langle\lambda,t|\mathbf{q}\rangle d\mathbf{q}\langle\mathbf{q}|\mu,t\rangle b_\lambda^* b_\mu \\ &= \sum_{\mu,\lambda}\langle\lambda,t|\mu,t\rangle b_\lambda^* b_\mu = \sum_\lambda b_\lambda^* b_\lambda = \mathbf{N}\end{aligned} \tag{8-121}$$

the total number operator for the system. We therefore call the operator $B^*(\mathbf{q},t)B(\mathbf{q},t)$ the total number density operator. Similarly for antisymmetrical systems we have

$$\begin{aligned}\int A^*(\mathbf{q},t)A(\mathbf{q},t)d\mathbf{q} &= \sum_{\mu,\lambda}\int \langle\lambda,t|\mathbf{q}\rangle d\mathbf{q}\langle\mathbf{q}|\mu,t\rangle a_\lambda^* a_\mu \\ &= \sum_{\mu,\lambda}\langle\lambda,t|\mu,t\rangle a_\lambda^* a_\mu = \sum_\lambda a_\lambda^* a_\lambda = \mathbf{N}\end{aligned} \tag{8-122}$$

so here again we interpret $A^*(\mathbf{q},t)A(\mathbf{q},t)$ as the total number density operator.

If H is the one-particle energy operator, the total energy operator for non-interacting systems can be written $\sum_\lambda Ha_\lambda^* a_\lambda$ or $\sum_\lambda Hb_\lambda^* b_\lambda$. The total energy density operator is then

$$A^*(\mathbf{q},t)H(\mathbf{q},t)A(\mathbf{q},t) \quad \text{or} \quad B^*(\mathbf{q},t)H(\mathbf{q},t)B(\mathbf{q},t)$$

It is worth while to write out some of these expressions in terms of the box-normalized states of Eq. (8–88). Thus we may write

$$\langle\mathbf{q}|\mathbf{k},t\rangle = L^{-3/2}\exp(i\mathbf{k}\cdot\mathbf{q} - iE_\mathbf{k}t/\hbar), \quad \mathbf{k} = \mathbf{p}/\hbar$$

and

$$B(\mathbf{q},t) = L^{-3/2}\sum_\mathbf{k}\exp(i\mathbf{k}\cdot\mathbf{q} - iE_\mathbf{k}t/\hbar)b_\mathbf{k}$$

while

$$B^*(\mathbf{q},t) = L^{-3/2}\sum_\mathbf{k}\exp(-i\mathbf{k}\cdot\mathbf{q} + iE_\mathbf{k}t/\hbar)b_\mathbf{k}^*$$

8.14. Some Theorems Concerning Particle Density Operators. Applying the theorem of Eq. (8–103) to the last factor of that same equation, we have:

$$\begin{aligned}\langle\mathbf{X}|\{n\},t\rangle_S &= \sum (n_\lambda/N)^{1/2}\langle\mathbf{q}_1|\lambda,t\rangle \\ &\quad\times \langle\mathbf{q}_2,\mathbf{q}_3,\cdots,\mathbf{q}_N|n_1,n_2,\cdots,n_\lambda - 1,\cdots,t\rangle_S \\ &= \sum_\lambda (n_\lambda/N)^{1/2}\langle\mathbf{q}_1|\lambda\rangle\sum_\mu (n_\mu/N-1)^{1/2}\langle\mathbf{q}_2|\mu\rangle \\ &\quad\times \langle\mathbf{q}_3\cdots\mathbf{q}_N|n_1\cdots n_\mu - 1,\cdots n_\lambda - 1\cdots t\rangle_S\end{aligned}$$

Then from the definition of b_λ in Eqs. (8–105) and (8–118) the right side here becomes

$$[N(N-1)]^{-1/2}\langle \mathbf{q}_3,\mathbf{q}_4,\cdots,\mathbf{q}_N|B(\mathbf{q}_2,t)B(\mathbf{q}_1,t)|n_1,n_2,\cdots,t\rangle_S \quad (8\text{–}123)$$

Continuing in this way we may prove

$$\langle \mathbf{X}|\{n\},t\rangle_S = (N!)^{-1/2}\langle t,0|B(\mathbf{q}_N,t)B(\mathbf{q}_{N-1},t)\cdots B(\mathbf{q}_1,t)|\{n\},t\rangle_S \quad (8\text{–}124)$$

Taking the hermitian conjugate of this also yields a theorem:

$$\langle\{n\},t|\mathbf{X}\rangle_S = (N!)^{-1/2}\langle\{n\},t|B^*(\mathbf{q}_1,t)B^*(\mathbf{q}_2,t)\cdots B^*(\mathbf{q}_N,t)|0,t\rangle_S \quad (8\text{–}125)$$

These theorems give explicit forms to the transformation functions relating configuration space to occupation number space.

Let us now multiply the last theorem on the left by $|\{n\},t\rangle_S$ and sum over all sets $\{n\}$, using Eqs. (8–84) and (8–100):

$$N!^{1/2}|\mathbf{X}\rangle_S = B^*(\mathbf{q}_1,t)B^*(\mathbf{q}_2,t)\cdots B^*(\mathbf{q}_N,t)|0,t\rangle_S \quad (8\text{–}126)$$

Similarly from Eq. (8–124) we can derive

$$N!^{1/2}{}_S\langle\mathbf{X}| = {}_S\langle 0,t|B(\mathbf{q}_1,t)B(\mathbf{q}_2,t)\cdots B(\mathbf{q}_N,t) \quad (8\text{–}127)$$

when we recall that from Eq. (8–120), all these B-operators commute. In words, we say that the eigenvector in $3N$ configuration space can be derived from the vacuum state by a succession of creation particle density operator amplitudes; a result that is by no means self-evident.

The following corollaries can also be proved (Schweber *loc. cit.*):

$$N^{1/2}|\mathbf{q},\mathbf{q}_1,\mathbf{q}_2,\cdots,\mathbf{q}_{N-1}\rangle_S = B^*(\mathbf{q})|\mathbf{q}_1,\mathbf{q}_2,\cdots,\mathbf{q}_{N-1}\rangle_S \quad (8\text{–}128)$$

$$N^{1/2}{}_S\langle\mathbf{q},\mathbf{q}_1,\mathbf{q}_2,\cdots,\mathbf{q}_{N-1}| = {}_S\langle\mathbf{q}_1,\mathbf{q}_2,\cdots,\mathbf{q}_{N-1}|B(\mathbf{q},t) \quad (8\text{–}129)$$

We may rationalize these by regarding them as similar to Eqs. (8–126) and (8–127) in that here, operating on a state containing $N-1$ particles, we produce a state with an additional particle at the position of the operator. From Eq. (8–104) we can derive in a somewhat similar fashion the following theorems:

$$B(\mathbf{q},t)|\mathbf{q}_1,\mathbf{q}_2,\cdots,\mathbf{q}_N\rangle_S = N^{-1/2}\prod_{j=1}^{N}\delta(\mathbf{q}_j-\mathbf{q})|\mathbf{q},\mathbf{q}_1,\mathbf{q}_2,\cdots,\mathbf{q}_{j-1},\mathbf{q}_{j+1},\cdots,\mathbf{q}_N\rangle_S \quad (8\text{–}130)$$

and

$${}_S\langle\mathbf{q}_1,\mathbf{q}_2,\cdots,\mathbf{q}_N|B^*(\mathbf{q},t) = N^{-1/2}\prod_{j=1}^{N}\delta(\mathbf{q}_j-\mathbf{q})\,{}_S\langle\mathbf{q}_1,\mathbf{q}_2,\cdots,\mathbf{q}_{j-1},\mathbf{q}_{j+1},\cdots,\mathbf{q}_N| \quad (8\text{–}131)$$

Taking the scalar product on the right of Eq. (8–129) with

$$|\mathbf{q}',\mathbf{q}_1',\mathbf{q}_2',\cdots,\mathbf{q}_{N-1}'\rangle_S$$

we obtain

$$_S\langle\mathbf{q}_1,\mathbf{q}_2,\cdots,\mathbf{q}_{N-1}|B(\mathbf{q},t)|\mathbf{q}',\mathbf{q}_1',\mathbf{q}_2',\cdots,\mathbf{q}_{N-1}'\rangle_S = N!^{1/2}\delta(\mathbf{q}-\mathbf{q}')\prod_{j=1}^{N-1}\delta(\mathbf{q}_j'-\mathbf{q}_i) \quad (8\text{–}132)$$

and similarly from Eq. (8–128):

$$_S\langle\mathbf{q}',\mathbf{q}_1',\mathbf{q}_2',\cdots,\mathbf{q}_{N-1}'|B^*(\mathbf{q},t)|\mathbf{q}_1,\mathbf{q}_2,\cdots,\mathbf{q}_{N-1}\rangle_S = N!^{1/2}\delta(\mathbf{q}-\mathbf{q}')\prod_{j=1}^{N-1}\delta(\mathbf{q}_j'-\mathbf{q}_j) \quad (8\text{–}133)$$

These expressions can be thought of as matrix expressions for the operators $B(\mathbf{q},t)$ and $B^*(\mathbf{q},t)$ respectively. We note that the number of particles represented on the left differs by unity from that on the right. The operators connect vectors having different populations.

8.15. Fock Space.—We have already discussed the Hilbert space $\mathscr{H}_N$ in which we postulate the existence of vectors represented by the states of a system of N particles. Let us now build a hyper-Hilbert space by uniting the Hilbert spaces for every possible population: the union of the Hilbert space $\mathscr{H}_0$ for an empty system, the Hilbert space $\mathscr{H}_1$ for a system with one particle, etc., without upper limit. This union is called Fock space:

$$\mathscr{H}_{\mathscr{F}} = \mathscr{H}_0 \oplus \mathscr{H}_1 \oplus \mathscr{H}_2 \oplus \cdots \oplus \mathscr{H}_N \oplus \cdots \quad (8\text{–}134)$$

The general vector in Fock space may have components in some or all of the Hilbert subspaces, which means that it is now possible to consider states in which there is a superposition of different populations. Thus, we may represent the Fock space vector at an arbitrary time t by a symbol $|t,\mathscr{F}\rangle$, and expand this state in terms of its components in each subspace:

$$|t,\mathscr{F}\rangle = \sum_N |t,N\rangle \quad (8\text{–}135)$$

where we have written $|t,N\rangle$ in place of the symbol $|t\rangle$ formerly used in order to indicate explicitly the population of the system in the subspace $\mathscr{H}_N$. One can still take the coordinate eigen vectors in the various subspaces, namely $|\mathbf{X}_N,t\rangle$, and note the relation

$$\int |\mathbf{X}_N\rangle d\mathbf{X}_N\langle\mathbf{X}_N| = I_N \quad (8\text{–}136)$$

I_N being the identity operator in the subspace $\mathscr{H}_N$. Then we have the expansion

$$|t,\mathscr{F}\rangle = \sum_N \int |\mathbf{X}_N\rangle d\mathbf{X}_N \langle \mathbf{X}_N|t,N\rangle \tag{8–137}$$

Thus $\langle \mathbf{X}_N|t,N\rangle$ is the component of $|t,\mathscr{F}\rangle$ with respect to $|\mathbf{X}_N\rangle$; it is the probability density in Fock space that the system have a population N. We recognize it as nothing other than the Schrödinger wave function for N particles—Section 8.10.

8.16. Fock Space Representation of Operators.—Let F be some operator that neither creates nor destroys particles, and is a known function in configuration space for N particles. In symbols such an operator must by definition have the following matrix elements in Fock space:

$$\langle \mathbf{X}'_M|F|\mathbf{X}_N\rangle = \delta_{MN} F(\mathbf{X}_N) \prod_{j=1}^{N} \delta(\mathbf{q}'_j - \mathbf{q}_j) \tag{8–138}$$

where $F(\mathbf{X}_N)$ is the known function in configuration space. We now take an outer product on the left with $|\mathbf{X}'_N\rangle$, and on the right with $\langle \mathbf{X}_N|$, and integrate with respect to both sets of coordinates; the left side of Eq. (8–138) with $M = N$ then becomes

$$\iint |\mathbf{X}'_N\rangle d\mathbf{X}'_N \langle \mathbf{X}'_N|F|\mathbf{X}_N\rangle d\mathbf{X}_N \langle \mathbf{X}_N| = F \tag{8–139}$$

because the two integrals are each identity operators. Meanwhile the right side of Eq. (8–138), following the same procedure, becomes

$$\begin{aligned} F &= \iint |\mathbf{X}'_N\rangle d\mathbf{X}'_N F(\mathbf{X}_N) \prod_{j=1}^{N} \delta(\mathbf{q}'_j - \mathbf{q}_j) d\mathbf{X}_N \langle \mathbf{X}_N| \\ &= \int |\mathbf{X}_N\rangle F(\mathbf{X}_N) \langle \mathbf{X}_N| d\mathbf{X}_N \end{aligned} \tag{8–140}$$

We may now make use of Eqs. (8–126) and (8–127) to express the vectors $\langle \mathbf{X}_N|$ and $|\mathbf{X}_N\rangle$ in terms of the density operators thus:

$$\begin{aligned} F = \int \cdots \int (1/N!) |B^*(\mathbf{q}_N,t) \cdots B^*(\mathbf{q}_1,t)|0\rangle F(\mathbf{X}_N) \\ \times \langle 0|B(\mathbf{q}_1,t) \cdots B(\mathbf{q}_N,t)| d\mathbf{X}_N \end{aligned} \tag{8–141}$$

From this we can find the occupation number matrix representation of the operator F; *viz.*, $\langle \{n'\}|F|\{n\}\rangle$ where $\sum_\lambda n'_\lambda = \sum_\lambda n_\lambda = N$, and

$\{n'\}$, $\{n\}$ are two different sets of occupation numbers, each corresponding to the same total population. Thus, we have from Eq. (8–141):

$$\langle\{n'\}|F|\{n\}\rangle = (1/N!) \int \cdots \int \langle\{n'\}|B^*(\mathbf{q}_N,t)\cdots B^*(\mathbf{q}_1,t)|0\rangle \times \langle 0|B(\mathbf{q}_1,t)\cdots B(\mathbf{q}_N,t)|\{n\}\rangle F(\mathbf{X}_N)d\mathbf{X}_N$$

Now $\langle\{n''\}|B(\mathbf{q}_1,t)\cdots B(\mathbf{q}_N,t)|\{n\}\rangle = 0$ unless $\{n''\} = 0$, so that the operator $|0\rangle\langle 0|$ in the center of the above expression can be replaced by a sum over all sets $|\{n''\}\rangle\langle\{n''\}|$, which then becomes the identity operator. Thus, we have finally

$$\langle\{n'\}|F|\{n\}\rangle = (1/N!) \int \cdots \int \langle\{n'\}|B^*(\mathbf{q}_N,t)\cdots B^*(\mathbf{q}_1,t)B(\mathbf{q}_1,t)\cdots \times B(\mathbf{q}_N,t)\ |\{n\}\rangle F(\mathbf{X}_N)d\mathbf{X}_N \quad (8\text{–}142)$$

Two cases are of interest in statistical problems. First let $F(\mathbf{X}_N)$ be a sum of one-particle functions:

$$F(\mathbf{X}_N) = \sum_{j=1}^{N} f(\mathbf{q}_j) \quad (8\text{–}143)$$

which is the case for an external field in which all the particles have a potential function, the same for each particle. In this case

$$\langle\{n'\}|F|\{n\}\rangle$$

becomes

$$(1/N!) \sum_j \int\int \langle\{n'\}|B^*(\mathbf{q}_N,t)\cdots B^*(\mathbf{q}_1,t)B(\mathbf{q}_1,t)\cdots B(\mathbf{q}_N,t)|\{n\}\rangle f(\mathbf{q}_j)d\mathbf{X}_N \quad (8\text{–}144)$$

Here the operators $B(\mathbf{q}_n,t)$ can be rearranged so that $B(\mathbf{q}_j,t)$ appears at the extreme right, and the operators $B^*(\mathbf{q}_n,t)$ can be rearranged so that $B^*(\mathbf{q}_j,t)$ appears on the extreme left. Then we can integrate over $d\mathbf{q}_1$, and the product $B^*(\mathbf{q}_1,t)B(\mathbf{q}_1,t)$ becomes the population operator, Eq. (8–121), while the state it operates on has the total population unity—it is the state $B(\mathbf{q}_2,t)\cdots B(\mathbf{q}_N,t)B(\mathbf{q}_j,t)|\{n\}\rangle$. The result is just one times this same state. Next we can integrate over $d\mathbf{q}_2$, and the product $B^*(\mathbf{q}_2,t)B(\mathbf{q}_2,t)$ now remaining at the center again integrates to the population operator, but this now operates on the state $B(\mathbf{q}_3,t)\cdots B(\mathbf{q}_N,t)B(\mathbf{q}_j,t)|\{n\}\rangle$, which has the population 2; the result is, therefore, this state multiplied by 2. Continuing in this way we finally get

$$\langle\{n'\}|F|\{n\}\rangle = \sum_j [(N-1)!/N!]\langle\{n'\}| \int B^*(\mathbf{q}_j,t)B(\mathbf{q}_j,t)f(\mathbf{q}_j)d\mathbf{q}_j|\{n\}\rangle \quad (8\text{–}145)$$

which is clearly the same as

$$\langle\{n'\}|F|\{n\}\rangle = \langle\{n'\}| \int B^*(\mathbf{q},t)f(\mathbf{q})B(\mathbf{q},t)d\mathbf{q}|\{n\}\rangle \tag{8–146}$$

Multiplying on the left by $|\{n'\}\rangle$ and on the right by $\langle\{n\}|$, then summing over both sets of numbers, we reach the operator expression

$$F = \int B^*(\mathbf{q},t)f(\mathbf{q})B(\mathbf{q},t)d\mathbf{q} \tag{8–147}$$

when

$$F(\mathbf{X}_N) = \sum_{j=1}^{N} f(\mathbf{q}_j)$$

This result should be compared with the statement near the end of Section 8.13.

The second case of interest arises when $F(\mathbf{X}_N)$ represents a pair interaction potential of the form

$$F(\mathbf{X}_N) = \sum_{i<j} V(\mathbf{q}_i,\mathbf{q}_j) = \tfrac{1}{2}\sum_{i,j} V(\mathbf{q}_i,\mathbf{q}_j) \tag{8–148}$$

By a similar argument in which all integrals are carried through except two, we are left with the following operator:

$$F = \tfrac{1}{2}\int\int B^*(\mathbf{q}',t)B^*(\mathbf{q},t)V(\mathbf{q}',\mathbf{q})B(\mathbf{q},t)B(\mathbf{q}',t)d\mathbf{q}d\mathbf{q}' \tag{8–149}$$

Both in Eq. (8–149) and Eq. (8–147), we have written the function in the center of the integrand simply for ease of visual memory; in fact both $f(\mathbf{q})$ and $V(\mathbf{q},\mathbf{q}')$ commute with all the B-operators and their positions are immaterial. The B-operators operate on vectors $|\{n\}\rangle$ in occupation number space, so that we can evaluate the matrix elements of F in occupation number representation, *viz.*, Eq. (8–145), either from Eq. (8–147) or from Eq. (8–149).

Here we have deduced the equivalence of the one-particle operator forms (8–147) and (8–149) with the N-particle forms (8–143) and (8–148). It is worthwhile to invert the argument as follows:

We first write down the coordinate representation of the effect of operating by (8–147) on the general state $|t,N\rangle$:

$$\langle\mathbf{X}_N|F|t,N\rangle = \langle\mathbf{X}_N| \int B^*(\mathbf{q}_j,t)B(\mathbf{q}_j,t)f(\mathbf{q}_j)|t,N\rangle d\mathbf{q}_j$$

Now we use Eq. (8–131) to reduce this to

$$N^{-1/2}\int\sum_{k=1}^{N}\delta(\mathbf{q}_k-\mathbf{q}_j)\langle\mathbf{q}_1,\mathbf{q}_2,\cdots,\mathbf{q}_{k-1},\mathbf{q}_{k+1},\cdots,\mathbf{q}_N| \times B(\mathbf{q}_j,t)f(\mathbf{q}_j)|t,N\rangle d\mathbf{q}_j$$

and again use Eq. (8–129) to reduce this to

$$\int\sum_{k=1}^{N}\delta(\mathbf{q}_k-\mathbf{q}_j)\langle\mathbf{q}_j,\mathbf{q}_1,\cdots,\mathbf{q}_{k-1},\mathbf{q}_{k+1},\cdots,\mathbf{q}_N|f(\mathbf{q}_j)|t,N\rangle d\mathbf{q}_j$$

At this point we can carry out the integration over $d\mathbf{q}_j$ and find

$$\sum_{k=1}^{N}\langle\mathbf{q}_k,\mathbf{q}_1,\cdots,\mathbf{q}_{k-1},\mathbf{q}_{k+1},\cdots,\mathbf{q}_N|f(\mathbf{q}_k)|t,N\rangle$$

Because the state is symmetrical, $\mathbf{q}_k$ can be placed in its normal position and the sum taken through to give

$$\langle\mathbf{X}_N|\sum_{k=1}^{N}f(\mathbf{q}_k)|t,N\rangle$$

which is exactly the Dirac symbol for $F(\mathbf{X}_N)\psi(\mathbf{X}_N,t)$, the Schrödinger wave function form for an operator operating in $3N$ configuration space. Thus we have shown that the Fock space representation and the Schrödinger representation are entirely equivalent for symmetrical states:

$$\langle\mathbf{X}_N|F|t,N\rangle = F(\mathbf{X}_N)\psi(\mathbf{X}_N,t) \tag{8–150}$$

A similar proof can be given for antisymmetrical systems.

The advantage of the Fock representation, Eqs. (8–147) and (8–149), is that we can avoid using a configuration space having an exceedingly large number of variables, and use instead either a single particle coordinate or, with the interaction operator, a single pair of particle coordinates. This becomes particularly apparent if we use the box-normalized wave functions of Eq. (8–88). Equation (8–147) would then be

$$F = \sum_{\mathbf{k},\mathbf{k}'}\sum\int d\mathbf{q}\,f(\mathbf{q})e^{i(\mathbf{k}-\mathbf{k}')\cdot\mathbf{q}}e^{-i(E_{\mathbf{k}}-E_{\mathbf{k}'})t/\hbar}b_{\mathbf{k}}^{*}b_{\mathbf{k}'} \tag{8–151}$$

The integral over $d\mathbf{q}$ now reduces to finding the Fourier transform of the potential function.

8.17. The Schrödinger Equation in Fock Representation.—Schrödinger's equation for the N-particle problem is

$$H\psi(\mathbf{X}_N,t) = i\hbar(\partial/\partial t)\psi(\mathbf{X}_N,t) \tag{8–152}$$

where we shall allow the hamiltonian to be

$$H = \sum_{k=1}^{N} H_o(\mathbf{q}_k) + \sum_{i<j} V(\mathbf{q}_i,\mathbf{q}_j) \tag{8–153}$$

In the Dirac notation Eq. (8–152) is

$$\langle \mathbf{X}_N|H|t,N\rangle = i\hbar(\partial/\partial t)\langle \mathbf{X}_N|t,N\rangle \tag{8–154}$$

The potential function on the left side of this can immediately be translated into the Fock representation by using Eq. (8–147) and (8–149):

$$\langle \mathbf{X}_N|\tfrac{1}{2}\iint d\mathbf{q}d\mathbf{q}'B^*(\mathbf{q}',t)B^*(\mathbf{q},t)V(\mathbf{q}',\mathbf{q})B(\mathbf{q},t)B(\mathbf{q}',t)|t,N\rangle \tag{8–155}$$

The Fock representation of the space derivatives, $(\partial/\partial q_k)^2$ and the time derivatives $(\partial/\partial t)$, involved in H_o, and on the right side of Eq. (8–154), require special attention. We start with Eq. (8–141) with F replaced by the appropriate derivative. For instance we rewrite Eq. (8–142) as:

$$\begin{aligned}\langle\{n'\}|(\partial/\partial t)|\{n\}\rangle = (1/N!)\int &\langle\{n'\}|B^*(\mathbf{q}_N,t)\cdots B^*(\mathbf{q}_1,t)\\ &\times (\partial/\partial t)B(\mathbf{q}_1,t)\cdots B(\mathbf{q}_N,t)|\{n\}\rangle d\mathbf{X}_N\end{aligned} \tag{8–156}$$

where the time derivative does not operate on $|\{n\}\rangle$. The differential operates on each B factor in turn, resulting in a sum of terms like

$$\sum_j [B(\mathbf{q}_1,t)\cdots\partial B(\mathbf{q}_j,t)/\partial t,\cdots,B(\mathbf{q}_N,t)]$$

Thus, the operator acts in the same fashion as that considered in Eq. (8–143), and results in a similar expression as Eqs. (8–145) and (8–146):

$$\langle\{n'\}|(\partial/\partial t)|\{n\}\rangle = \langle\{n'\}|\int B^*(\mathbf{q},t)(\partial/\partial t)B(\mathbf{q},t)d\mathbf{q}|\{n\}\rangle \tag{8–157}$$

This shows the operator relation to be

$$\partial/\partial t \rightarrow \int B^*(\mathbf{q},t)(\partial/\partial t)B(\mathbf{q},t)d\mathbf{q} \tag{8–158}$$

Similar comments apply to the operator $\partial/\partial q_k$. Finally, combining these remarks with Eq. (8–155), the Schrödinger equation in Fock representation may be written:

$$\int B^*(\mathbf{q},t)H_o(\mathbf{q})B(\mathbf{q},t)d\mathbf{q} + \tfrac{1}{2}\iint B^*(\mathbf{q}',t)B^*(\mathbf{q},t)V(\mathbf{q}',\mathbf{q})B(\mathbf{q},t)B(\mathbf{q}',t)d\mathbf{q}d\mathbf{q}' = i\hbar\int B^*(\mathbf{q},t)(\partial/\partial t)B(\mathbf{q},t)d\mathbf{q} \quad (8\text{–}159)$$

This is an operator relation and yields meaningful results so long as it operates on states in occupation number representation. Recalling that $B(\mathbf{q},t)$ has as one factor the Schrödinger wave function of one particle, Eq. (8–159) looks almost like an ordinary one-particle Schrödinger equation with the operator $B(\mathbf{q},t)$ replacing the one-particle wave function. It is customary to call the substitution of such an operator for a wave function, the process of "second quantization," and the process has been used as a formal device to derive operator equations from classical field equations in a general program of field quantization. Whether the process has any physical meaning in general is not really known; but we have seen here at least that Eq. (8–159) is derived directly from the accepted N-particle Schrödinger theory, and does not depend on, but rather justifies, the second quantization formalism in this case.

In practical applications one uses the definitions, Eq. (8–118), of the population density operators to write Eq. (8–159) in the form:

$$\sum_{\lambda,\mu} H_{o\lambda\mu}b_\lambda^* b_\mu + \sum_{\lambda'\lambda}\sum_{\mu'\mu} V_{\lambda'\lambda\mu'\mu}b_{\lambda'}^* b_\lambda^* b_{\mu'} b_\mu = \sum_\mu E_\mu b_\mu^* b_\mu \quad (8\text{–}160)$$

where $H_{o\lambda\mu}$ is the Heisenberg matrix of the operator H_o:

$$H_{o\lambda\mu} \equiv \int \langle\lambda,t|\mathbf{q}\rangle H_o\langle\mathbf{q}|\mu,t\rangle d\mathbf{q} \quad (8\text{–}161)$$

and $V_{\lambda'\lambda\mu'\mu}$ is a generalized form of Heisenberg matrix:

$$V_{\lambda'\lambda\mu'\mu} = \iint \langle\lambda',t|\mathbf{q}'\rangle\langle\lambda,t|\mathbf{q}\rangle V(\mathbf{q}',\mathbf{q})\langle\mathbf{q}|\mu,t\rangle\langle\mathbf{q}'|\mu',t\rangle d\mathbf{q}d\mathbf{q}' \quad (8\text{–}162)$$

while the right side of (8–160) arises from the familiar relation

$$i\hbar(\partial/\partial t)\langle\mathbf{q}|\lambda,t\rangle = E_\lambda\langle\mathbf{q}|\lambda,t\rangle$$

8.18. The von Neumann Projection Operators.—Consider the eigenstates $|\{n\}\rangle$ in the Hilbert space $\mathscr{H}_N$ of N particles with the properties:

$$\langle\{n'\}|\{n\}\rangle = \delta(\{n'\},\{n\}); \qquad \sum_{\{n\}} |\{n\}\rangle\langle\{n\}| = I \tag{8–163}$$

(for simplicity we are again omitting explicit indication that the vectors $|\{n\}\rangle$ are time-dependent). The von Neumann projection operator in occupation number representation is defined as

$$P\{n\} \equiv |\{n\}\rangle\langle\{n\}| \quad \text{(not summed)} \tag{8–164}$$

To rationalize the name "projection operator," we take a general vector $|t\rangle$ in $\mathscr{H}_N$ and operate on it with $P\{n\}$:

$$P\{n\}|t\rangle = |\{n\}\rangle\langle\{n\}|t\rangle \tag{8–165}$$

and the result on the right is a vector in the direction $|\{n\}\rangle$ with a length given by the component $\langle\{n\}|t\rangle$ of $|t\rangle$ in the direction $|\{n\}\rangle$.

The matrix of the projection operator in occupation number representation has a typical element

$$\begin{aligned}\langle\{n''\}|P\{n\}|n'\}\rangle &= \langle\{n''\}|\{n\}\rangle\langle\{n\}|\{n'\}\rangle \\ &= \delta(\{n''\},\{n\})\delta(\{n'\},\{n\})\end{aligned} \tag{8–166}$$

This has zero value unless both sets $\{n''\}$ and $\{n'\}$ are identical with the set $\{n\}$; so the matrix is a diagonal one with only one nonzero element, and its trace is obviously unity. Such a matrix is called an elementary matrix, see Chapter 7, Eq. (7–92).

We shall now express the projection operator as a matrix in coordinate representation, the typical element being

$$\langle\mathbf{X}''_N|P\{n\}|\mathbf{X}'_N\rangle = \langle\mathbf{X}''_N|\{n\}\rangle\langle\{n\}|\mathbf{X}'_N\rangle \tag{8–167}$$

Now we may use Eqs. (8–127) and (8–126) to express the vectors $\langle\mathbf{X}''_N|$ and $|\mathbf{X}'_N\rangle$ in terms of operators in occupation number representation:

$$\begin{aligned}\langle\mathbf{X}''_N|P\{n\}|\mathbf{X}'_N\rangle = (1/N!)\langle 0|B(\mathbf{q}''_1,t)\cdots B(\mathbf{q}''_N,t)|\{n\}\rangle \\ \times \langle\{n\}|B^*(\mathbf{q}'_1,t)\cdots B^*(\mathbf{q}'_N,t)|0\rangle\end{aligned}$$

The two factors here are just complex numbers, and their order can be inverted so that the expression now reads

$$(1/N!)\langle\{n\}|B^*(\mathbf{q}'_1,t)\cdots B^*(\mathbf{q}'_N,t)|0\rangle\langle 0|B(\mathbf{q}''_1,t)\cdots B(\mathbf{q}''_N,t)|\{n\}\rangle$$

By the same argument used in deriving Eq. (8–142) from a previous equation we can here replace the central expression $|0\rangle\langle 0|$ by $|\{n'\}\rangle\langle\{n'\}|$

and sum over all sets $\{n'\}$, the result being the identity operator. Thus

$$\langle \mathbf{X}''_N | P\{n\} | \mathbf{X}'_N \rangle = (1/N!) \langle \{n\} | B^*(\mathbf{q}'_1,t) \cdots B^*(\mathbf{q}'_N,t) B(\mathbf{q}''_1,t) \cdots B(\mathbf{q}''_N,t) | \{n\} \rangle \tag{8–168}$$

The diagonal elements of this matrix are found by setting $\mathbf{X}''_N = \mathbf{X}'_N$, and of course $\mathbf{q}''_j = \mathbf{q}'_j$, when the operators $B^*(\mathbf{q},t)B(\mathbf{q},t)$ become number density operators. Comparing the expression on the right of Eq. (8–168) with Eq. (8–142), setting $F = I$ and $F(X) = 1$, we see that the trace of this matrix is

$$\mathrm{Tr}\,\{P\{n\}\} \equiv \int \langle \mathbf{X}_N | P\{n\} | \mathbf{X}_N \rangle d\mathbf{X}_N = \langle \{n\} | I | \{n\} \rangle = 1 \tag{8–169}$$

The trace of the projection operator is again unity. It is, of course, invariant generally, regardless of the representation.

Let R be any linear operator in $\mathscr{H}_N$, and consider the product of the operators $P\{n\}$ and R operating on the vector $|t\rangle$ in $\mathscr{H}_N$. Thus

$$\begin{aligned} P\{n\}R|t\rangle &= |\{n\}\rangle\langle\{n\}|R|t\rangle \\ &= \sum_{\{m\}} |\{n\}\rangle\langle\{n\}|R|\{m\}\rangle\langle\{m\}|t\rangle \end{aligned} \tag{8–170}$$

In occupation number representation the matrix of $P\{n\}R$ has the typical element

$$\begin{aligned} \langle\{n''\}|P\{n\}R|\{n'\}\rangle &= \langle\{n''\}|\{n\}\rangle\langle\{n\}|R|\{n'\}\rangle \\ &= \delta(\{n''\},\{n\})\langle\{n\}|R|\{n'\}\rangle \end{aligned} \tag{8–171}$$

and the trace of this matrix is

$$\mathrm{Tr}\,\{P\{n\}R\} = \sum_{\{m\}} \delta(\{m\},\{n\})\langle\{n\}|R|\{m\}\rangle = \langle\{n\}|R|\{n\}\rangle \tag{8–172}$$

which is, by definition, the expectation value of R in the state $|\{n\}\rangle$ that defines the projection operator.

Suppose that R is an operator defined in configuration space so that its matrix is diagonal and of the form

$$\langle \mathbf{X}''|R|\mathbf{X}'\rangle = R(\mathbf{X}')\langle\mathbf{X}''|\mathbf{X}'\rangle = R(\mathbf{X}')\delta(\mathbf{X}'' - \mathbf{X}') \tag{8–173}$$

Now Eq. (8–172) can in fact be written as

$$\begin{aligned} \mathrm{Tr}\,\{P\{n\}R\} &= \int\int d\mathbf{X}''d\mathbf{X}'\langle\{n\}|\mathbf{X}''\rangle\langle\mathbf{X}''|R|\mathbf{X}'\rangle\langle\mathbf{X}'|\{n\}\rangle \\ &= \int\int d\mathbf{X}''d\mathbf{X}'\langle\{n\}|\mathbf{X}''\rangle\delta(\mathbf{X}'' - \mathbf{X}')\langle\mathbf{X}'|\{n\}\rangle R(\mathbf{X}') \\ &= \int d\mathbf{X}'\langle\{n\}|\mathbf{X}'\rangle R(\mathbf{X}')\langle\mathbf{X}'|\{n\}\rangle \end{aligned} \tag{8–174}$$

In Schrödinger notation, this reads

$$\text{Tr}\,\{P\{n\}R\} = \int \overline{\psi(\mathbf{X}')}R(\mathbf{X}')\psi(\mathbf{X}')d\mathbf{X}'$$

and this is obviously the expectation value of R in the state $\psi(\mathbf{X}')$ or $\langle \mathbf{X}'|\{n\}\rangle$.

Alternatively, consider the matrix of $P\{n\}R$ directly in coordinate representation:

$$\langle \mathbf{X}''|P\{n\}R|\mathbf{X}'\rangle = \sum_{\{m\}} \langle \mathbf{X}''|\{n\}\rangle\langle\{n\}|R|\{m\}\rangle\langle\{m\}|\mathbf{X}'\rangle$$

The trace of this matrix is found by setting $\mathbf{X}'' = \mathbf{X}'$ and integrating over $3N$ space. Changing the order of the first and last factor in the last equation we have

$$\text{Tr}\,\{P\{n\}R\} = \sum_{\{m\}} \int \langle\{m\}|\mathbf{X}\rangle d\mathbf{X}\langle \mathbf{X}|\{n\}\rangle\langle\{n\}|R|\{m\}\rangle$$

and from Eq. (8–73)

$$= \sum_{\{m\}} \langle\{m\}|\{n\}\rangle\langle\{n\}|R|\{m\}\rangle$$

Interchanging the order of these factors we find finally that

$$\text{Tr}\,\{P\{n\}R\} = \langle\{n\}|R|\{n\}\rangle \tag{8–175}$$

which again is the expectation value of R in the state $|\{n\}\rangle$.

Consider next the projection operator upon the coordinate space eigenvector $|\mathbf{X}\rangle$:

$$P(\mathbf{X}) = |\mathbf{X}\rangle\langle\mathbf{X}| \tag{8–176}$$

which has the following effect on the general vector $|t\rangle$ in $\mathscr{H}_N$:

$$P(\mathbf{X})|t\rangle = |\mathbf{X}\rangle\langle\mathbf{X}|t\rangle \tag{8–177}$$

This is a vector having magnitude equal to the Schrödinger N-particle wave function at the coordinates $\mathbf{X}$.

The coordinate representation matrix of this operator has the typical element:

$$\langle \mathbf{X}''|P(\mathbf{X})|\mathbf{X}'\rangle = \langle \mathbf{X}''|\mathbf{X}\rangle\langle\mathbf{X}|\mathbf{X}'\rangle = \delta(\mathbf{X}'' - \mathbf{X})\delta(\mathbf{X}' - \mathbf{X}) \tag{8–178}$$

Being a product of delta functions, it is an improper expression, and the trace is undefined. However, it is useful to consider the operator product $P(\mathbf{X})R$ where R is any linear operator defined in configuration space. The typical element of the matrix product is

$$\langle \mathbf{X}''|P(\mathbf{X})R|\mathbf{X}'\rangle = \delta(\mathbf{X}'' - \mathbf{X})\langle\mathbf{X}|R|\mathbf{X}'\rangle \tag{8–179}$$

The trace of this is

$$\text{Tr}\,\{P(\mathbf{X})R\} = \int d\mathbf{X}'\delta(\mathbf{X}' - \mathbf{X})\langle\mathbf{X}|R|\mathbf{X}'\rangle = \langle\mathbf{X}|R|\mathbf{X}\rangle \tag{8–180}$$

This is the expectation value of R at the position $\mathbf{X}$.

More generally, let us consider the projection onto an arbitrary state $|\emptyset\rangle$ which is a linear combination of the eigenstates $|\{n\}\rangle$:

$$|\emptyset\rangle = \sum_{\{n\}} a\{n\}|\{n\}\rangle$$

The projection operator can be written as

$$P(\emptyset) = |\emptyset\rangle\langle\emptyset| = \sum_{\{n\}}\sum_{\{n'\}} a\{n\}a^*\{n'\}|\{n\}\rangle\langle\{n'\}| \tag{8–181}$$

The matrix of this operator on the occupation number representation has the typical element

$$\begin{aligned}\langle\{m\}|P(\emptyset)|\{m'\}\rangle &= \sum_{\{n\}}\sum_{\{n'\}} a\{n\}a^*\{n'\}\langle\{m\}|\{n\}\rangle\langle\{n'\}|\{m'\}\rangle \\ &= a\{m\}a^*\{m'\}\end{aligned} \tag{8–182}$$

This is the statistical matrix, see Chapter 7.

Consider the product of $P(\emptyset)$ and an observable R. The matrix has the typical element

$$\begin{aligned}\langle\{m\}|P(\emptyset)R|\{m'\}\rangle &= \sum_{\{n\}}\sum_{\{n'\}} a\{n\}a^*\{n'\}\langle\{m\}|\{n\}\rangle\langle\{n'\}|R|\{m'\}\rangle \\ &= a\{m\}\sum_{\{n'\}} a^*\{n'\}\langle\{n'\}|R|\{m'\}\rangle\end{aligned}$$

and the trace of this matrix is

$$\text{Tr}\,\{P(\emptyset)R\} = \sum_{\{m\}}\sum_{\{n\}} a\{m\}a^*\{n\}\langle\{n\}|R|\{m\}\rangle \tag{8–183}$$

$$= \langle\emptyset|R|\emptyset\rangle \tag{8–184}$$

The expression in Eq. (8–183) is the one used in practical calculations, the form shown in Eq. (8–184) demonstrates that the result is the expectation value of the observable R in the state $|\emptyset\rangle$.

As a particularly simple example of this formalism, let us consider the spin states of a single electron with respect to the z-direction. In occupation number representation these states may be written as column vectors thus: $|\{n\}\rangle = \begin{pmatrix}1\\0\end{pmatrix}$ or $\begin{pmatrix}0\\1\end{pmatrix}$, and the conjugate forms are $\langle\{n\}| = (1\ 0)$ or $(0\ 1)$. Then let the general spin state be

$$|\emptyset\rangle = a\begin{pmatrix}1\\0\end{pmatrix} + b\begin{pmatrix}0\\1\end{pmatrix}$$

We can consider various projection operators, for example

$$P\begin{pmatrix}1\\0\end{pmatrix} \equiv \begin{pmatrix}1\\0\end{pmatrix}(1\quad 0) = \begin{pmatrix}1 & 0\\0 & 0\end{pmatrix};$$

$$P\begin{pmatrix}0\\1\end{pmatrix} \equiv \begin{pmatrix}0\\1\end{pmatrix}(0\quad 1) = \begin{pmatrix}0 & 0\\0 & 1\end{pmatrix}$$

More generally

$$P(\emptyset) \equiv \left[a\begin{pmatrix}1\\0\end{pmatrix} + b\begin{pmatrix}0\\1\end{pmatrix}\right][a^*(1\ 0) + b^*(0\ 1)] = \begin{pmatrix}aa^* & ab^*\\ba^* & bb^*\end{pmatrix}$$

We may now ask for the expectation value in the state $|\emptyset\rangle$ of spin in the x-direction, represented by the Pauli matrix $\sigma_x = \begin{pmatrix}0 & 1\\1 & 0\end{pmatrix}$? Taking the matrix product of $P(\emptyset)$ and σ_x we have

$$\mathrm{Tr}\begin{pmatrix}aa^* & ab^*\\ba^* & bb^*\end{pmatrix}\begin{pmatrix}0 & 1\\1 & 0\end{pmatrix} = ab^* + ba^*$$

The expectation value for σ_y is found similarly to be $i(ab^* - ba^*)$, while that for σ_z is $aa^* - bb^*$.

8.19. Ensembles and the Density Matrix.—So far we have considered only a single system of N particles, whose quantum states are represented either in terms of coordinates $\mathbf{X}$ or occupation numbers $\{n\}$. In statistics we deal rather with large numbers of such systems, and are generally unwilling, or even unable, to determine the quantum state of each system. All the information one generally has about any one system is the so-called macroscopic, or thermodynamic, state, characterized by specified values of one or more of the gross variables such as pressure, temperature, density, etc. Let us collect a large number of similar systems, all in the same thermodynamic state, and imagine that we can then determine the quantum state of each system. We should find a distribution among the quantum states, in the sense that for every set $\{n\}$ a certain fraction $w\{n\}$ of the systems are found in the quantum state $|\{n\}\rangle$. It is not assumed that this distribution is uniquely determined by the thermodynamic state of the system, but that there exists a most probable distribution corresponding to the given thermodynamic state. A collection with this most probable distribution is called an equilibrium ensemble; and it is assumed that its distribution determines the thermodynamic state of its members. It is also implied here that $w\{n\}$ is not a function of time.

There is thus assumed to be a one-to-one correspondence between the most probable distribution and the thermodynamic state. The equilibrium ensemble corresponding to any given thermodynamic state is then used to compute averages over the ensemble of other (not necessarily thermodynamic) properties of the systems represented in the ensemble. The first step in developing this theory is thus a suitable definition of the probability of a distribution in a collection of systems. In classical statistics we are familiar with the fact that the logarithm of the probability of a distribution $w\{n\}$ is $-\sum_{\{n\}} w\{n\} \ln w\{n\}$, and that the classical expression for entropy in the ensemble is[20]

$$S_{class} = -k \sum_{\{n\}} w\{n\} \ln w\{n\} \tag{8–185}$$

Consider the following operator, defined in any ensemble, and called the density operator:

$$W_N \equiv \sum_{\{n\}} w\{n\}P\{n\} = \sum_{\{n\}} w\{n\}|\{n\}\rangle\langle\{n\}| \tag{8–186}$$

Here the projection operator $P\{n\}$ is multiplied by the distribution probability $w\{n\}$, and the result summed over all states $|\{n\}\rangle$. A typical element of the matrix of this operator in occupation number representation, called the *density matrix*, is

$$\begin{aligned}\langle\{n''\}|W_N|\{n'\}\rangle &= \sum_{\{n\}} \langle\{n''\}|w\{n\}|\{n\}\rangle\langle\{n\}|\{n'\}\rangle \\ &= \sum_{\{n\}} w\{n\}\langle\{n''\}|\{n\}\rangle\langle\{n\}|\{n'\}\rangle \\ &= \sum_{\{n\}} w\{n\}\delta(\{n''\},\{n\})\delta(\{n\},\{n'\}) \\ &= w\{n'\}\delta(\{n'\},\{n''\}) \end{aligned} \tag{8–187}$$

This is evidently a diagonal matrix, and its diagonal elements are just $w\{n\}$ at the $\{n\} - \{n\}$ element. In other words W_N is an operator whose

[20] See, for example, Terrell L. Hill, *Statistical Mechanics*, Eq. (14.15), McGraw-Hill Book Co., New York, 1956.

eigenvalues are the distribution probabilities $w\{n\}$. The trace of the matrix of W_N is

$$\mathrm{Tr}\,\{W_N\} = \sum_{\{n\}} w\{n\} = 1 \tag{8–188}$$

provided we have normalized the probabilities to unity.

Let R be any linear operator in occupation number space, and consider the product $W_N R$. A typical matrix element of this operator is

$$\langle\{n''\}|W_N R|\{n'\}\rangle = \sum_{\{n\}} \langle\{n''\}w\{n\}|\{n\}\rangle\langle\{n\}|R|\{n'\}\rangle$$

and the trace of this is

$$\begin{aligned}\mathrm{Tr}\,\{W_N R\} &= \sum_{\{n'\}}\sum_{\{n\}} w\{n\}\langle\{n\}|R|\{n'\}\rangle\langle\{n'\}|\{n\}\rangle \\ &= \sum_{\{n\}} w\{n\}\langle\{n\}|R|\{n\}\rangle \equiv \langle\!\langle R\rangle\!\rangle_N \end{aligned}\tag{8–189}$$

Note that $\langle\{n\}|R|\{n\}\rangle$ is the expectation value of R in the state $|\{n\}\rangle$ and that $w\{n\}$ is the probability of this state in the ensemble. Therefore the expression $\langle\!\langle R\rangle\!\rangle_N$ is exactly the ensemble average of the observable R. That the trace of the matrix product of the density matrix and the observable is the ensemble average of the observable, is a basic theorem of quantum statistics.

It is worthwhile to consider the same theorem in terms of coordinate space instead of occupation number space. Thus, we may envision an ensemble of systems whose states are $|\mathbf{X}\rangle$, and whose distribution probabilities among these states are $w(\mathbf{X})$. We define the density operator

$$W_X \equiv \int d\mathbf{X} w(\mathbf{X})P(\mathbf{X}) \tag{8–190}$$

(see Eq. (8–176)). A typical element in the matrix of W_X is now

$$\begin{aligned}\langle\mathbf{X}''|W_X|\mathbf{X}'\rangle &= \int d\mathbf{X}\langle\mathbf{X}''|w(\mathbf{X})|\mathbf{X}\rangle\langle\mathbf{X}|\mathbf{X}'\rangle \\ &= \langle\mathbf{X}''|w(\mathbf{X}')|\mathbf{X}'\rangle = w(\mathbf{X}')\delta(\mathbf{X}'' - \mathbf{X}')\end{aligned}\tag{8–191}$$

which is a diagonal matrix again, with eigenvalues $w(\mathbf{X}')$. To be sure, the trace of this is not a proper expression; however, let R be any linear operator defined in configuration space, and consider the matrix of $W_X R$:

$$\langle\mathbf{X}''|W_X R|\mathbf{X}'\rangle = \int d\mathbf{X}\langle\mathbf{X}''|w(\mathbf{X})|\mathbf{X}\rangle\langle\mathbf{X}|R|\mathbf{X}'\rangle \tag{8–192}$$

The trace of this is

$$\begin{aligned}\mathrm{Tr}\,\{W_X R\} &= \int\!\!\int d\mathbf{X}'d\mathbf{X}\langle\mathbf{X}|R|\mathbf{X}'\rangle\langle\mathbf{X}'|\mathbf{X}\rangle w(\mathbf{X}) \\ &= \int d\mathbf{X}\langle\mathbf{X}|R|\mathbf{X}\rangle w(\mathbf{X}) = \langle\!\langle R\rangle\!\rangle_X \qquad (8\text{–}193)\end{aligned}$$

which again is the ensemble average of the observable R.

More generally, let the states of the ensemble be superposition states, or linear combinations of the eigenstates $|\{n\}\rangle$:

$$|\emptyset_s\rangle = \sum_{\{n\}} a_s\{n\}|\{n\}\rangle$$

and let w_s be the probability of the state $|\emptyset_s\rangle$ in the ensemble. The density operator for such an ensemble is

$$\begin{aligned}W_\emptyset &= \sum_s w_s P(\emptyset_s) = \sum_s w_s|\emptyset_s\rangle\langle\emptyset_s| \\ &= \sum_s \sum_{\{n\}} \sum_{\{n'\}} w_s a_s\{n\}a_s^*\{n'\}|\{n\}\rangle\langle\{n'\}| \qquad (8\text{–}194)\end{aligned}$$

A typical element of the matrix of this operator, the density matrix, is

$$\begin{aligned}\langle\{m\}|W_\emptyset|\{m'\}\rangle &= \sum_s \sum_{\{n\}} \sum_{\{n'\}} w_s a_s\{n\}a_s^*\{n'\}\langle\{m\}|\{n\}\rangle\langle\{n'\}|\{m'\}\rangle \\ &= \sum_s w_s a_s\{m\}a_s^*\{m'\} \qquad (8\text{–}195)\end{aligned}$$

This is a linear combination of statistical matrices, one for each of the states in the ensembles (compare Eq. (8–182)).

Consider the product of $W_\emptyset$ and an arbitrary linear operator R. The typical matrix element is

$$\begin{aligned}\langle\{m\}|W_\emptyset R|\{m'\}\rangle &= \sum_s \sum_{\{n\}} \sum_{\{n'\}} w_s a_s\{n\}a_s^*\{n'\}\langle\{m\}|\{n\}\rangle\langle\{n'\}|R|\{m'\}\rangle \\ &= \sum_s w_s a_s\{m\} \sum_{\{n'\}} a_s^*\{n'\}\langle\{n'\}|R|\{m'\}\rangle\end{aligned}$$

The trace of this matrix is then

$$\begin{aligned}\mathrm{Tr}\,\{W_\emptyset R\} &= \sum_s \sum_{\{n\}} \sum_{\{m\}} w_s a_s\{m\}a_s^*\{n\}\langle\{n\}|R|\{m\}\rangle \qquad (8\text{–}196) \\ &= \sum_s w_s\langle\emptyset_s|R|\emptyset_s\rangle = \langle\!\langle R\rangle\!\rangle_\emptyset \qquad (8\text{–}197)\end{aligned}$$

Here the form (8–196) is the one used in practice, while Eq. (8–197) shows that this is again the ensemble average of the observable R.

Let us develop further the simple example of a one-electron system discussed briefly at the end of Section 8.18. We may set up an ensemble of electrons to represent experimental data to the effect that the probability of the spin state $\begin{pmatrix}1\\0\end{pmatrix}$ is w_1, and that the spin state $\begin{pmatrix}0\\1\end{pmatrix}$ has probability w_2. The density matrix for such an ensemble is

$$W = w_1 \begin{pmatrix}1\\0\end{pmatrix} (1\ 0) + w_2 \begin{pmatrix}0\\1\end{pmatrix} (0\ 1) = \begin{pmatrix}w_1 & 0\\0 & w_2\end{pmatrix}$$

This is an example of Eq. (8–197). The ensemble average of positive spin represented by the operator σ_z, or the Pauli spin matrix $\begin{pmatrix}1 & 0\\0 & -1\end{pmatrix}$ is quite trivially

$$\langle\langle\sigma_z\rangle\rangle = \mathrm{Tr}\begin{pmatrix}w_1 & 0\\0 & -w_2\end{pmatrix}\begin{pmatrix}1 & 0\\0 & -1\end{pmatrix} = w_1 - w_2$$

The ensemble average of σ_x, or $\begin{pmatrix}0\ 1\\1\ 0\end{pmatrix}$ is similarly

$$\mathrm{Tr}\begin{pmatrix}w_1 & 0\\0 & w_2\end{pmatrix}\begin{pmatrix}0 & 1\\1 & 0\end{pmatrix} = 0$$

These are simple examples of Eq. (8–189).

Now consider two orthogonal superposition states

$$|\emptyset_1\rangle = a\begin{pmatrix}1\\0\end{pmatrix} + b\begin{pmatrix}0\\1\end{pmatrix} = \begin{pmatrix}a\\b\end{pmatrix}$$

and

$$|\emptyset_2\rangle = b^*\begin{pmatrix}1\\0\end{pmatrix} - a^*\begin{pmatrix}0\\1\end{pmatrix} = \begin{pmatrix}b^*\\-a^*\end{pmatrix}$$

and set up an ensemble with probability w_1 for $|\emptyset_1\rangle$, w_2 for $|\emptyset_2\rangle$. The density matrix for such an ensemble is

$$w_1|\emptyset_1\rangle\langle\emptyset_1| + w_2|\emptyset_2\rangle\langle\emptyset_2| = \begin{pmatrix}w_1aa^* + w_2bb^* & (w_1 - w_2)ab^*\\(w_1 - w_2)ba^* & w_1bb^* + w_2aa^*\end{pmatrix}$$

and ensemble average of the vector $(\sigma_x,\sigma_y,\sigma_z)$ or $\langle\langle\boldsymbol{\sigma}\rangle\rangle$ is

$$\langle\langle\boldsymbol{\sigma}\rangle\rangle = (w_1 - w_2)[ab^* + ba^*, i(ab^* - ba^*), aa^* - bb^*]$$

A more practical problem[21] is to determine the density matrix

[21] For a good discussion of spin problems, see Eugen Merzbacher, *Quantum Mechanics*, Chapter 13, John Wiley and Sons, Inc., New York, 1961.

representing a system when the ensemble average $\langle\langle \boldsymbol{\sigma} \rangle\rangle$ is known by laboratory measurement of the polarization vector. Thus, let $\langle\langle \boldsymbol{\sigma} \rangle\rangle$ be the vector (s_1,s_2,s_3), and let us seek the matrix W such that

$$\text{Tr}\,\{W\boldsymbol{\sigma}\} = \langle\langle \boldsymbol{\sigma} \rangle\rangle = (s_1,s_2,s_3) \tag{8–198}$$

Now W is necessarily expressible in the form

$$W = aI + a_1\sigma_x + a_2\sigma_y + a_3\sigma_z$$

The normalization of the density matrix, Eq. (8–188), and the fact that $\text{Tr}\, W = 2a$ yields $a = \frac{1}{2}$. Also $\text{Tr}\,\{W\sigma_x\} = 2a_1$, $\text{Tr}\,\{W\sigma_y\} = 2a_2$, $\text{Tr}\,\{W\sigma_z\} = 2a_3$, or the vector $\text{Tr}\,\{W\sigma\} = 2(a_1,a_2,a_3)$. This at once determines $a_1 = \frac{1}{2}s_1$, etc., and finally gives

$$W = \frac{1}{2}\begin{pmatrix} 1 + s_3 & s_1 - is_2 \\ s_1 + is_2 & 1 - s_3 \end{pmatrix} \tag{8–199}$$

8.20. Entropy and Equilibrium Ensembles.—If one can form an algebraic function of a linear operator L by means of a series of powers of L, then the eigenvalues of the operator so formed are the same algebraic function of the eigenvalues of L. Thus let us consider the operator W_N, *i.e.*, the statistical matrix, whose eigenvalues are $w\{n\}$:

$$W_N|\{n\}\rangle = w\{n\}|\{n\}\rangle$$

Taking the logarithm of this operator—which is an algebraic function of the kind just mentioned—we have the corresponding eigenvalue relation:

$$\ln W_N|\{n\}\rangle = \ln w\{n\}|\{n\}\rangle \tag{8–200}$$

Now introduce the operator $\ln W_N$ in place of R in the theorem of Eq. (8–189):

$$\begin{aligned} \langle\langle \ln W_N \rangle\rangle = \text{Tr}\,\{W_N \ln W_N\} &= \sum_{\{n\}} \langle\{n\}|\, W_N \ln W_N |\{n\}\rangle \\ &= \sum_{\{n\}} w\{n\} \ln w\{n\} \end{aligned} \tag{8–201}$$

Comparing this with Eq. (8–185), we see that we may define the entropy operator in quantum statistics as follows:

$$S \equiv -k \ln W_N \tag{8–202}$$

With this definition, the classical entropy per system equals the ensemble average of the expectation value of S in occupation number representation.

The probability of an ensemble distribution in classical statistics is maximized under the condition of given total energy in the ensemble, to yield the familiar Boltzmann distribution:

$$w\{n\} = \frac{\exp\left(-E\{n\}/kT\right)}{\sum_{\{m\}} \exp\left(-E\{m\}/kT\right)} \tag{8–203}$$

where $E\{n\}$ is the energy of a system in the state $|\{n\}\rangle$, and T is the absolute temperature—which is the thermodynamic variable that defines the equilibrium ensemble. The corresponding operator expression for W_N can be written down from Eqs. (8–186) and (8–203) thus:

$$\begin{aligned} W_N &= \frac{\sum_{\{n\}} \exp\left(-E\{n\}/kT\right)|\{n\}\rangle\langle\{n\}|}{\sum_{\{m\}} \exp\left(-E\{m\}/kT\right)} = \frac{\sum_{\{n\}} \exp\left(-E\{n\}/kT\right)|\{n\}\rangle\langle\{n\}|}{\mathrm{Tr}\,\{\exp\left(-H/kT\right)\}} \\ &= \frac{\exp\left(-H/kT\right) \sum_{\{n\}} |\{n\}\rangle\langle\{n\}|}{\mathrm{Tr}\,\exp\left(-H/kT\right)} = \frac{\exp\left(-H/kT\right)}{\mathrm{Tr}\,\exp\left(-H/kT\right)} \end{aligned} \tag{8–204}$$

where H is the hamiltonian operator: $H|\{n\}\rangle = E\{n\}|\{n\}\rangle$.

The corresponding operator expression for the equilibrium entropy in occupation number representation is then also seen to be

$$S = -k \ln W_N = H/T + k \ln \mathrm{Tr}\,\{\exp\left(-H/kT\right)\}I_N \tag{8–205}$$

where I_N is the identity operator in that representation, and H is the Schrödinger operator.

The equilibrium ensemble average of any observable represented by an operator R is given by Eqs. (8–189) and (8–204):

$$\langle\!\langle R \rangle\!\rangle = \mathrm{Tr}\,\{e^{-H/kT}R\}/\mathrm{Tr}\,\{e^{-H/kT}\} \tag{8–206}$$

In classical statistics all equilibrium properties of the system are expressed in terms of the partition function

$$Q_N = \sum_{\{n\}} \exp\left(-E\{n\}/kT\right) = \mathrm{Tr}\,\{e^{-H/kT}\} \tag{8–207}$$

where the last form is independent of the representation, because the trace of any operator is an invariant. With this form we can adopt all the classical relations, suitably modified, to give operators for the other thermodynamic variables. Thus, the classical expression for entropy [22]

[22] W. Band, *Introduction to Quantum Statistics*, Eq. (7.112), D. Van Nostrand Co., Inc., Princeton, N.J., 1955.

is $S = E/T + k \ln Q$, and this is the expectation value of the operator given in Eq. (8–205). Also the classical pressure relation is

$$P = (kT/Q)\partial Q/\partial V = (kT/Q)(\partial/\partial V) \operatorname{Tr} \{e^{-H/kT}\}$$
$$= -(1/Q) \operatorname{Tr} \{(\partial H/\partial V)e^{-H/kT}\} = \langle\!\langle -\partial H/\partial V \rangle\!\rangle \tag{8–208}$$

so that the operator for pressure in quantum statistics must be

$$P = -\partial H/\partial V \tag{8–209}$$

Classically the energy is

$$E = (kT^2/Q)(\partial/\partial T) \operatorname{Tr} \{e^{-H/kT}\} = (1/Q) \operatorname{Tr} \{He^{-H/kT}\}$$
$$= \langle\!\langle H \rangle\!\rangle \tag{8–210}$$

and the Helmholtz free energy $A = -kT \ln Q$ becomes

$$A = -kT \ln \operatorname{Tr} \{e^{-H/kT}\} I_N \tag{8–211}$$

Again, therefore, all thermodynamic properties of a system in quantum statistics can be derived from a knowledge of the partition function, and since this is the trace of an operator, we can choose any convenient representation in which to compute it. The most fruitful application of this method is probably to the theory of imperfect gases, and is well covered in the standard reference works.[23]

8.21. Grand Ensembles.—In the last section we considered ensembles of systems of given total population, but whose quantum states are distributed throughout the possible spectrum in some fashion determined by the density matrix of the ensemble. Here we shall consider systems whose total populations are also subject to uncertainty due to lack of information. For example, the system may be one phase (vapor) in contact with a "bath" consisting of a different phase (liquid) of the same substance, and we may be asking for the average population (concentration) among a large number of samples all having the same thermodynamic state. To represent this situation we let $w\{n\}_N$ be the number of systems in a collection, having each a population N in the state $|\{n\}_N\rangle$ where $\sum_j n_j = N$, and allow N to assume all possible values. Such a collection is called a grand ensemble.

We assume familiarity with the classical treatment of grand ensembles,[24] and know that the probability has a logarithm equal to

$$\sum_N \sum_{\{n\}} w\{n\}_N \ln w\{n\}_N$$

The states $|\{n\}_N\rangle$ are vectors in Fock space.

[23] W. Band, *Introduction to Quantum Statistics*, Chapter XI, D. Van Nostrand Co., Inc., Princeton, N.J., 1955; D. ter Haar, *Elements of Statistical Mechanics*, Chapter 8.4, Holt, Rinehart, and Winston, New York, 1954.

[24] W. Band, *Introduction to Quantum Statistics*, Chapter XII; T. L. Hill, *Statistical Mechanics*, Eq. (14.42); D. ter Haar, *Elements of Statistical Mechanics*, Chapter VI; G. S. Rushbrooke, *Introduction to Statistical Mechanics*.

We now define the projection operator in Fock space as an obvious generalization of Eq. (8–164):

$$P\{n\}_N = |\{n\}_N\rangle\langle\{n\}_N| \tag{8–212}$$

and let the density operator be defined as

$$W = \sum_N W_N = \sum_N \sum_{\{n\}_N} w\{n\}_N P\{n\}_N \tag{8–213}$$

It is now a simple exercise to go through the appropriate generalization of the steps leading to Eq. (8–187) for the matrix of W, and to show that

$$\langle\{n''\}_{N''}|W|\{n'\}_{N'}\rangle = w\{n'\}_{N'}\delta(\{n''\}_{N''}, \{n'\}_{N'})\cdot\delta(N'',N') \tag{8–214}$$

again a diagonal matrix with eigenvalues $w\{n\}_N$.

For any linear operator R defined in Fock space, we can similarly prove, by following an argument like that leading to Eq. (8–189), that the trace in Fock space of WR is the grand-ensemble-average of R:

$$\text{Tr}\,\{WR\} = \sum_N \sum_{\{n\}_N} w\{n\}_N\langle\{n\}_N|R|\{n\}_N\rangle = \langle\!\langle R\rangle\!\rangle \tag{8–215}$$

We also find that

$$\text{Tr}\,\{W \ln W\} = \sum_N \sum_{\{n\}_N} w\{n\}_N \ln w\{n\}_N \tag{8–216}$$

which shows that the operator

$$S = -k \ln W \tag{8–217}$$

has the grand ensemble average equal to the classical entropy.

It is shown in classical statistics that the probability of the grand ensemble is a maximum, under the restriction to given average energy and given average population per system, when the distribution is chosen to be

$$w\{n\}_N = \frac{\exp\,(\nu N - E\{n\}_N/kT)}{\sum_M \sum_{\{m\}_M} \exp\,(\nu M - E\{m\}_M/kT)} \tag{8–218}$$

where T is the parameter (absolute temperature) that determines the average energy, and ν is the parameter (chemical potential divided by kT) that determines the average population. The denominator of this expression is called the grand partition function for the system.

Using the expression (8–218) for the most probable (equilibrium) grand ensemble for the thermodynamic state, we find the density operator for the equilibrium grand ensemble from Eqs. (8–212) and (8–213):

$$W = (1/Z) \exp (\nu \mathbf{N} - H/kT) \tag{8–219}$$

where Z is the grand partition function

$$Z = \mathrm{Tr}\,\{\exp (\nu \mathbf{N} - H/kT)\} \tag{8–220}$$

and $\mathbf{N}$ is the population operator of Eq. (8–110):

$$\mathbf{N}|\{n\}_N\rangle = N|\{n\}_N\rangle \tag{8–221}$$

The equilibrium entropy operator, using Eqs. (8–217) and (8–219), is now

$$S = H/T - k\nu\,\mathbf{N} + k \ln Z \tag{8–222}$$

and the grand ensemble average in equilibrium of an observable R is

$$\langle\!\langle R \rangle\!\rangle = (1/Z)\,\mathrm{Tr}\,\{R \exp (\nu \mathbf{N} - H/kT)\} \tag{8–223}$$

The analog of Eq. (8–211) for the Helmholtz free energy is the grand potential

$$q = -kT \ln Z \tag{8–224}$$

and the equilibrium thermodynamic variables can be obtained from these equations.[25]

The appropriate expression for the operator H in the above equations is that appearing in Eq. (8–160). For a first example, consider an ideal gas without interactions. Assuming that the one-particle wave functions used in the population density operators are the energy eigenfunctions, then the matrix $H_{0\mu\lambda}$ is diagonal, and we can write

$$H = \sum_\mu E_{0\mu} b_\mu^* b_\mu \tag{8–225}$$

The eigenvalues of this operator are $n_\mu E_{0\mu}$, and those of the operator $\exp (H/kT)$ are therefore $\exp (n_\mu E_{0\mu}/kT)$. Using Eq. (8–220) for the grand partition function, we then find

$$\begin{aligned} Z &= \sum_N \sum_{\{n\}_N} \langle\{n\}_N| \exp [\nu \mathbf{N} - H/kT] |\{n\}_N\rangle \\ &= \sum_N \sum_{\{n\}_N} e^{\nu N} e^{-\sum_\mu n_\mu E_\mu/kT} \\ &= \sum_N \sum_{\{n\}_N} e^{-\sum_\mu n_\mu (E_\mu/kT - \nu)} \\ &= \prod_\mu \sum_{n_\mu} e^{-n_\mu (E_\mu/kT - \nu)} = \prod_\mu [1 - e^{-(E_\mu/kT - \nu)}]^{-1} \end{aligned} \tag{8–226}$$

[25] W. Band, *Introduction to Quantum Statistics*, Section 12.1.

Then from Eq. (8–224) we find the grand potential to be[26]

$$q = -kT \sum_{\mu} \ln \left[1 - e^{-(E_\mu/kT - \nu)}\right] \tag{8–227}$$

Before developing the theory when interactions are present, it is convenient to derive Bloch's equation for the density matrix.

8.22. Bloch's Equation for the Density Matrix.—Bloch's equation will be derived here both for the equilibrium ensemble density matrix of Eq. (8–204), and for the equilibrium grand ensemble density matrix of Eq. (8–219).

Write $\beta = 1/kT$, and regard W_N as a function of β. Taking the partial derivative of Eq. (8–204) with respect to β, remembering Eq. (8–207), we have

$$\begin{aligned} \partial W_N/\partial\beta &= -(1/Q)He^{-\beta H} - (1/Q^2)(\partial Q/\partial\beta)e^{-\beta H} \\ &= -HW_N - (1/Q)(\partial Q/\partial\beta)W_N \end{aligned} \tag{8–228}$$

Now from Eq. (8–210) we have

$$\begin{aligned} E &= (1/Q)\,\mathrm{Tr}\,\{He^{-\beta H}\} = -(1/Q)\,\mathrm{Tr}\,\{(\partial/\partial\beta)e^{-\beta H}\} \\ &= -(1/Q)(\partial/\partial\beta)(\mathrm{Tr}\,\{e^{-\beta H}\}) = -(1/Q)\partial Q/\partial\beta \end{aligned} \tag{8–229}$$

Combining this result with Eq. (8–228) we have

$$\partial W_N/\partial\beta = -(H - E)W_N \tag{8–230}$$

This is Bloch's equation. We note that this equation is essentially of the same form as Schrödinger's equation, with W_N playing the role of wave function, and β playing the role of time, $\beta \sim (i/\hbar)t$, and the operator $H - E$ representing deviation of the hamiltonian from the ensemble average.

Turning now to the grand ensemble, we differentiate Eq. (8–219) with respect to β and obtain

$$\begin{aligned} \partial W/\partial\beta &= -(1/Z)He^{\nu N - H/kT} - (1/Z^2)(\partial Z/\partial\beta)e^{\nu N - H/kT} \\ &= -HW - (1/Z)W\partial Z/\partial\beta \end{aligned} \tag{8–231}$$

Then from Eq. (8–223) with H replacing R, we have

$$\begin{aligned} E &= (1/Z)\,\mathrm{Tr}\,\{He^{\nu N - H/kT}\} = -(1/Z)\,\mathrm{Tr}\,\{(\partial/\partial\beta)e^{\nu N - \beta H}\} \\ &= -(1/Z)(\partial/\partial\beta)\,\mathrm{Tr}\,\{e^{\nu N - \beta H}\} = (1/Z)\partial Z/\partial\beta \end{aligned} \tag{8–232}$$

Combining Eqs. (8–231) and (8–232) we then have Bloch's equation again:

$$\partial W/\partial\beta = -(H - E)W \tag{8–233}$$

[26] See D. ter Haar, *loc. cit.*, Section 7.6.

Here of course H is the Fock-space operator, whereas in Eq. (8–230) it is the Schrödinger operator.

We now regard Eq. (8–233) as analogous to Schrödinger's equation, and proceed to carry out the transformation to the interaction representation described in Chapter 7, Section 7.7. We define the transformed density matrix R and the transformed potential U by

$$R \equiv e^{\beta(H_0 - E)}W, \qquad U \equiv e^{\beta(H_0 - E)}Ve^{-\beta(H_0 - E)} \tag{8–234}$$

where $H = H_0 + V$. We then have

$$\begin{aligned}\partial R/\partial\beta &= (H_0 - E)R - e^{\beta(H_0 - E)}(H - E)W \\ &= -e^{\beta(H_0 - E)}VW = -Ue^{\beta(H_0 - E)}W\end{aligned}$$

so that R satisfies the equation

$$\partial R/\partial\beta = -UR \tag{8–235}$$

With the boundary condition at $\beta = 0$, $R = W(0)$, $W(0) = e^{\nu N}/\mathrm{Tr}\,\{e^{\nu N}\}$, this equation can be integrated by Picard's method of successive approximation,[27] and the result is:

$$\begin{aligned}R(\beta) = W(0) + \sum_{n=1}^{\infty} (-1)^n \int_0^{\beta} d\beta_1 \int_0^{\beta_1} d\beta_2 \cdots \\ \times \int_0^{\beta_{n-1}} d\beta_n U(\beta_1)U(\beta_2)\cdots U(\beta_n)W(0)\end{aligned} \tag{8–236}$$

and then from Eq. (8–234) we can write down an expression for the density matrix. In making use of this result we must take H_0 as the operator in Eq. (8–225), and V the operator appearing in Eq. (8–160). In setting up the operators U in the integrand, we must remember that the various creation and destruction operators do not simply commute.

To obtain a similarly explicit expression for the grand partition function Z, we proceed in a somewhat different way. Thus we have

$$Z = \mathrm{Tr}\,\{e^{\nu N - \beta H}\} = \mathrm{Tr}\,\{e^{\nu N - \beta H_0}e^{\beta(H_0 - H)}\} = Z_0\,\mathrm{Tr}\,\{W_0 S(\beta)\}$$

where

$$W_0 \equiv (1/Z_0)e^{\nu N - \beta H_0}, \qquad S(\beta) \equiv e^{\beta(H_0 - H)}, \qquad Z_0 \equiv \mathrm{Tr}\,\{e^{\nu N - \beta H}\} \tag{8–237}$$

Thus

$$Z = Z_0 \langle\langle S(\beta) \rangle\rangle_0 \tag{8–238}$$

[27] Cf. Margenau and Murphy, *op. cit.*, Section 13.16.

where $\langle\!\langle S(\beta)\rangle\!\rangle_0$ is an ensemble average over a fictitious ensemble where the hamiltonian is H_0.

Because of the operator character of H and H_0, we must notice that functions of these operators do not commute, and $e^{\beta(H_0 - H)} \neq e^{-\beta(H - H_0)}$, and it is not safe to write either of them as $e^{\beta V}$. Now we have

$$\begin{aligned} \partial S(\beta)/\partial\beta &= H_0 e^{\beta(H_0 - H)} - e^{\beta H_0} H e^{-\beta H} = e^{\beta H_0} V e^{-\beta H} \\ &= -U(\beta) e^{\beta(H_0 - H)} = -U(\beta) S(\beta) \end{aligned} \tag{8–239}$$

Thus $S(\beta)$ satisfies the same differential equation as $R(\beta)$, Eq. (8–235), but with different boundary conditions, *i.e.*, $S(0) = 1$. The solution is

$$S(\beta) = \sum_{n=0}^{\infty} (-1)^n \int_0^{\beta} d\beta_1 \int_0^{\beta_1} d\beta_2 \cdots \int_0^{\beta_{n-1}} d\beta_n U(\beta_1) U(\beta_2) \cdots U(\beta_n) \tag{8–240}$$

This, combined with Eq. (8–238), yields the general explicit form for the grand partition function operator.

At the end of Section 8.16 we mentioned that the Fock representation avoids the use of multiple integrations of coordinate space when dealing with the many-body problem. We can see here, however, that the new method runs into complications of its own! To handle the immense bookkeeping problems involved in the multiple β-integrals and the ordered products of creation and annihilation operators, special diagram techniques have been developed. These are discussed in Chapter 11, "Quantum Electrodynamics." The reader who wishes to study further the many applications of these techniques to problems of quantum statistics will find an ample list of references in a review article by D. ter Haar, *Reports on Progress in Physics*, **24**, 1961, Inst. of Phys. and Phys. Soc. (London).

8.23. Rate of Change of Observables.—We start with the Schrödinger equation of motion, Eq. (8–154):

$$i\hbar(\partial/\partial t)\langle \mathbf{X}|\{n\},t\rangle = \langle \mathbf{X}|H|\{n\},t\rangle \tag{8–241}$$

and its complex conjugate

$$-i\hbar(\partial/\partial t)\langle\{n\},t|\mathbf{X}\rangle = \langle\{n\},t|H|\mathbf{X}\rangle \tag{8–242}$$

(remember the hermitian character of the hamiltonian, H). Now consider the expectation value of an operator L that does not depend explicitly on the time:

$$\langle\{n\},t|L|\{n'\},t\rangle = \iint \langle\{n\},t|\mathbf{X}\rangle d\mathbf{X} \langle \mathbf{X}|L|\mathbf{X}'\rangle d\mathbf{X}' \langle \mathbf{X}'|\{n'\},t\rangle$$

Taking the time derivative of this expression we obtain

$$i\hbar(\partial/\partial t)\langle\{n\},t|L|\{n'\},t\rangle$$
$$= \iint [i\hbar(\partial/\partial t)\langle\{n\},t|\mathbf{X}\rangle]d\mathbf{X}\langle\mathbf{X}|L|\mathbf{X}'\rangle d\mathbf{X}'\langle\mathbf{X}'|\{n'\},t\rangle$$
$$+ \iint \langle\{n\},t|\mathbf{X}\rangle d\mathbf{X}\langle\mathbf{X}|L|\mathbf{X}'\rangle d\mathbf{X}'[i\hbar(\partial/\partial t)\langle\mathbf{X}'|\{n'\},t\rangle] \quad (8\text{–}243)$$

Using Eqs. (8–241) and (8–242) on the right, one finds

$$- \iint \langle\{n\},t|H|\mathbf{X}\rangle d\mathbf{X}\langle\mathbf{X}|L|\mathbf{X}'\rangle d\mathbf{X}'\langle\mathbf{X}'|\{n'\},t\rangle$$
$$+ \iint \langle\{n\},t|\mathbf{X}\rangle d\mathbf{X}\langle\mathbf{X}|L|\mathbf{X}'\rangle d\mathbf{X}'\langle\mathbf{X}'|H|\{n'\},t\rangle$$

and finally, therefore

$$i\hbar(\partial/\partial t)\langle\{n\},t|L|\{n'\},t\rangle = \langle\{n\},t|(LH - HL)|\{n'\},t\rangle \quad (8\text{–}244)$$

This means that any observable not depending explicitly on time and commuting with H has an expectation value that does not depend on time.

Consider next the rate of change of the expectation value of an operator that does depend explicitly on time, say $R(t)$. Then in addition to the terms appearing in Eq. (8–244) there is also a term $\langle\{n\},t|\partial R/\partial t|\{n'\},t\rangle$ so that

$$i\hbar(\partial/\partial t)\langle\{n\},t|R|\{n'\},t\rangle = i\hbar\langle\{n\},t|\partial R/\partial t|\{n'\},t\rangle$$
$$+ \langle\{n\},t|(RH - HR)|\{n'\},t\rangle \quad (8\text{–}245)$$

As a somewhat exceptional example of this we shall find the rate of change of the ensemble density operator, Eq. (8–186), which we now rewrite more explicitly to bring out its time-dependence:

$$W_N = \sum_{\{n\}} w\{n\}|\{n\},t\rangle\langle\{n\},t|$$

where, however, we shall assume that $w\{n\}$ is not time dependent.[28] We have for the matrix components of W_N on the configuration representation

$$\langle\mathbf{X}|W_N|\mathbf{X}'\rangle = \sum_{\{n\}} \langle\mathbf{X}|\{n\},t\rangle w\{n\}\langle\{n\},t|\mathbf{X}'\rangle$$

[28] This restriction means that we shall consider ensembles representing equilibrium or stationary situations, and forego the discussion of quantum dynamical problems where the probabilities $w\{n\}$ are forced to change with time.

In view of Eqs. (8–241) and (8–242) the time derivative of this is seen to be

$$i\hbar(\partial/\partial t)\langle\mathbf{X}|W_N|\mathbf{X}'\rangle = \langle\mathbf{X}|H|\{n\},t\rangle\langle\{n\},t|\mathbf{X}'\rangle w\{n\} - \langle\mathbf{X}|\{n\},t\rangle\langle\{n\},t|H|\mathbf{X}'\rangle w\{n\} \quad (8\text{–}246)$$

Now if the states $|\{n\},t\rangle$ are composed of energy eigenstates, as was implicitly assumed up until now, we have

$$H|\{n\},t\rangle = E\{n\}|\{n\},t\rangle$$

and

$$H|\mathbf{X}'\rangle = \sum_{\{n'\}} H|\{n'\},t\rangle\langle\{n'\},t|\mathbf{X}'\rangle = \sum_{\{n'\}} E\{n'\}|\{n'\},t\rangle\langle\{n'\},t|\mathbf{X}'\rangle$$

From this it follows easily that the right side of Eq. (8–246) vanishes and so

$$i\hbar(\partial/\partial t)\langle\mathbf{X}|W_N|\mathbf{X}'\rangle = 0 \quad (8\text{–}247)$$

The expectation value of the density operator, and, indeed, all the components of the density matrix, are stationary in time for an ensemble set up in terms of energy eigenstates. If we use occupation number representation to set up the density matrix, it is at once seen from Eq. (8–187) that it also is independent of time:

$$i\hbar(\partial/\partial t)\langle\{n\},t|W_N|\{n'\},t\rangle = 0 \quad (8\text{–}248)$$

Now we shall consider the time dependence of the ensemble average of any operator R not explicitly a function of time, Tr $\{W_NR\}$. Because the trace is independent of the representation, we choose the one most convenient, which turns out to be the occupation number representation whose eigenvectors are eigenvectors of H. Thus we write

$$\text{Tr}\,\{W_NR\} = \sum_{\{n\}}\sum_{\{m\}}\langle\{n\},t|W_N|\{m\},t\rangle\langle\{m\},t|R|\{n\},t\rangle$$

Then using Eq. (8–248) we may write

$$i\hbar(\partial/\partial t)\,\text{Tr}\,\{W_NR\} = \sum_{\{n\}}\sum_{\{m\}}\langle\{n\},t|W_N|\{m\},t\rangle i\hbar(\partial/\partial t)\langle\{m\},t|R|\{n\},t\rangle$$

or, by Eq. (8–244)

$$= \sum_{\{n\}}\sum_{\{m\}}\langle\{n\},t|W_N|\{m\},t\rangle\langle\{m\},t|(RH - HR)|\{n\},t\rangle$$

From Eq. (8–187) this yields

$$i\hbar(\partial/\partial t)\,\mathrm{Tr}\,\{W_N R\} = \sum_{\{m\}} \delta(\{m\},\{n\})w\{n\}(E\{n\} - E\{m\})\langle\{m\},t|R|\{n\},t\rangle = 0 \tag{8–249}$$

In other words, the rate of change of the ensemble average of any observable is zero, even when the operator does not commute with H, provided it is not explicitly a function of time, and provided we have set up the ensemble in terms of the energy eigenstates.

Next, consider an ensemble defined in configuration space, so that the density matrix has the form of Eq. (8–190). We assume that the eigenvectors $|\mathbf{X}\rangle$ are not eigenvectors of the hamiltonian. We have

$$\langle\mathbf{X}|W_X|\mathbf{X}'\rangle = w(\mathbf{X})\delta(\mathbf{X} - \mathbf{X}')$$

and

$$\begin{aligned}\langle\mathbf{X}|W_X R|\mathbf{X}'\rangle &= w(\mathbf{X})\int \delta(\mathbf{X} - \mathbf{X}'')d\mathbf{X}''\langle\mathbf{X}''|R|\mathbf{X}'\rangle \\ &= w(\mathbf{X})\langle\mathbf{X}|R|\mathbf{X}'\rangle\end{aligned} \tag{8–250}$$

The rate of change of the ensemble average of R in this ensemble is then

$$\begin{aligned}i\hbar(\partial/\partial t)\,\mathrm{Tr}\,\{W_X R\} &= i\hbar(\partial/\partial t)\int w(\mathbf{X})\langle\mathbf{X}|R|\mathbf{X}\rangle d\mathbf{X} \\ &= i\hbar\sum_k w(\mathbf{X})(\partial/\partial t)\int \langle\mathbf{X}|k,t\rangle R_k\langle k,t|\mathbf{X}\rangle d\mathbf{X}\end{aligned} \tag{8–251}$$

where $|k,t\rangle$ are the eigenvectors of R: $\langle k,t|R|k',t\rangle = R_k\delta_{kk'}$. Applying the analogs of Eqs. (8–241) and (8–242) to these eigenvectors, we have for the right side of Eq. (8–251):

$$\begin{aligned}&\sum_k \int w(\mathbf{X})R_k[\langle\mathbf{X}|H|k,t\rangle\langle k,t|\mathbf{X}\rangle - \langle\mathbf{X}|k,t\rangle\langle k,t|H|\mathbf{X}\rangle]d\mathbf{X} \\ &\qquad = \sum_k \int w(\mathbf{X})[\langle\mathbf{X}|HR|k,t\rangle\langle k,t|\mathbf{X}\rangle - \langle\mathbf{X}|R|k,t\rangle\langle k,t|H|\mathbf{X}\rangle]d\mathbf{X} \\ &\qquad = \int w(\mathbf{X})\langle\mathbf{X}|(HR - RH)|\mathbf{X}\rangle d\mathbf{X}\end{aligned} \tag{8–252}$$

This looks as if it were not zero when H and R do not commute, but the appearance is deceptive. For we can write

$$\begin{aligned}w(\mathbf{X})\langle\mathbf{X}| = w(\mathbf{X})\langle\mathbf{X}|\int |\mathbf{X}'\rangle d\mathbf{X}'\langle\mathbf{X}'| &= \int w(\mathbf{X}')\langle\mathbf{X}|\mathbf{X}'\rangle d\mathbf{X}'\langle\mathbf{X}'| \\ &= \langle\mathbf{X}|W_X|\end{aligned}$$

and so (8–252) is in fact the same as

$$= \int \langle \mathbf{X} | (W_X HR - W_X RH) | \mathbf{X} \rangle d\mathbf{X} \tag{8–253}$$

This expression is the trace, in coordinate representation, of the operator $W_X HR - W_X RH$. But the trace of a product of matrices is independent of the order of the product, so the two parts of (8–253) cancel.[29]

The same result can be found by using energy eigenfunctions for the representation: the trace of $W_X R$ is independent of time.

We have carried out this discussion in occupation number representation or coordinate representation each with a definite number N of particles. Similar results follow for the Fock space representation and the properties of grand ensembles. Averages over grand ensembles are also independent of time when the probabilities $w\{n\}$ are independent of time, whether the observable commutes with H or not.

To sum up, the ensemble average of any observable not explicitly a function of time is independent of time even for an ensemble formed from configuration eigenstates that are not eigenstates of the hamiltonian, and even for observables that do not commute with the hamiltonian. This raises the suspicion that there is a more general proof that ensemble averages in any ensemble are independent of time, and in the next section we show that this is indeed the case.

8.24. Schrödinger's Equation as a Unitary Transformation.— We may write Schrödinger's equation in the form

$$i\hbar(\partial/\partial t)|k,t\rangle = H|k,t\rangle \tag{8–254}$$

where $|k,t\rangle$ is any complete orthonormal set of time-dependent states and H is not explicitly a function of time. A formal integration of this equation yields

$$|k,t\rangle = e^{-i(t-t_0)H/\hbar}|k,t_0\rangle \tag{8–255}$$

where $|k,t_0\rangle$ is an initial state at time t_0, which evolves into the state $|k,t\rangle$ at time t in a manner prescribed by the Schrödinger equation. That the operator

$$U(t,t_0) = e^{-i(t-t_0)H/\hbar} \tag{8–256}$$

is in fact unitary follows from the hermitian nature of H, so that

$$U^{-1}(t,t_0) = e^{+i(t-t_0)H/\hbar} = U^*(t,t_0) \tag{8–257}$$

[29] See Margenau and Murphy, *op. cit.*, p. 309.

Incidentally if $t - t_0$ is an infinitesimal time dt, the unitary transformation reduces in first order to

$$U(t + dt,t) = I - idtH/\hbar$$

and

$$|k,t + dt\rangle = U(t + dt)|k,t\rangle \tag{8–258}$$

It is interesting to compare this with Eq. (8–67).

Now let us use the set $|k,t_0\rangle$ to form a matrix representation of some operator Q at time t_0, assuming that Q is not explicitly a function of time. The expectation value of Q in the various states, changes in time only by virtue of the time-dependence of the state vectors used in the representation. However, because this dependence is equivalent to a unitary transformation, the matrix at time t is derived from the matrix at time t_0 by such a unitary transformation, and we know that this cannot change the trace of the matrix. Thus if $Q = W_X R$ our result entails that it is not possible to change the ensemble average of R, which is just the trace of Q.

The Schrödinger equation with its time-independent hamiltonian does not in fact constitute a dynamical theorem; it is simply a description of the time-dependence of the probability field corresponding to steady states or equilibrium conditions.

This result holds equally well, of course, when R happens to be the operator representing the entropy of an ensemble. Both Tr $\{W_X \ln W_X\}$ and Tr $\{W_N \ln W_N\}$ are invariant under unitary transformations, and so have no time dependence arising from the Schrödinger equation. This implies a paradox with the second law of thermodynamics in that apparently no increase in entropy can occur in an equilibrium isolated system. This paradox has been resolved by observing that no real laboratory system can in fact be conceived in which the hamiltonian is truly independent of time: the uncertainty principle allows virtual fluctuations of the hamiltonian with time at all boundaries that are used to define the configuration and isolate the system, and it is easy to prove that such fluctuations necessarily increase the entropy.[30]

To close this chapter we emphasize that the statistical mechanical definition of macroscopic parameters such as temperature and entropy are well designed to describe isentropic equilibrium systems, but are not immediately applicable to the discussion of transport processes where irreversible entropy increase is an essential feature. A macroscopic system through which heat is flowing does not possess a single tempera-

[30] W. Band, *Am. J. Phys.*, **26**, 540 (1958). For alternative explanations, see also van Hove, *Physica*, **21**, 517 (1957), and E. T. Jaynes, *Phys. Rev.*, **108**, 171 (1957).

ture, and the ensembles discussed in this chapter cannot be set up to contain all the information about the system that is in fact available.

One may attempt to approximate to such an experimental situation by considering a subsystem with small dimensions in the direction of the flow, so that a single temperature may be sufficiently precise in describing it. In this model one would have to provide a time-dependent hamiltonian operating in such a way as to feed energy into the system at one boundary and to remove energy from the other boundary. We would therefore be obliged to discuss systems with hamiltonians that are explicitly functions of time, and also located on the boundaries of the macrosystem.

All discussions of transport processes currently available in the literature are based on perturbation theory methods applied to kinetic pictures of micro-scattering processes within the macrosystem of interest. These methods do involve time-dependent hamiltonians in the sense that the interaction operates only during "collisions," while the wave functions are known only before and after the collision. However these interactions are purely internal, and their time-dependence is essentially implicit: the over-all hamiltonian of the entire system, such as the interaction term in Eq. (8–159) is not time-dependent, and such micro-scattering processes cannot lead to irreversible changes of thermodynamic (ensemble average) properties.

In general the transitions appearing between the "unperturbed" states in such perturbation theories are of no physical significance; they are simply a result of our attempt to express the true eigenstates of the true "perturbed" hamiltonian in terms of convenient but erroneous eigenstates of the unperturbed erroneous hamiltonian. If we were able to find the true eigenstates—and this is, of course, possible in principle—no such transitions would be discovered and the apparent time-dependence would disappear.

A physically acceptable theory of electrical resistance, or of heat conductivity, must contain a discussion of the explicitly time-dependent hamiltonian needed to supply the current at one boundary and remove it at another boundary of the macrosystem. Lacking this feature, recent theories of such transport phenomena contain no mechanism for irreversible entropy increase, and can be of little more than heuristic value.

CHAPTER 9

RELATIVISTIC QUANTUM MECHANICS[1]

by

S. S. SCHWEBER

Brandeis University

9.1. Historical Background.—Relativistic quantum mechanics had its beginning in 1900 with Planck's formulation of the law of black body radiation. Perhaps its inception should be attributed more accurately to Einstein (1905) who ascribed to electromagnetic radiation a corpuscular character: the photons. He endowed the photons with an energy and momentum $h\nu$ and $h\nu/c$, respectively, if the frequency of the radiation is ν. These assignments of energy and momentum for these zero rest mass particles were consistent with the postulates of relativity. It is to be noted that zero rest mass particles can only be understood within the framework of relativistic dynamics.

The first consistent attempt to "unify" quantum theory and relativity came after Schrödinger's and Heisenberg's work in 1925 and 1926 produced the rules for the quantum mechanical description of nonrelativistic systems of point particles. Mention should be made of the fact that in these developments de Broglie's hypothesis attributing wave-corpuscular properties to all matter played an important role. Central to this hypothesis are the relations between particle and wave properties: $E = h\nu$ and $\mathbf{p} = \hbar\mathbf{k}$, which de Broglie advanced on the basis of relativistic dynamics.

Actually Schrödinger's original paper on quantum mechanics already contained a relativistic wave equation, which, however, gave the wrong answer for the spectrum of the hydrogen atom. Due to this fact, and because of problems connected with the physical interpretation of this equation, which is of second order in the space and time variables, it was temporarily discarded. Dirac took seriously the notion of first

[1] Chapters 9, 10, and 11 form part of the content of a course on advanced quantum mechanics given by the author at the Massachusetts Institute of Technology during the academic year 1961–62. The author would like to take this opportunity to acknowledge the hospitality of the Department of Physics of that Institute. He also wishes to thank Professor H. Margenau and Professor H. N. Pendleton, III, for reading the manuscript critically, and commenting upon it constructively.

order equations and was thus led in 1928 to the equation bearing his name.

It is a characteristic feature of all these relativistic equations that in addition to positive energy solutions, they admit of negative energy solutions. The clarification of the problems connected with the interpretation of these negative energy solutions led to the realization that in the presence of interaction, a one particle interpretation of these equations is difficult and that in a consistent quantum mechanical formulation of the dynamics of relativistic systems it is convenient to deal from the start with an indefinite number of particles. In technical language this is the statement that one is to deal with quantized fields.

It is interesting to note that the basic notion of field quantization also had its origin in Planck's and Einstein's work on the light quantum hypothesis. Thus Ehrenfest in 1906 noted that Planck's distribution law could be derived by means of the Rayleigh-Jeans normal mode analysis of the electromagnetic field when coupled with Planck's hypothesis that the amount of field energy residing in a normal mode of frequency ν can only be an integral multiple of $h\nu$. Stated more precisely, an arbitrary field distribution obeying Maxwell's equations

$$\nabla \times \mathscr{E} + \frac{1}{c}\frac{\partial \mathscr{H}}{\partial t} = 0; \qquad \nabla \cdot \mathscr{E} = 0$$

$$\nabla \times \mathscr{H} - \frac{1}{c}\frac{\partial \mathscr{E}}{\partial t} = 0; \qquad \nabla \cdot \mathscr{H} = 0$$

can, upon a Fourier analysis of the field intensities $\mathscr{E}$ and $\mathscr{H}$, be thought of as a superposition of monochromatic waves. The dynamical properties of a monochromatic wave are thereby translated into that of a harmonic oscillator of the same frequency. The dynamical behavior of the electromagnetic field is thus transcribed into that of a doubly (due to the polarization) infinite set of harmonic oscillators. In the absence of charges and currents all these modes are uncoupled and the total field energy $H = \frac{1}{2}\int d^3\mathbf{r}(\mathscr{E}^2 + \mathscr{H}^2)$ is the sum of the energy of all these oscillators. Planck's hypothesis applied to the electromagnetic field, or equivalently the quantization of the electromagnetic field, results in the fact that electromagnetic energy of a frequency ν must always appear in "quanta" of the size $h\nu$. This, of course, is the light quantum hypothesis. The quantization of the field energy thus results in exhibiting the corpuscular aspect of the system. This connection between quantization and corpuscular aspects remained obscure, however, until 1927 when Dirac consistently applied the newly-discovered quantum rules to the quantization of the electromagnetic field.

There exists another, deeper, reason for the necessity of quantizing the electromagnetic field in order to describe in a consistent manner the interaction between charged particles and radiation. The reason is that if the mechanical parameters (coordinates and momenta) of the particles are to be quantized then the fields coupled to them must also be quantized because Heisenberg's uncertainty principle cannot possibly be valid for only part of nature. If the uncertainty principle did not apply to the field, then, as shown by Bohr and Rosenfeld, it would be possible to set up a "gedanken-experiment" which, in principle, would permit an accurate simultaneous determination of the position and momentum of a charged particle by observing and measuring the electromagnetic field generated by the particle. The quantization of the electromagnetic field is thus an inescapable consequence of the quantization of the dynamics of charged particles.

As noted above, the application of the quantum rules to the electromagnetic field is equivalent to the quantization of a set of harmonic oscillators. As with oscillators, the energy in a monochromatic wave can change only by multiples of $h\nu$ where ν is the frequency of the wave. Electromagnetic energy of a frequency ν must always appear in "quanta" of energy $h\nu$. As a result of the uncertainty principle, a harmonic oscillator even in its lowest energy state still has a finite amplitude of vibration. This fact when transcribed to the electromagnetic field implies that in its lowest energy state, although the electromagnetic field fluctuates about the mean value zero, the mean square value of the field strengths is different from zero and does not vanish. The strength of the field fluctuations in the vacuum, averaged over a volume V of linear dimensions a, is approximately given by

$$\langle \mathscr{E}^2 \rangle_{av} = \langle \mathscr{H}^2 \rangle_{av} \approx hc/a^4$$

These fluctuations will affect the motion of charged particles. A major part of the Lamb shift in a hydrogen atom can be understood as the contribution to the energy from the interaction of the electron with these zero point oscillations of the electromagnetic field. The qualitative explanation runs as follows: the mean square of the electric and magnetic field intensities in the vacuum state is equal to

$$\langle \mathscr{E}^2(\mathbf{x}) \rangle_{av} = \langle \mathscr{H}^2(\mathbf{x}) \rangle_{av} = \frac{2\hbar c}{\pi} \int_0^\infty k^3 dk$$

its value actually being independent of the position $\mathbf{x}$. Although the right-hand side is formally infinite, it can be reinterpreted to yield the statement that the strength of the fluctuations averaged over a volume of dimensions a^3 is proportional to hc/a^4. It is the larger the smaller the volume and in the limit as $a \rightarrow 0$ the fluctuations become "infinite." Consider now the motion of a charged nonrelativistic particle in the vacuum. As a result of its interaction with these fluctuations, the particle will perform what may be thought of as a brownian notion about its classical path. The root mean square deviations of its position coordinates $\Delta\mathbf{q}^2$ can readily be computed in terms of $\langle\mathscr{E}^2(\mathbf{x})\rangle_{av}$. If the particle moves in some external potential then the potential it "sees" is not $V(\mathbf{q})$ but

$$V(\mathbf{q} + \Delta\mathbf{q}) \approx V(\mathbf{q}) + \tfrac{1}{6}(\Delta\mathbf{q})^2\nabla^2 V(\mathbf{q}) + \cdots$$

(We have assumed the potential to be spherically symmetric.) It is precisely the perturbation $\frac{1}{6}(\Delta\mathbf{q})^2_{av}\nabla^2 V(\mathbf{q})$ that gives rise to the major part of the Lamb shift in the $2s$ state of the hydrogenic atom.

Although a qualitative explanation of a major part of the Lamb shift can thus be given in terms of the interaction of the bound electron with the zero point fluctuations of the quantized electromagnetic field, a more careful calculation is possible only after a host of difficulties connected with the description of the electron as a point charge are resolved. The resolution of these difficulties, or more accurately the bypassing of these difficulties, was achieved by the recognition that the parameters of mass and charge of the electron that enter in the electrodynamic formalism are in fact not the ordinarily measured electronic mass and charge. Just as in Lorentz's classical theory, a free electron is actually always accompanied by an electromagnetic field, its Coulomb and Biot-Savart field, which effectively alters the inertia of the system. Hence a "renormalization" whereby the initial mass parameter is eliminated and re-expressed in terms of the experimentally measured mass must be carried out before the predictions of the theory can be compared with experiments. Similarly, the electromagnetic field that accompanies the charged particle distorts the charge distribution of the matter-field (negaton-positon field) vacuum (vacuum polarization). The observed charge of the particle therefore corresponds to the bare charge, Q_0, plus induced charge $-\delta Q_0$ (which is always and unavoidably present). Unfortunately, the induced charge when calculated is infinite. The difficulty is circumvented by the process of charge renormalization, which *identifies* the quantity $Q_0 - \delta Q_0$ (cven though divergent) with the observed, finite, experimentally measured charge of the charged particle.

It is the purpose of this chapter to present the background material necessary for an outline of the modern formulation of quantum electrodynamics. We shall not consider any other field theory. The fact that the strong and weak interactions are of short range implies that no macroscopic analogues for these interactions exist. In quantum electrodynamics, on the other hand, where the interactions are of long range a correspondence limit does exist, namely classical electrodynamics, which is a valid description whenever the number of photons in a given mode is large compared to 1. The fact that a classical limit exists allows us to obtain quantum electrodynamics by writing down classical electrodynamics and quantizing this theory. In meson theories, on the other hand, we have no such guide and the correct formulation as well as the quantitative aspects of the theory are in a much less satisfactory state.

REFERENCES

Wentzel, G., "Quantum Theory of Fields," in *Theoretical Physics in the Twentieth Century*; A Memorial Volume to W. Pauli, M. Fierz, and V. F. Weisskopf, ed., Interscience Publishers, Inc., New York, 1960.

Villars, F., "Quantum Theory of Fields," in *Theoretical Physics in the Twentieth Century*; A Memorial Volume to W. Pauli, M. Fierz, and V. F. Weisskopf, ed., Interscience Publishers, Inc., New York, 1960.

Schwinger, J., *Selected papers on Quantum Electrodynamics*, Dover Publications, New York, 1958 (see particularly Schwinger's preface).

Weisskopf, V. F., *Rev. Mod. Phys.*, **21**, 305 (1949).

9.2. Notation.—Before embarking upon the subject matter of the present chapter let us briefly introduce the notation that will be used throughout the chapter.

We shall denote the space time coordinates by x^μ (which as a four-vector is denoted by a light face x) with $x^0 = t$, $x^1 = x$, $x^2 = y$, $x^3 = z$; $x = \{x^0, \mathbf{x}\}$. We shall use a metric tensor $g_{\mu\nu} = g^{\mu\nu}$ with components

$$g_{00} = -g_{11} = -g_{22} = -g_{33} = +1 \tag{9-1}$$

$$g_{\mu\nu} = 0 \quad \text{for } \mu \neq \nu \tag{9-2}$$

so that the determinant $|g|$

$$\det g = |g| = -1 \tag{9-3}$$

Contravariant vectors, those that transform like the coordinate vector x^μ, will be denoted by v^μ, and covariant ones (that transform like the gradient) by v_μ.

$$\begin{aligned} v^\mu &= (v^0, \mathbf{v}) \\ &= (v^0, v^k) \end{aligned} \tag{9-4}$$

and

$$v_\mu = (v^0, -\mathbf{v}) \tag{9-5}$$

In general, Greek indices will be used to denote the components (0,1,2,3) of a space-time tensor, whereas Latin indices will be used to denote spatial components (1,2,3). The raising and lowering of indices is defined by

$$v_\mu = g_{\mu\nu} v^\nu \tag{9-6}$$
$$v^\mu = g^{\mu\nu} v_\mu \tag{9-7}$$

where a repeated Greek index implies a summation over the index from 0 to 3. We shall in general adopt the rule of implied summation over repeated indices (0 to 3 for Greek indices, 1 to 3 for Latin indices). The Kronecker delta $\delta^\mu{}_\nu$ is equal to $g^\mu{}_\nu$, *i.e.*, $\delta^\mu{}_\nu = g^\mu{}_\nu = g^\nu{}_\mu$.

A homogeneous Lorentz transformation will be denoted by

$$x'^\mu = \Lambda^\mu{}_\nu x^\nu \tag{9-8}$$

It relates the space time coordinates x^μ of an event as labeled by an observer O, to the space-time coordinates of the same event as labeled by an observer O'. The most general homogeneous Lorentz transformation is the real linear transformation (9–8) which leaves invariant the quadratic form

$$\begin{aligned} x \cdot x = x^2 &= g^{\mu\nu} x_\mu x_\nu \\ &= x^\mu x_\mu = (x^0)^2 - \mathbf{x}^2 \\ &= (x^0)^2 - (x^1)^2 - (x^2)^2 - (x^3)^2 \end{aligned} \tag{9-9}$$

i.e., for which

$$x'^\mu x'_\mu = x^\mu x_\mu \tag{9-10}$$

The requirement that $x'^\mu x'_\mu = x^\mu x_\mu$ is the mathematical statement that light propagates with the same speed with respect to both O and O', if they are "equivalent" observers. In (9–8) the transformation coefficients $\Lambda^\mu{}_\nu$ are all real. The condition (9–10) requires that

$$\Lambda^\mu{}_\nu g_{\mu\rho} \Lambda^\rho{}_\sigma = g_{\nu\sigma} \tag{9-11}$$

or in matrix form with $(\Lambda)_{\mu\nu} = \Lambda^\mu{}_\nu$, and $(g)_{\mu\nu} = g_{\mu\nu}$

$$\Lambda^T g \Lambda = g \tag{9-12}$$

where Λ^T denotes the transpose of the matrix Λ. The Lorentz invariant scalar product of two vectors a_μ, b_μ is defined by

$$\begin{aligned} a \cdot b &= a_\mu g^{\mu\nu} b_\nu = a^\mu g_{\mu\nu} b^\nu = a_\mu b^\mu = a^\mu b_\mu \\ &= a^0 b^0 - \mathbf{a} \cdot \mathbf{b} = a^0 b^0 - a^1 b^1 - a^2 b^2 - a^3 b^3 \end{aligned} \tag{9-13}$$

Incidentally the tensor $g^{\mu\nu}$ satisfies

$$g^{\mu\nu} g_{\mu\sigma} = \delta^\nu{}_\sigma \tag{9-14}$$

where $\delta^{\mu}{}_{\sigma}$ is the Kronecker delta: $\delta^{\mu}{}_{\nu} = 1$ if $\mu = \nu$ and $\delta^{\mu}{}_{\nu} = 0$ otherwise. A vector a will be called time-like if $a \cdot a = a^2 > 0$, spacelike if $a^2 < 0$, and a null vector if $a^2 = 0$.

It follows from Eq. (9–12) that the determinant of Λ, det Λ, is equal to ± 1, so that for every homogeneous Lorentz transformation there exists an inverse transformation Λ^{-1} such that $\Lambda^{-1}\Lambda = \Lambda\Lambda^{-1} = 1 =$ the identity transformation. In fact, from Eq. (9–12) it follows that $\Lambda^{-1} = g\Lambda^T g$. One verifies that the product of two homogeneous Lorentz transformations is again a homogeneous Lorentz transformation so that the set of all homogeneous Lorentz transformations forms a group, known as the homogeneous Lorentz group.

Upon setting $\sigma = \nu = 0$ in Eq. (9–11), one obtains

$$(\Lambda^0{}_0)^2 = 1 + \sum_{i=1}^{3} (\Lambda^i{}_0)^2 \geq 1 \tag{9–15}$$

so that $\Lambda^0{}_0 \geq 1$ or $\Lambda^0{}_0 \leq -1$. A Lorentz transformation for which $\Lambda^0{}_0 \geq 1$ is called an orthochronous Lorentz transformation. The set of transformations with det $\Lambda = +1$ is called the set of proper Lorentz transformations. A transformation with det $\Lambda = -1$ is called an improper Lorentz transformation. The set of all Λ's can be divided into four subsets according to whether det $\Lambda = +1$ or det $\Lambda = -1$ and $\Lambda^0{}_0$ is equal to or greater than $+1$ or equal to or less than -1. The subset with det $\Lambda = +1$ and $\Lambda^0{}_0 \geq 1$ is usually called the group of restricted homogeneous Lorentz transformations and is a six-parameter group. The other subsets can be obtained by adjoining to the restricted homogeneous Lorentz group the following three discrete transformations.

(1) Space inversion

$$x'^{\mu} = \Lambda(i_s)^{\mu}{}_{\nu} x^{\nu} = \{x^0, -\mathbf{x}\} \tag{9–16}$$

$$\det \Lambda(i_s) = -1; \qquad \Lambda(i_s)^0{}_0 = +1 \tag{9–17}$$

(2) Time inversion

$$x'^{\mu} = \Lambda(i_t)^{\mu}{}_{\nu} x^{\nu} = \{-x^0, \mathbf{x}\} \tag{9–18}$$

$$\det \Lambda(i_t) = -1; \qquad \Lambda(i_t)^0{}_0 = -1 \tag{9–19}$$

(3) Space-time inversion

$$x'^{\mu} = \Lambda(i_{st})^{\mu}{}_{\nu} x^{\nu} = -x^{\mu} \tag{9–20}$$

$$\Lambda(i_{st}) = \Lambda(i_s)\Lambda(i_t) \tag{9–21}$$

$$\det \Lambda(i_{st}) = +1; \qquad \Lambda^0{}_0 = -1 \tag{9–22}$$

These subsets are disjoints and cannot be continuously connected by real Lorentz transformations.

An inhomogeneous Lorentz transformation $L = \{\Lambda,a\}$ is defined by

$$x'^{\mu} = \Lambda^{\mu}{}_{\nu}x^{\nu} + a^{\mu} \tag{9–23}$$

where Λ is a homogeneous Lorentz transformation and a^{μ} a constant four-vector. The multiplication law for two inhomogeneous Lorentz transformations is

$$\{\Lambda_1,a_1\}\{\Lambda_2,a_2\} = \{\Lambda_1\Lambda_2, a_1 + \Lambda_1 a_2\} \tag{9–24}$$

The set of all inhomogeneous Lorentz transformations form a ten-parameter group, usually called the Poincaré group.

We shall often have occasion to use the totally antisymmetric tensor (density) $\varepsilon^{\mu\nu\rho\sigma}$ which is defined as follows:

$$\varepsilon^{\mu\nu\rho\sigma} = \begin{cases} 0 & \text{if } \mu\nu\rho\sigma \text{ are not distinct} \\ 1 & \text{if } \mu\nu\rho\sigma \text{ is an even permutation of 0123} \\ -1 & \text{if } \mu\nu\rho\sigma \text{ is an odd permutation of 0123} \end{cases} \tag{9–25}$$

and whose indices can be lowered by using the metric tensor, *e.g.*

$$\varepsilon^{\mu}{}_{\nu}{}^{\rho\sigma} = g_{\nu\alpha}\varepsilon^{\mu\alpha\rho\sigma} \tag{9–26}$$

If $A^{\mu}{}_{\mu'}$ is an arbitrary four-by-four matrix, then[2]

$$\varepsilon^{\mu'\nu'\rho'\sigma'}A^{\mu}{}_{\mu'}A^{\nu}{}_{\nu'}A^{\rho}{}_{\rho'}A^{\sigma}{}_{\sigma'} = (\det A)\varepsilon^{\mu\nu\rho\sigma} \tag{9–27}$$

whence

$$\varepsilon_{\mu\nu\rho\sigma} = -\varepsilon^{\mu\nu\rho\sigma} \tag{9–28}$$

as is seen when we take A to be g. $\varepsilon^{\mu\nu\rho\sigma}$ is thus a tensor (density) whose components are the same in all proper Lorentz frames. It also satisfies the following identities

$$\varepsilon^{\mu\nu\rho\sigma}\varepsilon_{\mu\nu\rho\sigma} = -4! \tag{9–29}$$

$$\varepsilon^{\mu\nu\rho\sigma}\varepsilon_{\mu\nu\rho\lambda} = -3!g^{\sigma}{}_{\lambda} \tag{9–30}$$

$$\varepsilon^{\alpha\beta\mu\nu}\varepsilon_{\alpha\beta\rho\sigma} = -2!(g^{\mu}{}_{\rho}g^{\mu}{}_{\sigma} - g^{\mu}{}_{\sigma}g^{\mu}{}_{\rho}) \tag{9–31}$$

The corresponding three-dimensional antisymmetric tensor ε^{ijk} is defined by

$$\varepsilon^{ijk} \begin{cases} 0 & \text{if } ijk \text{ are not distinct} \\ +1 & \text{if } ijk \text{ is an even permutation of 123} \\ -1 & \text{if } ijk \text{ is an odd permutation of 123} \end{cases} \tag{9–32}$$

[2] Cf. Eq. 10–1 in H. Margenau and G. M. Murphy, *The Mathematics of Physics and Chemistry*, 2nd Ed., p. 302, D. Van Nostrand Co., Inc., Princeton, N.J., 1956.

It satisfies the identities

$$\varepsilon^{jkl}\varepsilon^{jkm} = 2\delta^{lm} \tag{9–33}$$

$$\varepsilon^{ijk}\varepsilon^{klm} = \delta^{il}\delta^{jm} - \delta^{im}\delta^{jl} \tag{9–34}$$

where δ^{il} is the Kronecker delta in the Latin indices 1, 2, 3.

We shall often denote by ∂_μ the covariant gradient operator

$$\partial_\mu = \frac{\partial}{\partial x^\mu} = \left\{\frac{\partial}{\partial x^0}, \boldsymbol{\nabla}\right\} \tag{9–35}$$

and by ∂^μ the operator

$$\partial^\mu = \frac{\partial}{\partial x_\mu} = \left\{\frac{\partial}{\partial x^0}, -\boldsymbol{\nabla}\right\} \tag{9–36}$$

The d'alembertian or wave operator will be denoted by

$$\square = \partial^\mu \partial_\mu = \frac{\partial^2}{\partial (x^0)^2} - \boldsymbol{\nabla}^2 \tag{9–37}$$

The operation of complex conjugation will be denoted by an overscore: $\bar{a}$ denotes the complex conjugate of a. For a matrix A, with matrix elements a_{ij} the hermitian conjugate matrix with elements $\bar{a}_{ji}$ will be denoted by A^*

$$(A^*)_{ij} = \bar{a}_{ji} \tag{9–38}$$

and the transpose by A^T

$$(A^T)_{ij} = a_{ji} \tag{9–39}$$

Finally, we shall almost always use natural units in which c, the velocity of light, and $\hbar$ Planck's constant divided by 2π are set equal to one. In this system of units, energy, mass, inverse length, and inverse time all have the same dimension.

REFERENCES

For further properties of the Lorentz group see:

Wightman, A. S., "L'invariance dans la Mécanique Quantique Relativiste," in *Dispersion Relations and Elementary Particles*, C. de Witt and R. Omnes, ed., John Wiley and Sons, Inc., New York, 1960, and references listed in these lectures.

9.3. Quantum Mechanical Generalities.—It will be recalled that in nonrelativistic quantum mechanics the state of a particle at a given instant t is represented by a vector in Hilbert space $|\psi(t)\rangle$. The evolution of the system in time is governed by the Schrödinger equation

$$H|\psi(t)\rangle = i\hbar\partial_t|\psi(t)\rangle \tag{9–40}$$

where H is the hamiltonian of the system. It is often convenient to specify the state vector $|\psi(t)\rangle$ by its components along some basis in the Hilbert space of realizable states. Thus in the representation in which $\mathbf{q}$, the position operator, is diagonal, the state vector is specified by its components along the basis vectors $|\mathbf{x}\rangle$, the eigenvectors of the position operator:

$$\mathbf{q}|\mathbf{x}\rangle = \mathbf{x}|\mathbf{x}\rangle \tag{9–41}$$

The spectrum of the operator $\mathbf{q}$ consists of the points in euclidean three space. The eigenfunctions $|\mathbf{x}'\rangle$ are not normalizable in the usual way as they correspond to eigenvalues in the continuous spectrum, but are normalized to a δ-function

$$\langle\mathbf{x}|\mathbf{x}'\rangle = \delta(\mathbf{x} - \mathbf{x}') \tag{9–42}$$

The components $\langle\mathbf{x}|\psi(t)\rangle = \psi(\mathbf{x},t)$ are then the probability amplitudes that if a position measurement is made at time t, the particle will be found at $\mathbf{x}$; more precisely, $|\langle\mathbf{x}|\psi(t)\rangle|^2 d^3\mathbf{x}$ is the probability that the particle will be found in the volume element $d^3\mathbf{x}$ about $\mathbf{x}$. In the $\mathbf{q}$ representation, Eq. (9–40) becomes

$$\int \langle\mathbf{x}|H|\mathbf{x}'\rangle d^3\mathbf{x}'\langle\mathbf{x}'|\psi(t)\rangle = i\hbar\partial_t\langle\mathbf{x}|\psi(t)\rangle \tag{9–43}$$

where to derive Eq. (9–43) we have made use of the completeness relation for the eigenstates $|\mathbf{x}\rangle$, namely the fact that

$$\int |\mathbf{x}\rangle d^3\mathbf{x}\langle\mathbf{x}| = 1 = (\text{unit operator}) \tag{9–44}$$

For a free nonrelativistic particle of mass m, H has the following form in the $\mathbf{q}$ representation

$$\begin{aligned}\langle\mathbf{x}|H|\mathbf{x}'\rangle &= -\frac{\hbar^2}{2m}\nabla_x^2\langle\mathbf{x}|\mathbf{x}'\rangle \\ &= -\frac{\hbar^2}{2m}\nabla_x^2\delta(\mathbf{x} - \mathbf{x}')\end{aligned} \tag{9–45}$$

and the Schrödinger equation in the $\mathbf{q}$ representation becomes

$$i\hbar\partial_t\psi(\mathbf{x},t) = -\frac{\hbar^2}{2m}\nabla_x^2\psi(\mathbf{x},t) \tag{9–46}$$

Formally, we recall that this equation can be derived by inserting the operator substitutions

$$E \rightarrow i\hbar\partial_t \tag{9–47}$$

$$\mathbf{p} \rightarrow -i\hbar\nabla \tag{9–48}$$

into the nonrelativistic relation between the energy and momentum for a free particle of mass m

$$E = \frac{\mathbf{p}^2}{2m} \tag{9–49}$$

Stated more abstractly, in quantum mechanics, a particle is characterized by a set of dynamical variables, $\mathbf{p},\mathbf{q}$, which are represented by operators that obey the fundamental commutation rules

$$[p^l,p^j] = [q^j,q^l] = 0 \tag{9–50}$$

$$[q^l,p^m] = i\hbar\delta^{lm} \quad j,l,m = 1,2,3 \tag{9–51}$$

and that under rotations transform as vectors. The eigenfunctions of these operators enable one to calculate the probabilities of finding the particle with a given position or momentum, provided the state vector $|\psi(t)\rangle$ describing the state of the particle is known.

The dynamical variables L^l that correspond to the three components of the orbital angular momentum pseudovector are related to the dynamical variables $\mathbf{q}$ and $\mathbf{p}$ corresponding to position and momentum by

$$L^l = \varepsilon^{ljk}q^jp^k \tag{9–52}$$

For a spinless particle the total angular momentum, $\mathbf{J}$, is equal to $\mathbf{L}$, the orbital angular momentum. It may, however, be the case that the total angular momentum is not equal to L^l as given by (9–52), but is of the form

$$J^l = \varepsilon^{ljk}q^jp^k + S^l \tag{9–53}$$

$$= L^l + S^l \tag{9–54}$$

with

$$[S^l,L^i] = 0 \qquad [S^l,p^j] = [S^l,q^j] = 0 \tag{9–55}$$

We then say that the particle has spin and the three components S^l constitute the (pseudovector) spin operator. Note that by virtue of Eq. (9–55) the spin variables are not expressible in terms of the variables $\mathbf{q}$ and $\mathbf{p}$. Since the angular momentum variables J^i are also the infinitesimal generators of rotations we deduce that

$$[J^l,S^m] = i\varepsilon^{lmn}S^n \tag{9–56}$$

which together with Eq. (9–53) implies that

$$[S^l,S^m] = i\varepsilon^{lmn}S^n \tag{9–57}$$

so that the S_j are the infinitesimal generators of an irreducible $(2s + 1)$ dimensional representation of the three-dimensional rotation group. In other words, by virtue of the commutation rules (9–57) obeyed by the spin variables, the spin of the particle is quantized, $\mathbf{S}^2$ having the possible values $s(s + 1)$ in units of $\hbar^2$, with $s = 0, \frac{1}{2}, 1, \frac{3}{2}, \cdots$.

For a free noninteracting spinning particle, invariance with respect to translations and rotations in three dimensional space, *i.e.*, invariance under the inhomogeneous euclidean group, requires that the momenta p^i and the total angular momenta J^l obey the following commutation rules

$$[J^l, J^k] = i\varepsilon^{jkl} J^l \tag{9–58}$$

$$[J^j, p^k] = i\varepsilon^{jkl} p^l \tag{9–59}$$

$$[p^k, p^l] = 0 \tag{9–60}$$

The above statements, when expressed in terms of the state vectors, imply that if the particle has no internal degrees of freedom, *i.e.*, has no spin, the "wave function" $\psi(\mathbf{x},t)$ is a one-component object. For a particle with spin s (*i.e.*, for a particle that in its rest frame has a total angular momentum whose square is equal to $s(s + 1)\hbar^2$) $\psi(\mathbf{x},t) = \langle \mathbf{x} | \psi(t) \rangle$ is a $2s + 1$ component object. If we regard $\psi(\mathbf{x},t)$ as a column vector and denote the various components by $\psi_\zeta(\mathbf{x},t)$, $\zeta = 1, \cdots, 2s + 1$, the scalar product of two vectors $|\psi(t)\rangle$, $|\phi(t)\rangle$ is defined as

$$\langle \psi(t) | \phi(t) \rangle = \sum_{\zeta=1}^{2s+1} \int d^3\mathbf{x} \overline{\psi_\zeta(\mathbf{x},t)} \phi_\zeta(\mathbf{x},t) \tag{9–61}$$

One easily shows by differentiation with respect to t and using the hermitian property of H that this scalar product is independent of time, if $|\psi(t)\rangle$ and $|\phi(t)\rangle$ are both solutions of (9–40). The probability interpretation of quantum mechanics is of course closely related to this fact. That $\langle \psi(t) | \phi(t) \rangle$ is independent of time can also be stated as the invariance of the scalar product under time translation. It should furthermore be noted that for a system whose hamiltonian is invariant under spatial rotations and spatial translations, the above scalar product is also invariant under rotations and spatial translations.

The aforementioned interpretation of $|\psi(\mathbf{x},t)|^2$ as a probability density is possible because $|\psi(\mathbf{x},t)|^2$ is (a) positive definite and (b) when integrated over all space, *i.e.*, $\int |\psi(\mathbf{x},t)|^2 d^3x$, is time independent. (By a suitable normalization of $|\psi(t)\rangle$ this integral can always be made equal to 1.)

In order to arrive at an equation for a relativistic particle of rest mass m and spin s we can proceed in essentially the same way. If in the relation between energy and momentum for a relativistic particle[3]

$$E = +c\sqrt{\mathbf{p}^2 + m^2c^2} \tag{9-62}$$

we again substitute the operator expressions (9–47) and (9–48), we arrive at an equation of the form

$$i\hbar\partial_t\chi(\mathbf{x},t) = c\sqrt{m^2c^2 - \hbar^2\nabla^2}\,\chi(\mathbf{x},t) \tag{9-63}$$

It should be noted that we have written $E = +c\sqrt{\mathbf{p}^2 + m^2c^2}$, rather than the more usual relation $E^2 = c^2\mathbf{p}^2 + m^2c^4$, so as to insure that the particles have positive energy. In equation (9–63), $\chi(\mathbf{x},t)$ is a $(2s + 1)$ component wave function whose components will be denoted by $\chi_\zeta(\mathbf{x},t)$ $(\zeta = 1,\cdots,2s + 1)$ and the square root operator $\sqrt{m^2c^2 - \hbar^2\nabla^2}$ is to be understood as an integral operator

$$\sqrt{m^2 - \nabla^2} = (m^2 - \nabla^2)\frac{1}{\sqrt{m^2 - \nabla^2}} \tag{9-64}$$

with[4]

$$\begin{aligned}\frac{1}{\sqrt{m^2 - \nabla^2}}\chi(\mathbf{x},t) &= \frac{1}{\sqrt{m^2 - \nabla^2}}\int\frac{d^3k}{(2\pi)^3}\,e^{i\mathbf{k}\cdot\mathbf{x}}\tilde{\chi}(\mathbf{k},t)\\ &= \int\frac{d^3k}{(2\pi)^3}\frac{1}{\sqrt{m^2 + \mathbf{k}^2}}\,e^{i\mathbf{k}\cdot\mathbf{x}}\tilde{\chi}(\mathbf{k},t)\\ &= \frac{1}{(2\pi)^3}\int d^3x'\int\frac{d^3k e^{i\mathbf{k}\cdot(\mathbf{x}-\mathbf{x}')}}{\sqrt{\mathbf{k}^2 + m^2}}\,\chi(\mathbf{x}',t)\\ &= \int d^3x' F(\mathbf{x} - \mathbf{x}')\chi(\mathbf{x}',t)\end{aligned} \tag{9-65}$$

where $\tilde{\phi}(\mathbf{k},t)$ denotes the Fourier transform with respect to $\mathbf{x}$ of $\phi(\mathbf{x},t)$ and

$$F(\mathbf{x} - \mathbf{x}') = \frac{1}{(2\pi)^3}\int e^{+i\mathbf{k}\cdot(\mathbf{x}-\mathbf{x}')}\cdot\frac{d^3k}{\sqrt{\mathbf{k}^2 + m^2}} \tag{9-66}$$

$F(\mathbf{x})$ can readily be evaluated in terms of Hankel functions. The salient property of $F(\mathbf{x})$ is that it decreases exponentially for $|\mathbf{x}| \gg \hbar/mc$.

[3] We shall often indicate factors $\hbar$ and c in the defining equations, although we shall consistently adopt a system of units wherein $\hbar = c = 1$.

[4] We define the inverse of the square root operator in order to deal with convergent expressions.

The solutions of Eq. (9–63) form a Hilbert space when the scalar product is defined by

$$(\chi,\phi) = \sum_{\zeta=1}^{2s+1} \int d^3x \overline{\chi_\zeta(\mathbf{x},t)} \phi_\zeta(\mathbf{x},t) \tag{9–67}$$

Note that the scalar product is formally the same as in the nonrelativistic case: it is, however, now required to be invariant under all orthochronous inhomogeneous Lorentz transformations. The requirement of invariance under orthochronous inhomogeneous Lorentz transformations stems of course from the homogeneity and isotropy of space-time, and corresponds to the assertion that all origins and orientation of the four-dimensional space time manifold are fully equivalent for the description of physical phenomena.

To make these notions precise, the transformation properties of the wavefunction χ under spatial and time translations as well as under spatial rotations and pure Lorentz transformations must be specified and it must be shown that the generators of these transformations form a unitary representation of the group of translations and proper Lorentz transformations. This can in fact be shown[5] but will not be here.

We shall only mention the fact, that a unitary representation of the inhomogeneous proper Lorentz group is exhibited in this Hilbert space through the following identification of the generators of the infinitesimal transformation of the group:

$$\mathbf{P} = \mathbf{p} \tag{9–68}$$

$$P^0 = H = \sqrt{\mathbf{p}^2 + m^2} \tag{9–69}$$

$$\mathbf{J} = \mathbf{r} \times \mathbf{p} + \mathbf{S} \tag{9–70}$$

$$\mathbf{N} = \tfrac{1}{2}(\mathbf{r}H + H\mathbf{r}) - \frac{\mathbf{S} \times \mathbf{p}}{m + H} - t\mathbf{p} \tag{9–71}$$

where the $\mathbf{S}$ are $(2s + 1) \times (2s + 1)$ irreducible hermitian matrices satisfying the commutation relations

$$[S^i,S^j] = i\varepsilon^{ijk}S^k \tag{9–72}$$

From Eq. (9–72) and the commutation rules

$$[r^l,p^j] = i\delta^{lj} \tag{9–73}$$

[5] See L. L. Foldy, *Phys. Rev.*, **102**, 568 (1956); *Phys. Rev.*, **122**, 275 (1961); or C. Fronsdal, *Phys. Rev.*, **113**, 1367 (1959).

one verifies that the operators **P**, P^0, **N**, and **J** so defined satisfy the commutation

$$[J^j,J^k] = i\varepsilon^{jkl}J^l \tag{9-74}$$

$$[J^j,N^k] = i\varepsilon^{jkl}N^l \tag{9-75}$$

$$[N^j,N^k] = -i\varepsilon^{jkl}J^l \tag{9-76}$$

$$[J^j,P^0] = 0 \tag{9-77}$$

$$[J^j,P^k] = i\varepsilon^{jkl}P^l \tag{9-78}$$

$$[N^j,P^0] = -iP^j \tag{9-79}$$

$$[P^j,P^k] = 0 = [P^0,P^j] \tag{9-80}$$

$$[N^j,P^k] = -i\delta^{jk}P^0 \tag{9-81}$$

which are the commutation rules for the infinitesimal generators of the inhomogeneous Lorentz group. This fact can now be used to prove the covariance of the formalism.[6]

It should be stressed that the amplitudes χ introduced above are *not* the usual covariant amplitudes. Their relation to the more familiar covariant Klein-Gordon amplitude for a spin 0 particle and the covariant Dirac amplitude for a spin $\frac{1}{2}$ particle will be discussed at the appropriate place. In the next section we turn to a discussion of the covariant amplitudes describing spin 0 particles.

REFERENCES

Dirac, P. A. M., *Principles of Quantum Mechanics*, 4th Ed., Clarendon Press, Oxford, 1958.

Foldy, L. L., *Phys. Rev.*, **102**, 568 (1956); **122**, 275 (1961).

Acharya, R., and Sudarshan, E. C. G., *J. Math. Phys.*, **1**, 532 (1960).

For the connection between group theory and relativistic wave equations, see:

Wigner, E. P., *Annals of Mathematics*, **40**, 149 (1939).

Bargmann, V., and Wigner, E. P., *Proc. Nat. Acad. Sciences*, **34**, 211 (1948).

Corson, E. M., *Tensors, Spinors and Relativistic Wave Equations*, Hafner Publishing Co., New York, 1953.

Wightman, A. S., "L'Invariance dans la Mécanique Quantique Relativiste," in *Dispersion Relations and Elementary Particles*, C. de Witt and R. Omnès, eds., John Wiley and Sons, Inc., New York, 1960.

9.4. Spin 0 Particles.—The covariant wave equation describing a spin 0, mass m particle is the Klein-Gordon equation:

$$(\Box + m^2)\phi(x) = 0 \tag{9-82}$$

[6] P. A. M. Dirac, *Rev. Mod. Phys.*, **21**, 392 (1949).

where the amplitude $\phi(x)$ is a (one-component) scalar function of the space time coordinates, which, under an inhomogeneous Lorentz transformation $x' = \Lambda x + a$, transforms according to

$$\phi'(x') = \phi(x) \tag{9–83}$$

Equation (9–82) admits of plane wave solutions of the form

$$\phi(x) = c_k e^{-i(k^0 x^0 - \mathbf{k}\cdot\mathbf{x})} \tag{9–84}$$

with $(k_0)^2 = \mathbf{k}^2 + m^2$ and c_k a one component amplitude. The manifold of positive energy solutions, *i.e.*, those for which $k_0 = +\sqrt{\mathbf{k}^2 + m^2}$, are the set of states that are physically realizable by a free particle of spin 0, mass m. The equation of motion for such a positive energy amplitude can be taken to be Eq. (9–82) together with the "constraint":

$$E\phi(x) = i\partial_0\phi(x) = \sqrt{m^2 - \nabla^2}\,\phi(x) \tag{9–85}$$

Although the Klein-Gordon equation is of second order in the time derivative, for a positive energy particle the knowledge of ϕ at some given time is sufficient to determine the subsequent evolution of the particle since $\partial\phi/\partial t$ is then given by Eq. (9–85). Alternatively Eq. (9–85) can be adopted as the equation of motion for a "free" spin zero particle of mass m. We shall do so here.

A Lorentz invariant scalar product can be defined in the linear vector space formed by the positive energy solutions which makes this vector space into a Hilbert space. For two positive energy Klein-Gordon amplitudes, this scalar product is defined as:

$$(\phi_1,\phi_2) = \frac{i}{2}\int d^3x\{\overline{\phi_1(x)}\partial_0\phi_2(x) - \overline{\partial_0\phi_1(x)}\phi_2(x)\} \tag{9–86}$$

$$= \tfrac{1}{2}\int d^3x\{\overline{\phi_1(x)}\sqrt{m^2 - \nabla^2}\phi_2(x) + \overline{\sqrt{m^2 - \nabla^2}\phi_1(x)}\phi_2(x)\} \tag{9–87}$$

$$= \int d^3x\, \overline{\sqrt[4]{m^2 - \nabla^2}\phi_1(x)}\cdot\sqrt[4]{m^2 - \nabla^2}\phi_2(x) \tag{9–88}$$

This scalar product is conserved in time if ϕ_1 and ϕ_2 obey the Klein-Gordon equation. It furthermore possesses all the properties usually required of a scalar product, namely

$$(\phi_1,\phi_2) = \overline{(\phi_2,\phi_1)} \tag{9–89}$$

$$(\alpha_1\phi_1 + \alpha_2\phi_2,\phi_3) = \bar{\alpha}_1(\phi_1,\phi_3) + \bar{\alpha}_2(\phi_2,\phi_3) \tag{9–90}$$

where α_1,α_2 are arbitrary complex numbers and

$$(\phi,\phi) \geq 0 \tag{9–91}$$

the equality sign in Eq. (9–91) holding if and only if $\phi = 0$. The positive definiteness of (ϕ,ϕ) if $\phi \neq 0$ is made evident by Eq. (9–88), or alternatively, by introducing the Fourier transform $\tilde{\phi}(\mathbf{k})$.

$$\phi(x) = \frac{1}{(2\pi)^{3/2}} \int_+ \frac{d^3k}{k_0} e^{-ik\cdot x}\tilde{\phi}(\mathbf{k}) \tag{9–92}$$

In the right side of Eq. (9–92) $k_0 = +\sqrt{\mathbf{k}^2 + m^2}$; this is the meaning of the subscript $+$ on the integral sign. Note further that given $\tilde{\phi}(\mathbf{k})$, the $\phi(x)$ defined by Eq. (9–92) is automatically a positive energy solution of the Klein-Gordon equation. In terms of these momentum space amplitudes the scalar product becomes

$$(\phi_1,\phi_2) = \int_+ \frac{d^3k}{k_0} \overline{\tilde{\phi}_1(\mathbf{k})}\tilde{\phi}_2(\mathbf{k}) \tag{9–93}$$

The relativistic invariance of the scalar product is also made explicit by Eq. (9–93) since ϕ as defined by Eq. (9–92) is a scalar, ($k\cdot x$ is an invariant and d^3k/k_0 is the invariant measure element over the hyperboloid $k^2 = m^2$).

From Eq. (9–88) we can obtain the relation between the Klein-Gordon amplitude ϕ and the Schrödinger amplitude χ for a spin 0, mass m particle discussed in Section 9.3, namely,

$$\chi(\mathbf{x},t) = \sqrt[4]{m^2 - \boldsymbol{\nabla}^2}\phi(\mathbf{x},t) \tag{9–94}$$

since in terms of the so defined Schrödinger amplitudes χ the scalar product takes the form (9–67), *i.e.*

$$(\phi_1,\phi_2) = \int d^3x\overline{\chi_1(\mathbf{x},t)}\chi_2(\mathbf{x},t) \tag{9–95}$$

The form of the scalar product in terms of Schrödinger amplitudes indicates that if we want to introduce into the theory a probability density it is $|\chi(\mathbf{x},t)|^2$ which must play this role. In fact, the reason for introducing the Schrödinger amplitude stems precisely from the circumstances that in terms of the latter the scalar product takes the simple form (9–95), and as a consequence of this $\int_V |\chi(\mathbf{x},t)|^2 d^3x$ may directly be interpreted as the probability of finding the particle within the volume V at time t.

However, in order to give an unambiguous answer to the question of how one is to calculate the probability of finding a Klein-Gordon particle at some point **x** at time t, we must first find a hermitian operator that can properly be called a position operator, and secondly find its eigenfunctions. It is somewhat easier to determine the latter since these should correspond to states wherein the particle is localized at a given point in space at a given time. Now the natural requirements to impose on localized states are:

(a) that this set of states localized at the origin at a given time form a linear manifold invariant under spatial rotations about the origin and
(b) that if a state is localized at some point **y** then a spatial displacement shall make it orthogonal to the set of states localized at **y**.

Let $\tilde{\phi}_0^\ell(\mathbf{k})$ be the Klein-Gordon amplitude corresponding to a spin zero particle localized at the origin at time $t = 0$. Since in momentum space the space displacement operator is multiplication by $\exp(-i\mathbf{k}\cdot\mathbf{a})$, the state localized at **y** at time $t = 0$ is given by $\exp(-i\mathbf{k}\cdot\mathbf{y})\tilde{\phi}_0^\ell(\mathbf{k})$. This displaced state by condition (b) above must be orthogonal to $\tilde{\phi}_0^\ell(\mathbf{k})$, *i.e.*

$$(\phi_0^\ell,\phi_y^\ell) = \int \frac{d^3k}{k_0} e^{-i\mathbf{k}\cdot\mathbf{y}}|\tilde{\phi}_0^\ell(\mathbf{k})|^2 \tag{9–96}$$

$$= \delta^{(3)}(\mathbf{0} - \mathbf{y}) \tag{9–97}$$

$$= \frac{1}{(2\pi)^3}\int d^3k e^{-i\mathbf{k}\cdot\mathbf{y}} \tag{9–98}$$

Hence

$$\begin{aligned} |\tilde{\phi}_0^\ell(\mathbf{k})|^2 &= (2\pi)^{-3}k_0 \\ \tilde{\phi}_0^\ell(\mathbf{k}) &= (2\pi)^{-3/2}k_0^{1/2} \\ &= (2\pi)^{-3/2}\sqrt[4]{\mathbf{k}^2 + m^2} \end{aligned} \tag{9–99}$$

The state localized at **y** at time $t = 0$ is therefore given by

$$\tilde{\phi}_{\mathbf{y},0}^\ell(\mathbf{k}) = (2\pi)^{-3/2}\sqrt[4]{\mathbf{k}^2 + m^2}e^{-i\mathbf{k}\cdot\mathbf{y}} \tag{9–100}$$

The configuration space amplitude at time $t = 0$ corresponding to a particle localized at $t = 0$ at the point **y** is obtained from $\tilde{\phi}_y^\ell(\mathbf{k})$ by substituting the latter expression into Eq. (9–92):

$$\phi_{\mathbf{y},0}^\ell(\mathbf{x},0) = \frac{1}{(2\pi)^3}\int \frac{d^3k}{k_0} e^{i\mathbf{k}\cdot(\mathbf{x}-\mathbf{y})}\sqrt[4]{\mathbf{k}^2 + m^2} \tag{9–101}$$

One verifies that

$$\phi^{\ell}_{\mathbf{y},0}(\mathbf{x},0) = \text{constant} \cdot \left(\frac{m}{r}\right)^{5/4} H^{(1)}_{5/4}(imr) \tag{9–102}$$

where $r = |\mathbf{x} - \mathbf{y}|$. The Hankel function has the property that it decreases exponentially as $\exp(-mr)$ as $r \to \infty$, and at $r = 0$ it becomes infinite as $r^{-5/2}$. This localized function is not square integrable. This is to be expected since we will show that it is an eigenfunction of a hermitian operator, the position operator, which has a purely continuous spectrum. It should be noted that these localized states do not correspond to δ-functions in coordinate space. It should also be noted that the localized states are not Lorentz covariant. They possess the maximum symmetry properties corresponding to a time-like plane in space time, *i.e.*, they are only covariant under three-dimensional spatial rotations and reflections. A state localized at the origin in one coordinate system is not localized in a moving coordinate system even if the origin of the two coordinate systems coincide at time $t = 0$. The concept of particle observables in relativistic quantum mechanics is a noncovariant one: it is associated with an observer in a given Lorentz frame.

More generally, the configuration space amplitude corresponding to a particle localized at time y_0 at the spatial point $\mathbf{y}$ is given by

$$\phi^{\ell}_{y}(x) = \frac{1}{(2\pi)^3} \int_{+} \frac{d^3k}{k_0} e^{-ik\cdot(x-y)} \sqrt[4]{\mathbf{k}^2 + m^2} \tag{9–103}$$

According to the usual rules of quantum mechanics the probability amplitude for finding a particle described by the amplitude $\phi(x)$ to be localized at y is then given by the scalar product (ϕ^{l}_{y},ϕ). This quantity is readily computed and one verifies that

$$\begin{aligned}(\phi^{\ell}_{y},\phi) &= \frac{1}{(2\pi)^{3/2}} \int_{+} \frac{d^3k}{k_0} e^{-ik\cdot y} \sqrt[4]{\mathbf{k}^2 + m^2}\,\tilde{\phi}(k) \\ &= \sqrt[4]{m^2 - \nabla_y^2}\,\phi(y) \\ &= \chi(y)\end{aligned} \tag{9–104}$$

proving that the probability for finding the particle at y is given by $|\chi(y)|^2$, so that the Schrödinger amplitude $\chi(y)$ indeed plays the role of a probability density for the Klein-Gordon theory.

We next turn our attention to the problem of finding the position operator $\mathbf{q}$, of which the localized state $\tilde{\phi}^{\ell}_{\mathbf{y}}(k)$ is an eigenfunction with eigenvalue $\mathbf{y}$. That this operator is not given by $\mathbf{q} = i\nabla_{\mathbf{k}}$ in the momentum representation becomes clear upon noting that the operator

$i\nabla_{\mathbf{k}}$ is not hermitian within the scalar product (9–93) due to the presence of the factor k_0^{-1} in the measure element. The operator[7]

$$\mathbf{q} = i\nabla_{\mathbf{k}} - \frac{1}{2}\frac{i\mathbf{k}}{\mathbf{k}^2 + m^2} \tag{9–105}$$

is easily seen to have the following properties:

(a) it is hermitian within the scalar product (9–93), *i.e.*

$$(\phi_1,\mathbf{q}\phi_2) = (\mathbf{q}\phi_1,\phi_2) \tag{9–106}$$

(b) the components of $\mathbf{q}$ commute with one another

$$[q^l,q^m] = 0 \tag{9–107}$$

(c) the commutation rules of the q_l with momentum operators are

$$[q^l,p^j] = i\delta^{lj} \tag{9–108}$$

(d) the time derivative of this operator $\mathbf{q}$ is equal to

$$\frac{d}{dt}\mathbf{q} = i[H,\mathbf{q}] = i[p_0,\mathbf{q}] \tag{9–109}$$

$$= \mathbf{p}/p_0 \tag{9–110}$$

which will be recognized as the velocity operator of the particle. The second time derivative, the acceleration operator, vanishes

$$[H,[H,\mathbf{q}]] = 0 \tag{9–111}$$

as is to be expected for a free particle,

(e) under spatial rotations $\mathbf{q}$ transforms like a vector,

(f) the localized wave function $\exp(-i\mathbf{k}\cdot\mathbf{y})k_0^{1/2}$ is an eigenfunction of $\mathbf{q}$ with eigenvalue $\mathbf{y}$

$$\mathbf{q}\{e^{-i\mathbf{k}\cdot\mathbf{y}}\sqrt{k_0}\} = i\left\{\nabla_{\mathbf{k}} - \frac{1}{2}\frac{\mathbf{k}}{k_0^2}\right\}\{e^{-i\mathbf{k}\cdot\mathbf{y}}\sqrt{k_0}\}$$

$$= \mathbf{y}\{e^{-i\mathbf{k}\cdot\mathbf{y}}\sqrt{k_0}\} \tag{9–112}$$

[7] For a particle with wave function $\tilde{\phi}(\mathbf{k})$ it is the Fourier transform of $\sqrt[4]{\mathbf{k}^2 + m^2}\tilde{\phi}(\mathbf{k})$ which gives the probability amplitude for finding the particle localized at a given point (see Eq. (9–104)). It is therefore natural to inquire as to the properties of the operator $U\mathbf{x}U^{-1}$, $\mathbf{x} = i\nabla_{\mathbf{k}}$, where U is the (nonunitary) operator such that if

$$\langle\mathbf{k}|\phi\rangle = \tilde{\phi}(\mathbf{k})$$

then

$$\langle\mathbf{k}|U|\phi\rangle = \sqrt[4]{\mathbf{k}^2 + m^2}\,\tilde{\phi}(\mathbf{k})$$

In this fashion one is led to the operator

$$\mathbf{q} = U\mathbf{x}U^{-1} = i\nabla_{\mathbf{k}} - \frac{1}{2}\frac{i\mathbf{k}}{\mathbf{k}^2 + m^2}$$

for the position operator.

The above properties justify calling $\mathbf{q}$ the position operator for a relativistic spin 0, mass m particle.

We have thus far only considered the relativistic quantum mechanical description of a single spin 0, mass m particle. We next turn to the problem of describing a system of n such noninteracting spin 0, mass m, particles. The most concise description of a system of such identical particles is in terms of an operator formalism known as "second quantization." It is described in Chapter 8, "The Mathematical Formalism of Quantum Statistics," and the reader is referred to that chapter for detailed exposition of the formalism. We here shall assume familiarity with it.

We denote the no particle state by $|0\rangle$. It is normalized as follows:

$$\langle 0|0\rangle = 1 \tag{9–113}$$

The one-particle state of momentum $\mathbf{k}$ will be denoted by $|\mathbf{k}\rangle$. Since the particle is noninteracting and free, its energy is $k_0 = \sqrt{\mathbf{k}^2 + m^2}$. We shall normalize the one-particle states in such a way that

$$\langle \mathbf{k}'|\mathbf{k}\rangle = k_0\delta(\mathbf{k} - \mathbf{k}') \tag{9–114}$$

and the completeness relation for these one particle states is then given by

$$\int_+ \frac{d^3k}{k_0} |\mathbf{k}\rangle\langle\mathbf{k}| = 1 \quad \text{(in one particle subspace)} \tag{9–115}$$

since operating on a one-particle state $|\mathbf{k}'\rangle$, the left-hand side of Eq. (9–115) reproduces this state. Given a one particle state, we can construct many-particle states by taking suitable linear combinations of products of one-particle states. A properly symmetrized n-particle state consisting on n particles with momenta $\mathbf{k}_1,\cdots,\mathbf{k}_n$, energies $k_{01},\cdots,k_{0n}$ can be constructed from the product $|\mathbf{k}_1\rangle\cdots|\mathbf{k}_n\rangle$ by applying the symmetrizer S to it. We shall denote this properly symmetrized state by

$$|\mathbf{k}_1,\cdots,\mathbf{k}_n\rangle = S\{|\mathbf{k}_1\rangle\cdots|\mathbf{k}_n\rangle\} \tag{9–116}$$

Its orthonormality properties are

$$\langle \mathbf{k}_1',\mathbf{k}_2',\cdots,\mathbf{k}_m'|\mathbf{k}_1,\cdots,\mathbf{k}_n\rangle = \delta_{nm}\frac{1}{n!}\sum_p k_{01}\delta(\mathbf{k}_1' - \mathbf{k}_{\alpha_1})\cdots k_{0n}\delta(\mathbf{k}_n' - \mathbf{k}_{\alpha_n}) \tag{9–117}$$

where the summation is over all the permutations of the set $\{\alpha_1,\cdots\alpha_n\}$.

We now define the annihilation operator $a_{\mathbf{k}}$ by the equations

$$a_{\mathbf{k}}|0\rangle = 0 \tag{9–118}$$

$$a_{\mathbf{k}}|\mathbf{k}'\rangle = k_0\delta(\mathbf{k} - \mathbf{k}')|0\rangle \tag{9–119}$$

Since the one-particle states are orthogonal to the no-particle state, *i.e.* $\langle 0|\mathbf{k}\rangle = 0$, Eqs. (9–118) and (9–119) imply that

$$\langle 0|a_{\mathbf{k}}|0\rangle = \langle \mathbf{k}'|a_{\mathbf{k}}|0\rangle = \langle \mathbf{k}'|a_{\mathbf{k}}|\mathbf{k}''\rangle = 0 \tag{9–120}$$

$$\langle 0|a_{\mathbf{k}}|\mathbf{k}'\rangle = k_0\delta(\mathbf{k} - \mathbf{k}') \tag{9–121}$$

The creation operator $a_{\mathbf{k}}^*$ is defined by

$$a_{\mathbf{k}}^*|0\rangle = [a_{\mathbf{k}}]^*|0\rangle \tag{9–122}$$

$$= |\mathbf{k}\rangle \tag{9–123}$$

and more generally by

$$|\mathbf{k}_1,\cdots,\mathbf{k}_n\rangle = \frac{1}{\sqrt{n!}}\, a_{\mathbf{k}_1}^* \cdots a_{\mathbf{k}_n}^*|0\rangle \tag{9–124}$$

The symmetric character of the vector $|\mathbf{k}_1,\cdots,\mathbf{k}_n\rangle$ then implies that

$$[a_{\mathbf{k}}^*,a_{\mathbf{k}'}^*] = 0 \tag{9–125}$$

and taking the hermitian adjoint of this equation, we find that

$$[a_{\mathbf{k}},a_{\mathbf{k}'}] = 0 \tag{9–126}$$

The normalization of the one-particle states together with the definition of the vacuum now implies that

$$\begin{aligned}\langle \mathbf{k}'|\mathbf{k}\rangle &= \langle 0|a_{\mathbf{k}'}a_{\mathbf{k}}^*|0\rangle = \langle 0|[a_{\mathbf{k}'},a_{\mathbf{k}}^*]|0\rangle \\ &= k_0\delta(\mathbf{k} - \mathbf{k}')\end{aligned} \tag{9–127}$$

so that if we require the commutator to be a c-number we have in general

$$[a_{\mathbf{k}},a_{\mathbf{k}'}^*] = k_0\delta(\mathbf{k} - \mathbf{k}') \tag{9–128}$$

The occupation number operator for particles of momentum $\mathbf{k}$ can be defined as $n_{\mathbf{k}} = k_0^{-1}a_{\mathbf{k}}^*a_{\mathbf{k}}$, and the total number of particles operator as

$$N = \int \frac{d^3k}{k_0}\, a_{\mathbf{k}}^*a_{\mathbf{k}} \tag{9–129}$$

it has the property that

$$N|0\rangle = 0 \tag{9–130}$$

$$N|\mathbf{k}_1,\cdots,\mathbf{k}_n\rangle = n|\mathbf{k}_1,\cdots,\mathbf{k}_n\rangle \tag{9–131}$$

as is easily verified using the commutation relations of N with the creation operator $a_{\mathbf{k}}^*$:

$$[N,a_{\mathbf{k}}^*] = a_{\mathbf{k}}^* \tag{9–132}$$

and the definition (9–124) of an n-particle state in terms of creation operators. Similarly we can define the total energy and total momentum operators as follows:

$$H = \int \frac{d^3k}{k_0}\, k_0 a_{\mathbf{k}}^* a_{\mathbf{k}} \tag{9–133}$$

$$\mathbf{P} = \int \frac{d^3k}{k_0}\, \mathbf{k} a_{\mathbf{k}}^* a_{\mathbf{k}} \tag{9–134}$$

They have the property that

$$H|\mathbf{k}_1,\cdots,\mathbf{k}_n\rangle = \sum_{i=1}^{n} k_{0\,i}|\mathbf{k}_1,\cdots,\mathbf{k}_n\rangle \tag{9–135}$$

$$\mathbf{P}|\mathbf{k}_1,\cdots,\mathbf{k}_n\rangle = \sum_{i=1}^{n} \mathbf{k}_i|\mathbf{k}_1,\cdots,\mathbf{k}_n\rangle \tag{9–136}$$

$$H|0\rangle = \mathbf{P}|0\rangle = 0 \tag{9–137}$$

The defining equations (9–133) and (9–134) for H and $\mathbf{P}$ reflect the fact that the particles are free and do not interact with one another. The total energy and total momentum of the system is, therefore, the sum of energies and momenta of the individual particles as indicated by Eqs. (9–135) to (9–137).

We shall see that we may consider the operators H,$\mathbf{P}$ as the time and space components of the four-vector P_μ

$$P_\mu = \int \frac{d^3k}{k_0}\, k_\mu a_{\mathbf{k}}^* a_{\mathbf{k}} \tag{9–138}$$

$$k_0 = \sqrt{\mathbf{k}^2 + m^2} \tag{9–139}$$

The commutation rules of P_μ with $a_{\mathbf{k}}$ and $a_{\mathbf{k}}^*$ are

$$[P_\mu,a_{\mathbf{k}}] = -k_\mu a_{\mathbf{k}} \tag{9–140}$$

$$[P_\mu,a_{\mathbf{k}}^*] = k_\mu a_{\mathbf{k}}^* \tag{9–141}$$

These commutation rules imply that if the state $|p\rangle$ is an eigenstate of P_μ with eigenvalue p_μ

$$P_\mu|p\rangle = p_\mu|p\rangle \tag{9–142}$$

then the state $a_{\mathbf{k}}|p\rangle$ is an eigenfunction of P_μ with eigenvalue $p_\mu - k_\mu(k_0 = \sqrt{\mathbf{k}^2 + m^2})$:

$$\begin{aligned} P_\mu a_{\mathbf{k}}|p\rangle &= a_{\mathbf{k}} P_\mu|p\rangle + [P_\mu, a_{\mathbf{k}}]|p\rangle \\ &= (p_\mu - k_\mu)|p\rangle \end{aligned} \tag{9–143}$$

Similarly the state $a_{\mathbf{k}}^*|p\rangle$ is a state with energy-momentum eigenvalues $p_\mu + k_\mu(k_0 = \sqrt{\mathbf{k}^2 + m^2})$. These facts further validate the interpretation of $a_{\mathbf{k}}$ and $a_{\mathbf{k}}^*$ as destruction and creation operators for a particle of momentum $\mathbf{k}$ and energy $\sqrt{\mathbf{k}^2 + m^2}$.

Using the defining equations (9–118), (9–124), and the commutation rules (9–124), (9–125), and (9–128), one verifies that

$$a_{\mathbf{k}}|\mathbf{k}_1, \cdots, \mathbf{k}_n\rangle = \frac{1}{\sqrt{n}} \sum_{j=1} k_0 \delta(\mathbf{k} - \mathbf{k}_j)|\mathbf{k}_1, \cdots, \mathbf{k}_{j-1}, \mathbf{k}_{j+1}, \cdots, \mathbf{k}_n\rangle \tag{9–144}$$

$$a_{\mathbf{k}}^*|\mathbf{k}_1, \cdots, \mathbf{k}_n\rangle = \sqrt{n+1}|\mathbf{k}, \mathbf{k}_1, \cdots, \mathbf{k}_n\rangle \tag{9–145}$$

One speaks of Eqs. (9–144) and (9–145) as a representation of the operators $a_{\mathbf{k}}$ and $a_{\mathbf{k}}^*$ satisfying the commutation rules (9–128), (9–124), and (9–125). The states $|\mathbf{k}_1, \cdots, \mathbf{k}_n\rangle$ $n = 0,1,2,\cdots$ are the basis vectors spanning the Hilbert space in which the operators $a_{\mathbf{k}}$ and $a_{\mathbf{k}}^*$ operate. The representation (9–144) and (9–145) is characterized by the fact that a no-particle state $|0\rangle$ exists which is annihilated by $a_{\mathbf{k}}$. Furthermore this representation is irreducible since in this representation $a(a^*)$ operating upon an n-particle state, results in an $n - 1$ $(n + 1)$ particle state so that there are no invariant subspaces. Besides the above representation there exist other inequivalent irreducible representations of the commutation rules for which neither a no-particle state nor a number operator exists.[8]

We next introduce the configuration space Heisenberg operator

$$\phi^{(+)}(x) = \int_{k_0>0} \frac{d^3k}{k_0} \frac{1}{\sqrt{2(2\pi)^3}} e^{-ik\cdot x} a_{\mathbf{k}} \tag{9–146}$$

This operator is a destruction operator and has the property that it annihilates the vacuum

$$\phi^{(+)}(x)|0\rangle = 0 \quad \text{for all } x \tag{9–147}$$

and obeys the Klein-Gordon equation

$$(\Box + \mu^2)\phi^{(+)}(x) = 0 \tag{9–148}$$

[8] See A. S. Wightman and S. S. Schweber, *Phys. Rev.*, **98**, 812 (1955), or R. Haag, *Kgl. Danske Videnshab Selskab, Mat. fys. Medd*, **29**, No. 12 (1955); *Lectures in Theoretical Physics*, Vol. III, pp. 353–381, Interscience Publishers, Inc., New York, 1961.

In fact, by virtue of the circumstance that in the defining equation for $\phi^{(+)}(x)$ only positive frequencies occur ($k_0 = +\sqrt{\mathbf{k}^2 + m^2} > 0$), $\phi^{(+)}(x)$ obeys the following first order equation

$$i \frac{\partial}{\partial x_0} \phi^{(+)}(x) = \sqrt{m^2 - \nabla^2}\phi^{(+)}(x) \tag{9–149}$$

We define the configuration space Heisenberg creation operator by the equation

$$\phi^{(-)}(x) = \int_{k_0 > 0} \frac{d^3k}{k_0} \frac{1}{\sqrt{2(2\pi)^3}} e^{ik\cdot x} a_{\mathbf{k}}^* \tag{9–150}$$

$$= \phi^{(+)*}(x) \tag{9–151}$$

which satisfies the following first order equation

$$i \frac{\partial}{\partial x_0} \phi^{(-)}(x) = -\sqrt{m^2 - \nabla^2}\phi^{(-)}(x) \tag{9–152}$$

Since in (9–150), $k^2 = m^2$, $\phi^{(-)}(x)$ also satisfies the Klein-Gordon equation

$$(\Box + \mu^2)\phi^{(-)}(x) = 0 \tag{9–153}$$

Upon taking the adjoint of Eq. (9–147) we deduce that $\phi^{(-)}(x)$ annihilates the vacuum when operating on it from the right:

$$\langle 0|\phi^{(-)}(x) = 0 \quad \text{for all } x \tag{9–154}$$

The commutation rules of $\phi^{(+)}(x)$ and $\phi^{(-)}$ are easily derived from those of $a_{\mathbf{k}}, a_{\mathbf{k}}^*$. They are

$$[\phi^{(+)}(x), \phi^{(+)}(x')] = [\phi^{(-)}(x), \phi^{(-)}(x')] = 0 \tag{9–155}$$

$$[\phi^{(+)}(x), \phi^{(-)}(x')] = i\Delta^{(+)}(x - x') \tag{9–156}$$

where

$$\Delta^{(+)}(x) = -\frac{i}{2(2\pi)^3} \int_+ \frac{d^3k}{k_0} e^{-ik\cdot x} \tag{9–157}$$

$$= -\frac{i}{(2\pi)^3} \int d^4k \theta(k_0) \delta(k^2 - m^2) e^{-ik\cdot x} \tag{9–158}$$

In (9–158), $\theta(k_0)$ is defined by

$$\begin{aligned} \theta(k_0) &= 1 \quad \text{if } k_0 > 0 \\ &= 0 \quad \text{if } k_0 < 0 \end{aligned} \tag{9–159}$$

We shall at times write $\theta(k)$ for $\theta(k_0)$. The equivalence of (9–158) and (9–159) is established by recalling that

$$\delta(k^2 - m^2) = \frac{1}{2|k_0|}\left[\delta(k_0 - \sqrt{\mathbf{k}^2 + m^2}) + \delta(k_0 + \sqrt{\mathbf{k}^2 + m^2})\right] \tag{9–160}$$

and recognizing that the $\theta(k_0)$ factor implies that only the

$$\delta(k_0 - \sqrt{\mathbf{k}^2 + m^2})$$

contributes. Note incidentally that the δ function also asserts that k^2 in (9–158) is a time-like vector. The $\theta(k_0)$ then implies that k lies in the forward light cone. This specification is Lorentz invariant, since under Lorentz transformations a vector that lies in the forward light cone remains in the forward light cone, *i.e.*

$$\theta(k) = \theta(\Lambda k) \quad \text{if } k^2 > 0 \tag{9–161}$$

The representation (9–158) makes explicit two of the important properties of $\Delta^{(+)}(x)$, namely that

(a) it satisfies the Klein-Gordon equation

$$(\Box + \mu^2)\Delta^{(+)}(x) = 0 \tag{9–162}$$

(it actually also satisfies the first order equation

$$i\frac{\partial}{\partial x_0}\Delta^{(+)}(x) = \sqrt{m^2 - \nabla^2}\Delta^{(+)}(x) \tag{9–163}$$

(b) for any proper homogeneous Lorentz transformation Λ which does not invert the sign of the time

$$\Delta^{(+)}(\Lambda x) = \Delta^{(+)}(x) \tag{9–164}$$

Similarly one may show:

$$[\phi^{(-)}(x),\phi^{(+)}(x')] = i\Delta^{(-)}(x - x') \tag{9–165}$$

where

$$\Delta^{(-)}(x) = -\Delta^{(+)}(-x) \tag{9–166}$$

$$= \overline{\Delta^{(+)}(x)} \tag{9–167}$$

We can construct from the operators $\phi^{(+)}(x)$ and $\phi^{(-)}(x)$ the following *hermitian* operator:

$$\phi(x) = \phi^{(+)}(x) + \phi^{(-)}(x) \tag{9–168}$$

$$= \frac{1}{\sqrt{2(2\pi)^3}}\int\frac{d^3k}{k_0}\,(a_{\mathbf{k}}e^{-ik\cdot x} + a_{\mathbf{k}}^* e^{ik\cdot x}) \tag{9–169}$$

which satisfies the Klein-Gordon equation

$$(\Box + \mu^2)\phi(x) = 0 \tag{9–170}$$

and the following commutation rules

$$[\phi(x),\phi(x')] = i\Delta(x - x') \tag{9–171}$$

where

$$\Delta(x) = \Delta^{(+)}(x) + \Delta^{(-)}(x) \tag{9–172}$$

An explicit representation of $\Delta(x)$ is given by

$$\Delta(x) = -\frac{i}{2(2\pi)^3}\int_{k_0>0}\frac{d^3k}{k_0}\,(e^{-ik\cdot x} - e^{ik\cdot x}) \tag{9–173}$$

$$= -\frac{1}{(2\pi)^3}\int_{k_0>0}\frac{d^3k}{k_0}\,e^{i\mathbf{k}\cdot\mathbf{x}}\sin k_0x_0 \tag{9–174}$$

$$= -\frac{i}{(2\pi)^3}\int d^4k\varepsilon(k_0)\delta(k^2 - \mu^2)e^{-ik\cdot x} \tag{9–175}$$

where $\varepsilon(k_0) = k_0/|k_0|$. The important properties of $\Delta(x)$ that can be deduced from the above representation are:

$$-\Delta(-x) = \Delta(x) \tag{9–176}$$

$$\Delta(\Lambda x) = \Delta(x) \tag{9–177}$$

$$(\Box + \mu^2)\Delta(x) = 0 \tag{9–178}$$

$$\Delta(x_0 = 0,\mathbf{x}) = 0 \tag{9–179}$$

$$\left(\frac{\partial\Delta(x)}{\partial x_0}\right)_{x_0=0} = -\delta(\mathbf{x}) \tag{9–180}$$

From the invariance of $\Delta(x)$ under proper homogeneous Lorentz transformation and the fact that $\Delta(x)$ is odd, $\Delta(-x) = -\Delta(x)$, one can deduce that $\Delta(x)$ vanishes when x^2 is spacelike. The proof of this assertion is as follows: the Lorentz invariance of $\Delta(x)$, $\Delta(\Lambda x) = \Delta(x)$, implies that $\Delta(x)$ is a function only of the invariants which can be formed from x, *i.e.*, it is a function of x^2 for $x^2 < 0$ and of x^2 and $\varepsilon(x_0) = x_0/|x_0|$, the sign of the time, for $x^2 \geq 0$:

$$\text{for } x^2 \geq 0 \qquad \Delta(x) = G_1(x^2) + \varepsilon(x_0)G_2(x^2) \tag{9–181}$$

$$\text{for } x^2 < 0 \qquad \Delta(x) = F_1(x^2) \tag{9–182}$$

However, since a function of x^2 cannot be an odd function of x, $F_1(x^2) = 0$, which was to be demonstrated. Within the light cone

$\Delta(x)$ must have the form $\Delta(x) = \varepsilon(x_0)G_2(x^2)$ in order to be odd and invariant, that is, $G_1(x^2)$ must be equal to zero. In other words

$$\Delta(x) = 0 \qquad \text{for } x^2 < 0 \tag{9-183}$$

$$\Delta(x) = \varepsilon(x_0)G(x^2) \quad \text{for } x^2 \geq 0 \tag{9-184}$$

Equation (9–183) states that the commutator $[\phi(x),\phi(x')]$ vanishes if $x - x'$ lies outside the light cone, which can be regarded as the statement of microscopic causality for our theory. The reason for this is as follows: in quantum mechanics, the vanishing of the commutator of two *hermitian* operators implies that these operators can both be brought to diagonal form, which in turn, in the light of the physical interpretation of the theory, implies that the observables corresponding to these hermitian operators can be both measured with arbitrary accuracy, no mutual interference effects occurring. Now the statement of causality within the framework of the theory of special relativity is that no signal can be propagated faster than the speed of light, so that measurements at space-time points separated by a space like distance can never interfere. Hence, within a consistent relativistic quantum theory, causality requires that local observables separated by a space like distance commute with one another.

The covariant amplitudes describing one-, two-, etc., particle systems can be defined in terms of the Heisenberg field operators $\phi(x)$ as follows: consider a one-particle system described by the state vector $|\Psi\rangle$: Since it describes a one-particle system, it has the property that

$$N|\Psi\rangle = 1|\Psi\rangle \tag{9-185}$$

We now define the covariant (Fock) amplitude describing this system by

$$\varphi(x) = \langle 0|\phi(x)|\Psi\rangle \tag{9-186}$$

By virtue of Eq. (9–154) only the positive frequency part of $\phi(x)$, *i.e.*, $\phi^{(+)}(x)$, gives a nonvanishing contribution to the matrix element. Since $\phi^{(+)}(x)$ obeys Eq. (9–149), so will $\varphi(x)$:

$$i\frac{\partial}{\partial x_0}\varphi(x) = \sqrt{m^2 - \nabla^2}\varphi(x) \tag{9-187}$$

proving that $\varphi(x)$ is identical with the covariant Klein-Gordon amplitude previously used to describe a one-particle system and extensively studied at the beginning of the present section. If furthermore $|\Psi\rangle$ is an eigenstate of the total momentum operator with eigenvalue $\mathbf{k}$

$$\mathbf{P}|\Psi\rangle = \mathbf{k}|\Psi\rangle \tag{9-188}$$

then upon using the commutation relation

$$[\phi(x),P^l] = i\frac{\partial\phi}{\partial x_l} \tag{9–189}$$

(which is easily deduced using Eqs. (9–169), (9–134), (9–140), and (9–141), and the fact that $\mathbf{P}|0\rangle = 0$ we find that

$$\begin{aligned} \langle 0|[\phi(x),P^l]|\Psi\rangle &= i\frac{\partial}{\partial x_l}\langle 0|\phi(x)|\Psi\rangle \\ &= i\frac{\partial\varphi(x)}{\partial x_l} \\ &= k^l\langle 0|\phi(x)|\Psi\rangle \\ &= k^l\varphi(x) \end{aligned} \tag{9–190}$$

i.e., under these circumstances

$$-i\frac{\partial}{\partial x^l}\varphi(x) = k^l\varphi(x)$$

These considerations can be extended to noninteracting two-, three-, etc., particle systems.

The theory outlined above is adequate for the description of a system of noninteracting bosons of mass m and spin 0 that are electrically neutral and that have no other quantum numbers to characterize them, for example, the neutral pions. It is, however, observed in nature that for particles with spin 0 that do have other quantum numbers specifying them, such as charge and strangeness, there always exist two kinds of particles with the same mass and spin but opposite additive quantum numbers such as charge and strangeness. By additive we mean that the quantum number for a system of such particles is the algebraic sum of the quantum numbers for the individual particles.

Consider for example the case of positively charged and negatively charged pions. These particles both have the same mass and both have spin 0. However, they have opposite electric charge quantum numbers: the positively charged pion having a charge quantum number $+e$, whereas the negatively charged pion has a charge quantum number $-e$. Let us describe the positively charged particles by creation and annihilation operators $a^*_{\mathbf{k}}$ and $a_{\mathbf{k}}$ and the negatively charged ones by creation and annihilation operators $b^*_{\mathbf{k}}$ and $b_{\mathbf{k}}$. They obey the commutation rules

$$[a_{\mathbf{k}},a^*_{\mathbf{k}'}] = k_0\delta(\mathbf{k} - \mathbf{k}') \tag{9–191}$$

$$[a_{\mathbf{k}},a_{\mathbf{k}'}] = [a^*_{\mathbf{k}},a^*_{\mathbf{k}'}] = 0 \tag{9–192}$$

$$[b_{\mathbf{k}},b^*_{\mathbf{k}'}] = k_0\delta(\mathbf{k} - \mathbf{k}') \tag{9–193}$$

$$[b_{\mathbf{k}},b_{\mathbf{k}'}] = [b^*_{\mathbf{k}},b^*_{\mathbf{k}'}] = 0 \tag{9–194}$$

and since the $a_{\mathbf{k}}$ and $b_{\mathbf{k}}$ operators refer to different degrees of freedom they commute

$$[a_{\mathbf{k}},b_{\mathbf{k}}] = [a_{\mathbf{k}}^*,b_{\mathbf{k}}^*] = 0 \tag{9–195}$$

$$[a_{\mathbf{k}},b_{\mathbf{k}}^*] = [a_{\mathbf{k}}^*,b_{\mathbf{k}}] = 0 \tag{9–196}$$

We shall refer to the positively charged particles as the particles and the negatively charged ones as the "antiparticles."

The number operators N_+,N_- for the number of positively and negatively charged particles are then given by the following expressions

$$N_- = \int_+ \frac{d^3k}{k_0}\, b_{\mathbf{k}}^* b_{\mathbf{k}} \tag{9–197}$$

$$N_+ = \int_+ \frac{d^3k}{k_0}\, a_{\mathbf{k}}^* a_{\mathbf{k}} \tag{9–198}$$

and the operators corresponding to the total energy and momentum by

$$H = \int_+ \frac{d^3k}{k_0}\, k_0^*(a_{\mathbf{k}}^* a_{\mathbf{k}} + b_{\mathbf{k}}^* b_{\mathbf{k}}) \tag{9–199}$$

$$\mathbf{P} = \int_+ \frac{d^3k}{k_0}\, \mathbf{k}(a_{\mathbf{k}}^* a_{\mathbf{k}} + b_{\mathbf{k}}^* b_{\mathbf{k}}) \tag{9–200}$$

A state of m particles and n antiparticles can be constructed from the no-particle state $|0\rangle$, which now is annihilated by both the $b_{\mathbf{k}}$ and the $a_{\mathbf{k}}$ operators:

$$b_{\mathbf{k}}|0\rangle = a_{\mathbf{k}}|0\rangle = 0 \quad \text{for all } \mathbf{k} \tag{9–201}$$

as follows:

$$|\mathbf{k}_1,\mathbf{k}_2,\cdots,\mathbf{k}_m;\,\mathbf{p}_1,\cdots,\mathbf{p}_n\rangle = \frac{1}{\sqrt{m!n!}}\, a_{\mathbf{k}_1}^* \cdots a_{\mathbf{k}_m}^* b_{\mathbf{p}_1}^* \cdots b_{\mathbf{p}_n}^* |0\rangle \tag{9–202}$$

Note that by virtue of Eqs. (9–192) and (9–194), the vector

$$|\mathbf{k}_1,\cdots,\mathbf{k}_m;\,\mathbf{p}_1,\cdots,\mathbf{p}_n\rangle$$

is symmetric under the interchange of any two particles, and any two antiparticles. This is as required by the Bose character of the particles and antiparticles. Let us next introduce the *hermitian* operator Q which is to describe the electric charge properties of our particles. We define the operator Q by

$$Q|0\rangle = 0 \tag{9–203}$$

$$Q|\mathbf{k};\,\rangle = e|\mathbf{k};\,\rangle \tag{9–204}$$

$$Q|\,;\mathbf{p}\rangle = -e|\,;\mathbf{p}\rangle \tag{9–205}$$

and additivity requires that

$$Q|\mathbf{k}_1,\cdots,\mathbf{k}_m;\,\mathbf{p}_1,\cdots,\mathbf{p}_n\rangle = (m-n)e|\mathbf{k}_1,\cdots,\mathbf{k}_m;\,\mathbf{p}_1,\cdots,\mathbf{p}_n\rangle \tag{9-206}$$

Since by virtue of Eq. (9–203)

$$\begin{aligned} Q\frac{1}{\sqrt{n!m!}}a^*_{\mathbf{k}_1}\cdots a^*_{\mathbf{k}_m}b^*_{\mathbf{p}_1}\cdots b^*_{\mathbf{p}_n}|0\rangle &= \frac{1}{\sqrt{n!m!}}[Q,a^*_{\mathbf{k}_1}]a^*_{\mathbf{k}_2}\cdots b^*_{\mathbf{p}_n}|0\rangle \\ &\quad+\frac{1}{\sqrt{n!m!}}a^*_{\mathbf{k}_1}[Q,a^*_{\mathbf{k}_2}]a^*_{\mathbf{k}_3}\cdots b^*_{\mathbf{p}_n}|0\rangle \\ &\quad+\cdots+\frac{1}{\sqrt{n!m!}}a^*_{\mathbf{k}_1}\cdots a^*_{\mathbf{k}_m}b^*_{\mathbf{p}_1}\cdots[Q,b^*_{\mathbf{p}_n}]|0\rangle \end{aligned} \tag{9-207}$$

The desired "additive" result expressed by Eq. (9–206) will follow if

$$[Q,a^*_{\mathbf{k}}] = ea^*_{\mathbf{k}} \tag{9-208}$$

$$[Q,b^*_{\mathbf{k}}] = -eb^*_{\mathbf{k}} \tag{9-209}$$

Since e is the eigenvalue of a hermitian operator, it is real; hence, upon taking the hermitian adjoint of Eqs. (9–208) and (9–209) we deduce that

$$[Q,a_{\mathbf{k}}] = -ea_{\mathbf{k}} \tag{9-210}$$

$$[Q,b_{\mathbf{k}}] = eb_{\mathbf{k}} \tag{9-211}$$

The above commutation rules suggest that an explicit representation of Q is given by

$$\begin{aligned} Q &= e\int\frac{d^3k}{k_0}(a^*_{\mathbf{k}}a_{\mathbf{k}} - b^*_{\mathbf{k}}b_{\mathbf{k}}) \\ &= e(N_+ - N_-) \end{aligned} \tag{9-212}$$

This operator in fact satisfies all the requirements placed on the total charge operator, *i.e.*, it satisfies Eqs. (9–203), (9–204), (9–205), (9–206), and (9–208)–(9–212). In addition, it is a constant of the motion, since

$$[H,Q] = 0 \tag{9-213}$$

We next introduce the configuration space operators

$$\phi^{(+)}(x) = \frac{1}{\sqrt{2(2\pi)^3}}\int_+\frac{d^3k}{k_0}a_{\mathbf{k}}e^{-ik\cdot x} \tag{9-214}$$

and

$$\phi^{(-)}(x) = \frac{1}{\sqrt{2(2\pi)^3}} \int_+ \frac{d^3k}{k_0} b_{\mathbf{k}}^* \overline{e^{-ik\cdot x}}$$
$$= \frac{1}{\sqrt{2(2\pi)^3}} \int_+ \frac{d^3k}{k_0} b_{\mathbf{k}}^* e^{ik\cdot x} \tag{9-215}$$

whose commutations are

$$[\phi^{(\pm)}(x), \phi^{(\pm)}(x')] = 0 \tag{9-216}$$
$$[\phi^{(+)}(x), \phi^{(+)*}(x')] = i\Delta^{(+)}(x - x') \tag{9-217}$$
$$[\phi^{(-)}(x), \phi^{(-)*}(x')] = i\Delta^{(-)}(x - x') \tag{9-218}$$

Consider now the operator

$$\phi(x) = \phi^{(+)}(x) + \phi^{(-)}(x)$$
$$= \frac{1}{\sqrt{2(2\pi)^3}} \int_+ \frac{d^3k}{k_0} (a_{\mathbf{k}} e^{-ik\cdot x} + b_{\mathbf{k}}^* e^{ik\cdot x}) \tag{9-219}$$

which has been so constructed that it has simple commutation rules with Q

$$[Q,\phi(x)] = -e\phi(x) \tag{9-220}$$

so that $\phi(x)$ destroys an amount of charge e.

Upon taking the hermitian adjoint of this equation, we obtain

$$[Q,\phi^*(x)] = e\phi^*(x) \tag{9-221}$$

hence $\phi^*(x)$ is an operator that creates an amount of charge e. The explicit representation of $\phi^*(x)$ in terms of $a_{\mathbf{k}}^*$ and $b_{\mathbf{k}}$ is

$$\phi^*(x) = \frac{1}{\sqrt{2(2\pi)^3}} \int \frac{d^3k}{k_0} (a_{\mathbf{k}}^* e^{ik\cdot x} + b_{\mathbf{k}} e^{-ik\cdot x}) \tag{9-222}$$

These operators satisfy the following commutation rules

$$[\phi(x),\phi^*(x')] = i\Delta^{(+)}(x - x') + i\Delta^{(-)}(x - x')$$
$$= i\Delta(x - x') \tag{9-223}$$

We note in passing that the operator

$$\phi'(x) = \alpha_+\phi^{(+)}(x) + \alpha_-\phi^{(-)}(x) \tag{9-224}$$

would satisfy the same commutation rules with Q as did the operator $\phi(x)$. However, its commutation with $\phi'^*(x)$ would be

$$[\phi'(x),\phi'^*(x')] = i|\alpha_+|^2\Delta^{(+)}(x - x') + i|\alpha_-|^2\Delta^{(-)}(x - x') \tag{9-225}$$

which would result in certain local hermitian observables not necessarily commuting with one another for spacelike separations of their arguments—which is unacceptable on the basis of causality.

Although we have outlined the particle-antiparticle formalism for the case of the $\pi^+ - \pi^-$ system identical considerations can be applied to the $K^0 - \overline{K^0}$ system, where particle and antiparticle differ in having opposite strangeness quantum number:[9] $+1$ for K^0 and -1 for $\overline{K^0}$, and to the $K^+ - K^-$ system where particle and antiparticle differ in both charge and strangeness quantum number.

In concluding this section we note that the hamiltonian describing the system of noninteracting charged spin 0 particles, Eq. (9–199), can be expressed in terms of the configuration space operators $\phi(x)$ and $\phi^*(x)$ as follows:

$$H = N \int d^3x \left\{ \frac{\partial \phi^*(x)}{\partial x^0} \frac{\partial \phi(x)}{\partial x^0} + \nabla\phi^*(x)\cdot\nabla\phi(x) + \mu^2\phi^*(x)\phi(x) \right\} \tag{9–226}$$

where the normal product operation N is defined as follows: Operating on a product of creation and annihilation operators it rewrites the product in "normal form" with all creation operators standing to the left of all destruction operators, the rearrangement being made as if all Boson operator commutation rules were equal to zero. Thus, *e.g.*

$$\begin{aligned} N(\phi^{(-)}(x)\phi^{(+)}(x)) &= N(\phi^{(+)}(x)\phi^{(-)}(y)) \\ &= \phi^{(-)}(x)\phi^{(+)}(x) \end{aligned} \tag{9–227}$$

By definition the distributive law is valid for the normal product operation N; *i.e.*

$$\begin{aligned} &N(\phi^{(+)}(x)\{\phi^{(+)}(y) + \phi^{(-)*}(z)\}) \\ &\qquad = N(\phi^{(+)}(x)\phi^{(+)}(y)) + N(\phi^{(+)}(x)\phi^{(-)*}(z)) \end{aligned} \tag{9–228}$$

The total charge operator Q when expressed in terms of the operators ϕ and ϕ^* takes the form

$$Q = +ieN \int d^3x \left(\frac{\partial \phi^*(x)}{\partial x_0} \phi(x) - \phi^*(x) \frac{\partial \phi(x)}{\partial x_0} \right) \tag{9–229}$$

This expression for the total charge suggests that one can define the current operator $j_\mu(x)$ as follows:

$$j_\mu(x) = +ieN \left(\frac{\partial \phi^*(x)}{\partial x^\mu} \phi(x) - \phi^*(x) \frac{\partial \phi(x)}{\partial x^\mu} \right) \tag{9–230}$$

[9] For the "meaning" of the strangeness quantum number, see E. C. G. Sudarshan and R. Marshak, *loc. cit.*

This operator is conserved, *i.e.*,

$$\frac{\partial j_\mu(x)}{\partial x_\mu} = 0 \tag{9-231}$$

by virtue of the equations of motion

$$(\Box + \mu^2)\phi(x) = 0 \tag{9-232}$$

$$(\Box + \mu^2)\phi^*(x) = 0 \tag{9-233}$$

obeyed by the operators $\phi(x)$ and $\phi^*(x)$. The total charge operator

$$Q = \int d^3x j_0(x) \tag{9-234}$$

is, therefore, time independent.

Note incidentally that for a charge self-conjugate spin 0 field, *i.e.*, one for which particle and antiparticle are identical (*e.g.*, the π^0 system) so that $a = b$ and $\phi^* = \phi$, the current operator j^μ vanishes identically.

REFERENCES

Position operator:

Newton, R., and Wigner, E. P., *Rev. Mod. Phys.*, **21**, 400 (1949).

Second quantization and configuration space description of spin 0 particles:

Schweber, S. S., *An Introduction to Relativistic Quantum Field Theory*, Harper and Row, New York, 1961.

Representation of commutation rules:

Wightman, A. S., and Schweber, S. S., *Phys. Rev.*, **98**, 812 (1955).

Garding, L., and Wightman, A. S., *Proc. Nat. Acad. Sciences US*, **40**, 617 (1956).

Segal, I. E., *Kgl. Danske Videnskab Selskab Mat-fys. Medd*, **31**, Nr. 12 (1959).

Haag, R., "Canonical Commutation Relations in Field Theory and Functional Integration," in W. E. Britten and B. W. and J. Downs, eds., *Lectures in Theoretical Physics*, Vol. III, Interscience Publishers, Inc., New York, 1961.

9.5. Spin $\frac{1}{2}$ Particles.—The covariant relativistic wave equation which describes a free spin $\frac{1}{2}$ particle of mass m is Dirac's equation:

$$(-i\gamma^\mu \partial_\mu + m)\psi(x) = 0 \tag{9-235}$$

where the γ^μ are four-by-four matrices satisfying the commutation rules

$$\gamma^\mu\gamma^\nu + \gamma^\nu\gamma^\mu = 2g^{\mu\nu} \tag{9-236}$$

$g^{\mu\nu}$ being the metric tensor: $g^{00} = -g^{11} = -g^{22} = -g^{33} = +1$, $g^{\mu\nu} = 0$ for $\mu \neq \nu$. The right-hand side of Eq. (9-236) should really read $2g^{\mu\nu}I$, with I the four-by-four unit matrix. We shall, however, often suppress this factor.

Dirac was led to this equation for a spin $\frac{1}{2}$ particle by demanding that:

(a) it be of first order in the time, so that the knowledge of the amplitude ψ at some initial time determines the subsequent history of the particle. Relativistic covariance, by requiring that there be essentially complete symmetry between space and time, then implies the equation that be of first order in the spatial derivatives also;
(b) that it be linear, so that the superposition principle holds;
(c) since for a free particle the Einstein relation $E^2 = \mathbf{p}^2 + m^2$ must hold, one must also require that ψ obey the equation

$$(\Box + m^2)\psi(x) = 0 \tag{9–237}$$

When ψ is a one component scalar function, one can take the "square root" of Eq. (9–237) and one thus obtains the relativistic equation describing a spin 0 particle discussed in Section 9.4. This procedure, however, does not work for a spin $\frac{1}{2}$ particle since we know that in the present situation the amplitude ψ must be a multicomponent object, because in the nonrelativistic limit the amplitude ψ must go over into the 2-component nonrelativistic wave function describing a spin $\frac{1}{2}$ particle. Dirac, therefore, argued that the "square root" operator in the present case must involve something operating on these components.

Let us, therefore, assume that the amplitude $\psi(x)$ describing a relativistic spin $\frac{1}{2}$ particle is an N-component object. We are then looking for a hermitian operator H, the hamiltonian or energy operator, which is linear in $\mathbf{p}$ and has the property that $H^2 = c^2\mathbf{p}^2 + m^2c^4 = -\hbar^2c^2\nabla^2 + m^2c^4$. We also require H to be the infinitesimal operator for time translations, *i.e.*, that

$$i\hbar\partial_t\psi(x) = H\psi(x) \tag{9–238}$$

Since H is to be an operator that acts upon the components of ψ, Dirac wrote

$$H = c\boldsymbol{\alpha}\cdot\mathbf{p} + \beta mc^2 = \sum_{j=1}^{3} c\alpha^j p^j + \beta mc^2 \tag{9–239}$$

where $\boldsymbol{\alpha} = (\alpha^1,\alpha^2,\alpha^3)$ and β are operators that act only on the components of ψ, are independent of $\mathbf{x}$ and $\mathbf{p}$, and hence commute with these operators. Explicitly, in matrix notation Eq. (9–239) becomes ($\hbar = c = 1$)

$$i\partial_t\psi_l(x) = \sum_{n=1}^{N} H_{ln}\psi_n(x) \quad l = 1,\cdots,N \tag{9–240}$$

with

$$H_{ln} = \sum_{k=1}^{3} (\alpha^k)_{ln} p^k + \beta_{ln} m \tag{9–241}$$

The scalar product of two Dirac wave functions is defined as

$$(\psi,\phi) = \sum_{l=1}^{N} \int d^3x \overline{\psi_l(x)} \phi_l(x) \tag{9–242}$$

The operator H must be hermitian within this scalar product. One verifies that for this to be the case α and β must be hermitian matrices

$$\overline{(\alpha^k)_{nl}} = (\alpha^k)_{ln} \tag{9–243}$$

$$\overline{\beta_{nl}} = \beta_{ln} \tag{9–244}$$

The requirement that $H^2 = \mathbf{p}^2 + m^2$ means that

$$\tfrac{1}{2}(\alpha^k\alpha^l + \alpha^l\alpha^k) = \delta^{kl} \tag{9–245}$$

$$\alpha^k\beta + \beta\alpha^k = 0 \tag{9–246}$$

$$(\alpha^k)^2 = \beta^2 = 1 \quad k,l = 1,2,3 \tag{9–247}$$

i.e., that the α's as well as any α and β anticommute, and that the square of all four operators is unity. It is clear that the problem of finding $\boldsymbol{\alpha}$'s and β's satisfying (9–245), (9–246), and (9–247) does not have a unique solution since the operators $\boldsymbol{\alpha}' = S\boldsymbol{\alpha}S^{-1}$, and $\beta' = S\beta S^{-1}$, with S nonsingular, satisfy identical equations. The best that can be hoped for is uniqueness up to similarity transformations. Two facts concerning the operators $\boldsymbol{\alpha}$ and β can easily be verified, namely that

(a) their dimensionality must be even;
(b) their traces vanish.

The proof of the first assertion involves taking the determinant of Eq. (9–246). Since the determinant of any of these four matrices cannot vanish (since by virtue of Eq. (9–247) $\det \alpha^k = \det \beta = \pm 1$), the identity

$$\begin{aligned}\det \alpha^k\beta &= \det(-\beta\alpha^k) \\ &= \det(-I\beta\alpha^k) = \det(-I)\det\beta\det\alpha^k = (-1)^N \det\beta\det\alpha^k \\ &= \det\alpha^k\det\beta\end{aligned} \tag{9–248}$$

indicates that N must be even. Similarly since each of the matrices α^k,β has an inverse (Eq. (9–247) in fact indicates that they are their own inverses), Eq. (9–246) can be rewritten as

$$(\alpha^k)^{-1}\beta\alpha^k = -\beta \tag{9–249}$$

and taking the trace[10] of both sides we obtain

$$\operatorname{Tr} \beta = -\operatorname{Tr} \beta = 0 \tag{9–250}$$

Similarly

$$\begin{aligned}\operatorname{Tr} \alpha^k &= -\operatorname{Tr} \beta\alpha^k\beta^{-1} = -\operatorname{Tr} \alpha^k \\ &= 0\end{aligned} \tag{9–251}$$

If we introduce the matrices

$$\gamma^k = \beta\alpha^k \quad (k = 1,2,3) \tag{9–252}$$

$$\gamma^0 = \beta \tag{9–253}$$

the commutation rules (9–245), (9–246), and (9–247), imply that $(\gamma^k)^2 = -1$ and $(\gamma^0)^2 = +1$, and that these matrices anticommute with one another. These facts can be summarized in the following commutation rules

$$\gamma^\mu\gamma^\nu + \gamma^\nu\gamma^\mu = 2g^{\mu\nu} \tag{9–254}$$

In terms of the γ matrices, Eq. (9–240) and (9–241), upon multiplication by γ^0, can be written as

$$(-i\gamma^\mu\partial_\mu + m)\psi(x) = 0 \tag{9–255}$$

A set of matrices satisfying Eq. (9–254), together with all their products and linear combinations with complex coefficient is called a *Clifford algebra.* The basic facts concerning such algebras are the following:[11]

Theorem A.—The γ^μ's and their products yield sixteen linearly independent matrices.

Consider the following sixteen matrices:

$$I, \gamma^\mu, [\gamma^\mu,\gamma^\nu] = \gamma^\mu\gamma^\nu - \gamma^\nu\gamma^\mu, \gamma^5 = i\gamma^0\gamma^1\gamma^2\gamma^3, \gamma^5\gamma^\mu$$

All other products of γ-matrices can, by using the commutation rules, be reduced to one of these sixteen elements. The proof of their linear independence is based upon the fact that the trace of any of these matrices except for the unit matrix, I, is zero. If Γ_r is any one of these matrices, then $\Gamma_r\Gamma_s$ generates again one of the Γ's, the unit matrix

[10] Recall that the trace of a matrix A is defined by

$$\operatorname{Tr} A = \sum A_{ll}$$

from which it follows that

$$\operatorname{Tr} AB = \operatorname{Tr} BA$$

See Margenau and Murphy, *op. cit.*, p. 309.

[11] For detailed proofs, see W. Pauli, *Ann. Institut H. Poincaré*, **6**, 137 (1936), or R. H. Good, Jr., *Rev. Mod. Phys.*, **27**, 187 (1955).

resulting only if $r = s$. Now if the Γ_r were linearly dependent it would be possible to satisfy the linear relation

$$\sum_{r=1}^{16} c_r \Gamma_r = 0$$

for nontrivial c_r. However, multiplying by Γ_s and taking the trace yields $c_s = 0$ for all s. It is, therefore, not possible to represent the γ^μ's by matrices whose dimension is less than 4, since it is impossible to construct sixteen linearly independent matrices from such matrices. Conversely since there exist precisely sixteen linearly independent four-by-four matrices we can try to represent the γ-matrices by four-by-four matrices. In fact, the explicit representation given by Eqs. (9–302)–(9–305) below, shows that this is possible.

Corollary.—Any four-dimensional matrix can be written as a linear combination of these sixteen linearly independent matrices.

Theorem B.—Any four-by-four matrix that commutes with a set of γ^μ is a multiple of the identity.

The proof of this theorem follows from theorem A: A four-by-four matrix that commutes with the γ^μ commutes with their products and hence with an arbitrary matrix. However, the only matrices that commute with every matrix are constant multiples of the identity. Theorem B is *valid* only in four dimensions, *i.e.*, when $N = 4$. In other words the irreducible representations of (9–254) are four-dimensional.

We shall henceforth always assume the γ^μ to be irreducible, *i.e.*, four-dimensional.

Theorem C.—If γ'^μ and γ^μ are two sets of matrices both satisfying Eq. (9–254), *i.e.*

$$\gamma'^\mu \gamma'^\nu + \gamma'^\nu \gamma'^\mu = 2g^{\nu\mu} \tag{9–256}$$

$$\gamma^\mu \gamma^\nu + \gamma^\nu \gamma^\mu = 2g^{\mu\nu} \tag{9–257}$$

there exists a nonsingular matrix S, such that

$$\gamma'^\mu = S\gamma^\mu S^{-1} \tag{9–258}$$

Theorem C establishes the fact that there exists essentially only one irreducible representation of the γ-matrices (all others are related to it by a similarity transformation). As a corollary to this theorem, theorem B allows us to assert that S is uniquely defined up to a factor. For suppose there were two such S's, say S_1 and S_2 such that $\gamma'^\mu = S_1\gamma^\mu S_1{}^{-1}$ and $\gamma'^\mu = S_2\gamma^\mu S_2{}^{-1}$ then by equating γ'^μ in these equations we find that $\gamma^\mu = (S_2^{-1}S_1)\gamma^\mu(S_2^{-1}S_1)^{-1}$, *i.e.*, $S_2^{-1}S_1$ commutes with γ^μ and hence is a constant multiple of the identity, *i.e.*, $S_2 = cS_1$.

Since the matrices $-\gamma^\mu, \gamma^{\mu *}, \gamma^{\mu T}$, and $\overline{\gamma^\mu}$ all obey the same commutation rules as γ^μ (take the hermitian adjoint, transpose and complex conjugate of Eq. (9–254)!) it follows from theorem C, that there exist nonsingular matrices A, B, C, D, such that

$$\gamma^{\mu *} = A\gamma^\mu A^{-1} \tag{9–259}$$

$$\gamma^{\mu T} = B\gamma^\mu B^{-1} \tag{9–260}$$

$$\overline{\gamma^\mu} = C\gamma^\mu C^{-1} \tag{9–261}$$

$$-\gamma^\mu = D\gamma^\mu D^{-1} \tag{9–262}$$

The matrix $\gamma^5 = i\gamma^0\gamma^1\gamma^2\gamma^3[(\gamma^5)^2 = +1]$, anticommutes with all the γ^μ's. It therefore has the property that $\gamma^5\gamma^\mu(\gamma^5)^{-1} = -\gamma^\mu$. Hence, a possible choice for D is γ^5. Further properties of the matrices A,B,D can be obtained as follows: Consider for example the matrix A. Upon taking the hermitian adjoint of Eq. (9–259) and substituting therein Eq. (9–259) again, we obtain

$$\begin{aligned}\gamma^\mu &= A^{-1*}\gamma^{\mu *}A^* \\ &= A^{-1*}A\gamma^\mu(A^{-1*}A)^{-1}\end{aligned} \tag{9–263}$$

so that $A^{*-1}A$ commutes with γ^μ and hence is a multiple of the identity:

$$A^{*-1}A = a \quad \text{or} \quad A = aA^* \tag{9–264}$$

Upon taking the hermitian adjoint of Eq. (9–264) we deduce that $A^* = \bar{a}A = |a|^2A^*$ whence $|a|^2 = 1$. We can adjust A such that $\det A = 1$. Upon choosing the phase of A such that $a = 1$, A is hermitian

$$A = A^* \tag{9–265}$$

Similarly upon taking the transpose of Eq. (9–260), we deduce:

$$\begin{aligned}\gamma^\mu &= B^{-1T}\gamma^{\mu T}B^T \\ &= B^{-1T}B\gamma^\mu(B^{-1T}B)^{-1}\end{aligned} \tag{9–266}$$

so that $B^{-1T}B$ is a constant multiple of the identity:

$$B = bB^T \tag{9–267}$$

The transpose of Eq. (9–267) is $B^T = bB = b^2B^T$ so that $b^2 = +1$.

To answer the question: "Is $b = +1$ or is $b = -1$?" we calculate $(B\Gamma_i)^T$. A simple computation indicates that:

$$(BI)^T = B^T = bBI \tag{9-268}$$

$$(B\gamma^\mu)^T = b\gamma^{\mu T}B = bB\gamma^\mu \tag{9-269}$$

$$(B\gamma^5)^T = b\gamma^{5T}B = bB\gamma^5 \tag{9-270}$$

$$(B\gamma^\mu\gamma^5)^T = bB\gamma^5\gamma^\mu = -bB\gamma^\mu\gamma^5 \tag{9-271}$$

$$\begin{aligned}(B[\gamma^\mu,\gamma^\nu])^T &= b[\gamma^{\nu T},\gamma^{\mu T}]B = b[B\gamma^\nu B^{-1}, B\gamma^\mu B^{-1}]B \\ &= -bB[\gamma^\mu,\gamma^\nu]\end{aligned} \tag{9-272}$$

If now b were equal to $+1$, there would be six symmetric $B\Gamma_i$ and ten antisymmetric $B\Gamma_i$, whereas if $b = -1$ there are six antisymmetric ones and ten symmetric ones. Since there exist only six antisymmetric four-by-four matrices we conclude that b must be equal to -1:

$$B^T = -B \tag{9-273}$$

Finally upon taking the complex conjugate of Eq. (9–261), we infer that $\bar{C}C = c1$, from which one deduces that $\bar{c}^2 = c^2 = |c|^2$ so that c is real and with the normalization $\det C = 1$

$$\bar{C} = C^{-1} \tag{9-274}$$

Since for any matrix M, $(\bar{M})^T = M^*$, the matrices A, B, C must be related. By substituting into

$$(\gamma^\mu)^* = (\overline{\gamma^\mu})^T \tag{9-275}$$

the relations (9–259)–(9–261) we indeed deduce that

$$A = \bar{B}C = C^*B \tag{9-276}$$

We next define for any matrix X, the matrices $\tilde{X}$, $X^\dagger$, and X^c by

$$\tilde{X} = A^{-1}X^*A = (AXA^{-1})^* \tag{9-277}$$

$$X^\dagger = B^{-1}X^TB = (BXB^{-1})^T \tag{9-278}$$

$$X^c = C^{-1}\bar{X}C = \overline{(CXC^{-1})} \tag{9-279}$$

It should be noted that the operations $X \to \tilde{X}$, $X \to X^\dagger$, and $X \to X^c$ are isomorphic to the $*$ operation (*i.e.*, taking hermitian conjugate) to the ^{T} operation and to complex conjugation, respectively, in the sense that

$$\tilde{\tilde{X}} = A^{-1}\tilde{X}^*A = A^{-1}(AXA^{-1})A = X \tag{9-280}$$

$$X^{\dagger\dagger} = B^{-1}X^{\dagger T}B = B^{-1}(BXB^{-1})B = X \tag{9-281}$$

$$X^{cc} = C^{-1}\bar{X}^cC = C^{-1}(CXC^{-1})C = X \tag{9-282}$$

and that $\tilde{X} = X^{\dagger c}$, etc.

Similarly, for wave functions, hereafter called spinors, we define operations isomorphic to $*,^T$ and complex conjugation. Thus if u is a column spinor we define

$$\tilde{u} = u^*A \tag{9–283}$$
$$u^\dagger = u^TB \tag{9–284}$$
$$u^c = C^{-1}u \tag{9–285}$$

(Note that $\tilde{u}$ and $u^\dagger$ are row spinors.) If μ is a row spinor we define

$$\tilde{\mu} = A^{-1}\mu^* \tag{9–286}$$
$$\mu^\dagger = B^{-1}\mu^T \tag{9–287}$$
$$\mu^c = \bar{\mu}C \tag{9–288}$$

(Note that $\tilde{\mu}$ and $\mu^\dagger$ are then column spinors.) One again verifies that $\tilde{\tilde{u}} = u$, $\tilde{u} = u^{\dagger c}$, etc.

The isomorphism between the tilde operation and hermitian conjugation, implies that upon performing this "A-operation" on the Dirac equation we find that ψ satisfies the equation:

$$\tilde{\psi}(x)(i\widetilde{\gamma_\mu\overleftarrow{\partial}^\mu} + m) = 0 \tag{9–289}$$

But

$$\begin{aligned}\widetilde{\gamma_\mu} &= A^{-1}\gamma_\mu^*A \\ &= A^{-1}A\gamma_\mu A^{-1}A = \gamma_\mu\end{aligned} \tag{9–290}$$

hence

$$\tilde{\psi}(x)(i\gamma\cdot\overleftarrow{\partial} + m) = 0$$

Similarly $\psi^c(x)$ satisfies

$$(i\gamma\cdot\partial + m)\psi^c(x) = 0 \tag{9–291}$$

One of the principal reasons for the usefulness of these definitions lies in the fact that they are invariant under a change of representation. One verifies that under a change of representation wherein

$$\gamma^\mu \to \gamma'^\mu = S\gamma^\mu S^{-1} \tag{9–292}$$

and

$$u \to u' = Su \tag{9–293}$$

with S nonsingular, the following relations hold:

$$\begin{aligned}(\gamma'^\mu)^* &= A'\gamma'^\mu A'^{-1} = A'S\gamma^\mu S^{-1}A'^{-1} \\ &= (S^{-1})^*\gamma^{\mu*}S^* \\ &= (S^{-1})^*A\gamma^\mu A^{-1}S^*\end{aligned} \tag{9–294}$$

Hence $S^{-1}A'^{-1}S^{-1*}A$ commutes with γ^μ and is, therefore, a constant multiple of the identity, whence by a suitable choice of phases

$$A' = (S^{-1})^*AS^{-1} \tag{9–295}$$

Note also that it follows from the defining relation

$$\tilde{u}' = (Su)^* A' \tag{9-296}$$

that the quantity

$$\tilde{u}_2 u_1 = \sum_{\alpha=1}^{4} \tilde{u}_{2\alpha} u_{1\alpha} = \sum_{\beta,\alpha=1}^{4} \overline{u}_{2\alpha} (\gamma^0)_{\alpha\beta} u_{1\beta}$$

is invariant under a change of representation:

$$\begin{aligned} \tilde{u}_2' u_1' &= u_2^* S^* A' S u_1 = u_2^* A u_1 \\ &= u_2 u_1 \end{aligned} \tag{9-297}$$

Although the previous discussion assumed no properties of the γ-matrices beyond their commutation rules, in most of our subsequent discussion we shall specialize to a particular representation of these matrices, namely the one in which γ^0 is hermitian and the γ^i are antihermitian. In this representation $A = \gamma^0$ and $\tilde{u} = u^* \gamma^0$.

We shall also have occasion to use the following matrices

$$\boldsymbol{\alpha} = \beta \boldsymbol{\gamma} = \gamma^0 \boldsymbol{\gamma} \tag{9-298}$$

and

$$\boldsymbol{\Sigma} = \tfrac{1}{2} i (\boldsymbol{\gamma} \times \boldsymbol{\gamma}) \tag{9-299}$$

More precisely

$$\begin{aligned} \Sigma^l = \tfrac{1}{2} i \varepsilon^{lmn} \gamma^m \gamma^n &= \frac{i}{2} (\gamma^m \gamma^n - \gamma^n \gamma^m) \\ &= i \gamma^m \gamma^n \quad (l \neq m \neq n) \end{aligned} \tag{9-300}$$

Note further that

$$\begin{aligned} \alpha^k = \gamma^0 \gamma^k &= \gamma^0 \gamma^1 \gamma^2 \gamma^3 \gamma^1 \gamma^2 \gamma^3 \gamma^k \\ &= -i \gamma^5 \gamma^1 \gamma^2 \gamma^3 \gamma^k \\ &= \Sigma^k \gamma^5 = \gamma^5 \Sigma^k \end{aligned} \tag{9-301}$$

An explicit representation can be exhibited by

$$\boldsymbol{\alpha} = \begin{pmatrix} 0 & \boldsymbol{\sigma} \\ \boldsymbol{\sigma} & 0 \end{pmatrix} \qquad \beta = \begin{pmatrix} 1 & 0 \\ 0 & -1 \end{pmatrix} \tag{9-302}$$

$$\boldsymbol{\gamma} = \begin{pmatrix} 0 & \boldsymbol{\sigma} \\ -\boldsymbol{\sigma} & 0 \end{pmatrix} \tag{9-303}$$

$$\boldsymbol{\Sigma} = \tfrac{1}{2} i \boldsymbol{\gamma} \times \boldsymbol{\gamma} = \begin{pmatrix} \boldsymbol{\sigma} & 0 \\ 0 & \boldsymbol{\sigma} \end{pmatrix} \tag{9-304}$$

$$\gamma^5 = \begin{pmatrix} 0 & 1 \\ 1 & 0 \end{pmatrix} \tag{9-305}$$

where the $\boldsymbol{\sigma}$'s are the two-by-two Pauli matrices.[12] This representation is usually called the "standard representation."

Next we investigate the physical content of the Dirac equation. To that end we inquire as to the solutions of the Dirac equation corresponding to free particles moving with definite energy and momentum. One easily checks that the Dirac equation admits of plane wave solutions of the form

$$\psi(x) = N_{\mathbf{p}} e^{i(\mathbf{p}\cdot\mathbf{x} - E(\mathbf{p})t)} u(\mathbf{p}) \tag{9–306}$$

if the four-component object $u(\mathbf{p})$ satisfies

$$H(\mathbf{p})u(\mathbf{p}) = (\boldsymbol{\alpha}\cdot\mathbf{p} + \beta m)u(\mathbf{p}) = E(\mathbf{p})u(\mathbf{p}) \tag{9–307}$$

and $E^2(\mathbf{p}) = m^2 + \mathbf{p}^2$; $N_{\mathbf{p}}$ is a normalization constant. Before considering the case of a moving particle, let us further simplify the problem and consider the case of a particle at rest, *i.e.*, the case when $\mathbf{p} = 0$. Under these circumstances $u(\mathbf{0})$ must satisfy

$$\beta m u(\mathbf{0}) = E(\mathbf{0})u(\mathbf{0}) \tag{9–308}$$

with $E(\mathbf{0})^2 = m^2$. When $E(\mathbf{0}) = +m$, there clearly exist two linearly independent solutions (recall the representation (9–302) for β) which can be taken to be:

$$u_{\uparrow}(\mathbf{0}) = \begin{pmatrix} 1 \\ 0 \\ 0 \\ 0 \end{pmatrix} \qquad u_{\downarrow}(\mathbf{0}) = \begin{pmatrix} 0 \\ 1 \\ 0 \\ 0 \end{pmatrix} \tag{9–309}$$

That there exist two solutions is a reflection of the fact that the equation describes a particle of spin $\frac{1}{2}$. In general there will be $2(\frac{1}{2}) + 1$ solutions for a given momentum and sign of the energy.

In order to construct solutions corresponding to a particle in motion, consider the hermitian operators

$$P_+(\mathbf{p}) = \frac{E_{\mathbf{p}} + \boldsymbol{\alpha}\cdot\mathbf{p} + \beta m}{2E_{\mathbf{p}}} = \frac{1}{2}\left(1 + \frac{\boldsymbol{\alpha}\cdot\mathbf{p} + \beta m}{E_{\mathbf{p}}}\right) \tag{9–310}$$

$$P_-(\mathbf{p}) = \frac{E_{\mathbf{p}} - (\boldsymbol{\alpha}\cdot\mathbf{p} + \beta m)}{2E_{\mathbf{p}}} = \frac{1}{2}\left(1 - \frac{\boldsymbol{\alpha}\cdot\mathbf{p} + \beta m}{E_{\mathbf{p}}}\right) \tag{9–311}$$

where

$$E_{\mathbf{p}} = +\sqrt{\mathbf{p}^2 + m^2} \tag{9–312}$$

[12] H. Margenau and G. M. Murphy, *The Mathematics of Physics and Chemistry*, 2nd Ed., p. 407, D. Van Nostrand Co., Inc., Princeton, N.J., 1956.

Since $(\boldsymbol{\alpha}\cdot\mathbf{p} + \beta m)^2 = \mathbf{p}^2 + m^2 = E_{\mathbf{p}}^2$, the operators $P_{\pm}(\mathbf{p})$ are projection operators

$$[P_{\pm}(\mathbf{p})]^* = P_{\pm}(\mathbf{p}) \tag{9–313}$$

$$[P_{\pm}(\mathbf{p})]^2 = P_{\pm}(\mathbf{p}) \tag{9–314}$$

and furthermore

$$P_{+}(\mathbf{p}) + P_{-}(\mathbf{p}) = 1 \tag{9–315}$$

It follows from the identity

$$(\boldsymbol{\alpha}\cdot\mathbf{p} + \beta m)P_{\pm}(\mathbf{p}) = \pm E_{\mathbf{p}}P_{\pm}(\mathbf{p}) \tag{9–316}$$

that if w is an arbitrary four-component spinor, then $P_{+}(\mathbf{p})w = u_{+}(\mathbf{p})$ is a solution of

$$(\boldsymbol{\alpha}\cdot\mathbf{p} + \beta m)u_{+}(\mathbf{p}) = +E_{\mathbf{p}}u_{+}(\mathbf{p}) \tag{9–317}$$

and $P_{-}(\mathbf{p})w = u_{-}(\mathbf{p})$ is a solution of

$$(\boldsymbol{\alpha}\cdot\mathbf{p} + \beta m)u_{-}(\mathbf{p}) = -E_{\mathbf{p}}u_{-}(\mathbf{p}) \tag{9–318}$$

Hence two solutions for $E(\mathbf{p}) = E_{\mathbf{p}} = +\sqrt{\mathbf{p}^2 + m^2}$ are

$$u_{+\uparrow}(\mathbf{p}) = N_{+\mathbf{p}}P_{+}(\mathbf{p})\begin{pmatrix}1\\0\\0\\0\end{pmatrix} = N_{+\mathbf{p}}\frac{1}{2}\left(1 + \frac{\boldsymbol{\alpha}\cdot\mathbf{p} + \beta m}{E_{\mathbf{p}}}\right)\begin{pmatrix}1\\0\\0\\0\end{pmatrix}$$

$$= \frac{N_{+\mathbf{p}}}{2E_{\mathbf{p}}}\begin{pmatrix}m + E_{\mathbf{p}}\\0\\p_3\\p_1 + ip_2\end{pmatrix} \tag{9–319}$$

and

$$u_{+\downarrow}(\mathbf{p}) = N_{+\mathbf{p}}P_{+}(\mathbf{p})\begin{pmatrix}0\\1\\0\\0\end{pmatrix} = N_{+\mathbf{p}}\frac{1}{2}\left(1 + \frac{\boldsymbol{\alpha}\cdot\mathbf{p} + \beta m}{E_{\mathbf{p}}}\right)\begin{pmatrix}0\\1\\0\\0\end{pmatrix} \tag{9–320}$$

If we normalize our spinors so that $u^*u = 1$, then

$$N_{+\mathbf{p}} = \sqrt{\frac{2E_{\mathbf{p}}}{E_{\mathbf{p}} + m}} \tag{9–321}$$

and

$$u_{+\uparrow}(\mathbf{p}) = \sqrt{\frac{E_\mathbf{p} + m}{2E_\mathbf{p}}} \begin{pmatrix} 1 \\ 0 \\ \dfrac{\boldsymbol{\sigma}\cdot\mathbf{p}}{E_\mathbf{p} + m}\begin{pmatrix}1\\0\end{pmatrix} \end{pmatrix} \tag{9–322}$$

$$u_{+\downarrow}(\mathbf{p}) = \sqrt{\frac{E_\mathbf{p} + m}{2E_\mathbf{p}}} \begin{pmatrix} 0 \\ 1 \\ \dfrac{\boldsymbol{\sigma}\cdot\mathbf{p}}{E_\mathbf{p} + m}\begin{pmatrix}0\\1\end{pmatrix} \end{pmatrix} \tag{9–323}$$

It should be noted that these two solutions are orthogonal to each other $u_\uparrow^*(\mathbf{p})u_\downarrow(\mathbf{p}) = 0$. By noting that the projection operator $P_+(\mathbf{p})$ operating on the remaining two basis spinors

$$\begin{pmatrix}0\\0\\1\\0\end{pmatrix} \quad \text{and} \quad \begin{pmatrix}0\\0\\0\\1\end{pmatrix}$$

merely yields linear combinations of $u_{+\uparrow}(\mathbf{p})$ and $u_{+\downarrow}(\mathbf{p})$, one concludes that there exist only two linearly independent solutions for

$$E(\mathbf{p}) = E_\mathbf{p} = +\sqrt{\mathbf{p}^2 + m^2}$$

Similarly there exist two linearly independent solutions for

$$E(\mathbf{p}) = -\sqrt{\mathbf{p}^2 + m^2}$$

which can be taken as

$$N_{-,\mathbf{p}}P_-(\mathbf{p})\begin{pmatrix}0\\0\\0\\1\end{pmatrix} \quad \text{and} \quad N_{-,\mathbf{p}}P_-(\mathbf{p})\begin{pmatrix}0\\0\\1\\0\end{pmatrix}$$

These four solutions of Eq. (9–307) for the momentum $\mathbf{p}$ are linearly independent and orthogonal to each other.

For the case of the particle at rest the solutions (9–309) are also eigensolutions of the operator Σ_3. In the standard representation, the representation (9–304) indicates that these two solutions correspond to two different possible orientations of the spin of the particle. However, $\boldsymbol{\Sigma}$ and H do not commute in general, *i.e.*, when $\mathbf{p} \neq 0$. A more systematic way of obtaining eigenfunctions under these circumstances is to note that the hermitian operator

$$s(\mathbf{p}) = \frac{\mathbf{\Sigma}\cdot\mathbf{p}}{|\mathbf{p}|} = [s(\mathbf{p})]^* \tag{9–324}$$

which is usually called the helicity operator, does commute with the hamiltonian since the latter can be written in the form

$$H = \gamma_5\mathbf{\Sigma}\cdot\mathbf{p} + \beta m \tag{9–325}$$

and γ_5 and $\mathbf{\Sigma}$ commute. Note further that

$$s(\mathbf{p})^2 = \left(\frac{\mathbf{\Sigma}\cdot\mathbf{p}}{|\mathbf{p}|}\right)^2 = 1 \tag{9–326}$$

hence, the eigenvalues of $s(\mathbf{p})$ are ± 1. Hence, for a given $\mathbf{p}$ we can construct states that are simultaneous eigenstates of $s(\mathbf{p})$ and H. Let us denote these four states by $u(\mathbf{p},E(\mathbf{p}),s)$ where s can assume the values ± 1, and $E(\mathbf{p})$ the values $\pm E_\mathbf{p}$. Being eigenfunctions of hermitian operators corresponding to different eigenvalues, these solutions are orthonormal, *i.e.*

$$u^*(\mathbf{p},E'(\mathbf{p}),s')u(\mathbf{p},E(\mathbf{p}),s) = \delta_{EE'}\delta_{ss'} \tag{9–327}$$

They, in fact, form a complete set for the spinors of momentum $\mathbf{p}$, in the sense that an arbitrary spinor w of momentum $\mathbf{p}$ can be expanded in terms of the above solutions as follows:

$$w(\mathbf{p}) = \sum_{E(\mathbf{p}),s} c(E(\mathbf{p}),s)u(\mathbf{p},E(\mathbf{p}),s) \tag{9–328}$$

From the orthonormality relations (9–327) it follows that

$$c(E(\mathbf{p}),s) = u^*(\mathbf{p},E(\mathbf{p}),s)w(\mathbf{p}) \tag{9–329}$$

hence

$$w(\mathbf{p}) = \sum_{E(\mathbf{p}),s} u(\mathbf{p},E(\mathbf{p}),s)u^*(\mathbf{p},E(\mathbf{p}),s)w(\mathbf{p}) \tag{9–330}$$

Therefore, since $w(\mathbf{p})$ is an arbitrary spinor,

$$1 = \sum_{E(\mathbf{p}),s} u(\mathbf{p},E(\mathbf{p}),s)u^*(\mathbf{p},E(\mathbf{p}),s) \tag{9–331}$$

and

$$\beta = \sum_{E(\mathbf{p}),s} u(\mathbf{p},E(\mathbf{p}),s)\tilde{u}(\mathbf{p},E(\mathbf{p}),s) \tag{9–332}$$

Since

$$(E(\mathbf{p}) + \boldsymbol{\alpha}\cdot\mathbf{p} + \beta m)(s + s(\mathbf{p}))u(\mathbf{p},s',E'(\mathbf{p}))$$
$$= \begin{cases} 0, & \text{if } E(\mathbf{p}) \neq E'(\mathbf{p}) \quad \text{and/or} \quad s \neq s' \qquad (9\text{–}333) \\ 2E'(\mathbf{p})2s', & \text{if } E(\mathbf{p}) = E'(\mathbf{p}) \quad \text{and} \quad s = s' \qquad (9\text{–}334) \end{cases}$$

it follows that

$$(E(\mathbf{p}) + \boldsymbol{\alpha}\cdot\mathbf{p} + \beta m)(s + s(\mathbf{p}))\beta$$
$$= 2E(\mathbf{p})2su(\mathbf{p},E(\mathbf{p}),s)\cdot\tilde{u}(\mathbf{p},E(\mathbf{p}),s) \qquad (9\text{–}335)$$

If we denote by $u_+(\mathbf{p},s)$ the positive energy solutions corresponding to helicity s, and by $v_-(\mathbf{p},s)$, the negative energy solutions of momentum $-\mathbf{p}$ and helicity s, *i.e.*,

$$v_-(\mathbf{p},s) = u_-(-\mathbf{p},-E_{\mathbf{p}},+s) \qquad (9\text{–}336)$$

then upon noting that $\beta = \gamma^0$ and $\boldsymbol{\Sigma}$ commute we can rewrite Eq. (9–335) to read

$$\frac{\gamma\cdot p + m}{2E_{\mathbf{p}}}\frac{s + s(\mathbf{p})}{2s} = u_+(\mathbf{p},s)\tilde{u}_+(\mathbf{p},s) \qquad (9\text{–}337)$$

$$\frac{-\gamma\cdot p + m}{-2E_{\mathbf{p}}}\frac{s + s(\mathbf{p})}{2s} = v_-(\mathbf{p},s)\tilde{v}_-(\mathbf{p},s) \qquad (9\text{–}338)$$

These relations were derived on the assumption that the normalization of the spinors was $u^*u = 1$. It is oftentimes useful (for covariance reasons) to normalize the spinors so that $\tilde{u}u$ = constant. The relation between these two normalizations is readily obtained. Upon multiplying Eq. (9–307) by $\tilde{u}(\mathbf{p},E(\mathbf{p}),s)$ on the left, we obtain

$$\tilde{u}(\mathbf{p},E(\mathbf{p}))(\boldsymbol{\alpha}\cdot\mathbf{p} + \beta m)u(\mathbf{p},E(\mathbf{p})) = E(\mathbf{p})\tilde{u}(\mathbf{p},E(\mathbf{p}))u(\mathbf{p},E(\mathbf{p})) \qquad (9\text{–}339)$$

Similarly, upon multiplying the equation which $\tilde{u}(\mathbf{p},E(\mathbf{p}))$ satisfies, by $u(\mathbf{p},E(\mathbf{p}))$ on the right we obtain

$$\tilde{u}(\mathbf{p},E(\mathbf{p}))(-\boldsymbol{\alpha}\cdot\mathbf{p} + \beta m)u(\mathbf{p},E(\mathbf{p})) = E(\mathbf{p})\tilde{u}(\mathbf{p},E(\mathbf{p}))u(\mathbf{p},E(\mathbf{p})) \qquad (9\text{–}340)$$

Adding together Eqs. (9–339) and (9–340) we deduce that

$$\tilde{u}(\mathbf{p},E(\mathbf{p}),s)u(\mathbf{p},E(\mathbf{p}),s) = \frac{m}{E(\mathbf{p})}u^*(\mathbf{p},E(\mathbf{p}),s)u(\mathbf{p},E(\mathbf{p}),s) \qquad (9\text{–}341)$$

Hence if we normalize our spinors so that

$$u^*(\mathbf{p},E(\mathbf{p}),s)u(\mathbf{p},E(\mathbf{p}),s) = \frac{E_{\mathbf{p}}}{m} \qquad (9\text{–}342)$$

then

$$\tilde{u}(\mathbf{p},E(\mathbf{p}),s)u(\mathbf{p},E(\mathbf{p}),s) = \frac{E_{\mathbf{p}}}{E(\mathbf{p})} = \frac{E(\mathbf{p})}{|E(\mathbf{p})|} \tag{9–343}$$

We adopt this latter normalization henceforth; consequently

$$u_+(\mathbf{p},s)\tilde{u}_+(\mathbf{p},s) = \frac{\gamma\cdot p + m}{2m}\frac{s + s(\mathbf{p})}{2s} \tag{9–344}$$

$$v_-(\mathbf{p},s)\tilde{v}_-(\mathbf{p},s) = \frac{-\gamma\cdot p + m}{2m}\frac{s + s(\mathbf{p})}{2s} \tag{9–345}$$

The usefulness of these representations stems from the fact that in certain applications we shall have to evaluate quantities of the form $|M|^2$, where

$$M = \tilde{w}_2 Q w_1 \tag{9–346}$$

w_1 and w_2 are spinors, and Q is a four-by-four matrix. Now

$$\begin{aligned}|M|^2 &= (\tilde{w}_2 Q w_1)(w_1^* Q^* \tilde{w}_2^*)\\ &= (\tilde{w}_2 Q w_1)(w_1^* A A^{-1} Q^* A w_2)\\ &= (\tilde{w}_2 Q w_1)(\tilde{w}_1 \tilde{Q} w_2)\end{aligned} \tag{9–347}$$

which expression can also be written in the form

$$\begin{aligned}|M|^2 &= \sum_{\alpha,\beta,\rho,\sigma=1}^{4} \tilde{w}_{2\alpha} Q_{\alpha\beta} w_{1\beta} \tilde{w}_{1\rho} \tilde{Q}_{\rho\sigma} w_{2\sigma}\\ &= \sum_{\alpha,\beta,\rho,\sigma=1}^{4} w_{2\sigma}\tilde{w}_{2\alpha} Q_{\alpha\beta} w_{1\beta}\tilde{w}_{1\rho}\tilde{Q}_{\rho\sigma}\end{aligned} \tag{9–348}$$

If we consider $w_{2\sigma}\tilde{w}_{2\alpha}$ as the $\sigma\alpha$ matrix element of the square matrix $w_2 \otimes \tilde{w}_2$, and similarly for $w_{1\beta}\tilde{w}_{1\rho}$, then expression (9–348) is in fact a trace and

$$|M|^2 = \mathrm{Tr}\,(w_2\tilde{w}_2 Q w_1 \tilde{w}_1 \tilde{Q}) \tag{9–349}$$

If w_1 and w_2 are spinors corresponding to definite energy, momentum, and helicity, the matrices $w\tilde{w}$ are explicitly given by Eqs. (9–344) or (9–345). Finally the resulting traces involving γ-matrices can always be evaluated using the commutation relations $[\gamma^\mu,\gamma^\nu]_+ = 2g^{\mu\nu}$. Thus, for example

$$\mathrm{Tr}\,\gamma^\mu = 0 \tag{9–350}$$

$$\begin{aligned}\mathrm{Tr}\,\gamma^\mu\gamma^\nu &= \tfrac{1}{2}\,\mathrm{Tr}\,(\gamma^\mu\gamma^\nu + \gamma^\nu\gamma^\mu) = g^{\mu\nu}\,\mathrm{Tr}\,I\\ &= 4g^{\mu\nu}\end{aligned} \tag{9–351}$$

We next inquire as to the transformation property of the quantity $\psi(x)$ under a homogeneous Lorentz transformation

$$x'_\mu = \Lambda_\mu{}^\nu x_\nu \tag{9–352}$$

Since $\psi(x)$ is a multicomponent object, we expect as in the case of the electromagnetic field intensities, that the components will be "shuffled" by such a transformation. We, therefore, write for the transformed amplitude $\psi'(x')$

$$\psi'_\alpha(x') = \sum_{\beta=1}^{4} S_{\alpha\beta}(\Lambda)\psi_\beta(x) \tag{9–353}$$

where $S(\Lambda)$ is a four-by-four nonsingular matrix, which will depend only upon the Lorentz transformation Λ. In fact, due to the group property of Lorentz transformations, the $S(\Lambda)$ must form a representation up to a factor of the Lorentz group

$$S(\Lambda_1)S(\Lambda_2) = \omega(\Lambda_1,\Lambda_2)S(\Lambda_1\Lambda_2) \tag{9–354}$$

where $\omega(\Lambda_1,\Lambda_2)$ is a phase factor of modulus one, which may depend on Λ_1 and Λ_2. Equation (9–353) can also be written in the more succinct form

$$\psi'(x') = S(\Lambda)\psi(\Lambda^{-1}x') \tag{9–355}$$

The condition that serves to determine $S(\Lambda)$ is the requirement of relativistic invariance; ψ' must satisfy the Dirac equation in the new coordinate system; *i.e.*, $\psi'(x')$ must satisfy the equation

$$\left(-i\gamma^\mu \frac{\partial}{\partial x'^\mu} + m\right)\psi'(x') = 0 \tag{9–356}$$

with the same γ matrices. By multiplying the Dirac equation

$$\left(-i\gamma^\mu \frac{\partial}{\partial x^\mu} + m\right)\psi(x) = 0 \tag{9–357}$$

for $\psi(x)$ by $S(\Lambda)^{-1}$ and noting that

$$\frac{\partial}{\partial x^\mu} = \frac{\partial x'^\nu}{\partial x^\mu}\frac{\partial}{\partial x'^\nu} = \Lambda_\mu{}^\nu \frac{\partial}{\partial x'^\nu} \tag{9–358}$$

the condition that Eqs. (9–357) and (9–358) be identical is seen to be

$$\Lambda^\nu{}_\mu\gamma^\mu = S(\Lambda)^{-1}\gamma^\nu S(\Lambda) \tag{9–359}$$

Now one readily verifies that for proper Lorentz transformations the matrices

$$\gamma'^\nu = \Lambda^\nu{}_\mu\gamma^\mu \tag{9–360}$$

satisfy the same anticommutation rules as the γ matrices by virtue of the property

$$\Lambda_\nu{}^\mu g_{\mu\rho}\Lambda^\rho{}_\sigma = g_{\nu\sigma} \tag{9–361}$$

of Lorentz transformations. By theorem B of the present section, a nonsingular $S(\Lambda)$, therefore, always exists. Furthermore, it is possible to choose $S(\Lambda)$ in such a way that the operations of taking adjoints, transposition, and complex conjugation are invariant, *i.e.*, are such that

$$(\gamma'^\mu)^* = A\gamma'^\mu A^{-1} \tag{9–362}$$

$$(\gamma'^\mu)^T = B\gamma'^\mu B^{-1} \tag{9–363}$$

$$\overline{(\gamma'^\mu)} = C\gamma'^\mu C^{-1} \tag{9–364}$$

with the matrices A, B, C the same as in the old coordinate system. Since, in general, under a change of representation the matrices A transform according to (recall Eqs. (9–292), (9–293), and (9–295))

$$A' = (S^{-1})^* A S^{-1} \tag{9–365}$$

the above requirement is that

$$S^*(\Lambda)A = AS^{-1}(\Lambda) \tag{9–366}$$

or equivalently

$$\tilde{S}(\Lambda) = S^{-1}(\Lambda) \tag{9–367}$$

In the standard representation, where $A = \gamma^0$, this requirement becomes

$$S^*(\Lambda)\gamma^0 = \gamma^0 S^{-1}(\Lambda) \tag{9–368}$$

More generally, one can derive that

$$\tilde{S}(\Lambda) = A^{-1}S^*(\Lambda)A = \alpha S^{-1}(\Lambda) \tag{9–369}$$

where $\alpha = +1$ for a Lorentz transformation for which $\Lambda_0{}^0 \geq 1$ and $\alpha = -1$ for a Lorentz transformation that inverts the sign of the time, *i.e.*, one for which $\Lambda_0{}^0 \leq -1$.

Equation (9–369) allows us to infer that the transformation of the adjoint spinor under Lorentz transformation is given by

$$\begin{aligned} \tilde{\psi}' &= (\psi')^* A' = \psi^* S^* A' \\ &= \alpha\psi^* A S^{-1}(\Lambda) \\ &= \alpha\tilde{\psi} S^{-1}(\Lambda) \end{aligned} \tag{9–370}$$

Hence, under a proper homogeneous Lorentz transformation without time inversion the quantity $\tilde{\psi}\psi$ transforms like a scalar:

$$\tilde{\psi}'\psi' = \tilde{\psi}S^{-1}S\psi = \tilde{\psi}\psi \tag{9–371}$$

$\tilde{\psi}\gamma^\mu\psi$ transforms like a 4-vector since

$$\begin{aligned}\tilde{\psi}'\gamma^\mu\psi' &= \tilde{\psi}S(\Lambda)^{-1}\gamma^\mu S(\Lambda)\psi \\ &= \Lambda^\mu{}_\nu\tilde{\psi}\gamma^\nu\psi\end{aligned} \tag{9–372}$$

Moreover $\tilde{\psi}\sigma^{\mu\nu}\psi$, where $\sigma^{\mu\nu} = (i/2)(\gamma^\mu\gamma^\nu - \gamma^\nu\gamma^\mu) = -\sigma^{\nu\mu}$, transforms like an antisymmetric tensor of rank 2 because

$$\begin{aligned}\tilde{\psi}'\sigma^{\mu\nu}\psi' &= \tilde{\psi}S(\Lambda)^{-1}\sigma^{\mu\nu}S(\Lambda)\psi \\ &= \Lambda^\mu{}_{\mu'}\Lambda^\nu{}_{\nu'}\tilde{\psi}\sigma^{\mu'\nu'}\psi\end{aligned} \tag{9–373}$$

The quantity $\tilde{\psi}\gamma_5\psi$, wherein

$$\begin{aligned}\gamma_5 = -\gamma^5 &= \frac{i}{4!}\,\varepsilon^{\mu\nu\rho\sigma}\gamma_\mu\gamma_\nu\gamma_\rho\gamma_\sigma \\ &= \frac{i}{4!}\,\varepsilon_{\mu\nu\rho\sigma}\gamma^\mu\gamma^\nu\gamma^\rho\gamma^\sigma\end{aligned} \tag{9–374}$$

transforms like a pseudoscalar

$$\begin{aligned}\tilde{\psi}'\gamma_5\psi' &= \tilde{\psi}S(\Lambda)^{-1}\gamma_5 S(\Lambda)\psi \\ &= \det\Lambda\tilde{\psi}\gamma_5\psi\end{aligned} \tag{9–375}$$

In obtaining Eq. (9–375) we have made use of the defining equation for det Λ, namely

$$(\det\Lambda)\varepsilon^{\alpha\beta\gamma\delta} = \Lambda^\alpha{}_\mu\Lambda^\beta{}_\nu\Lambda^\gamma{}_\rho\Lambda^\delta{}_\sigma\varepsilon^{\mu\nu\rho\sigma} \tag{9–376}$$

Finally, since

$$\gamma_5\gamma^\mu = \frac{i}{3!}\,\varepsilon^{\mu\nu\rho\sigma}\gamma_\nu\gamma_\rho\gamma_\sigma \tag{9–377}$$

the quantity $\tilde{\psi}'\gamma^5\gamma^\mu\psi'$ transform like a pseudovector

$$\begin{aligned}\tilde{\psi}'\gamma^5\gamma^\mu\psi' &= \tilde{\psi}S(\Lambda)^{-1}\gamma^5 S(\Lambda)S(\Lambda)^{-1}\gamma^\mu S(\Lambda)\psi \\ &= \det(\Lambda)\Lambda^\mu{}_\nu\tilde{\psi}\gamma^5\gamma^\nu\psi\end{aligned} \tag{9–378}$$

The explicit construction of the $S(\Lambda)$ is most readily accomplished by a consideration of the infinitesimal transformations. Consider an infinitesimal transformation, $\Lambda^\mu{}_\nu = \delta^\mu{}_\nu + \lambda\varepsilon^\mu{}_\nu$, *i.e.*,

$$x'_\mu = x_\mu + \lambda\varepsilon_{\mu\nu}x^\nu \tag{9–379}$$

where λ is infinitesimal. In order that the transformation so defined be a Lorentz transformation, $\varepsilon_{\mu\nu}$ must satisfy

$$\varepsilon_{\mu\nu} = -\varepsilon_{\nu\mu} \tag{9–380}$$

so that $x_\mu x^\mu = x'^\mu x'_\mu$ to order λ^2. Let us denote the $S(\Lambda)$ corresponding to this infinitesimal transformation by

$$S(\Lambda) = 1 + \lambda T \tag{9–381}$$
$$S(\Lambda)^{-1} = 1 - \lambda T \tag{9–382}$$

Equation (9–359) for the infinitesimal case then reads

$$[\gamma^\mu, T] = \varepsilon^\mu{}_\nu \gamma^\nu \tag{9–383}$$

The requirement that det $S = 1$, implies that Tr $T = 0$. Note that T is then uniquely determined by this requirement and Eq. (9–383). For assume that there were two such T's that satisfied Eq. (9–383). This difference would then commute with γ^μ, and, hence, by theorem A, their difference would be a constant multiple of the identity. But both of these T's can have trace zero only if this constant is equal to zero. This unique T is given by

$$T = \tfrac{1}{8}\varepsilon^{\mu\nu}(\gamma_\mu\gamma_\nu - \gamma_\nu\gamma_\mu) \tag{9–384}$$

The T corresponding to various infinitesimal transformations (*e.g.*, an infinitesimal rotation about the z-axis, or an infinitesimal Lorentz transformation about the x-axis) can be explicitly computed from this representation. The finite transformations can then be obtained by exponentiation. For example, for a pure rotation about the 1-direction (x-axis) through the angle θ, S is given by

$$S = e^{(i/2)\theta\Sigma_1} = \cos\frac{\theta}{2} + i\Sigma_1 \sin\frac{\theta}{2} \tag{9–385}$$

$$S(\theta + 2\pi) = -S(\theta) \tag{9–386}$$

For a pure Lorentz transformation along the 1-direction corresponding to a hyperbolic angle θ, S has the form

$$S = e^{\frac{1}{2}\theta\alpha} = \cosh\frac{\theta}{2} + \alpha_1 \sinh\frac{\theta}{2} \tag{9–387}$$

It should be noted that S is unitary and two-valued for a pure rotation, and is hermitian (but single-valued and nonunitary) for a pure Lorentz transformation.

To conclude this section we make a few remarks concerning the physical interpretation of the covariant amplitude $\psi(x)$. For a free particle one would surmise that adoption of the manifold of positive energy solutions of the Dirac equation (9–235) with the scalar product defined by Eq. (9–242) would yield a straightforward relativistic quantum mechanical description of a spin $\frac{1}{2}$ particle. This, however, is not so.

Consider for example the commutator of $\mathbf{x}$ with H

$$\dot{\mathbf{x}} = \frac{i}{\hbar}[H,\mathbf{x}] = c\boldsymbol{\alpha} \tag{9–388}$$

This result implies that if one tries to identify the amplitude $\psi(\mathbf{x},t)$ satisfying the Dirac equation (9–235) with the Schrödinger amplitude giving the position probability amplitude, so that $\mathbf{x}$ is the operator identified with the position operator, then according to Eq. (9–388), $\boldsymbol{\alpha}$ is the operator to be identified with the velocity operator. But this would have the consequence that the components of the "velocity" operator do not commute with each other (and hence are not simultaneously diagonalizable) and that the eigenvalue of any component of the velocity is ± 1 (in units of the velocity of light). This identification would furthermore imply that the velocity and the sign of the energy cannot be simultaneously diagonalized. Another "strange" feature of this representation is the time dependence of the orbital angular momentum $\mathbf{L} = \mathbf{x} \times \mathbf{p}$ for a free particle since $[\mathbf{L},H] \neq 0$. For a certain time, rather than rejecting the identification of $\psi(x)$ with the Schrödinger amplitude, the above unusual features were attributed to be a "mysterious" feature of relativistic equations.

The correct position operator and localized amplitudes were worked out by various investigators,[13] in particular Newton and Wigner[14] and Foldy and Wouthuysen.[15] The latter authors indicated that the amplitude

$$\phi(\mathbf{x},t) = -i\exp\left\{\frac{\beta\boldsymbol{\alpha}\cdot\mathbf{p}}{2|\mathbf{p}|}\tan^{-1}\left(\frac{|\mathbf{p}|}{m}\right)\right\}\psi(\mathbf{x},t) \tag{9–389}$$

$$= U_{FW}\psi(\mathbf{x},t) \quad (\mathbf{p} = -i\boldsymbol{\nabla}) \tag{9–390}$$

satisfies the Schrödinger-like equation

$$i\frac{\partial\phi(\mathbf{x},t)}{\partial t} = \beta\sqrt{m^2 - \boldsymbol{\nabla}^2}\,\phi(\mathbf{x},t) \tag{9–391}$$

Notice that according to Eq. (9–389), $\phi(\mathbf{x},t)$ is unitarily related to

[13] See, for example, M. L. Pryce, *Proc. Roy. Soc.*, A, **195**, 62 (1948).
[14] R. Newton and E. P. Wigner, *Rev. Mod. Phys.*, **21**, 400 (1949).
[15] L. Foldy and S. A. Wouthuysen, *Phys. Rev.*, **78**, 29 (1950). See also S. Tani, *Prog. Theor. Phys.*, **6**, 267 (1951).

$\psi(\mathbf{x},t)$ so that the probability density is unaltered. (The probability current is, however, altered in going from ψ to ϕ.) Within this representation, hereafter called the Foldy-Wouthuysen representation, the position operator $\mathbf{q}$ has the representative $\mathbf{x}$.

The components of the position operator, therefore, commute with one another; furthermore they are canonically conjugate to the momentum operators

$$[x^r,p^s] = i\delta^{rs} \tag{9–392}$$

In the Foldy-Wouthuysen representation the hamiltonian is given by

$$\begin{aligned} H_{FW} &= U_{FW}H_D U_{FW}^{-1} \\ &= U_{FW}(\boldsymbol{\alpha}\cdot\mathbf{p} + \beta m)U_{FW}^{-1} \\ &= \beta\sqrt{\mathbf{p}^2 + m^2} \end{aligned} \tag{9–393}$$

so that in this representation the operator $\mathbf{x}$ has the property that

$$i[H_{FW},\mathbf{x}] = \beta\frac{\mathbf{p}}{\sqrt{\mathbf{p}^2 + m^2}} \tag{9–394}$$

$$[H_{FW},[\mathbf{x},H_{FW}]] = 0 \tag{9–395}$$

i.e., that the velocity operator is given by β times $\mathbf{p}/\sqrt{\mathbf{p}^2 + m^2} = \mathbf{p}/E_{\mathbf{p}}$, and that the acceleration is zero (as should be the case for a free particle).

Equation (9–392) together with (9–394) and (9–395) are the proofs of the assertions that $\mathbf{x}$ is the position operator in the Foldy-Wouthuysen representation.[16] (Note also that $\mathbf{x}$ commutes with β the sign of the energy.) We further note that in the FW-representation the operators $\mathbf{x} \times \mathbf{p}$ and $\boldsymbol{\Sigma}$ commute with H_{FW} separately and, hence, are constants of the motion. In the FW-representation the orbital and spin angular momentum operators are thus separately constants of the motion. The fact that

$$\Sigma^l\Sigma^m = \delta^{lm} + i\varepsilon^{lmn}\Sigma^n \tag{9–396}$$

and $\boldsymbol{\Sigma}^2 = 3$ is now the proof that the Dirac equation describes a spin $\frac{1}{2}$ particle since the $\frac{1}{2}\boldsymbol{\Sigma}$ matrices form a (reducible) representation of $J = \frac{1}{2}$ angular momentum operators.

[16] In the Dirac representation, the position operator has the following representation

$$\begin{aligned} q_{jD} &= U_{FW}^{-1}q_{jFW}U_{FW} = U_{FW}^{-1}x_jU_{FW} \\ &= x_j + U_{FW}^{-1}[x_j,U_{FW}] \\ &= x_j + \frac{i\beta\alpha_j}{2E_{\mathbf{p}}} - \frac{i\beta(\boldsymbol{\alpha}\cdot\mathbf{p})\mathbf{p}_j + (\boldsymbol{\Sigma}\times\mathbf{p})_j|\mathbf{p}|}{2E_{\mathbf{p}}(E_{\mathbf{p}} + m)|\mathbf{p}|} \end{aligned}$$

Actually there exists in the FW representation another "polarization" operator, $\mathscr{S}$, which also satisfies the commutation rules

$$\mathscr{S}^l \mathscr{S}^m = \delta^{lm} + i\varepsilon^{lmr}\mathscr{S}^r\beta \tag{9–397}$$

and hence on the positive energy states satisfies the commutation rule $\mathscr{S}_l\mathscr{S}_m = \delta_{lm} + i\varepsilon_{lmr}\mathscr{S}_r$, commutes with the hamiltonian, *i.e.*

$$[\mathscr{S},\beta] = [\mathscr{S},H_{FW}] = 0 \tag{9–398}$$

and has the property that

$$(\mathscr{S}\cdot\mathbf{n})^2 = 1 \tag{9–399}$$

for any unit vector $\mathbf{n}$. The operator $\mathscr{S}$ having these properties is $\beta\mathbf{\Sigma}$. It is often called the Stech operator.[17] Its properties, as well as those of its eigenfunctions, are discussed in the excellent review article by Fradkin and Good.[18] We here note only two facts about this polarization operator. In the Dirac picture it has the form

$$\begin{aligned}\mathbf{O} &= U_{FW}^{-1}\beta\mathbf{\Sigma}U_{FW}\\ &= \beta\left[\mathbf{\Sigma} + \mathbf{p}\frac{\mathbf{\Sigma}\cdot\mathbf{p}}{|\mathbf{p}|^2}\left\{\beta\frac{\boldsymbol{\alpha}\cdot\mathbf{p}+\beta m}{E_{\mathbf{p}}} - 1\right\}\right]\end{aligned} \tag{9–400}$$

and satisfies the commutation rules

$$O^iO^j = \delta^{ij} + i\varepsilon^{ijk}O^k\frac{\boldsymbol{\alpha}\cdot\mathbf{p}+\beta m}{E_{\mathbf{p}}} \tag{9–401}$$

most easily verified in the FW-representation. For any unit vector $\mathbf{n}$, $(\mathbf{O}\cdot\mathbf{n})^2 = 1$ so that $\mathbf{O}\cdot\mathbf{n}$ has eigenvalues ± 1. Furthermore this operator $\mathbf{O}$ commutes with the hamiltonian; hence, one can obtain a complete set of simultaneous eigenfunctions of H_0 and $\mathbf{O}\cdot\mathbf{n}$. A system in an eigenstate of $\mathbf{O}\cdot\mathbf{n}$ will be said to be polarized in the $\mathbf{n}$-direction. The second and most important property of this polarization operator is that the polarization when thus defined is the same no matter from which Lorentz frame the particle is viewed.

We have noted that in the FW-representation the operator β plays the role of the sign of the energy. Hence, the proper Schrödinger equation describing a relativistic spin $\frac{1}{2}$ particle is obtained by restricting ϕ in Eq. (9–391) to contain only positive energy solutions. It is given by

$$i\frac{\partial\chi}{\partial t} = \sqrt{\mathbf{p}^2 + m^2}\,\chi \tag{9–402}$$

where χ is a two-component amplitude.

[17] B. Stech, *Z. Physik*, **144**, 214 (1956).

[18] D. M. Fradkin and R. H. Good, Jr., *Rev. Mod. Phys.*, **33**, 343 (1961).

REFERENCES

Historical:

Dirac, P. A. M., "The Quantum Theory of the Electron," *Proc. Roy. Soc.*, A, **117**, 610 (1928), and *Proc. Roy. Soc.*, A, **118**, 351 (1928).

See also:

Van der Waerden, B. L., "Exclusion Principle and Spin," in *Theoretical Physics in the Twentieth Century*, M. Fierz and V. F. Weisskopf, eds., Interscience Publishers, Inc., New York, 1950.

Dirac Algebra:

Good, R. H., Jr., *Rev. Mod. Phys.*, **27**, 187 (1955).

Pauli, W., *Ann. de l'Institut Henri Poincaré*, **6**, 137 (1936).

Jauch, J. M., and Rohrlich, F., *Theory of Electrons and Photons*, Appendix A2, Addison-Wesley, Cambridge, Mass., 1954.

Solutions of Dirac equation:

Rose, M. E., *Relativistic Electron Theory*, John Wiley and Sons, Inc., New York, 1961.

Position operator:

Newton, R., and Wigner, E. P., *Rev. Mod. Phys.*, **21**, 400 (1949).

Foldy, L., and Wouthuysen, S. A., *Phys. Rev.*, **78**, 29 (1950).

See also:

Bardacki, K., and Acharya, R., *Nuovo Cimento*, **21**, 802 (1961).

Transformation properties of Dirac spinors in particular under inversions:

Marshak, R. E., and Sudarshan, E. C. G., *Introduction to Elementary Particle Physics*, Interscience Publishers, Inc., New York, 1961.

Electron polarization operators:

Michel, L., *Nuovo Cimento Supplemento*, **14**, 95 (1959).

Fradkin, D. M., and Good, R. H., Jr., *Rev. Mod. Phys.*, **33**, 343 (1961).

See also:

Wightman, A. S., "L'Invariance dans la Mécanique Quantique," in C. de Witt and R. Omnès, eds., *Dispersion Relations and Elementary Particles*, John Wiley and Sons, Inc., New York, 1960. This last reference also contains a discussion of the spin $\frac{1}{2}$, mass 0 case.

9.6. Second Quantized Description of a System of Noninteracting Spin $\frac{1}{2}$ Particles.—All the spin $\frac{1}{2}$ particles discovered thus far in nature have the property that particles and antiparticles are distinct from one another. In fact there operates in nature conservation laws (besides charge conservation) which prevent such a particle from turning into its antiparticle. These laws operate independently for "light" particles (leptons) and "heavy" particles (baryons). For the light fermions, *i.e.*, the leptons: neutrinos, muons, and electrons, the conservation law is that of leptons, requiring that the number of leptons minus the number of antileptons is conserved in any process. For the baryons (nucleons, Λ, Σ, and Ξ hyperons) the conservation law is the heavy particle or baryon conservation law, requiring the number of baryons minus the number of antibaryons to be conserved in any process. No violations of these laws have been observed.

In formulating the second-quantized description of a system of noninteracting fermions, we shall, therefore, have to introduce distinct creation and annihilation operators for particle and antiparticle. Furthermore, since all the fermions that have been discovered thus far obey the Pauli Exclusion principle we shall have to make sure that the formalism describes a many particle system in terms of properly antisymmetrized amplitudes so that the particles obey Fermi-Dirac statistics. For definiteness, we shall in the present section consider only the negaton-positon system, and call the negaton the particle and the positon the antiparticle.

We shall denote the creation and annihilation operators for a negaton of momentum $\mathbf{p}$ energy $E_{\mathbf{p}} = \sqrt{\mathbf{p}^2 + m^2}$ and polarization s by $b^*(\mathbf{p},s)$ and $b(\mathbf{p},s)$ respectively. In the following, by the polarization s we shall always mean the eigenvalue of the operator $\mathbf{O}\cdot\mathbf{n}$, where $\mathbf{O}$ is the Stech polarization operator and $\mathbf{n}$ some fixed unit vector. We denote the creation and annihilation operators for a positon (the antiparticle) of momentum $\mathbf{q}$ energy $E_{\mathbf{q}} = \sqrt{\mathbf{q}^2 + m^2}$, polarization t, by $d^*(\mathbf{q},t)$ and $d(\mathbf{q},t)$ respectively. A vacuum or no-particle state $|0\rangle$ will be assumed to exist with the property that

$$b(\mathbf{p},s)|0\rangle = d(\mathbf{q},t)|0\rangle = 0 \tag{9–403}$$

for all $\mathbf{p},\mathbf{q}$ and s,t. The one-particle and one-antiparticle states are then defined by

$$|\mathbf{p},s;\rangle = b^*(\mathbf{p},s)|0\rangle \tag{9–404}$$

$$b(\mathbf{p},s)|\mathbf{p}',s';\rangle = p_0\delta_{ss'}\delta(\mathbf{p} - \mathbf{p}')|0\rangle; \quad p_0 = E_{\mathbf{p}} \tag{9–405}$$

$$|;\mathbf{q},t\rangle = d^*(\mathbf{q},t)|0\rangle \tag{9–406}$$

$$d(\mathbf{q},t)|;\mathbf{q}',t'\rangle = \delta_{tt'}q_0\delta(\mathbf{q} - \mathbf{q}')|0\rangle; \quad q_0 = E_{\mathbf{q}} \tag{9–407}$$

We normalize these states invariantly as follows:

$$\langle\mathbf{p}',s'|\mathbf{p},s\rangle = \delta_{ss'}p_0\delta(\mathbf{p} - \mathbf{p}') = \langle 0|b(\mathbf{p}',s)b^*(\mathbf{p},s)|0\rangle \tag{9–408}$$

$$\langle\mathbf{q}',t'|\mathbf{q},t\rangle = \delta_{tt'}q_0\delta(\mathbf{q} - \mathbf{q}') = \langle 0|d(\mathbf{q}',t')d^*(\mathbf{q},t)|0\rangle \tag{9–409}$$

where

$$p_0 = E_{\mathbf{p}} = \sqrt{\mathbf{p}^2 + m^2} \tag{9–410}$$

$$q_0 = E_{\mathbf{q}} = \sqrt{\mathbf{q}^2 + m^2} \tag{9–411}$$

More generally a state containing m particles with momenta $\mathbf{p}_1,\mathbf{p}_2,\cdots,$

$\mathbf{p}_m$, polarization $s_1, \cdots, s_m$ and n antiparticles of momenta $\mathbf{q}_1, \cdots, \mathbf{q}_n$, polarization $t_1, \cdots, t_n$ is defined as

$$|\mathbf{p}_1,s_1,\cdots,\mathbf{p}_m,s_m;\,\mathbf{q}_1,t_1,\cdots,\mathbf{q}_n,t_n\rangle = \frac{1}{\sqrt{m!n!}}\, b^*(\mathbf{p}_1,s_1)\cdots b^*(\mathbf{p}_m,s_m)d^*(\mathbf{q}_1,t_1)\cdots d(\mathbf{q}_n,t_n)|0\rangle \quad (9\text{–}412)$$

It is required, in accordance with the Fermi character of particles and antiparticles, to be separately antisymmetric in the particle and antiparticle variables, which in turn requires that the operator b^* and d^* satisfy the following anticommutation rules:

$$\{b^*(\mathbf{p},s)b^*(\mathbf{p}',s')\} = \{d^*(\mathbf{q},t),d^*(\mathbf{q}',t')\} = 0 \quad (9\text{–}413)$$

where $\{A,B\} = [A,B]_+ = AB + BA$. Note that when $\mathbf{p} = \mathbf{p}'$, $s = s'$, Eq. (9–413) asserts that $b^*(\mathbf{p},s)b^*(\mathbf{p},s) = 0$ which, of course, is the operator statement of the fact that it is impossible to realize a state in which two particles have all their quantum numbers identical. By taking the hermitian adjoint of Eq. (9–413) we deduce that

$$\{b(\mathbf{p},s),b(\mathbf{p}',s')\} = \{d(\mathbf{q},t),d(\mathbf{q}',t')\} = 0 \quad (9\text{–}414)$$

which, of course, reflects the required antisymmetry of the adjoint vectors $\langle\mathbf{p}_1,s_1,\cdots,\mathbf{p}_n,s_n;\,\mathbf{q}_1,t_1,\cdots,\mathbf{q}_n,t_n|$. We shall normalize the nm particle states as follows

$$\langle\mathbf{p}_1',s_1',\cdots,\mathbf{p}_m',s_m';\,\mathbf{q}_1',t_1',\cdots,\mathbf{q}_n',t_n'|\mathbf{p}_1,s_1,\cdots,\mathbf{p}_m s_m;\,\mathbf{q}_1,t_1,\cdots,\mathbf{q}_n,t_n\rangle = \delta_{mm'}\delta_{nm'}\frac{1}{n!m!}\det|p_{0j}\delta(\mathbf{p}_j-\mathbf{p}_k')\delta_{s_js_k'}| \times \det|q_{0j}\delta(\mathbf{q}_j-\mathbf{q}_k')\delta_{t_jt_k'}| \quad (9\text{–}415)$$

The normalization requirement of the one and many particle states is satisfied if we impose the following commutation rules on the b and d operators:

$$\{b(\mathbf{p},s),b^*(\mathbf{p}',s')\} = \delta_{ss'}p_0\delta(\mathbf{p}-\mathbf{p}') \quad (9\text{–}416)$$

$$\{d(\mathbf{q},t),d^*(\mathbf{q}',t')\} = \delta_{tt'}q_0\delta(\mathbf{q}-\mathbf{q}') \quad (9\text{–}417)$$

$$\{b(\mathbf{p},s),d(\mathbf{q},t)\} = \{b(\mathbf{p},s),d^*(\mathbf{q},t)\} = 0 \quad (9\text{–}418)$$

$$\{b^*(\mathbf{p},s),d^*(\mathbf{q},t)\} = \{b^*(\mathbf{p},s),d^*(\mathbf{q},t)\} = 0 \quad (9\text{–}419)$$

The occupation number operator for particles of momentum $\mathbf{p}$ polarization s and antiparticle of momentum $\mathbf{q}$ polarization t are given by

$$N_-(\mathbf{p},s) = p_0^{-1}b^*(\mathbf{p},s)b(\mathbf{p},s) \quad (9\text{–}420)$$

$$N_+(\mathbf{q},t) = q_0^{-1}d^*(\mathbf{q},t)d(\mathbf{q},t) \quad (9\text{–}421)$$

and the total number of particle operator by

$$N_{-} = \sum_{s} \int_{+} \frac{d^3p}{p_0} b^*(\mathbf{p},s)b(\mathbf{p},s) \tag{9–422}$$

and the corresponding number operator for the antiparticles by

$$N_{+} = \sum_{t} \int \frac{d^3q}{q_0} d^*(\mathbf{q},t)\, d\,(\mathbf{q},t) \tag{9–423}$$

The commutations (9–416)–(9–419) guarantee that the state vectors are antisymmetric and that the occupation number operators $N_{-}(\mathbf{p},s)$ and $N_{+}(\mathbf{q},t)$ can have only eigenvalues 0 and 1 (which is, of course, what is meant by the statement that particles and antiparticles separately obey Fermi-Dirac statistics). In fact one readily verifies that

$$[N_{\pm}(\mathbf{p},s)]^2 = [N_{\pm}(\mathbf{p},s)] \tag{9–424}$$

which proves our assertion.

The total energy operator and total momentum operator can be defined as

$$H = \sum_{s} \int_{+} \frac{d^3p}{p_0} \{b^*(\mathbf{p},s)b(\mathbf{p},s) + d^*(\mathbf{p},s)d(\mathbf{p},s)\}E_{\mathbf{p}} \tag{9–425}$$

$$\mathbf{P} = \sum_{s} \int_{+} \frac{d^3p}{p_0} \{b^*(\mathbf{p},s)b(\mathbf{p},s) + d^*(\mathbf{p},s)d(\mathbf{p},s)\}\mathbf{p} \tag{9–426}$$

respectively; they have the following commutation rules with b,b^* and d,d^*

$$\left[H, \begin{matrix} d(\mathbf{p},s) \\ b(\mathbf{p},s) \end{matrix}\right] = -E_{\mathbf{p}} \begin{matrix} d(\mathbf{p},s) \\ b(\mathbf{p},s) \end{matrix}; \quad \left[H, \begin{matrix} d^*(\mathbf{p},s) \\ b^*(\mathbf{p},s) \end{matrix}\right] = E_{\mathbf{p}} \begin{matrix} d^*(\mathbf{p},s) \\ b^*(\mathbf{p},s) \end{matrix} \tag{9–427}$$

and

$$\left[\mathbf{P}, \begin{matrix} d(\mathbf{p},s) \\ b(\mathbf{p},s) \end{matrix}\right] = -\mathbf{p} \begin{matrix} d(\mathbf{p},s) \\ b(\mathbf{p},s) \end{matrix}; \quad \left[\mathbf{P}, \begin{matrix} d^*(\mathbf{p},s) \\ b^*(\mathbf{p},s) \end{matrix}\right] = \mathbf{p} \begin{matrix} d^*(\mathbf{p},s) \\ b^*(\mathbf{p},s) \end{matrix} \tag{9–428}$$

This confirms our interpretation of the operators b,b^* and d,d^* as creation and annihilation operators for particles of definite momentum and energy. Similar consideration can be made for the angular momentum operator. The total electric charge operator is defined as

$$Q = -e \sum_{s} \int \frac{d^3p}{p_0} \{b^*(\mathbf{p},s)b(\mathbf{p},s) - d^*(\mathbf{p},s)d(\mathbf{p},s)\} \tag{9–429}$$

$$= -e(N_{-} - N_{+}) \tag{9–430}$$

and has the property that

$$[Q,H] = 0 \tag{9–431}$$

and

$$Q|\mathbf{p}_1,s_1,\cdots,\mathbf{p}_m,s_m;\ \mathbf{q}_1,t_1,\cdots,\mathbf{q}_n,t_n\rangle = -e(m-n)|\mathbf{p}_1,s_1,\cdots;\ \cdots,\mathbf{q}_n,t_n\rangle \tag{9–432}$$

as required by the additive attribute of the charge quantum number. Equations (9–431) and (9–432) can be verified by using the commutation rules of Q with the b,b^* and d,d^* operators.

As in our discussion of the spin 0 theory, we next introduce configuration space operators. We define the operators $\psi^{(+)}(x)$ and $\psi^{(-)}(x)$ as follows:

$$\psi^{(+)}(x) = \sum_s \int \frac{d^3p}{p_0}\, b(\mathbf{p},s)w_{+,\mathbf{p},s}(x) \tag{9–433}$$

$$\psi^{(-)}(x) = \sum_s \int \frac{d^3q}{q_0}\, d^*(\mathbf{q},t)w_{-,\mathbf{q},t}(x) \tag{9–434}$$

In Eq. (9–433) $w_{+,\mathbf{p},s}(x)$ is given by

$$w_{+,\mathbf{p},s}(x) = \sqrt{\frac{m}{(2\pi)^3}}\, u_{+,s}(\mathbf{p})e^{-ip\cdot x} \tag{9–435}$$

and $u_{+,s}(\mathbf{p})$ is a *positive* energy spinor of momentum $\mathbf{p}$, polarization s normalized so that $\tilde{u}u = +1$ and

$$\sum_s u_{+,s}(\mathbf{p}) \otimes \tilde{u}_{+,s}(\mathbf{p}) = \frac{\gamma\cdot p + m}{2m} \tag{9–436}$$

Similarly in Eq. (9–434) $w_{-,\mathbf{p},t}(x)$ is given by

$$w_{-,\mathbf{p},t}(x) = \sqrt{\frac{m}{(2\pi)^3}}\, v_{-,t}(\mathbf{p})e^{+ip\cdot x} \tag{9–437}$$

with $v_{-,t}(\mathbf{p})$ as a *negative* energy Dirac spinor of momentum $-\mathbf{p}$ (*i.e.*, it satisfies $(-\boldsymbol{\alpha}\cdot\mathbf{p} + \beta m)v_{-,t}(\mathbf{p}) = -E_\mathbf{p}v_{-,t}(\mathbf{p})$) polarization t, normalized so that $\tilde{v}v = -1$ and

$$\sum_t v_{-,t}(\mathbf{p}) \otimes \tilde{v}_{-,t}(\mathbf{p}) = \frac{-\gamma\cdot p + m}{2m} \tag{9–438}$$

The commutation relation satisfied by the operators $\psi^{(+)}(x)$ and $\widetilde{\psi^{(+)}}(x)$, where $\widetilde{\psi^{(+)}}(x)$ is defined as

$$\widetilde{\psi^{(+)}}(x) = [\psi^{(+)}(x)]^*\gamma^0 = \sum_s \int \frac{d^3p}{p_0}\, b^*(\mathbf{p},s)\, \tilde{w}_{+,\mathbf{p},s}(x) \tag{9–439}$$

$$\tilde{w}_{+,\mathbf{p},s}(x) = \sqrt{\frac{m}{(2\pi)^3}}\, \tilde{u}_{+,s}(\mathbf{p})e^{+ip\cdot x} \tag{9–440}$$

are readily derived using Eqs. (9–425) and (9–436). One finds

$$\begin{aligned}\{\psi_\alpha^{(+)}(x),\widetilde{\psi_\beta^{(+)}}(x')\} &= \frac{m}{(2\pi)^3}\int_+ \frac{d^3p}{p_0}\, e^{-ip\cdot(x-x')}\cdot \sum_s u_{+,s,\alpha}(\mathbf{p})\tilde{u}_{+,s,\beta}(\mathbf{p}) \\ &= \frac{1}{2(2\pi)^3}\int_+ \frac{d^3p}{p_0}\, e^{-ip\cdot(x-x')}(\gamma\cdot p + m)_{\alpha\beta} \\ &= (i\gamma^\mu\partial_\mu + m)_{\alpha\beta}\frac{1}{2(2\pi)^3}\int_{p_0>0}\frac{d^3p}{p_0}\, e^{-ip\cdot(x-x')} \\ &= (i\gamma^\mu\partial_\mu + m)_{\alpha\beta}\, i\Delta^{(+)}(x-x';m) \\ &= -iS^{(+)}(x-x';m)\end{aligned} \tag{9–441}$$

Similarly, one obtains

$$[\psi_\alpha^{(-)}(x),\widetilde{\psi_\beta^{(-)}}(x')]_+ = -iS_{\alpha\beta}^{(-)}(x-x') \tag{9–442}$$

where

$$S^{(-)}(x-x') = -(i\gamma^\mu\partial_\mu + m)\Delta^{(-)}(x-x';m) \tag{9–443}$$

The operator

$$\psi(x) = \psi^{(+)}(x) + \psi^{(-)}(x) \tag{9–444}$$

$$= \sum_s \int_+ \frac{d^3p}{p_0}\{b(\mathbf{p},s)u_{+,s}(\mathbf{p})e^{-ip\cdot x} + d^*(\mathbf{p},s)v_{-,s}(\mathbf{p})e^{ip\cdot x}\}$$

$$(p_0 = E_{\mathbf{p}}) \tag{9–445}$$

has the following properties:

(a) It has simple commutation rules with Q, namely

$$[Q,\psi(x)] = -e\psi(x) \tag{9–446}$$

so that $\psi(x)$ can be interpreted as a destruction operator for an amount of charge $-e$. Proof; if $|Q'\rangle$ is an eigenstate of Q with eigenvalue Q' then the state $\psi(x)|Q'\rangle$ is an eigenstate of Q with eigenvalue $Q' - e$:

$$\begin{aligned}Q\psi(x)|Q'\rangle &= \psi(x)Q|Q'\rangle + [Q,\psi(x)]|Q'\rangle \\ &= (Q'-e)\psi(x)|Q'\rangle\end{aligned} \tag{9–447}$$

(b) It satisfies the Dirac equation

$$(-i\gamma\cdot\partial + m)\psi(x) = 0 \tag{9–448}$$

(c) It obeys the following commutation rules

$$\{\psi_\alpha(x),\tilde{\psi}_\beta(x')\} = -iS_{\alpha\beta}(x-x';\, m) \tag{9–449}$$

where

$$\begin{aligned}S(x) &= S^{(+)}(x) + S^{(-)}(x) \\ &= -(i\gamma\cdot\partial + m)\Delta(x;\, m)\end{aligned} \tag{9–450}$$

The singular function $S(x)$ satisfies Dirac's equation

$$(-i\gamma\cdot\partial + m)S(x) = 0 \tag{9–451}$$

since

$$-(-i\gamma\cdot\partial + m)(i\gamma\cdot\partial + m)\Delta(x,m) = -(\Box + m^2)\Delta(x;m) = 0 \tag{9–452}$$

Furthermore, from the equal time properties of $\Delta(x; m)$, Eq. (9–176)–(9–180), it follows that

$$S(x)\bigg|_{x_0=0} = -i\gamma^0 \frac{\partial\Delta(x)}{\partial x^0}\bigg|_{x^0=0} = i\gamma^0\delta(\mathbf{x}) \tag{9–453}$$

The number operators, when expressed in terms of the configuration space operators, assume the following form

$$N_- = \int d^3x \widetilde{\psi^{(+)}}(x)\gamma^0\psi^{(+)}(x) \tag{9–454}$$

$$N_+ = \int d^3x \widetilde{\psi_c^{(+)}}(x)\gamma^0\psi_c^{(+)}(x) \tag{9–455}$$

where ψ_c, the charge conjugate operator is defined by

$$\psi_c(x) = C^{-1}\tilde{\psi}^T(x) \tag{9–456}$$

and C is a unitary matrix[18a] with the property

$$C\gamma_\mu C^{-1} = -\gamma_\mu^T \tag{9–457}$$

$$C^T = -C \tag{9–458}$$

This matrix C is essentially $B\gamma^5$, B being the matrix defined in Section 9.5 by the equation $B\gamma^\mu B^{-1} = \gamma^{\mu T}$. The total charge operator

$$Q = -e(N_- - N_+) \tag{9–459}$$

which, due to charge conservation is time independent, should be the integral over-all space of the 0-component of a conserved charge-current four-vector $j_\mu(x)$

$$Q = \int d^3x j_0(x) \tag{9–460}$$

with $\partial_\mu j^\mu(x) = 0$. These criteria are satisfied if we define the charge-current four-vector as

$$j_\mu(x) = eN(\tilde{\psi}(x)\gamma_\mu\psi(x)) \tag{9–461}$$

where the normal product operator N operating on fermion operators is defined as follows: acting on a product of creation and annihilation

[18a] This matrix C is not to be confused with that defined by Eq. (9–261).

operators, it rewrites the expression with all creation operators standing to the left of all destruction operators, the rearrangement being effected as if all the anticommutators of the fermion operators were equal to zero. Thus, for example

$$\begin{aligned} N(\psi^{(+)}(x)\psi^{(-)}(y)) &= -N(\psi^{(-)}(y)\psi^{(+)}(x)) \\ &= -\psi^{(-)}(y)\psi^{(+)}(x) \qquad (9\text{–}462) \\ N(\psi^{(+)}(x)\psi^{(+)}(y)) &= -N(\psi^{(+)}(y)\psi^{(+)}(x)) \\ &= \psi^{(+)}(x)\psi^{(+)}(y) = -\psi^{(+)}(y)\psi^{(+)}(x) \qquad (9\text{–}463) \end{aligned}$$

It is again postulated that the distributive law be valid for the normal product operation. Similarly one readily verifies that the hamiltonian and the momentum operator can be expressed in terms of $\psi(x)$ and $\tilde{\psi}(x)$ as follows:

$$P_\mu = \tfrac{1}{2}iN\int d^3x(\tilde{\psi}(x)\gamma^0\partial_\mu\psi(x) - \partial_\mu\tilde{\psi}(x)\gamma^0\psi(x)) \qquad (9\text{–}464)$$

In concluding this section we briefly establish the connection between the Dirac theory for a single isolated free particle described in the previous section and the present formalism. If $|\Psi\rangle$ is the state vector describing a one-particle state, $N_-|\Psi\rangle = 1|\Psi\rangle$ consider the amplitude

$$f(x) = \langle 0|\psi(x)|\Psi\rangle \qquad (9\text{–}465)$$

It satisfies the Dirac equation, $(-i\gamma\cdot\partial + m)f(x) = 0$, because $\psi(x)$ does [Eq. (9–448)]. Since $\langle 0|d^*(\mathbf{q},t) = 0$, upon inserting the representation (9–445) for $\psi(x)$ into the right-hand side of Eq. (9–465), we deduce that

$$f(x) = \sqrt{\frac{m}{(2\pi)^3}}\sum_s\int_+ \frac{d^3p}{p_0}\langle 0|b(\mathbf{p},s)|\Psi\rangle u_{+,s}(\mathbf{p})e^{-ip\cdot x} \qquad (9\text{–}466)$$

so that $f(x)$ is a superposition of *positive* energy solutions of the Dirac equation, in agreement with the discussion of Section 9.5. Similarly, if $|\Phi\rangle$ is the state vector corresponding to a one-antiparticle system: $N_+|\Phi\rangle = 1|\Phi\rangle$, the amplitude

$$g(x) = \langle 0|\psi_c(x)|\Phi\rangle \qquad (9\text{–}467)$$

corresponds to the amplitude for finding the antiparticle. Using the definition (9–456) of $\psi_c(x)$ we find that

$$g(x) = \sqrt{\frac{1}{(2\pi)^3}}\sum_t\int_+ \frac{d^3q}{q_0}\langle 0|d(\mathbf{q},t)|\Phi\rangle u^c_{+,t}(\mathbf{q})e^{-iq\cdot x}$$

$$q_0 = \sqrt{\mathbf{q}^2 + m^2} \qquad (9\text{–}468)$$

where the spinor u^c is given by

$$u^c_{+,t}(\mathbf{q}) = C\tilde{v}_{-,t}(\mathbf{q}) \tag{9-469}$$

and it satisfies the Dirac equation $(\gamma\cdot q - m)u^c_+(\mathbf{q}) = 0$. Note particularly that $g(x)$ satisfies the Dirac equation and that it is a superposition of *positive* energy solutions since its time dependence is given by factors $\exp(-iq_0x_0)$ with $q_0 > 0$.

REFERENCES

For the configuration space treatment of a spin ½ operator, see:

Wightman, A. S., and Schweber, S. S., *Phys. Rev.*, **98**, 812 (1954). A discussion of the transformation properties of the operators $\psi(x)$ and $\tilde{\psi}(x)$ under Lorentz transformation is also included in this reference.

For a discussion of the transformation of the field operators under improper Lorentz transformations and discrete symmetry operations such as charge conjugation, see:

Feinberg, G., and Weinberg, S., *Nuovo Cimento*, **14**, 571 (1959).

also:

Marshak, R. E., and Sudarshan, E. C. G., *Introduction to Elementary Particle Physics*, Interscience Publishers, Inc., New York, 1961.

9.7. Spin 1, Mass Zero Particles. *Photons.*—For a mass zero, spin 1 particle, the set of relativistic wave equations describing the particle is Maxwell's equations. We adopt the vector $\mathfrak{E}(x)$ and the pseudovector $\mathfrak{H}(x)$ which are positive energy (frequency) solutions of

$$\nabla\cdot\mathfrak{E}(x) = 0 \tag{9-470}$$

$$\nabla\cdot\mathfrak{H}(x) = 0 \tag{9-471}$$

$$\frac{\partial\mathfrak{E}(x)}{\partial t} = \nabla\times\mathfrak{H}(x) \tag{9-472}$$

$$\frac{\partial\mathfrak{H}(x)}{\partial t} = -\nabla\times\mathfrak{E}(x) \tag{9-473}$$

as the quantities characterizing the state of photon. Since it follows from Eqs. (9-472) and (9-473) that div $\mathfrak{E}$ and div $\mathfrak{H}$ are constant in time, one need in fact only consider the solutions of Eqs. (9-472) and (9-473), which initially have zero divergence. The real vector quantities $\mathfrak{E}$ and $\mathfrak{H}$ can be combined in the complex vector valued "wave function"

$$\mathfrak{G}(x) = \frac{1}{\sqrt{2}}(\mathfrak{E}(x) + i\mathfrak{H}(x)) \tag{9-474}$$

obeying the equations

$$\operatorname{div} \mathfrak{G}(x) = 0 \tag{9–475}$$

$$i\partial_t \mathfrak{G}(x) = -\nabla \times \mathfrak{G}(x) \tag{9–476}$$

which in component form read

$$\partial_j \mathfrak{G}^j(x) = 0 \tag{9–477}$$

$$\varepsilon^{lmn}\partial^m \mathfrak{G}^n(x) = -i\partial_t \mathfrak{G}^l(x) \tag{9–478}$$

Let us next introduce the three hermitian matrices s^l defined by the equation

$$-i\varepsilon^{lmn} = (s^m)_{ln} \tag{9–479}$$

so that upon writing $-i\hbar\partial^m = p^m$, Eq. (9–478) becomes

$$-i\varepsilon^{lmn} p^m \mathfrak{G}^n = i\hbar\partial_t \mathfrak{G}^l \tag{9–480}$$

or, equivalently,

$$-(\mathbf{s}\cdot\mathbf{p})_{ln}\mathfrak{G}^n = i\hbar\partial_t \mathfrak{G}^l \tag{9–481}$$

In vector notation,

$$-(\mathbf{s}\cdot\mathbf{p})\mathfrak{G} = i\hbar\partial_t \mathfrak{G} \tag{9–482}$$

This equation can be taken as the Schrödinger form of the one photon equation, with the hamiltonian

$$H = -(\mathbf{s}\cdot\mathbf{p}) \tag{9–483}$$

However, an acceptable wave function $\mathfrak{G}$ must satisfy the subsidiary condition (9–475), *i.e.*, $\mathbf{p}\cdot\mathfrak{G} = 0$.

Explicitly the matrices s^l have the following representation:

$$s^1 = i\begin{pmatrix} 0 & 0 & 0 \\ 0 & 0 & +1 \\ 0 & -1 & 0 \end{pmatrix} \quad s^2 = i\begin{pmatrix} 0 & 0 & -1 \\ 0 & 0 & 0 \\ +1 & 0 & 0 \end{pmatrix}$$

$$s^3 = i\begin{pmatrix} 0 & +1 & 0 \\ -1 & 0 & 0 \\ 0 & 0 & 0 \end{pmatrix} \tag{9–484}$$

and their commutation rules are easily calculated to be

$$[s^l, s^m] = i\varepsilon^{lmr}s^r \tag{9–485}$$

The s^j, therefore, satisfy angular momentum commutation rules. Since each of these matrices has eigenvalues ± 1 and 0, they form a representation of the angular momentum operators for spin 1.

The plane wave solutions of (9–475) and (9–476) are found by writing

$$\mathfrak{G}(x) = \mathfrak{g}_{\mathbf{k}} e^{i(\mathbf{k}\cdot\mathbf{x} - Wt)} \tag{9–486}$$

Nontrivial solutions exist only when

$$\det |\mathbf{s}\cdot\mathbf{k} - W| = 0 \tag{9–487}$$

i.e., when $W = \pm k$ or 0 ($k = |\mathbf{k}|$). Consider the case of a photon moving along the z-axis, so that only k^3 is different from zero and

$$\mathbf{s}\cdot\mathbf{k} = i\begin{pmatrix} 0 & +k^3 & 0 \\ -k^3 & 0 & 0 \\ 0 & 0 & 0 \end{pmatrix} \tag{9–488}$$

The requirement of positive frequency implies that we must restrict ourselves to the cases in which $W = +k$ or $W = 0$. When $W = +k$, one readily finds that apart from a normalization factor

$$\mathfrak{G}_{+,\mathbf{k}} = \begin{pmatrix} 1 \\ -1 \\ 0 \end{pmatrix} e^{+i(\mathbf{k}\cdot\mathbf{x} - kt)} \tag{9–489}$$

whereas when $W = 0$, $\mathfrak{g}_{0,\mathbf{k}}$ is given by

$$\mathfrak{g}_{0,\mathbf{k}} = \begin{pmatrix} 0 \\ 0 \\ 1 \end{pmatrix} \tag{9–490}$$

However, clearly the solution for $W = 0$ does not satisfy the subsidiary condition $\mathbf{k}\cdot\mathfrak{g}_{0,\mathbf{k}} = 0$. There exists, therefore, only one acceptable solution of Eq. (9–482) and it corresponds to a one-photon state of momentum $\mathbf{k}$ and negative helicity ($\mathbf{s}\cdot\mathbf{k} = -k$). The $\mathfrak{g}_{+,\mathbf{k}}$ for that situation satisfies

$$(\mathbf{s}\cdot\mathbf{k})\mathfrak{g}_{+,\mathbf{k}} = -|\mathbf{k}|\mathfrak{g}_{+,\mathbf{k}} \tag{9–491}$$

$$\mathbf{k}\cdot\mathfrak{g}_{+,\mathbf{k}} = 0 \tag{9–492}$$

One verifies that the vector $\hat{\mathfrak{G}} = 1/\sqrt{2}(\mathfrak{E} - i\mathfrak{H})$, constructed from positive energy solutions of (9–470), (9–471), (9–472), and (9–473), corresponds in the case of a photon of definite energy, to the photon having its spin parallel to its direction of motion, *i.e.*, positive helicity ($\mathbf{s}\cdot\mathbf{k} = +|\mathbf{k}|$).

The scalar product of two wave functions is defined as

$$(\mathfrak{G}_1,\mathfrak{G}_2) = \int d^3x \overline{\mathfrak{G}_1(x)}\mathfrak{G}_2(x) \tag{9–493}$$

and is time independent for $\mathfrak{G}$'s satisfying (9–475) and (9–476). We note that the norm $\mathfrak{G}$ is related to the energy since

$$(\mathfrak{G},\mathfrak{G}) = \int d^3x \overline{\mathfrak{G}(x)} \cdot \mathfrak{G}(x) \tag{9–494}$$

$$= \frac{1}{2} \int d^3x (\mathfrak{E}^2 + \mathfrak{H}^2) \tag{9–495}$$

The formalism can be carried further to discuss the particle observables and also the transformation properties of the $\mathfrak{G}$'s and of the scalar product under Lorentz transformations. Since in our subsequent discussion we shall be primarily interested in the covariant amplitudes describing the photon, we shall not here carry out these considerations. We only mention that a position operator $\mathbf{q}$ having the properties that:

(a) it transforms under spatial rotations like a vector;
(b) it satisfies the commutation rules

$$[q_i,q_j] = 0 \tag{9–496}$$

$$[q_l,p_j] = i\delta_{lj} \tag{9–497}$$

$$[[q_i,H],H] = 0 \tag{9–498}$$

does not exist for spin 1, mass zero particles. We shall return to this point. For a manifestly covariant description of the state of a photon it is useful to introduce the real antisymmetric tensor

$$\mathfrak{F}_{\mu\nu} = \begin{pmatrix} 0 & \mathfrak{E}^1 & \mathfrak{E}^2 & \mathfrak{E}^3 \\ -\mathfrak{E}^1 & 0 & \mathfrak{H}^3 & -\mathfrak{H}^2 \\ -\mathfrak{E}^2 & -\mathfrak{H}^3 & 0 & \mathfrak{H}^1 \\ -\mathfrak{E}^3 & \mathfrak{H}^2 & -\mathfrak{H}^1 & 0 \end{pmatrix} = -\mathfrak{F}_{\nu\mu} \tag{9–499, 9–500}$$

with $\mathfrak{F}_{0i} = \mathfrak{E}^i$ and $\mathfrak{F}_{kl} = \epsilon_{klm}\mathfrak{H}^m$. The Maxwell equations (9–470) and (9–472), can be written in terms of $\mathfrak{F}_{\mu\nu}$ in the form

$$\partial^\mu \mathfrak{F}_{\mu\nu}(x) = 0 \tag{9–501}$$

and Eqs. (9–471) and (9–473) as

$$\partial_\lambda \mathfrak{F}_{\mu\nu} + \partial_\mu \mathfrak{F}_{\nu\lambda} + \partial_\nu \mathfrak{F}_{\lambda\mu} = 0 \tag{9–502}$$

Equation (9–502) can also be written as follows:

$$\varepsilon^{\rho\mu\nu\sigma} \partial_\sigma \mathfrak{F}_{\mu\nu} = 0 \tag{9–503}$$

where $\varepsilon^{\rho\mu\nu\sigma}$ is the completely antisymmetric tensor of rank 4. If we introduce the dual tensor

$$\hat{\mathfrak{F}}_{\mu\nu} = \tfrac{1}{2}\varepsilon_{\mu\nu\kappa\rho}\mathfrak{F}^{\kappa\rho}$$

then Maxwell's equations take on the symmetric form

$$\partial^\mu \hat{\mathfrak{F}}_{\mu\nu} = 0 \qquad \partial^\mu \mathfrak{F}_{\mu\nu} = 0 \tag{9–504}$$

(The set of equations $\partial^\mu \hat{\mathfrak{F}}_{\mu\nu} = 0$ remains homogeneous even in the presence of charge, because of the nonexistence of magnetic monopoles.) It follows from Eqs. (9–501) and (9–503) together with the antisymmetry of the $\mathfrak{F}_{\mu\nu}$'s that each component of $\mathfrak{F}_{\mu\nu}$ satisfies the wave equation

$$\Box \mathfrak{F}_{\mu\nu}(x) = 0 \tag{9–505}$$

One verifies that upon representing the $\mathfrak{F}_{\mu\nu}$ as the four-dimensional curl of the four vector $\mathfrak{A}_\mu(x)$

$$\mathfrak{F}_{\mu\nu} = \partial_\nu \mathfrak{A}_\mu(x) - \partial_\mu \mathfrak{A}_\nu(x) \tag{9–506}$$

Equation (9–502) is automatically satisfied.[19] The potentials $\mathfrak{A}_\mu(x)$ are, however, not fixed by Eq. (9–506) since under the gauge transformation:

$$\mathfrak{A}_\mu(x) \to \mathfrak{A}_\mu(x) + \partial_\mu \mathfrak{L}(x) \tag{9–507}$$

where $\mathfrak{L}(x)$ is an arbitrary scalar function of x, which possesses partial derivatives of first and second order, the fields $\mathfrak{F}_{\mu\nu}$ remain unchanged. The field equations will therefore clearly also remain invariant. Two vector potentials differing by $\partial_\mu \mathfrak{L}$ describe the same physical configuration. If one imposes the Lorentz condition

$$\partial^\mu \mathfrak{A}_\mu(x) = 0 \tag{9–508}$$

the vector potential $\mathfrak{A}_\mu(x)$ is fixed in gauge up to the addition of some $\partial_\mu \mathfrak{L}(x)$, with $\mathfrak{L}(x)$ satisfying the wave equation

$$\Box \mathfrak{L}(x) = 0 \tag{9–509}$$

[19] In simpler language since div $\mathfrak{H} = 0$, we can represent $\mathfrak{H}$ as the curl of some vector: $\mathfrak{H} = \nabla \times \mathfrak{A}$. Equation (9–473) can then be written as

$$\nabla \times (\mathfrak{E} + \partial_t \mathfrak{A}) = 0$$

The vector $\mathfrak{E} + \partial_t \mathfrak{A}$ has a vanishing curl and can, therefore, be represented as the gradient of some scalar $\mathfrak{A}_0$

$$\mathfrak{E} + \partial_t \mathfrak{A} = \nabla \mathfrak{A}_0$$

In the Lorentz gauge, Maxwell's equations when expressed in terms of the potentials assume the following form

$$\Box\mathfrak{A}_\mu(x) = 0 \tag{9–510}$$

$$\partial^\mu\mathfrak{A}_\mu(x) = 0 \tag{9–511}$$

Equations (9–510) and (9–511) together with the defining equation for the fields in terms of the potential, Eq. (9–506), are equivalent to the original Maxwell equations.

We shall adopt Eqs. (9–510) and (9–511) as the covariant wave equation for the covariant four-vector amplitude $\mathfrak{A}_\mu(x)$ describing a photon. The physically realizable amplitudes correspond to positive frequency solutions of Eq. (9–510), which in addition satisfy the subsidiary condition (9–511). In other words the admissible "wave functions" satisfy

$$i\frac{\partial}{\partial t}\mathfrak{A}_\mu(x) = \sqrt{-\nabla^2}\mathfrak{A}_\mu(x) \tag{9–512}$$

$$\partial^\mu\mathfrak{A}_\mu(x) = 0 \tag{9–513}$$

Such admissible wave functions are most concisely expressed in terms of their Fourier transform, $a_\mu(k)$. An admissible "wave function" must be of the form

$$\mathfrak{A}_\mu(x) = \int_+ e^{-ik\cdot x}a_\mu(k)\frac{d^3k}{2k_0} \tag{9–514}$$

$$= \int d^4k\theta(k_0)\delta(k^2)a_\mu(k)e^{-ik\cdot x} \tag{9–515}$$

In the expression (9–514), $k_0 = |\mathbf{k}|$ so that in fact $a_\mu(k)$ is only a function of $\mathbf{k}$. In Eq. (9–514) the integration is carried out over the positive light cone. Clearly the so defined $\mathfrak{A}_\mu(x)$ will satisfy the wave equation (9–510). In order for this $\mathfrak{A}_\mu(x)$ to satisfy the Lorentz condition $a_\mu(k)$ must be such that

$$k^\mu a_\mu(k) = 0 \tag{9–516}$$

We shall call an amplitude $a_\mu(k)$, which satisfies Eq. (9–516), a transversal amplitude.[20] We can summarize the above statements as follows: in momentum space, a one-photon amplitude $a_\mu(k)$ is defined on the forward light cone, *i.e.*, for $k^2 = 0$, $k_0 > 0$, and satisfies the subsidiary

[20] We shall call a four-vector $\Phi_\mu(k)$ "transversal" if it satisfies $k^\mu\Phi_\mu(k) = 0$, in contradistinction to a three-dimensional "transverse" vector $\Psi_i(\mathbf{k})$, *i.e.*, one that satisfies $\sum_{i=1}^3 k^i\Psi^i(\mathbf{k}) = 0$.

condition $k^\mu a_\mu(k) = 0$. The freedom of gauge transformations, Eqs. (9–507), (9–509), however, implies that a photon is not specified by a unique wave function $a_\mu(k)$, but rather by an equivalence class of functions $\{a_\mu(k)\}$. Two functions $a'_\mu(k)$ and $a''_\mu(k)$ will belong to the same equivalence class if their difference is parallel to k_μ, *i.e.*, if

$$a'_\mu(k) - a''_\mu(k) = k_\mu \lambda(k) \tag{9–517}$$

The scalar product of two wave functions $a^{(1)}_\mu(k)$ and $a^{(2)}_\mu(k)$ is defined as

$$(a^{(1)}, a^{(2)}) = -\int_+ \overline{a^{(1)}_\mu(k)} g^{\mu\nu} a^{(2)}_\nu(k) \frac{d^3k}{k_0} \tag{9–518}$$

where the integration is again carried out over the positive light cone. This scalar product is positive definite for "physically realizable" wave functions (those satisfying $k^2 a_\mu(k) = 0$, $k^\mu a_\mu(k) = 0$, $k_0 > 0$); *i.e.*, such "physically admissible" wave functions will have positive norms within the scalar product (9–518). Before proving this assertion we first recall a few properties of Lorentzian four vectors.

Lemma.—If $k^2 = 0$, then if $k \cdot \ell = 0$, either ℓ_μ is space like or $\ell_\mu = \alpha k_\mu$ (α a constant).

Proof.—If $k \cdot \ell = 0$, $k^0 \ell^0 = \mathbf{k} \cdot \boldsymbol{\ell}$. Applying Schwartz inequality to this last equation, we obtain

$$|k^0|\,|\ell^0| = |\mathbf{k} \cdot \boldsymbol{\ell}| \le |\mathbf{k}|\,|\boldsymbol{\ell}| \tag{9–519}$$

and recalling that $|k^0| = |\mathbf{k}|$, we deduce that

$$|\ell^0| \le |\boldsymbol{\ell}| \tag{9–520}$$

i.e., that ℓ_μ is a spacelike vector if the inequality ($<$) sign holds. The equality sign holds only if $\ell_\mu = \alpha k_\mu$.

It therefore follows from the transversality condition [Eq. (9–516)] that a physically admissible wave function $a_\mu(k)$ can only be spacelike or a multiple of k_μ, since k_μ is a null vector. In the coordinate system in which

$$k^\mu = |\mathbf{k}|\,(1,1,0,0) \tag{9–521}$$

construct the three real linearly independent vectors

$$v^{(1)\mu} = (1,-1,0,0) \tag{9–522}$$

$$v^{(2)\mu} = (0,0,1,0) \tag{9–523}$$

$$v^{(3)\mu} = (0,0,0,1) \tag{9–524}$$

Then

$$v_\mu^{(1)}v^{(1)\mu} = 0; \qquad v^{(1)\mu}k_\mu > 0 \tag{9–525}$$

$$v_\mu^{(2)}v^{(2)\mu} = v_\mu^{(3)}v^{(3)\mu} = -1 \tag{9–526}$$

$$v^{(2)\mu}k_\mu = v^{(3)\mu}k_\mu = 0 \tag{9–527}$$

The vectors $v^{(1)\mu}$, $v^{(2)\mu}$, $v^{(3)\mu}$, and k^μ are linearly independent. In this coordinate system an arbitrary vector can be written as follows

$$a_\mu(k) = \sum_{i=1}^{3} \alpha_i v_\mu^{(i)} + \alpha_0 k_\mu \tag{9–528}$$

Clearly for a vector $a_\mu(k)$ to be transversal it is necessary and sufficient that $\alpha_1 = 0$. These transversal vectors lie in a hyperplane that is tangent to the light cone along k_μ. For a transversal vector one now verifies that

$$\begin{aligned} -\overline{a_\mu(k)}g^{\mu\nu}a_\nu(k) = -\overline{a_\mu(k)}a^\mu(k) &= -\left(|\alpha_2|^2 v_\mu^{(2)}v^{(2)\mu} + |\alpha_3|^2 v_\mu^{(3)}v^{(3)\mu}\right) \\ &= |\alpha_2|^2 + |\alpha_3|^2 \geq 0 \end{aligned} \tag{9–529}$$

the equality holding only if $\alpha_2 = \alpha_3 \equiv 0$. Equation (9–529) indicates that for a transversal amplitude $a_\mu(k)$ the norm

$$\|a\|^2 = -\int_+ \overline{a_\mu(k)}a^\mu(k)\,\frac{d^3k}{k_0} \tag{9–530}$$

is non-negative. The norm may vanish if $a_\mu(k) = \alpha k_\mu$. But according to our previous observation regarding gauge transformations, an amplitude that is proportional to k_μ is equivalent to zero. A transversal vector $b_\mu(k)$ (*i.e.*, one satisfying $k_\mu b^\mu(k) = 0$) is said to be equivalent to zero if and only if $b_\mu(k) = \beta(k)k_\mu$. We shall write $b_\mu \sim 0$ if $b_\mu = \beta k_\mu$. Alternatively, two vectors b'_μ and b''_μ are equivalent, $b'_\mu \sim b''_\mu$, if and only if $b'_\mu - b''_\mu \sim 0$. Note that if $b_\mu \sim 0$ and a_μ is some transversal vector then $-b_\mu a^\mu = 0$. The proof of this follows upon recognizing that the statement $b_\mu \sim 0$ implies that $b_\mu = \beta k_\mu$, hence $b_\mu a^\mu = \beta k_\mu a^\mu = 0$ since a_μ is transversal. We also note for future reference that if $b'_\mu \sim b_\mu$ and $a'_\mu \sim a_\mu$ and a_μ, b_μ are transversal then

$$b'_\mu a'^\mu = b_\mu a^\mu \tag{9–531}$$

Proof.—

$$\begin{aligned} b'_\mu a'^\mu - b_\mu a^\mu &= (b'_\mu - b_\mu)a^\mu - b'_\mu(a'^\mu - a^\mu) \\ &= \beta k_\mu a^\mu - \alpha k_\mu b'^\mu = 0 \end{aligned} \tag{9–532}$$

In the language of equivalence classes, the norm $-b_\mu b^\mu$ vanishes only if $b_\mu \sim 0$.

Note incidentally that in any particular Lorentz frame we could choose as the representative of an equivalence class that vector that has zero time component. For example, for the vectors equivalent to $\mathscr{b}_\mu(k)$ we could choose as the representative of that equivalence class the vector

$$\mathscr{b}'_\mu(k) = \mathscr{b}_\mu(k) - \frac{k_\mu}{k_0}\mathscr{b}_0(k) \tag{9-533}$$

which has the property that $\mathscr{b}'_0 = 0$. Note also that for this representative the transversality condition takes the form

$$\mathbf{k}\cdot\mathscr{b}'(k) = 0 \tag{9-534}$$

i.e., it becomes a three-dimensional transversality condition that ensures that the photon is always transversely polarized with just two independent polarizations. The configuration space amplitude

$$\mathfrak{A}'(x) = \int \frac{d^3k}{2k_0}\, e^{-ik\cdot x}\mathscr{a}'(k) \tag{9-535}$$

corresponding to such a three dimensionally transverse amplitude $\mathscr{a}'(k)$ $(\mathbf{k}\cdot\mathscr{a}'(k) = 0)$ clearly satisfies the equation

$$i\partial_t\mathfrak{A}'(x) = \sqrt{-\nabla^2}\mathfrak{A}'(x) \tag{9-536}$$

$$\nabla\cdot\mathfrak{A}'(x) = 0 \tag{9-537}$$

(compare with Klein-Gordon case). The absence of a position operator for a photon can now be understood in the following heuristic fashion. For a Klein-Gordon particle a localized state at a given point in space could be constructed since all momenta were available. For a photon on the other hand, because of the transversality condition, only the momenta orthogonal to $\mathscr{a}$ are available so that we cannot localize the photon along the direction of $\mathscr{a}$, *i.e.*, the direction of polarization.[21]

We have noted that if k_μ is the energy-momentum four vector of a photon (*i.e.*, $k^2 = 0$, $k_0 > 0$) there exist only two other linearly independent vectors orthogonal to k_μ. We shall denote these as $e_\mu^{(1)}(k)$ and $e_\mu^{(2)}(k)$. They satisfy

$$-e_\mu^{(i)}(k)g^{\mu\nu}e_\nu^{(j)}(k) \equiv \langle e^{(i)},e^{(j)}\rangle \tag{9-538}$$

$$= \delta_{ij} \quad (i,j = 1,2) \tag{9-539}$$

$$e_\mu^{(i)}(k)k^\mu = 0 \quad (i,j = 1,2) \tag{9-540}$$

and

$$\mathbf{e}^{(1)}(k) \times \mathbf{e}^{(2)}(k)\cdot\mathbf{k} > 0 \tag{9-541}$$

[21] See T. O. Newton and E. P. Wigner, *Rev. Mod. Phys.*, **21**, 400 (1949).

Equation (9–538) defines the "polarization" scalar product, $\langle e^{(i)},e^{(j)}\rangle$, of two amplitudes. It should be noted that the unit vector $e_\mu^{(1)}(k)$ and $e_\mu^{(2)}(k)$ are only defined up to an arbitrary component along k_μ. The particular choice

$$e^{(i)\mu}(k) = (0,\mathbf{e}^{(i)}(k)) \tag{9–542}$$

will often be made in the following.

An arbitrary transversal amplitude (which is not equivalent to zero) can, therefore, be written in the form

$$a_\mu(k) = \sum_{i=1}^{2} e_\mu^{(i)}(k)\alpha_i(k) + \alpha_0(k)k_\mu \tag{9–543}$$

where the term $\alpha_0(k)k_\mu$ can always be "gauged away." The specification of the $e_\mu^{(i)}$ corresponds to a specification of the state of polarization of the photon. Thus the momentum space wave function corresponding to a photon of momentum $\mathbf{q}$ energy $q_0 = |\mathbf{q}|$ and polarization $e_\mu^{(i)}(q)$ is given by

$$a_\mu^{(\mathbf{q}i)}(k) = k_0\delta(\mathbf{q} - \mathbf{k})e_\mu^{(i)}(k) \qquad (k_0 = |\mathbf{k}|) \tag{9–544}$$

With the choice $e^\mu(k) = (0,\mathbf{e}(k))$, $\mathbf{e}$ is proportional to the electric vector of the photon. In writing Eq. (9–544) we have normalized our wave functions in the following way: let $a_\mu^{(q'i')}(k)$ be the amplitude for a photon of momentum q'_μ, polarization i' and $a_\mu^{(q''i'')}(k)$ that of a photon of momentum q'' polarization i''; then

$$(a^{(q'i')},a^{(q''i'')}) = \delta_{i'i''}q'_0\delta(\mathbf{q}' - \mathbf{q}'') \tag{9–545}$$

Consider next a photon of definite energy-momentum k_μ. Let its state of polarization be denoted by $n_\mu(k)$. This vector can be decomposed along $e_\mu^{(1)}(k)$ and $e_\mu^{(2)}(k)$

$$n_\mu(k) = \eta_1 e_\mu^{(1)}(k) + \eta_2 e_\mu^{(2)}(k) \tag{9–546}$$

We can normalize the polarization vector in such a way that

$$\langle n,n\rangle = 1 = -\overline{n_\mu(k)}g^{\mu\nu}n_\nu(k) \tag{9–547}$$

$$= |\eta_1|^2 + |\eta_2|^2 \tag{9–548}$$

When defined in terms of a real basis such as the vectors $e_\mu^{(1)}(k)$ and $e_\mu^{(2)}(k)$, the complex conjugate vector is

$$\overline{n_\mu(k)} = \bar{\eta}_1 e_\mu^{(1)}(k) + \bar{\eta}_2 e_\mu^{(2)}(k) \tag{9–549}$$

If we introduce the circular polarization vectors $\varepsilon_\mu^{(\pm)}(k)$ defined by

$$\varepsilon_\mu^{(\pm)}(k) = \frac{1}{\sqrt{2}}\,(e_\mu^{(1)}(k) \pm ie_\mu^{(2)}(k)) \tag{9–550}$$

and satisfying the two relations

$$\langle \varepsilon^{(\lambda)},\varepsilon^{(\lambda')}\rangle = -\overline{\varepsilon_\mu^{(\lambda)}(k)}g^{\mu\nu}\varepsilon_\nu^{(\lambda')}(k) = \delta_{\lambda\lambda'} \tag{9-551}$$

$$\overline{\varepsilon^{(\lambda)}} = \varepsilon^{(-\lambda)} \tag{9-552}$$

then the "polarization" wave function of a photon of momentum k, can be expanded in terms of these basis vectors as follows:

$$n_\mu(k) = \sum_{\lambda=\pm} \xi^{(\lambda)}\varepsilon_\mu^{(\lambda)}(k) \tag{9-553}$$

where

$$\xi^{(\lambda)} = \langle \varepsilon^{(\lambda)},n\rangle = -\varepsilon^{(\lambda)}(k)\cdot n(k) \tag{9-554}$$

Consider next the correspondence

$$\varepsilon_\mu^{(\lambda)}(k) \to |k,\lambda\rangle \tag{9-555}$$

where the $|k,\lambda\rangle$ are ket vectors in a Hilbert space. This correspondence can be shown to be linear in this sense that if a general pure state of polarization is represented by

$$n_\mu(k) = \xi^+\varepsilon_\mu^{(+)}(k) + \xi^-\varepsilon_\mu^{(-)}(k) \tag{9-556}$$

with

$$\langle n,n\rangle = |\xi^+|^2 + |\xi^-|^2 = 1 \tag{9-557}$$

then the corresponding ket is

$$\xi^+|k,+\rangle + \xi^-|k,-\rangle = |k,\xi\rangle \tag{9-558}$$

We may now construct the density matrix for the polarization of a one-photon state. If we choose for our basic states the states of right and left circular polarization $|k,\lambda\rangle$, then for an arbitrary pure state $|k,\xi\rangle$, the density matrix is

$$\rho(k) = |k,\xi\rangle\langle k,\xi| \tag{9-559}$$

For a pure state, it has the property (since the $|k,\xi\rangle$ are normalized to 1) that

$$\rho^2 = \rho \tag{9-560}$$

and also

$$\rho^* = \rho \tag{9-561}$$

i.e., it is a projection operator. Furthermore

$$\mathrm{Tr}\,\rho = 1 \tag{9-562}$$

If we represent the ket $|\xi\rangle$ by its components along $|+\rangle$ and $|-\rangle$

$$|\xi\rangle \to \begin{pmatrix} \xi^+ \\ \xi^- \end{pmatrix} \tag{9–563}$$

then the density matrix is representable as a two-by-two hermitian matrix with components

$$\begin{pmatrix} \xi^+ \\ \xi^- \end{pmatrix} \otimes (\overline{\xi^+}\,\overline{\xi^-}) = \begin{pmatrix} |\xi^+|^2 & \xi^+\overline{\xi^-} \\ \xi^-\overline{\xi^+} & |\xi^-|^2 \end{pmatrix} \tag{9–564}$$

Since ρ is hermitian, it can be expanded in terms of the two-by-two matrices τ^j and the unit matrix; thus

$$\rho = \frac{1}{2}\left(a1 + \sum_{i=1}^{3} \xi^j \tau^j\right) \tag{9–565}$$

Because of the hermiticity of ρ, the coefficients a and ξ are real. The requirement that $\operatorname{Tr}\rho = 1$ implies that $a = 1$, while the equation $\rho^2 = \rho$ requires that $\xi^2 = 1$; hence

$$\rho = \tfrac{1}{2}(1 + \boldsymbol{\xi}\cdot\boldsymbol{\tau}) \quad \text{with } \boldsymbol{\xi}^2 = 1 \tag{9–566}$$

The expectation value of $\boldsymbol{\tau}$ in the state $|\xi\rangle$ is

$$\begin{aligned} \langle\xi|\boldsymbol{\tau}|\xi\rangle &= \operatorname{Tr} \boldsymbol{\tau}|\xi\rangle\langle\xi| \\ &= \operatorname{Tr} \boldsymbol{\tau}\rho \\ &= \boldsymbol{\xi} \end{aligned} \tag{9–567}$$

Since τ_3 is diagonal, $\tau_3 = \pm 1$ corresponds to pure right and left polarization, respectively, and $\tau_3 = 0$ to plane polarization. If we do not wish to consider just pure states, but also wish to include in our discussion partially polarized states, the density matrix for the polarization for such a mixture is still given by

$$\rho = \tfrac{1}{2}(1 + \boldsymbol{\xi}\cdot\boldsymbol{\tau}) \tag{9–568}$$

but now

$$0 \le |\boldsymbol{\xi}| = \left|\sum_{i=1}^{3} \xi_i^2\right|^{1/2} \le 1 \tag{9–569}$$

The generalization of the previous formalism to encompass systems of n (noninteracting) photons is straightforward. In the Lorentz gauge, an n photon amplitude is a tensor $a_{\mu_1 \ldots \mu_n}(k_1, \cdots, k_n)$; ($k_1^2 = k_2^2 = \cdots = k_n^2 = 0$) which is symmetric in the set of variables (μ, k) by virtue of the Bose character of photons. It is transversal in the sense that

$$k^{\mu_i} a_{\mu_1 \cdots \mu_i \cdots \mu_n}(k_1, \cdots, k_i, \cdots, k_n) = 0 \quad (i = 1, 2, \cdots, n) \tag{9-570}$$

Actually transversality in all the k variables already follows from transversality in any one of the k variables because of the symmetric character of the tensor $a_{\mu_1 \cdots \mu_n}(k_1, \cdots, k_n)$. Again due to the freedom of gauge transformations an n photon configuration is not described by a unique amplitude but rather by an equivalence class of tensors. We define the notion of equivalence for these tensors, as follows: a tensor $b_{\mu_1 \cdots \mu_n}(k_1, \cdots, k_n)$ will be said to be equivalent to zero:

$$b_{\mu_1 \cdots \mu_n}(k_1, \cdots, k_n) \sim 0 \tag{9-571}$$

if and only if

$$b_{\mu_1 \cdots \mu_n}(k_1, \cdots, k_n) = \alpha S\{k_{\mu_1} \beta_{\mu_2 \cdots \mu_n}(k_2, \cdots, k_n)\} \tag{9-572}$$

where $\beta_{\mu_2 \cdots \mu_n}(k_2, \cdots, k_n)$ is transversal, satisfying

$$k_i^{\mu_i} \beta_{\mu_2 \cdots \mu_i \cdots \mu_n}(k_2, \cdots, k_n) = 0 \quad (i = 2, \cdots, n) \tag{9-573}$$

but otherwise arbitrary. In Eq. (9–572), S is the symmetrizer. Explicitly since $\beta_{\mu_2 \cdots \mu_n}$ is symmetric,

$$S\{k_{\mu_1} \beta_{\mu_2 \cdots \mu_n}(k_2, \cdots, k_n)\} = \frac{1}{n} \sum_{j=1}^{n} k_{\mu_j} \beta_{\mu_1 \cdots \mu_{j-1} \mu_{j+1} \mu_n}(k_1, \cdots, k_{j-1}, k_{j+1}, \cdots, k_n) \tag{9-574}$$

Two transversal n photon amplitudes

$$a'_{\mu_1 \cdots \mu_n}(k_1, \cdots, k_n) \quad \text{and} \quad a''_{\mu_1 \cdots \mu_n}(k_1, \cdots, k_n)$$

will be said to be equivalent if

$$a'_{\mu_1 \cdots, \mu_n}(k_1, \cdots, k_n) - a''_{\mu_1 \cdots \mu_n}(k_1, \cdots, k_n) \sim 0 \tag{9-575}$$

One then proves in the manner employed in the one-particle case that if $b_{\mu_1 \cdots \mu_n} \sim 0$ and $a_{\mu_1 \cdots \mu_n}$ is a transversal n photon amplitude, *i.e.*, one satisfying Eq. (9–570), then

$$(-1)^n \overline{a^{\mu_1 \cdots \mu_n}(k_1, \cdots, k_n)} b_{\mu_1 \cdots \mu_n}(k_1, \cdots, k_n) = 0 \tag{9-576}$$

Similarly for transversal amplitudes, if

$$b_{\mu_1 \cdots \mu_n} \sim b'_{\mu_1 \cdots \mu_n} \quad \text{and} \quad a_{\mu_1 \cdots \mu_n} \sim a'_{\mu_1 \cdots \mu_n}$$

then

$$a^{\mu_1 \cdots \mu_n} b_{\mu_1 \cdots \mu_n} = a'^{\mu_1 \cdots \mu_n} b'_{\mu_1 \cdots \mu_n} \tag{9-577}$$

Finally one again verifies that the expression

$$(-1)\overline{a_{\mu_1\cdots\mu_n}(k_1,\cdots,k_n)}a^{\mu_1\cdots\mu_n}(k_1,\cdots,k_n) \geq 0 \tag{9–578}$$

i.e., it is non-negative if $a_{\mu_1\cdots\mu_n}$ is a transversal n photon amplitude. It is equal to zero if and only if $a_{\mu_1\cdots\mu_n} \sim 0$. Hence we can define the scalar product of two transversal n photon amplitudes $a_{\mu_1\cdots\mu_n}$ and $b_{\mu_1\cdots\mu_n}$ by the expression

$$(a,b) = (-1)^n \int_+ \frac{d^3k_1}{k_{10}} \cdots \int \frac{d^3k_n}{k_{n0}} \overline{a_{\mu_1\cdots\mu_n}(k_1,\cdots,k_n)} b^{\mu_1\cdots\mu_n}(k_1,\cdots,k_n) \tag{9–579}$$

As in the spin 0 and spin $\frac{1}{2}$ case we could next introduce creation and annihilation operators. This is most conveniently done by working with the representatives that satisfy in a given Lorentz frame the *three* dimensional transversality condition, *i.e.*, by working in the radiation gauge. We shall, however, adopt a slightly different procedure, which is outlined in the next section.

REFERENCES

For the covariant density matrix treatment of relativistic one-particle systems, see:

Wightman, A. S., "L'Invariance dans la Mécanique Quantique," in C. de Witt and R. Omnès, eds., *Dispersion Relations and Elementary Particles*, John Wiley and Sons, Inc., New York, 1960.

For the Schrödinger form of the photon equation, see:

Good, R. H., Jr., *Phys. Rev.*, **105**, 1914 (1957).

Position operator for photon:

Newton, R., and Wigner, E. P., *Rev. Mod. Phys.*, **21**, 400 (1949).
Acharya, R., and Sudarshan, E. C. G., *J. Math. Physics*, **1**, 532 (1960).
Bardacki, K., and Acharya, R., *Nuovo Cimento*, **21**, 802 (1961).

9.8. Quantization of the Electromagnetic Field.—Instead of proceeding as in the previous discussion of spin 0 and spin $\frac{1}{2}$ particles, we shall here adopt essentially the opposite point of view. Namely, instead of formulating the quantum theory of a system of many photons in terms of operators and showing the equivalence of this formalism to the imposition of quantum rules on classical electrodynamics, we shall take as our point of departure certain commutation rules which we assume the field operators to satisfy. We shall then show that a satisfactory quantized theory results provided that we adopt for the hamiltonian of our field system, the expression

$$H = \tfrac{1}{2} \int d^3x \{\mathscr{E}^2(x) + \mathscr{H}^2(x)\} \tag{9–580}$$

and for the total momentum of the field system the expression

$$\mathbf{P} = \int d^3x \{(\mathscr{E}x) \times \mathscr{H}(x)\} \tag{9–581}$$

where $\mathscr{E}(x)$ and $\mathscr{H}(x)$ are the hermitian (Heisenberg picture) *operators* corresponding to the electric and magnetic field intensities. The resulting theory will be shown to be consistent in the sense that the postulated commutations will be such that the hamiltonian is indeed the time translation operator, *i.e.*, for any operator $Q(x)$

$$i\hbar\partial_t Q(x) = [Q(x),H] \tag{9–582}$$

and that $\mathbf{P}$ is the space translation operator

$$-i\hbar\nabla Q(x) = [Q(x),\mathbf{P}] \tag{9–583}$$

In particular, the postulated commutation rules for $\mathscr{E}$ and $\mathscr{H}$ will be such that Eq. (9–582) when $Q(x)$ is taken to be $\mathscr{E}(x)$ and $\mathscr{H}(x)$ gives back Maxwell's equation for $\partial_t\mathscr{E}(x)$ and $\partial_t\mathscr{H}(x)$.

This method has the advantage of formulating the theory in terms of the (observable) field intensities. The more usual procedure which starts from a lagrangian formulation [22] expresses the theory in terms of the potentials $A^\mu(x)$. A gauge transformation

$$A_\mu(x) \to A_\mu(x) + \partial_\mu S(x) \tag{9–584}$$

where $S(x)$ is an arbitrary scalar function then leaves the field intensities unchanged, and hence Maxwell's equations as well. One usually restricts the potentials by the condition

$$\frac{\partial A_\mu}{\partial x_\mu} = 0 \tag{9–585}$$

in which case, in order that the gauge transformation (9–584) preserve the Lorentz condition (9–585), it is necessary that

$$\frac{\partial^2 S}{\partial x_\mu \partial x^\mu} = 0 \tag{9–586}$$

[22] G. Wentzel, *Quantum Theory of Fields*, Interscience Publishers, Inc., New York, 1949.

so that the gauge transformations are restricted. However, if the Lorentz condition (9–585) is imposed on the potentials, one finds a contradiction with the commutation rules deduced from the canonical formalism for the (operators) $A_\mu(x)$.[23] It is precisely to avoid these difficulties that we formulate the quantization of the radiation field directly in terms of the field intensity operators.[24] We shall thereafter introduce potentials and obtain the connection with the description of one-photon states outlined in Section 9.7.

We postulate the equal time commutation rules for the field operators to be

$$[\mathscr{E}^j(x),\mathscr{E}^k(x')]_{x_0=x_0'} = [\mathscr{H}^j(x),\mathscr{H}^k(x')]_{x_0=x_0'} = 0 \tag{9–587}$$

$$[\mathscr{E}^l(x),\mathscr{H}^r(x')]_{x_0=x_0'} = -i\hbar\varepsilon^{lrs}\frac{\partial}{\partial x^s}\delta(\mathbf{x}-\mathbf{x}') \tag{9–588}$$

It should be noted that these commutation rules are compatible with the transverse nature of $\boldsymbol{\mathscr{E}}$ and $\boldsymbol{\mathscr{H}}$, *i.e.*, with the fact both div $\boldsymbol{\mathscr{E}}$ and div $\boldsymbol{\mathscr{H}}$ vanish. In fact, it follows from the antisymmetry in the subscripts l and r in the commutation rules for $\mathscr{E}^l$ and $\mathscr{H}^r$ that div $\boldsymbol{\mathscr{E}}(x)$ commutes with $\boldsymbol{\mathscr{H}}(x')$ for $x_0 = x_0'$, and similarly, div $\boldsymbol{\mathscr{H}}(x)$ commutes with $\boldsymbol{\mathscr{E}}(x')$ for $x_0 = x_0'$. Furthermore, from (9–587) it follows that div $\boldsymbol{\mathscr{H}}(x)$ commutes with $\boldsymbol{\mathscr{H}}(x')$ for $x_0 = x_0'$, and div $\boldsymbol{\mathscr{E}}(x)$ commutes with $\boldsymbol{\mathscr{E}}(x')$ for $x_0 = x_0'$.

Consider next the equation of motion satisfied by $\boldsymbol{\mathscr{E}}(x)$ and $\boldsymbol{\mathscr{H}}(x)$ if one adopts for H, the hamiltonian of the system, the expression one would have written down classically for the field energy, *i.e.*, the expression given by Eq. (9–580). One obtains

$$\begin{aligned} i\hbar\partial_t\mathscr{E}^j(x) = [\mathscr{E}^j(x),H] &= \tfrac{1}{2}\int d^3x'[\mathscr{E}^j(x),\boldsymbol{\mathscr{E}}^2(x') + \boldsymbol{\mathscr{H}}^2(x')]_{x_0=x_0'} \\ &= \int d^3x'[\mathscr{E}^j(x),\mathscr{H}^i(x')]_{x_0=x_0'}\mathscr{H}^i(x') \\ &= +i\hbar\varepsilon^{jlm}\frac{\partial\mathscr{H}^m(x)}{\partial x^l} \end{aligned} \tag{9–589}$$

where use has been made of the fact that H is time independent, $[H,H] = 0$, to set $x_0' = x_0$. Equation (9–589) will be recognized as the Maxwell equation for $\partial_t\boldsymbol{\mathscr{E}}(x)$

$$\frac{\partial\boldsymbol{\mathscr{E}}(x)}{\partial t} = \boldsymbol{\nabla}\times\boldsymbol{\mathscr{H}}(x) \tag{9–590}$$

[23] It is, however, not necessary to impose the Lorentz condition, in which case S is an arbitrary function of x. Such a theory can be quantized; see P. A. M. Dirac, *Canadian Journal of Physics*, 650 (1955).

[24] W. Pauli, *Handbuch der Physik*, 2nd Ed., **24/1**, J. Springer, Berlin, 1933.

Similarly, the commutation rules (9–587) and (9–588) allow us to deduce that

$$i\hbar\partial_t \mathscr{H}^j(x) = [\mathscr{H}^j(x),H] = -i\hbar\varepsilon^{jlm}\frac{\partial \mathscr{E}^m(x)}{\partial x^l} \tag{9–591}$$

Since div $\mathscr{E}(x)$ and div $\mathscr{H}(x)$ commute with $\mathscr{E}(x')$ and $\mathscr{H}(x')$ for $x_0 = x_0'$, they have vanishing commutators with the hamiltonian and hence, they are time-independent operators. In fact, their constancy in time implies that they commute with $\mathscr{H}(x)$ and $\mathscr{E}(x)$ at all times and hence they must be c-number multiples of the unit operator. If these c-numbers are set equal to zero initially, they will remain zero for all times. With this initial choice for div $\mathscr{E}(x)$ and div $\mathscr{H}(x)$, the operators $\mathscr{E}$ and $\mathscr{H}$ satisfy all of the Maxwell equations (these now are operator equations!):

$$\frac{\partial \mathscr{E}(x)}{\partial t} = \nabla \times \mathscr{H}(x); \qquad \text{div}\, \mathscr{E}(x) = 0 \tag{9–592}$$

$$\frac{\partial \mathscr{H}(x)}{\partial t} = -\nabla \times \mathscr{E}(x); \qquad \text{div}\, \mathscr{H}(x) = 0 \tag{9–593}$$

In a manner similar to the above, one verifies that the commutation rules (9–587) and (9–588) guarantee that $\mathbf{P}$ as given by Eq. (9–581) is the generator for an infinitesimal spatial translation in the sense that Eq. (9–583) is satisfied for the field operators. Similarly, one verifies that the three components of the vector operator

$$\mathbf{M} = \int d^3x{:}\boldsymbol{r} \times (\mathscr{E}(x) \times \mathscr{H}(x)){:} \tag{9–594}$$

(which classically corresponds to the total angular momentum) are the generators for infinitesimal rotations about the three coordinate axis, respectively. One verifies that the components of $\mathbf{M}$, by virtue of (9–587) and (9–588) satisfy the commutation rules

$$[M^j,M^l] = i\varepsilon^{jlm}M^m \tag{9–595}$$

The total momentum operator $\mathbf{P}$, as well as the total angular momentum operator $\mathbf{M}$, commute with H and hence are constants of the motion. However, they do not commute with another, their commutator being equal to

$$[P^j,M^l] = -i\varepsilon^{jlm}P^m \tag{9–596}$$

In order to deduce the physical content of the quantized theory, we shall try to obtain a representation in which $\mathbf{P}$ and H are simultaneously diagonal. To this end we shall introduce the Fourier transforms of the Schrödinger operators. These latter operators are defined as the Heisenberg operators at time $x_0 = 0$. We thus write

$$\begin{aligned} \mathscr{E}(\mathbf{x}) &= \mathscr{E}(\mathbf{x},x_0 = 0) \\ &= \frac{1}{(2\pi)^{3/2}} \int e^{i\mathbf{k}\cdot\mathbf{x}} \tilde{\mathscr{E}}(\mathbf{k}) d^3k \end{aligned} \tag{9-597}$$

$$\begin{aligned} \mathscr{H}(\mathbf{x}) &= \mathscr{H}(\mathbf{x},x_0 = 0) \\ &= \frac{1}{(2\pi)^{3/2}} \int e^{i\mathbf{k}\cdot\mathbf{x}} \tilde{\mathscr{H}}(\mathbf{k}) \end{aligned} \tag{9-598}$$

where from the hermiticity of $\mathscr{E}(\mathbf{x})$ and $\mathscr{H}(\mathbf{x})$

$$\mathscr{E}^*(\mathbf{x}) = \mathscr{E}(\mathbf{x}) \tag{9-599}$$

$$\mathscr{H}^*(\mathbf{x}) = \mathscr{H}(\mathbf{x}) \tag{9-600}$$

it follows that

$$\tilde{\mathscr{H}}^*(\mathbf{k}) = \tilde{\mathscr{H}}(-\mathbf{k}) \tag{9-601}$$

$$\tilde{\mathscr{E}}^*(\mathbf{k}) = \tilde{\mathscr{E}}(-\mathbf{k}) \tag{9-602}$$

The fact that div $\mathscr{H} = 0$ and div $\mathscr{E} = 0$ implies that $\tilde{\mathscr{E}}$ and $\tilde{\mathscr{H}}$ are transverse

$$\mathbf{k}\cdot\tilde{\mathscr{H}}(\mathbf{k}) = 0 \tag{9-603}$$

$$\mathbf{k}\cdot\tilde{\mathscr{E}}(\mathbf{k}) = 0 \tag{9-604}$$

Thus $\tilde{\mathscr{E}}(\mathbf{k})$ and $\mathscr{H}(\mathbf{k})$ have only two components since they have no component along $\mathbf{k}$.

It proves convenient instead of working with the operator $\tilde{\mathscr{H}}$ to work with the operator $\tilde{\mathscr{A}}(\mathbf{k})$ defined by the equations

$$\tilde{\mathscr{A}}^*(\mathbf{k}) = \tilde{\mathscr{A}}(-\mathbf{k}) \tag{9-605}$$

$$\tilde{\mathscr{H}}(\mathbf{k}) = i\mathbf{k} \times \tilde{\mathscr{A}}(\mathbf{k}) \tag{9-606}$$

where in order to have $\tilde{\mathscr{H}}$ uniquely specify $\tilde{\mathscr{A}}(\mathbf{k})$, and conversely, we shall require that $\tilde{\mathscr{A}}(\mathbf{k})$ be transverse:

$$\mathbf{k}\cdot\tilde{\mathscr{A}}(\mathbf{k}) = 0 \tag{9-607}$$

The operator $\tilde{\mathscr{A}}(\mathbf{k})$ will be recognized as the Fourier transform of the vector potential $\mathscr{A}(x)$, $\nabla \times \mathscr{A}(\mathbf{x}) = \mathscr{H}(\mathbf{x})$,

$$\mathscr{A}(\mathbf{x}) = \frac{1}{(2\pi)^{3/2}} \int d^3x e^{i\mathbf{k}\cdot\mathbf{x}} \tilde{\mathscr{A}}(\mathbf{k}) \tag{9-608}$$

and Eq. (9–607) as fixing the "gauge" to be the radiation gauge, *i.e.*, that gauge in which

$$\nabla \cdot \mathscr{A}(\mathbf{x}) = 0 \tag{9–609}$$

It should be stressed, however, that the introduction of the operator $\tilde{\mathscr{A}}(\mathbf{k})$ in the present context is purely for mathematical convenience. All the subsequent development could also be carried out without its introduction. It is only when we consider the interaction of the quantized electromagnetic field with charged particles that the potentials assume new importance—at least in the usual formulation with its particular way of fixing the phase factors in the operators of the charged fields—since the potentials themselves then appear in the equations of motion of the interacting electromagnetic and matter fields.

Equation (9–606) specifies $\tilde{\mathscr{H}}(\mathbf{k})$ given $\tilde{\mathscr{A}}(\mathbf{k})$ and conversely. This is made explicit upon noting that

$$\begin{aligned} \mathbf{k} \times \tilde{\mathscr{H}}(\mathbf{k}) &= i\mathbf{k} \times (\mathbf{k} \times \tilde{\mathscr{A}}(\mathbf{k})) \\ &= -i\mathbf{k}^2\tilde{\mathscr{A}}(\mathbf{k}) \end{aligned} \tag{9–610}$$

since $\tilde{\mathscr{A}}(\mathbf{k})$ is transverse. From Eq. (9–610) we deduce that

$$\tilde{\mathscr{A}}(\mathbf{k}) = i\,\frac{\mathbf{k} \times \tilde{\mathscr{H}}(\mathbf{k})}{\mathbf{k}^2} \tag{9–611}$$

which determines $\tilde{\mathscr{A}}(\mathbf{k})$ given $\tilde{\mathscr{H}}(\mathbf{k})$. Note incidentally that this last equation implies that to obtain $\mathscr{A}(\mathbf{x})$ we must know $\mathscr{H}(\mathbf{x})$ over all space since

$$\begin{aligned} \mathscr{A}^j(\mathbf{x}) &= \frac{i}{(2\pi)^{3/2}} \int d^3k e^{i\mathbf{k}\cdot\mathbf{x}} \frac{(\mathbf{k} \times \tilde{\mathscr{H}}(\mathbf{k}))^j}{\mathbf{k}^2} \\ &= \int d^3x' \mathscr{D}^{jm}(\mathbf{x} - \mathbf{x}',0)\mathscr{H}^m(\mathbf{x}') \end{aligned} \tag{9–612}$$

where

$$\mathscr{D}^{jm}(\mathbf{x} - \mathbf{x}'; 0) = \frac{i}{(2\pi)^3} \int \frac{d^3k}{\mathbf{k}^2} e^{i\mathbf{k}\cdot(\mathbf{x}-\mathbf{x}')}\varepsilon^{jlm}k^l \tag{9–613}$$

The commutation relations for the dynamical variables $\tilde{\mathscr{A}}(\mathbf{k})$ and $\tilde{\mathscr{E}}(\mathbf{k})$ are readily obtained by a Fourier inversion of Eqs. (9–587) and (9–588). They are

$$[\tilde{\mathscr{E}}^l(\mathbf{k}),\tilde{\mathscr{E}}^m(\mathbf{k}')] = [\tilde{\mathscr{A}}^l(\mathbf{k}),\tilde{\mathscr{A}}^m(\mathbf{k}')] = 0 \tag{9–614}$$

and

$$i\varepsilon^{rmn}[\tilde{\mathscr{E}}^j(\mathbf{k}),k'^m\tilde{\mathscr{A}}^n(\mathbf{k}')]$$

$$= i\hbar\varepsilon^{jlr}\frac{1}{(2\pi)^3}\int d^3x\int d^3x' e^{-i\mathbf{k}\cdot\mathbf{x}-i\mathbf{k}'\cdot\mathbf{x}'}\partial^l\delta(\mathbf{x}-\mathbf{x}')$$

$$= -\varepsilon^{jlr}k^l\delta(\mathbf{k}+\mathbf{k}') \qquad (9\text{–}615)$$

or equivalently

$$\varepsilon^{rmn}k'^m[\tilde{\mathscr{E}}^j(\mathbf{k}),\tilde{\mathscr{A}}^n(\mathbf{k}')] = i\hbar\varepsilon^{jlr}k^l\delta(\mathbf{k}+\mathbf{k}') \qquad (9\text{–}616)$$

Multiplying both sides of Eq. (9–582) by ε^{str} and summing over r we obtain

$$[\tilde{\mathscr{E}}^j(\mathbf{k}),\tilde{\mathscr{A}}^l(\mathbf{k}')] = i\hbar\delta(\mathbf{k}+\mathbf{k}')\left(\delta^{jl}-\frac{k^jk^l}{\mathbf{k}^2}\right)$$

$$= i\hbar d^{jl}(\mathbf{k})\delta(\mathbf{k}+\mathbf{k}') \qquad (9\text{–}617)$$

The factor

$$d^{jl}(\mathbf{k}) = \{\delta^{jl} - (k^jk^l/\mathbf{k}^2)\} \qquad (9\text{–}618)$$

is a projection operator onto the directions perpendicular to $\mathbf{k}$, and guarantees that the commutation rules are compatible with the transverse nature of $\tilde{\mathscr{E}}$ and $\tilde{\mathscr{A}}$, *i.e.*, with the fact that

$$\mathbf{k}\cdot\tilde{\mathscr{A}}(\mathbf{k}) = \mathbf{k}\cdot\tilde{\mathscr{E}}(\mathbf{k}) = 0$$

The hamiltonian can be expressed in terms of the $\tilde{\mathscr{E}}$ and $\tilde{\mathscr{A}}$ variables, and it then takes the following form:

$$H = \tfrac{1}{2}\int d^3x\{\mathscr{E}^2(\mathbf{x}) + \mathscr{H}^2(\mathbf{x})\}$$

$$= \tfrac{1}{2}\int d^3k\{\tilde{\mathscr{E}}^*(\mathbf{k})\cdot\tilde{\mathscr{E}}(\mathbf{k}) + \tilde{\mathscr{H}}^*(\mathbf{k})\cdot\tilde{\mathscr{H}}(\mathbf{k})\}$$

$$= \tfrac{1}{2}\int d^3k\{\tilde{\mathscr{E}}^*(\mathbf{k})\cdot\tilde{\mathscr{E}}(\mathbf{k}) + \mathbf{k}^2\tilde{\mathscr{A}}^*(\mathbf{k})\cdot\tilde{\mathscr{A}}(\mathbf{k})\} \qquad (9\text{–}619)$$

since by virtue of the transversality of $\tilde{\mathscr{A}}(\mathbf{k})$

$$(\mathbf{k}\times\tilde{\mathscr{A}}^*(\mathbf{k}))\cdot(\mathbf{k}\times\tilde{\mathscr{A}}(\mathbf{k})) = \mathbf{k}^2\tilde{\mathscr{A}}^*(\mathbf{k})\cdot\tilde{\mathscr{A}}(\mathbf{k}) \qquad (9\text{–}620)$$

One verifies that $\tilde{\mathscr{E}}(\mathbf{k})$ and $\tilde{\mathscr{A}}(\mathbf{k})$ are indeed conjugate variables, *i.e.*

$$\frac{i}{\hbar}[\tilde{\mathscr{A}}^j(\mathbf{k}),H] = \tilde{\mathscr{E}}^j(\mathbf{k}) \qquad (9\text{–}621)$$

$$\frac{i}{\hbar}[\tilde{\mathscr{E}}^j(\mathbf{k}),H] = -\mathbf{k}^2\tilde{\mathscr{A}}^j(\mathbf{k}) \qquad (9\text{–}622)$$

For the physical interpretation of the theory it is convenient to be able to express the hamiltonian in the form $\int d^3k\omega_{\mathbf{k}}c^*(\mathbf{k})c(\mathbf{k})$, with $c^*(\mathbf{k}),c(\mathbf{k})$ satisfying δ-function commutation rules so that number operators can be introduced into the theory. The form (9–619) for the hamiltonian suggests that we define the operators:

$$\tilde{C}_l(\mathbf{k}) = \sqrt{\frac{|\mathbf{k}|}{2\hbar}}\,\tilde{\mathscr{A}}_l(\mathbf{k}) - i\sqrt{\frac{1}{2\hbar|\mathbf{k}|}}\,\tilde{\mathscr{E}}_l(\mathbf{k}) \tag{9–623}$$

$$\tilde{C}_l^*(\mathbf{k}) = \sqrt{\frac{|\mathbf{k}|}{2\hbar}}\,\tilde{\mathscr{A}}_l(-\mathbf{k}) + i\sqrt{\frac{1}{2\hbar|\mathbf{k}|}}\,\tilde{\mathscr{E}}_l(-\mathbf{k}) \tag{9–624}$$

The operator $\tilde{C}_l(\mathbf{k})$ is *not* hermitian. By virtue of the transverse nature of $\tilde{\mathscr{A}}_i(\mathbf{k})$ and $\tilde{\mathscr{E}}_i(\mathbf{k})$ it is also transverse:

$$k_j\tilde{C}_j(\mathbf{k}) = 0 \tag{9–625}$$

The commutation rules satisfied by the $\tilde{C}_i(\mathbf{k})$ and $\tilde{C}_i^*(\mathbf{k})$ operators are readily deduced from those obeyed by $\tilde{\mathscr{A}}_i(\mathbf{k})$ and $\tilde{\mathscr{E}}_l(\mathbf{k})$. One finds that

$$[\tilde{C}_i(\mathbf{k}),\tilde{C}_i(\mathbf{k}')] = 0 \tag{9–626}$$

$$[\tilde{C}_l(\mathbf{k}),\tilde{C}_j^*(\mathbf{k}')] = \left(\delta_{lj} - \frac{k_ik_j}{\mathbf{k}^2}\right)\delta(\mathbf{k}-\mathbf{k}') \tag{9–627}$$

Hamiltonian and total momentum, when expressed in terms of $\tilde{C}$ and $\tilde{C}^*$ operators, are

$$H = \sum_{i=1}^{3}\int d^3k\hbar|\mathbf{k}|c\tilde{C}_i^*(\mathbf{k})\tilde{C}_i(\mathbf{k}) \tag{9–628}$$

$$\mathbf{P} = \sum_{i=1}^{3}\int d^3k\hbar\mathbf{k}\tilde{C}_i^*(\mathbf{k})\tilde{C}_i(\mathbf{k}) \tag{9–629}$$

We have now achieved one objective, that of expressing the hamiltonian in essentially diagonal form. In order to deal with operators that satisfy δ-function commutation rules rather than δ_{ij}^T commutation rules, where

$$\delta_{ij}^T(\mathbf{k}-\mathbf{k}') = \left(\delta_{ij} - \frac{k_ik_j}{\mathbf{k}^2}\right)\delta(\mathbf{k}-\mathbf{k}') = d_{ij}(\mathbf{k})\delta(\mathbf{k}-\mathbf{k}') \tag{9–630}$$

we shall introduce as new dynamical variables the two components of $\tilde{\mathbf{C}}(\mathbf{k})$ which are perpendicular to $\mathbf{k}$. To do so, we define the three real unit vectors

$$\mathbf{e}^{(1)}(\mathbf{k}),\quad \mathbf{e}^{(2)}(\mathbf{k})\quad\text{and}\quad \mathbf{e}^{(3)}(\mathbf{k}) = \mathbf{k}/|\mathbf{k}|$$

which are orthogonal

$$\mathbf{e}^{(i)}(\mathbf{k})\cdot\mathbf{e}^{(j)}(\mathbf{k}) = \sum_{l=1}^{3} e_l^{(i)}(\mathbf{k})e_l^{(j)}(\mathbf{k}) = \delta_{ij} \tag{9-631}$$

and which are complete:

$$\sum_{i=1}^{3} e_r^{(i)}(\mathbf{k})e_s^{(i)}(\mathbf{k}) = \delta_{rs} \tag{9-632}$$

Note that in terms of these vectors, the projection operator onto the directions transverse to $\mathbf{k}$ is given by

$$d_{rs}(\mathbf{k}) = \sum_{\lambda=1}^{2} e_r^{(\lambda)}(\mathbf{k})e_s^{(\lambda)}(\mathbf{k}) = \left(\delta_{rs} - \frac{k_r k_s}{\mathbf{k}^2}\right) \tag{9-633}$$

When decomposed along these three unit vectors $\tilde{\mathbf{C}}(\mathbf{k})$, being transverse, has components along $\mathbf{e}^{(1)}(\mathbf{k})$ and $\mathbf{e}^{(2)}(\mathbf{k})$ only, hence

$$\tilde{\mathbf{C}}(\mathbf{k}) = \sum_{\lambda=1}^{2} c_{(\lambda)}(\mathbf{k})\mathbf{e}^{(\lambda)}(\mathbf{k}) \tag{9-634}$$

Using the orthogonality properties of the $\mathbf{e}^{\lambda}$'s one can invert Eq. (9-634) and one finds that the operators $c_\lambda(\mathbf{k})$ are given by

$$c_\lambda(\mathbf{k}) = \mathbf{e}^{(\lambda)}(\mathbf{k})\cdot\tilde{\mathbf{C}}(\mathbf{k}) = \sum_{l=1}^{3} e_l^{(\lambda)}(\mathbf{k})\tilde{C}_l(\mathbf{k}) \tag{9-635}$$

They, therefore, satisfy the following commutation rules:

$$[c_\lambda(\mathbf{k}),c_{\lambda'}(\mathbf{k}')] = [c_\lambda^*(\mathbf{k}),c_{\lambda'}^*(\mathbf{k}')] = 0 \tag{9-636}$$

and

$$[c_\lambda(\mathbf{k}),c_{\lambda'}^*(\mathbf{k}')] = \sum_{rs} e_r^{(\lambda)}(\mathbf{k})e_s^{(\lambda')}(\mathbf{k}')d_{rs}(\mathbf{k})\delta(\mathbf{k}-\mathbf{k}') = \delta_{\lambda\lambda'}\delta(\mathbf{k}-\mathbf{k}') \tag{9-637}$$

In terms of the $c_\lambda(\mathbf{k})$ operators, the expressions for H and $\mathbf{P}$ now become

$$H = \sum_{\lambda=1,2}\int d^3k\hbar c|\mathbf{k}|c_\lambda^*(\mathbf{k})c_\lambda(\mathbf{k}) \tag{9-638}$$

$$\mathbf{P} = \sum_{\lambda=1,2}\int d^3k\hbar\mathbf{k}c_\lambda^*(\mathbf{k})c_\lambda(\mathbf{k}) \tag{9-639}$$

Due to the δ-function commutation rules that the $c_\lambda(\mathbf{k})$ operators satisfy, Eqs. (9–636) and (9–637), we can interpret the hermitian operators

$$n^{(\lambda)}(\mathbf{k}) = c_\lambda^*(\mathbf{k})c_\lambda(\mathbf{k}) \tag{9–640}$$

as the operators for the number of photons of momentum $\mathbf{k}$ and polarization $\mathbf{e}^{(\lambda)}(\mathbf{k})$ since they have as their spectrum the positive integers and zero. Furthermore, its commutation rules with $c_\lambda^*(\mathbf{k})$ and $c_\lambda(\mathbf{k})$

$$[n^{(\lambda)}(\mathbf{k}),c_{\lambda'}^*(\mathbf{k}')] = \delta(\mathbf{k} - \mathbf{k}')\delta_{\lambda\lambda'}c_\lambda^*(\mathbf{k}) \tag{9–641}$$

$$[n^{(\lambda)}(\mathbf{k}),c_{\lambda'}(\mathbf{k})] = -\delta(\mathbf{k} - \mathbf{k}')\delta_{\lambda\lambda'}c_\lambda(\mathbf{k}) \tag{9–642}$$

allow us to interpret $c_\lambda(\mathbf{k})$ and $c_\lambda^*(\mathbf{k})$ as destruction and creation operators, respectively, for photons of momentum $\mathbf{k}$ and polarization λ. We note finally that since

$$\begin{aligned}\tilde{\mathscr{A}}_i(\mathbf{k}) &= \sqrt{\frac{\hbar}{2|\mathbf{k}|}}\,(\tilde{C}_i(\mathbf{k}) + \tilde{C}_i^*(-\mathbf{k})) \\ &= \sqrt{\frac{\hbar}{2|\mathbf{k}|}}\sum_{\lambda=1}^{2} e_i^{(\lambda)}(\mathbf{k})(c_\lambda(\mathbf{k}) + c_\lambda^*(-\mathbf{k}))\end{aligned} \tag{9–643}$$

the configuration space operator $\mathscr{A}_i(\mathbf{x})$ is given by

$$\begin{aligned}\mathscr{A}_i(\mathbf{x}) = \frac{1}{(2\pi)^{3/2}}\int d^3k\,\sqrt{\frac{\hbar c}{2|\mathbf{k}|}} \\ \times \sum_{\lambda=1}^{2} e_i^{(\lambda)}(\mathbf{k})(c_\lambda(\mathbf{k})e^{i\mathbf{k}\cdot\mathbf{x}} + c_\lambda^*(\mathbf{k})e^{-i\mathbf{k}\cdot\mathbf{x}})\end{aligned} \tag{9–644}$$

This operator is a Schrödinger picture operator. The corresponding Heisenberg operator is

$$\begin{aligned}\mathscr{A}_i(x) &= e^{iHt/\hbar}\mathscr{A}_i(\mathbf{x})e^{-iHt/\hbar} \quad (ct = x_0) \\ &= \int d^3k\,\sqrt{\frac{\hbar c}{(2\pi)^3 2|\mathbf{k}|}}\sum_{\lambda=1}^{2} \mathbf{e}_i^{(\lambda)}(\mathbf{k}) \\ &\qquad \times (c_\lambda(\mathbf{k})e^{-ik\cdot x} + c_\lambda^*(\mathbf{k})e^{+ik\cdot x})\end{aligned} \tag{9–645}$$

where $k_o = \omega_\mathbf{k} = c|\mathbf{k}|$.

Next we establish the connection of the previous formalism with the Fock space description of photons. From the interpretation of $n^{(\lambda)}(\mathbf{k})$ as the number operator for photons of momentum $\mathbf{k}$ polarization λ, and of $c_\lambda(\mathbf{k})$ and $c_\lambda^*(\mathbf{k})$ as destruction and creation operators for such photons, upon denoting by $|0\rangle$ the no-photon state characterized by $n_\lambda(\mathbf{k})|0\rangle = 0$ for all $\mathbf{k}$ and λ, or equivalently by

$$c_\lambda(\mathbf{k})|0\rangle = 0, \quad \text{for all } \mathbf{k} \text{ and } \lambda \tag{9–646}$$

it follows that $c_\lambda^*(\mathbf{k})|0\rangle$ is a one-photon state of momentum $\mathbf{k}$ and polarization λ:

$$|\mathbf{k},\lambda\rangle = c_\lambda^*(\mathbf{k})|0\rangle \tag{9–647}$$

Indeed one verifies that this vector is an eigenstate of the operator N which represents the total number of photons

$$N = \int d^3k \sum_{\lambda=1}^{2} n_\lambda(\mathbf{k}) \tag{9–648}$$

with eigenvalue 1. Thus from the commutation rule (9–641) it is seen that

$$[N,c_\lambda^*(\mathbf{k})] = c_\lambda^*(\mathbf{k}) \tag{9–649}$$

whence

$$\begin{aligned} Nc_\lambda^*(\mathbf{k})|0\rangle &= [N,c_\lambda^*(\mathbf{k})]|0\rangle \\ &= c_\lambda^*(\mathbf{k})|0\rangle \end{aligned} \tag{9–650}$$

Similarly one verifies that the state $c_{\lambda_1}^*(\mathbf{k}_1)c_{\lambda_2}^*(\mathbf{k}_2)|0\rangle$ is a two-photon state

$$|\mathbf{k}_1,\lambda_1,\mathbf{k}_2,\lambda_2\rangle = \frac{1}{\sqrt{2!}} c_{\lambda_1}^*(\mathbf{k}_1)c_{\lambda_2}^*(\mathbf{k}_2)|0\rangle \tag{9–651}$$

corresponding to the presence of two photons of momentum $\mathbf{k}_1$ and $\mathbf{k}_2$ and polarization λ_1,λ_2, etc. If $|\Psi\rangle$ is an arbitrary state of the photon system then the components:

$$\begin{aligned} \Psi^{(n)}(\mathbf{k}_1,\lambda_1,\cdots,\mathbf{k}_n,\lambda_n) &= \frac{1}{\sqrt{n!}} \langle 0|c_{\lambda_1}(\mathbf{k}_1)\cdots c_{\lambda_n}(\mathbf{k}_n)|\Psi\rangle \\ &= \langle \mathbf{k}_1,\lambda_1,\cdots,\mathbf{k}_n,\lambda_n|\Psi\rangle \end{aligned} \tag{9–652}$$

are the Fock space amplitudes, which are the probability amplitudes for finding the system to consist of n photons with momenta $\mathbf{k}_1,\cdots,\mathbf{k}_n$ and polarization $\lambda_1,\cdots,\lambda_n$.

By virtue of the commutation rules (9–636) these amplitudes are symmetric under the interchange $(\mathbf{k}_i\lambda_i \rightleftharpoons \mathbf{k}_l\lambda_l)$ thus verifying the Bose character of photons. The norm of $|\Psi\rangle$ is given in terms of the Fock space amplitudes by

$$\begin{aligned}\|\Psi\|^2 &= \langle\Psi|\Psi\rangle \\ &= \sum_{n=0}^{\infty}\int d^3k_1\cdots\int d^3k_n \\ &\quad\times\sum_{\lambda_1,\cdots,\lambda_n}^{1,2}\langle\Psi|\mathbf{k}_1,\lambda_1,\cdots,\mathbf{k}_n,\lambda_n\rangle\langle\mathbf{k}_1,\lambda_1,\cdots,\mathbf{k}_n,\lambda_n|\Psi\rangle \\ &= \sum_{n=0}^{\infty}\int d^3k_1\cdots\int d^3k_n\sum_{\lambda_1\cdots\lambda_n}|\Psi^{(n)}(\mathbf{k}_1,\lambda_1,\cdots,\mathbf{k}_n,\lambda_n)|^2 \qquad (9\text{–}653)\end{aligned}$$

A particular representation of the commutation rules (9–636) and (9–637) characterized by the existence of a no-particle state $|0\rangle$ is exhibited by the equations

$$\begin{aligned}&c_\lambda^*(\mathbf{k})\left\{\frac{1}{\sqrt{n!}}c_{\lambda_1}^*(\mathbf{k}_1)\cdots c_{\lambda_n}^*(\mathbf{k}_n)|0\rangle\right\} \\ &\qquad= \sqrt{n+1}\left\{\frac{1}{\sqrt{(n+1)!}}c_\lambda^*(\mathbf{k})c_{\lambda_1}^*(\mathbf{k}_1)\cdots c_{\lambda_n}^*(\mathbf{k}_n)|0\rangle\right\} \qquad (9\text{–}654)\end{aligned}$$

or equivalently

$$c_\lambda^*(\mathbf{k})|\mathbf{k}_1,\lambda_1,\cdots,\mathbf{k}_n,\lambda_n\rangle = \sqrt{n+1}|\mathbf{k},\lambda,\mathbf{k}_1,\lambda_1,\cdots,\mathbf{k}_n,\lambda_n\rangle \qquad (9\text{–}655)$$

and

$$\begin{aligned}&c_\lambda(\mathbf{k})\left\{\frac{1}{\sqrt{n!}}c_{\lambda_1}^*(\mathbf{k}_1)\cdots c_{\lambda_n}^*(\mathbf{k}_n)|0\rangle\right\} \\ &\quad= \frac{1}{\sqrt{n}}\sum_{i=1}^{n}\delta_{\lambda\lambda_i}\delta(\mathbf{k}-\mathbf{k}_i) \\ &\qquad\times\left\{\frac{1}{\sqrt{(n-1)!}}c_\lambda^*(\mathbf{k}_1)\cdots c_{\lambda_{i-1}}^*(\mathbf{k}_{i-1})c_{\lambda_{i+1}}^*(\mathbf{k}_{i+1})\right. \\ &\qquad\qquad\left.\cdots c_{\lambda_n}^*(\mathbf{k}_n)|0\rangle\right\} \qquad (9\text{–}656)\end{aligned}$$

or equivalently

$$\begin{aligned}&c_\lambda(\mathbf{k})|\mathbf{k}_1,\lambda_1,\cdots,\mathbf{k}_n,\lambda_n\rangle \\ &= \frac{1}{\sqrt{n}}\sum_{i=1}^{n}\delta_{\lambda\lambda_i}\delta(\mathbf{k}-\mathbf{k}_i)|\mathbf{k}_1,\lambda_1,\cdots,\mathbf{k}_{i-1},\lambda_{i-1},\mathbf{k}_{i+1},\lambda_{i+1},\mathbf{k}_n,\lambda_n\rangle \qquad (9\text{–}657)\end{aligned}$$

Hence, if $|\Psi\rangle$ is an arbitrary vector,

$$(c_\lambda(\mathbf{k})\Psi)^{(n)}(\mathbf{k}_1,\lambda_1,\cdots,\mathbf{k}_n,\lambda_n) \equiv \langle\mathbf{k}_1,\lambda_1,\cdots,\mathbf{k}_n,\lambda_n|c_\lambda(\mathbf{k})|\Psi\rangle$$
$$= \sqrt{n+1}\langle\mathbf{k},\lambda,\mathbf{k}_1,\lambda_1,\cdots,\mathbf{k}_n,\lambda_n|\Psi\rangle \quad (9\text{–}658)$$
$$= \sqrt{n+1}\Psi^{(n+1)}(\mathbf{k},\lambda,\mathbf{k}_1,\lambda_1,\cdots,\mathbf{k}_n,\lambda_n)$$

and similarly

$$(c_\lambda^*(\mathbf{k})\Psi)^{(n)}(\mathbf{k}_1,\lambda_1,\cdots,\mathbf{k}_n,\lambda_n)$$
$$= \frac{1}{\sqrt{n}}\sum_{i=1}^{n}\delta_{\lambda\lambda_i}\delta(\mathbf{k}-\mathbf{k}_i)\Psi^{(n-1)}$$
$$\times(\mathbf{k}_1,\lambda_1,\cdots,\mathbf{k}_{i-1},\lambda_{i-1},\mathbf{k}_{i+1},\lambda_{i+1},\cdots,\mathbf{k}_n,\lambda_n) \quad (9\text{–}659)$$

Instead of the amplitudes $\Psi^{(n)}(\mathbf{k}_1,\lambda_1,\cdots,\mathbf{k}_n,\lambda_n)$ consider the amplitudes

$$\Psi^{(n)}_{i_1\cdots i_n}(\mathbf{k}_1,\cdots,\mathbf{k}_n)$$
$$= \sum_{\lambda_1\cdots\lambda_n}^{1,2} e_{i_1}^{(\lambda_1)}(\mathbf{k}_1)\cdots e_{i_1}^{(\lambda_1)}(\mathbf{k}_n)\Psi^{(n)}(\mathbf{k}_1,\lambda_1,\cdots,\mathbf{k}_n,\lambda_n) \quad (9\text{–}660)$$

These tensor amplitudes have the property that:

(a) they are symmetric under the interchange $(\mathbf{k}_l,i_l) \rightleftharpoons (\mathbf{k}_j,i_j)$ $j,l = 1,2,\cdots,n$;

(b) they are transverse in the sense that

$$\sum_{i_j=1}^{3} k_{i_j}\Psi^{(n)}_{i_1\cdots i_j\cdots i_n}(\mathbf{k}_1,\cdots,\mathbf{k}_{i_j},\cdots,\mathbf{k}_n) = 0 \quad (9\text{–}661)$$

They are in fact the components of $|\Psi\rangle$ with respect to the basis vectors

$$\frac{1}{\sqrt{n!}}\tilde{C}_{i_1}^*(\mathbf{k}_1)\cdots\tilde{C}_{i_n}^*(\mathbf{k}_n)|0\rangle$$

i.e.,

$$\Psi_{i_1\cdots i_n}(\mathbf{k}_1,\cdots,\mathbf{k}_n) = \frac{1}{\sqrt{n!}}\langle 0|\tilde{C}_{i_1}(\mathbf{k}_1)\cdots\tilde{C}_{i_n}(\mathbf{k}_n)|\Psi\rangle \quad (9\text{–}662)$$

The representation of the operators $\tilde{C}_i(\mathbf{k})$ and $\tilde{C}_i^*(\mathbf{k})$ is

$$(\tilde{C}_i(\mathbf{k})\Psi)^{(n)}_{i_1\cdots i_n}(\mathbf{k}_1,\cdots,\mathbf{k}_n) = \sqrt{n+1}\Psi^{(n+1)}_{i i_1\cdots i_n}(\mathbf{k},\mathbf{k}_1,\cdots,\mathbf{k}_n) \quad (9\text{–}663)$$

$$(\tilde{C}_i^*(\mathbf{k})\Psi)^{(n)}_{i_1\cdots i_n}(\mathbf{k}_1,\cdots,\mathbf{k}_n)$$
$$= \frac{1}{\sqrt{n}}\sum_{j=1}^{n}\delta(\mathbf{k}-\mathbf{k}_j)d_{ii_j}$$
$$\times\Psi^{(n-1)}_{i_1\cdots i_{j-1}i_{j+1}\cdots i_n}(\mathbf{k}_1,\cdots,\mathbf{k}_{j-1},\mathbf{k}_{j+1},\cdots,\mathbf{k}_n) \quad (9\text{–}664)$$

The norm of $|\Psi\rangle$ in terms of the amplitudes $\Psi'^{(n)}_{i_1\cdots i_n}(\mathbf{k}_1,\cdots,\mathbf{k}_n)$ is given by

$$\|\Psi\|^2 = \sum_{n=0}^{\infty} \int d^3k_1 \cdots \int d^3k_n \sum_{i_1,\cdots,i_n=1}^{3} |\Psi'^{(n)}_{i_1\cdots i_n}(\mathbf{k}_1,\cdots,\mathbf{k}_n)|^2 \tag{9–665}$$

The description of the photon system in terms of either the amplitudes $\Psi^{(n)}(\mathbf{k}_1,\lambda_1,\cdots,\mathbf{k}_n,\lambda_n)$ or $\Psi'^{(n)}_{i_1\cdots i_n}(\mathbf{k}_1,\cdots,\mathbf{k}_n)$ operates within one particular gauge, namely the gauge in which $\nabla\cdot\mathscr{A}(\mathbf{x}) = 0$, the radiation gauge. Although the description is in appearance not invariant with respect to Lorentz transformations—one can nevertheless pass from one Lorentz frame to another by means of a canonical transformation (which in fact is actually a gauge transformation) so that the physical predictions will be independent of the frame used for the quantization and specification of the amplitudes.

Instead of exhibiting at this point the invariance of the above formalism, let us see whether the above formulation can be recast so as to be manifestly covariant. The essential steps for such a procedure have in fact been outlined in the previous section.

Thus consider first the one-photon amplitude $\Psi'^{(1)}_{i_1}(\mathbf{k}_1)$ $i = 1,2,3$. To this three dimensional vector amplitude, which is transverse, *i.e.*

$$\sum_{i_1=1}^{3} k_{1i_1}\Psi'^{(1)}_{i_1}(\mathbf{k}_1) = 0 \tag{9–666}$$

and has the positive definite norm

$$0 < \sum_{i_1=1} \int d^3k_1 |\Psi'^{(1)}_{i_1}(\mathbf{k}_1)|^2 < \infty \tag{9–667}$$

we correlate an equivalence class of four-dimensional vectors $\{\Phi^{(1)}_{\mu_1}(k_1)\}$ where $k_1^\mu = \{k_1^0 = |\mathbf{k}_1|,\mathbf{k}_1\}$ (and therefore $k_{1\mu}k_1^\mu = 0$) the members of which are transversal in the Minkowski metric, *i.e.*

$$k_1^{\mu_1}\Phi^{(1)}_{\mu_1}(k_1) = 0 \tag{9–668}$$

Two such transversal vectors Φ_μ and Φ'_μ will be said to be equivalent ($\equiv$) if and only if their difference is equivalent to zero

$$\Phi'_\mu(k) - \Phi_\mu(k) \equiv 0 \tag{9–669}$$

a vector $b_\mu(k)$ being equivalent to zero, $b_\mu(k) \equiv 0$, if and only if $b_\mu(k) = \beta(k)k_\mu$. Given $\Psi'^{(1)}_i(\mathbf{k})$ we can consider it as proportional to that particular member of the equivalence class of transversal vectors

$\{\Psi_\mu^{(1)}(k)\}$ for which $\Phi_0^{(1)}(k) = 0$. More precisely, the representative of the equivalence class will be taken to be that $\Phi_\mu^{(1)}(k)$ for which

$$\Phi_0^{(1)}(k) = 0 \tag{9–670}$$

$$\Phi_i^{(1)}(k) = \sqrt{k_0}\Psi_i^{(1)}(\mathbf{k}) \quad (i = 1,2,3) \tag{9–671}$$

The reader will recall that we proved at the end of the last section that the quantity $(-)\overline{\Phi_\mu(k)}\Phi^\mu(k)$ is never negative if $\Phi_\mu(k)$ is transversal, *i.e.*, if $k^\mu\Phi_\mu(k) = 0$, $k^2 = 0$. In fact $(-)^1\overline{\Phi_\mu(k)}\Phi^\mu(k)$ will be positive definite for any vector $\Phi_\mu(k)$ not equivalent to zero, *i.e.*, for any transverse vector $\Phi_\mu(k)$ not of the form $\phi(k)k_\mu$. Hence

$$(-)^1\overline{\Phi_\mu^{(1)}(k)}\Phi^{(1)\mu}(k) > 0$$

and the contribution to the norm of $|\Psi\rangle$ from the one-photon subspace can be written in the form

$$\sum_i \int d^3k |\Psi_i^{(1)}(\mathbf{k})|^2 = (-)^1 \int_+ \frac{d^3k}{k_0} \overline{\Phi_\mu^{(1)}(k)}\Phi^{(1)\mu}(k) > 0 \tag{9–672}$$

where in the right-hand side of Eq. (9–672) the integration is carried out over the positive light cone $k^2 = 0$, $k_o > 0$.

The correlation can readily be extended to the higher photon configurations. We shall choose as the representative of the n photon configuration the tensor $\Phi_{\mu_1\cdots\mu_n}^{(n)}(k_1,\cdots,k_n)$ defined on the positive light cones $k_i^2 = 0$, $k_{i0} = |\mathbf{k}_i| > 0$ with the property that

$$\Phi_{\mu_1\cdots\mu_{j-1}0\mu_{j+1}\cdots\mu_n}^{(n)}(k_1,\cdots,k_n) = 0 \quad (j = 1,\cdots,n) \tag{9–673}$$

$$\Phi_{i_1\cdots i_n}^{(n)}(k_1,\cdots,k_n) = \sqrt{k_{1o}\cdots k_{no}}\,\Psi_{i_1\cdots i_n}^{(n)}(\mathbf{k}_1,\cdots,\mathbf{k}_n) \tag{9–674}$$

These tensors are transversal in the four-dimensional sense in each index by virtue of the three-dimensional transversality of the tensors $\Psi_{i_1\cdots in}^{(n)}$. The factor $\sqrt{k_{1o}\cdots k_{no}}$ is introduced so that the norm of $|\Psi\rangle$ will become

$$\|\Psi\|^2 = \sum_{n=0}^{\infty} \int_+ \frac{d^3k_1}{k_{1o}} \cdots \int \frac{d^3k_n}{k_{no}} (-1)^n \cdot \overline{\Phi^{(n)\mu_1\cdots\mu_n}(k_1,\cdots,k_n)}\Phi_{\mu_1\cdots\mu_n}^{(n)}(k_1,\cdots,k_n) \tag{9–675}$$

which is invariant, provided that the $\Phi_{\mu_1\cdots\mu_n}^{(n)}$ are four-dimensional tensors of rank n (d^3k/k_o is the invariant measure element over the light cone).

We next investigate the representation of the field operators in terms of the amplitude $\Phi^{(n)}_{\mu_1\cdots\mu_n}$. Recall that in the Heisenberg picture, in the radiation gauge, *i.e.*, in the gauge in which div $\mathscr{A}(x) = 0$,

$$\mathscr{E}(x) = -\frac{\partial \mathscr{A}(x)}{\partial x_o} \tag{9–676}$$

and

$$\mathscr{H}(x) = \nabla \times \mathscr{A}(x) \tag{9–677}$$

If we introduce the electromagnetic field tensor operator $F_{\mu\nu}(x)$, which can be decomposed as follows:

$$F_{\mu\nu}(x) = -i\sqrt{\frac{\hbar c}{2(2\pi)^3}} \times \int_+ \frac{d^3k}{k_o}\,(\tilde{F}_{\mu\nu}(k)e^{-ik\cdot x} - \tilde{F}^*_{\mu\nu}(k)e^{-k\cdot x}) \qquad k_o = |\mathbf{k}| > 0 \tag{9–678}$$

then from Eqs. (9–676) and (9–677) and the properties of the $\tilde{C}_i$ and $\tilde{C}_i^*$ operators, we deduce the following representation for $\tilde{F}_{\mu\nu}(k)$ and $\tilde{F}^*_{\mu\nu}(k)$

$$(\tilde{F}_{\mu\nu}(k)\Psi)^{(n)}_{\mu_1\cdots\mu_n}(k_1,\cdots,k_n) = \sqrt{n+1}\{k_\nu\Phi^{(n+1)}_{\mu\mu_1\cdots\mu_n}(k,k_1,\cdots,k_n) - k_\mu\Phi^{(n+1)}_{\nu\mu_1\cdots\mu_n}(k,k_1,\cdots,k_n)\} \tag{9–679}$$

$$(\tilde{F}^*_{\mu\nu}(k)\Psi)^{(n)}_{\mu_1\cdots\mu_n}(k_1,\cdots,k_n) = \frac{1}{\sqrt{n}}\sum_{j=1}^{n} k_{j0}\delta(\mathbf{k}-\mathbf{k}_j)(k_\nu d_{\mu\mu_j} - k_\mu d_{\nu\mu_j}) \cdot \Phi^{(n-1)}_{\mu_1\cdots\mu_{j-1}\mu_{j+1}\cdots\mu_n}(k_1,\cdots,k_{j-1},k_{j+1},\cdots,k_n) \tag{9–680}$$

where

$$d_{\mu\nu} = g_{\mu\nu} - \frac{k_\mu k_\nu}{k_0^2} \tag{9–681}$$

However, since the $\Phi^{(n)}_{\mu_1\cdots\mu_n}$ are only significant up to an equivalence, we can in Eq. (9–680) replace $-d_{\mu\nu}$ by $g_{\mu\nu}$, thus obtaining the following representation for $\tilde{F}^*_{\mu\nu}$

$$(\tilde{F}^*_{\mu\nu}(k)\Psi)^{(n)}_{\mu_1\cdots\mu_n}(k_1,\cdots,k_n) = \frac{1}{\sqrt{n}}\sum_{j=1}^{n} k_{jo}\delta(\mathbf{k}-\mathbf{k}_j)(k_\mu g_{\nu\mu_j} - k_\nu g_{\mu\mu_j}) \cdot \Phi^{(n-1)}_{\mu_1\cdots\mu_{j-1}\mu_{j+1}\cdots\mu_n}(k_1,\cdots,k_{j-1},k_{j+1},\cdots,k_n) \tag{9–682}$$

Note that these representations imply that $\tilde{F}_{\mu\nu}(k)|\Psi\rangle$ as well as

$\tilde{F}^*_{\mu\nu}(k)|\Psi\rangle$ are vectors whose components are again transversal (in the four-dimensional sense). Furthermore, $\tilde{F}_{\mu\nu}(k)$ and $\tilde{F}^*_{\mu\nu}(k)$ have the property that they carry equivalent vectors into equivalent vectors, where two vectors $|\Psi\rangle$ and $|\Psi'\rangle$ are said to be equivalent if

$$\Phi^{(n)}_{\mu_1\cdots\mu_n} - \Phi'^{(n)}_{\mu_1\cdots\mu_n} \equiv 0 \quad \text{for all } n \tag{9–683}$$

It should be noted that up to this point we have worked only in the system where the potential $\mathscr{A}(x)$ is transverse and the $\Phi'^{(n)}_{\mu_1\cdots\mu_n}$ have no time-like components.

Next let us introduce operators $a_\mu(k)$ by the equation

$$\tilde{F}_{\mu\nu}(k) = k_\nu a_\mu(k) - k_\mu a_\nu(k) \tag{9–684}$$

By comparing with Eqs. (9–679) and (9–682), we infer that we can define the operators $a_\mu(k)$ by the following representation

$$(a_\mu(k)\Psi)^{(n)}_{\mu_1\mu_2\cdots\mu_n}(k_1,\cdots,k_n) = \sqrt{n+1}\,\Phi^{(n+1)}_{\mu\mu_1\cdots\mu_n}(k,k_1,\cdots,k_n) \tag{9–685}$$

and

$$\begin{aligned}(a^*_\mu(k)\Psi)^{(n)}_{\mu_1\cdots\mu_n}&(k_1,\cdots,k_n)\\ &= -\frac{1}{\sqrt{n}}\sum_{j=1}^{n} k_{jo}\delta(\mathbf{k}-\mathbf{k}_j)g_{\mu\mu_j}\\ &\qquad \times \Phi^{(n-1)}_{\mu_1\cdots\mu_{j-1}\mu_{j+1}\cdots\mu_n}(k_1,\cdots,k_{j-1},k_{j+1},\cdots,k_n)\end{aligned} \tag{9–686}$$

The operator $a^*_\mu(k)$ so defined has the property that it takes a vector $|\Psi\rangle$ with transversal components into a vector $a^*_\mu(k)|\Psi\rangle$ whose components are no longer transversal. Hence, in order to define the operators $a_\mu(k)$ and $a^*_\mu(k)$, we need a larger vector space than the one whose elements have only transversal components. Within the scalar product

$$\begin{aligned}(\Psi_A,\Psi_B) = \sum_{n=0}^{\infty}(-1)^n \int\frac{d^3k_1}{k_{10}}\cdots\int\frac{d^3k_n}{k_{n0}}&\\ \times\, \overline{\Phi^{(n)}_{A\,\mu_1\cdots\mu_n}(k_1,\cdots,k_n)}\,\Phi^{(n)}_{B\,\mu_1\cdots\mu_n}&(k_1,\cdots,k_n)\end{aligned} \tag{9–687}$$

such nontransversal vectors may have a *negative* norm. However, for vectors that have physical meaning, *i.e.*, vectors whose components are transversal, the norm is positive definite. We, therefore, speak of the metric (9–687) in this larger vector space as indefinite, *i.e.*, not necessarily positive definite. This larger vector space can be made into a Hilbert space wherein all vectors have positive norm by defining a scalar product in accordance with the rule

$$(\Psi_A,\Psi_B)_H = \sum_{n=0}^{\infty} \int \frac{d^3k_1}{k_{10}} \cdots \int \frac{d^3k_n}{k_{n0}} \times \sum_{\mu_1,\cdots\mu_n=0}^{3} \overline{\Phi_{A\mu_1\cdots\mu_n}(k_1,\cdots,k_n)}\Phi_{B\mu_1\cdots\mu_n}(k_1,\cdots,k_n) \tag{9–688}$$

The indefinite bilinear form (Ψ_A,Ψ_B) as defined by Eq. (9–687) can be expressed in terms of the Hilbert space scalar product $(\Psi,\chi)_H$ as follows:

$$(\chi,\Psi) = (\chi,\eta\Psi)_H \tag{9–689}$$

where η is a linear operator. Comparing Eqs. (9–688) and (9–687) we infer

$$(\eta\Psi)^{(n)}_{\mu_1\cdots\mu_n}(k_1,\cdots,k_n) = \sum_{\nu_1\cdots\nu_n=0}^{3} \prod_{j=1}^{n} (-g_{\mu_j\nu_j})\Phi^{(n)}_{\nu_1\cdots\nu_n}(k_1,\cdots,k_n) \tag{9–690}$$

and

$$\eta^2 = 1 \tag{9–691}$$

$$\eta^* = \eta \tag{9–692}$$

In effect the scalar product in (9–688), which makes the vector space into a Hilbert space, omits the factor $(-1)^n$ from the bilinear form (9–687). We shall always work with the indefinite bilinear form (9–687). Thus, for example, one verifies that with this indefinite metric

$$(\chi,a_\mu(k)\Psi) = (a^*_\mu(k)\chi,\Psi) \tag{9–693}$$

The above defined operators $a_\mu(k)$ and $a^*_\mu(k)$ are hermitian. Furthermore, they satisfy by virtue of their representations the following commutation rules

$$[a_\mu(k),a_\nu(k')] = 0 \tag{9–694}$$

$$[a_\mu(k),a^*_\nu(k')] = -g_{\mu\nu}k_0\delta(\mathbf{k} - \mathbf{k}') \tag{9–695}$$

If we define the operators $A_\mu(x)$ by

$$A_\mu(x) = \sqrt{\frac{\hbar c}{2(2\pi)^3}} \int \frac{d^3k}{k_0} (a_\mu(k)e^{-ik\cdot x} + a^*_\mu(k)e^{ik\cdot x}) \tag{9–696}$$

the commutation rules (9–694)–(9–695) for the a_μ imply that the $A_\mu(x)$ operators obey the following commutation rules:

$$[A_\mu(x),A_\nu(x')] = -i\hbar c g_{\mu\nu} D(x - x') \tag{9–697}$$

where the singular function $D(x)$

$$\begin{aligned} D(x) &= -\frac{i}{(2\pi)^3}\int d^4k e^{-ik\cdot x}\varepsilon(k)\delta(k)^2 \\ &= -\frac{1}{(2\pi)^3}\int_{k_0>0}\frac{d^3k}{k_0}\, e^{i\mathbf{k}\cdot\mathbf{x}}\sin k_0x_0 \\ &= -\frac{1}{2\pi}\,\varepsilon(x_0)\delta(x^2) \end{aligned} \tag{9–698}$$

is that solution of the hyperbolic equation

$$\square D(x) = 0 \tag{9–699}$$

which satisfies the initial conditions

$$D(\mathbf{x},0) = 0 \tag{9–700}$$

$$\left.\frac{\partial D}{\partial x_0}\right|_{x_0=0} = -\delta(\mathbf{x}) \tag{9–701}$$

It should be noted that by virtue of Eq. (9–693), $A_\mu(x)$ is self-adjoint within the indefinite metric. The vacuum state can now be characterized by the relation

$$a_\mu(k)|0\rangle = 0 \tag{9–702}$$

or equivalently by

$$A_\mu^{(+)}(x)|0\rangle = 0 \tag{9–703}$$

where $A_\mu^{(+)}(x)$ is the positive frequency part of the operator $A_\mu(x)$, *i.e.*

$$A_\mu^{(+)}(x) = \sqrt{\frac{\hbar c}{2(2\pi)^3}}\int\frac{d^3k}{k_0}\, a_\mu(k)e^{-ik\cdot x} \tag{9–704}$$

The physically realizable states $|\Psi\rangle$ can be characterized by

$$k_\mu a^\mu(k)|\Psi\rangle = 0 \tag{9–705}$$

since this equation, in terms of the components of $|\Psi\rangle$ reads as follows:

$$k^\mu \Phi^{(n)}_{\mu\mu_1\cdots\mu_{n-1}}(k,k_1,\cdots,k_n) = 0 \quad \text{for all } n \tag{9–706}$$

which, of course, is the transversality condition for the components. In configuration space, Eq. (9–705) becomes

$$\left(\frac{\partial A_\mu^{(+)}(x)}{\partial x_\mu}\right)|\Psi\rangle = 0 \tag{9–707}$$

or equivalently

$$\left(\frac{\partial A_\mu(x)}{\partial x_\mu}\right)^{(+)}|\Psi\rangle = 0 \tag{9–708}$$

CHAPTER 10

EXTERNAL FIELD PROBLEMS

by

S. S. SCHWEBER

Brandeis University

Before embarking on the problem of the interaction of the negaton-positon field with the quantized electromagnetic field, we shall first consider the case of the negaton-positon field interacting with an external, classical (prescribed) electromagnetic field. We shall also outline in the present chapter those aspects of the theory of the S-matrix that will be required for the treatment of quantum electrodynamics. Section 10.4 presents a treatment of the Dirac equation in an external field.

10.1. The Negaton-Positon Field in an External Field.—In the Heisenberg picture, the operators describing the negaton-positon field in the presence of an external (classically prescribed) electromagnetic field, $A_\mu^e(x)$, satisfy the following equations of motion

$$\gamma^\mu \left(i\partial_\mu + \frac{e}{\hbar c} A_\mu^e(x) \right) \psi(x) - \frac{mc}{\hbar} \psi(x) = 0 \tag{10–1}$$

$$\left(i\partial_\mu - \frac{e}{\hbar c} A_\mu^e(x) \right) \tilde{\psi}(x)\gamma^\mu + \frac{mc}{\hbar} \tilde{\psi}(x) = 0 \tag{10–2}$$

These field equations are derivable from the following lagrangian density

$$\begin{aligned} \mathscr{L} = {} & \frac{\hbar c}{4} \left[\tilde{\psi}(x), \left(i\gamma^\mu\partial_\mu + \frac{e}{\hbar c} \gamma^\mu A_\mu^e(x) \right) \psi(x) \right] \\ & + \frac{\hbar c}{4} \left[\left(-i\partial_\mu + \frac{e}{\hbar c} A_\mu^e(x) \right) \tilde{\psi}(x)\gamma^\mu, \psi(x) \right] \\ & - \frac{mc^2}{2} [\tilde{\psi}(x), \psi(x)] - J^{e\mu}(x) A_\mu^e(x) \end{aligned} \tag{10–3}$$

$$\begin{aligned} = {} & \mathscr{L}_{\text{Dirac}} + \frac{e}{2} [\tilde{\psi}(x)\gamma^\mu, \psi(x)] A_\mu^e(x) \\ & - J^{e\mu}(x) A_\mu^e(x) \end{aligned} \tag{10–4}$$

where e is the magnitude of the electric charge of a negaton ($-e$ is the electronic charge). We have included in the lagrangian (10–3) and (10–4) the contribution from the interaction energy $J^{e\mu}(x)A_\mu^e(x)$ of the external field. Although the external potential $A_\mu^e(x)$ and external current are prescribed, and are assumed to be unaffected by their interaction with the negaton-positon field, we have included the interaction energy density $J^{e\mu}(x)A_\mu^e(x)$ so that the hamiltonian, which corresponds to this lagrangian, is the *total* energy of the system. We shall assume that the external potential has been so chosen that it satisfies the Lorentz condition

$$\partial^\mu A_\mu^e(x) = 0 \tag{10–5}$$

The relation between the external potential and the external current, which is the source of the external electromagnetic field, is

$$(g_{\mu\nu}\Box - \partial_\mu\partial_\nu)A^{e\nu}(x) = J_\mu^e(x) \tag{10–6}$$

or equivalently, by virtue of Eq. (10–5)

$$\Box A_\mu^e(x) = J_\mu^e(x) \tag{10–7}$$

The canonical commutation rules, which the equal-time operators satisfy, are

$$\{\psi(x),\bar{\psi}(x')\}|_{x_0=x_0} = \gamma^0\delta(\mathbf{x} - \mathbf{x}') \tag{10–8}$$

all other equal-time anti-commutators vanishing. These commutation rules can be generalized to arbitrary space-like separations. They then read

$$\{\psi(x),\bar{\psi}(x')\} = -iS(x - x') \tag{10–9}$$

$$\{\psi(x),\psi(x')\} = \{\bar{\psi}(x),\bar{\psi}(x')\} = 0 \tag{10–10}$$

for $(x - x')^2 < 0$. Since the external electromagnetic field variables are c-numbers the negaton-positon variables commute with $J^{e\mu}$ and $A^{e\mu}$. The above commutation rules guarantee that the commutator $[\psi(x),H(t)]_{t=x_0}$ reproduces the correct equation (of motion) obeyed by $\partial_t\psi(x)$. In this commutator $H(t)$ is the hamiltonian of the system [1]

$$H(t) = \int d^3x\mathscr{H}(x) \tag{10–11}$$

[1] In this chapter the symbol $\mathscr{H}$, which stood for the magnetic field in Chapter 9, will be used for energy density.

with $\mathscr{H}(x)$, the energy density, given by

$$\mathscr{H}(x) = \Big\{\tilde{\psi}(x)(-i\boldsymbol{\gamma}\cdot\boldsymbol{\nabla} + m)\psi(x) + J^{e\mu}(x)A_\mu^e(x) \\ - \frac{e}{2}[\tilde{\psi}(x)\gamma^\mu,\psi(x)]A_\mu^e(x)\Big\} \quad (10\text{–}12)$$

This hamiltonian is time-dependent if the external field $A_\mu^e(x)$ is time-dependent.

The charge and current density operator [2]

$$j_\mu(x) = -\frac{e}{2}[\tilde{\psi}(x)\gamma_\mu,\psi(x)] \quad (10\text{–}13)$$

is conserved, *i.e.*, satisfies the equation

$$\partial^\mu j_\mu(x) = 0 \quad (10\text{–}14)$$

by virtue of the equations of motion (10–1)–(10–2). This also follows from the invariance of the lagrangian (10–3) and (10–4) under the gauge transformations

$$\psi(x) \rightarrow e^{i\alpha}\psi(x) \quad (10\text{–}15)$$

$$\psi(x) \rightarrow e^{-i\alpha}\tilde{\psi}(x) \quad (10\text{–}16)$$

where α is a constant. From the fact that $j_\mu(x)$ is conserved, we conclude that the hermitian operator, Q, the total charge operator

$$Q = \int_t d^3x j_0(x) \quad (10\text{–}17)$$

is independent of the space-like surface t = constant and is a constant of the motion. This allows us to compute the commutation rule of $\psi(x)$ and $\tilde{\psi}(x)$ with Q by choosing for t, the space-like surface $t = x_0$. One then verifies that

$$[Q,\psi(x)] = e\psi(x) \quad (10\text{–}18)$$

$$[Q,\tilde{\psi}(x)] = -e\psi(x) \quad (10\text{–}19)$$

[2] Actually due to the coincidence of the space time point x in $\tilde{\psi}$ and ψ the operator $j_\mu(x)$ as given by (10–13) is ill-defined. This difficulty is remedied by defining the current in terms of the limit $\varepsilon \rightarrow 0$ applied to the operator

$$-\frac{e}{2}\left[\tilde{\psi}(x+\varepsilon)\gamma_\mu\psi(x)e^{i\int_x^{x+\varepsilon}d\xi^\mu A_\mu^e(\xi)} - \psi(x)\tilde{\psi}(x-\varepsilon)\gamma_\mu e^{-i\int_{x-\varepsilon}^{x}d\xi^\mu A_\mu^e(\xi)}\right]$$

where ε is a time-like vector. See K. A. Johnson, *Nuclear Phys.*, **25,** 431 (1961).

Therefore, if the state $|q\rangle$ is an eigenstate of the total charge operator Q with eigenvalue q

$$Q|q\rangle = q|Q\rangle \tag{10–20}$$

the state $\psi(x)|q\rangle$ is an eigenstate of Q with eigenvalue $q - e$; proof:

$$\begin{aligned} Q\psi(x)|q\rangle &= \psi(x)Q|q\rangle + [Q,\psi(x)]|q\rangle \\ &= (q + e)\psi(x)|q\rangle \end{aligned} \tag{10–21}$$

Similarly the state $\tilde{\psi}(x)|q\rangle$ is an eigenfunction of Q with eigenvalue $q - e$. This argument allows us to infer that the Heisenberg operator $\psi(x)$ destroys an amount of charge $-e$ or creates an amount of charge $+e$, and that $\psi(x)$ destroys an amount of charge $+e$ or creates an amount of charge $-e$.

In all the following discussion of the negaton-positon field interacting with an external field, $A^{e}_{\mu}(x)$, we shall assume that the external field $A^{e}_{\mu}(x)$ cannot bind any particles; more precisely we shall assume that there exist no bound state solutions of the one-particle Dirac equation (10–1) in the presence of this external field. The situation in the presence of bound states is somewhat more complicated. However, all the following development can be generalized so as to include bound states. Furthermore, since we are dealing with given external electromagnetic fields, we shall assume that these external fields have the property that in the remote past and in the remote future they are adiabatically switched off. (In other words, $A^{e}_{\mu}(x)$ really stands for $A^{e}_{\mu}(x)\cdot\exp(-\alpha|x_0|)$, where α is a positive small number that will go to zero at the end of the calculation.)

Under the above assumptions, we shall try to solve the operator equations (10–1) and (10–2) by writing ($\hbar = c = 1$)

$$\psi(x) = \psi_{\text{in}}(x) + e\int S_R(x - x'; m)\gamma^{\mu}A^{e}_{\mu}(x')\psi(x')d^4x' \tag{10–22}$$

where $S_R(x;m)$ is the retarded Green's function

$$S_R(x;m) = -(i\gamma\cdot\partial + m)\Delta_R(x;m^2) \tag{10–23}$$

which satisfies the equation

$$(-i\gamma\cdot\partial + m)S_R(x;m) = \delta^{(4)}(x) \tag{10–24}$$

and the boundary condition $S_R(x;m) = 0$ for $x_0 < 0$. The integration in Eq. (10–22) is, therefore, within the past light cone. A representation of Δ_R is given by[3]

$$\Delta_R(x;m^2) = \frac{-1}{(2\pi)^4} \int_{C_R} \frac{e^{-ik\cdot x}}{k^2 - m^2} d^4k \tag{10–25}$$

where C_R is the contour indicated in Fig. 10–1, which is so chosen as to make $\Delta_R(x)$ vanish for $x_0 < 0$. One readily verifies that for $x_0 > 0$

$$\Delta_R(x) = -\Delta(x) \quad (\text{for } x_0 > 0) \tag{10–26}$$

and as stated above $\Delta_R(x) = 0$ for $x_0 < 0$. Hence

$$\Delta_R(x) = -\theta(x)\Delta(x) \tag{10–27}$$

Alternatively, we may write

$$\begin{aligned} \Delta_R(x) &= -\frac{1}{(2\pi)^4} \lim_{\varepsilon\to 0} \int_{-\infty}^{+\infty} \frac{e^{-ik\cdot x}}{(k+i\varepsilon)^2 - m^2} d^4k \\ &= -\frac{1}{(2\pi)^4} \int \frac{e^{-ik\cdot x}}{(k^2 - m^2)_R} d^4k \end{aligned} \tag{10–28}$$

where ε^μ is a positive time-like vector ($\varepsilon^0 > 0$). This particular representation allows us to write, upon taking the limit $\varepsilon^0 \to 0$

$$\Delta_R(x;m^2) = -\frac{1}{(2\pi)^4} \int_{-\infty}^{+\infty} e^{-ik\cdot x} \left\{ \mathscr{P} \frac{1}{k^2 - m^2} - i\pi\varepsilon(k_0)\delta(k^2 - m^2) \right\} \tag{10–29}$$

a form which will prove useful later. In Eq. (10–28), $\mathscr{P}$ denotes that the principal part of the integral is to be taken.

Equation (10–22) will be a (formal) solution of (10–1) if the Heisenberg operator $\psi_{\text{in}}(x)$ satisfies the free field equation

$$(-i\gamma\partial + m)\psi_{\text{in}}(x) = 0 \tag{10–30}$$

as is verified by applying the operator $(-i\gamma\cdot\partial + m)$ on both sides of Eq. (10–1) and making use of Eq. (10–24). Furthermore, we note that as $x_0 \to -\infty$ the region of integration recedes to the infinite past so that by our adiabatic hypothesis

$$\lim_{x_0\to -\infty} \psi(x) \to \psi_{\text{in}}(x) \tag{10–31}$$

[3] When no ambiguity can result we shall suppress the dependence of S_R and Δ_R on m. Later on we shall have occasion to make explicit reference to the mass dependence of Δ_R and we shall then denote the function by $\Delta_R(x;m^2)$.

The sense of this operator convergence will have to be made more precise later. We shall further assert that $\psi_{\text{in}}(x)$ obeys field-free commutation rules

$$\{\psi_{\text{in}}(x),\tilde{\psi}_{\text{in}}(x')\} = -iS(x - x') \tag{10–32}$$

and define the no-particle "in" state, $|0\rangle_{\text{in}}$, the "in" vacuum by

$$\psi_{\text{in}}^{(+)}(x)|0\rangle_{\text{in}} = \tilde{\psi}_{\text{in}}^{(+)}(x)|0\rangle_{\text{in}} = 0 \quad \text{for all } x \tag{10–33}$$

These "in" operators now allow us to build up a complete set of states that span the Hilbert space of physical states in the manner discussed in Section 9.6 of the previous chapter for the free-field case. These

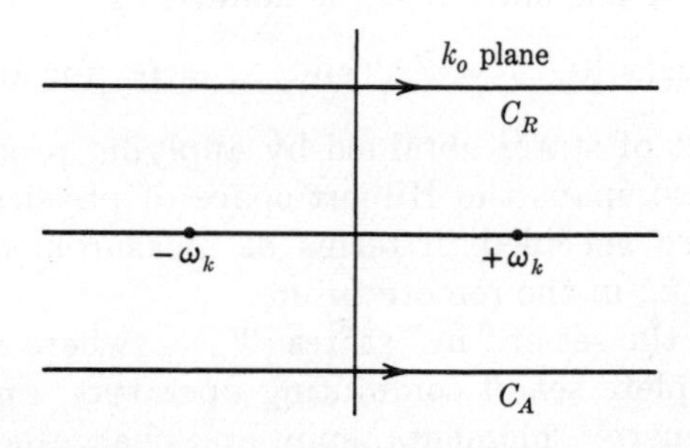

Fig. 10–1.

"in" states are Heisenberg states that are specified in terms of measurements performed at time $t = -\infty$.

In a manner analogous to the above we can define the "out" Heisenberg operators $\psi_{\text{out}}(x)$ by the formal solution

$$\psi(x) = \psi_{\text{out}}(x) + e\int S_A(x - x')\gamma^{\mu}A_{\mu}^{e}(x')\psi(x')d^4x' \tag{10–34}$$

where

$$S_A(x) = -(i\gamma\cdot\partial + m)\Delta_A(x) \tag{10–35}$$

and $\Delta_A(x)$ is given by

$$\Delta_A(x) = -\frac{1}{(2\pi)^4}\int_{C_A}\frac{e^{-ik\cdot x}}{k^2 - m^2}\,d^4k \tag{10–36}$$

with C_A the contour indicated in Fig. 10–1. Hence

$$\Delta_A(x) = \theta(-x)\Delta(x) \tag{10–37}$$

$$= \overline{\Delta_R(-x)} \tag{10–38}$$

Similarly one verifies that in the representation of the γ matrices where γ^0 is hermitian and γ^i antihermitian, *i.e.*, in the representation where

$$(\gamma^\mu)^* = \gamma^0\gamma^\mu\gamma^0 \tag{10–39}$$

the relation between S_A and S_R is

$$S_A(-x) = \gamma^0 S_R^*(x)\gamma^0 \tag{10–40}$$

which, incidentally, implies that $\tilde{\psi}(x)$ satisfies the following equation

$$\tilde{\psi}(x) = \tilde{\psi}_{\text{in}}(x) + e\int \tilde{\psi}(x')\gamma^\mu S_A(x' - x)A_\mu^{\text{e}}(x')d^4x' \tag{10–41}$$

The "out" no-particle state $|0\rangle_{\text{out}}$ is defined by

$$\psi_{\text{out}}^{(+)}(x)|0\rangle_{\text{out}} = \tilde{\psi}_{\text{out}}^{(+)}(x)|0\rangle_{\text{out}} = 0 \quad \text{for all } x \tag{10–42}$$

The complete set of states obtained by applying products of $\psi_{\text{out}}^{(-)}$ and $\tilde{\psi}_{\text{out}}^{(-)}$ on $|0\rangle_{\text{out}}$ also spans the Hilbert space of physical states. These "out" states are specified in terms of measurements performed at time $t = +\infty$, *i.e.*, in the remote future.

Summarizing, the set of "in" states $|\Psi_\alpha\rangle_{\text{in}}$ (where α labels the eigenvalues of a complete set of commuting operators, *e.g.*, the number of particles, their energy, momenta, spin, and charge) and $|\Psi_\alpha\rangle_{\text{out}}$ represent the answer to the query: "What is the state vector of the system?" the question being asked at $t = -\infty$ for the case of "in" states and at time $t = +\infty$ for the "out" states. Furthermore, since the set $\{|\Psi_\alpha\rangle_{\text{in}}\}$ is complete and so is the set $\{|\Psi_\alpha\rangle_{\text{out}}$, there exists a unitary transformation S, $S^* = S^{-1}$, between these two sets of basis vectors:

$$|\Psi_\alpha\rangle_{\text{out}} = S^*|\Psi_\alpha\rangle_{\text{in}} \tag{10–43}$$

Equivalently, this unitary operator S can be defined by the relation

$$S^{-1}\psi_{\text{in}}(x)S = \psi_{\text{out}}(x) \tag{10–44}$$

which follows from the fact that ψ_{in} and ψ_{out} form an equivalent representation of the commutation rules and, hence, must be unitarily related.

The formulation of the theory outlined above is particularly well-suited for the description of scattering processes, *i.e.*, experiments consisting of the preparation of a number of physical, free noninteracting particles at $t = -\infty$, allowing these particles to interact (with one another and/or any external field present), and finally measuring the state of these particles and whatever other particles are present at time $t = +\infty$ when they once again move freely. The infinite time involved in the mathematical formulation of the theory is a convenient artifice—all that actually need be required is that the time between the initial preparation and the final measurement is long compared to the characteristic times involved in the interaction of the particles (for example, if the range of the force is a, the characteristic time would be a/c). The free field operators $\psi_{\text{in}}(x)$ and $\tilde{\psi}_{\text{in}}(x)$ are to be used to construct the Heisenberg state vector $|\Psi\rangle_{\text{in}}$ that describe the knowledge of the system at $t = -\infty$. The state vectors $|\Phi\rangle_{\text{out}}$ which represent the eigenfunctions of the various types of measurements that we wish to make on the system at $t = +\infty$ are to be constructed from the operators ψ_{out} and $\tilde{\psi}_{\text{out}}$ operating on $|0\rangle_{\text{out}}$. The amplitude for the transition from an initial state $|\Psi\rangle_{\text{in}}$ at $t = -\infty$, to the state $|\Phi\rangle_{\text{out}}$ at $t = +\infty$ is then given by ${}_{\text{out}}\langle\Phi|\Psi\rangle_{\text{in}}$. By virtue of Eqs. (10–43) and (10–44) this amplitude can be written as

$$ {}_{\text{out}}\langle\Phi|\Psi\rangle_{\text{in}} = {}_{\text{in}}\langle\Phi|S|\Psi\rangle_{\text{in}} \tag{10–45} $$

The square of this matrix element $|{}_{\text{in}}\langle\Phi|S|\Psi\rangle_{\text{in}}|^2$ is the probability that a system that was prepared in the state $|\Psi\rangle$ at $t = -\infty$ will be found in the state $|\Phi\rangle$ at $t = +\infty$. The transformation operator S is the S-matrix of Heisenberg. We shall return later in this section to the problem of evaluating the S-matrix.

Besides such scattering experiments we shall assume that it is also possible to perform local measurements, for example, of the measurements of such quantities as the current density in a given state, *i.e.*, of $\langle\Psi|j_\mu(x)|\Psi\rangle$ or more accurately of such quantities as

$$ \langle\Psi|\int_\Omega j_\mu(x)f(x)d^4x|\Psi\rangle $$

where $f(x)$ is a "testing function" which is different from zero only in some space-time region Ω. That only such averages of field quantities are measurable is a consequence of the fact that the classical measuring apparatus used in any measurement is always of finite size. Similarly, a finite time is always necessary to determine any force through its effect on the velocity of macroscopic test bodies.[4]

Let us in fact consider the expectation value of the current operator in the no-particle state: ${}_{\text{in}}\langle 0|j_\mu(x)|0\rangle_{\text{in}}$. In order to obtain an insight into this quantity, we first treat the case of a very weak external field so that only effects to first order in the external field need be

[4] Strictly speaking the description of such local measurements can be carried out only within the framework of quantum electrodynamics, *i.e.*, in a theory wherein photons can be exchanged between the measuring apparatus and the current distribution being measured.

considered. By iterating Eq. (10–22) and (10–34) we obtain an expression for the Heisenberg field valid to first order in $A^{\rm e}_\mu$

$$\psi(x) = \psi_{\rm in}(x) + e\int S_R(x - x')\gamma^\mu A^{\rm e}_\mu(x')\psi_{\rm in}(x')d^4x' \qquad (10\text{–}46)$$

$$\tilde{\psi}(x) = \tilde{\psi}_{\rm in}(x) + e\int \tilde{\psi}_{\rm in}(x')\gamma^\mu A^{\rm e}_\mu(x')S_A(x' - x)d^4x' \qquad (10\text{–}47)$$

from which we can calculate the current operator

$$+\frac{e}{2}[\tilde{\psi}(x)\gamma^\mu,\psi(x)]$$
$$= \tfrac{1}{2}e[\tilde{\psi}_{\rm in}(x)\gamma^\mu,\psi_{\rm in}(x)]$$
$$+ \tfrac{1}{2}e^2\left[\tilde{\psi}_{\rm in}(x)\gamma^\mu, \int S_R(x - x')\gamma^\nu A^{\rm e}_\mu(x')\psi_{\rm in}(x')d^4x'\right]$$
$$+ \tfrac{1}{2}e^2\left[\int \tilde{\psi}_{\rm in}(x')\gamma^\nu A^{\rm e}_\nu(x')S_A(x' - x)\gamma^\mu,\psi_{\rm in}(x)\right]$$
$$+ \text{ terms of order } (A^{\rm e})^2 \qquad (10\text{–}48)$$

Recalling that

$${}_{\rm in}\langle 0|[\psi_{{\rm in}\,\alpha}(x),\tilde{\psi}_{{\rm in}\,\beta}(x')]|0\rangle_{\rm in} = S^{(1)}_{\alpha\beta}(x - x')$$
$$= -(i\gamma\cdot\partial + m)_{\alpha\beta}\Delta^{(1)}(x - x') \qquad (10\text{–}49)$$

and that ${}_{\rm in}\langle 0|j^\mu_{\rm in}(x)|0\rangle_{\rm in} = 0$, we obtain to first order in the external field

$${}_{\rm in}\langle 0|j_\mu(x)|0\rangle_{\rm in} = \tfrac{1}{2}e^2\int d^4x'\{{\rm Tr}\,[\gamma^\mu S_R(x - x')\gamma^\nu S^{(1)}(x' - x)]$$
$$+ {\rm Tr}\,[\gamma^\nu S_A(x' - x)\gamma^\mu S^{(1)}(x - x')]\}A^{\rm e}_\nu(x') \qquad (10\text{–}50)$$
$$= \int d^4x' K^{\mu\nu}(x - x')A^{\rm e}_\nu(x') \qquad (10\text{–}51)$$

where

$$K_{\mu\nu}(x - x') = \tfrac{1}{2}e^2\,{\rm Tr}\,\{\gamma_\mu S_R(x - x')\gamma_\nu S^{(1)}(x' - x)$$
$$+ \gamma_\nu S_A(x' - x)\gamma_\mu S^{(1)}(x - x')\} \qquad (10\text{–}52)$$

and Tr denotes that the trace of the expression in parenthesis to be taken. The properties of $K^{\mu\nu}(x)$ which will be of importance in what follows are:

(a) Lorentz invariance: from the invariant character of the singular S functions appearing in the definition of $K_{\mu\nu}$

$$S(\Lambda)^{-1}S_{(\,)}(x)S(\Lambda) = S_{(\,)}(\Lambda^{-1}x) \qquad (10\text{–}53)$$

where $S_{(\ )}$ can be either S_R, S_A, or $S_{(1)}$ and $S(\Lambda)$ is the finite dimensional spinor representation of the homogeneous Lorentz group

$$S(\Lambda_1)S(\Lambda_2) = \omega_{\Lambda_1\Lambda_2}S(\Lambda_1\Lambda_2) \tag{10-54}$$

$$S(\Lambda)^{-1}\gamma^\mu S(\Lambda) = \Lambda^\mu{}_\nu\gamma^\nu \tag{10-55}$$

[recall Eq. (9–353)–(9–359) in Chapter 9] one readily deduces that under Lorentz transformations $K^{\mu\nu}$ transforms like a tensor of rank 2

$$K^{\mu\nu}(x - x') = \Lambda^\mu{}_{\mu'}\Lambda^\nu{}_{\nu'}K^{\mu'\nu'}(\Lambda^{-1}(x - x')) \tag{10-56}$$

(b) Gauge invariance: the requirement that $j_\mu(x)$ be conserved, *i.e.*, that $\partial^\mu j_\mu(x) = 0$ implies that

$$\partial_\mu K^{\mu\nu}(x) = 0 \tag{10-57}$$

The related requirement that when $A^e_\mu(x) = \partial_\mu G(x)$ (*i.e.*, zero external *field*) there be no induced current, *i.e.*, ${}_{\text{in}}\langle 0|j_\mu(x)|0\rangle_{\text{in}} = 0$ (since by a gauge transformation we can revert to the free field case) implies that

$$0 = \int d^4x' K_{\mu\nu}(x - x')\partial'^\nu G(x') \tag{10-58}$$

or

$$\partial_\nu K^{\mu\nu}(x) = 0 \tag{10-59}$$

In fact, it turns out that $K^{\mu\nu}$ is symmetric so that the requirements (10–57), (10–58), and (10–59) are identical.

(c) Causality: due to the presence of the factor $\theta(x_0 - x_0')$ in $S_R(x - x')$ and $S_A(x' - x)$, $K_{\mu\nu}(x - x')$ vanishes unless $x_0 > x_0'$; $K_{\mu\nu}(x - x') = 0$ for $x_0 - x_0' < 0$.

If we suppress all the indices and space variables, Eqs. (10–50) and (10–51) can be written in the form

$$R(t) = \frac{1}{\sqrt{2\pi}}\int_{-\infty}^{+\infty} T(t - t')I(t')dt' \tag{10-60}$$

where $R(t)$ can be considered as the response of the physical system, to the input $I(t)$, in the present case the external electromagnetic field, and $T(t)$, the time delay distribution function, is the output corresponding to a δ-function input. By causality we then mean the condition that the response of the system to the input must vanish for times earlier than the application of the input—in other words, no output can occur before the input. If we denote by $r(\omega)$, $t(\omega)$, and $i(\omega)$ the Fourier transforms of R, T, and I respectively, *i.e.*,

$$G(t) = \frac{1}{\sqrt{2\pi}}\int_{-\infty}^{+\infty} g(\omega)e^{-i\omega t}d\omega \tag{10-61}$$

Equation (10–60) can be written as[5]

$$r(\omega) = t(\omega)i(\omega) \tag{10–62}$$

The causality principle asserts that if $I(t) = 0$ for $t < 0$, then $R(t) = 0$ for $t < 0$. Since

$$i(\omega) = \frac{1}{\sqrt{2\pi}} \int_{-\infty}^{+\infty} e^{i\omega t} I(t) dt \tag{10–63}$$

if $I(t) = 0$ for $t < 0$, then

$$i(\omega) = \frac{1}{\sqrt{2\pi}} \int_0^{\infty} e^{i\omega t} I(t) dt \tag{10–64}$$

so that $i(\omega)$ considered as a function of the complex variable $\omega = \omega_1 + i\omega_2$ will be analytic for $\text{Im}\,\omega = \omega_2 > 0$, *i.e.*, in the upper half of the complex ω-plane, for $I(t)$ bounded or square integrable. $R(t)$ will also vanish for $t < 0$ if the function $t(\omega)i(\omega)$ is analytic in the upper half of the complex ω plane. Since $i(\omega)$ is analytic in the upper half plane, the system will, therefore, be causal if $t(\omega)$ is analytic in $\text{Im}\,\omega > 0$ or equivalently if $T(t) = 0$ for $t < 0$.

Now if the function $t(\omega)$ is analytic in the upper half of the complex plane, and if C is a contour lying entirely in $\text{Im}\,\omega > 0$, then by Cauchy's theorem[6]

$$t(\omega) = \frac{1}{2\pi i} \oint \frac{t(\xi)}{\xi - \omega} d\xi \tag{10–65}$$

provided ω lies within C. Let us suppose that the behavior at infinity of $t(\xi)$ is such that the contour can be extended to a large semicircle with the contribution from the integration over the circumference vanishing in the limit as the radius $R \to \infty$; then

$$t(\omega) = \frac{1}{2\pi i} \int_{-\infty}^{+\infty} \frac{t(\xi)}{\xi - \omega} d\xi \tag{10–66}$$

Finally in the limit as $\omega \to \omega_1 + i\varepsilon$

$$\begin{aligned} \lim_{\omega \to \omega_1 + i\varepsilon} t(\omega) &= t(\omega_1) \\ &= \frac{1}{2\pi i} \int_{-\infty}^{+\infty} d\xi \frac{t(\xi)}{\xi - \omega_1 - i\varepsilon} \\ &= \frac{1}{2\pi i} \mathscr{P} \int_{-\infty}^{+\infty} d\xi \frac{t(\xi)}{\xi - \omega_1} + \tfrac{1}{2} t(\omega_1) \end{aligned} \tag{10–67}$$

[5] Cf. H. Margenau and G. M. Murphy, *The Mathematics of Physics and Chemistry*, 2nd Ed., p. 262, D. Van Nostrand Co., Inc., Princeton, N.J., 1956.

[6] Margenau and Murphy, *op. cit.*, p. 90.

where $\mathscr{P}$ denotes that the principal value of the integral is to be taken. Hence for real ω's

$$t(\omega) = \frac{1}{i\pi} \mathscr{P} \int_{-\infty}^{\infty} d\xi \frac{t(\xi)}{\xi - \omega_1} \tag{10–68}$$

By taking the real and imaginary parts of this last integral representation one obtains the Hilbert relations, which in physical applications have become known under the name "dispersion relations":

$$\operatorname{Re} t(\omega) = \frac{1}{\pi} \mathscr{P} \int_{-\infty}^{+\infty} \frac{\operatorname{Im} t(\omega')}{\omega' - \omega} d\omega' \tag{10–69}$$

$$\operatorname{Im} t(\omega) = -\frac{1}{\pi} \mathscr{P} \int_{-\infty}^{+\infty} \frac{\operatorname{Re} t(\omega)}{\omega' - \omega} d\omega' \tag{10–70}$$

Alternatively, since $\operatorname{Im} t(\omega) = \int_{-\infty}^{+\infty} \operatorname{Im} t(\omega')\delta(\omega - \omega')d\omega'$ upon adding this expression to (10–69) we obtain

$$t(\omega) = \frac{1}{\pi} \lim_{\varepsilon \to 0+} \int_{-\infty}^{+\infty} \frac{\operatorname{Im} t(\omega')}{\omega' - \omega - i\varepsilon} d\omega' \tag{10–71}$$

This last representation is completely equivalent to the analyticity of $t(\omega)$ in $\operatorname{Im} \omega > 0$ and the statement that $\omega t(\omega)$ go to zero as $|\omega| \to \infty$. The analyticity property in turn is a direct consequence of the retarded or causal character of $T(t)$, namely that it vanishes for $t > 0$. If $t(\omega)$ is analytic in the upper half plane, but instead of having the requisite asymptotic properties to allow the neglect of the contribution from the semicircle at infinity, behaves like a constant as $|\omega| \to \infty$, we can apply Cauchy's integral to $t(\omega)/(\omega - \omega_0)$ where ω_0 is some fixed point in the upper half plane within the contour. The result in this case, valid if $t(\omega) \to$ constant as $|\omega| \to \infty$ is

$$t(\omega) - t(\omega_0) = \frac{\omega - \omega_0}{\pi} \lim_{\varepsilon \to 0} \int d\omega' \frac{\operatorname{Im} t(\omega')}{(\omega' - \omega - i\varepsilon)(\omega' - \omega_0 - i\varepsilon)} \tag{10–72}$$

Note that this expression could have been obtained from (10–71) by subtracting from $t(\omega)$, as given by that expression, the value $t(\omega_0)$.

We now apply these results to compute $\tilde{K}_{\mu\nu}(p)$, the Fourier transform of $K_{\mu\nu}(x)$, in terms of its imaginary part $\operatorname{Im} \tilde{K}_{\mu\nu}(p)$. Causality asserts that $\tilde{K}_{\mu\nu}(p)$ is an analytic function of p_0 in $\operatorname{Im} p_0 > 0$, and hence that there exists a dispersion relation relating the real and imaginary parts of $\tilde{K}_{\mu\nu}$.

In terms of the Fourier transform $\tilde{K}_{\mu\nu}(p)$ of $K_{\mu\nu}(x)$

$$K_{\mu\nu}(x) = \frac{1}{(2\pi)^4}\int d^4p e^{-ip\cdot x}\tilde{K}_{\mu\nu}(p) \tag{10–73}$$

Equation (10–56) asserts that $\tilde{K}^{\mu\nu}(p)$ is of the form

$$\tilde{K}^{\mu\nu}(p) = p^\mu p^\nu \tilde{K}_{(1)}(p^2) + g^{\mu\nu}p^2\tilde{K}_{(2)}(p^2) \tag{10–74}$$

since p_μ is the only vector available. Note that the invariant functions $K_{(1)}$ and $K_{(2)}$ can also depend on $\varepsilon(p)$, the sign of p^0 when $p^2 > 0$, *i.e.*, within the light cone. We have suppressed this dependence. Equations (10–57), (10–58), and (10–59) further entail

$$p^\mu \tilde{K}_{\mu\nu}(p) = 0 \tag{10–75}$$

so that $\tilde{K}_{(1)} = -\tilde{K}_{(2)} = \tilde{K}$ and we can therefore write

$$\tilde{K}_{\mu\nu}(p) = (p_\mu p_\nu - g_{\mu\nu}p^2)\tilde{K}(p^2) \tag{10–76}$$

Hence it will prove sufficient to compute $\tilde{K}(p^2)$ since $\tilde{K}_{\mu\nu}(p)$ can easily be constructed from it. In fact, from Eq. (10–76) it follows that

$$\tilde{K}(p^2) = -\frac{1}{3p^2}K^\mu{}_\mu(p) \tag{10–77}$$

If we introduce into the expression for $K^\mu{}_\mu(x)$ the explicit representations for S_R, S_A, and $S_{(1)}$ we obtain

$$\begin{aligned}\tilde{K}^\mu{}_\mu(p) = \frac{1}{2}\frac{e^2}{(2\pi)^3}&\int d^4k' \int d^4k''\delta(p - k' + k'')\\ &\times \operatorname{Tr}\{\gamma^\mu(\gamma\cdot k' + m)\gamma_\mu(\gamma\cdot k'' + m)\}\\ &\times\left\{\left(\mathscr{P}\frac{1}{k'^2 - m^2} - i\pi\varepsilon(k_0')\delta(k'^2 - m^2)\right)\delta(k''^2 - m^2)\right.\\ &\left.+\left(\mathscr{P}\frac{1}{k''^2 - m^2} + i\pi\varepsilon(k_0'')\delta(k''^2 - m^2)\right)\delta(k'^2 - m^2)\right\}\end{aligned} \tag{10–78}$$

so that if we write

$$\tilde{K}(p) = \operatorname{Re}\tilde{K}(p) + i\operatorname{Im}\tilde{K}(p) \tag{10–79}$$

then

$$\begin{aligned}\operatorname{Re}\tilde{K}(p) = -\frac{1}{3p^2}\frac{1}{2}\frac{e^2}{(2\pi)^2}&\int d^4k' \int d^4k''\delta(p - k' + k'')\\ &\times \operatorname{Tr}\{\gamma^\mu(\gamma\cdot k' + m)\gamma_\mu(\gamma\cdot k'' + m)\}\\ &\times\left\{\mathscr{P}\frac{1}{k'^2 - m^2}\delta(k''^2 - m^2) + \mathscr{P}\frac{1}{k''^2 - m^2}\delta(k'^2 - m^2)\right\}\end{aligned} \tag{10–80}$$

and

$$\text{Im}\,\tilde{K}(p) = +\frac{\pi}{3p^2}\frac{1}{2}\frac{e^2}{(2\pi)^3}\int d^4k' \int d^4k''\delta(p - k' + k'')$$
$$\times\ \text{Tr}\,\{\gamma^\mu(\gamma\cdot k' + m)\gamma_\mu(\gamma\cdot k'' + m)\}$$
$$\times\ (\varepsilon(k_0') - \varepsilon(k_0''))\delta(k'^2 - m^2)\delta(k''^2 - m^2) \quad (10\text{–}81)$$

The trace appearing in expressions (10–80) and (10–81) is readily evaluated. Using the fact that

$$\gamma^\mu\gamma_\mu = 4 \quad (10\text{–}82)$$
$$\gamma^\mu\gamma^\nu\gamma_\mu\gamma^\sigma = -2\gamma^\nu\gamma^\sigma \quad (10\text{–}83)$$
$$\text{Tr}\,\{\gamma^\mu\gamma^\nu\} = 4g^{\nu\sigma} \quad (10\text{–}84)$$

one finds that

$$\text{Tr}\,\{\gamma^\mu(\gamma\cdot k' + m)\gamma_\mu(\gamma\cdot k'' + m)\} = \text{Tr}\,\{\gamma^\mu\gamma\cdot k\gamma_\mu\gamma\cdot k'' + \gamma^\mu\gamma_\mu m^2\}$$
$$= 4(-2k'\cdot k'' + 4m^2) \quad (10\text{–}85)$$

From Eqs. (10–80), (10–81), and (10–85), we deduce that

$$\text{Im}\,\tilde{K}(p) = -\ \text{Im}\,\tilde{K}(-p) \quad (10\text{–}86)$$
$$\text{Re}\,\tilde{K}(p) = \text{Re}\,\tilde{K}(-p) \quad (10\text{–}87)$$

The symmetry properties expressed by Eqs. (10–81) and (10–83), coupled with the fact that $\tilde{K}$ must be an invariant function of the invariants p^2 and $\varepsilon(p)$, imply that

$$\text{Re}\,\tilde{K}(p) = \text{P}(p^2) \quad (10\text{–}88)$$

and that

$$\text{Im}\,\tilde{K}(p) = \pi\varepsilon(p)\Pi(p^2) \quad (10\text{–}89)$$

with $\Pi(p^2)$ vanishing for $p^2 < 0$. We shall verify explicitly this last assertion.

Upon introducing Eq. (10–85) into the expression for Im $K(p)$, and putting $-2k'\cdot k'' = (k' - k'')^2 - k'^2 - k''^2$ the δ functions appearing therein allow us to write

$$\text{Im}\,\tilde{K}(p) = +\frac{e^2}{12\pi^2}\frac{p^2 + 2m^2}{p^2}\int d^4k' \int d^4k''\delta(p - k' + k'')$$
$$\times\ (\varepsilon(k_0') - \varepsilon(k_0''))\delta(k'^2 - m^2)\delta(k''^2 - m^2)$$
$$= +\frac{e^2}{12\pi^2}\frac{p^2 + m^2}{p^2}\int d^4k\,\{\varepsilon(p_0 + k_0) - \varepsilon(k_0)\}$$
$$\times\ \delta((p + k)^2 - m^2)\delta(k^2 - m^2) \quad (10\text{–}90)$$

We can differentiate between two cases, namely: (a) p is space-like; and (b) p is time-like. In the case that p is space-like, due to the invariance of $\tilde{K}$ we can choose without loss of generality a coordinate system in which $p = (0,\mathbf{p})$, in which case Im $\tilde{K}(p) = 0$, since

$$\varepsilon(p_0 + k_0) - \varepsilon(k_0) = \varepsilon(k_0) - \varepsilon(k_0) = 0$$

Therefore, Im $\tilde{K}(p)$ is different from zero only when p is time-like. If p is time-like, choose a coordinate system in which $p = (p_0,\mathbf{0})$, so that

$$\begin{aligned}
\text{Im } \tilde{K}(p) &= +\frac{e^2}{12\pi^2}\frac{p_0^2 + 2m^2}{p_0^2}\int d^4k(\varepsilon(p_0 + k_0) - \varepsilon(k_0)) \\
&\qquad \times \delta((p_0 + k_0)^2 - \mathbf{k}^2 - m^2)\delta(k^2 - m^2) \\
&= +\frac{e^2}{12\pi^2}\frac{p_0^2 + 2m^2}{p_0^2}\int d^4k \\
&\qquad \times \left\{\frac{1}{2E_{\mathbf{k}}}(\delta(p_0 + k_0 - E_{\mathbf{k}}) - \delta(p_0 + k_0 + E_{\mathbf{p}})) \right. \\
&\qquad \times \delta(k^2 - m^2) - \frac{e^2}{2E_{\mathbf{k}}}(\delta(k_0 - E_{\mathbf{k}}) - \delta(k_0 + E_{\mathbf{k}})) \\
&\qquad \left. \times \delta((p_0 + k_0)^2 - \mathbf{k}^2 - m^2)\right\} \\
&= +\frac{e^2}{12\pi^2}\frac{p_0^2 + 2m^2}{p_0^2}\int \frac{d^3k}{E_{\mathbf{k}}}\{\delta((E_{\mathbf{k}} - p_0)^2 - \mathbf{k}^2 - m^2) \\
&\qquad - \delta((p_0 + E_{\mathbf{k}})^2 - \mathbf{k}^2 - m^2)\} \qquad (10\text{–}91)
\end{aligned}$$

Upon introducing $E_{\mathbf{k}}$ as the variable of integration after performing the angular integrations, we obtain

$$\begin{aligned}
\text{Im } \tilde{K}(p) &= +\frac{e^2}{3\pi}\frac{p_0^2 + 2m^2}{p_0^2}\int_m^\infty dE_{\mathbf{k}}\sqrt{E_{\mathbf{k}}^2 - m^2} \\
&\qquad \times \{\delta(2p_0E_{\mathbf{k}} - p_0^2) - \delta(p_0^2 + 2p_0E_{\mathbf{k}})\} \qquad (10\text{–}92)
\end{aligned}$$

since $E_{\mathbf{k}}dE_{\mathbf{k}} = kdk$, $k = \sqrt{E_{\mathbf{k}}^2 - m^2}$. Now the first δ function in (10–92) asserts that $E_{\mathbf{k}} = \frac{1}{2}p_0$ for $\frac{1}{2}p_0 > m$, whereas the second asserts that $E_{\mathbf{k}} = \frac{1}{2}p_0$ for $-\frac{1}{2}p_0 > m$, hence

$$\begin{aligned}
\text{Im } \tilde{K}(p) &= +\frac{e^2}{3\pi}\frac{p_0^2 + 2m^2}{p_0^2}\left\{\frac{1}{2p_0}\sqrt{\tfrac{1}{4}p_0^2 - m^2}\,\theta(p_0 - 2m)\right. \\
&\qquad \left. - \frac{1}{2p_0}\sqrt{\tfrac{1}{4}p_0^2 - m^2}\,\theta(-p_0 - 2m)\right\} \\
&= +\frac{e^2}{12\pi}\frac{p_0^2 + 2m^2}{p_0^2}\sqrt{\frac{p_0^2 - 4m^2}{p_0^2}}\,\varepsilon(p)\theta(p_0^2 - 4m^2) \qquad (10\text{–}93)
\end{aligned}$$

From invariance, in an arbitrary coordinate system, we have

$$\text{Im}\,\tilde{K}(p) = +\varepsilon(p)\frac{e^2}{12\pi}\frac{p^2+2m^2}{p^2}\sqrt{\frac{p^2-4m^2}{p^2}}\,\theta(p^2-4m^2) \tag{10–94}$$

verifying the form (10–85) for Im $K(p)$ and indicating that to this order

$$\Pi(p^2) = +\frac{e^2}{12\pi^2}\frac{p^2+2m^2}{p^2}\sqrt{\frac{p^2-4m^2}{p^2}}\,\theta(p^2-4m^2) \tag{10–95}$$

Note that $\Pi(p^2)$ approaches a constant as $p^2 \to \infty$ so that if we wish to calculate $\tilde{K}(p)$ from Im $\tilde{K}(p)$ we must use the once subtracted dispersion relations (10–72). We, furthermore, note that due to the symmetry relation (10–86), and (10–87) we can write the unsubtracted dispersion relation as follows:

$$\begin{aligned}\text{Re}\,\tilde{K}(p^2) &= \mathrm{P}(p^2)\\ &= \mathscr{P}\int_{-\infty}^{+\infty} dp_0'\varepsilon(p_0')\frac{\Pi(p_0'^2-\mathbf{p}^2)}{p_0'-p_0}\\ &= \mathscr{P}\int_0^{\infty} dp_0'\Pi(p_0'^2-p^2)\left\{\frac{1}{p_0'-p_0}+\frac{1}{p_0'+p_0}\right\}\\ &= \mathscr{P}\int_0^{\infty} dp'^2\frac{\Pi(p_0'^2-\mathbf{p}^2)}{p_0'^2-p_0^2}\end{aligned} \tag{10–96}$$

If we call $p_0^2 - \mathbf{p}^2 = a$, and recall that $\Pi(a)$ vanishes unless $a > 4m^2$, we can write

$$\mathrm{P}(p^2) = \mathscr{P}\int_{4m^2}^{\infty} da\,\frac{\Pi(a)}{a-p^2} \tag{10–97}$$

As $\Pi(a)$ approaches a constant as $a \to \infty$ the function $\Pi(p^2)$ as defined by Eq. (10–97) is logarithmically divergent. The once subtracted dispersion relation is well defined, and reads

$$\mathrm{P}(p^2) - \mathrm{P}(0) = p^2\mathscr{P}\int_{4m^2}^{\infty} da\,\frac{\Pi(a)}{a(a-p^2)} \tag{10–98}$$

the subtraction at $p^2 = 0$ rendering the quantity $\mathrm{P}(p^2) - \mathrm{P}(0)$ finite. Finally, therefore

$$\tilde{K}(p^2) - \tilde{K}(0) = \text{Re}\,\tilde{K}(p^2) + i\,\text{Im}\,\tilde{K}(p^2) - \text{Re}\,\tilde{K}(0) \tag{10–99}$$

$$= \mathrm{P}(p^2) + i\pi\varepsilon(p)\Pi(p^2) - \text{Re}\,\tilde{K}(0) \tag{10–100}$$

$$= -\int_{4m^2}^{\infty} da\Pi(a)\frac{1}{(p^2-a)_R} - \tilde{K}(0) \tag{10–101}$$

where to arrive at (10–101) we have written $\Pi(p^2)$ as

$$\int_0^\infty da\delta(a - p^2)\Pi(a)$$

and have again adopted the notation

$$\frac{1}{(p^2 - a)_R} = \frac{1}{p^2 - a} - i\pi\varepsilon(p_0)\delta(p^2 - a) \tag{10–102}$$

(recall also that Im $\tilde{K}(0) = 0$).

The induced current

$$_{\text{in}}\langle 0|\tilde{j}_\mu(p)|0\rangle_{\text{in}} = \tilde{K}(p^2)\tilde{J}^{\text{e}}_\mu(p)$$

is therefore given by

$$_{\text{in}}\langle 0|\tilde{j}_\mu(p)|0\rangle_{\text{in}} = -\int_0^\infty \frac{da}{(p^2 - a)_R}\,\Pi(a)\tilde{J}^{\text{e}}_\mu(p) \tag{10–103}$$

which in configuration space becomes

$$\begin{aligned} _{\text{in}}\langle 0|j_\mu(x)|0\rangle_{\text{in}} &= -\frac{1}{(2\pi)^4}\int d^4p \int_0^\infty \frac{da}{(p^2 - a)_R}\,\Pi(a)\tilde{J}^{\text{e}}_\mu(p)e^{-ip\cdot x} \\ &= +\int d^4x' \int_0^\infty da\Pi(a)\cdot\frac{-1}{(2\pi)^4}\int d^4p\,\frac{e^{-ip\cdot(x-x')}}{(p^2 - a)_R}\,J^{\text{e}}_\mu(x') \end{aligned} \tag{10–104}$$

$$= \int d^4x' \int_0^\infty da\Pi(a)\Delta_R(x - x'; a)J^{\text{e}}_\mu(x') \tag{10–105}$$

The right-hand side of Eq. (10–105) is, however, ill-defined as

$$\int^\infty \frac{\Pi(a)}{a}\,da$$

is divergent. We note that to the order in which we are working

$$\Pi(a) = \frac{e^2}{12\pi^2}\frac{a + 2m^2}{a}\sqrt{\frac{a - 4m^2}{a}}\;\theta(a - 4m^2) \tag{10–106}$$

so that

$$\int_0^\infty \frac{\Pi(a)}{a}\,da = \frac{e^2}{12\pi^2}\int_{4m^2}^\infty \frac{da}{a^2}\,(a + 2m^2)\sqrt{\frac{a - 4m^2}{a}} = e^2C \tag{10–107}$$

where C is logarithmically divergent. However, since

$$(\Box + a)\Delta_R(x;a) = \delta(x)$$

we may write

$$\Delta_R(x;a) = \frac{1}{a}\,\delta(x) - \frac{1}{a}\,\Box\Delta_R(x;a) \tag{10–108}$$

in which case Eqs. (10–104) and (10–105) becomes

$$\begin{aligned}{}_{\text{in}}\langle 0|j_\mu(x)|0\rangle_{\text{in}} &= \int_0^\infty da\,\frac{\Pi(a)}{a}\,J^{\text{e}}_\mu(x)\\ &\quad - \int d^4x' \int_0^\infty da\,\frac{\Pi(a)}{a}\,\Box\Delta_R(x-x';a)\,J^{\text{e}}_\mu(x')\end{aligned} \tag{10–109}$$

thus isolating in the first term the divergent contribution to

$${}_{\text{in}}\langle 0|j_\mu(x)|0\rangle_{\text{in}}$$

The decomposition (10–109) above is of course equivalent to writing

$$\frac{1}{(p^2+a)_R} = \frac{1}{a} + \frac{p^2}{a(p^2+a)_R} \tag{10–110}$$

or alternatively

$${}_{\text{in}}\langle 0|\tilde{j}_\mu(p)|0\rangle_{\text{in}} = \tilde{K}(0)\,\tilde{J}^{\text{e}}_\mu(p) + (\tilde{K}(p^2) - \tilde{K}(0))\tilde{J}^{\text{e}}_\mu(p) \tag{10–111}$$

In order to interpret the above results, consider the expectation value of the total energy density in the vacuum state, *i.e.*, of the hamiltonian density, Eq. (10–12). There is a contribution $J^{\text{e}\mu}(x)A^{\text{e}}_\mu(x)$ from the external field and a contribution ${}_{\text{in}}\langle 0|j^\mu(x)|0\rangle_{\text{in}}A^{\text{e}}_\mu(x)$ from the induced current, hence to lowest order

$$\langle\mathscr{H}(x)\rangle_0 = J^{\text{e}\mu}(x)A^{\text{e}}_\mu(x) + {}_{\text{in}}\langle 0|j^\mu(x)|0\rangle_{\text{in}}A^{\text{e}}_\mu(x) \tag{10–112}$$

$$\begin{aligned}&= (1+e^2C)\,J^{\text{e}\mu}A^{\text{e}}_\mu(x)\\ &\quad - \int d^4x' \int_0^\infty da\,\frac{\Pi(a)}{a}\,\Box\Delta_R(x-x';a)\,J^{\text{e}}_\mu(x')A^{\text{e}\mu}(x)\end{aligned} \tag{10–113}$$

In writing (10–113) we have combined that part of the induced current that is a constant (infinite) multiple of the inducing current with the original current. Doing so recognizes the fact that it is impossible experimentally to separate the external charge-current J^{e}_μ from the induced current proportional to it; the external current will always polarize the vacuum and in all measurements the inducing current is given by

$$J^{\text{e}}_{R\mu}(x) = (1+e^2C)^{1/2}J^{\text{e}}_\mu(x) \tag{10–114}$$

$J^{\text{e}}_{R\mu}(x)$ is called the "renormalized" charge-current density.

By virtue of Eq. (10–6) clearly the external potential is renormalized in the same way

$$A^{e}_{R\mu}(x) = (1 + e^2C)^{1/2}A^{e}_{\mu}(x) \tag{10–115}$$

A finite and consistent theory is now obtained if, together with this renormalization of the external field strength, the renormalized unit of charge is defined as

$$e_R = \frac{e}{(1 + e^2C)^{1/2}} \tag{10–116}$$

Note that this definition implies that

$$eA^{e}_{\mu}(x) = e_R A^{e}_{R\mu}(x) \tag{10–117}$$

To second order, then

$$\begin{aligned}\Pi_R(a) &= \frac{e_R^2}{12\pi^2}\,\frac{a + 2m^2}{p^2}\sqrt{\frac{a - 4m^2}{a}}\,\theta(a - 4m^2) \\ &= \frac{\Pi(a)}{(1 + e^2C)}\end{aligned} \tag{10–118}$$

whence the energy density $= J^{e\mu}_{R}(x)A^{e}_{R\mu}(x)$

$$- \int d^4x \int_0^\infty da\, \frac{\Pi_R(a)}{a}\,\Box\Delta_R(x - x';a) \times J^{e}_{R\mu}(x')A^{e\mu}_{R}(x) \tag{10–119}$$

is well defined and finite.

REFERENCES

For other modern discussions of the problem of vacuum polarization by an external field, see:

Schwinger, J., *Phys. Rev.*, **82**, 664 (1951); **93**, 615 (1954).

Thirring, W. E., *Principles of Quantum Electrodynamics*, Academic Press, New York, 1958.

Källén, G., *Handbuch der Physik*, Band V, Teil 1, Springer Verlag, Berlin-Göttingen, 1958.

For a mathematical discussion of the relation between causality and dispersion relations, see:

Toll, J. S., *Phys. Rev.*, **104**, 1760 (1956).

For a discussion of the quantized electromagnetic field interacting with a given (prescribed) external current, see:

Thirring, W. E., *Principles of Quantum Electrodynamics*, Academic Press, New York, 1958.

10.2. The S-Matrix.—We next turn to the problem of formulating a systematic procedure for calculating higher order contributions.[7] The methods that we shall develop have the property that they will also be applicable to the computation of the S-matrix elements.

To facilitate the derivation we shall assume that we are in the Heisenberg picture and dealing with a time-independent hamiltonian, *i.e.*, $H(t) = H(0) = H$, in which case Heisenberg operators at different times are related by the equation

$$Q(t) = e^{+iH(t-t')}Q(t')e^{-iH(t-t')} \tag{10–120}$$

We shall take the Heisenberg and Schrödinger pictures to coincide at time $t = 0$. We next correlate with the complete hamiltonian $H(0)$ (*i.e.*, the total hamiltonian in the Heisenberg picture at time $t = 0$, which by the above convention is also the total hamiltonian in the Schrödinger picture) an unperturbed hamiltonian $H_o(0)$. We shall write

$$H(0) = H_o(0) + H_I(0) \tag{10–121}$$

thereby defining the "interaction" or perturbed part of the hamiltonian, $H_I(t)$. We shall furthermore assume that a certain set of eigenfunctions of $H(0)$ obeying specified boundary conditions can be correlated in a one-to-one fashion with the eigenstates of $H_o(0)$. We shall designate these eigenfunctions of $H(0)$ by $|\Psi_n\rangle$, and their correlated eigenstates by $|\Phi_n\rangle$. More specifically, we shall assume that this set $\{|\Psi_n\rangle\}$ corresponds to states representing incoming plane waves plus outgoing spherical waves, and to make this specification explicit, we shall write $|\Psi_n\rangle_+$. Formally we can write

$$|\Psi_n\rangle_+ = |\Phi_n\rangle_+ + \lim_{\varepsilon\to 0+} \frac{1}{E_n - H_o(0) + i\varepsilon} H_I(0)|\Psi_n\rangle_+ \tag{10–122}$$

if we suitably adjust the zero of energy of $H_o(0)$ so that the spectra of $H(0)$ and $H_0(0)$ coincide. The $|\Psi_n\rangle_+$ so defined satisfy the equation

$$H(0)|\Psi_n\rangle_+ = E_n|\Psi_n\rangle_+ \tag{10–123}$$

together with the outgoing wave boundary condition (the $|\Phi_n\rangle$ satisfy the equation $H_o|\Phi_n\rangle = E_n|\Phi_n\rangle$). They can be normalized so that they have the same normalization as the $|\Phi_n\rangle$, *i.e.*

$$_+\langle\Psi_n|\Psi_m\rangle_+ = \delta_{nm} \tag{10–124}$$

$$\langle\Phi_n|\Phi_m\rangle = \delta_{nm} \tag{10–125}$$

[7] M. Gell-Mann and M. L. Goldberger, *Phys. Rev.*, **91**, 398 (1953).

In (10–124) and (10–125), n and m refer to the eigenvalues of a complete set of commuting observables so δ_{nm} stands for a delta function in those observables in the set $\{n\}$ that have a continuous spectrum, and a Kronecker δ in those that have a discrete spectrum.

We next introduce the Møller wave operator $\Omega^{(+)}$ which transforms the state vectors $|\Phi_n\rangle$ into $|\Psi_n\rangle_+$

$$\Omega^{(+)}|\Phi_n\rangle = |\Psi_n\rangle_+ \tag{10–126}$$

If the hamiltonians $H(0)$ and $H_o(0)$ are such that there exist no bound states, and the states $|\Psi_n\rangle_+$ are properly normalized, $\Omega^{(+)}$ is a unitary operator. Furthermore, it has the property that

$$\Omega^{(+)}H_o(0)\Omega^{(+)-1} = H(0) \tag{10–127}$$

Next we define the operator

$$V_+(t) = e^{iH(0)t}\Omega^{(+)}e^{-iH(0)t}$$

which by virtue of Eq. (10–127) obeys the following equation

$$\begin{aligned} i\partial_t V_+(t) &= e^{iH(0)t}(\Omega^{(+)}H(0) - H(0)\Omega^{(+)})e^{-iH(0)t} \\ &= e^{iH(0)t}\Omega^{(+)}(H(0) - H_o(0)e^{-iH(0)t} \\ &= V_+(t)H_I(t) = V_+(t)H_I(t)V_+(t)^{-1}V_+(t) \end{aligned} \tag{10–128}$$

where

$$H_I(t) = e^{iH(0)t}H_I(0)e^{-iH(0)t} \tag{10–129}$$

The Heisenberg operators $Q_+(t)$ defined by

$$Q_+(t) \equiv V_+(t)Q(t)V_+(t)^{-1} \tag{10–130}$$

have the property that they obey the Heisenberg equations of motion

$$i\partial_t Q_+(t) = [Q_+(t),H(t)] \tag{10–131}$$

However, since

$$\begin{aligned} H_{o+}(t) &= V_+(t)H_o(t)V_+(t)^{-1} \\ &= e^{iH(0)t}\Omega^{(+)}H_o(0)\Omega^{(+)-1}e^{-iH(0)t} \\ &= e^{iH(0)t}H(0)e^{-iH(0)t} = H(0) \\ &= H(t) \end{aligned} \tag{10–132}$$

Equation (10–131) above can be rewritten as

$$\begin{aligned} i\partial_t Q_+(t) &= [Q_+(t),H_{o+}(t)] \\ &= [Q_+(t),H_{o+}(0)] \end{aligned} \tag{10–133}$$

so that the operator $Q_+(t)$ obeys free field equations. Finally we note, since

$$\langle\Phi_m| = {}_+\langle\Psi_m|\Omega^{(+)} \tag{10–134}$$

and

$$\langle\Phi_m|\Psi_n\rangle_+ = \delta_{mn} - \frac{R_{mn}}{E_n - E_m + i\varepsilon} \tag{10–135}$$

where

$$\langle\Phi_m|H_I(0)|\Psi_n\rangle_+ = R_{mn} \tag{10–136}$$

that

$$\begin{aligned} {}_+\langle\Psi_m|V_+(t)|\Psi_n\rangle_+ &= e^{+i(E_m - E_n)t}\,{}_+\langle\Psi_m|\Omega^{(+)}|\Psi_n\rangle_+ \\ &= e^{+i(E_m - E_n)t}\left\{\delta_{mn} - \lim_{\varepsilon\to 0+}\frac{R_{mn}}{E_n - E_m + i\varepsilon}\right\} \end{aligned} \tag{10–137}$$

so that in the limit as $t \to \pm\infty$

$$\lim_{t\to+\infty}\ {}_+\langle\Psi_m|V_+(t)|\Psi_n\rangle_+ = \delta_{mn} - 2\pi i\delta(E_n - E_m)R_{mn} \tag{10–138}$$

and

$$\lim_{t\to-\infty}\ {}_+\langle\Psi_m|V_+(t)|\Psi_n\rangle_+ = \delta_{mn} \tag{10–139}$$

Proof: Write

$$\lim_{\varepsilon\to 0+}\frac{1}{E + i\varepsilon} = \lim_{\varepsilon\to 0+} i\int_0^\infty e^{i(E+i\varepsilon)\lambda}d\lambda \tag{10–140}$$

$$= \delta(E) - i\pi\mathscr{P}\frac{1}{E} \tag{10–141}$$

The presence of the δ-function indicates that the factor $(E + i\varepsilon)^{-1}$ in the limit as $\varepsilon \to 0$ only has a meaning in the sense of distribution theory, *i.e.*, when multiplied by a sufficiently smooth function $f(E)$ whose support is closed and bounded, and then integrated over the range of the possible values of E. Consider, therefore, the limit $t \to \pm\infty$ of the expression

$$\int_{-\infty}^{+\infty}\frac{e^{-iEt}f(E)}{E + i\varepsilon}\,dE = I(t) \tag{10–142}$$

where $f(E)$ is a function with the above properties, whose Fourier transform $\tilde{f}$ will be assumed to satisfy the condition that

$$\int_{-\infty}^{+\infty}|\tilde{f}(\lambda)|d\lambda < \infty$$

Substituting into (10–142) the expression (10–140) we find

$$\begin{aligned}\lim_{\varepsilon\to 0}\int_{-\infty}^{+\infty}\frac{e^{-iEt}f(E)}{E+i\varepsilon}\,dE &= i\int_0^{\infty}d\lambda\int_{-\infty}^{+\infty}e^{i(\lambda-t)E}f(E)dE\\ &= 2\pi i\int_0^{\infty}d\lambda\tilde{f}(\lambda-t) = 2\pi i\int_{-t}^{\infty}\tilde{f}(\lambda)d\lambda\end{aligned} \tag{10–143}$$

Hence in the limit as $t\to-\infty$, $I(t)$ goes to zero whereas in the limit as $t\to+\infty$

$$\begin{aligned}\lim_{t\to+\infty}I(t) &= 2\pi i\,f(0)\\ &= 2\pi i\int_{-\infty}^{+\infty}\delta(E)f(E)dE \quad \text{Q.E.D.}\end{aligned} \tag{10–144}$$

Expression (10–138) will be recognized as the expression for the mn matrix element of the S-matrix. Hence

$$_{+}\langle\Psi_m|V_+(\infty)|\Psi_n\rangle_+ = S_{mn} \tag{10–145}$$

Summarizing, we have noted that the Heisenberg operators $Q_+(t)$ obey field free equations; *i.e.*, that their time derivatives are given by the commutator of the operator with $H_{o+}(t) = H_{o+}(0)$ and that this operator $H_{o+}(t)$ is equal to $H(t) = H(0)$. The eigenstates of H_{o+} are, therefore, just the eigenstates of H. We can, therefore, identify the states $|\Psi_n\rangle_+$ with the previously defined $|\Psi_n\rangle_{\text{in}}$ and the operator $\psi_+(\mathbf{x},t)$ as defined by Eq. (10–130), with $\psi_{\text{in}}(x)$. The S-matrix is given by

$$S = \lim_{t\to\infty}V_+(t) \tag{10–146}$$

The operator $V_+(t)$ transforms Heisenberg operators into "in" operators

$$Q_{\text{in}}(t) = V_+(t)Q(t)V_+(t)^{-1} \tag{10–147}$$

It satisfies the differential equation

$$i\partial_t V_+(t) = H_{I\,\text{in}}(t)V_+(t) \tag{10–148}$$

and the initial conditions

$$\lim_{t\to-\infty}V_+(t) = 1 \tag{10–149}$$

(See Eqs. (10–128) and (10–139).)

It is possible to replace the above differential equation and initial condition by a single integral equation that $V_+(t)$ must satisfy, namely

$$V_+(t) = 1 - i\int_{-\infty}^{t} dt' H_{I\,\mathrm{in}}(t')V_+(t') \tag{10–150}$$

By iterating this equation the Liouville-Neumann expansion for $V_+(t)$ is obtained. This expansion is given by[8]

$$\begin{aligned} V_+(t) = 1 &+ (-i)\int_{-\infty}^{t} dt_1 H_{I\,\mathrm{in}}(t_1) \\ &+ (-i)^2\int_{-\infty}^{t} dt_1 \int_{-\infty}^{t_1} dt_2 H_{I\,\mathrm{in}}(t_1)H_{I\,\mathrm{in}}(t_2) + \cdots \end{aligned} \tag{10–151}$$

By introducing the time-ordering chronological operator[9] P which rewrites a product of time labeled operators as the product of these same operators ordered according to their time label, the one with the earliest time label standing farthest to the right, we can rewrite the expansion (10–151) in the form

$$\begin{aligned} V_+(t) &= 1 - i\int_{-\infty}^{t} dt_1 H_{I\,\mathrm{in}}(t_1) \\ &\quad + \frac{(-i)^2}{2!}\int_{-\infty}^{t} dt_1 \int_{-\infty}^{t} dt_2 P(H_{I\,\mathrm{in}}(t_1)H_{I\,\mathrm{in}}(t_2)) + \cdots \\ &= \sum_{n=0}^{\infty} \frac{(-i)^n}{n!}\int_{-\infty}^{t} dt_1 \cdots \int_{-\infty}^{t} dt_n P(H_{I\,\mathrm{in}}(t_1)\cdots H_{I\,\mathrm{in}}(t_n)) \end{aligned} \tag{10–152}$$

where

$$P(H_{I\,\mathrm{in}}(t_1)\cdots H_{I\,\mathrm{in}}(t_n)) = H_{I\,\mathrm{in}}(t_i)\cdots H_{I\,\mathrm{in}}(t_j)\cdots H_{I\,\mathrm{in}}(t_k) \quad \text{if } t_i > \cdots t_j \cdots > t_k \tag{10–153}$$

That the series (10–152) is indeed a solution of (10–148) is readily verified by differentiating it with respect to t,

$$\begin{aligned} i\partial_t V_+(t) = H_{I\,\mathrm{in}}(t) \sum_{n=1}^{\infty} \frac{1}{(n-1)!}(-i)^{n-1} \int_{-\infty}^{t} dt_1 \cdots \int_{-\infty}^{t} dt_{n-1} \\ \times P(H_{I\,\mathrm{in}}(t_1)\cdots H_{I\,\mathrm{in}}(t_{n-1})) \end{aligned} \tag{10–154}$$

[8] See also H. Margenau and G. M. Murphy, *The Mathematics of Physics and Chemistry*, 2nd Ed., D. Van Nostrand Co., Inc., Princeton, N.J., 1956.

[9] See Chapter 1.

In obtaining the right-hand side of (10–154) we have made use of the symmetry of the integrand and the fact that

$$P(H_{I\,\mathrm{in}}(t_1)\cdots H_{I\,\mathrm{in}}(t_{n-1})H_{I\,\mathrm{in}}(t)) = H_{I\,\mathrm{in}}(t)P(H_{I\,\mathrm{in}}(t_1)\cdots H_{I\,\mathrm{in}}(t)) \tag{10–155}$$

since the time label of $H_{I\,\mathrm{in}}(t)$ is always later than $t_1,t_2,\cdots,t_{n-1}$. By rewriting the right side of Eq. (10–154) as:

$$H_{I\,\mathrm{in}}(t)\sum_{n=0}^{\infty}\frac{(-i)^n}{n!}\int_{-\infty}^{t}dt_1\cdots\int_{-\infty}^{t}dt_n P(H_{I\,\mathrm{in}}(t_1)\cdots H_{I\,\mathrm{in}}(t_n)) = H_{I\,\mathrm{in}}(t)V_+(t) \tag{10–156}$$

we have verified that $V_+(t)$ as defined by Eq. (10–152) is indeed a solution of Eq. (10–148) provided the series converges. Very little is known concerning the convergence of the series except in certain special cases.

Although the previous development was based on the assumption that $H(t) = H(0)$, it can readily be verified that the formulae (10–148)–(10–152) are valid more generally. In particular for the negaton-positon field interacting with an external electromagnetic field, we have

$$H_{I\,\mathrm{in}}(t) = \frac{1}{c}\int d^3\mathbf{x}\, j^{\mu}_{\mathrm{in}}(x)A^{\mathrm{e}}_{\mu}(x) \quad (x^0 = t) \tag{10–157}$$

$$j^{\mu}_{\mathrm{in}}(x) = -\frac{e}{2}[\tilde{\psi}_{\mathrm{in}}(x)\gamma^{\mu},\psi_{\mathrm{in}}(x)] \tag{10–158}$$

with $\psi_{\mathrm{in}}(x)$ satisfying the free-field equation of motion and free-field commutation rules; $V_+(t)$ is given by the expansion (10–152) with $H_{I\,\mathrm{in}}(t)$ given by Eqs. (10–157) and (10–158). We are, therefore, now in a position to compute such quantities as

$${}_{\mathrm{out}}\langle 0|0\rangle_{\mathrm{in}} = {}_{\mathrm{in}}\langle 0|S|0\rangle_{\mathrm{in}}$$

the probability amplitude that the vacuum remain a vacuum under the influence of $A^{\mathrm{e}}_{\mu}(x)$, or ${}_{\mathrm{in}}\langle \mathbf{p}'s'|S|\mathbf{p}s\rangle_{\mathrm{in}}$ the amplitude for the scattering of an electron from a state of momentum $\mathbf{p}$, polarization s to a final state $\mathbf{p}'s'$.

Let us first consider the amplitude ${}_{\mathrm{out}}\langle 0|0\rangle_{\mathrm{in}}$. This amplitude need not be equal to one since for sufficiently rapidly varying external fields (*i.e.*, external fields having Fourier components for $k^2 > 4m^2$) there exists the possibility of pair creation. To second order in A_μ^{e} this amplitude is given by

$$
\begin{aligned}
{}_{\text{out}}\langle 0|0\rangle_{\text{in}} &= {}_{\text{in}}\langle 0|S|0\rangle_{\text{in}} \\
&= 1 + \frac{i^2}{2!}\int d^4x_1 \int d^4x_2 \; {}_{\text{in}}\langle 0|P(j_{\text{in}}^{\mu_1}(x_1)j_{\text{in}}^{\mu_2}(x_2))|0\rangle_{\text{in}} \\
&\qquad \times A_{\mu_1}^{\text{e}}(x_1)A_{\mu_2}^{\text{e}}(x_2) + \cdots
\end{aligned}
\tag{10–159}
$$

(since ${}_{\text{in}}\langle 0|j_{\text{in}}^\mu(x)|0\rangle_{\text{in}} = 0$ the first order term vanishes). The vacuum expectation value of the P bracket can be evaluated as follows:

$$
\begin{aligned}
{}_{\text{in}}\langle 0|P(j_{\text{in}}^{\mu_1}(x_1)j_{\text{in}}^{\mu_2}(x_2)|0\rangle_{\text{in}} &= \theta(x_1 - x_2)\; {}_{\text{in}}\langle 0|j_{\text{in}}^{\mu_1}(x_1)j_{\text{in}}^{\mu_2}(x_2)|0\rangle_{\text{in}} \\
&\quad + \theta(x_2 - x_1)\; {}_{\text{in}}\langle 0|j_{\text{in}}^{\mu_2}(x_2)j_{\text{in}}^{\mu_1}(x_1)|0\rangle_{\text{in}}
\end{aligned}
\tag{10–160}
$$

Since we shall integrate over x_1 and x_2 and sum over μ_1 and μ_2, we may interchange x_1 and μ_1 and μ_2 in the second term of the right side of Eq. (10–160) and thus find it identical to the first. Upon decomposing the operators $j_{\text{in}}^\mu(x)$ in terms of the operator $\psi_{\text{in}}^{(\pm)}(x)$ and $\tilde{\psi}_{\text{in}}^{(\pm)}(x)$ and recalling that

$$\psi_{\text{in}}^{(+)}(x)|0\rangle_{\text{in}} = \tilde{\psi}_{\text{in}}^{(+)}(x)|0\rangle_{\text{in}} = 0 \tag{10–161}$$

$${}_{\text{in}}\langle 0|\tilde{\psi}_{\text{in}}^{(-)}(x) = {}_{\text{in}}\langle 0|\psi_{\text{in}}^{(-)}(x) = 0 \tag{10–162}$$

we find that the only term that survives in ${}_{\text{in}}\langle 0|j_{\text{in}}^{\mu_1}(x_1)j_{\text{in}}^{\mu_2}(x_2)|0\rangle_{\text{in}}$ is

$$
\begin{aligned}
&{}_{\text{in}}\langle 0|j_{\text{in}}^{\mu_1}(x_1)j_{\text{in}}^{\mu_2}(x_2)|0\rangle_{\text{in}} \\
&\quad = e^2 \sum_{\alpha_1\alpha_2\beta_1\beta_2=1}^{4} {}_{\text{in}}\langle 0|\tilde{\psi}_{\text{in}\alpha_1}^{(+)}(x_1)\psi_{\text{in}\beta_1}^{(+)}(x_1)\tilde{\psi}_{\text{in}\alpha_2}^{(-)}(x_2)\psi_{\text{in}\beta_2}^{(-)}(x_2)|0\rangle_{\text{in}} \\
&\qquad\qquad \times (\gamma^{\mu_1})_{\alpha_1\beta_1}(\gamma^{\mu_2})_{\alpha_2\beta_2} \\
&\quad = +e^2 \sum_{\alpha_1\alpha_2\beta_1\beta_2} (-iS_{\beta_1\alpha_1}^{(+)}(x_1 - x_2))(-iS_{\beta_2\alpha_1}^{(-)}(x_2 - x_1)) \\
&\qquad\qquad \times (\gamma^{\mu_1})_{\alpha_1\beta_1}(\gamma^{\mu_2})_{\alpha_2\beta_2} \\
&\quad = -e^2\,\text{Tr}\,\{S^{(+)}(x_1 - x_2)\gamma^{\mu_2}S^{(-)}(x_2 - x_1)\gamma^{\mu_1}\}
\end{aligned}
\tag{10–163}
$$

Hence to this order

$$
{}_{\text{in}}\langle 0|S|0\rangle_{\text{in}} = 1 + e^2 \int d^4x_1 \int d^4x_2 \, \text{Tr}\,\{S^{(+)}(x_1 - x_2)\gamma^{\mu_2}S^{(-)}(x_2 - x_1)\gamma^{\mu_1}\} \\ \times \theta(x_1 - x_2)A^{\text{e}}_{\mu_1}(x_1)A^{\text{e}}_{\mu_2}(x_2) + \cdots \quad (10\text{–}164)
$$

If we call $-\frac{1}{2}S_F(x)$ the function which is equal to

$$
\left.\begin{matrix} -iS^{(+)}(x) & \text{for } x_0 > 0 \\ +iS^{(-)}(x) & \text{for } x_0 < 0 \end{matrix}\right\} = -\tfrac{1}{2}S_F(x) \quad (10\text{–}165)
$$

i.e.,

$$
-\tfrac{1}{2}S_F(x) = -i(\theta(x)S^{(+)}(x) - \theta(-x)S^{(-)}(x)) \quad (10\text{–}166)
$$

we can rewrite the amplitude as

$$
{}_{\text{in}}\langle 0|S|0\rangle_{\text{in}} = 1 + \frac{e^2}{4} \int d^4x_1 \int d^4x_2 \\ \times \text{Tr}\,\{S_F(x_1 - x_2)\gamma^{\mu_2}S_F(x_2 - x_1)\gamma^{\mu_1}\}A^{\text{e}}_{\mu_1}(x_1)A^{\text{e}}_{\mu_2}(x_2) \quad (10\text{–}167)
$$

This expression can be evaluated readily. It is, in fact, closely related to the polarization tensor previously evaluated. We shall, however, not do so at this juncture. Rather we first inquire whether it is possible to evaluate higher order contributions to ${}_{\text{in}}\langle 0|S|0\rangle_{\text{in}}$ using the explicit form (10–152) for S. Clearly the use of techniques similar to the one that we employed to arrive at Eq. (10–167) is possible, but not very efficient. Fortunately there exists a very powerful theorem, due to Wick, which enables one to express a chronological product of time-dependent operators as a sum of products of normal ordered operators. A normal ordered product of operators is one in which all creation operators stand to the left of all destruction operators. Given any two "in" states specified by a definite number of particles with specified spins and momenta, there exists one and only one normal product of creation and annihilation operators with a nonzero matrix element between these states. A decomposition of the S-matrix into normal products of in-operators is thus equivalent to the listing of all the matrix elements of S in a representation in which the occupation numbers are diagonal. There exists a simple graphical way, called a Feynman diagram, of representing a normal product. We now proceed to prove Wick's theorem.

Definition of Normal Product.—Given a product of free field creation and annihilation operators $U,X,\cdots,YV$, we define the operator N as follows: acting on this product it rearranges it in normal order, with all creation operators standing to the left of all annihilation operators, this rearrangement being made as if all commutation rules (for boson operators) and all anticommutation rules (for fermion operators) which the operators satisfy had a vanishing right-hand side. Thus

$$N(UX\cdot R\cdots YZV) = \delta_P \underbrace{UV\cdots R}_{\substack{\text{creation}\\ \text{operation}}}\underbrace{X\cdots YZ}_{\substack{\text{annihilation}\\ \text{operation}}} \tag{10–168}$$

where δ_P is the sign which arises due to the change in the order of anticommuting fields.

By definition the distributive law is valid for the normal product operation:

$$N((A + B)(C + D)) = N(AC) + N(AD) + N(BC) + N(BD) \tag{10–169}$$

Example. If we denote by $\phi_{\text{in}}(x)$, a spin zero neutral scalar field, satisfying $(\Box + \mu^2)\phi_{\text{in}}(x) = 0$ and such that $\phi^{(+)}(x)|0\rangle_{\text{in}} = 0$ and $[\phi_{\text{in}}(x),\phi_{\text{in}}(x')] = i\Delta(x - x';\mu^2)$, then

$$N(\phi_{\text{in}}^{(+)}(x)\phi_{\text{in}}^{(+)}(x')) = \phi_{\text{in}}^{(+)}(x)\phi_{\text{in}}^{(+)}(x') \tag{10–170}$$

$$N(\phi_{\text{in}}^{(+)}(x)\phi_{\text{in}}^{(-)}(x')) = \phi_{\text{in}}^{(-)}(x')\phi_{\text{in}}^{(+)}(x) \tag{10–171}$$

$$\begin{aligned} N(\phi_{\text{in}}(x)\phi_{\text{in}}(x')) &= \phi_{\text{in}}^{(+)}(x)\phi_{\text{in}}^{(+)}(x') + \phi_{\text{in}}^{(-)}(x')\phi_{\text{in}}^{(+)}(x) \\ &\quad + \phi_{\text{in}}^{(-)}(x)\phi_{\text{in}}^{(-)}(x') + \phi_{\text{in}}^{(-)}(x)\phi_{\text{in}}^{(-)}(x') \end{aligned} \tag{10–172}$$

If $\psi_{\text{in}}(x)$, $\tilde{\psi}_{\text{in}}(x)$ are the fermion field operators discussed at length above, then

$$N(\psi_{\text{in}}^{(+)}(x)\psi_{\text{in}}^{(+)}(x')) = \psi_{\text{in}}^{(+)}(x)\psi_{\text{in}}^{(+)}(x') \tag{10–173}$$

$$N(\psi_{\text{in}}^{(+)}(x)\psi_{\text{in}}^{(-)}(x')) = -\psi_{\text{in}}^{(-)}(x')\psi_{\text{in}}^{(+)}(x') \tag{10–174}$$

$$= -N(\psi_{\text{in}}^{(-)}(x')\psi_{\text{in}}^{(+)}(x)) \tag{10–175}$$

$$N(\psi_{\text{in}}^{(+)}(x)\tilde{\psi}_{\text{in}}^{(-)}(x')) = -\tilde{\psi}_{\text{in}}^{(-)}(x')\psi_{\text{in}}^{(+)}(x') \tag{10–176}$$

One of the most important properties of a normal-ordered product of operators is that its vacuum expectation value vanishes, because in such a normal-ordered product there is always either a destruction operator on the extreme right (which would give zero when operating on the vacuum state standing to the right of it) or a creation operator at the extreme left (which would give zero when operating on the vacuum state standing to the left it). Hence

$$\langle 0|N(XY\cdots Z)|0\rangle = 0 \tag{10–177}$$

where the state $|0\rangle$ is the vacuum state defined by $X|0\rangle = 0$ if X is any destruction operator, *i.e.*, $|0\rangle$ stands for $|0\rangle_{\text{in}}$ if the operators $X, Y, \cdots$ are "in" field operators. Since the commutator of two boson "in" operators or of a boson and fermion "in" operator and the anticommutator for two fermion "in" factors is a c-number, it is an immediate corollary to the above that for two factors XY

$$N(XY) = XY - \langle 0|XY|0\rangle \tag{10–178}$$

Definition of Wick Chronological Operator.—We define the Wick chronological operator T as follows: operating on a product of time labeled operators $UV \cdots Z$, it rewrites the product in chronological order $XY \cdots$, the operator having the latest time standing furthest to the left, the whole product being the sign $+$ or $-$ (δ_p) according to whether the permutation of fermion factors in going from the left side to the right side of Eq. (10–179) is even or odd

$$T(UV \cdots Z) = \delta_p XY \cdots W$$
$$t_X > t_Y \cdots > t_W \tag{10–179}$$

The Wick chronological operator T is, therefore, defined in the same way as the P operator previously introduced, except that the T operator includes in its definition the sign of the permutation of the fermion factors.

Example:

$$T(\phi_{\text{in}}(x)\phi_{\text{in}}(x')) = \phi_{\text{in}}(x)\phi_{\text{in}}(x') \quad \text{if } x_0 > x_0' \tag{10–180}$$
$$= \phi_{\text{in}}(x')\phi_{\text{in}}(x) \quad \text{if } x_0' > x_0 \tag{10–181}$$

i.e.,

$$T(\phi_{\text{in}}(x)\phi_{\text{in}}(x')) = \theta(x - x')\phi(x)\phi(x') + \theta(x' - x)\phi(x')\phi(x) \tag{10–182}$$

and

$$T(\psi_{\text{in}}(x)\psi_{\text{in}}(x')) = \psi_{\text{in}}(x)\psi_{\text{in}}(x') \qquad \text{if } x_0 > x_0' \tag{10–183}$$
$$= -\psi_{\text{in}}(x')\psi_{\text{in}}(x) \quad \text{if } x_0' > x_0 \tag{10–184}$$
$$= \theta(x - x')\psi_{\text{in}}(x)\psi_{\text{in}}(x') - \theta(x' - x)\psi_{\text{in}}(x')\psi_{\text{in}}(x) \tag{10–185}$$

similarly

$$T(\psi_{\text{in}\,\alpha}(x)\tilde{\psi}_{\text{in}\,\beta}(x')) = \theta(x - x')\psi_{\text{in}\,\alpha}(x)\tilde{\psi}_{\text{in}\,\beta}(x') - \theta(x' - x)\tilde{\psi}_{\text{in}\,\beta}(x')\psi_{\text{in}\,\alpha}(x) \tag{10–186}$$

Definition of Contraction Symbol.—We next define the contraction of two time labeled operators U and V, denoted by $U^{\cdot}V^{\cdot}$, as the difference between the chronological and the normal product of these two operators

$$U^{\cdot}V^{\cdot} = T(UV) - N(UV) \qquad (10\text{–}187)$$

Using Eq. (10–178) we immediately deduce the fact that

$$U^{\cdot}V^{\cdot} = \langle 0|T(UV)|0\rangle = c\text{-number} \qquad (10\text{–}188)$$

Proof.—If U and V are such that the time labels satisfy $t_U > t_V$ so that

$$T(UV) = UV \qquad (10\text{–}189)$$

then Eq. (10–178) allows us to rewrite the right-hand side of Eq. (10–187) as follows:

$$T(UV) = N(UV) + \langle 0|UV|0\rangle \qquad (10\text{–}190)$$

whence

$$\begin{aligned} U^{\cdot}V^{\cdot} &= \langle 0|UV|0\rangle \\ &= \langle 0|T(UV)|0\rangle \end{aligned} \qquad (10\text{–}191)$$

as is asserted by Eq. (10–188). If on the other hand $t_V > t_U$, then

$$T(UV) = \pm VU \qquad (10\text{–}192)$$

(the $-$ sign arising in the case that both U and V are fermion operators). In this case

$$\begin{aligned} U^{\cdot}V^{\cdot} &= \pm VU - N(UV) \\ &= \pm(VU - N(VU)) \end{aligned} \qquad (10\text{–}193)$$

and again using Eq. (10–178) we obtain

$$\begin{aligned} U^{\cdot}V^{\cdot} &= \pm\langle 0|VU|0\rangle \\ &= \pm\langle 0|T(VU)|0\rangle = \langle 0|T(UV)|0\rangle \end{aligned} \qquad (10\text{–}194)$$

which was to be proved. Note that Eq. (10–188) states that the contraction of two creation operators and that of two annihilation operators gives zero. Similarly, the contraction of a creation operator and an annihilation operator gives zero if the time label of the destruction operator is earlier than that of the destruction operator. By virtue of the distributive property of the normal product operator N, Eq. (10–188) is also valid for sums of field operators.

We now introduce a notation involving a normal product with one or more contracted pairs of factors. If $U, V, \cdots$ denote a set of free-field creation and annihilation operators, we define the mixed product by

$$N(U^{\cdot}VW^{\cdot\cdot}X^{\cdot}\cdots Y^{\cdot\cdot}Z) = \delta_p(U^{\cdot}X^{\cdot})(W^{\cdot\cdot}Y^{\cdot\cdot})N(V\cdots Z) \qquad (10\text{–}195)$$

where δ_p is again the parity of the permutation of the fermion factors in going from the left to the right side of Eq. (10–195). We can now prove the following:

Lemma.—If Z is an operator whose time label t_Z is earlier than any of the times $t_U, t_V, \cdots, t_Y$, then

$$\begin{aligned} N(UV\cdots XY)Z = {} & N(UV\cdots XYZ) + N(UV\cdots XY^{\cdot}Z^{\cdot}) \\ & + N(UV\cdots X^{\cdot}YZ^{\cdot}) + \cdots N(U^{\cdot}V\cdots XYZ^{\cdot}) \end{aligned} \tag{10–196}$$

The proof is by induction. It is clearly true for two factors since then it reduces to the definition of the contraction symbol. Furthermore, it is sufficient to prove the theorem under the assumption that Z is a creation operator and that all the operators $UV\cdots XY$ are destruction operators. If $UV\cdots XY$ are all destruction operators and Z is a creation operator, we may then add any number of creation operators to the left of all factors on both sides of Eq. (10–196) within the N product, without impairing the validity of our theorem, since the contraction between two creation operators gives zero. If on the other hand Z is a destruction operator and $UV\cdots$ are creation operators, then Eq. (10–196) reduces to a trivial identity

$$N(UV\cdots XY)Z = N(UV\cdots XYZ)$$

since the contraction of a destruction and a creation operator gives zero if the time label of the destruction operator is earlier than that of the creation operator. Assume then that Eq. (10–196) is true for n factors, and multiplying (10–196) by another destruction operator D on the left, D having a time label that is later than that of Z. On the right-hand side the D factor can then be brought within all the N product wherein Z is contracted, *i.e.*, wherein only $Z^{\cdot}$ appears. Using the properties of the N-operator and the fact that t_D is later than t_Z, we can cast the last term into the form

$$DN(UV\cdots XYZ) = N(D^{\cdot}UV\cdots XYZ^{\cdot}) + N(DUV\cdots XYZ) \tag{10–197}$$

Since $DN(UV\cdots XY)Z = N(DUV\cdots XY)Z$, the theorem is proved for $n+1$ factors. This lemma can be generalized by multiplying both sides of Eq. (10–196) by an arbitrary number of contracted factors, and using Eq. (10–195) to bring these factors within the N products. Wick's theorem now states that a T product can be decomposed into a unique sum of normal products as follows:

$$\begin{aligned} T(UV\cdots XYZ) = {} & N(UV\cdots XYZ) + N(U^{\cdot}V^{\cdot}\cdots XYZ) \\ & + \cdots + N(U^{\cdot}V^{\cdot\cdot}\cdots X^{\cdot\cdot}YZ^{\cdot}) \\ & + \cdots + N(U^{\cdot}V^{\cdot\cdot}W^{\cdot\cdot\cdot}\cdots X^{\cdot}Y^{\cdot\cdot}Z^{\cdot\cdot\cdot}) \end{aligned} \tag{10–198}$$

where the sum on the right-hand side includes all possible sets of contraction. The proof is again by induction. It is certainly true for one and two factors. Assume it to be true for n factors. Then multiply Eq. (10–198) by an operator Ω, whose time label is earlier than that of any other fact, so that

$$T(UV\cdots XYZ)\Omega = T(UV\cdots XYZ\Omega) \qquad (10\text{–}199)$$

On the right-hand side of Eq. (10–198) the terms of the form

$$N(UV\cdots XYZ)\Omega$$

can be brought into normal product form using the previous lemma, Eq. (10–196). The theorem is thus proved for $n + 1$ factor provided that $t_\Omega < t_U, t_V, \cdots, t_Z$. However, once Ω is inside the T product on the left-hand side, and within the N products on the right-hand side we may rearrange the order of the operators, since by the definition of the T and N product Eq. (10–198) is invariant under the same regrouping of factors on both sides of the equation. QED.

We are not yet quite ready to apply these theorems to the reduction of the S-matrix as given in the form (10–152), since in the latter it is the P operator that appears. Furthermore, in each factor $H_{I\,\text{in}}(t)$ there occurs a product of operators having the same time label, *i.e.*, the $j^\mu_{\text{in}}(x)$ operator, which is of the form $[\tilde{\psi}_{\text{in}}(x)\gamma^\mu, \psi_{\text{in}}(x)]$, for which the P or T operators do not prescribe an order. But these difficulties are easily overcome. We first of all note that the fermion factors in $H_{I\,\text{in}}(t)$ will always appear in pairs due to covariance requirements. More precisely in any local theory they will generally be of the form $[\tilde{\psi}_{\text{in}}(x)\Gamma_i, \psi_{\text{in}}(x)]$ where Γ_i is any of the sixteen linearly independent four-by-four matrices. A direct consequence of this is that the P operator can be replaced by the T operator, since in rearranging the product

$$P(H_{I\,\text{in}}(t_1)\cdots H_{I\,\text{in}}(t_n))$$

in chronological order, the number of permuted fermion factors will always be even. Thus, in the expansion (10–152), we can replace the P operator by a T operator. The removal of the second difficulty is achieved by noting that we may write

$$\tfrac{1}{2}[\tilde{\psi}_{\text{in}}(x)\gamma^\mu, \psi_{\text{in}}(x)] = N(\tilde{\psi}_{\text{in}}(x)\gamma^\mu\psi_{\text{in}}(x)) \qquad (10\text{–}200)$$

so that the normal ordering operator N prescribes the order for those factors having the same time label. Finally Wick's theorem can easily be generalized to the decomposition of a T product containing such normal products. The decomposition rule for such a "mixed" T product then reads:

A mixed T product can be decomposed into a unique sum of normal products according to the same rule as an ordinary T product, but with the omission of contractions between factors already in normal product form.

The above rules are readily applied to the case of the S-matrix for the interaction under discussion, namely the electron-positron field interacting with an external field for which

$$H_I(t) = -\frac{e}{2}\int d^3x[\tilde{\psi}_{\text{in}}(x)\gamma_\mu,\psi_{\text{in}}(x)]A^{e\mu}(x) \qquad (10\text{–}201)$$

The expansion of any T product occurring in the S-matrix expansion in terms of normal products gives rise then to many terms whose enumeration is aided by the use of Feynman diagrams, each of which consists of a number of vertices and lines joining them. The vertices represent the different space-time points that are the arguments of the operators in the S-matrix. The rules for drawing a diagram corresponding to a given term are then:

(1) for each contracted pair of factors $\psi(x)^{\cdot}\tilde{\psi}(y)^{\cdot}$ draw a directed solid line from x to y, the direction being indicated by an arrow on the line;

(2) for each $\tilde{\psi}(x)$ factor, which is not contracted, draw a directed line *from* x to "the edge of the diagram," *i.e.*, the other end of the line is free and not a vertex of the diagram;

(3) for each factor $\psi(x)$, which is not contracted, draw a directed solid line from the "edge of the diagram" *to* x;

(4) for each $A^{e}_{\mu}(x)$ draw a dotted line from x, the other end having an X appended to it (to denote the external field).

Examples of such diagrams will be given in the next section.

Since there are three factors $\tilde{\psi}(x)$, $\psi(x)$, and $A^{e}(x)$ associated with each point in the integrand of S, there are always two solid lines and one dotted line meeting at each point. Since each operator is the sum of an annihilation and a creation operator, the above graphs have a nonunique meaning. Thus, a solid line going into the diagram (representing an uncontracted $\psi(x)$) might correspond to either a negaton in an initial state or a positon in a final state. Similarly a solid line pointed out of the diagram represents either a negaton in the final state or a positon in the initial state.

Finally the contraction between two fermion operators can explicitly be computed and one finds that

$$\psi^{\cdot}_{\text{in}\,\alpha}(x)\tilde{\psi}^{\cdot}_{\text{in}\,\beta}(y) = {}_{\text{in}}\langle 0|T(\psi_{\text{in}\,\alpha}(x)\tilde{\psi}_{\text{in}\,\beta}(y))|0\rangle_{\text{in}} \tag{10–202}$$

$$= -i\theta(x_o - y_o)S^{(+)}_{\alpha\beta}(x-y) + i\theta(y_o - x_o)S^{(-)}_{\alpha\beta}(x-y) \tag{10–203}$$

$$= -\tfrac{1}{2}S_{F\alpha\beta}(x-y) \tag{10–204}$$

$$= -\tilde{\psi}^{\cdot}_{\text{in}\,\beta}(y)\psi^{\cdot}_{\text{in}\,\alpha}(x) \tag{10–205}$$

$$\psi^{\cdot}_{\text{in}\,\alpha}(x)\psi^{\cdot}_{\text{in}\,\beta}(y) = \tilde{\psi}^{\cdot}_{\text{in}\,\alpha}(x)\tilde{\psi}^{\cdot}_{\text{in}\,\beta}(x) = 0 \tag{10–206}$$

$$-\tfrac{1}{2}S_F(x) = \frac{i}{(2\pi)^4}\lim_{\varepsilon\to 0}\int \frac{1}{\gamma\cdot p - m + i\varepsilon}\, e^{-ip\cdot x}d^4p \tag{10–207}$$

$$= \frac{i}{(2\pi)^4}\lim_{\varepsilon\to 0}\int \frac{\gamma\cdot p + m}{p^2 - m^2 + i\varepsilon}\, e^{-ip\cdot x}d^4p \tag{10–208}$$

REFERENCES

Dyson, F. J., *Phys. Rev.*, **83**, 1207 (1951).
Gill-Mann, M., and Goldberger, M. L., *Phys. Rev.*, **91**, 398 (1953).
Wick, G. C., *Phys. Rev.*, **80**, 268 (1950).

10.3. Scattering of a Negaton by an External field.—In the present section we apply the formalism just developed to the analysis of the scattering of a negaton by an external field $A^{e}_{\mu}(x)$, neglecting radiative corrections.

If we expand the "in" and "out" operators in terms of operators creating particles of definite momentum, *i.e.*,

$$\psi^{(+)}_{\substack{\text{in}\\ \text{out}}}(x) = \sqrt{\frac{m}{(2\pi)^3}}\int\frac{d^3p}{E_{\mathbf{p}}}\sum_{s=1,2} b_{\substack{\text{in}\\ \text{out}}}(\mathbf{p},s)u_s(\mathbf{p})e^{-ip\cdot x} \tag{10–209}$$

$$\{b_{\substack{\text{in}\\ \text{out}}}(\mathbf{p},s), b^{*}_{\substack{\text{in}\\ \text{out}}}(\mathbf{p}',s')\} = \delta_{ss'}\delta(\mathbf{p} - \mathbf{p})p_o \tag{10–210}$$

$$p_o = E_{\mathbf{p}} \tag{10–211}$$

then the S-matrix element describing the scattering of a negaton from an initial state $|\mathbf{p},s\rangle_{\text{in}}$ to the final state $|\mathbf{p}',s'\rangle_{\text{out}}$ is given by

$${}_{\text{out}}\langle\mathbf{p}',s'|\mathbf{p},s\rangle_{\text{in}} = {}_{\text{out}}\langle 0|b_{\text{out}}(\mathbf{p}',s')b^{*}_{\text{in}}(\mathbf{p},s)|0\rangle_{\text{in}} \tag{10–212}$$

Upon inverting Eq. (10–209) by making use of the orthogonality properties of plane wave solutions of the Dirac equation, we obtain the result that

$$b_{\text{in}}(\mathbf{p},s) = \sqrt{\frac{m}{(2\pi)^3}}\int d^3x\,\tilde{u}_s(\mathbf{p})e^{ip\cdot x}\gamma^0\psi_{\text{in}}(x) \tag{10–213}$$

Upon noting that $u_s(\mathbf{p})e^{-ip\cdot x}$ and $\psi_{\text{in}}(x)$ both obey the (free) Dirac equation, Eq. (10–213) can also be written in the form

$$b_{\text{in}}(\mathbf{p},s) = \sqrt{\frac{m}{(2\pi)^3}} \int_\sigma d\sigma^\mu(x)\tilde{u}_s(\mathbf{p})e^{ip\cdot x}\gamma_\mu\psi_{\text{in}}(x) \qquad (10\text{–}214)$$

the integration being carried out over an arbitrary space-like surface σ, since the right-hand side of Eq. (10–214) is independent of σ. The scattering amplitude can, therefore, be written as

$$\begin{aligned} {}_{\text{out}}\langle \mathbf{p}',s'|\mathbf{p},s\rangle_{\text{in}} &= \frac{m}{(2\pi)^3}\int d^3x \int d^3x' \\ &\quad \times \tilde{u}_{s'}(\mathbf{p}')e^{ip'\cdot x'}\gamma^0 {}_{\text{out}}\langle 0|\psi_{\text{out}}(x')\tilde{\psi}_{\text{in}}(x)|0\rangle_{\text{in}}\,\gamma^0 u_s(\mathbf{p})e^{-ip\cdot x} \end{aligned} \qquad (10\text{–}215)$$

where the times x_0' and x_0 are arbitrary. We make use of this arbitrariness, and choose x_0' to be in the remote future and x_0 in the remote past, in which case we can write

$$\begin{aligned} {}_{\text{out}}\langle 0|b_{\text{out}}(\mathbf{p}',s')b^*_{\text{in}}(\mathbf{p},s)|0\rangle_{\text{in}} &= \lim_{x_0'\to+\infty}\ \lim_{x_0\to-\infty}\int d^3x\int d^3x'\,\frac{m}{(2\pi)^3} \\ &\quad \times \tilde{u}_{s'}(\mathbf{p}')e^{ip'\cdot x'}\gamma^0 G_+^A(x',x)\,\gamma^0 u_s(\mathbf{p})e^{-ip\cdot x} \end{aligned} \qquad (10\text{–}216)$$

where

$$G_+^A(x',x) = {}_{\text{out}}\langle 0|T(\psi(x')\tilde{\psi}(x)|0\rangle_{\text{in}} \qquad (10\text{–}217)$$

In Eq. (10–217) $\psi(x)$ and $\tilde{\psi}(x)$ are the Heisenberg operators that obey the equations (10–1) and (10–2) of the present chapter. The equivalence of the representations (10–216) and (10–215) for the scattering amplitude follows from the asymptotic condition, which can be stated heuristically as

$$\lim_{x_0\to+\infty} \psi(x) = \psi_{\text{out}}(x) \qquad (10\text{–}218)$$

$$\lim_{x_0\to-\infty} \psi(x) = \psi_{\text{in}}(x) \qquad (10\text{–}219)$$

and from the fact that x_0' is always later than x_0 so that the T product is always equal to $\psi(x')\tilde{\psi}(x)$.

$$T(\psi(x')\tilde{\psi}(x)) = \psi(x')\tilde{\psi}(x) \quad \text{for } x_0' > x_0 \qquad (10\text{–}220)$$

Before proceeding further, let us make the statement of the asymptotic condition somewhat more precise. Since the operators $\psi_{\substack{\text{in}\\\text{out}}}(x)$ are unbounded as indicated by their commutation rules [10] we will have to convert these operators in some fashion to bounded ones in order to

[10] Consider, for example, the norm of $\tilde{\psi}_{\text{in}}(x)|0\rangle_{\text{in}}$, which is proportional to $S^{(+)}(0)$.

make meaningful the motion of convergence of ψ to $\psi_{\substack{\text{in}\\ \text{out}}}$. To this end we introduce a set of square integrable (wave packet solutions) of the Dirac equation $\{f^i(x)\}$

$$(-i\gamma\cdot\partial + m)f^i(x) = 0 \tag{10–221}$$

which are orthogonal in the scalar product

$$(f^i,f^j) = \int_\sigma d\sigma^\mu \tilde{f}^i(x)\gamma_\mu f^j(x) \tag{10–222}$$

$$= \delta_{ij} \tag{10–223}$$

and complete in the sense that

$$\sum_j f^j(x)\tilde{f}^j(x') = -iS(x - x') \tag{10–224}$$

Recall that the scalar product (10–222) is independent of σ (and hence of time) for spinors satisfying Eq. (10–221). If we now define the operators

$$\psi(f,t) = \int_{\sigma=t} d\sigma^\mu(x)\tilde{f}(x)\gamma_\mu\psi(x) \tag{10–225}$$

the completeness relation (10–224) yields

$$\psi(x) = \sum_f f(\mathbf{x},x_0 = t)\psi(f,t) \tag{10–226}$$

Notice that the operator

$$\psi_{\text{in}}(f) = \int d\sigma^\mu(x)\tilde{f}(x)\gamma_\mu\psi_{\text{in}}(x) \tag{10–227}$$

is time-independent, since both f and ψ_{in} obey the Dirac equation. The operators $\psi(f,t)$ and $\psi_{\text{in}}(f)$ are bounded operators.

Consider now the equation defining for example $\psi_{\text{in}}(x)$:

$$\psi(x) = \psi_{\text{in}}(x) + e\int S_R(x - x';m)\gamma^\mu A^{\text{e}}_\mu(x')\psi(x')d^4x' \tag{10–228}$$

Upon multiplying this equation by $\tilde{f}(x)\gamma_\mu$ and integrating over the space-like surface $x_0 = t$, we obtain

$$\begin{aligned}\psi(f,x_0) &= \psi_{\text{in}}(f) + \int\int d\sigma^\mu(x)\tilde{f}(x)\gamma_\mu S_R(x - x';m)\gamma\cdot A^{\text{e}}(x')\psi(x')d^4x' \\ &= \psi_{\text{in}}(f) + \int_{-\infty}^{x_0} d^4x\tilde{f}(x)\gamma\cdot A^{\text{e}}(x)\psi(x) \end{aligned}\tag{10–229}$$

The precise formulation of the asymptotic condition can now be given as follows: the operator $\psi_{\text{in}}(x)$ will be said to be the asymptotic limit of $\psi(x)$ if

$$\lim_{x_0 \to -\infty} \langle \Psi | \psi(f,x_0) | \Phi \rangle = \langle \Psi | \psi_{\text{in}}(f) | \Phi \rangle \tag{10–230}$$

for all physical state vectors $|\Psi\rangle$ and $|\Phi\rangle$ in the Hilbert space and for all functions f. The essence of the asymptotic condition is, therefore, the requirement that

$$\lim_{t \to -\infty} \langle \Psi | \int_{-\infty}^{t} d^4x \tilde{f}(x) \gamma \cdot A^{\text{e}}(x) \psi(x) | \Phi \rangle = 0 \tag{10–231}$$

for all physically realizable states $|\Psi\rangle$ and $|\Phi\rangle$. Note we require only that the matrix elements of the operator $\psi(f,t)$ converge to $\psi_{\text{in}}(f)$ and we do not require that the norm of $\psi(f,t)|\Phi\rangle$ converge to the norm of $\psi_{\text{in}}(f)|\Phi\rangle$. Such a convergence is called weak (operator) convergence. The requirement of convergence in the norms is called "strong" (operator) convergence. To have strong convergence in the present situation would require that

$$\lim_{t \to -\infty} \| (\psi(f,t) - \psi_{\text{in}}(f)) | \Phi \rangle \| = 0 \tag{10–232}$$

for all $|\Phi\rangle$ in the Hilbert space of realizable state vectors. This would require, in particular, that

$$\lim_{t \to -\infty} \left\| \int_{-\infty}^{t} d^4x \tilde{f}(x) \gamma \cdot A^{\text{e}}(x) \psi(x) | 0 \rangle \right\|^2 \tag{10–233}$$

$$= \lim_{t \to -\infty} \langle 0 | \int_{-\infty}^{t} d^4y \bar{\psi}(y) \gamma \cdot A^{\text{e}}(y) f(y) \times \int_{-\infty}^{t} d^4x \tilde{f}(x) \gamma \cdot A^{\text{e}}(x) \psi(x) | 0 \rangle \tag{10–234}$$

$$= \lim_{t \to -\infty} \sum_{|n\rangle} \langle 0 | \int_{-\infty}^{t} d^4y \bar{\psi}(y) \gamma \cdot A^{\text{e}}(y) f(y) | n \rangle \times \langle n | \int_{-\infty}^{t} d^4x \tilde{f}(x) \gamma \cdot A^{\text{e}}(x) \psi(x) | 0 \rangle \tag{10–235}$$

$$= \lim_{t \to -\infty} \sum_{|n\rangle} \left| \langle n | \int_{-\infty}^{t} d^4x \tilde{f}(x) \gamma \cdot A^{\text{e}}(x) \psi(x) | 0 \rangle \right|^2 \tag{10–236}$$

converge to zero. In Eq. (10–235) the $\{|n\rangle\}$ represent a complete set of states in the Hilbert space of physically realizable states. The asymptotic condition, as formulated above in the sense of weak convergence, requires the convergence of each of the terms of the sum to zero. Strong convergence would in addition require the sum to converge, and in fact, converge to zero. In the present situation, although it is easy to guarantee that

$$\lim_{t\to-\infty}\int_{-\infty}^{t} d^4x\tilde{f}(x)\gamma\cdot A^e(x)\langle\Psi|\psi(x)|\Phi\rangle \to 0 \qquad (10\text{–}237)$$

by suitably restricting the class of external potentials considered, particularly if $A^e(x)$ vanishes in the remote past, we have no guarantee that the sum (10–236) converges, much less that it converges to zero. However, we require only weak convergence in the formulation of the asymptotic condition. We shall continue to write the asymptotic condition in the formal and heuristic way

$$\lim_{\substack{t\to+\infty\\ -\infty}} \psi(x) = \psi_{\substack{\text{in}\\ \text{out}}}(x) \qquad (10\text{–}238)$$

with the tacit understanding that this limiting procedure implies convergence of matrix elements of $\psi(f,t)$ to those of $\psi_{\substack{\text{in}\\ \text{out}}}(f)$ in the limit $t \to \mp\infty$.

The above remarks indicate that strictly speaking, the amplitude ${}_{\text{out}}\langle\mathbf{p}',s'|\mathbf{p}s\rangle_{\text{in}}$ when expressed in the form (10–216), is to be understood as the limit of

$$\lim_{x_0'\to+\infty}\ \lim_{x_0\to-\infty}\int d^3x\int d^3x'\tilde{f}_{\mathbf{p}'s'}(x')\gamma^0{}_{\text{out}}\langle 0|T(\psi(x')\tilde{\psi}(x))|0\rangle_{\text{in}}\gamma^0 f_{\mathbf{p}s}(x) \qquad (10\text{–}239)$$

where after the limiting procedures in x_0 and x_0' have been taken, the spinors $f_{\mathbf{p}'s'}, f_{\mathbf{p}s}$, which in Eq. (10–239) are wave packet solutions of the Dirac equation centering about a mean momentum $\mathbf{p}$ and $\mathbf{p}'$, are allowed to go over to their plane wave limit

$$f_{\mathbf{p}s}(x) \to \sqrt{\frac{m}{(2\pi)^3}}\, e^{-ip\cdot x}u_s(\mathbf{p}) \qquad (10\text{–}240)$$

The above discussion, thus, has made somewhat more precise the sense of the limiting procedure involved in writing down the representation (10–216) for the scattering amplitude. This representation also makes clear that a knowledge of Green's function

$$G^A(x,x') = {}_{\text{out}}\langle 0|T(\psi(x)\tilde{\psi}(x')|0\rangle_{\text{in}} \qquad (10\text{–}241)$$

is sufficient for the computation of the scattering amplitude. Now since

$$T(\psi(x)\tilde{\psi}(x')) = \tfrac{1}{2}\epsilon(x - x')[\psi(x),\tilde{\psi}(x')]_+ + \tfrac{1}{2}[\psi(x),\tilde{\psi}(x')] \qquad (10\text{–}242)$$

upon differentiation of $T(\psi(x),\bar{\psi}(x'))$ with respect to $\partial/\partial x^0$ two contributions are obtained: one from the differentiation of the step function $\frac{1}{2}\varepsilon(x - x')$, and the other from the differentiation of $\psi(x)$, so that

$$i\gamma^0\partial^0 T(\psi(x),\bar{\psi}(x')) = i\gamma^0\delta(x_0 - x_0')\{\psi(x),\bar{\psi}(x')\} + T(i\gamma^0\partial^0\psi(x)\bar{\psi}(x')) \tag{10-243}$$

Hence, by virtue of the equation of motion (10–1), which $\psi(x)$ obeys, and the equal time commutation rules (10–8), the Green function G^A obeys the following equation

$$[i\gamma^\mu(\partial_\mu - ieA_\mu^{\mathrm{e}}(x)) - m]G^A(x,x') = i\delta^{(4)}(x - x')\ {}_{\mathrm{out}}\langle 0|0\rangle_{\mathrm{in}} \tag{10-244}$$

For the particular case that A_μ^{e} is time-independent, we could obtain the boundary conditions that G^A is to satisfy by inserting into the defining relation, Eq. (10–241), a complete set of states that are eigenstates of H. Thus, when $x_0 > x_0'$, we can write

$$G^A(x,x') = \sum_{|n\rangle} {}_{\mathrm{out}}\langle 0|\psi(x)|n\rangle\langle n|\bar{\psi}(x')|0\rangle_{\mathrm{in}} \tag{10-245}$$

Furthermore, since H, the hamiltonian, is the time translation operator

$$\psi(\mathbf{x},t) = e^{iHt}\psi(\mathbf{x},0)e^{-iHt} \tag{10-246}$$

and since by assumption $H|n\rangle = E_n|n\rangle$, whence for $x_0 > x_0'$

$$G^A(x,x') = \sum_{|n\rangle} {}_{\mathrm{out}}\langle 0|\psi(\mathbf{x},0)|n\rangle\langle n|\bar{\psi}(\mathbf{x}',0)|0\rangle_{\mathrm{in}}e^{-i(E_n - E_0)(t-t')} \tag{10-247}$$

Since E_0, the vacuum energy, must for obvious physical reasons, be the lowest energy of the negaton-positon field system, $E_n - E_0 \geq 0$, so that Eq. (10–247) indicates that for $x_0 > x_0'$, G^A contains only positive frequencies. Similarly one verifies that (under the assumption of a stable vacuum state, the state of lowest energy) G^A for $x_0 < x_0'$ contains only negative frequencies.

We shall, however, proceed somewhat differently, and obtain directly the perturbation expansion for G^A. Consider the case $x_0 > x_0'$; using the fact that

$${}_{\mathrm{out}}\langle 0| = {}_{\mathrm{in}}\langle 0|S \tag{10-248}$$

we can write G^A for that case in the form

$$\begin{aligned} {}_{\mathrm{out}}\langle 0|\psi(x)\bar{\psi}(x')|0\rangle_{\mathrm{in}} &= {}_{\mathrm{in}}\langle 0|S\psi(x)\bar{\psi}(x')|0\rangle_{\mathrm{in}} \\ &= {}_{\mathrm{in}}\langle 0|SV_+(t)^{-1}\psi_{\mathrm{in}}(x)V_+(t)V_+(t')^{-1} \\ &\qquad \times \bar{\psi}_{\mathrm{in}}(x')V_+(t')|0\rangle_{\mathrm{in}} \end{aligned} \tag{10-249}$$

Now since

$$S = \lim_{\tau \to +\infty} V_+(\tau) = \lim_{\tau \to +\infty} V(\tau, -\infty) \tag{10–250}$$

and

$$V_+(t)^{-1} = V_+(t, -\infty)^{-1} = V_+(-\infty, t) \tag{10–251}$$

we deduce from the group property of $V_+(t)$ that

$$SV_+(t)^{-1} = \lim_{\tau \to +\infty} V(\tau, t) \tag{10–252}$$

and also that

$$V_+(t, -\infty)V_+(t', -\infty)^{-1} = V_+(t, t') \tag{10–253}$$

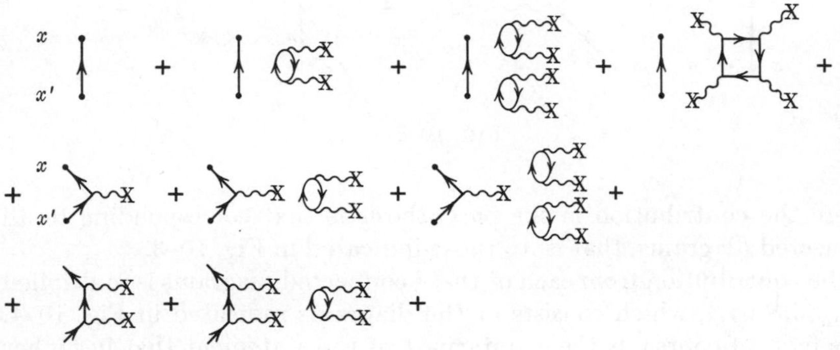

FIG. 10–2.

so that the above matrix element reduces to

$$\begin{aligned} {}_{\text{out}}\langle 0|\psi(x)\tilde{\psi}(x')|0\rangle_{\text{in}} &= {}_{\text{in}}\langle 0|V(\infty, t)\psi_{\text{in}}(x)V_+(t, t')\tilde{\psi}_{\text{in}}(x')V(t', -\infty)|0\rangle_{\text{in}} \qquad (10\text{–}254) \\ &= {}_{\text{in}}\langle 0|T(S\psi_{\text{in}}(x)\tilde{\psi}_{\text{in}}(x'))|0\rangle_{\text{in}} \qquad (10\text{–}255) \end{aligned}$$

where the introduction of the T product allows us to rewrite Eq. (10–254) as (10–255). One readily verifies that, in fact, the representation (10–255) is generally valid, *i.e.*,

$$\begin{aligned} {}_{\text{out}}\langle 0|T(\psi(x)\tilde{\psi}(x'))|0\rangle_{\text{in}} &= {}_{\text{in}}\langle 0|T(S\psi_{\text{in}}(x)\tilde{\psi}_{\text{in}}(x'))|0\rangle_{\text{in}} \\ &= \sum_{n=0}^{\infty} \frac{(-i)^n}{n!} \int d^4x_1 \cdots \int d^4x_n A^{\text{e}}_{\mu_1}(x_1) \cdots A^{\text{e}}_{\mu_n}(x_n) \\ &\quad \times {}_{\text{in}}\langle 0|T(j^{\mu_1}_{\text{in}}(x_1) \cdots j^{\mu_n}_{\text{in}}(x_n)\psi_{\text{in}}(x)\tilde{\psi}_{\text{in}}(x'))|0\rangle_{\text{in}} \end{aligned} \tag{10–256}$$

The application of Wick's theorem to the above expansion indicates that it consists of a sum of contributions that can be represented diagrammatically in the form shown in Fig. 10–2.

In other words, the matrix element can be factored in the form

$$
{}_{\rm in}\langle 0|T(S\psi(x)\tilde{\psi}(x'))|0\rangle_{\rm in} = \left(-\tfrac{1}{2}S_F(x-x') - \frac{i}{1!}\int d^4x_1\, \tfrac{1}{2}S_F(x-x_1)e\gamma\cdot A^{\rm e}(x_1)\tfrac{1}{2}S_F(x_1-x') + \cdots\right){}_{\rm in}\langle 0|S|0\rangle_{\rm in} \qquad (10\text{–}257)
$$

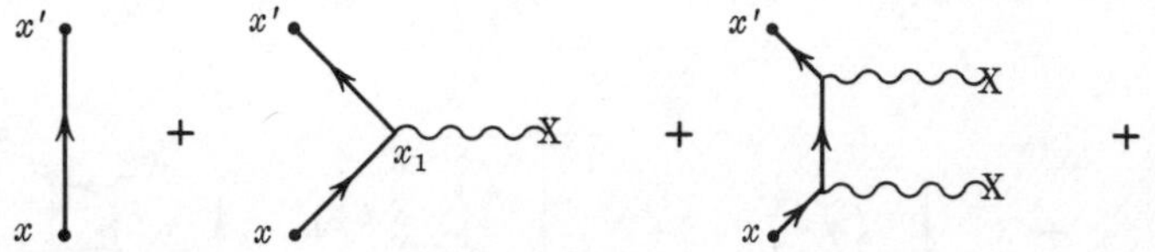

FIG. 10–3.

where the contribution in the parenthesis is that corresponding to all connected diagrams, that is, to those indicated in Fig. 10–3.

The contribution from each of these connected diagrams is multiplied by ${}_{\rm in}\langle 0|S|0\rangle_{\rm in}$, which consists of the diagrams indicated in Fig. 10–4. This fact, of course, is the counterpart of the statement that in higher order each of the connected diagrams appears together with the

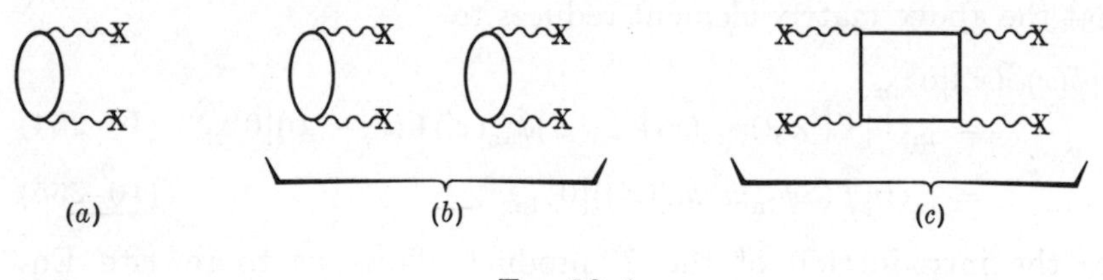

FIG. 10–4.

vacuum fluctuation diagrams, and that for a given connected diagram, the contribution of all such disconnected vacuum fluctuation can be summed into a multiplicative factor ${}_{\rm in}\langle 0|S|0\rangle_{\rm in}$. Hence if we call

$$
\frac{{}_{\rm out}\langle 0|T(\psi(x)\tilde{\psi}(x'))|0\rangle_{\rm in}}{{}_{\rm out}\langle 0|0\rangle_{\rm in}} = K_+^A(x,x') \qquad (10\text{–}258)
$$

then

$$K_+^A(x,x') = -\tfrac{1}{2}S_F(x - x') + (-i)\int d^4x_1\, \tfrac{1}{2}S_F(x - x_1)e\gamma \times A^e(x_1)\tfrac{1}{2}S_F(x_1 - x')$$
$$+\frac{(-i)^2}{2!}\int d^4x_1 \int d^4x_2\, \tfrac{1}{2}S_F(x - x_1)e\gamma\cdot A^e(x_1)\tfrac{1}{2}S_F(x_1 - x_2) \times e\gamma\cdot A^e(x_2)\tfrac{1}{2}S_F(x_2 - x') + \cdots \quad (10\text{–}259)$$

$$= -\tfrac{1}{2}S_F(x - x') + i\int d^4x_1\, \tfrac{1}{2}S_F(x - x_1)e\gamma\cdot A^e(x_1)K_+^A(x_1,x') \quad (10\text{–}260)$$

since Eq. (10–259) is, in fact, the Liouville-Neumann expansion of Eq. (10–260). If we denote by $K_+(x,x') = K_+(x - x')$ the contraction factor

$$-\tfrac{1}{2}S_F(x - x') = K_+(x - x') \quad (10\text{–}261)$$

then Eq. (10–259) reads

$$K_+^A(x,x') = K_+(x - x') - ie\int d^4x_1 K_+(x - x_1)\gamma\cdot A^e(x_1)K_+^A(x_1,x') \quad (10\text{–}262)$$

Note that K_+^A satisfies the differential equation (10–244), and, by virtue of the properties of $S_F(x - x')$, it will contain only positive frequencies when $(x - x')_0 > 0$ and negative frequencies when $(x - x')_0 < 0$.

The propagator K_+^A can be interpreted as the Green's function for computing amplitudes for one-particle processes relative to the amplitude that the vacuum remain a vacuum under the influence of the external potential. To lowest order the amplitude that the vacuum remain a vacuum is given by

$$_{\text{out}}\langle 0|0\rangle_{\text{in}} = {_{\text{in}}}\langle 0|S|0\rangle_{\text{in}}$$
$$= 1 + \frac{e^2}{2!}\int d^4x_1 \int d^4x_2\, \mathrm{Tr}\,\{\gamma^{\mu_1}A^e_{\mu_1}(x_1)K_+(x_1 - x_2)\gamma^{\mu_2}A^e_{\mu_2}(x_2) \times K_+(x_2 - x_1)\} + \cdots$$
$$= 1 + M_V^{(2)} + \cdots \quad (10\text{–}263)$$

The factor 1 can be interpreted as the amplitude that the vacuum remains a vacuum with nothing happening, the next term as the amplitude for the creation and annihilation of one pair (Fig. 10–5), etc. The quantity $M_V^{(2)}$ diverges, independently of the external field. This divergence is the result of the coincidence of the singularities of $K^+(x_1 - x_2)$ and $K_+(x_2 - x_1)$ at $x_1 = x_2$. The quantity $M_V^{(2)}$ turns out to be logarithmically divergent (if the gauge invariance of the theory is enforced). Thus upon introducing the representation (10–207) for K_+ and the Fourier transform $a_\mu^{\text{e}}(k)$ of $A_\mu^{\text{e}}(x)$

$$A_\mu^{\text{e}}(x) = \int d^4k e^{-ik\cdot x} a_\mu^{\text{e}}(k) \tag{10–264}$$

we find that

$$M_V^{(2)} = \frac{e^2}{2} \int d^4k a_\mu^{\text{e}}(k) \Pi_V^{\mu\nu}(k) a_\nu^{\text{e}}(-k) \tag{10–265}$$

with

$$\begin{aligned} \Pi_V^{\mu\nu}(k) &= -\int d^4q \operatorname{Tr}\left\{\gamma^\mu \frac{1}{\gamma\cdot(q+k) - m + i\varepsilon} \gamma^\nu \frac{1}{\gamma\cdot q - m + i\varepsilon}\right\} \\ &= \Pi_V^{\nu\mu}(k) \end{aligned} \tag{10–266}$$

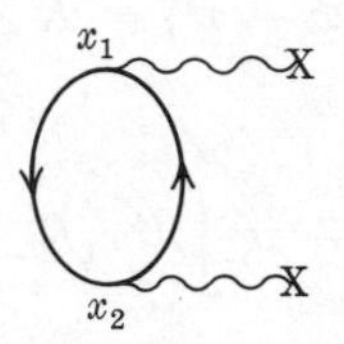

FIG. 10–5.

Gauge invariance requires that if we replace $a_\mu^{\text{e}}(k)$ by $a_\mu^{\text{e}}(k) + k_\mu \Lambda(k)$, the matrix element $M_V^{(2)}$ remain unchanged. Stated differently, if $a_\mu^{\text{e}}(k)$ is of the form k_μ times a function of k, then $M_V^{(2)}$ must vanish; hence

$$k_\mu \Pi_V^{\mu\nu}(k) = k_\nu \Pi_V^{\mu\nu}(k) = 0 \tag{10–267}$$

This together with the requirements of relativistic invariance (recall discussion in Section 10.1) implies that

$$\Pi_{V\mu\nu}(k) = (k_\mu k_\nu - g_{\mu\nu} k^2) \Pi_V(k^2) \tag{10–268}$$

The $\Pi_V(k^2)$ defined by Eq. (10–268) is closely related to the $\Pi(k^2)$ defined in Section 10.1 (they correspond to different boundary values of the same analytic function).

If we sum all the contributions of the closed loops diagrams indicated in Fig. 10–6, we shall obtain a contribution to ${}_{\text{out}}\langle 0|0\rangle_{\text{in}}$ of the form $\exp M_V^{(2)}$.

Although $M_V^{(2)}$ is divergent

$$|e^{M_V^{(2)}}|^2 = e^{+2\text{Re}\, M_V^{(2)}} \tag{10–269}$$

is finite since only the Im $M_V^{(2)}$ is divergent:

$$M_V^{(2)} = -iC \int d^4x \tfrac{1}{4} F^{\mathrm{e}}_{\mu\nu}(x) F^{\mathrm{e}\mu\nu}(x) + \text{finite terms} \tag{10–270}$$

where

$$C = \frac{1}{6\pi^2} (\log (M/m) - \tfrac{5}{6})_{M \to \infty} \tag{10–271}$$

All other higher order contributions to ${}_{\text{out}}\langle 0|0\rangle_{\text{in}}$ are finite.

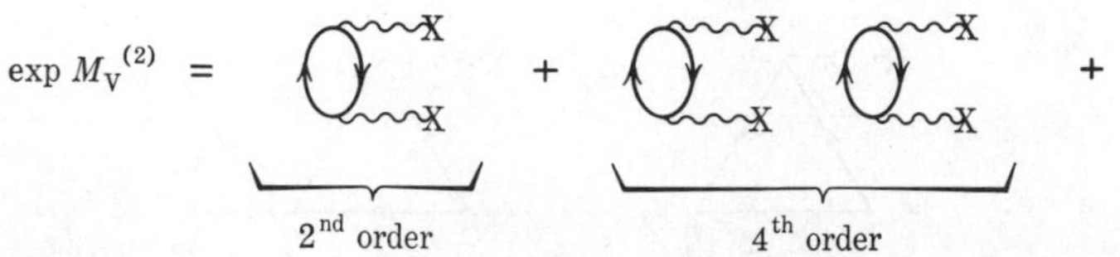

$\exp M_V^{(2)} =$ + +

2nd order 4th order

FIG. 10–6.

The third order contribution to the amplitude that the vacuum remain a vacuum under the influence of the external field is exhibited by the two diagrams of Fig. 10–7, and is given by

$$\begin{aligned} M_V^{(3)} = -\frac{1}{3!}\left(\frac{ie}{\hbar c}\right)^3 &\int d^4x_1 \int d^4x_2 \int d^4x_3 \\ &\times \operatorname{Tr} \{\gamma^{\mu_1} A^{\mathrm{e}}_{\mu_1}(x_1) K_+(x_1 - x_2) \gamma^{\mu_2} A^{\mathrm{e}}_{\mu_2}(x_2) \\ &\qquad \times K_+(x_2 - x_2) \gamma^{\mu_3} A^{\mathrm{e}}_{\mu_3}(x_3) K_+(x_3 - x_1) \\ &+ \gamma^{\mu_1} A^{\mathrm{e}}_{\mu_1}(x_1) K_+(x_1 - x_3) \gamma^{\mu_3} A^{\mathrm{e}}_{\mu_3}(x_3) K_+(x_3 - x_2) \\ &\qquad \times \gamma^{\mu_2} A^{\mathrm{e}}_{\mu_2}(x_2) K_+(x_2 - x_1)\} \end{aligned} \tag{10–272}$$

The matrix element (10–272) actually vanishes.

Proof.—There exists a unitary skew symmetric matrix C with the property that

$$C\gamma^{\mu}C^{-1} = -\gamma^{\mu T} \tag{10–273}$$

$$C^*C = CC^* = 1 \tag{10–274}$$

$$C^T = -C \tag{10–275}$$

If we now insert in the first term of Eq. (10–272) the factor $C^{-1}C = I$, and note that

$$\begin{aligned} CK_+(x_1 - x_2)C^{-1} &= K_+^T(x_2 - x_1) \\ &= \frac{i}{(2\pi)^4} \int \frac{\gamma^T \cdot p + m}{p^2 - m^2 + i\varepsilon} e^{-ip\cdot(x_2 - x_1)} d^4p \end{aligned} \tag{10–276}$$

we then find that

$$\begin{aligned}
\operatorname{Tr}\{C\gamma^{\mu}\cdot C^{-1}CK_{+}(x_1 - x_2)C^{-1}C\gamma^{\mu_2}C^{-1}CK_{+}(x_2 - x_3)C^{-1}C \\
\times \gamma^{\mu_3}C^{-1}CK_{+}(x_3 - x_1)C^{-1}\}A^{\mathrm{e}}_{\mu_1}(x_1)A^{\mathrm{e}}_{\mu_2}(x_2)A^{\mathrm{e}}_{\mu_3}(x_3) \\
= (-1)^3 \operatorname{Tr}\{\gamma^{\mu_1 T}K^T_{+}(x_2 - x_1)\gamma^{\mu_2 T}K^T_{+}(x_3 - x_2)\gamma^{\mu_3 T}K^T_{+}(x_1 - x_3)\} \\
\times A^{\mathrm{e}}_{\mu_1}(x_1)A^{\mathrm{e}}_{\mu_2}(x_2)A^{\mathrm{e}}_{\mu_3}(x_3) \\
= (-1)^3 \operatorname{Tr}\{\gamma^{\mu_1}K_{+}(x_1 - x_3)\gamma^{\mu_3}K_{+}(x_3 - x_2)\gamma^{\mu_2}K_{+}(x_2 - x_1)\} \\
\times A^{\mathrm{e}}_{\mu_1}(x_1)A^{\mathrm{e}}_{\mu_2}(x_2)A^{\mathrm{e}}_{\mu_3}(x_3) \quad (10\text{–}277)
\end{aligned}$$

so that the two terms in Eq. (10–272) cancel and $M_V^{(3)} = 0$.

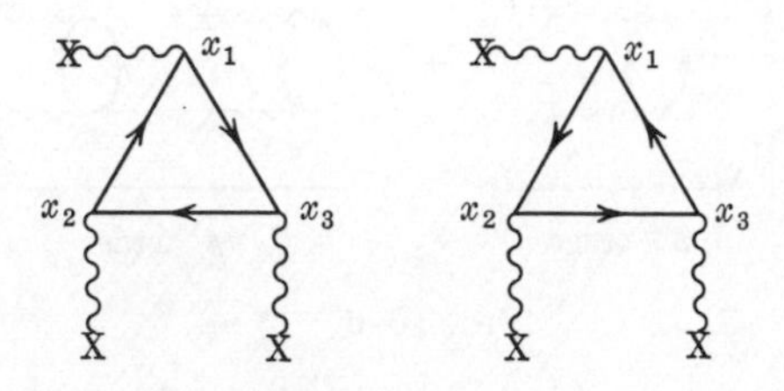

FIG. 10-7.

Quite generally a closed loop with an odd number of corners vanishes by a similar argument. This is the reason why we have not included these diagrams in Fig. 10–2. This result is connected with the invariance of the theory under charge conjugation to which subject we shall return in Section 11.3 of Chapter 11. We conclude this section by computing the scattering cross-section (valid to lowest order) for the scattering of an electron by an external field $A^{\mathrm{e}}_{\mu}(x)$. To this end we note that the Green function $K_{+}(x - x') = -\frac{1}{2}S_F(x - x')$ has the following properties

$$(-i\gamma\cdot\overrightarrow{\partial}_x + m)S_F(x - x') = 2i\delta^{(4)}(x - x') \quad (10\text{–}278)$$

$$S_F(x - x')(i\gamma\cdot\overleftarrow{\partial}_{x'} + m) = 2i\delta^{(4)}(x - x') \quad (10\text{–}279)$$

Hence, upon applying Gauss' theorem

$$\int_{\Omega} \partial_{\mu}F^{\mu}(x)d^4(x) = \int_S d\sigma_{\mu}(x)F^{\mu}(x) \quad (10\text{–}280)$$

where S denotes the surface enclosing the four-dimensional volume Ω, to the function

$$F_{\mu}(x') = S_F(x - x')\gamma_{\mu}f(x') \quad (10\text{–}281)$$

where $f(x)$ is a solution of the Dirac equation, $(-i\gamma\cdot\partial + m)f(x) = 0$, we obtain the result that if x is within Ω then

$$f(x) = i\int_S d\sigma_\mu(x)[-\tfrac{1}{2}S_F(x - x')]\gamma^\mu f(x') \tag{10–282}$$

If $f(x)$ is a wave packet solution that vanishes for large spatial distances, then the surface integral over S extends over the two space-like surfaces σ_1, σ_2 bounding Ω (see Fig. 10–8).

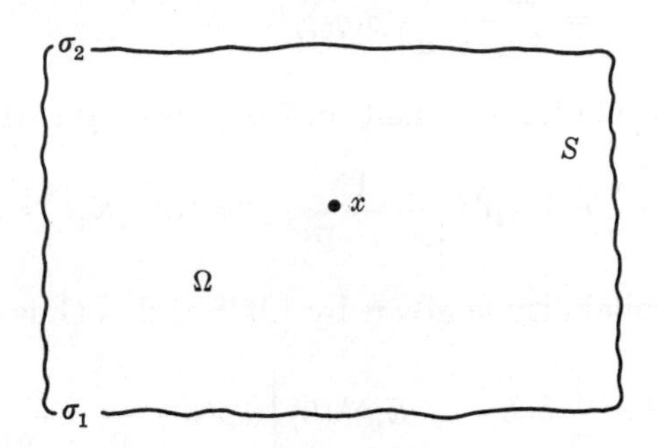

FIG. 10–8.

Since for $x_0 - x_0' > 0$, $-\tfrac{1}{2}S_F(x - x') = -iS^{(+)}(x - x')$, only the positive frequency part of $f(x')$ on σ_1 is propagated from σ_1 to x, and similarly since $-\tfrac{1}{2}S_F(x - x') = iS^{(-)}(x - x')$ for $x_0 - x_0' < 0$, only the negative frequency part of $f(x')$ on σ_2 is propagated from σ_2 to x.

Hence, if we substitute into the expression

$$\lim_{\substack{x_0'\to+\infty \\ x_0\to-\infty}} \int d\sigma^{\mu'}(x')\int d\sigma\,^{\mu}(x)\tilde{f}_{\mathbf{p}'s'}(x')\gamma_{\mu'}K_+^A(x',x)\gamma_\mu f_{\mathbf{p}s}(x) \tag{10–283}$$

for the scattering amplitude, the first order approximation for $K_+^A(x',x)$ namely

$$K_+^A(x',x) = K_+(x' - x) - ie\int d^4x_1 K_+(x' - x_1)\gamma\cdot A^e(x_1)K_+(x_1 - x) \tag{10–284}$$

then upon making use of Eq. (10–282), we obtain the following expression for the scattering amplitude in the limit as the $f_{\mathbf{p}s}(x)$'s become plane wave, positive energy solutions of the Dirac equation:

$$_{\text{out}}\langle\mathbf{p}'s'|\mathbf{p}s\rangle_{\text{in}} \simeq \delta_{ss'}\delta(\mathbf{p} - \mathbf{p}')p_0 - 2\pi ime\tilde{u}_{s'}(\mathbf{p}')\gamma_\mu a^{e\mu}(\mathbf{p}' - \mathbf{p})u_s(\mathbf{p}) \tag{10–285}$$

where

$$a_\mu^e(q) = \frac{1}{(2\pi)^4}\int d^4x_1 e^{iq\cdot x_1}A_\mu^e(x_1) \tag{10–286}$$

If the external field is the Coulomb field of a point charge located at the origin; in particular, if

$$A_0^e(x) = A_0^e(\mathbf{x}) = \frac{Ze}{4\pi|\mathbf{x}|} \tag{10–287}$$

then

$$\begin{aligned}\gamma \cdot a^e(q) &= \frac{1}{(2\pi)^4}\int dx_0 e^{+iq_0x_0}\int d^3re^{-i\mathbf{q}\cdot\mathbf{x}}\frac{Ze}{4\pi|\mathbf{x}|} \\ &= \frac{Ze}{4\pi}\frac{1}{2\pi^2\mathbf{q}^2}\,\delta(q_0)\gamma^0\end{aligned} \tag{10–288}$$

so that the amplitude for a transition from $\mathbf{p}s \to \mathbf{p}'s'$ ($\mathbf{p} \neq \mathbf{p}'$) is

$$M = \frac{Ze^2}{4\pi}\frac{i}{\pi}\,m\tilde{u}_{s'}(\mathbf{p}')\,\frac{1}{|\mathbf{p}' - \mathbf{p}|^2}\,\gamma^0 u_s(\mathbf{p})\delta(E_{\mathbf{p}'} - E_{\mathbf{p}}) \tag{10–289}$$

The transition probability is given by $|M|^2$ and is thus equal to

$$|M|^2 = Z^2e^4m^2\frac{1}{\pi}\,\delta(E_{\mathbf{p}'} - E_{\mathbf{p}})\delta(0)\left|\tilde{u}_{s'}(\mathbf{p}')\,\frac{1}{|\mathbf{p}' - \mathbf{p}|}\,\gamma^0u_s(\mathbf{p})\right|^2 \tag{10–290}$$

The factor $\delta(0)$ is to be interpreted as

$$\begin{aligned}\delta(0) &= \lim_{T\to\infty}\lim_{E - E'}\frac{1}{2\pi}\int_{-T/2}^{T/2} e^{i(E'-E)t}dt \\ &= \lim_{T\to\infty}\frac{T}{2\pi}\end{aligned} \tag{10–291}$$

where T is the time elapsed between the preparation of the initial state and the measurement of the properties of the final state. Hence, the transition probability per unit time, to the final state $u_{s'}(\mathbf{p}')$ is given by

$$\begin{aligned}W_{\mathbf{p}s\to\mathbf{p}'s'} &= |M|^2/T \\ &= \frac{Z^2e^4}{2\pi^3}\,m^2\left|\tilde{u}_{s'}(\mathbf{p}')\,\frac{1}{|\mathbf{p}' - \mathbf{p}|^2}\,\gamma^0u_s(\mathbf{p})\right|^2\delta(E_{\mathbf{p}'} - E_{\mathbf{p}})\end{aligned} \tag{10–292}$$

Actually, we are always interested only in the transition probability per unit time to a group of final states with density $\rho_f = dn_f/dE_f$. This transition rate is given by

$$w = \frac{4Z^2e^4}{(2\pi)^3}\,m^2\left(\frac{dn_f}{dE_f}\right)_{E_f=E_i}\left|\tilde{u}_{s'}(\mathbf{p}')\,\frac{1}{|\mathbf{p}' - \mathbf{p}|^2}\,\gamma^0u_s(\mathbf{p})\right|^2 \tag{10–293}$$

The density of final states is obtained by noting that in the one-particle subspace the operator

$$\sum_s \int dn_f b^*_{\text{in } s}(\mathbf{p}_f)|0\rangle_{\text{in in}}\langle 0|b_{\text{in } s}(\mathbf{p}_f) \tag{10–294}$$

must be the identity operator. In particular, operating on the state $b^*_{\text{in } s}(\mathbf{p})|0\rangle_{\text{in}}$ the operator must reproduce it, hence

$$dn_f = \frac{d^3p}{p_0} \tag{10–295}$$

where $p_0 = E_{\mathbf{p}} = \sqrt{\mathbf{p}^2 + m^2}$ and

$$\frac{dn_f}{dE} = \frac{p^2 dp d\Omega}{dE} = Epd\Omega \tag{10–296}$$

since

$$\frac{dE}{dp} = \frac{d}{dp}\sqrt{\mathbf{p}^2 + m^2} = \frac{p}{E} \tag{10–297}$$

In case we are not interested in the spin of the scattered electron, and the initial beam is unpolarized, we must sum w over the final states s', and average over the two initial spin states. We have seen in Section 5 of Chapter 9, that

$$\tfrac{1}{2}\sum_{s'}\sum_{s} |\tilde{u}_{s'}(\mathbf{p}')\gamma^0 u_s(\mathbf{p})|^2 = \tfrac{1}{2}\,\mathrm{Tr}\left(\frac{\gamma\cdot p' + m}{2m}\,\gamma^0\,\frac{\gamma\cdot p + m}{2m}\,\gamma^0\right) \tag{10–298}$$

The trace can readily be evaluated, and one finds that

$$\begin{aligned}\tfrac{1}{2}\,\mathrm{Tr}\left(\frac{\gamma\cdot p' + m}{2m}\,\gamma^0\,\frac{\gamma\cdot p + m}{2m}\,\gamma^0\right) &= \frac{1}{8m^2}(2p_0'p_0 - p'\cdot p + m^2)\\ &= \frac{1}{m^2}(E^2 + \mathbf{p}'\cdot\mathbf{p} + m^2)\end{aligned} \tag{10–299}$$

where $E = E_{\mathbf{p}} = E_{\mathbf{p}'}$, since the field is time-independent, so that the energy of the scattered electron is conserved. If we call the scattering angle θ then

$$\begin{aligned}\mathbf{p}'\cdot\mathbf{p} &= |\mathbf{p}|\,|\mathbf{p}'|\cos\theta\\ &= \mathbf{p}^2\cos\theta = (E^2 - m^2)\cos\theta\end{aligned} \tag{10–300}$$

where

$$|\mathbf{p}'| = |\mathbf{p}| \tag{10–301}$$

since

$$E_{\mathbf{p}} = E_{\mathbf{p}'} = \sqrt{\mathbf{p}^2 + m^2} = \sqrt{\mathbf{p}'^2 + m^2} \tag{10–302}$$

Hence the expression (10–298) for the trace becomes

$$\tfrac{1}{2}\,\mathrm{Tr}\left(\frac{\gamma\cdot p' + m}{2m}\,\gamma^0\,\frac{\gamma\cdot p + m}{2m}\,\gamma^0\right) = \frac{E^2}{m^2}\,(1 - v^2 \sin^2 \tfrac{1}{2}\theta) \quad (10\text{–}303)$$

where v is the velocity of the electron:

$$\frac{m^2}{E^2} = 1 - v^2 \quad (10\text{–}304)$$

Similarly, since the magnitude of the momentum is conserved

$$|\mathbf{p}' - \mathbf{p}| = 2|\mathbf{p}|\sin\tfrac{1}{2}\theta \quad (10\text{–}305)$$

the spin-averaged transition probability per unit of time is given by

$$w = \frac{Z^2e^4}{4\mathbf{p}^4 \sin^4 \frac{1}{2}\theta}\,(1 - v^2\sin^2\tfrac{1}{2}\theta)\,\frac{1}{(2\pi)^3}\left(\frac{dn_f}{dE}\right)_{Ef=Ei} \quad (10\text{–}306)$$

To obtain the differential cross-section we must divide w by the incident flux

$$\text{flux} = \frac{1}{(2\pi)^3}\,v = \frac{1}{(2\pi)^3}\,\frac{p}{E} \quad (10\text{–}307)$$

The differential cross-section to this order is, therefore, given by

$$\frac{d\sigma}{d\Omega} = \frac{Z^2e^4}{4\mathbf{p}^2v^2\sin^4\frac{1}{2}\theta}\,(1 - v^2\sin^2\tfrac{1}{2}\theta) \quad (10\text{–}308)$$

This is the Rutherford formula $Z^2e^4/4\mathbf{p}^2v^2\sin^4\frac{1}{2}\theta$ multiplied by $(1 - v^2\sin^2\frac{1}{2}\theta)$, which is the correction to the Rutherford formula arising from the spin of the electron.

To second order in the external field, the scattering amplitude is given by

$$\begin{aligned}\frac{{}_{\text{out}}\langle\mathbf{p}'s'|\mathbf{p}s\rangle_{\text{in}}}{{}_{\text{out}}\langle 0|0\rangle_{\text{in}}} &= \delta_{ss'}\,p_0\,\delta(\mathbf{p} - \mathbf{p}') - 2\pi i m e\,\tilde{u}_{s'}(\mathbf{p}) \\ &\quad\times\left[\gamma_\mu a^{e\mu}(p' - p) - \frac{e}{(2\pi)^4}\int d^4q\,\gamma^{\mu_1}a^{e}_{\mu_1}(p' - q)\right. \\ &\quad\left.\times\,\frac{1}{\gamma\cdot q - m + i\varepsilon}\,\gamma^{\mu_2}a^{e}_{\mu_2}(q - p) + \cdots\right]u_s(\mathbf{p})\end{aligned} \quad (10\text{–}309)$$

The differential cross-section, averaged over the initial electron spin states and summed over the final spin states for the potential

$$A^0(\mathbf{x}) = \frac{Ze}{|\mathbf{x}|}\,e^{-\lambda|\mathbf{x}|} \quad (10\text{–}310)$$

has the form

$$\frac{d\sigma}{d\Omega} = \frac{4Z^2e^4E^2}{(\lambda^2 + 4\mathbf{p}^2 \sin^4 \frac{1}{2}\theta)} \left\{ (1 - v^2 \sin^2 \tfrac{1}{2}\theta) \times \left[(1 - \lambda^2 + 4\mathbf{p}^2 \sin^2 \tfrac{1}{2}\theta) \frac{Ze^2}{\pi^2} E \operatorname{Re}(I + J) \right] - \frac{m^2}{E} \frac{Ze^2}{\pi^2} (\lambda^2 + 4\mathbf{p}^2 \sin^2 \tfrac{1}{2}\theta) \operatorname{Re}(I + J) \right\} \quad (10\text{–}311)$$

where in the limit $\lambda \to 0$

$$I - J = \frac{\pi^3}{4|\mathbf{p}|^3 \cos^2 \frac{1}{2}\theta} (\operatorname{cosec} \tfrac{1}{2}\theta - 1) + \frac{\pi^2 i}{4|\mathbf{p}|^3 \cos^2 \frac{1}{2}\theta} \ln (\sin^2 \tfrac{1}{2}\theta) \quad (10\text{–}312)$$

and

$$I \simeq \frac{\pi^2 i}{2|\mathbf{p}|^3 \sin^2 \frac{1}{2}\theta} \ln \left(\frac{2|\mathbf{p}| \sin \frac{1}{2}\theta}{\lambda} \right) \quad (10\text{–}313)$$

Hence, in the limit $\lambda \to 0$, the differential cross-section diverges. This is due to the long range character of the Coulomb field, which entails that the expansion (10–259) of K^A does not converge. Alternatively, the asymptotic condition is not valid in this case.

It can be shown, however, that the λ-dependent term occurring in the amplitude (10–311)–(10–313), can to this order in Z be regarded as a phase factor multiplying the amplitude, thus having no physical consequence.

REFERENCES

For discussions of the scattering of a spin $\frac{1}{2}$ particle by an external time-independent field, see:

Feynman, R. P., *Phys. Rev.*, **76**, 749 (1949).
Schwinger, J., *Phys. Rev.*, **94**, 1362 (1954).

For the particular case of scattering by a Coulomb field, see:

Dalitz, R. H., *Proc. Roy. Society, A*, **206** (1951).
Nagel, B., *Kungl. Tekniska Hogskolans*, Handlingar No. **157** (1960).

10.4. The Dirac Equation in a Central Field.

—The previous sections have indicated that at times it is useful to have an explicit representation of the matrix element $\langle 0|\psi(x)|n\rangle$ where $\psi(x)$ is the Heisenberg operator satisfying Eq. (10–1). Of particular interest is the case when the external field $A^e(x)$ is time-independent, $A^e = A^e(\mathbf{x})$, so that the states $|n\rangle$ can be assumed to be eigenstates of the then time-independent hamiltonian operator H. For the states $|n\rangle$ which are eigenstates of the total charge Q with eigenvalue $-e$, the amplitude

$$\langle 0|\psi(x)|n\rangle = \psi_n(x) \tag{10–314}$$

can be identified with the one-particle Dirac amplitude. Since $\psi(x)$ obeys Eq. (10–1), the amplitude $\psi_n(x)$ obeys the same equation. Furthermore, since by assumption

$$H|n\rangle = E_n|n\rangle \tag{10–315}$$

and $\langle 0|H = 0$, and since in the Heisenberg picture

$$-i\hbar\partial_t\psi(x) = [H,\psi(x)] \tag{10–316}$$

we deduce that

$$\begin{aligned}\langle 0|[\psi(x),H]|n\rangle &= i\hbar\partial_t\psi_n(x)\\ &= E_n\psi_n(x)\end{aligned} \tag{10–317}$$

To obtain the representation of the matrix element $\langle 0|\psi(x)|n\rangle$ we, therefore, need to study the solutions of the equation

$$\begin{aligned}\left[-i\hbar c\gamma^0\boldsymbol{\gamma}\cdot\left(\boldsymbol{\nabla} - \frac{e}{\hbar c}\mathbf{A}(\mathbf{x})\right) + \gamma^0 mc^2 + eA^0(\mathbf{x})\right]\psi_n(\mathbf{x}) &= \mathrm{h}\psi_n(\mathbf{x})\\ &= E_n\psi_n(\mathbf{x})\end{aligned} \tag{10–318}$$

We can speak of h as the hamiltonian for the one-particle case, and avail ourselves of the familiar methods to study the solutions of Eq. (10–318).

For a central electrostatic field h takes the form

$$\mathrm{h} = c\boldsymbol{\alpha}\cdot\mathbf{p} + \beta mc^2 + eA^0(r) \tag{10–319}$$

$$A^0(r) = A^0(|\mathbf{r}|); \quad \mathbf{r} = \mathbf{x} \tag{10–320}$$

We first inquire as to the constants of the motion in this situation. Since h is invariant under the group of spatial rotations, and under spatial inversions, the total angular momentum and the parity operator are constants of the motion. The total angular momentum operator is

$$\mathbf{J} = \mathbf{L} + \tfrac{1}{2}\hbar\boldsymbol{\Sigma} \tag{10–321}$$

$$\mathbf{L} = \mathbf{r}\times\mathbf{p} \tag{10–322}$$

and one readily verifies that it commutes with h. The three components of $\mathbf{J}$, however, do not commute with one another,

$$[J^l,J^m] = i\hbar\varepsilon^{lmn}J^n \tag{10–323}$$

so that only $\mathbf{J}^2$ and one of the J_i can be diagonalized simultaneously, which is possible since

$$[\mathbf{J}^2,J^m] = 0 \tag{10–324}$$

We have exhibited two constants of the motion that can be diagonalized simultaneously with h. A third constant of motion is the parity operator

$$P = \beta R \tag{10-325}$$

where R is the operator with the property that

$$R\mathbf{r}R^{-1} = -\mathbf{r} \tag{10-326}$$

$$R\mathbf{p}R^{-1} = -\mathbf{p} \tag{10-327}$$

The constancy of P is a consequence of the invariance of h under spatial inversion, *i.e.*, $P\mathrm{h}P^{-1} = \mathrm{h}$. P commutes with J_i so that the eigenstates of h can be taken to be eigenstates of J^2, J_3, and P. Note that due to the presence of the β operator in P, the upper and lower components of a four-component spinor must behave oppositely under R. Since it is the eigenvalues of L^2 that basically determine the behavior of a wave function under the operation R, upper and lower components must belong to different eigenvalues l. This is basically the reason why it is not possible to construct a four-component spinor that is a simultaneous eigenstate of $\mathbf{J}^2$, $\mathbf{L}^2$, and P. When using a classification of the eigenstates in terms of $\mathbf{J}^2$ and J_3 it is often convenient to deal with the operator

$$K = \beta(\mathbf{\Sigma}\cdot\mathbf{J} - \tfrac{1}{2}\hbar) \tag{10-328}$$

$$= \beta(\mathbf{\Sigma}\cdot\mathbf{L} + \hbar) \tag{10-329}$$

instead of the operator P to which it is closely related. Since K is proportional to $\mathbf{J}\cdot\mathbf{\Sigma}$, it is to be expected that the eigenvalues of this operator will differentiate between spin parallel or antiparallel to $\mathbf{J}$, *i.e.*, whether $j = l + \frac{1}{2}$ or $j = l - \frac{1}{2}$. Furthermore, since

$$K^2 = \mathbf{J}^2 + \tfrac{1}{4}\hbar^2 \tag{10-330}$$

if the eigenvalues of $\mathbf{J}^2$ are $j(j+1)\hbar^2$ and those of K, kh, Eq. (10-330) asserts that $k = \pm(j + \frac{1}{2})$. Since j is an odd half-integer, K has as its eigenvalues the positive and negative integers but not zero. It will be noted that K commutes with J_i as well as with h

$$[K,J_i] = 0 \tag{10-331}$$

$$[K,\mathrm{h}] = 0 \tag{10-332}$$

so that we could just as well have chosen h, $\mathbf{J}^2$, J_3, and K as our commuting set of observables. If we denote by $\psi_{j\mu k}$ a simultaneous eigenfunction of $\mathbf{J}^2$, J_3, and K with eigenvalues $j(j+1)\hbar^2$, $\mu\hbar$, and $k\hbar$, respectively, and write

$$\psi_{j\mu k}(\mathbf{r}) = \begin{pmatrix} \psi^L(\mathbf{r}) \\ \psi^S(\mathbf{r}) \end{pmatrix} \tag{10–333}$$

where ψ^L and ψ^S are two-component spinors, the requirement that

$$J_3\psi_{j\mu k} = \mu\psi_{j\mu k} \tag{10–334}$$

when expressed in terms of ψ^L and ψ^S, becomes

$$\begin{pmatrix} \frac{1}{2}\hbar\sigma_3 + L_3 & 0 \\ 0 & \frac{1}{2}\hbar\sigma_3 + L_3 \end{pmatrix}\begin{pmatrix} \psi^L \\ \psi^S \end{pmatrix} = \mu\begin{pmatrix} \psi^L \\ \psi^S \end{pmatrix} \tag{10–335}$$

If we denote by ψ^{L1} and ψ^{L2} the two components of ψ^L (and similarly ψ^{S1} and ψ^{S2}), Eq. (10–335) asserts that

$$(\tfrac{1}{2}\hbar + L_3)\psi^{L1} = \mu\psi^{L1} \tag{10–336}$$

$$(-\tfrac{1}{2}\hbar + L_3)\psi^{L2} = \mu\psi^{L2} \tag{10–337}$$

(Identical equations hold for ψ^S.) Since

$$L_3 Y_{lm}(\theta,\phi) = m\hbar Y_{lm}(\theta,\phi) \tag{10–338}$$

where the Y_{lm} are the spherical harmonics discussed in Chapter 9, we can satisfy Eqs. (10–336) and (10–337) by writing

$$\psi^{L1}(\mathbf{r}) = f_1(r) Y_{l,\mu-1/2} \tag{10–339}$$

$$\psi^{L2}(\mathbf{r}) = f_2(r) Y_{l,\mu+1/2} \tag{10–340}$$

Let us next try to satisfy the requirement that

$$K\psi_{j\mu k} = \beta(\mathbf{\Sigma}\cdot\mathbf{L} + \hbar)\psi_{j\mu k} \tag{10–341}$$

$$= k\hbar\psi_{j\mu k} \tag{10–342}$$

For the large component ψ^L, Eqs. (10–341) and (10–342) become

$$\begin{pmatrix} L_3 + \hbar & L_1 - iL_2 \\ L_1 + iL_2 & -L_3 + \hbar \end{pmatrix}\begin{pmatrix} f_1 Y_{l,\mu-1/2} \\ f_2 Y_{l,\mu+1/2} \end{pmatrix} = k\hbar\begin{pmatrix} f_1 Y_{l,\mu-1/2} \\ f_2 Y_{l,\mu+1/2} \end{pmatrix} \tag{10–343}$$

Since

$$(L_1 \pm iL_2) Y_{l,m} = \hbar\sqrt{(l \mp m)(l \pm m + 1)}\, Y_{l,m\pm 1} \tag{10–344}$$

and

$$\int d\Omega |Y_{l,m}|^2 = 1 \tag{10–345}$$

we can reduce Eq. (10–343) to the following set of homogeneous equations for f_1 and f_2

$$(m - k + 1)f_1 + \sqrt{(l + m + 1)(l - m)}f_1 = 0 \tag{10–346}$$

$$\sqrt{(l - m)(l + m + 1)}f_1 - (m + k)f_2 = 0 \tag{10–347}$$

Nontrivial solutions will exist only if the determinant D

$$D = \begin{vmatrix} m - k + 1 & \sqrt{(l + m + 1)(l - m)} \\ \sqrt{(l - m)(l + m + 1)} & -(m + k) \end{vmatrix} \tag{10–348}$$

vanishes. One readily verifies that $D = 0$ if either $k = l + 1$ or $k = -l$. When $k = l + 1 > 0$

$$f_2 = \sqrt{\frac{l - \mu + \frac{1}{2}}{l + \mu + \frac{1}{2}}}f_1 \quad \text{if } k > 0 \tag{10–349}$$

whereas when $k = -l < 0$

$$f_2 = -\sqrt{\frac{l + \mu + \frac{1}{2}}{l - \mu + \frac{1}{2}}}f_1 \quad \text{if } k < 0 \tag{10–350}$$

so that f_1 and f_2 differ only by a constant factor in both cases. Now when operating on ψ^L with

$$\mathbf{J}^2 = \mathbf{L}^2 + \hbar\mathbf{\Sigma}\cdot\mathbf{L} + \tfrac{3}{4}\hbar^2 = \mathbf{L}^2 + \hbar K - \tfrac{1}{4}\hbar^2 \tag{10–351}$$

we find on equating the eigenvalues that

$$j(j + 1) = l(l + 1) + k - \tfrac{1}{4} \tag{10–352}$$

Hence, when $k = l + 1$

$$j(j + 1) = (l + \tfrac{1}{2})(l + \tfrac{1}{2} + 1) \tag{10–353}$$

i.e., $j = l + \frac{1}{2}$, and similarly when $k = -l, j = l - \frac{1}{2}$. Equivalently, we can write

$$k = j + \tfrac{1}{2} \qquad \text{when } j = l + \tfrac{1}{2} \tag{10–354}$$

$$k = -(j + \tfrac{1}{2}) \quad \text{when } j = l - \tfrac{1}{2} \tag{10–355}$$

so that $k = \pm 1, \pm 2, \pm 3, \cdots$. The fact that $k^2 = (j + \frac{1}{2})^2$ follows, of course, immediately from the fact that $K^2 = J^2 + \hbar^2/4$. Combining Eqs. (10–353) and (10–354) we can write

$$k = (-1)^{l+1/2-j}(j + \tfrac{1}{2}) \tag{10–356}$$

Since R, when operating on the large components, has eigenvalues $(-1)^l$, the difference between the eigenvalues of P and K is a factor $(-1)^{j-1/2}(j + \frac{1}{2})$, *i.e.*, when operating on eigenfunctions of $\mathbf{J}^2$

$$K = P(-1)^{j-1/2}(j + \tfrac{1}{2}) \tag{10–357}$$

If we write for $k > 0$

$$\psi^L_{j\mu} = f(r)\xi^+_{j\mu} \tag{10–358}$$

with

$$\xi^+ = \begin{pmatrix} c_1 Y_{j-1/2,\mu-1/2} \\ c_2 Y_{j-1/2,\mu+1/2} \end{pmatrix}; \quad \frac{c_1}{c_2} = \sqrt{\frac{j+\mu}{j-\mu}} \tag{10–359}$$

then upon normalizing the spinors so that

$$\int d\Omega |\xi^+_{j\mu}|^2 = 1 \tag{10–360}$$

we find that the components ψ^L of $\psi_{j\mu k}$ have the following form, for $k = l + 1 > 0, j = l + \frac{1}{2}$

$$\psi^L_{j\mu k} = f(r) \begin{pmatrix} \sqrt{\dfrac{j+\mu}{2j}} & Y_{j-1/2,\mu-1/2} \\ \sqrt{\dfrac{j-\mu}{2j}} & Y_{j-1/2,\mu+1/2} \end{pmatrix} \tag{10–361}$$

$$= f(r)\xi^+_{j\mu} \tag{10–362}$$

for $k = -l < 0, j = l - \frac{1}{2}$

$$\psi^L_{j\mu k} = f(r) \begin{pmatrix} \sqrt{\dfrac{j-\mu+1}{2(j+1)}} & Y_{j+1/2,\mu-1/2} \\ -\sqrt{\dfrac{j+\mu+1}{2(j+1)}} & Y_{j+1/2,\mu+1/2} \end{pmatrix} \tag{10–363}$$

$$= f(r)\xi^-_{j\mu} \tag{10–364}$$

Finally, the complete normalized spinor for the case $k > 0, j = l + \frac{1}{2}$ has the form

$$\psi_{j\mu k}(\mathbf{r}) = \begin{pmatrix} \sqrt{\dfrac{j+\mu}{2j}} & Y_{j-1/2,\mu-1/2}(\theta,\phi)f(r) \\ \sqrt{\dfrac{j-\mu}{2j}} & Y_{j-1/2,\mu+1/2}(\theta,\phi)f(r) \\ \sqrt{\dfrac{j-\mu+1}{2(j+1)}} & Y_{j+1/2,\mu-1/2}(\theta,\phi)g(r) \\ -\sqrt{\dfrac{j+\mu+1}{2(j+1)}} & Y_{j+1/2,\mu+1/2}(\theta,\phi)g(r) \end{pmatrix} \tag{10–365}$$

$$= \begin{pmatrix} f(r) & \xi^+_{j\mu} \\ g(r) & \xi^-_{j\mu} \end{pmatrix} \tag{10–366}$$

since, for $\psi_{j\mu k}$ to be an eigenfunction of $K = \beta(\mathbf{\Sigma}\cdot\mathbf{L} + \hbar)$, the lower two components must be eigenvalues of $\boldsymbol{\sigma}\cdot\mathbf{L} + \hbar$ with eigenvalue $-k\hbar$ if the upper two components are eigenfunctions of $\boldsymbol{\sigma}\cdot\mathbf{L} + \hbar$ with eigenvalue $k\hbar$. For $k < 0$, $k = -l$, $j = l - \frac{1}{2}$ the normalized spinor is of the form

$$\psi_{j\mu k}(\mathbf{r}) = \begin{pmatrix} \sqrt{\dfrac{j-\mu+1}{2(j+1)}} & Y_{j+1/2,\mu-1/2}(\theta,\phi)f(r) \\ -\sqrt{\dfrac{j+\mu+1}{2(j+1)}} & Y_{j+1/2,\mu+1/2}(\theta,\phi)f(r) \\ \sqrt{\dfrac{j+\mu}{2j}} & Y_{j-1/2,\mu-1/2}(\theta,\phi)g(r) \\ \sqrt{\dfrac{j-\mu}{2j}} & Y_{j-1/2,\mu+1/2}(\theta,\phi)g(r) \end{pmatrix} \tag{10–367}$$

$$= \begin{pmatrix} f(r) & \xi_{j\mu}^{-} \\ g(r) & \xi_{j\mu}^{+} \end{pmatrix} \tag{10–368}$$

It remains for us to exhibit the hamiltonian in a form that allows us to make use of the above results. To this end we note that we can decompose the vector $\mathbf{p}$ into components parallel and perpendicular to an arbitrary unit vector $\mathbf{n}$ as follows

$$\mathbf{p} = \mathbf{n}(\mathbf{n}\cdot\mathbf{p}) - \mathbf{n}\times(\mathbf{n}\times\mathbf{p}) \tag{10–369}$$

whence

$$\boldsymbol{\alpha}\cdot\mathbf{p} = (\boldsymbol{\alpha}\cdot\mathbf{n})(\mathbf{n}\cdot\mathbf{p}) - \boldsymbol{\alpha}\cdot\mathbf{n}\times(\mathbf{n}\times\mathbf{p}) \tag{10–370}$$

Choose $\mathbf{n} = \mathbf{r}/r$, in which case

$$\mathbf{r}\times(\mathbf{r}\times\mathbf{p}) = \mathbf{r}\times\mathbf{L} \tag{10–371}$$

so that with $p_r = \mathbf{n}\cdot\mathbf{p} = -i\hbar(\partial/\partial r)$ and $\alpha_r = \mathbf{n}\cdot\boldsymbol{\alpha}$

$$\boldsymbol{\alpha}\cdot\mathbf{p} = \alpha_r p_r - \boldsymbol{\alpha}\cdot(\mathbf{r}\times\mathbf{L}) \tag{10–372}$$

If we write $\boldsymbol{\alpha} = \gamma_5\mathbf{\Sigma}$, and note that, if $\mathbf{A}$ and $\mathbf{B}$ are operators that commute with $\mathbf{\Sigma}$, then

$$\begin{aligned}(\mathbf{\Sigma}\cdot\mathbf{A})(\mathbf{\Sigma}\cdot\mathbf{B}) &= \tfrac{1}{2}(\Sigma_i\Sigma_j + \Sigma_j\Sigma_i)A_iB_j + \tfrac{1}{2}(\Sigma_i\Sigma_j - \Sigma_j\Sigma_i)A_iB_j \\ &= A_iB_i + i\varepsilon_{ljk}\Sigma_lA_jB_k \\ &= \mathbf{A}\cdot\mathbf{B} + i\mathbf{\Sigma}\cdot(\mathbf{A}\times\mathbf{B})\end{aligned} \tag{10–373}$$

Upon applying this last formula to $\mathbf{\Sigma}\cdot(\mathbf{r}\times\mathbf{L})$, and noting that $\mathbf{r}\cdot\mathbf{L} = 0$, Eq. (10–372) can be rewritten as

$$\boldsymbol{\alpha}\cdot\mathbf{p} = \alpha_r p_r + i(\boldsymbol{\alpha}\cdot\mathbf{r})(\mathbf{\Sigma}\cdot\mathbf{L})r^{-2} \tag{10–374}$$

After inserting into this equation the expressions (10–328) and (10–329) for K, we can finally write the hamiltonian in the form

$$\mathrm{h} = c\alpha_r p_r + ic\alpha_r \frac{\beta K - \hbar}{r} + \beta mc^2 + eA^0(r)$$

$$= i\hbar c\alpha_r \left(\frac{\beta K\hbar^{-1} - 1}{r} - \frac{\partial}{\partial r}\right) + \beta mc^2 + eA^0(r) \qquad (10\text{–}375)$$

Note incidentally that K commutes with α_r.

In computing $\alpha_r \psi_{j\mu k}$ we shall have to evaluate quantities such as $(\boldsymbol{\sigma}\cdot\mathbf{n})\xi^{\pm}$ since

$$\alpha_r \psi_{j\mu k} = \begin{pmatrix} 0 & \boldsymbol{\sigma}\cdot\mathbf{n} \\ \boldsymbol{\sigma}\cdot\mathbf{n} & 0 \end{pmatrix} \begin{pmatrix} f(r) & \xi^{+}_{j\mu} \\ g(r) & \xi^{-}_{j\mu} \end{pmatrix} \qquad (10\text{–}376)$$

in the case that $k > 0$. To do so we note that the operator $N = \boldsymbol{\sigma}\cdot\mathbf{n}$ has the following properties:

(a) $N^2 = 1$;
(b) N commutes with $\mathbf{L} + \frac{1}{2}\hbar\boldsymbol{\sigma}$, being a scalar operator;
(c) N anticommutes with $\boldsymbol{\sigma}\cdot\mathbf{L} + \hbar = \kappa$, $[N,\kappa]_+ = 0$.

These properties allow us to determine $N\xi^{+}_{j\mu}$ up to a constant. Since the $\xi^{\pm}_{j\mu}$ are eigenfunctions of $L_3 + \frac{1}{2}\hbar\sigma_3$ with eigenvalue μ, and of $\boldsymbol{\sigma}\cdot\mathbf{L} + \hbar$ with eigenvalue $\pm k$, we have

$$\kappa(N\xi^{\pm}_{j\mu}) = -N\kappa\xi^{\pm}_{j\mu} = \mp k(N\xi^{\pm}_{j\mu}) \qquad (10\text{–}377)$$

and

$$(L_3 + \tfrac{1}{2}\hbar\sigma_3)(N\xi^{\pm}_{j\mu}) = N(L_3 + \tfrac{1}{2}\hbar\sigma_3)\xi^{\pm}_{j\mu} = \mu\hbar N\xi^{\pm}_{j\mu} \qquad (10\text{–}378)$$

$N\xi^{\pm}_{j\mu}$, therefore, belongs to the same values of $j\mu$ as does $\xi^{\pm}_{j\mu}$ but to the opposite value of k; hence

$$(\boldsymbol{\sigma}\cdot\mathbf{n})\xi^{\pm}_{j\mu} = d_{j\mu}\xi^{\mp}_{j\mu} \qquad (10\text{–}379)$$

where $d_{j\mu}$ are certain constants to be determined. Since $N = \boldsymbol{\sigma}\cdot\mathbf{n}$ commutes with the operators $L_1 \pm iL_2 + \frac{1}{2}\hbar(\sigma_1 \pm i\sigma_2)$ (the latter are step up (+) and step down (−) operators for the μ-value), one deduces that $d_{j,\mu} = d_{j,\mu-1}$ so that the $d_{j\mu}$ are independent of μ. We write $(\boldsymbol{\sigma}\cdot\mathbf{n})\xi^{\pm}_{j\mu} = d_j\xi^{\mp}_{j\mu}$. From the normalization property of the $\xi^{\pm}_{j\mu}$ and the fact that $N^2 = 1$, one further concludes that $|d_j| = 1$. Finally from the action of N on the spinor ξ^{+}_{jj}, one establishes that in fact $d_j = +1$, so that

$$(\boldsymbol{\sigma}\cdot\mathbf{n})\xi^{\pm}_{j\mu} = \xi^{\mp}_{j\mu} \qquad (10\text{–}380)$$

Upon substituting the forms (10–365) and (10–366) for ψ into the equation

$$\mathrm{h}\psi_{j\mu k} = E\psi_{j\mu k} \tag{10–381}$$

and making use of the identity (10–379), one finds the following coupled equations for f and g

$$(E - mc^2 - eA^0(r))f + i\hbar c\left(\frac{dg}{dr} + \frac{1}{r}g + \frac{k}{r}g\right) = 0 \tag{10–382}$$

$$(E + mc^2 - eA^0(r))g + i\hbar c\left(\frac{df}{dr} + \frac{1}{r}f - \frac{k}{r}f\right) = 0 \tag{10–383}$$

The normalization of f and g is such that

$$\int_0^\infty r^2 dr(|f|^2 + |g|^2) = 1 \tag{10–384}$$

The above equations assume a somewhat simpler form on introducing the functions

$$F = rf \qquad G = irg \tag{10–385}$$

They take the form

$$(E - mc^2 - eA^0(r))F + \hbar c\left(\frac{dG}{dr} + \frac{k}{r}G\right) = 0 \tag{10–386}$$

$$(E + mc^2 - eA^0(r))F - \hbar c\left(\frac{dF}{dr} - \frac{k}{r}F\right) = 0 \tag{10–387}$$

and the normalization condition becomes

$$\int_0^\infty dr(|F|^2 + |G|^2) = 1 \tag{10–388}$$

For the case of a Coulomb field, special methods exist that reduce the equation to a form where the nonrelativistic solutions can be used.[11] Thus, if we denote by ψ the wave function of the electron moving in a Coulomb field, then ψ obeys the Dirac equation

$$\left[c\boldsymbol{\gamma}\cdot\mathbf{p} + mc^2 - \gamma_0\left(E + \frac{Zc^2}{4\pi r}\right)\right]\psi = 0 \tag{10–389}$$

Here E denotes the energy and $\mathbf{p} = -i\hbar\boldsymbol{\nabla}$. It turns out to be convenient to express ψ in terms of a function ϕ by the relation

$$\begin{aligned}\psi &= \frac{1}{2mc^2}\left[-c\boldsymbol{\gamma}\cdot\mathbf{p} + \gamma_0\left(E + \frac{Ze^2}{4\pi r}\right) + mc^2\right]\phi \\ &= \mathscr{P}_+\phi\end{aligned} \tag{10–390}$$

[11] P. C. Martin and R. J. Glauber, *Phys. Rev.*, **109**, 1306 (1958).

By substituting this expression for ψ into (10–389) one finds that ϕ must satisfy the following second-order Dirac equation

$$0 = \left[c\boldsymbol{\gamma}\cdot\mathbf{p} - \gamma_0\left(E + \frac{Ze^2}{4\pi r}\right) + mc^2\right] \times \left[-c\boldsymbol{\gamma}\cdot\mathbf{p} + \gamma_0\left(E + \frac{Ze^2}{4\pi r}\right) + mc^2\right]\phi \qquad (10\text{–}391)$$

Since Eq. (10–391) is a second-order equation for the four-component spinor ϕ, it will have twice as many solutions as Eq. (10–389), the solutions of which we are interested in obtaining. Equation (10–391) can be further simplified by multiplying out the two bracketed factors

$$0 = \left[\mathbf{p}^2c^2 + m^2c^4 - c\left[\boldsymbol{\alpha}\cdot\mathbf{p}, \frac{Ze^2}{4\pi r}\right] - \left(E + \frac{Ze^2}{4\pi r}\right)^2\right]\phi \qquad (10\text{–}392)$$

$$= \left[\mathbf{p}^2c^2 + m^2c^4 - \left(E + \frac{Ze^2}{4\pi r}\right)^2 - \alpha_r\frac{i\hbar cZe^2}{4\pi r^2}\right]\phi \qquad (10\text{–}393)$$

where $\alpha_r = \boldsymbol{\alpha}\cdot\mathbf{r}/|\mathbf{r}|$. The adjoint spinors $\tilde{\phi} = \phi^*\gamma_0$ and $\tilde{\psi}$ satisfy the equation

$$\tilde{\psi}\left[c\boldsymbol{\gamma}\cdot\mathbf{p} - \gamma_0\left(E + \frac{Ze^2}{4\pi r}\right) + mc^2\right] = 0 \qquad (10\text{–}394)$$

$$\tilde{\phi}\left[\mathbf{p}^2c^2 + m^2c^4 - \left(E + \frac{Ze^2}{4\pi r}\right) - i\hbar\alpha_r c\frac{Ze^2}{4\pi r^2}\right] = 0 \qquad (10\text{–}395)$$

in which $\mathbf{p} = -i\hbar\boldsymbol{\nabla}$ is assumed to act on the left. The normalization of ϕ is so chosen as to agree with the normalization of the ψ, *i.e.*,

$$\mathbf{1} = \int d^3r\tilde{\psi}\gamma_0\psi = \int d^3r\tilde{\phi}\mathscr{P}_+\gamma_0\mathscr{P}_+\phi$$

$$= \int d^3r\tilde{\phi}\left(\frac{E + Ze^2/4\pi r}{mc^2}\right)\mathscr{P}_+\phi \qquad (10\text{–}396)$$

The orthogonality relations satisfied by solutions ϕ_i,ϕ_j corresponding to the energies E_i and E_j, are found from (10–393) and (10–395) to be

$$\int d^3r\tilde{\phi}_j\left(E_i + E_j + \frac{2Ze^2}{4\pi r}\right)\phi_i = 0 \qquad (10\text{–}397)$$

for $E_j \neq E_i$.

The second-order equation (10–393) is more useful than the first-order equation (10–389) because (10–393) involves only one of the Dirac matrices, α_r, and can, therefore, be solved more easily than

(10–389). If we multiply Eq. (10–369) by $\mathbf{p}$, and again choose for $\mathbf{n}$ the vector $\mathbf{r}/r$, we obtain the following familiar decomposition of $\mathbf{p}^2$

$$\mathbf{p}^2 = r^{-1}p_r^2 r + \mathbf{L}^2 r^{-2}$$

where $p_r = -i\hbar\partial/\partial r$ is the radial momentum and $\mathbf{L}$ the orbital angular momentum. If then we express $\mathbf{L}^2$ in terms of K by squaring Eq. (10–329)

$$\mathbf{L}^2 = K(K - \beta\hbar) \tag{10–398}$$

we may rewrite Eqs. (10–392) and (10–393) as follows

$$\left[p_r^2 + \frac{K(K-\beta\hbar) - \left(\dfrac{Ze^2}{4\pi c}\right)^2 - i\hbar\alpha_r \dfrac{Ze^2}{4\pi c}}{r^2} - \frac{2EZe^2}{c^2 r} + m^2c^2 - \left(\frac{E}{c}\right)^2\right]\phi = 0 \tag{10–399}$$

The coefficient of $1/r^2$ now takes the place of the operator for the square of the orbital angular momentum in the nonrelativistic Schrödinger equation. This correspondence can be made more explicit by introducing the Johnson operator

$$\mathscr{J} = -\frac{1}{\hbar}\left(K\beta + i\frac{Ze^2}{4\pi c}\alpha_r\right) \tag{10–400}$$

since in terms of this operator Eq. (10–399) reads

$$\left[p_r^2 + \frac{\mathscr{J}(\mathscr{J}+1)\hbar^2}{r^2} - \frac{2EZe^2}{4\pi c^2 r} + m^2c^2 - \left(\frac{E}{c}\right)^2\right]\phi = 0 \tag{10–401}$$

Since the operator $\mathscr{J}$ satisfies the equation

$$\mathscr{J}^2 = \frac{K^2}{\hbar^2} - \left(\frac{Ze^2}{4\pi c\hbar}\right)^2 \tag{10–402}$$

its eigenvalues, Λ, are

$$\begin{aligned}\Lambda &= \pm\left[(j+\tfrac{1}{2})^{1/2} - \left(\frac{Ze^2}{4\pi\hbar c}\right)^2\right]^{1/2} \\ &= \pm\lambda\end{aligned} \tag{10–403}$$

where

$$\frac{e^2}{4\pi\hbar c} = \alpha \simeq (137)^{-1} \tag{10–404}$$

Eigenfunctions of the operator $\mathscr{J}$, which are also eigenfunctions of Eqs. (10–392) and (10–393), satisfy

$$\left[p_r^2 + \frac{\Lambda(\Lambda + 1)\hbar^2}{r^2} - \frac{2EZe^2}{4\pi c^2 r} + m^2c^2 - \left(\frac{E}{c}\right)^2\right]\phi = 0 \tag{10–405}$$

The pair of uncoupled equations for $\Lambda = \pm\sqrt{(j + \frac{1}{2})^{1/2} - (Z\alpha)^2} = \pm\lambda$ now replaces the coupled first order equations for f and g (Eqs. (10–382)–(10–383)). Since J_z, $\mathscr{J}$, K all commute with one another the solutions of (10–405) may be taken as eigenfunctions of K and J_z.

The eigenfunctions and eigenvalues of Eq. (10–405) can be obtained as in the nonrelativistic case upon introducing the variables

$$\mu_i^2 = m^2c^2 - \left(\frac{E_i}{c}\right)^2 \tag{10–406}$$

$$x = 2\mu r/\hbar \tag{10–407}$$

$$\eta_i = \frac{Ze^2}{4\pi\hbar c}\frac{E_i}{\mu c} \tag{10–408}$$

and the spinor

$$\phi_i(r) = [u_i(x)/x]v^k_{\pm\lambda} \tag{10–409}$$

which is an eigenfunction of $\mathscr{J}$ and K

$$Kv^k_{\pm\lambda} = kv^k_{\pm\lambda} \tag{10–410}$$

$$\mathscr{J}v^k_{\pm\lambda} = \pm\lambda v^k_{\pm\lambda} \tag{10–411}$$

The amplitude $u_i(x)$ then satisfies the equation

$$\left[\frac{d^2}{dx^2} + \frac{\eta_i}{x} - \frac{1}{4} - \frac{\lambda(\lambda \pm 1)}{x^2}\right]u_i(x) = 0 \tag{10–412}$$

which will be recognized as being identical to that encountered in the nonrelativistic Coulomb problem. The eigenvalues E_i are

$$E_i = mc^2\frac{1}{\sqrt{1 + \dfrac{Z^2\alpha^2}{n_r + \lambda + \frac{1}{2} \pm \frac{1}{2}}}} \tag{10–413}$$

where n_r is the radial quantum number, which takes on the value $0,1,2,\cdots$ and where the alternative signs refer to $\Lambda = \pm\lambda$ respectively.

The solutions of Eq. (10–405) include the solutions to *two* first-order equations, namely, the first-order Dirac equation and this first-order equation with the sign of the mass term reversed. Equivalently, if ϕ_i is an eigenfunction of either of the operator factors occurring in (10–391), it satisfies the second-order Eq. (10–393).

The eigenfunctions of the first-order equation (10–389) may also be taken to be eigenfunctions of the operators K and J_z as we have noted earlier in this section. These eigenfunctions must be expressible as combinations of the solutions of (10–405), which have the same eigenvalue E_i,k,m. In general, there are two such wave functions, one for each value $\pm\lambda$. Neither of them need be an eigenfunction of the first-order equation since $\mathscr{J}$, unlike K, does not commute with the ordinary first-order Dirac hamiltonian. The correct linear combinations are most simply obtained by applying the projection operator occurring in Eq. (10–390) to remove the negative mass part of the function ϕ_i in (10–392) and (10–393).

According to the Dirac equation the $2S_{1/2}$ and $2P_{1/2}$ states coincide. It was, however, observed by Lamb and Rutherford that the $2S_{1/2}$ is higher than the $2P_{1/2}$ state by ~ 1060 Mc/s. For the explanation of this level shift, one must take into account the quantum aspect of the electromagnetic field as well as those of the negaton-positon field.

REFERENCES

For the treatment of the Dirac equation in an external field, see:

Bethe, H. A., and Salpeter, E. E., *Handbuch der Physik*, Vol. 35, Band 1, Springer Verlag, Berlin-Göttingen, 1955.

Rose, M. E., *Relativistic Electron Theory*, John Wiley and Sons, Inc., New York, 1961.

For the case of the Coulomb field, particularly elegant methods of solution are due to:

Hylleraas, E. A., *Z. Physik*, **140**, 626 (1955).

Martin, P. C., and Glauber, R. J., *Phys. Rev.*, **109**, 1306 (1958).

The experimental results for the hydrogenic spectrum are reviewed in:

Series, G. W., *Spectrum of Atomic Hydrogen*, Oxford University Press, 1957.

CHAPTER 11

QUANTUM ELECTRODYNAMICS

by

S. S. SCHWEBER

Brandeis University

11.1. Quantum Electrodynamics in the Heisenberg Picture.—

With the present section we begin our discussion of the quantum theoretical description of the interaction between the negaton-positon field and the radiation field; *i.e.*, of quantum electrodynamics proper.

In the Heisenberg picture the electromagnetic field operators satisfy the equations of motion

$$-\frac{\partial \mathscr{H}(x)}{\partial x_0} = \nabla \times \mathscr{E}(x) \tag{11–1}$$

$$\frac{\partial \mathscr{E}(x)}{\partial x_0} = \nabla \times \mathscr{H}(x) - \mathbf{j}(x) \tag{11–2}$$

$$\text{div}\, \mathscr{E}(x) = \rho(x) \tag{11–3}$$

$$\text{div}\, \mathscr{H}(x) = 0 \tag{11–4}$$

where

$$j^0(x) = \rho(x) = \frac{e}{2}[\tilde{\psi}(x)\gamma_0, \psi(x)] \tag{11–5}$$

and

$$\mathbf{j}(x) = \frac{e}{2}[\tilde{\psi}(x)\boldsymbol{\gamma}, \psi(x)] \tag{11–6}$$

are the charge and current density operators for the negaton-positon field. These operators will by virtue of the equation of motion of the negaton-positon field obey the continuity equation

$$\partial^\mu j_\mu(x) = \frac{\partial \rho(x)}{\partial x_0} + \nabla \cdot \mathbf{j}(x) = 0 \tag{11–7}$$

If we decompose the electric field operator into a transverse and longitudinal part

$$\mathscr{E}(x) = \mathscr{E}_t(x) + \mathscr{E}_\ell(x) \tag{11–8}$$

with

$$\nabla \cdot \mathscr{E}_t(x) = 0 \tag{11–9}$$

$$\nabla \times \mathscr{E}_\ell(x) = 0 \tag{11–10}$$

then since the curl of $\mathscr{E}_\ell(x)$ vanishes, it can be written as the gradient of the scalar operator function

$$\mathscr{E}_\ell(x) = -\nabla\phi(x) \tag{11–12}$$

From Eq. (11–12) it now follows that

$$\text{div}\,\mathscr{E}(x) = -\nabla^2\phi(x) = \rho(x) \tag{11–13}$$

so that

$$\phi(\mathbf{x},t) = \frac{1}{4\pi}\int \frac{\rho(\mathbf{x}',t)}{|\mathbf{x}-\mathbf{x}'|}\, d^3x' \tag{11–14}$$

$\phi(\mathbf{x},t)$, of course, will be recognized as the Coulomb potential due to the charge distribution $\rho(\mathbf{x}',t)$. Since $\nabla \times \mathscr{E}_\ell(x) = 0$, the Maxwell equation (11–1) now reads

$$\frac{\partial \mathscr{H}(x)}{\partial x_0} = -\nabla \times \mathscr{E}_t(x) \tag{11–15}$$

with

$$\nabla\cdot\mathscr{E}_t(x) = 0 \tag{11–16}$$

Furthermore, by virtue of the continuity equation (11–7), we can write

$$\begin{aligned}
\frac{\partial \mathscr{E}(x)}{\partial x_0} &= \frac{\partial \mathscr{E}_t(x)}{\partial x_0} + \frac{\partial \mathscr{E}_\ell(x)}{\partial x_0} \\
&= \frac{\partial \mathscr{E}_t(x)}{\partial x_0} - \nabla\int \frac{\partial_t\rho(\mathbf{x}',t)}{4\pi|\mathbf{x}-\mathbf{x}'|}\, d^3x' \\
&= \frac{\partial \mathscr{E}_t(x)}{\partial x_0} + \nabla\int \frac{\nabla_{x'}\cdot\mathbf{j}(\mathbf{x}',t)}{4\pi|\mathbf{x}-\mathbf{x}'|}\, d^3x'
\end{aligned} \tag{11–17}$$

so that the Maxwell equation (11–2) now reads

$$\frac{\partial \mathscr{E}_t(x)}{\partial x_0} = \nabla \times \mathscr{H}(x) - \mathbf{j}_t(x) \tag{11–18}$$

where $\mathbf{j}_t(x)$ is equal to

$$\mathbf{j}_t(x) = \mathbf{j}(x) + \nabla_x \int \frac{\nabla_{x'}\cdot\mathbf{j}(\mathbf{x}',t)}{4\pi|\mathbf{x}-\mathbf{x}'|}\, d^3x' \tag{11–19}$$

It should be noted that since

$$\nabla_x^2 \frac{1}{4\pi|\mathbf{x}-\mathbf{x}'|} = -\delta(\mathbf{x}-\mathbf{x}') \tag{11–20}$$

the current operator $\mathbf{j}_t(x)$ is transverse

$$\nabla\cdot\mathbf{j}_t(x) = 0 \tag{11–21}$$

which property is, of course, required, in order that Eq. (11–18) be consistent. We have, therefore, rewritten Maxwell's equations in a form where they involve only $\mathscr{E}_t(x)$ and $\mathscr{H}(x)$:

$$\frac{\partial \mathscr{H}(x)}{\partial x_0} = -\nabla \times \mathscr{E}_t(x); \qquad \nabla \cdot \mathscr{H} = 0 \tag{11–22}$$

$$\frac{\partial \mathscr{E}_t(x)}{\partial x_0} = \nabla \times \mathscr{H}(x) - \mathbf{j}_t(x); \quad \nabla \cdot \mathscr{E}_t(x) = 0 \tag{11–23}$$

We shall adopt these variables as the dynamical variables describing the quantized electromagnetic field.

As in the case of the radiation field, since $\nabla \cdot \mathscr{H}(x) = 0$, we introduce a vector potential $\mathscr{A}(x)$ by the equation [1]

$$\mathscr{H}(x) = \nabla \times \mathscr{A}(x) \tag{11–24}$$

and to make the correspondence unique we shall require $\mathscr{A}(x)$ to be transverse

$$\nabla \cdot \mathscr{A}(x) = 0 \tag{11–25}$$

in which case

$$\mathscr{A}(\mathbf{x},t) = \int \frac{\nabla_{x'} \times \mathscr{H}(\mathbf{x}',t)}{4\pi|\mathbf{x} - \mathbf{x}'|} d^3x' \tag{11–26}$$

and

$$\Box \mathscr{A}(x) = \mathbf{j}_t(x) \tag{11–27}$$

Thus, given $\mathscr{H}$, $\mathscr{A}$ is uniquely determined so that $\mathscr{H}$ and $\mathscr{A}$ are equivalent dynamical variables.

The description of the quantized electromagnetic field in terms of $\mathscr{E}_t$ and $\mathscr{A}$, with $\mathscr{A}(\mathbf{x},t)$ satisfying Eqs. (11–25) and (11–27) is called the transverse or Coulomb gauge.

More generally we could write $\mathscr{H} = \nabla \times \mathscr{A}$ with $\mathscr{A}$ given by

$$\mathscr{A}(x) = \mathscr{A}_t(x) + \nabla Z(x) \tag{11–28}$$

$$\nabla \cdot \mathscr{A}_t(x) = 0 \tag{11–29}$$

where $Z(x)$, the longitudinal part of $\mathscr{A}$ commutes with all other

[1] This vector potential $\mathscr{A}$ should not be confused with the vector potential for the radiation field introduced in Section 9.8 of Chapter 9. The vector potential $\mathscr{A}$ of the present section obeys the equation $\Box \mathscr{A} = \mathbf{j}_t$. We have denoted it by script cap $\mathscr{A}$ to indicate that it satisfies the transversality condition div $\mathscr{A} = 0$ in contradistinction to the Lorentz gauge potentials A_μ to be introduced later, which satisfy $\partial_\mu A^\mu(x) = 0$ and $\Box A_\mu = j_\mu$.

operators. (It can, therefore, be taken as an arbitrary c-number.) Under these circumstances, Maxwell equations become

$$\mathscr{E}_t(x) = -\frac{\partial \mathscr{A}_t(x)}{\partial x_0} \tag{11-30}$$

so that

$$\mathscr{E}(x) = -\frac{\partial \mathscr{A}_t}{\partial x_0} - \nabla\phi \tag{11-31}$$

If we define $\mathscr{A}^0$ by the equation

$$\mathscr{A}^0(x) = \phi(x) - \frac{\partial Z(x)}{\partial x_0} \tag{11-32}$$

we can then write

$$\mathscr{E}(x) = -\frac{\partial \mathscr{A}(x)}{\partial t} - \nabla\mathscr{A}^0(x) \tag{11-33}$$

In the following we shall fix the gauge by choosing $Z = 0$.

The advantage of introducing the vector potentials $\mathscr{A}(\mathbf{x},t)$ lies in the fact that it is in terms of these variables that the matter-field equations assume their simplest and *local* form, namely

$$i\frac{\partial\psi(x)}{\partial x_0} = (-i\boldsymbol{\alpha}\cdot\nabla + \beta m)\psi(x) - e\boldsymbol{\alpha}\cdot\mathscr{A}(x)\psi(x) + \frac{e}{2}\{\phi(x),\psi(x)\} \tag{11-34}$$

The hamiltonian describing the negaton-positon field interacting with the electromagnetic field is

$$H = H_0(t) + H_I(t) \tag{11-35}$$

$$H_0(t) = \int_{x_0=t} d^3x\psi^*(x)(-i\boldsymbol{\alpha}\cdot\nabla + \beta m)\psi(x) + \tfrac{1}{2}\int d^3x(\mathscr{E}^2(x) + \mathscr{H}^2(x)) \tag{11-36}$$

$$H_I(t) = -\int_{x_0=t} d^3x\mathbf{j}(x)\cdot\mathscr{A}(x) \tag{11-37}$$

By decomposing $\mathscr{E}$ into its longitudinal and transverse part, and noting that

$$\int d^3x\mathscr{E}_t(x)\cdot\mathscr{E}_\ell(x) = -\int d^3x\mathscr{E}_t(x)\cdot\nabla\phi(x) = +\int d^3x\nabla\cdot\mathscr{E}_t(x)\phi(x) = 0 \tag{11-38}$$

we can write

$$\int d^3x \mathscr{E}^2(x) = \int d^3x\{\mathscr{E}_t^2(x) + \mathscr{E}_\ell^2(x)\} \tag{11–39}$$

However, for any charge distribution extending only over a finite region of space

$$\begin{aligned}\int \mathscr{E}_\ell^2(x) d^3x &= \int d^3x \nabla\phi(x)\cdot\nabla\phi(x) \\ &= \int d^3x \phi(x)\rho(x) \\ &= \int d^3x \int d^3x' \frac{\rho(\mathbf{x},t)\rho(\mathbf{x}',t)}{4\pi|\mathbf{x} - \mathbf{x}'|}\end{aligned} \tag{11–40}$$

Hence we can rewrite the hamiltonian in the form

$$\begin{aligned}H = \tfrac{1}{2} \int & d^3x(\mathscr{E}_t^2(x) + \mathscr{H}^2(x)) \\ &+ \int d^3x \psi^*(x)(-i\boldsymbol{\alpha}\cdot\nabla + \beta m)\psi(x) \\ &+ \frac{1}{8\pi} \int d^3x \int d^3x \frac{\rho(\mathbf{x},t)\rho(\mathbf{x}',t)}{|\mathbf{x} - \mathbf{x}'|} \\ &- \int d^3x \mathbf{j}(x)\cdot\mathscr{A}(x)\end{aligned} \tag{11–41}$$

We shall again postulate commutation rules which have the property that the equations of motion of the matter field and of the electromagnetic field are consequences of the Heisenberg equation of motion:

$$[Q(x_0),H] = i\frac{\partial}{\partial x_0} Q(x_0) \tag{11–42}$$

This, in fact, is how the commutation rules are determined.

The commutation rules that satisfy these criteria are

$$\begin{aligned}0 = [\mathscr{E}_t^j(x),\mathscr{E}_t^r(x')]_{x_0=x_0'} &= [\mathscr{H}^j(x),\mathscr{H}^r(x')]_{x_0=x_0'} \\ &= [\mathscr{A}^j(x),\mathscr{A}^r(x')]_{x_0=x_0'} = 0\end{aligned} \tag{11–43}$$

$$\{\psi_\rho(x),\psi_\sigma(x')\}_{x_0=x_0'} = \{\tilde{\psi}_\rho(x),\tilde{\psi}_\sigma(x')\}_{x_0=x_0'} = 0 \tag{11–44}$$

and

$$[\mathscr{E}_t^j(x),\mathscr{A}^r(x')]_{x_0=x_0'} = i\left(\delta^{jk} - \frac{\partial^j\partial^r}{\partial^2}\right)\delta(\mathbf{x} - \mathbf{x}') \tag{11–45}$$

$$\{\psi_\rho(x),\psi_\sigma^*(x')\}_{x_0=x_0'} = \delta_{\rho\sigma}\delta(\mathbf{x} - \mathbf{x}') \tag{11–46}$$

Furthermore, since $\mathscr{H}, \mathscr{E}_t$ and ψ, ψ^* refer to different degrees of freedom, they commute for equal times. It should be noted that the above commutation rules are consistent with the operator conditions div $\mathscr{E}_t = 0$ and div $\mathscr{H}$ = div $\mathscr{A} = 0$. They also guarantee that div $\mathscr{E}_t$ and div $\mathscr{H}$ commute with the hamiltonian, and, hence, are constant in time. Since they commute with the dynamical variables $\mathscr{E}_t$, $\mathscr{H}$, ψ and ψ^* for all times they are multiples of the identity operator, and, therefore, constant c numbers. If the value of these c numbers is taken to be zero initially, div $\mathscr{E}_t$ and div $\mathscr{H}$ will be zero for all times. Now the hamiltonian (11–41) together with the commutation rules (11–43)–(11–46) determine [via Eq. (11–42)] the equation of motion for the electromagnetic field operators to be Maxwell's equations (11–15) and (11–18). By requiring that div $\mathscr{E}_t$ and div $\mathscr{H}$ be equal to zero initially, we have then guaranteed that the theory under discussion is that of the electromagnetic field in interaction with a charge current density $\rho(x), \mathbf{j}(x)$. Explicitly, the hamiltonian (11–41) gives rise to the following equation of motion for the Heisenberg operators:

$$i\partial_0\psi(x) = (m\beta - i\boldsymbol{\alpha}\cdot\boldsymbol{\nabla} - e\boldsymbol{\alpha}\cdot\mathscr{A}(x))\psi(x) + \frac{e}{2}\{\phi(x),\psi(x)\} \tag{11–47}$$

$$\partial_0\mathscr{E}_t(x) = \text{curl}\,\mathscr{H}(x) - \mathbf{j}_t(x) \tag{11–48}$$

$$\partial_0\mathscr{A}(x) = -\mathscr{E}_t(x) \tag{11–49}$$

Recall also that

$$\mathscr{H} = \text{curl}\,\mathscr{A} \tag{11–50}$$

$$\text{div}\,\mathscr{A} = 0 \tag{11–51}$$

Equation (11–48) becomes, therefore

$$-\partial_0^2\mathscr{A}(x) = -\boldsymbol{\nabla}^2\mathscr{A}(x) - \mathbf{j}_t(x) \tag{11–52}$$

or

$$\Box\mathscr{A}(x) = \mathbf{j}_t(x) \tag{11–53}$$

wherein both $\mathscr{A}$ and $\mathbf{j}_t(x)$ are transverse

$$\boldsymbol{\nabla}\cdot\mathscr{A}(x) = 0 \tag{11–54}$$

$$\boldsymbol{\nabla}\cdot\mathbf{j}_t(x) = 0 \tag{11–55}$$

To deduce the physical content of the theory we first proceed in a heuristic manner. We define "in" and "out" fields in a manner analogous to the case of the negaton-positon field interacting with an external electromagnetic field (see Chapter 10)

$$\psi(x) = \psi_{\text{in}}(x) + e\int S_R(x - x')\gamma^\mu \mathscr{A}_\mu(x')\psi(x')d^4x' \tag{11–56}$$

$$= \psi_{\text{out}}(x) + e\int S_A(x - x')\gamma^\mu \mathscr{A}_\mu(x')\psi(x')d^4x' \tag{11–57}$$

where $\mathscr{A}^i(x)$ is the transverse three-vector defined above, and

$$\mathscr{A}^0(x) = \phi(x) = \int \frac{\rho(\mathbf{x}',t)}{4\pi|\mathbf{x} - \mathbf{x}'|}\, d^3x'$$

$$= -\frac{e}{2}\int \frac{[\tilde{\psi}(\mathbf{x}',t)\gamma^0,\psi(\mathbf{x}',t)]}{4\pi|\mathbf{x} - \mathbf{x}'|}\, d^3x' \tag{11–58}$$

Note that $\mathscr{A}^0$ is, therefore, not an electromagnetic field variable: it is determined by the matter field operators.

In (11–56) and (11–57) above, ψ_{in} and ψ_{out} satisfy free field equations:

$$(-i\gamma\cdot\partial + m)\psi_{\substack{\text{in}\\\text{out}}}(x) = 0 \tag{11–59}$$

and it is postulated that they obey free field commutation rules:

$$\{\psi_{\text{in}}(x),\tilde{\psi}_{\text{in}}(x')\} = \{\psi_{\text{out}}(x),\tilde{\psi}_{\text{out}}(x')\}$$

$$= -iS(x - x') \tag{11–60}$$

The representation of these commutation rules is fixed by the requirement that there exist no-particle states $|0\rangle_{\text{in}}$ and $|0\rangle_{\text{out}}$ which are annihilated by the corresponding positive frequency operators, *i.e.*

$$\psi^{(+)}_{\substack{\text{in}\\\text{out}}}(x)|0\rangle_{\substack{\text{in}\\\text{out}}} = \tilde{\psi}^{(+)}_{\substack{\text{in}\\\text{out}}}(x)|0\rangle_{\substack{\text{in}\\\text{out}}} = 0 \tag{11–61}$$

Similarly we define the $\mathscr{A}^j_{\substack{\text{in}\\\text{out}}}(x)$ fields by the equation

$$\mathscr{A}^j(x) = \mathscr{A}^j_{\substack{\text{in}\\\text{out}}}(x) + \int\left(\delta^{jl} - \frac{\partial^j\partial^l}{\boldsymbol{\partial}^2}\right)\cdot D_{\substack{R\\A}}(x - x')j^l_t(x')d^4x' \tag{11–62}$$

They satisfy the equation of motion

$$\Box\mathscr{A}^j_{\substack{\text{in}\\\text{out}}}(x) = 0 \tag{11–63}$$

the subsidiary condition:

$$\operatorname{div}\mathscr{A}^j_{\substack{\text{in}\\\text{out}}}(x) = 0 \tag{11–64}$$

and the commutation rules

$$[\mathscr{A}^j_{\substack{\text{in}\\ \text{out}}}(x), \mathscr{A}^l_{\substack{\text{in}\\ \text{out}}}(x')] = i\left(\delta^{jl} - \frac{\partial^j\partial^l}{\partial^2}\right) D(x - x') \tag{11-65}$$

The representation of these commutation rules is again fixed by the requirement that there exist no-particle states $|0\rangle_{\text{out}}$ and $|0\rangle_{\text{in}}$. The S-matrix is defined as the unitary operator which relates the "in" and "out" fields:

$$S^{-1}\mathscr{A}_{\text{in}\,\mu}(x)S = \mathscr{A}_{\text{out}\,\mu}(x) \tag{11-66}$$

$$S^{-1}\psi_{\text{in}}(x)S = \psi_{\text{out}}(x) \tag{11-67}$$

Such a unitary operator S must exist since ψ_{in} and ψ_{out} (and $\mathscr{A}_{\text{in}\,\mu}$ and $\mathscr{A}_{\text{out}\,\mu}$) form equivalent representation of the commutation rules (11–60) and (11–65). Explicitly it can be computed as follows

$$S = \lim_{t\to+\infty} V^C_+(t) \tag{11-68}$$

where $V^C_+(t)$ satisfies the equation

$$i\hbar\partial_t V^C_+(t) = H^C_{I\,\text{in}}(t)V^C_+(t) \tag{11-69}$$

and the boundary condition

$$\lim_{t\to-\infty} V^C_+(t) = 1 \tag{11-70}$$

with $H_{I\,\text{in}}(t)$ given by

$$H^C_{I\,\text{in}}(t = x_0) = -\int d^3x\,\mathbf{j}_{\text{in}}(x)\cdot\mathscr{A}_{\text{in}}(x) + \int d^3x \int d^3x' \,\frac{\rho_{\text{in}}(x)\rho_{\text{in}}(x')|_{x_0=x_0'}}{8\pi|\mathbf{x} - \mathbf{x}'|} \tag{11-71}$$

What has been accomplished by defining "in" and "out" fields via equations (11–56), (11–57), and (11–62) is the possibility of solving the field equations by iteration. This iteration procedure can be started with the "in" fields. We can then make use of the properties of the free-field operators studied in Chapter 9.

It should be stressed at this point that, as we shall see, the "in" and "out" negaton-positon and electromagnetic fields given by Eqs. (11–56), (11–57), and (11–62) are ill-defined. For the matter field, the reason is that the Coulomb field has an infinite range, and, hence, charged particles, no matter how far apart, still interact with one another and never move freely. Hence, it will not be possible in a many-particle situation to assert, that

$$\lim_{t\to-\infty} \psi(x) \to \psi_{\text{in}}(x) \tag{11–72}$$

$$\lim_{t\to+\infty} \psi(x) \to \psi_{\text{out}}(x) \tag{11–73}$$

Secondly, as we shall see shortly, self-interaction processes occur which alter the properties of even a single-particle system with the result that even "heuristically" Eqs. (11–72) and (11–73) cannot be correct if $\psi_{\substack{\text{in}\\\text{out}}}$ are defined by Eqs. (11–56) and (11–57). However, before turning to these questions we shall show that the above formulation of quantum electrodynamics is equivalent to another, in which the covariance of the theory is manifest. It will turn out, furthermore, that it is simpler to calculate when this latter formalism is employed.

To establish this equivalence, we note that the S-matrix is given by

$$S = 1 + \frac{-i}{\hbar c}\int_{-\infty}^{+\infty} dt H_{I\,\text{in}}^{C}(t) + \frac{1}{2!}\left(\frac{-i}{\hbar c}\right)^2 \int_{-\infty}^{+\infty} dt_1 \int_{-\infty}^{+\infty} dt_2 T(H_{I\,\text{in}}^{C}(t_1)H_{I\,\text{in}}^{C}(t_2)) + \cdots \tag{11–74}$$

with $H_{I\,\text{in}}^{C}(t)$ given by Eq. (11–71). The contraction symbols are readily computed and are given by

$$\begin{aligned}\psi^{\bullet}_{\text{in}\,\alpha}(x)\bar{\psi}^{\bullet}_{\text{in}\,\beta}(x') &= {}_{\text{in}}\langle 0|T(\psi_{\text{in}\,\alpha}(x)\bar{\psi}_{\text{in}\,\beta}(x'))|0\rangle_{\text{in}} \\ &= -\tfrac{1}{2}S_{F\alpha\beta}(x-x') \\ &= \frac{i}{(2\pi)^4}\int d^4p e^{-ip\cdot(x-x')}\frac{(\gamma\cdot p+m)_{\alpha\beta}}{p^2-m^2+i\varepsilon}\end{aligned} \tag{11–75}$$

and

$$\begin{aligned}\mathscr{A}^{j\,\bullet}_{\text{in}}(x)\mathscr{A}^{l\,\bullet}_{\text{in}}(y) &= {}_{\text{in}}\langle 0|T(\mathscr{A}^{j}_{\text{in}}(x)\mathscr{A}^{l}_{\text{in}}(y))|0\rangle_{\text{in}} \\ &= \tfrac{1}{2}\hbar c\left(\delta^{jl} - \frac{\partial^j\partial^l}{\boldsymbol{\partial}^2}\right)D_F(x-y)\end{aligned} \tag{11–76}$$

with

$$D_F(x) = \frac{2i}{(2\pi)^4}\int d^4k \frac{e^{-ik\cdot x}}{k^2+i\varepsilon} \tag{11–77}$$

As a specific application of Wick's theorem and the above contraction rules, consider the scattering of two negatons by one another. To order e^2 the scattering amplitude will be given by

$$
\begin{aligned}
{}_{\text{in}}\langle \mathbf{p}_1's_1',\mathbf{p}_2's_2'|S|\mathbf{p}_1s_1,\mathbf{p}_2s_2\rangle_{\text{in}}
&= {}_{\text{in}}\langle \mathbf{p}_1's_1',\mathbf{p}_2's_2'|1 + \left(\frac{-i}{\hbar c}\right)\int d^4x \mathscr{H}_{I\,\text{in}}^C(x_1) \\
&\quad + \frac{1}{2!}\int d^4x_1 \int d^4x_2 T(\mathscr{H}_{I\,\text{in}}^C(x_1)\mathscr{H}_{I\,\text{in}}^C(x_2)) + \cdots |\mathbf{p}_1s_1,\mathbf{p}_2s_2\rangle_{\text{in}}
\end{aligned}
\tag{11–78}
$$

This matrix element represents the amplitude for the scattering of two negatons from an initial state

$$|\mathbf{p}_1s_1,\mathbf{p}_2s_2\rangle_{\text{in}} = b_{\text{in}}^*(\mathbf{p}s_1)b_{\text{in}}^*(\mathbf{p}s_2)|0\rangle_{\text{in}} \tag{11–79}$$

in which they have momenta $\mathbf{p}_1$ and $\mathbf{p}_2$ and polarization s_1,s_2, to a final state in which they have momenta $\mathbf{p}_1',\mathbf{p}_2'$ and polarization s_1',s_2'.

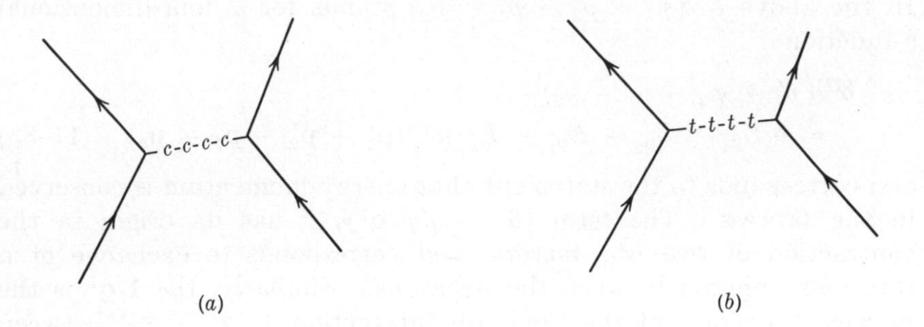

FIG. 11–1.

To order e^2 the Coulomb interaction term contributes to the first-order term in the S-matrix expansion, *i.e.*, to $\int d^4x \mathscr{H}_{I\,\text{in}}^C(x)$, and the $\boldsymbol{j}\cdot\boldsymbol{\mathscr{A}}$ term contributes to second-order. Diagrammatically, we have illustrated these contributions in Fig. 11–1 (c stands for Coulomb, t for transverse photons). To the order indicated, the part of the S-matrix contributing to the process is

$$
\begin{aligned}
&\frac{e^2}{8\pi}\left(-\frac{i}{\hbar c}\right)\int dt \int d^3x_1 \int d^3x_2 \,\frac{\widetilde{\psi_{\text{in}}^{(+)}}(x_1)\gamma^0\psi_{\text{in}}^{(+)}(x_1)\widetilde{\psi_{\text{in}}^{(+)}}(x_2)\gamma^0\psi^{(+)}(x_2)}{|\mathbf{x}_1 - \mathbf{x}_2|} \\
&\quad + \frac{e^2}{2}\left(-\frac{i}{\hbar c}\right)^2 \int d^4x_1 \int d^4x_2 \widetilde{\psi_{\text{in}}^{(+)}}(x_1)\gamma^j\psi_{\text{in}}^{(+)}(x_1) \\
&\quad \times \widetilde{\psi_{\text{in}}^{(+)}}(x_2)\gamma^l\psi_{\text{in}}^{(+)}(x_2)\cdot\frac{\hbar c}{2}\left(\delta^{jl} - \frac{\partial_1^j\partial_1^l}{\boldsymbol{\partial}_1^2}\right) D_F(x_1 - x_2)
\end{aligned}
\tag{11–80}
$$

where the first term is the contribution of the Coulomb interaction between the particles (Fig. 11–1(a)), and the second is that due to the exchange of a transverse photon between the particles (Fig. 11–1(b)). It makes the following contribution to ${}_{\text{in}}\langle \mathbf{p}_2'\mathbf{p}_1'|S|\mathbf{p}_1\mathbf{p}_2\rangle_{\text{in}}$ for $\mathbf{p}_1,\mathbf{p}_2 \neq \mathbf{p}_1',\mathbf{p}_2'$

$$\begin{aligned}
&{}_{\text{out}}\langle \mathbf{p}_2's_2',\mathbf{p}_1's_1'|\mathbf{p}_1s_1,\mathbf{p}_2s_2\rangle_{\text{in}} \\
&\quad = -i\frac{e^2}{\hbar c}\frac{1}{(2\pi)^2}\,\delta^{(4)}(p_1' + p_2' - p_1 - p_2)\tilde{w}_{s_2'}(\mathbf{p}_2')\tilde{w}_{s_1'}(\mathbf{p}_1') \\
&\quad \times \left\{\gamma^{(1)j}\frac{1}{q^2 + i\varepsilon}\left(\delta^{jl} - \frac{q^jq^l}{\mathbf{q}^2}\right)\gamma^{(2)l} + \frac{\gamma_o^{(1)}\gamma_o^{(2)}}{\mathbf{q}^2}\right\} w_{s_1}(\mathbf{p}_1)w_{s_2}(\mathbf{p}_2) \\
&\quad - \text{term with } (\mathbf{p}_1's_1') \text{ and } (\mathbf{p}_2's_2') \text{ interchanged}
\end{aligned} \tag{11–81}$$

where

$$\mathbf{q} = \mathbf{p}_1' - \mathbf{p}_1 \tag{11–82}$$

In the above $\delta^{(4)}(p_1' + p_2' - p_1 - p_2)$ stands for a four-dimensional δ-function

$$\begin{aligned}
&\delta^{(4)}(p_1' + p_2' - p_1 - p_2) \\
&\quad = \delta(E_{\mathbf{p}_1'} + E_{\mathbf{p}_2'} - E_{\mathbf{p}_1} - E_{\mathbf{p}_2})\delta^{(3)}(\mathbf{p}_1' + \mathbf{p}_2' - \mathbf{p}_1 - \mathbf{p}_2)
\end{aligned} \tag{11–83}$$

and corresponds to the statement that energy-momentum is conserved in the process. The term $(\delta^{jl} - q^jq^l/\mathbf{q}^2)q^{-2}$ has its origin in the contraction of two $\mathscr{A}_{\text{in}}$ factors, and corresponds to exchange of a transverse photon between the negatons. Similarly, the $1/\mathbf{q}^2$ is the Fourier transform of the Coulomb interaction $1/|\mathbf{x}_1 - \mathbf{x}_2|$ between the two negatons. The superscripts (1) and (2) on the γ matrices indicate that they act on the spinors labeled by

$$\mathbf{p}_1s_1,\mathbf{p}_1's_1' \quad \text{and} \quad \mathbf{p}_2s_2,\mathbf{p}_2's_2'$$

respectively. The w's are positive-energy spinor solutions of the Dirac equation:

$$(\gamma^0p^0 - \boldsymbol{\gamma}\cdot\mathbf{p} - m)w(\mathbf{p}) = 0 \quad p_0 = E_{\mathbf{p}} \tag{11–84}$$

$$\tilde{w}(\mathbf{p})(\gamma^0p^0 - \boldsymbol{\gamma}\cdot\mathbf{p} - m) = 0 \tag{11–85}$$

Since $\mathbf{q} = (\mathbf{p}_1' - \mathbf{p}_1)$, it follows that

$$\begin{aligned}
\tilde{w}(\mathbf{p}_1')\boldsymbol{\gamma}^{(1)}\cdot\mathbf{q}w(\mathbf{p}_1) &= \tilde{w}(\mathbf{p}_1')(\boldsymbol{\gamma}^{(1)}\cdot\mathbf{p}_1' - \boldsymbol{\gamma}^{(1)}\cdot\mathbf{p}_1)w(\mathbf{p}_1) \\
&= \tilde{w}(\mathbf{p}_1')\gamma^{(1)o}(p_{1o}' - p_{1o})w(\mathbf{p}_1)
\end{aligned} \tag{11–86}$$

and similarly

$$\tilde{w}(\mathbf{p}_2')\boldsymbol{\gamma}^{(2)}\cdot\mathbf{q}w(\mathbf{p}_2) = \tilde{w}(\mathbf{p}_2')\gamma^{(2)o}(p_{2o} - p_{2o}')w(\mathbf{p}_2) \tag{11–87}$$

so that the term $\boldsymbol{\gamma}^{(1)}\cdot\mathbf{q}\,\boldsymbol{\gamma}^{(2)}\cdot\mathbf{q}/\mathbf{q}^2$ when standing between the w spinors can also be written in the form

$$-\frac{1}{q^2}\boldsymbol{\gamma}^{(1)}\cdot\mathbf{q}\,\boldsymbol{\gamma}^{(2)}\cdot\mathbf{q} = -\frac{1}{q^2}\frac{\gamma_0^{(1)}\gamma_0^{(2)}q_0^2}{\mathbf{q}^2} \tag{11–88}$$

This term can be combined with the contribution from the Coulomb interaction to yield a factor

$$-\frac{1}{q^2}\frac{q_o^2}{\mathbf{q}^2}+\frac{1}{\mathbf{q}^2} = -\frac{1}{\mathbf{q}^2}\left(\frac{q^2-q_o^2}{q^2}\right) = \frac{1}{q^2} \tag{11–89}$$

multiplied by $\gamma_0^{(1)}\gamma_0^{(2)}$, which combines with the remaining terms to give

$$\begin{aligned}(\boldsymbol{\gamma}^{(1)}\cdot\boldsymbol{\gamma}^{(2)} - \gamma_0^{(1)}\gamma_0^{(2)})\frac{1}{q^2} &= -\frac{\gamma_\mu^{(1)}\gamma^{(2)\mu}}{q^2}\\ &= -\frac{g_{\mu\nu}}{q^2}\gamma^{(1)\mu}\gamma^{(2)\nu}\end{aligned} \tag{11–90}$$

In other words the matrix element can also be written in the form

$$\begin{aligned}&= -i\frac{e^2}{\hbar c}\frac{1}{(2\pi)^2}\delta^{(4)}(p_1'+p_2'-p_1-p_2)\\ &\quad\times\tilde{w}_{s_2'}(\mathbf{p}_2')\tilde{w}_{s_1'}(\mathbf{p}_1')\gamma^{(1)\mu}\left(\frac{-g_{\mu\nu}}{q^2+i\varepsilon}\right)\gamma^{(2)\nu}w_{s_1}(\mathbf{p}_1)w_{s_2}(\mathbf{p}_2)\end{aligned} \tag{11–91}$$

Essentially what has enabled us to rewrite the matrix element in this form is the fact that the sources of the electromagnetic potential, that is, the currents $j_{\text{in}\,\mu}$ of the charged particles obey the continuity equation $\partial_\mu j_{\text{in}}^\mu(x) = 0$.

Precisely the result (11–91) would have been obtained if, instead of working in the Coulomb gauge, we had adopted the Lorentz gauge. The theory is then described by Heisenberg operators satisfying the following equations of motion [2]

$$(-i\gamma\cdot\partial + m)\psi(x) = -e\gamma\cdot A(x)\psi(x) \tag{11–92}$$

$$\Box A_\mu(x) = j_\mu(x) = -\frac{e}{2}[\tilde{\psi}(x)\gamma_\mu,\psi(x)] \tag{11–93}$$

[2] The matter field operators, although denoted by the same symbol, should not be confused with those defined in the Coulomb gauge by the equations of motion (11–47). The same is true for the "in," "out" operators. The two are related by a transformation of the form

$$\psi_{\text{Coulomb}}(x) = e^{i\Lambda(x)}\psi_{\text{Lorentz}}(x)$$

with $\Lambda(x)$ an operator gauge function. In fact (in the Gupta formalism) $\psi_{\text{Lorentz}}(x)$ operates in a larger Hilbert space than the one in which $\psi_{\text{Coulomb}}(x)$ is defined.

and the physically realizable states of the system satisfy the subsidiary condition

$$(\partial^\mu A_\mu(x)^{(+)}|\Psi\rangle = 0 \tag{11–94}$$

Since the operator $\partial^\mu A_\mu(x)$ by virtue of the equations of motion (11–93) satisfies

$$\Box(\partial^\mu A_\mu(x)) = 0 \tag{11–95}$$

($j_\mu(x)$ is conserved: $\partial_\mu j^\mu(x) = 0$), it can be decomposed into only positive and negative frequency parts in an invariant fashion, hence the subsidiary condition (11–94) is covariant.

We again define "in" and "out" fields by the equations

$$\psi(x) = \psi_{\substack{\text{in}\\\text{out}}}(x) + e\int S_{\substack{R\\A}}(x - x')\gamma^\mu A_\mu(x')\psi(x')d^4x' \tag{11–96}$$

$$A_\mu(x) = A_{\substack{\text{in}\\\text{out}}}(x) + \int D_{\substack{R\\A}}(x - x')j_\mu(x')d^4x' \tag{11–97}$$

These satisfy free-field equations and free-field commutation rules, *e.g.*

$$\Box A_{\text{in}\,\nu}(x) = 0$$

$$[A_{\text{in}\,\mu}(x), A_{\text{in}\,\nu}(x')] = -ig_{\mu\nu}D(x - x') \tag{11–98}$$

$$= -\frac{i}{2\pi}\,g_{\mu\nu}\varepsilon(x_o)\delta(x^2) \tag{11–99}$$

with

$$A_{\text{in}\,\mu}(x) = \sqrt{\frac{1}{2(2\pi)^3}}\int_{k_o>0}\frac{d^3k}{k_o}\sum_{\lambda=0}^{3}\varepsilon_\mu^{(\lambda)}(\mathbf{k})$$

$$\cdot\,\{a_{\text{in}}^{(\lambda)}(\mathbf{k})e^{-ik\cdot x} + a_{\text{in}}^{(\lambda)*}(\mathbf{k})e^{ik\cdot x}\} \tag{11–100}$$

$$\varepsilon_\mu^{(\lambda)}(\mathbf{k})\varepsilon^{(\lambda')\mu}(\mathbf{k}) = g^{\lambda\lambda'} \tag{11–101}$$

$$[a_{\text{in}\,\mu}(\mathbf{k}), a^*_{\text{in}\,\nu}(\mathbf{k}')] = -g_{\mu\nu}k_o\delta(\mathbf{k} - \mathbf{k}') \tag{11–102}$$

with

$$a_{\text{in}\,\mu}(k) = \sum_{\lambda=0}^{3}\varepsilon_\mu^{(\lambda)}(k)a_{\text{in}}^{(\lambda)}(\mathbf{k}) \tag{11–103}$$

We further assume the existence of a no-particle state such that

$$a_{\text{in}\,\mu}(k)|0\rangle_{\text{in}} = 0 \tag{11–104}$$

Note that in the Lorentz gauge we have to adopt the Gupta-Bleuler quantization scheme, with its indefinite metric in a vector space that contains, in addition to the physically realizable states, unphysical states whose norm may be zero or negative. The physical states are characterized by

$$k^{\mu}a_{\text{in}\,\mu}(k)|\Psi\rangle = 0 \tag{11–105}$$

and have a positive norm. The S-matrix is now given by

$$S = \lim_{t \to +\infty} V_{+}^{L}(t) \tag{11–106}$$

where $V_{+}^{L}(t)$ satisfies the integral equation

$$V_{+}^{L}(t) = 1 - i\int_{-\infty}^{t} dt' H_{I\,\text{in}}^{L}(t') V_{+}^{L}(t') \tag{11–107}$$

with

$$H_{I\text{in}}^{L}(t) = \int d^3x j_{\text{in}\,\mu}(x) A_{\text{in}}^{\mu}(x) \tag{11–108}$$

It has the property that

$$S^{-1}A_{\text{in}}(x)S = A_{\text{out}}(x) \tag{11–109}$$

$$S^{-1}\psi_{\text{in}}(x)S = \psi_{\text{out}}(x) \tag{11–110}$$

The contractions that are encountered in applying Wick's theorem in the computation of the S-matrix are given by

$${}_{\text{in}}\langle 0|T(A_{\text{in}\,\mu}(x)A_{\text{in}\,\nu}(x'))|0\rangle_{\text{in}} = -\frac{\hbar c}{2} D_F(x - x')g_{\mu\nu} \tag{11–111}$$

and

$${}_{\text{in}}\langle 0|T(\psi_{\text{in}}(x)\bar{\psi}_{\text{in}}(x'))|0\rangle_{\text{in}} = -\tfrac{1}{2}S_F(x - x') \tag{11–112}$$

A procedure similar to the one outlined for the external field case can now be used to establish a one-to-one correspondence between the nth order elements of the S-matrix in normal form and Feynman diagrams with n vertices, in which the points $x_1, \cdots, x_n$ are identified. This correspondence, of course, is the basis of the usefulness of the Feynman diagram. Thus, in practice, one draws all possible topologically different graphs (graphs that differ from one another by the interchange of the labels of the vertices are not considered different) consistent with the interaction $j_{\text{in}\,\mu}(x)A_{\text{in}}^{\mu}(x)$. Thus, at every vertex two electron lines and one photon line must meet. The matrix element corresponding to any n^{th} order diagram can be obtained by writing down the following factors:

(1) a factor $(-i/\hbar c)^n$ for the diagram as a whole arising from the perturbation expansion;

(2) a factor $-e(\gamma^\mu)_{\alpha\beta}$ for each vertex;

(3) a factor $-\frac{1}{2}\hbar c g_{\mu\nu} D_F(x_j - x_l)$ for each photon (wavy undirected) line connecting the points x_j and x_l arising from a contraction

$$A_{\text{in}\,\mu}^{\cdot}(x_j)A_{\text{in}\,\nu}^{\cdot}(x_l)$$

in S_n. It is assumed that the factors $(-e\gamma^\mu)$ and $(-e\gamma^\nu)$ act at these vertices. The summation convention is used with respect to the polarization indices μ and ν;

(4) a factor $[-\frac{1}{2}S_F(x_l - x_j)]_{\alpha\beta}$ for an internal line directed from x_j to x_l. The factor $(-e\gamma^\mu)_{\sigma\alpha}$ is assumed to occur at the vertex labeled by x_l and the factor $(-e\gamma^\nu)_{\beta\delta}$ at the vertex labeled by x_j. This factor corresponds to the contraction $\psi_{\text{in}\,\alpha}^{\cdot}(x_l)\tilde{\psi}_{\text{in}\,\beta}^{\cdot}(x_j)$ in S_n;

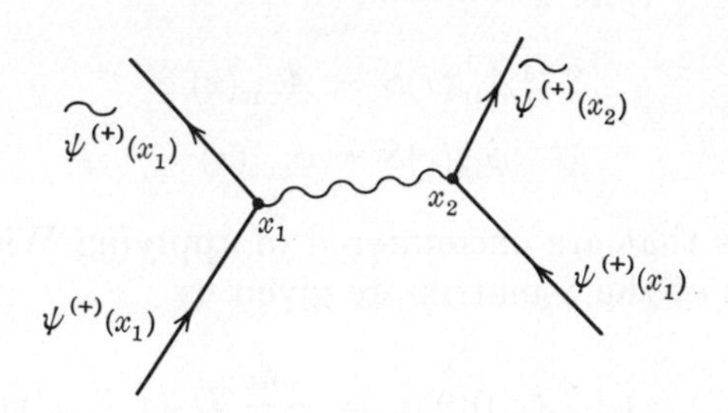

FIG. 11–2.

(5) the correct creation or annihilation operator $\psi_{\text{in}}^{(\pm)}$, $\tilde{\psi}_{\text{in}}^{(\pm)}$, $A_{\text{in}\,\mu}^{(\pm)}$ for each external free negaton, positon, or photon line arriving or leaving at x. (These factors arise from the ψ_{in}, $\tilde{\psi}_{\text{in}}$ and A_{in} not contracted in S_n);

(6) a factor (-1) for each internal closed electron loop;

(7) integrate over $x_1, x_2, \cdots, x_n$.

The factor $1/n!$ in the perturbation expansion is not to be included since we have agreed to consider only topologically different diagrams. As there are $n!$ permutations of the points $x_1, \cdots, x_n$ among themselves which leave the graph topologically unchanged, the correct answer is obtained by omitting the $n!$. This last remark does not apply to vacuum diagrams, *i.e.*, diagrams with no external lines.

Starting from this formulation of quantum electrodynamics, the lowest-order contribution to the scattering amplitude for negaton-negaton scattering (Fig. 11–2) is given by the following term in the S-matrix

$$\frac{e^2}{2}\left(-\frac{i}{\hbar c}\right)^2 \int d^4x_1 \int d^4x_2 \bar{\psi}^{(+)}_{\text{in}\,\alpha_1}(x_1)\bar{\psi}^{(+)}_{\text{in}\,\alpha_2}(x_2)$$

$$\times\ (\gamma^{\mu_1})_{\alpha_1\beta_1}(\gamma^{\mu_2})_{\alpha_2\beta_2}\psi^{(+)}_{\text{in}\,\beta_1}(x_1)\psi^{(+)}_{\text{in}\,\beta_2}(x_2)g_{\mu_1\mu_2}\left(-\frac{\hbar c}{2}\right) D_F(x - x') \tag{11–113}$$

which when evaluated between the states ${}_{\text{in}}\langle \mathbf{p}_2's_2', \mathbf{p}_1's_1'|$ and $|\mathbf{p}_1s_1, \mathbf{p}_2s_2\rangle_{\text{in}}$ is readily verified to be equal to the expression (11–91).

The Coulomb gauge theory and the Lorentz gauge theory thus both describe the same physical phenomena, but they handle one aspect of the physical situation, namely, the Coulomb interaction, in fundamentally different ways. In the Coulomb gauge the interaction is

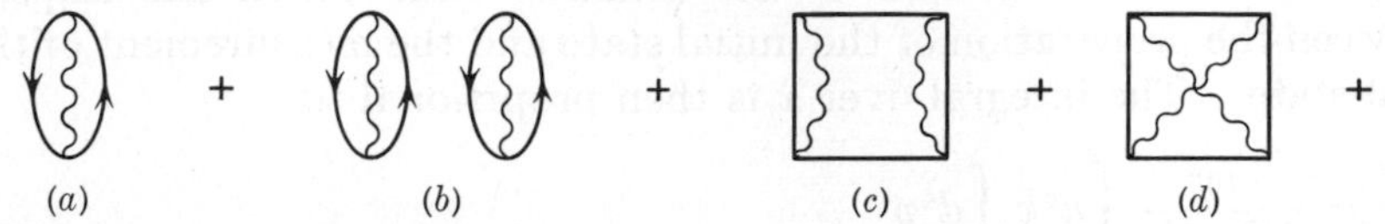

(a) + (b) + (c) + (d) +

Fig. 11–3.

incorporated into the electron field, while in the Lorentz gauge it appears as being caused by the emission and absorption of longitudinal quanta. It is because the Coulomb interaction does not involve observable quanta that this freedom of choosing the gauge exists.

Next, let us check whether the theory as formulated above satisfies certain reasonable physical requirements. One of these is clearly the "steadiness" of the vacuum and one-particle states. The "steadiness" of the vacuum would correspond to the statement that ${}_{\text{out}}\langle 0|0\rangle_{\text{in}} = 1$. Let us, therefore, compute this quantity explicitly:

$$\begin{aligned}
{}_{\text{out}}\langle 0|0\rangle_{\text{in}} &= {}_{\text{in}}\langle 0|S|0\rangle_{\text{in}} \\
&= 1 - \frac{1}{2!}\left(\frac{i}{\hbar c}\right)^2 \int d^4x_1 \int d^4x_2 \frac{e^2}{4} \\
&\qquad \text{Tr}\,\{\gamma^\mu S_F(x_2 - x_1)\gamma_\mu S_F(x_1 - x_2)\} \cdot \frac{\hbar c}{2} D_F(x_1 - x_2) + \cdots
\end{aligned} \tag{11–114}$$

$$= 1 - L_v^{(1)} + \cdots \tag{11–115}$$

where the contribution from the term written down in (11–115) stems from Fig. 11–3(a). Other higher order contributions will arise from the diagrams indicated in Figs. 11–3(c) and 11–3(d). Upon introducing "relative" and "center of mass" coordinates

$$x_1 - x_2 = x \tag{11–116}$$

$$\tfrac{1}{2}(x_1 + x_2) = X \tag{11–117}$$

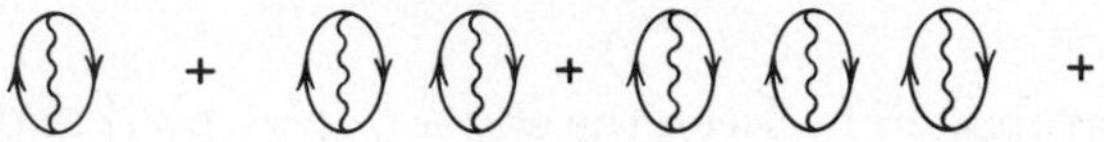

FIG. 11–4.

the integration in $L_v^{(1)}$ over X can immediately be carried out since the integrand in (11–114) depends only on $x_1 - x_2$. We thus obtain a result that is proportional to VT, where V is the volume of space (quantization volume) and T the (infinite) time which has elapsed between the preparation of the initial state and the measurement of the final state. The integral over x is then proprtional to

$$\frac{E_0^{(2)}}{V} = \frac{ie^2}{2(2\pi)^4\hbar c}\int d^4k \int d^4p \times \operatorname{Tr}\left\{\gamma^\mu \frac{\gamma\cdot p + m}{p^2 - m^2 + i\varepsilon}\gamma_\mu \frac{\gamma\cdot(p-k) + m}{(p-k)^2 - m^2 + i\varepsilon}\right\}\cdot\frac{1}{k^2 + i\delta} \tag{11–118}$$

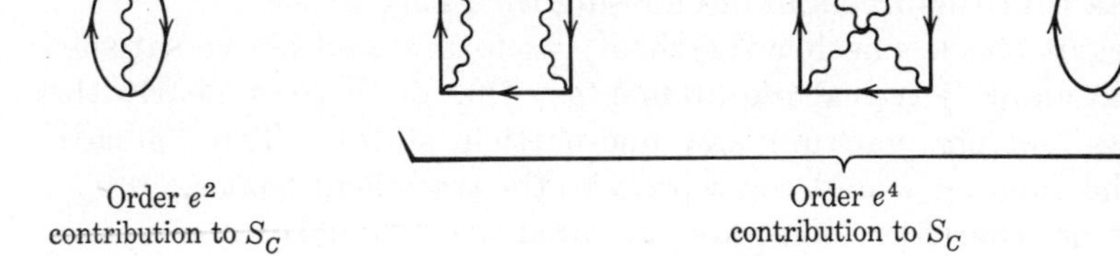

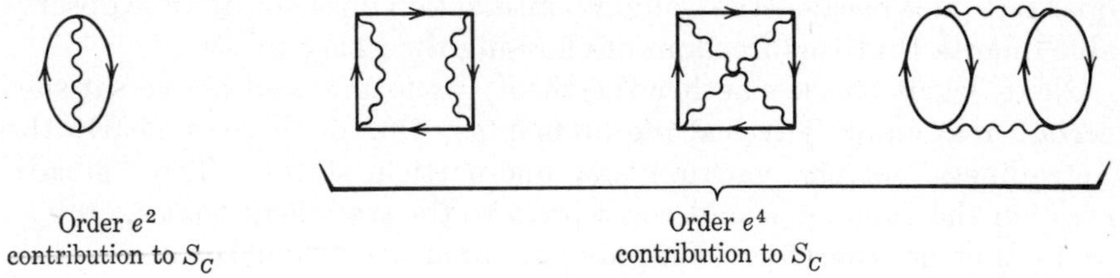

FIG. 11–5.

a highly divergent quantity. For our purposes it is sufficient, however, to note that the contribution of the diagrams indicated in Fig. 11–4 can be summed to yield a factor exp $(+iE_o^{(2)}T)$. In fact it can be shown that the totality of all the vacuum-fluctuation diagrams sums to a contribution

$${}_{\text{out}}\langle 0|0\rangle_{\text{in}} = {}_{\text{in}}\langle 0|S|0\rangle_{\text{in}} = e^{+iE_oT} \tag{11–119}$$

with E_o real, and given by

$$+iE_oT = {}_{\text{in}}\langle 0|S_C|0\rangle_{\text{in}} \tag{11–120}$$

In Eq. (11–120) S_C denotes the contribution to S from connected diagrams only, *i.e.*, from the diagrams shown in Fig. 11–5. The energy E_o in this phase factor, exp $(+iE_oT)$, can be interpreted as the vacuum "self-energy" due to the interaction $j_{\text{in}\,\mu}A^\mu_{\text{in}}$. By redefining the interaction hamiltonian as

$$\mathscr{H}_{I\,\text{in}\,t}(x) = j_{\text{in}\,\mu}(x)A^\mu_{\text{in}}(x) - E_0/V \tag{11–121}$$

the energy of the vacuum is so adjusted that

$${}_{\text{out}}\langle 0|0\rangle_{\text{in}} = {}_{\text{in}}\langle 0|S|0\rangle_{\text{in}} = 1 \tag{11–122}$$

This is most readily seen by writing the following formal expression for S

$$S = P(e^{-i\int_{-\infty}^{+\infty}d^4x\mathscr{H}_{\text{in}\,I}(x)}) \tag{11–123}$$

which is obtained by formally summing the defining series for S. By taking the interaction hamiltonian to be (11–121), we have guaranteed

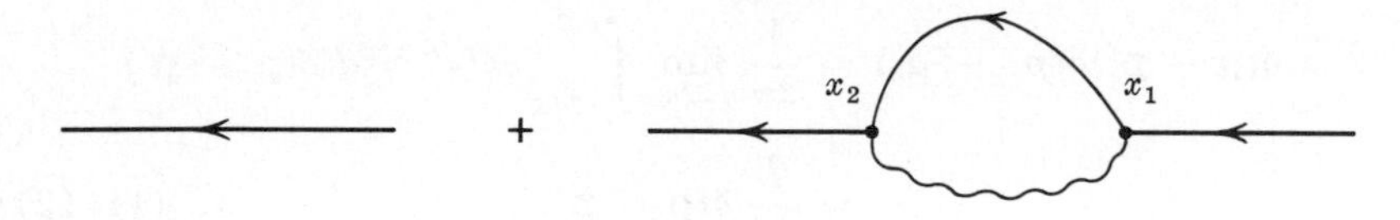

Fig. 11–6.

that the vacuum is steady, *i.e.*, that, apart from an irrelevant phase factor,

$$|0\rangle_{\text{in}} = |0\rangle_{\text{out}} \tag{11–124}$$

As no confusion can arise, we shall often in the subsequent exposition omit the "in" or "out" subscript and denote the vacuum state by $|0\rangle$.

Alternatively, one can drop the E_o/V factor in (11–121) and, whenever computing any matrix element, omit from consideration the contribution from disconnected vacuum fluctuation diagrams. We shall do so hereafter.

Consider next the single-electron states. We would expect that the state $|\mathbf{p},s\rangle$ corresponding to a single negaton in the "universe" would have the property that

$${}_{\text{out}}\langle \mathbf{p}'s'|\mathbf{p}s\rangle_{\text{in}} = {}_{\text{in}}\langle \mathbf{p}'s'|S|\mathbf{p}s\rangle_{\text{in}} = p_o\delta(\mathbf{p} - \mathbf{p}')\delta_{ss'} \tag{11–125}$$

In other words that a negaton initially in a state of momentum $\mathbf{p}$, energy $\sqrt{\mathbf{p}^2 + m^2}$ helicity s, would remain forever in that state (since it does not interact with anything). Let us, however, compute the left-hand side of Eq. (11–123) with the S-matrix given in terms of the interaction hamiltonian (11–121). To lowest order the diagrams indicated in Fig. 11–6 contribute and give rise to the following contribution to the matrix element of S between one-particle states

$$
\begin{aligned}
{}_{\text{in}}\langle \mathbf{p}'s|S|\mathbf{p}s\rangle_{\text{in}} &\cong p_o\delta(\mathbf{p} - \mathbf{p}')\delta_{ss'} \\
&\quad + \frac{e^2}{\hbar c}\frac{m}{(2\pi)^3}\,\delta^{(4)}(\mathbf{p} - \mathbf{p}') \\
&\quad \times \tilde{u}_{s'}(\mathbf{p}')\left\{\int d^4k\gamma^\mu \frac{\gamma\cdot(p - k) + m}{(p - k)^2 - m^2 + i\varepsilon}\gamma_\mu \frac{1}{k^2 + i\delta}\right\} u_s(\mathbf{p})
\end{aligned} \tag{11–126}
$$

Since p and p' refer to the four-momenta of a free particle with $p_o = \sqrt{\mathbf{p}^2 + m^2}$, $p_o' = \sqrt{\mathbf{p}^2 + m}$, the delta function occurring in (11–126) can also be rewritten as

$$
\begin{aligned}
\delta(\mathbf{p} - \mathbf{p}')\delta(p_o - p_o') &= \frac{1}{2\pi}\lim_{T\to\infty}\int_{-T/2}^{T/2} e^{i(p_o - p_o')t}dt\,\delta(\mathbf{p} - \mathbf{p}') \\
&= \frac{T}{2\pi}\,\delta(\mathbf{p} - \mathbf{p}')
\end{aligned} \tag{11–127}
$$

where T is the time difference between the times at which "in" and "out" states are specified. The integral in the bracket can readily be evaluated. Thus using the fact that

$$\gamma^\mu\gamma_\nu\gamma_\mu = -2\gamma_\nu \tag{11–128}$$

and that $\gamma\cdot pu(\mathbf{p}) = mu(\mathbf{p})$, one can cast the integral into the form

$$2\int \frac{\gamma\cdot k + m}{-2p\cdot k + k^2 + i\varepsilon}\frac{d^4k}{k^2 + i\delta} \tag{11–129}$$

For large k both denominators become equal to k^2. In this limit the contribution of the $\gamma\cdot k$ vanishes by symmetry and we are left with an integrand proportional to k^3dk/k^4 for large k. The integral is, therefore, logarithmically divergent. Although the fact that we are integrating over a hyperbolic space has been overlooked, we shall see that a more careful analysis substantiates this result. The other point to notice is that the integral is proportional to m. Hence, to second order we may write

$$
{}_{\text{in}}\langle \mathbf{p}'s'|S|\mathbf{p}s\rangle_{\text{in}} = p_o\delta(\mathbf{p} - \mathbf{p}')\delta_{ss'}\cdot\left\{1 + i\,\frac{m}{p_o}\,\Delta m_{(2)}T + \cdots\right\} \tag{11–130}
$$

where $\Delta m_{(2)}$ is a logarithmically divergent relativistically invariant constant (which is proportional to m). If we were to sum the contributions to the matrix element (11–125) of all the diagrams of the form shown in Fig. 11–7, the result would be equal to

$$
p_o\delta(\mathbf{p} - \mathbf{p}')\delta_{ss'}e^{i(m/p_o)\Delta m_{(2)}T} \tag{11–131}
$$

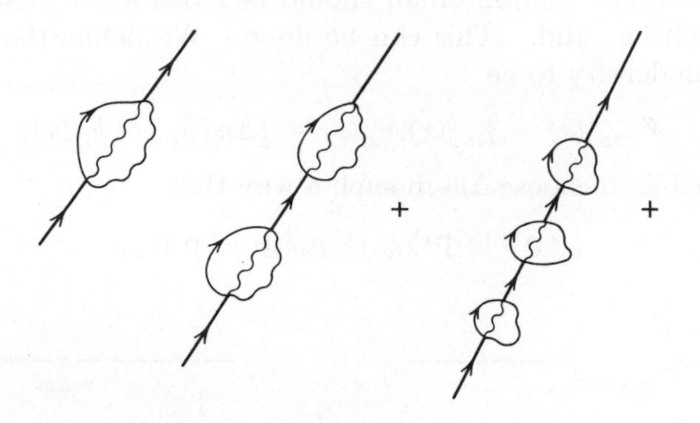

FIG. 11–7.

This is precisely the form that would be expected if the self interaction gave rise to a change of the mass of the particle from m to $\Delta m_{(2)} + m$, in which case the change in the energy of the particle would be

$$
\begin{aligned}
E_{\mathbf{p}} + \Delta E_{(2)} &= \sqrt{(m + \Delta m_{(2)})^2 + \mathbf{p}^2} \\
&\simeq \sqrt{m^2 + \mathbf{p}^2} + \frac{\Delta m_{(2)}m}{E_{\mathbf{p}}} + \mathrm{O}((\Delta m)^2)
\end{aligned} \tag{11–132}
$$

i.e., to first order

$$
\Delta E_{(2)} = \frac{m}{E_{\mathbf{p}}}\,\Delta m_{(2)} = \frac{m}{p_o}\,\Delta m_{(2)} \tag{11–133}
$$

Hence, the phase factor appearing in (11–131) can be written

$$
e^{i\Delta E_{(2)}T}
$$

justifying the interpretation of the self-interaction as giving rise to a change of the mass of the particle. Physically, however, as noted above, we would expect that the theory should be such that the one-particle state is steady, namely is such that

$$ {}_{\text{in}}\langle \mathbf{p},s|S = {}_{\text{out}}\langle \mathbf{p},s| \tag{11–134}$$

$$ = {}_{\text{in}}\langle \mathbf{p},s| \tag{11–135}$$

and, therefore

$$ {}_{\text{out}}\langle \mathbf{p}',s'|\mathbf{p},s\rangle_{\text{in}} = {}_{\text{in}}\langle \mathbf{p}',s'|\mathbf{p},s\rangle_{\text{in}} $$

$$ = \delta_{ss'}p_o\delta(\mathbf{p} - \mathbf{p}') \tag{11–136}$$

and that no phase factors appear on the right-hand side of Eq. (11–136). We, therefore, argue as in the case of the vacuum self energy, namely that the interaction hamiltonian should be redefined to guarantee that Eq. (11–136) be valid. This can be done. We define the "correct" hamiltonian density to be

$$ \mathscr{H}_{I\,\text{in}\,t}(x) = j_{\text{in}\,\mu}(x)A^{\mu}_{\text{in}}(x) - \tfrac{1}{2}\Delta m[\tilde{\psi}_{\text{in}}(x),\psi_{\text{in}}(x)] \tag{11–137}$$

If it is possible to choose Δm in such a way that

$$ {}_{\text{in}}\langle \mathbf{p}'s'|S|\mathbf{p}s\rangle_{\text{in}} = p_o\delta(\mathbf{p} - \mathbf{p}')\delta_{ss'} \tag{11–138}$$

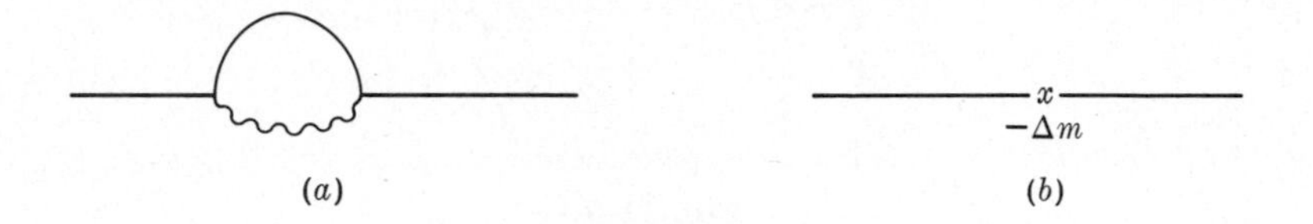

FIG. 11–8.

we shall have succeeded in our aim. This is in fact possible. Thus, for example, if we compute the S-matrix with the interaction hamiltonian (11–137) to lowest order, in addition to the contribution of the $j_{\text{in}\,\mu}A^{\mu}_{\text{in}}$ term (Fig. 11–8(a)), there will also be a contribution from the Δm term (diagrammatically represented in Fig. 11–8(b)). If Δm is thought of as being expanded in a power series in $\alpha = e^2/4\pi\hbar c$

$$ \Delta m = \Delta m_{(2)} + \Delta m_{(4)} + \cdots \tag{11–139}$$

then the requirement that the contributions from Fig. 11–8(a) and (b) cancel one another fixes Δm to order α, *i.e.*, fixes $\Delta m_{(2)}$ similarly in higher orders. We have thus insured that the one-negaton and one-positon states are steady, *i.e.*, that

$$ |\mathbf{p},s\rangle_{\text{in}} = |\mathbf{p},s\rangle_{\text{out}} \tag{11–140}$$

Since no confusion can arise we shall often in the following discussion omit the subscript "in" or "out" on one-particle states and denote these by $|\mathbf{p},s,\pm e\rangle$.

The addition of the $\Delta m\bar{\psi}_{\text{in}}\psi_{\text{in}}$ term to $H_{\text{in}\,I}$ implies, of course, that the equation of motion which the Heisenberg operator obeys is also altered and now reads

$$(-i\gamma\cdot\partial + m)\psi(x) = -e\gamma\cdot A(x)\psi(x) - \Delta m\psi(x) \qquad (11\text{–}141)$$

The equation defining the "in" field now reads

$$\psi(x) = \psi_{\text{in}}(x) + e\int d^4x' S_R(x - x',m)\{\gamma\cdot A(x') - \Delta m\}\psi(x') \qquad (11\text{–}142)$$

That the Δm term must, in fact, be present can also be inferred from the requirement that $\psi_{\text{in}}(x)$ be the asymptotic field to which $\psi(x)$ converges weakly in the limit as $x_0 \to -\infty$. We shall give a discussion of the asymptotic condition in Section 11.5 of the present chapter.

However, before closing this section we remark that the hamiltonian (11–137), although guaranteeing that the vacuum and the one-negaton and one-positon states are steady, does not as yet guarantee that the one-photon states are steady, namely that

$${}_{\text{in}}\langle\mathbf{k},\lambda|S = {}_{\text{out}}\langle\mathbf{k},\lambda| = {}_{\text{in}}\langle\mathbf{k},\lambda| \qquad (11\text{–}143)$$

i.e., that

$${}_{\text{out}}\langle\mathbf{k}',\lambda'|\mathbf{k},\lambda\rangle_{\text{in}} = \delta_{\lambda\lambda'}k_0\delta(\mathbf{k} - \mathbf{k}') \qquad (11\text{–}144)$$

We could inquire in a manner similar to the electron case as to what changes must be made in the hamiltonian so as to guarantee that Eq. (11–144) be satisfied. Since the change should affect the one-photon states, we would expect that the "counter terms" to be added are of the form

$$L'A^{\mu}_{\text{in}}(x)\partial_{\mu}\partial_{\nu}A^{\nu}_{\text{in}}(x) + L''A^{\mu}_{\text{in}}(x)\Box A_{\text{in}\,\mu}(x')$$

It turns out that this choice is correct and that L' and L'' can be so chosen that (11–144) is satisfied. We shall return to this question in our discussion of the asymptotic condition in Section 11.5 of the present chapter. As preparation for these considerations, we turn in the next few sections to a discussion of the invariance properties of quantum electrodynamics and their consequences.

This section has outlined the current formulations of quantum electrodynamics. Since the theory assumes its local form when expressed in terms of potentials, these formulations were in terms of the electromagnetic potentials rather than in terms of the electromagnetic field. Stated differently, they operated with particular gauges.

The disadvantages of such gauges were noted. In the Lorentz gauge, the most convenient for calculational purposes, it is necessary to quantize in terms of an indefinite metric (Gupta-Bleuler method) and one has to introduce unphysical states with negative norms. But the resulting theory is covariant in appearance. In the Coulomb gauge, no unphysical states appear. However, the covariance of the theory is not manifest nor for that matter is the gauge-invariance manifestly maintained. Actually, the matter field operators are not gauge covariant in either of these two gauges.

It is possible to formulate the Coulomb gauge theory in terms of radiation operators $\mathscr{A}_\mu(x)$ which satisfy the subsidiary condition

$$[\partial_\mu - n_\mu(n\cdot\partial)]\mathscr{A}^\mu(x) = 0 \qquad (11\text{–}145)$$

where n_μ is a unit time-like vector. The theory then appears more covariant but actually depends on the choice of the unit vector n_μ.

REFERENCES

Osaki, S., *Progr. Theoret. Phys.*, **14**, 511 (1955); *Nuclear Physics*, **15**, 501 (1960).
Zumino, B., *J. Math. Phys.*, **1**, 1 (1960).
Evans, L. E., Feldman, G., and Matthews, P. T., *Ann. Phys.*, **13**, 268 (1961).
Evans, L., and Fulton, T., *Nuclear Phys.*, **21**, 492 (1960).

For a quantization scheme without the use of potentials, see:

Goldberg, I., *Phys. Rev.*, **112**, 1361 (1958).
Pauli, W., *Handbuch der Physik*, Vol. 5, J. Springer Verlag, Berlin, 1958.
Mandelstam, S., *Ann. Phys.*, **19**, 1 (1962).

General reference:

Källén, G., *Handbuch der Physik*, Vol. 5, Part I, J. Springer Verlag, Berlin, 1958.

11.2. Invariance Properties.—Before delving into the mathematical formulation of the invariance properties of quantum electrodynamics, let us briefly state what is meant by an invariance principle in general. As we shall be primarily concerned with the formulation of invariance principles in the Heisenberg picture, it is useful to introduce the concept of the complete description of a physical system. By this is meant at the classical level a specification of the trajectories of all particles together with a full description of all fields at all points of space for all time. The equations of motion then allow one to determine whether the system could, in fact, have evolved in the way specified by the complete description.

An invariance principle then requires that the following three postulates be satisfied:

(1) it should be possible to translate a complete description of a physical system, from one coordinate system into every *equivalent* coordinate system;

(2) the description that results from the translation of a dynamically possible description should again be a dynamically possible one;

(3) the criteria for the dynamic possibility of a complete description should be identical for *equivalent* observers.

Postulate 1 is the statement that there must exist a well-defined correspondence between the description of physical phenomena by different observers.

Postulate 2 is the statement that a possible motion to one observer must also appear possible to any other observer.

Postulate 3 demands what is called the form invariance of the equations of motion.

In a quantum mechanical framework, Postulate 1 remains as stated. It implies that there exists a well-defined connection and correspondence between the labels attributed to the space-time points by each observer, between the state vectors each observer attributes to a given physical system, and between observables of the system. Postulate 2 is usually formulated in terms of transition probabilities, and requires that the transition probability be independent of the frame of reference. It should be stated explicitly at this point that we shall formulate the notion of invariance in terms of the concept of bodily identity, wherein a single physical system is viewed by two observers who, in general, will have different relations to the system.

Now in quantum theory the description of a physical system in the Heisenberg picture for a given observer O is by means of operators Q, which satisfy certain equations of motion and commutation rules with respect to O's frame of reference (coordinate system x). The above notion of an invariance principle can be stated alternatively as follows: If, when we change this coordinate frame of reference (*i.e.*, for observer O') we are able to find a new set of operators that obeys the same equations of motion and the same commutation rules with respect to the new frame of reference (coordinate system x') we then say that these observers are equivalent and the theory invariant under the transformation $x \to x'$. The observable consequences of theory in the new frame (for observer O') will then clearly be the same as those in the old frame.

Consider for example the theory under discussion, namely, quantum electrodynamics under the circumstance that the frame of reference with respect to which phenomena are described is changed from a right-handed to a left-handed coordinate system, *i.e.*, from one in which the space-time coordinates are labeled by x to one in which they are labeled by x', with

$$x' = \Lambda(i_s)x \tag{11–146}$$

with

$$\mathbf{x}' = -\mathbf{x} \tag{11–147}$$

$$x_o' = x_o \tag{11–148}$$

We shall often abbreviate $\Lambda(i_s)$ by i_s, *i.e.*,

$$(i_s)_\mu{}^\nu = -(-1)^{\delta_{\nu o}}\delta_\mu{}^\nu \tag{11–149}$$

The statement that quantum electrodynamics is invariant under such a spatial inversion (parity operation) can be taken as the statement that there exist new field operators $\psi'(x')$ and $A_\mu'(x')$ expressible in terms of $\psi(x)$ and $A_\mu(x)$ which satisfy the same commutation rules and equations of motion in terms of x' as do $\psi(x)$ and $A_\mu(x)$ written in terms of x. In fact one readily verifies that the operators

$$\psi'(x) = \bar{\eta}_P\gamma_0\psi(i_s x) \tag{11–150}$$

$$\tilde{\psi}'(x) = \eta_P\tilde{\psi}(i_s x)\gamma_0 \tag{11–151}$$

$$A_\mu'(x) = \lambda_P(-1)^{\delta_{\mu o}}A_\nu(i_s x) \tag{11–152}$$

where η_P and λ_P are c numbers, satisfy the same commutation rules as do $\psi(x)$ and $A_\mu(x)$ provided

$$|\eta_P|^2 = |\lambda_P|^2 = 1 \tag{11–153}$$

Furthermore since $A_\mu(x)$ is hermitian, by taking hermitian adjoints of both sides of Eq. (11–152), one concludes that λ_P must be real so that $\lambda_P = \pm 1$.

One next verifies that the primed operators will satisfy the same equations of motion with respect to the x' coordinates as do the unprimed operators with respect to the x coordinates (Postulate 3 of an invariance principle) provided that

$$\lambda_P = -1 \tag{11–154}$$

Hence, the laws of nature formulated in terms of the primed variables yield the same observable consequences as they do when formulated in terms of the unprimed ones. Furthermore, since the primed operators obey the same equations of motion with respect to the primed coordinate system, the criteria for the dynamic possibility of a motion is identical for these equivalent observers. More precisely stated, from this (primed) set of field operators, which obey the same commutation rules and equations of motion as the unprimed ones, we can construct a complete set of observables (such as the total energy-momentum, total charge, etc.) whose eigenvalue spectrum will be the same as that of the corresponding unprimed set.

We must next consider more precisely the connection between the description of bodily identical states by the two observers (the requirements of Postulate 1). Quite in general, in fact, a physical theory, and quantum electrodynamics in particular, is fully defined only if the connection between the description of bodily identical states by (equivalent) observers is known for every state of the system and for every pair of observers. Since the observers are equivalent every state which can be described by O can also be described by O'. Given a bodily state of the same system, observer O will ascribe to it a state vector $|\Psi_O\rangle$ in his Hilbert space and observer O' will attribute to it a state vector $|\Psi_{O'}\rangle$ in his Hilbert space. The above formulation of invariance means that there exists a one-to-one correspondence between the vectors $|\Psi_O\rangle$ and $|\Psi_{O'}\rangle$ used by observers O and O' to describe bodily the same state.[3] This correspondence guarantees that the two Hilbert spaces are in fact isomorphic. It is, therefore, possible for the two observers to agree to describe states of the system by vectors in the same Hilbert space. A similar statement can be made for the observables: there exists a one-to-one correspondence between the operators Q_O and $Q_{O'}$, which observers O and O' attribute to observables. The consistency of the theory (Postulate 2) demands, however, that the two observers make the same prediction as the outcome of the same experiment performed on bodily the same system. This requires the relation

$$|(\Psi_O,\Phi_O)|^2 = |(\Psi_{O'},\Phi_{O'})|^2 \qquad (11\text{–}155)$$

There are now two alternate consistent ways for the observers to relate their observables and state vectors, the Heisenberg-type and the Schrödinger-type descriptions.

[3] Actually this statement is not quite correct because a state of the physical system is represented by each observer not by a vector in his (private) Hilbert space, but by a *ray*, since the normalization and phase of the state is not pertinent to the description of the state. What one has, therefore, is a correspondence between rays rather than between vectors. We shall, however, ignore this fact in the interests of simplicity. Its relevance to the present discussion is fully treated by E. P. Wigner, *Nuovo Cimento*, **3**, 517 (1956); *Rev. Mod. Phys.*, **29**, 255 (1957); and *Group Theory*, Academic Press, New York, 1959.

Heisenberg-Type Description.—Observer O and O' ascribe to bodily the same state, the *same* state vector $|\Psi\rangle$ (*i.e.*, $|\Psi_O\rangle = |\Psi_{O'}\rangle$ apart from possible phase factors), but describe observables by operators Q and Q', respectively, which are in one-to-one correspondence.

Schrödinger-Type Description.—Observer O and O' ascribe to bodily the same state two different vectors $|\Psi\rangle$ and $|\Psi'\rangle$, but ascribe to observables the same operators.

Equation (11–155), which is the statement that the transition probabilities for bodily identical pairs of states be the same for all observers, is trivially satisfied for the Heisenberg-type description. On the other hand, for the Schrödinger-type description, Eq. (11–155) asserts that the one-to-one correspondence between the vectors $|\Psi\rangle$ and $|\Psi'\rangle$ is, in fact, either a unitary or anti-unitary[4] (norm preserving) one

$$|\Psi_{O'}\rangle = U(L)|\Psi_O\rangle \tag{11–156}$$

with $U(L)$ depending upon only the relation between the coordinate systems of O and O' and not on the intrinsic properties of either.

Since both types of description must give the same expectation value for the observables for observer O', we must have

$$\langle\Psi'_s|Q'_s|\Psi'_s\rangle = \langle\Psi'_h|Q'_h|\Psi'_h\rangle \tag{11–157}$$

where the super prime denotes the fact that we are referring to observables and vectors of observer O' and the subscripts s and h indicate whether a Schrödinger-type (s) or Heisenberg-type (h) description is adopted.

Since in a Heisenberg-type description the vector $|\Psi'_h\rangle$ that O' ascribes to bodily the same physical system is the same as that which O ascribes to it, call it $|\Psi\rangle$, whereas in the Schrödinger-type description

$$|\Psi'_s\rangle = U(L)|\Psi\rangle \tag{11–158}$$

but the observables are represented by the same operators, Eq. (11–157) can be rewritten as

$$(U(L)\Psi, Q_s\, U(L)\Psi) = (\Psi, Q'_h\Psi) \tag{11–159}$$

or dropping the subscript s and h, as the prime on Q makes clear the designation

$$(\Psi, Q'\Psi) = (\Psi', Q\Psi') = (U\Psi, QU\Psi) \tag{11–160}$$

hence

$$Q' = U^*(L)QU(L) \quad \text{if } U \text{ is unitary} \tag{11–161}$$

[4] See footnote 6 of the present chapter (p. 687), for the definition of the term "anti-unitary."

and

$$Q' = U^*(L)Q^*U(L) \quad \text{if } U \text{ is anti-unitary} \tag{11–162}$$

In the Heisenberg-type description the existence of such a unitary or anti-unitary operator U is inferred from the fact that the set of observable Q and Q' satisfy the same commutation rules.

The discussion at the beginning of this section, when coupled with the fact that the observers O and O' agree to describe bodily the same state by the same state vector, has exhibited the invariance of quantum electrodynamics under space inversion in the Heisenberg-type description.

Let us next adopt the Schrödinger-type description. The statement that quantum electrodynamics is invariant under space inversion can now be translated into the statement that there exists a unitary operator $U(i_s)$ such that

$$\begin{gathered} U(i_s)^{-1}\psi(x)U(i_s) = \eta_P\gamma_0\psi(i_s x) \\ |\eta_P|^2 = 1 \end{gathered} \tag{11–163}$$

or more generally

$$U(i_s)^{-1}\psi(x)U(i_s) = \eta_P S(i_s)\psi(i_s x) \tag{11–164}$$

where

$$S(i_s)\gamma^\mu S(i_s)^{-1} = \Lambda(i_s)^\mu{}_\nu\gamma^\nu \tag{11–165}$$

and such that

$$U(i_s)^{-1}A_\mu(x)U(i_s) = -(-1)^{\delta_{\mu 0}}A_\mu(i_s x) \tag{11–166}$$

Observers O and O' describe bodily the same state by vectors $|\Psi\rangle$ and $|\Psi'\rangle$, which are related by

$$|\Psi'\rangle = U(i_s)|\Psi\rangle \tag{11–167}$$

but use the same operators to describe observables.

Consider next the relativistic invariance of quantum electrodynamics. Again, loosely speaking, we say that quantum electrodynamics is relativistically invariant if its observable consequences are the same in all frames connected by an inhomogeneous Lorentz transformation $\{a,\Lambda\}$

$$x' = \Lambda x + a \tag{11–168}$$

The above discussion asserts that the theory will be invariant if there exist operators $\psi'(x')$ and $A'_\mu(x')$ which obey the same commutation rules and equation of motion with respect to x' as did $\psi(x)$ and $A(x)$ with respect to x. If such primed operators exist, then by virtue of obeying the same commutation rules as the unprimed ones (and thus composing the same Hilbert space of states) they must be unitarily (or anti-unitarily) related to them; hence

$$\psi'(x') = U^{-1}(a,\Lambda)\psi(x')U(a,\Lambda) \tag{11–169}$$

$$A'_\mu(x') = U^{-1}(a,\Lambda)A_\mu(x')U(a,\Lambda) \tag{11–170}$$

Now since the Lorentz transformations form a group

$$\{a_2,\Lambda_2\}\{a_1,\Lambda_1\} = \{\Lambda_2 a_1 + a_2, \Lambda_2\Lambda_1\} \tag{11–171}$$

the $U(a,\Lambda)$ must form an up to a factor unitary (or anti-unitary) representation of the inhomogeneous Lorentz group

$$U(a_2,\Lambda_2)U(a_1,\Lambda_1) = \omega(\Lambda_1,\Lambda_2,a_1,a_2)\cdot U(\Lambda_2 a_1 + a_2, \Lambda_2\Lambda_1) \tag{11–172}$$

Equation (11–172) is verified by considering the relation between the operators in the coordinates system O, O', O'' where

$$x'' = \{a_2,\Lambda_2\}x' \tag{11–173}$$

$$= \{a_2,\Lambda_2\}\{a_1,\Lambda_1\}x \tag{11–174}$$

It can actually be shown that the factor ω can be chosen to be ± 1.[5] Furthermore, for restricted Lorentz transformations $U(a,\Lambda)$ must be unitary since every element of the group $\{a,\Lambda\}$ can be written as the product of elements that are the same

$$\{a,\Lambda\} = \{b,\Lambda'\}\{b,\Lambda'\} \tag{11–175}$$

and the product of two anti-unitary operators is a unitary operator.

The requirement of Postulate 3 that the equations of motion be form-invariant (*i.e.*, that $\psi'(x')$ and $A'_\mu(x')$ satisfy the same equation of motion with respect to x' as did $\psi(x)$ and $A_\mu(x)$ with respect to x demands that the field variables transform under such transformations according to a finite dimensional representation of the Lorentz group. In other words it demands that ψ transform like a spinor

$$\psi'(x') = S(\Lambda)\psi(x) \tag{11–176}$$

where $S(\Lambda)$ satisfies

$$S(\Lambda)^{-1}\gamma^\mu S(\Lambda) = \Lambda^\mu{}_\nu\gamma^\nu \tag{11–177}$$

$$S(\Lambda_1)S(\Lambda_2) = \omega(\Lambda_1\Lambda_2)S(\Lambda_1\Lambda_2) \tag{11–178}$$

and forms a four-by-four finite dimensional (*non*unitary) spinor representation of homogeneous Lorentz group, and that $A_\mu(x)$ transforms like a vector

$$A'_\mu(x') = \Lambda_\mu{}^\nu A_\nu(x) \tag{11–179}$$

[5] V. Bargmann, *Ann. Math.*, **59**, 1 (1954).

Combining Eqs. (11–176)–(11–179) and (11–169)–(11–170), we deduce that

$$U^{-1}(a,\Lambda)\psi(x')U(a,\Lambda) = S(\Lambda)\psi(x) \tag{11–180}$$

$$U^{-1}(a,\Lambda)A_\mu(x')U(a,\Lambda) = \Lambda_\mu{}^\nu A_\nu(x) \tag{11–181}$$

Alternatively since $U(a,\Lambda)$ and $S(\Lambda)$ are both representations of a group

$$U(a,\Lambda)^{-1} = U(-\Lambda^{-1}a,\Lambda^{-1}) \tag{11–182}$$

$$S(\Lambda)^{-1} = S(\Lambda^{-1}) \tag{11–183}$$

so that we can rewrite Eqs. (11–180) and (11–181) as follows:

$$U(a,\Lambda)\psi(x)U(a,\Lambda)^{-1} = S(\Lambda)^{-1}\psi(\Lambda x + a) \tag{11–184}$$

$$U(a,\Lambda)A_\mu(x)U(a,\Lambda)^{-1} = (\Lambda^{-1})_\mu{}^\nu A_\nu(\Lambda x + a) \tag{11–185}$$

which is the form most useful when stating the invariance properties in terms of a Schrödinger-type description. Equations (11–184) and (11–185) can be regarded as characterizing the operators $\psi(x)$ and $A_\mu(x)$ as spinor and vector field operators, respectively.

The previous results become somewhat more transparent when consideration is given to the manner in which matrix elements transform under Lorentz transformations. The matrix elements are c numbers and express the results of measurements. Since relativistic invariance is a statement concerning the observable consequences of the theory, it is perhaps more natural to state the requirements of invariance as a requirement that matrix elements transform properly.

If $A_\mu(x)$ is a vector field, call

$$(\Psi,A_\mu(x)\Psi) = a_\mu(x) \tag{11–186}$$

The (four-vector) $a_\mu(x)$ represents the result of some local measurement at the point x performed by a (Lorentz) observer O. An observer O' (related to O by a Lorentz transformation $x' = \Lambda x$) describes this measurement by

$$(\Psi',A_\mu(x')\Psi') = a'_\mu(x') \tag{11–187}$$

where we have adopted the Schrödinger-type description so that the state vectors $|\Psi\rangle$ and $|\Psi'\rangle$ are the vectors which observers O and O' attribute to bodily the same state. The covariance of the theory can then be expressed by equation

$$a'_\nu(x') = \Lambda_\nu{}^\mu a_\mu(x) \tag{11–188}$$

which will be guaranteed if there exists for any Lorentz transformation $\{a,\Lambda\}$ a unitary operator $U(a,\Lambda)$

$$U(a,\Lambda)^{-1} = U^*(a,\Lambda) \tag{11–189}$$

such that

$$|\Psi'\rangle = U(a,\Lambda)|\Psi\rangle \tag{11–190}$$

and

$$U(a,\Lambda)A_\mu(x)U(a,\Lambda)^{-1} = (\Lambda^{-1})_\mu{}^\nu A_\nu(\Lambda x + a) \tag{11–191}$$

We have noted that the unitary operators $U(a,\Lambda)$ define a representation of the inhomogeneous group. If we denote by P_μ and $M_{\mu\nu}$ the (hermitian) generators for infinitesimal translations and Lorentz transformations respectively, then

$$U(a,1) = e^{ia_\mu P^\mu} \tag{11–192}$$

is the generator for a translation

$$x'_\mu \rightarrow x_\mu + a \tag{11–193}$$

and

$$U(0,\Lambda) = e^{\frac{1}{2}i\Lambda_{\mu\nu}M^{\mu\nu}} \tag{11–194}$$

is the generator for a homogeneous Lorentz transformation

$$x'_\mu = \Lambda_\mu{}^\nu x_\nu \tag{11–195}$$

For an inhomogeneous transformation

$$U(a,\Lambda) = \exp\{ia_\mu P^\mu + \tfrac{1}{2}i\Lambda_{\mu\nu}M^{\mu\nu}\} \tag{11–196}$$

The commutation rules that are obeyed by the generators for infinitesimal translations and rotations are

$$[P_\mu,P_\nu] = 0 \tag{11–197}$$

$$[P_\mu,M_{\kappa\lambda}] = -i(g_{\mu\kappa}P_\lambda - g_{\lambda\mu}P_\kappa) \tag{11–198}$$

$$[M_{\kappa\lambda},M_{\mu\nu}] = i(g_{\lambda\mu}M_{\kappa\nu} + g_{\kappa\nu}M_{\lambda\mu} - g_{\kappa\mu}M_{\lambda\nu} - g_{\lambda\nu}M_{\kappa\mu}) \tag{11–199}$$

These are the structure relations for the Poincaré group and are consequences of the multiplication law (11–171) and (11–172) for the inhomogeneous Lorentz group. In terms of the three vectors

$$\mathbf{J} = (M^{23},M^{31},M^{12}) \tag{11–200}$$

$$\mathbf{N} = (M^{01},M^{02},M^{03}) \tag{11–201}$$

the above commutation rules imply

$$[J^j,J^k] = i\varepsilon^{jkl}J^l \tag{11–202}$$

$$[N^j,N^k] = -i\varepsilon^{jql}J^l \tag{11–203}$$

$$[J^j, N^k] = i\varepsilon^{jkl} N^l \tag{11-204}$$

$$[J^j, P^o] = 0 \tag{11-205}$$

$$[J^j, P^k] = i\varepsilon^{jkl} P^k \tag{11-206}$$

$$[N^j, P^o] = -iP^j \tag{11-207}$$

$$[N^j, P^k] = -i\delta^{jk} P^o \tag{11-208}$$

The existence of a unitary transformation $U(a,\Lambda)$ which relates the field operators in the two frames imposes certain conditions on the operators themselves: they must satisfy certain commutation rules with P_μ and $M_{\mu\nu}$. Consider first the case of a space-time translation

$$x' = x + a \tag{11-209}$$

Under this transformation the field operators transform as follows:

$$\psi'(x') = \psi(x) \tag{11-210}$$

$$A'_\mu(x') = A_\mu(x) \tag{11-211}$$

The transformation is induced by the unitary operator $U(a,1)$ with the property that

$$U(a,1)\psi(x)U(a,1)^{-1} = \psi(x + a) \tag{11-212}$$

$$U(a,1)A_\mu(x)U(a,1)^{-1} = A_\mu(x + a) \tag{11-213}$$

For an infinitesimal transformation, $a_\mu = \varepsilon_\mu$, Eqs. (11–212) and (11–213) read

$$(1 + i\varepsilon\cdot P + \cdots)\psi(x)(1 - i\varepsilon\cdot P + \cdots) = \psi(x) + \varepsilon\cdot\partial\psi(x) + \cdots \tag{11-214}$$

$$(1 + i\varepsilon\cdot P + \cdots)A_\mu(x)(1 - i\varepsilon\cdot P + \cdots) = A_\mu(x) + \varepsilon\cdot\partial A_\mu(x) + \cdots \tag{11-215}$$

whence, since ε is arbitrary,

$$i[P_\mu, \psi(x)] = \partial_\mu\psi(x) \tag{11-216}$$

$$i[P_\mu, A_\nu(x)] = \partial_\mu A_\nu(x) \tag{11-217}$$

For $\mu = 0$ the above equation must coincide with the equation of motion, hence P_0 is the hamiltonian of the system. Similarly one deduces that the P_i ($i = 1,2,3$) must be the components of the total momentum operator. We call the operator P_μ the displacement operators for space time translations in the sense that for an arbitrary operator $F(x)$ which is a function of $\psi(x)$ and $A_\mu(x)$

$$U(a,1)F(x)U(a,1)^{-1} = F(x + a) \tag{11-218}$$

Again for infinitesimal a this equation reads

$$(1 + iP\cdot a)F(x)(1 - iP\cdot a) = F(x) + a\cdot\partial F(x) \tag{11–219}$$

or since a_μ is arbitrary

$$i[P_\mu,F(x)] = \partial_\mu F(x) \tag{11–220}$$

Since the operators P_μ commute with one another we can choose a representation in which every basis vector is an eigenfunction of all the P_μ's with eigenvalue p_μ. It should be noted that the specification of the energy and momentum of a state vector does not uniquely characterize the state. The energy-momentum operators are merely four operators of a complete set of commuting observables. We shall denote by α,β the other eigenvalues necessary to specify the state. Thus

$$P_\mu|p,\alpha\rangle = p_\mu|p,\alpha\rangle \tag{11–221}$$

In a representation specified by basis vectors $|p,\alpha\rangle$, since

$$\begin{aligned} U(a,1)|p,\alpha\rangle &= e^{iP\cdot a}|p,\alpha\rangle \\ &= e^{ip\cdot a}|p,\alpha\rangle \end{aligned} \tag{11–222}$$

the matrix element of an arbitrary operator $F(x)$ can be written as follows:

$$\begin{aligned} \langle p',\beta|F(x)|p,\alpha\rangle &= \langle p',\beta|e^{iP\cdot x}F(0)e^{-iP\cdot x}|p,\alpha\rangle \\ &= e^{i(p'-p)\cdot x}\langle p',\beta|F(0)|p,\alpha\rangle \end{aligned} \tag{11–223}$$

thus giving explicitly the x-dependence of the matrix element in terms of the matrix element of the operator $F(0)$, *i.e.*, of the operator $F(x)$ evaluated at $x = 0$. Similar remarks apply to the case of homogeneous Lorentz transformations. One thus derives for example that the commutation rule between $M_{\mu\nu}$ and $\psi(x)$ must be

$$\begin{aligned} [M_{\mu\nu},\psi_\alpha(x)] &= i(x_\mu\partial_\nu - x_\nu\partial_\mu)\psi_\alpha(x) \\ &\quad + i\sum_{\beta=1}^{4}(\sigma_{\mu\nu})_{\alpha\beta}\psi_\beta(x) \end{aligned} \tag{11–224}$$

where

$$\sigma_{\mu\nu} = \frac{1}{2i}(\gamma_\mu\gamma_\nu - \gamma_\nu\gamma_\mu) \tag{11–225}$$

The right side is again determined by the fact that $\psi(x)$ must transform like a spinor under a homogeneous Lorentz transformation. Its form is made transparent by recalling that for an infinitesimal homogeneous Lorentz transformation

$$x'^\mu = x^\mu + \omega^\mu{}_\nu x^\nu \tag{11–226}$$

$$S(\Lambda) = 1 + \frac{i}{4}\omega^{\mu\nu}\sigma_{\mu\nu} \tag{11–227}$$

Consider next the transformation properties of state vectors, in particular one-particle states, under Lorentz transformation. The theory under discussion, quantum electrodynamics, must describe states of one positon, states of one negaton and states of one photon. We, therefore, assume the existence of discrete eigenvalues of the mass operator $P^2 = P_\mu P^\mu$ corresponding to the mass 0 (one-photon state) and corresponding to the mass m (1-negaton, 1-positon states). In other words we assume the existence of states $|\mathbf{p},s,-e\rangle$ corresponding to a negaton of momentum $\mathbf{p}$, helicity s, charge $-e$, energy $p_o = \sqrt{\mathbf{p}^2 + m^2}$ and mass m, with the property that

$$P_\mu|\mathbf{p},s,-e\rangle = p_\mu|\mathbf{p},s,-e\rangle \tag{11-228}$$

$$Q|\mathbf{p},s,-e\rangle = -e|\mathbf{p},s,-e\rangle \tag{11-229}$$

$$P^2|\mathbf{p},s,-e\rangle = m^2|\mathbf{p},s,-e\rangle \tag{11-230}$$

i.e., states such that

$$p^2 = m^2 \tag{11-231}$$

$$p_o = +\sqrt{\mathbf{p}^2 + m^2} \tag{11-232}$$

Similarly for the one-positon states $|\mathbf{p},s,+e\rangle$ for which

$$Q|\mathbf{p},s,e\rangle = e|\mathbf{p},s,e\rangle \tag{11-233}$$

The one-photon states will have the property that

$$P_\mu|\mathbf{k},\lambda\rangle = k_\mu|\mathbf{k},\lambda\rangle \tag{11-234}$$

$$P^2|\mathbf{k},\lambda\rangle = k^2|\mathbf{k},\lambda\rangle = 0 \tag{11-235}$$

$$Q|\mathbf{k},\lambda\rangle = 0 \tag{11-236}$$

where $\mathbf{k}$ denotes the momentum, $k_o = |\mathbf{k}|$ the energy, and λ the polarization of the photon. Actually we shall see that by virtue of the zero photon mass such *discrete* eigenvalues of the operator P^2 do not really exist and that, in fact, P^2 has a continuous spectrum starting at $P^2 = 0$. Similarly, the point $P^2 = m^2$ is a branch point of the resolvent operator $(P^2 - z)^{-1}$. For the present we shall not concern ourselves with these particular difficulties. They can be bypassed (at a formal level) by assuming that the photon has a very small mass μ. However, the lack of analyticity of the theory in the parameter μ and the fact that gauge invariance is destroyed by its introduction, make this device unattractive. The following statements should therefore be regarded as formal consequences of the above assumptions.

The one-particle states are steady and they can be regarded as being created by the action of the "in" operators on the vacuum state. The vacuum state $|0\rangle$ is an eigenfunction of P_μ and $M_{\mu\nu}$ with eigenvalue 0

$$P_\mu|0\rangle = 0 \tag{11–237}$$

$$M_{\mu\nu}|0\rangle = 0 \tag{11–238}$$

(hence it is an invariant state)

$$U(a,\Lambda)|0\rangle = 0 \tag{11–239}$$

In order to establish the transformation properties of the one-particle states, let us obtain the transformation properties of the "in" operators.

The transformation properties (11–184) and (11–185) of the fields and $A_\mu(x)$ and $\psi(x)$ together with the invariance properties of the D_R and S_R functions, *e.g.*, that for proper inhomogeneous Lorentz transformations:

$$D_R(\Lambda x + a - y) = D_R(x - \Lambda^{-1}(y - a)) \tag{11–240}$$

imply that $A_{\text{in}}(x)$ and $\psi_{\text{in}}(x)$ transform as follows:

$$U(a,\Lambda)\psi_{\text{in}}(x)U(a,\Lambda)^{-1} = S(\Lambda)^{-1}\psi_{\text{in}}(\Lambda x + a) \tag{11–241}$$

$$U(a,\Lambda)A_{\text{in}\,\mu}(x)U(a,\Lambda)^{-1} = (\Lambda^{-1})_\mu{}^\nu A_{\text{in}\,\nu}(\Lambda x + a) \tag{11–242}$$

This is verified by applying $U(a,\Lambda)$ to the left and $U(a,\Lambda)^{-1}$ to the right of both sides of Eqs. (11–142) and (11–97), and making use of the transformation properties of (11–184) and (11–185) of the fields. Equations (11–241) and (11–242) were to be expected. They guarantee that $\psi_{\text{in}}(x)$ and $A_{\text{in}\,\mu}(x)$ transform like a spinor and four-vector, respectively. We are now in a position to discuss the transformation properties of the one-particle states. Consider the one-negaton state, $|\mathbf{p},s,-e\rangle$. Upon taking the adjoint of Eq. (11–241) and multiplying by γ_o we obtain

$$U(a,\Lambda)\tilde{\psi}_{\text{in}}(x)U(a,\Lambda)^{-1} = \tilde{\psi}_{\text{in}}(\Lambda x + a)S(\Lambda) \tag{11–243}$$

with

$$S(\Lambda)\gamma_\mu S(\Lambda)^{-1} = (\Lambda^{-1})_\mu{}^\nu\gamma_\nu \tag{11–244}$$

since for a Lorentz transformation such that $\Lambda_o^o \geq 1$ (no time inversion)

$$S^*(\Lambda)\gamma^o = \gamma^o S(\Lambda)^{-1} \tag{11–245}$$

Hence, since

$$\begin{aligned}|\mathbf{p},s,-e\rangle &= b_{\text{in}}^*(\mathbf{p},s)|0\rangle \\ &= \sqrt{\frac{m}{(2\pi)^3}}\int d\sigma^\mu(x)\tilde{\psi}_{\text{in}}(x)\gamma_\mu w(\mathbf{p},s)e^{-ip\cdot x}|0\rangle\end{aligned} \tag{11–246}$$

where $w(\mathbf{p},s)$ is a positive energy solution of the Dirac equation of momentum $\mathbf{p}$ and helicity s, it follows that

$$U(a,\Lambda)|\mathbf{p},s,-e\rangle$$

$$= \sqrt{\frac{m}{(2\pi)^3}} \int d\sigma^\mu(x)\tilde{\psi}_{\text{in}}(\Lambda x + a)S(\Lambda)\gamma_\mu w(\mathbf{p},s)e^{-ip\cdot x}|0\rangle \quad (11\text{–}247)$$

$$= \sqrt{\frac{m}{(2\pi)^3}} \int d\sigma^\mu(x)(\Lambda^{-1})_\mu{}^\nu\tilde{\psi}_{\text{in}}(\Lambda x + a)\gamma_\nu S(\Lambda)w(\mathbf{p},s) \cdot e^{i\Lambda p\cdot a}e^{-i\Lambda p\cdot(\Lambda x+a)}|0\rangle \quad (11\text{–}248)$$

$$= \sqrt{\frac{m}{(2\pi)^3}} \int d\sigma^\nu(y)\tilde{\psi}_{\text{in}}(y)\gamma_\nu S(\Lambda)w(\mathbf{p},s)\cdot e^{-i\Lambda p\cdot y}e^{i\Lambda p\cdot a}|0\rangle \quad (11\text{–}249)$$

In arriving at Eq. (11–249) we have made use of Eq. (11–241), of the (pseudo)vector character of the surface element $d\sigma^\mu(x)$ and of the invariance of the vacuum state expressed by Eq. (11–239). We now insert into the right-hand side of Eq. (11–249) the expansion of $\psi_{\text{in}}(x)$ in terms of b^*_{in} operators, and find

$$U(a,\Lambda)b^*_{\text{in}}(\mathbf{p},s)|0\rangle = \sum_t \tilde{w}(\Lambda p,t)\gamma_\nu S(\Lambda)w(\mathbf{p},s)\,\frac{m}{p'_0}\cdot e^{i\Lambda p\cdot a}b^*_{\text{in}}(\Lambda p,t)|0\rangle \quad (11\text{–}250)$$

where

$$p' = \Lambda p \quad (11\text{–}251)$$

Equivalently we can write

$$U(a,\Lambda)b^*_{\text{in}}(p,s)U(a,\Lambda)^{-1} = e^{i\Lambda p\cdot a}\sum_t \sigma_{ts}(p,\Lambda)b^*_{\text{in}}(\Lambda p,t) \quad (11\text{–}252)$$

where

$$\sigma_{ts}(p,\Lambda) = \frac{m}{p'_o}\,\tilde{w}(\Lambda p,t)\gamma_o S(\Lambda)w(p,s) \quad (11\text{–}253)$$

The following relation which is satisfied by $\sigma_{ts}(p,\Lambda)$ is often useful in explicit computations:

$$\sum_s \sigma_{ts}(p,\Lambda)\overline{\sigma_{rs}(p,\Lambda)}$$

$$= \frac{m^2}{p_o'^2}\sum_s \tilde{w}(\Lambda p,t)\gamma_o S(\Lambda)w(\mathbf{p},s)\tilde{w}(\mathbf{p},s)\cdot S(\Lambda)^{-1}\gamma_o w(\Lambda p,r)$$

$$= \frac{m^2}{p_o'^2}\tilde{w}(\Lambda p,t)\gamma_o S(\Lambda)\,\frac{\gamma\cdot p + m}{2m}\,S(\Lambda)^{-1}\gamma_o w(\Lambda p,r)$$

$$= \frac{m^2}{p_o'^2}\tilde{w}(\Lambda p,t)\gamma_o\,\frac{\gamma\cdot\Lambda p + m}{2m}\,\gamma_o w(\Lambda p,r)$$

$$= \frac{m}{p_o}\,\tilde{w}(\Lambda p,t)\gamma_o w(\Lambda p,s)$$

$$= \delta_{ts} \quad (11\text{–}254)$$

Similar considerations lead to the transformation properties of the one-photon states and of the photon "in"-operators which create photons of definite momentum and helicity. We shall, however, omit them here. Suffice it to remark that the above transformation properties imply that the interaction hamiltonian density $\mathscr{H}_{\text{in}\,I}(x) = j_{\text{in}\,\mu}(x)A^{\mu}_{\text{in}}(x)$ transforms like a scalar under restricted inhomogeneous Lorentz transformation

$$U(a,\Lambda)j_{\text{in}\,\mu}(x)A^{\mu}_{\text{in}}(x)U(a,\Lambda)^{-1} = j_{\text{in}\,\mu}(\Lambda x + a)A^{\mu}_{\text{in}}(\Lambda x + a) \tag{11–255}$$

Hence, since for $(x - x')^2 < 0$

$$[j_{\text{in}\,\mu}(x),j_{\text{in}\,\nu}(x')] = [A_{\text{in}\,\mu}(x),A_{\text{in}\,\nu}(x')] = 0$$

the S matrix

$$S = P(e^{i\int_{-\infty}^{+\infty} d^4x j_{\text{in}\,\mu}(x)A^{\mu}_{\text{in}}(x)}) \tag{11–256}$$

is invariant under restricted inhomogeneous Lorentz transformations

$$U(\Lambda,a)SU(\Lambda,a)^{-1} = S \tag{11–257}$$

This last equation can also be written in the form

$$[S,U(\Lambda,a)] = 0 \tag{11–258}$$

Several consequences can immediately be drawn from Eq. (11–257) by considering infinitesimal transformations

$$U = 1 + i\varepsilon G \tag{11–259}$$

where G is hermitian. Equation (11–258) then asserts that $[S,G] = 0$, and it follows that the transition amplitude ${}_{\text{in}}\langle g''|S|g'\rangle_{\text{in}}$ between two different eigenvalues of G vanishes.

Finally before concluding this section a word should be said concerning the relation between gauge invariance of electrodynamics and the uniqueness of the unitary operators $U(a,\Lambda)$ inducing inhomogeneous Lorentz transformations. We have adopted a description of the electromagnetic field in terms of potential operators $A_{\mu}(x)$ satisfying the Lorentz gauge condition for both observers O and O'. There exists, therefore, always the arbitrariness that the observer O' may use the operators

$$A'_{G\mu}(x') = A'_{\mu}(x') + \partial_{\mu}\Lambda'(x') \tag{11–260}$$

and

$$\psi'_G(x') = \exp(i\varepsilon\Lambda'(x'))\cdot\psi'(x') \tag{11–261}$$

with

$$\Box'\Lambda'(x') = 0 \tag{11–262}$$

which obey the same equations of motion and commutation rules as ψ and A, rather than the operators $\psi'(x')$ and $A'_\mu(x')$. Clearly the unitary operator $U_G(a,\Lambda)$ which relates ψ,A and ψ'_G,A'_G provides just as acceptable a transformation. There exists, therefore, a whole class of $U(a,\Lambda)$ that are *equivalent*.

11.3. Invariance of Quantum Electrodynamics under Discrete Transformations.—In the present section we consider the invariance of quantum electrodynamics under discrete symmetry operations, such as space-inversion, time-inversion, and charge conjugation.

Space Inversion.

As indicated at the beginning of the last section, to say that quantum electrodynamics is invariant under space inversion ($x' = i_s x$) means that we can find new field operators $\psi'(x'),A'_\nu(x')$ expressible in terms of $\psi(x)$ and $A_\mu(x)$ which satisfy the same equations of motion and commutation rules with respect to the primed coordinate system ($x' = i_s x$) as did $\psi(x)$ and $A_\nu(x)$ in terms of x. Since the commutation rules are to be the same for both sets of operators and the *set* of realizable states must be invariant, there must exist a unitary (or anti-unitary) transformation connecting these two sets of operators if the theory is invariant. For the case of space inversions, such a unitary operator is exhibited by $U(i_s)$, with the properties

$$\psi'(x) = U(i_s)^{-1}\psi(x)U(i_s) \tag{11–263}$$

$$U(i_s)\psi(x)U(i_s)^{-1} = \bar{\eta}_P S(i_s)^{-1}\psi(i_s x) \tag{11–264}$$

$$|\eta_P|^2 = 1; \qquad S(i_s) = \gamma_o \tag{11–265}$$

$$A'_\mu(x) = U(i_s)^{-1}A_\mu(x)U(i_s) \tag{11–266}$$

$$U(i_s)A_\mu(x)U(i_s)^{-1} = -(-1)^{\delta_{\mu o}}A_\mu(i_s x) \tag{11–267}$$

By convention the vacuum is invariant under $U(i_s)$

$$U(i_s)|0\rangle = |0\rangle \tag{11–268}$$

These transformation properties can be transcribed into transformation properties of state vectors in a Schrödinger-type description. The in-fields will satisfy equations similar to the above, *e.g.*

$$U(i_s)\psi_{\text{in}}(x)U(i_s)^{-1} = \bar{\eta}_P\gamma_o\psi_{\text{in}}(i_s x) \tag{11–269}$$

We next substitute in both sides of this equation the expansion

$$\psi_{\text{in}}(x) = \sqrt{\frac{m}{(2\pi)^3}}\sum_s \int \frac{d^3p}{p_o}\,(b_{\text{in}}(\mathbf{p},s)u(\mathbf{p},s)e^{-ip\cdot x} + d^*_{\text{in}}(\mathbf{p},s)v(\mathbf{p},s)e^{+ip\cdot x}) \tag{11–270}$$

In Eq. (11–270) $u(\mathbf{p},s) = w(\mathbf{p},s)$ is a positive energy spinor of momentum $\mathbf{p}$ and helicity s

$$(\gamma \cdot p - m)u(\mathbf{p},s) = 0 \tag{11–271}$$

$$(\mathbf{\Sigma} \cdot \mathbf{p})u(\mathbf{p},s) = |\mathbf{p}|su(\mathbf{p},s) \tag{11–272}$$

Upon noting that $\gamma_0 u(\mathbf{p},s)$ is a solution of the Dirac equation of momentum $-\mathbf{p}$, and helicity $-s$, *i.e.*

$$\gamma_0 u_+(\mathbf{p},s) = u_+(-\mathbf{p},-s) \tag{11–273}$$

whereas if $v_-(\mathbf{p},s)$ is a negative energy solution of momentum $-\mathbf{p}$,

$$\gamma_0 v_-(\mathbf{p},s) = -v_-(-\mathbf{p},-s) \tag{11–274}$$

one deduces from Eqs. (11–269) and (11–270) that

$$U(i_s)b_{\text{in}}(\mathbf{p},s)U(i_s)^{-1} = \bar{\eta}_P b_{\text{in}}(-\mathbf{p},-s) \tag{11–275}$$

$$U(i_s)d^*_{\text{in}}(\mathbf{p},s)U(i_s)^{-1} = -\bar{\eta}_P d^*_{\text{in}}(-\mathbf{p},-s) \tag{11–276}$$

Note the minus sign on the right side of Eq. (11–276), stemming from the relation (11–274). These transformation properties imply the following transformation rule of a one-negaton state under space inversion

$$\begin{aligned} U(i_s)|\mathbf{p},s,-e\rangle &= U(i_s)b^*(\mathbf{p},s)|0\rangle \\ &= U(i_s)b^*(\mathbf{p},s)U(i_s)^{-1}U(i_s)|0\rangle \\ &= \eta_P|-\mathbf{p},-s,-e\rangle \end{aligned} \tag{11–277}$$

In writing Eq. (11–277) we have also made use of our postulate that the vacuum remains invariant under the operation $U(i_s)$

$$U(i_s)|0\rangle = |0\rangle \tag{11–278}$$

The result (11–277) is consistent with the transformation property

$$U(i_s)\mathbf{P}U(i_s)^{-1} = -\mathbf{P} \tag{11–279}$$

of the total momentum operator, which is necessary in order that the equation

$$[\mathbf{P},Q(x)] = -i\nabla Q(x) \tag{11–280}$$

remain invariant under space inversion. Likewise, invariance of the commutation rules

$$\mathbf{J} \times \mathbf{J} = i\mathbf{J} \tag{11–281}$$

for the total angular momentum operator under space inversion requires that

$$U(i_s)\mathbf{J}U(i_s)^{-1} = \mathbf{J} \tag{11–282}$$

Hence

$$U(i_s)\mathbf{J} \cdot \mathbf{P}U(i_s)^{-1} = -\mathbf{J} \cdot \mathbf{P} \tag{11–283}$$

(so that the helicity of a given one-particle state will be changed under $U(i_s)$). The additional $(-)$ sign occurring in (11–276) means that the state of one negaton and one positon

$$|\mathbf{p}s;\, \mathbf{q}t\rangle_{\text{in}} = b^*_{\text{in}}(\mathbf{p},s)d^*_{\text{in}}(\mathbf{q},t)|0\rangle \tag{11–284}$$

transforms as follows under space-inversion

$$\begin{aligned} U(i_s)|\mathbf{p}s;\, \mathbf{q}t\rangle_{\text{in}} &= -|\eta_P|^2 b^*_{\text{in}}(-\mathbf{p},-s)d^*_{\text{in}}(-\mathbf{q},-t)|0\rangle \\ &= -|-\mathbf{p},-s;\, -\mathbf{q},-t\rangle_{\text{in}} \end{aligned} \tag{11–285}$$

so that a negaton-positon system in an s orbital state of relative angular momentum has a parity opposite to that of the vacuum.

Note that the above transformation properties for the ψ operators force the current operator to transform as expected under i_s, namely like a vector. Since

$$\begin{aligned} U(i_s)\tilde{\psi}(x)\gamma_\mu\psi(x)U(i_s)^{-1} &= |\eta_P|^2\tilde{\psi}(i_sx)\gamma_0\gamma_\mu\gamma_0\psi(i_sx) \\ &= \begin{cases} \tilde{\psi}(i_sx)\gamma_0\psi(i_sx) \\ -\tilde{\psi}(i_sx)\gamma_i\psi(i_sx) \end{cases} \end{aligned} \tag{11–286}$$

we see that

$$U(i_s)j_\mu(x)U(i_s)^{-1} = -(-1)^{\delta_{\mu 0}}j_\mu(i_sx) \tag{11–287}$$

Thus the current operator indeed transforms like a vector. This must be the case in order that the equation $\Box A_\mu(x) = j_\mu(x)$ transform properly, assuming the transformation property (11–267) for $A_\mu(x)$. We now inquire briefly into the question of the uniqueness of the $U(i_s)$ operator, in particular into the question of the phase associated with the fermion field operator. Note that the phase of the photon field operator is uniquely determined (Eq. (11–267)) by the fact that A_μ is a hermitian field which commutes with the total charge operator Q. The negaton-positon field operator on the other hand does not commute with the total charge operator, in fact

$$e^{iQ\alpha/e}\psi(x)e^{-iQ\alpha/e} = e^{i\alpha}\psi(x) \tag{11–288}$$

The theory is, however, invariant under a gauge transformation whereby

$$\psi(x) \to e^{i\alpha}\psi(x) \tag{11–289}$$

Hence the transformation (11–263)–(11–266) with $|\eta_P|^2 = 1$ and $\bar{\eta}_P$ fixed, is not the only one which produces a negaton-positon field operator for which the commutation rules and field equations are invariant. An $U'(i_s)$ satisfying

$$U'(i_s)\psi(x)U'(i_s)^{-1} = \bar{\eta}_P e^{i\alpha}\gamma_0\psi(i_sx) \tag{11–290}$$

would do just as well. Clearly this $U'(i_s)$ is related to $U(i_s)$ (see (11-263)-(11-266)) by

$$U'(i_s) = e^{iQ\alpha/e}U(i_s) \tag{11-291}$$

Hence, there is a whole class of $U(i_s)$'s that are equivalent and admissible. We can make use of this freedom to choose a particular $U(i_s)$ for which

$$\begin{aligned} U(i_s)^2 A_\mu(x) U(i_s)^{-2} &= A_\mu(x) \\ U(i_s)^2 \psi(x) U(i_s)^{-2} &= \psi(x) \end{aligned} \tag{11-292}$$

and, in fact, such that $U(i_s)^2 = 1$, *i.e.*, such that $U(i_s)$ is hermitian.

The interaction hamiltonian density $j_{\text{in}\,\mu}(x)A^\mu_{\text{in}}(x)$ transforms like a scalar:

$$U(i_s)j_{\text{in}\,\mu}(x)A^\mu_{\text{in}}(x)U(i_s)^{-1} = j_{\text{in}\,\mu}(i_s x)A^\mu_{\text{in}}(i_s x) \tag{11-293}$$

The hamiltonian is, therefore, invariant under $U(i_s)$. Similarly the S-matrix is invariant under $U(i_s)$

$$U(i_s)SU(i_s)^{-1} = S \tag{11-294}$$

and it follows that

$$[S,U(i_s)] = 0 \tag{11-295}$$

If we restrict ourselves to the case of a hermitian $U(i_s)$, the vanishing of this commutator implies that the S-matrix element between any two states characterized by two different eigenvalues of the (hermitian) operator $U(i_s)$ must vanish. Thus, for example, positronium in a triplet S state cannot decay into two photons. (Note that since $U(i_s)$ anticommutes with $\mathbf{P}$, the total momentum of the states under consideration must vanish.) Equation (11-294) when written in the form

$$U(i_s)^*SU(i_s) = S \tag{11-296}$$

(again for the case of a hermitian $U(i_s)$) asserts that the S-matrix element between any two states is equal to the corresponding S-matrix element between the spatially inverted states

$${}_{\text{in}}\langle\Psi|S|\Phi\rangle_{\text{in}} = {}_{\text{in}}\langle\Psi|U(i_s)^*SU(i_s)|\Phi\rangle_{\text{in}} \tag{11-297}$$

Particle-Antiparticle Conjugation.—If quantum electrodynamics is invariant under space inversion, then it does not matter whether we employ a right- or left-handed coordinate system in the description of purely electrodynamic phenomena. To speak of "right" and "left" is an arbitrary convention in a world in which only electrodynamics operates.

Similarly the recognition that it is a convention to call the negaton the particle and the positon the antiparticle (we could just as well have called the negaton the antiparticle and the positon the particle) suggests that the theory possesses an additional invariance property, namely it must be invariant under the operation of interchanging particles and antiparticles.

If these inferences are correct an operator U_c must exist such that

$$U_c b_{\text{in}}(\mathbf{p},s) U_c^{-1} = \eta_C d_{\text{in}}(\mathbf{p},s) \tag{11–298}$$

$$U_c d_{\text{in}}(\mathbf{p},s) U_c^{-1} = \bar{\eta}_C b_{\text{in}}(\mathbf{p},s) \tag{11–299}$$

under which the theory is invariant. The resulting U_c clearly will have the property that operating on any "in"-state it will change particles into antiparticles (and vice-versa) leaving all other quantum numbers the same. We assert that this is, in fact, the case and prove our assertion by exhibiting an operator U_c with the requisite properties, under which the theory is invariant.

Before doing so we note a certain peculiarity of negative energy spinors. Let $u(\mathbf{p},s)$ be a positive energy solution of the Dirac equation corresponding to helicity s so that

$$(\gamma \cdot p - m) u(\mathbf{p},s) = 0 \tag{11–300}$$

$$(\mathbf{\Sigma} \cdot \mathbf{p}) u(\mathbf{p},s) = s|\mathbf{p}| u(\mathbf{p},s) \tag{11–301}$$

The adjoint spinor $\tilde{u}(\mathbf{p},s)$ then satisfies the equation

$$\tilde{u}(\mathbf{p},s)(\gamma \cdot p - m) = 0 \tag{11–302}$$

Upon taking the transpose of this last equation we find that $\tilde{u}^T(\mathbf{p},s)$ (a column spinor!) satisfies the equation

$$(\gamma^T \cdot p - m)\tilde{u}^T(\mathbf{p},s) = 0 \tag{11–303}$$

With the help of the matrix C, satisfying

$$C\gamma^\mu C^{-1} = -\gamma^{\mu T} \tag{11–304}$$

$$C^*C = CC^* = 1; \qquad C^T = -C \tag{11–305}$$

Equation (11–303) can also be written, as follows:

$$-C(\gamma \cdot p + m)C^{-1}\tilde{u}^T(\mathbf{p},s) = 0 \tag{11–306}$$

Hence the spinor

$$u_c(\mathbf{p},s) = C^{-1}\tilde{u}^T(\mathbf{p},s) \tag{11–307}$$

is a negative energy solution for momentum $-\mathbf{p}$ and spin parallel to $-s\mathbf{p}$, *i.e.*,

$$u_c(\mathbf{p},s) = v(\mathbf{p},s) \tag{11–308}$$

(which in the formalism of the hole theory can be reinterpreted as the amplitude of an antiparticle of momentum $\mathbf{p}$, energy $\sqrt{\mathbf{p}^2 + m^2}$ and spin parallel to $s\mathbf{p}$). We can, therefore, write the decomposition of $\psi_{\text{in}}(x)$ in terms of creation and annihilation operators for particles of definite helicity and momentum as follows:

$$\psi_{\text{in}}(x) = \sqrt{\frac{m}{(2\pi)^3}} \int \frac{d^3p}{p_o} \{b_{\text{in}}(\mathbf{p},s)u(\mathbf{p},s)e^{-ip\cdot x} + d^*_{\text{in}}(\mathbf{p},s)u_c(\mathbf{p},s)e^{ip\cdot x}\} \tag{11–309}$$

If we now define the unitary operator U_c in accordance with (11–298) and (11–299) above, then

$$U_c\psi_{\text{in}}(x)U_c{}^{-1} = \eta_c \sqrt{\frac{m}{(2\pi)^3}} \int \frac{d^3p}{p_o} \{d_{\text{in}}(\mathbf{p},s)C^{-1}\tilde{v}^T(\mathbf{p},s)e^{-ip\cdot x} + b^*_{\text{in}}(\mathbf{p},s)C^{-1}\tilde{u}^T(\mathbf{p},s)e^{ip\cdot x}\} \tag{11–310}$$

$$= \eta_C C^{-1}\tilde{\psi}^T_{\text{in}}(x) \tag{11–311}$$

More generally let us define U_c by

$$U_c\psi(x)U_c^{-1} = \eta_C C^{-1}\tilde{\psi}^T(x) \tag{11–312}$$

$$= \psi_C(x) \tag{11–313}$$

Since U_c is assumed unitary

$$\begin{aligned} U_c\tilde{\psi}(x)U_c^{-1} &= \bar{\eta}_C[C^{-1}\tilde{\psi}^T(x)]^*\gamma_o \\ &= \bar{\eta}_C(C\psi(x))^T \end{aligned} \tag{11–314}$$

The equal time commutations rules obeyed by ψ and $\tilde{\psi}$ will be invariant provided that

$$|\eta_C|^2 = 1 \tag{11–315}$$

Furthermore, one readily verifies that under U_c the equation of motion for $\psi(x)$ goes over into that for $\tilde{\psi}(x)$, and conversely. The current operator transforms under U_c as follows:

$$\begin{aligned} U_c[\tilde{\psi}(x)\gamma_\mu,\psi(x)]U_c^{-1} &= U_c[\tilde{\psi}_\alpha(x),\psi_\beta(x')]U_c^{-1}(\gamma_\mu)_{\alpha\beta} \\ &= -[\psi_\alpha(x),\tilde{\psi}_\beta(x')](C\gamma_\mu C^{-1})_{\alpha\beta} \\ &= -[\tilde{\psi}(x)\gamma_\mu,\psi(x)] \end{aligned} \tag{11–316}$$

i.e.,

$$U_c j_\mu(x)U_c^{-1} = -j_\mu(x) \tag{11–317}$$

Hence the total charge anticommutes with U_c,

$$U_c Q U_c^{-1} = -Q \tag{11–318}$$

This is as expected since U_c change particles into antiparticles, and antiparticles have opposite electric charge from particles. Thus, since

$$U_c|\mathbf{p},s,-e\rangle = |\mathbf{p},s,+e\rangle \tag{11–319}$$

hence

$$QU_c|\mathbf{p},s,-e\rangle = +e|\mathbf{p},s,e\rangle \tag{11–320}$$

whereas

$$U_cQ|\mathbf{p},s,-e\rangle = -e|\mathbf{p},s,e\rangle \tag{11–321}$$

so that

$$U_cQ + QU_c = 0 \tag{11–322}$$

The above transformation properties of the current operator make quantum electrodynamics invariant under the operation U_c, usually called charge conjugation, provided

$$U_cA_\mu(x)U_c^{-1} = -A_\mu(x) \tag{11–323}$$

for then the equation $\Box A_\mu(x) = j_\mu(x)$ is invariant under U_c, and the equal time commutation rules obeyed by $A_\mu(x)$ remain invariant.

Note that U_c^2 commutes with all the operators

$$U_c^2\psi(x)U_c^{-2} = \psi(x) \tag{11–324}$$

$$U_c^2A_\mu(x)U_c^{-2} = A_\mu(x) \tag{11–325}$$

Again, the definition of U_c lacks uniqueness because of the freedom of gauge transformations

$$\psi(x) \to \psi(x)e^{i\alpha} \tag{11–326}$$

This arbitrariness can be made use of to define U_c such that $U_c^2 = 1$, *i.e.*, such that U_c is hermitian

$$U_c^* = U_c \tag{11–327}$$

Since U_c anticommutes with the total charge, clearly the only interesting eigenstates of U_c are those with zero total charge. Furthermore, if $|\lambda\rangle$ is such an eigenstate, *i.e.*, if

$$U_c|\lambda\rangle = \lambda|\lambda\rangle \tag{11–328}$$

then since $U_c^2 = +1$, it follows that $\lambda^2 = 1$ and hence $\lambda = \pm 1$. Clearly eigenstates with $\lambda = +1$ are orthogonal to those with $\lambda = -1$. It is usual to define the vacuum state as eigenstate of U_c with eigenvalue $+1$

$$U_c|0\rangle = |0\rangle \tag{11–329}$$

As in the case of space inversion, one readily verifies that

$$U_cSU_c^{-1} = S \tag{11–330}$$

The invariance of quantum electrodynamics under charge conjugation has several immediate consequences.

(1) A state of n incoming (outgoing) photons has the charge conjugation eigenvalue $(-1)^n$.

Proof:

$$U_c A_{\substack{\text{in}\\ \text{out}}\,\mu_1}(x_1)\cdots A_{\substack{\text{in}\\ \text{out}}\,\mu_n}(x_n)|0\rangle$$

$$= U_c A_{\substack{\text{in}\\ \text{out}}\,\mu_1}(x_1) U_c^{-1} U_c \cdots U_c A_{\substack{\text{in}\\ \text{out}}\,\mu_n}(x_n) U_c^{-1} U_c|0\rangle$$

$$= (-1)^n A_{\substack{\text{in}\\ \text{out}}\,\mu_1}(x_1)\cdots A_{\substack{\text{in}\\ \text{out}}\,\mu_n}(x_n)|0\rangle \tag{11–331}$$

(2) The vacuum expectation value of an odd number of (Heisenberg) photon operators vanishes.

Proof: Since U_c is unitary

$$\langle 0|A_{\mu_1}(x_1)\cdots A_{\mu_n}(x_n)|0\rangle$$

$$= \langle 0|U_c^* U_c A_{\mu_1}(x_1) U_c^{-1} U_c \cdots U_c A_{\mu_n}(x_n) U_c^{-1} U_c|0\rangle$$

$$= (-1)^n \langle 0|A_{\mu_1}(x_1)\cdots A_{\mu_n}(x_n)|0\rangle \tag{11–332}$$

This statement is closely related to Furry's theorem.

(3) Equation (11–330) implies

$$_{\text{in}}\langle b|S|a\rangle_{\text{in}} = {}_{\text{in}}\langle b|U_c^* S U_c|a\rangle_{\text{in}}$$

$$= {}_{\text{in}}\langle b_c|S|a_c\rangle_{\text{in}} \tag{11–333}$$

where the states $|b_c\rangle, |a_c\rangle$ are obtained by replacing every particle (antiparticle) in the states $|a\rangle$ and $|b\rangle$ by its antiparticle (particle).

(4) The magnetic moment of a positon is opposite in sign from that of the negaton.

Proof: The magnetic moment of a particle is given by the expectation value of the operator $\int d^3x\, \mathbf{r} \times \mathbf{j}(x)$. Hence since U_c is unitary, and anticommutes with $\mathbf{j}$

$$\boldsymbol{\mu}_e = \langle e| \int d^3\, x\, \mathbf{r} \times \mathbf{j}(x)|e\rangle$$

$$= \langle e|U_c^* U \int d^3x\; \mathbf{r} \times \mathbf{j}(x) U_c^* U_c|e\rangle$$

$$= -\langle -e| \int d^3x\; \mathbf{r} \times \mathbf{j}(x)|-e\rangle$$

$$= -\boldsymbol{\mu}_{-e} \tag{11–334}$$

(5) Because eigenstates of U_c with eigenvalues $+1$ and -1 are orthogonal to each other, the following selection rules hold:

(a) a ^3S state of positronium cannot decay into an even number of photons;

(b) a ^1S state of positronium cannot decay into an odd number of photons;

Time inversion.

Finally, we consider the invariance of quantum electrodynamics under time reversal: $x' = i_t x$ where

$$x_o' = -x_o \tag{11-335}$$

$$\mathbf{x}' = \mathbf{x} \tag{11-336}$$

The transformation $U(i_t)$ which maps the operator algebra $\psi(x), A_\mu(x)$ onto the operator algebra of the time reversed operators is fundamentally different from the unitary mappings previously considered. This can most easily be seen as follows:

Assume that there exists a unitary operator $U(i_t)$ which maps the Heisenberg operator $Q(t)$ at time t into the operator $Q^\tau(-t)$. Assume further that this mapping has the property of leaving the hamiltonian invariant, *i.e.*, that $U(i_t)HU(i_t)^{-1} = H$. Consider then the equation satisfied by the transformed operator

$$Q^\tau(-t) = U(i_t)^{-1}Q(t)U(i_t) \tag{11-337}$$

Since the original operator $Q(t)$ obeyed the Heisenberg equation of motion

$$[Q(t),H] = i\partial_t Q(t) \tag{11-338}$$

the transformed one, by virtue of the assumed invariance of H under $U(i_t)$, will satisfy

$$U(i_t)^{-1}[Q(t),H]U(i_t) = [Q^\tau(-t),H] \tag{11-339}$$

$$= i \lim_{\Delta t \to 0} U(i_t)^{-1} \frac{Q(t + \Delta t) - Q(t)}{\Delta t} U(i_t) \tag{11-340}$$

$$= -i \lim_{\Delta t \to 0} \frac{Q^\tau(-t - \Delta t) - Q^\tau(-t)}{-\Delta t} \tag{11-341}$$

$$= -i\partial_t Q^\tau(-t) \tag{11-342}$$

contradicting the Heisenberg form of the equation of motion, Eq. (11–338). This difficulty can be overcome by making $U(i_t)$ an antilinear operator[6] so that

[6] An antilinear operator A is defined by

$$A(\alpha|\Psi\rangle + \beta|\Phi\rangle) = \bar{\alpha}A|\Psi\rangle + \bar{\beta}A|\Phi\rangle \tag{a}$$

where α,β are arbitrary complex numbers. The antilinearity is characterized by the fact that it is the complex conjugate of α and β, $\bar{\alpha}$ and $\bar{\beta}$ which appear on the right-hand side of the defining relation, Eq. (a), *i.e.*,

$$A\lambda = \bar{\lambda}A \tag{b}$$

$$U(i_t)(\alpha|\Psi\rangle + \beta|\Phi\rangle) = \bar{\alpha}U(i_t)|\Psi\rangle + \bar{\beta}U(i_t)|\Phi\rangle \tag{11–343}$$

in which case the right hand of (11–339) becomes equal to

$$\begin{aligned}[Q^\tau(-t),H] &= -i \lim_{\Delta t\to 0} U(i_t)^{-1} \frac{Q(t+\Delta t) - Q(t)}{\Delta t} U(i_t) \\ &= i\partial_t Q^\tau(-t)\end{aligned} \tag{11–344}$$

Thus $Q^\tau(-t)$ does satisfy the correct Heisenberg equation of motion. It should be recalled, incidentally, that the correct definition of the adjoint A^* of an antilinear operator A is

$$(\Psi,A\Phi) = \overline{(A^*\Psi,\Phi)} \tag{11–345}$$

We next inquire as to the transformation properties of the total momentum operator $\mathbf{P}$ under time inversion in order that the equation

$$[\mathbf{P},Q(\mathbf{x},t)] = i\hbar\nabla Q(\mathbf{x},t) \tag{11–346}$$

From the definitions (a)–(b) it follows that a product of an even number of antilinear operators is a linear operator, whereas the product of an odd number of antilinear operators is an antilinear operator. Similarly a product of any number of linear operators and an even (odd) number of antilinear operators is a linear (antilinear) operator.

If A induces a one-to-one mapping of the Hilbert space on itself then the inverse operator A^{-1} exists. It is an antilinear operator with the property that

$$A^{-1}A = AA^{-1} = 1 \tag{c}$$

If we assume that the adjoint A^* of an antilinear operator is defined as in the case of a linear operator by the equation

$$(\Psi,A\Phi) = (A^*\Psi,\Phi)$$

we are led to a contradiction since under such circumstances

$$\begin{aligned}(\alpha\Psi,A\Phi) &= \bar{\alpha}(\Psi,A\Phi) = \bar{\alpha}(A^*\Psi,\Phi) \\ &= (A^*\alpha\Psi,\Phi) = (\bar{\alpha}A^*\Psi,\Phi) \\ &= \alpha(A^*\Psi,\Phi)\end{aligned} \tag{d}$$

so that

$$\bar{\alpha}(A^*\Psi,\Phi) = \alpha(A^*\Psi,\Phi) \tag{e}$$

which is not true for arbitrary α. A consistent definition of the adjoint A^* of an antilinear operator is obtained by postulating that

$$\begin{aligned}(\Psi,A\Phi) &= \overline{(A^*\Psi,\Phi)} \\ &= (\Phi,A^*\Psi)\end{aligned} \tag{f}$$

hold for all $|\Psi\rangle$ and $|\Phi\rangle$. A^* is an antilinear operator sometimes called the antihermitian adjoint of A. One easily verifies that if L is a linear operator and A an antilinear one

$$(LA)^* = A^*L^* \tag{g}$$

where A^* is the antihermitian adjoint of A and L^* is the hermitian adjoint of L.

An antilinear operator A is called antihermitian if

$$A^* = A \tag{h}$$

and antiunitary if

$$A^* = A^{-1} \tag{i}$$

be invariant under time inversion. Applying $U(i_t)^{-1},U(i_t)$ on the left and right of this equation, we find

$$[U(i_t)^{-1}\mathbf{P}U(i_t), Q^\tau(\mathbf{x},-t)] = -i\hbar\nabla Q^\tau(\mathbf{x},t) \tag{11–347}$$

so that, if

$$U(i_t)^{-1}\mathbf{P}U(i_t) = -\mathbf{P} \tag{11–348}$$

the equation is invariant. Similarly, the invariance of the commutation rules $\mathbf{J} \times \mathbf{J} = i\mathbf{J}$ for the total angular momentum operators requires that $\mathbf{J}$ transform as follows under time inversion[7]

$$U(i_t)^{-1}\mathbf{J}U(i_t) = -\mathbf{J} \tag{11–349}$$

We next note that if $H_o(0)$, $H_I(0)$, and H are invariant under $U(i_t)$

$$U(i_t)HU(i_t)^{-1} = H \tag{11–350}$$

$U(i_t)$ will have the property that it changes "in" states into "out" states and conversely.

Proof: Consider the formal definition of the "in" and "out" states $|\Psi_\alpha\rangle_{\substack{\text{in}\\\text{out}}}$ in terms of eigenstates of $H_o(0): |\Phi_\alpha\rangle$

$$|\Psi_\alpha\rangle_{\text{in}} = |\Phi_\alpha\rangle + \lim_{\varepsilon\to 0+} \frac{1}{E_\alpha - H_o(0) + i\varepsilon} H_I(0)|\Psi_\alpha\rangle_{\text{in}} \tag{11–351}$$

$$|\Psi_\alpha\rangle_{\text{out}} = |\Phi_\alpha\rangle + \lim_{\varepsilon\to 0+} \frac{1}{E_\alpha - H_o(0) - i\varepsilon} H_I(0)|\Psi_\alpha\rangle_{\text{out}} \tag{11–352}$$

Call

$$U(i_t)|\Phi_\alpha\rangle = |\Phi_{\tau\alpha}\rangle \tag{11–353}$$

the time reversed state. From Eqs. (11–348) and (11–349), $|\Phi_{\tau\alpha}\rangle$ is the state obtained by reversing the momenta and spins of all the particles in the state $|\Phi_\alpha\rangle$. Since

$$U(i_t)H_o(0)U(i_t)^{-1} = H_o(0), \quad U(i_t)H_I(0)U(i_t)^{-1} = H_I(0)$$

[7] As a consequence of this transformation property if $|j,m\rangle$ is an eigenfunction of $\mathbf{J}^2,J_3$ with eigenvalue $j(j+1)$ and m respectively, with the phase convention

$$(J_1 \pm iJ_2)|j,m\rangle = \sqrt{(j \mp m)(j \pm m + 1)}\,|j,m \pm 1\rangle \tag{a}$$

$$J_3|j,m\rangle = m|j,m\rangle \tag{b}$$

then applying $U(i_t)$ to this last equation we infer that

$$U(i_t)|j,m\rangle = \varepsilon_m|j,-m\rangle \tag{c}$$

The constant ε_m can be determined by applying $U(i_t)$ on Eq. (a), and one finds that $\varepsilon_m = (-1)^m\varepsilon$, so that

$$U(i_t)|j,m\rangle = \varepsilon(-1)^m|j,-m\rangle$$

it follows that the vector $U(i_t)|\Psi_\alpha\rangle_{\rm in}$ satisfies the equation

$$U(i_t)|\Psi_\alpha\rangle_{\rm in} = |\Phi_{\tau\alpha}\rangle + \lim_{\varepsilon\to 0+} \frac{1}{E_\alpha - H_o - i\varepsilon} H_I(0)U(i_t)|\Psi_\tau\rangle_{\rm in} \tag{11-354}$$

Hence apart from a phase factor

$$U(i_t)|\Psi_\alpha\rangle_{\rm in} = |\Psi_{\tau\alpha}\rangle_{\rm out} \tag{11-355}$$

Here $|\Psi_{\tau\alpha}\rangle_{\rm out}$ is an outgoing wave solution corresponding to a plane wave state $|\Phi_{\tau\alpha}\rangle$ at time $t = +\infty$, *i.e.*,

$$|\Psi_{\tau\alpha}\rangle_{\rm out} = |\Phi_{\tau\alpha}\rangle + \lim_{\varepsilon\to 0+} \frac{1}{E_\alpha - H_o - i\varepsilon} H_I(0)|\Psi_{\tau\alpha}\rangle_{\rm out} \tag{11-356}$$

We, therefore, expect in the field theoretical case, in a Schrödinger-type description, that

$$U(i_t)\psi_{\rm in}(x)U(i_t)^{-1} = \bar{\eta}_T S(i_t)\psi_{\rm out}(i_t x) \tag{11-357}$$

where $S(i_t)$ must be so chosen as to guarantee that $\psi_{\rm out}(x)$ obeys the free Dirac equation and the phase factor η_T so as to leave the commutation rules invariant under $U(i_t)$.

Upon applying $U(i_t)$ to the left and $U(i_t)^{-1}$ on the right of the equation of motion for $\psi_{\rm in}(x)$

$$(-i\gamma\cdot\partial + m)\psi_{\rm in}(x) = 0 \tag{11-358}$$

we obtain

$$(i\bar{\gamma}\cdot\partial + m)U(i_t)\psi_{\rm in}(x)U(i_t)^{-1} = 0 \tag{11-359}$$

$$= \bar{\eta}_T(i\bar{\gamma}\cdot\partial + m)S(i_t)\psi_{\rm out}(-x_o,\mathbf{x}) = 0 \tag{11-360}$$

Therefore, if

$$S(i_t)^{-1}\overline{\gamma^o}S(i_t) = \gamma^o \tag{11-361}$$

$$S(i_t)^{-1}\overline{\gamma^i}S(i_t) = -\gamma^i \tag{11-362}$$

$\psi_{\rm out}(x)$ will obey the Dirac equation

$$(-i\gamma\cdot\partial + m)\psi_{\rm out}(x) = 0 \tag{11-363}$$

Now for our particular system of γ matrices, wherein γ^i is antihermitian and γ^o hermitian,

$$(\gamma^i)^* = -\gamma^i \tag{11-364}$$

$$(\gamma^o)^* = \gamma^o \tag{11-365}$$

since

$$(\gamma^\mu)^* = \gamma^o\gamma^\mu\gamma^o \tag{11-366}$$

and

$$(\gamma^\mu)^* = \overline{(\gamma^\mu)}^T \tag{11-367}$$

we can write

$$\overline{\gamma^\mu} = \gamma^{oT}\gamma^{\mu T}\gamma^{oT} \tag{11-368}$$

If C is the unitary skew-symmetric matrix

$$C^* = C^{-1} \tag{11-369}$$

$$C^T = -C \tag{11-370}$$

with the property that

$$-(\gamma^\mu)^T = C\gamma^\mu C^{-1} \tag{11-371}$$

we can then write Eq. (11–368) in the form

$$\overline{(\gamma^\mu)} = -C\gamma^o\gamma^\mu\gamma^o C^{-1} \tag{11-372}$$

or equivalently

$$\overline{\gamma^o} = -C\gamma^o C^{-1} \tag{11-373}$$

$$\overline{\gamma^i} = C\gamma^i C^{-1} \tag{11-374}$$

Hence Eqs. (11–361) and (11–362) can be satisfied with the choice

$$S(i_t) = C\gamma_5 \tag{11-375}$$

The transformation of the adjoint spinor reads

$$U(i_t)\tilde{\psi}_{\text{in}}(x)U(i_t)^{-1} = \eta_T\tilde{\psi}_{\text{out}}(i_t x)\gamma_5 C^{-1} \tag{11-376}$$

The reader will further see that with the choice $|\eta_T|^2 = 1$, the commutation rules of the "in" field operators go over into the proper commutation rules for the "out" fields, and conversely.

More generally, let us define the transformation properties of the Heisenberg field to be

$$U(i_t)\psi(x)U(i_t)^{-1} = \bar{\eta}_T C\gamma_5\psi(i_t x) \tag{11-377}$$

$$U(i_t)\tilde{\psi}(x)U(i_t)^{-1} = \eta_T\tilde{\psi}(i_t x)\gamma_5 C^{-1} \tag{11-378}$$

The choice of $|\eta_T|^2 = 1$, together with the antiunitary character of $U(i_t)$, guarantees the invariance of the equal time commutation rules under $U(i_t)$. With these definitions of the transformation properties of the spin $\frac{1}{2}$ field operators one verifies that

$$U(i_t)\psi_c(x)U(i_t)^{-1} = \eta_T C\gamma_5\psi_c(i_t x) \tag{11-379}$$

If we take the transformation properties of the electromagnetic potential operators to be

$$U(i_t)A_i(x)U(i_t)^{-1} = -A_i(i_t x) \tag{11–380}$$

$$U(i_t)A_o(x)U(i_t)^{-1} = A_o(i_t x) \tag{11–381}$$

then the equal time commutation rules for $A_\mu(x)$ are preserved. The particular choice of the phase for the right side of Eqs. (11–380) and (11–381) is a consequence of the hermiticity of the $A_\mu(x)$ field and the fact that we want the electromagnetic potential to transform like the current operator. The latter has the following transformation properties:

$$\begin{aligned} U(i_t)\tilde{\psi}(x)\gamma^\mu\psi(x)U(i_t)^{-1} &= U(i_t)\tilde{\psi}(x)U(i_t)^{-1}\overline{\gamma^\mu}U(i_t)\psi(x)U(i_t)^{-1} \\ &= |\eta_T|^2\tilde{\psi}(i_t x)S(i_t)^{-1}\overline{\gamma^\mu}S(i_t)\psi(i_t x) \\ &= -(-1)^{\delta_{\mu o}}\tilde{\psi}(i_t x)\gamma^\mu\psi(i_t x) \end{aligned} \tag{11–382}$$

Hence

$$U(i_t)\begin{Bmatrix} j_o(x) \\ j^i(x) \end{Bmatrix} U(i_t)^{-1} = \begin{Bmatrix} j_o(i_t x) \\ -j^i(i_t x) \end{Bmatrix} \tag{11–383}$$

i.e., the current operator transforms like a pseudovector under time inversion. The transformation properties of $A_\mu(x)$ are thus correct to assure the invariance of the field equation

$$\Box A_\mu(x) = j_\mu(x) \tag{11–384}$$

under time inversion.

Incidentally, note that

$$U(i_t)^2\psi(x)U(i_t)^{-2} = -\psi(x) \tag{11–385}$$

$$U(i_t)^2 A_\mu(x)U(i_t)^{-2} = +A_\mu(x) \tag{11–386}$$

Equations (11–377)–(11–381) for the field operators entail that under time inversion the interaction hamiltonian transforms like a scalar

$$U(i_t)\mathscr{H}_{\text{in}\,I}(x)U(i_t)^{-1} = \mathscr{H}_{\text{in}\,I}(i_t x) \tag{11–387}$$

and that the total hamiltonian H, being independent of time, is invariant under time inversion:

$$U(i_t)HU(i_t)^{-1} = H \tag{11–388}$$

The S-matrix, due to the time ordering operator in its definition is not invariant under time inversion. The invariance of the theory under time inversion has the following important consequence for the S-matrix: since this operator's matrix elements are given by:

$$S_{\beta\alpha} = {}_{\text{out}}\langle\Psi_\beta|\Psi_\alpha\rangle_{\text{in}} \tag{11–389}$$

upon inserting $U^*(i_t)U(i_t)$ into this matrix element we obtain

$$\begin{aligned} S_{\beta\alpha} &= (\Psi_\beta^{\text{out}}, U^*(i_t)U(i_t)\Psi_\alpha^{\text{in}}) \\ &= \overline{(U(i_t)\Psi_\beta^{\text{out}}, U(i_t)\Psi_\alpha^{\text{in}})} \\ &= \overline{(\Psi_{\tau\beta}^{\text{in}}, \Psi_{\tau\alpha}^{\text{out}})} \\ &= (\Psi_{\tau\alpha}^{\text{out}}, \Psi_{\tau\beta}^{\text{in}}) \\ &= S_{\tau\alpha,\,\tau\beta} \end{aligned} \tag{11–390}$$

which is the theorem of detailed balancing.

11.4. Spectral Representation.—As an application of the invariance properties of quantum electrodynamics we shall now use the results obtained in the last section to deduce a representation of the vacuum expectation value of a product of two fermion operators and of two boson operators. The invariance of the theory under time inversion and more particularly the fact that

$$U(i_t)^2\psi(x)U(i_t)^{-2} = -\psi(x) \tag{11–391}$$

and that the vacuum is invariant under $U(i_t)$, imply

$$\langle 0|\psi(x)|0\rangle = \langle 0|\tilde{\psi}(x)|0\rangle = 0 \tag{11–392}$$

This result also follows from the fact that the state $\psi(x)|0\rangle$ is an eigenstate of the total charge Q with eigenvalue e, whereas the vacuum is an eigenstate of Q with eigenvalue O. These two states are, therefore, orthogonal. Consider next the quantity

$$\begin{aligned} \langle 0|\psi_\alpha(x)\tilde{\psi}_\beta(y)|0\rangle &= (\Psi_o, \psi_\alpha(x)\tilde{\psi}_\beta(y)\Psi_o) \\ &= f_{\alpha\beta}(x,y) \end{aligned} \tag{11–393}$$

The invariance of the theory under inhomogeneous Lorentz transformation implies that a unitary $U(a,\Lambda)$ exists, such that

$$U(a,\Lambda)\psi_\alpha(x)U(a,\Lambda)^{-1} = \sum_{\beta=1}^{4} S(\Lambda)^{-1}_{\alpha\beta}\psi_\beta(\Lambda x + a) \tag{11–394}$$

$$U(a,\Lambda)\tilde{\psi}_\beta(x)U(a,\Lambda)^{-1} = \sum_{\alpha=1}^{4} \tilde{\psi}_\alpha(\Lambda x + a)S(\Lambda)_{\alpha\beta} \tag{11–395}$$

$\{a,\Lambda\}$ being any element of the inhomogeneous Lorentz group with $\Lambda_o{}^o \geq 1$, under which the vacuum remains invariant

$$U(a,\Lambda)|0\rangle = 0 \tag{11–396}$$

Upon inserting the factor $U^*(a,\Lambda)U(a,\Lambda) = 1$ into the matrix element (11–393) we find

$$f_{\alpha\beta}(x,y) = \sum_{\delta\varepsilon} S(\Lambda^{-1})_{\alpha\delta}f_{\delta\varepsilon}(\Lambda x + a, \Lambda y + a)S(\Lambda)_{\varepsilon\beta} \tag{11–397}$$

If we specialize to the case of pure translations $\Lambda = 1$, Eq. (11–397) asserts that for arbitrary displacements

$$f_{\alpha\beta}(x,y) = f_{\alpha\beta}(x + a, y + a) \tag{11–398}$$

whence $f_{\alpha\beta}$ is only a function of the difference of the coordinates x,y:

$$f_{\alpha\beta}(x,y) = f_{\alpha\beta}(x - y) \tag{11–399}$$

Then, by virtue of the invariance under proper homogeneous transformations,

$$f_{\alpha\beta}(x) = \sum_{\delta\varepsilon} S(\Lambda^{-1})_{\alpha\delta} f_{\delta\varepsilon}(\Lambda x) S(\Lambda)_{\varepsilon\beta} \tag{11–400}$$

or, in matrix notation,

$$f(x) = S(\Lambda)^{-1} f(\Lambda x) S(\Lambda) \tag{11–401}$$

Being a four-by-four matrix $f(x)$ can be expanded in terms of the sixteen linearly independent matrices $\Gamma^{(i)}$ formed of the γ-matrices and their products

$$f_{\alpha\beta}(x) = \sum_{i=1}^{16} [\Gamma^{(i)}]_{\alpha\beta} f^{(i)}(x) \tag{11–402}$$

with

$$f^{(i)}(x) = \tfrac{1}{4} \operatorname{Tr} (f(x)\Gamma^{(i)}) \tag{11–403}$$

Grouping the $\Gamma^{(i)}$ into sets with well-defined transformation properties, we can write Eq. (11–402) more explicitly in the form

$$\begin{aligned} f_{\alpha\beta}(x) = \delta_{\alpha\beta} f^S(x) &+ (\gamma^\mu)_{\alpha\beta} f^V_\mu(x) \\ &+ (\gamma_5)_{\alpha\beta} f^P(x) + \tfrac{1}{2}(\sigma^{\mu\nu})_{\alpha\beta} f^T_{\nu\mu}(x) \\ &+ i(\gamma_5\gamma^\mu) f^A_\mu(x) \end{aligned} \tag{11–404}$$

If we substitute this decomposition of f into Eq. (11–400), and make use of

$$S(\Lambda)^{-1}\gamma^\mu S(\Lambda) = \Lambda^\mu{}_\nu \gamma^\nu \tag{11–405}$$

we find upon taking appropriate traces that

$$f^S(x) = f^S(\Lambda x) \tag{11–406}$$

$$f^V_\mu(x) = (\Lambda^{-1})_\mu{}^\nu f^V_\nu(\Lambda x) \tag{11–407}$$

$$f^T_{\mu\nu}(x) = (\Lambda^{-1})_\mu{}^\alpha (\Lambda^{-1})_\nu{}^\beta f^T_{\alpha\beta}(\Lambda x) \tag{11–408}$$

$$f^P(x) = (\det \Lambda) f^P(\Lambda x) \tag{11–409}$$

$$f^A_\mu(x) = (\det \Lambda)(\Lambda^{-1})_\mu{}^\nu f^A_\nu(\Lambda x) \tag{11–410}$$

The labels S (scalar), V (vector), T (tensor), A (axial vector), and P

(pseudoscalar) are, therefore, justified. The invariance of the theory under time inversion requires that

$$\begin{aligned} f_{\alpha\beta}(x,y) &= \overline{(U(i_t)\Psi_o, U(i_t)\psi_\alpha(x)\tilde{\psi}_\beta(y)\Psi_o)} \\ &= \sum_{\delta\varepsilon} (C\gamma_5)_{\alpha\delta} \overline{f_{\delta\varepsilon}(i_t x, i_t y)} (\gamma_5 C^{-1})_{\varepsilon\beta} \end{aligned} \tag{11–411}$$

and this leads to the relations

$$f^S(x) = \overline{f^S(i_t x)} \tag{11–412}$$

$$f^V_\mu(x) = -(-1)^{\delta_{\mu o}} \overline{f^V_\mu(i_t x)} \tag{11–413}$$

$$f^A_\mu(x) = (-1)^{\delta_{\mu o}} \overline{f^A_\mu(i_t x)} \tag{11–414}$$

$$f^T_{\mu\nu}(x) = (-1)^{\delta_{\mu o} + \delta_{\nu o}} \overline{f^T_{\mu\nu}(i_t x)} \tag{11–415}$$

$$f^P(x) = \overline{-f^P(i_t x)} \tag{11–416}$$

The hermiticity of the scalar product implies that

$$\begin{aligned} f_{\alpha\beta}(x,y) &= (\Psi_o, \psi_\alpha(x)\tilde{\psi}_\beta(y)\Psi_o) \\ &= \overline{(\psi_\alpha(x)\tilde{\psi}_\beta(y)\Psi^o, \Psi^o)} \end{aligned} \tag{11–417}$$

from which one readily deduces that

$$f(x) = \gamma^o f(-x)^* \gamma^o \tag{11–418}$$

or equivalently

$$f^i(x) = \overline{f^{(i)}(-x)} \tag{11–419}$$

From the invariance of the theory under space inversion, it follows that the axial vector and tensor amplitudes transform as follows:

$$f^A_\mu(x) = -(-1)^{\delta_{\mu o}} f^A_\mu(i_s x) \tag{11–420}$$

and

$$f^T_{\mu\nu}(x) = -(-1)^{\delta_{\mu o} + \delta_{\nu o}} f^T_{\mu\nu}(i_s x) \tag{11–421}$$

so that if we carry out a space and time inversion in succession, we obtain

$$f^A_\mu(x) = -\overline{f^A_\mu(-x)} \tag{11–422}$$

$$f^T_{\mu\nu}(x) = -\overline{f^T_{\mu\nu}(-x)} \tag{11–423}$$

since $i_t i_s x = -x$. This, together with the hermiticity relation (11–419) for these amplitudes, implies that they vanish. Using Eq. (11–409), together with the transformation properties of f^P under space and time inversion, one can similarly establish that $f^P(x) = 0$, whence

$$f_{\alpha\beta}(x) = (1)_{\alpha\beta} f^S(x) + (\gamma^\mu)_{\alpha\beta} f^V_\mu(x) \tag{11–424}$$

If we next assume that the spectrum of the basis $\{|p,\alpha\rangle\}$ spanning the Hilbert space of states is such that

$$p_{no} \geq 0 \tag{11–425}$$

$$p_n^2 \geq 0 \tag{11–426}$$

then a further statement concerning $f(x)$ can be made. Thus, if we insert into the representation (11–393) for $f(x)$, a complete set of states we obtain

$$\begin{aligned} f_{\alpha\beta}(x - x') &= \sum_{p,\alpha} \langle 0|\psi_\alpha(x)|p,\alpha\rangle\langle p,\alpha|\bar{\psi}_\beta(x')|0\rangle \\ &= \sum_{p,\alpha} \langle 0|\psi_\alpha(0)|p,\alpha\rangle\langle p,\alpha|\bar{\psi}_\beta(0)|0\rangle e^{-ip\cdot(x-x')} \\ &= \int d^4p\tilde{f}(p)e^{-ip(x-x')}\theta(p_o)\theta(p^2) \end{aligned} \tag{11–427}$$

with

$$\tilde{f}(p) = \sum_\alpha \langle 0|\psi_\alpha(0)|p,\alpha\rangle\langle p,\alpha|\bar{\psi}_\beta(0)|0\rangle \tag{11–428}$$

In (11–427) we have explicitly indicated the fact that the p's are the momenta of physical states and hence are restricted to the forward light cone.[8] The previous arguments when translated in terms of the Fourier transform $\tilde{f}(p)$ imply that

$$\tilde{f}_\mu^V(p) = (\Lambda^{-1})_\mu{}^\nu f_\nu^V(p) \tag{11–429}$$

$$f^S(p) = f^S(\Lambda p) \tag{11–430}$$

with p lying in the forward light cone. Equation (11–430) immediately asserts that

$$f^S(p) = f_{(1)}(p^2) \tag{11–431}$$

i.e., that it is only a function of p^2. Similarly Eq. (11–429) states that

$$\tilde{f}_\mu^V(p) = p_\mu\tilde{f}_{(2)}(p^2) \tag{11–432}$$

hence, on the basis of invariance and the assumption that the physical states have a spectrum whose support is the forward light cone, we have deduced the following representation for $f(x)$

$$f(x) = \int d^4pe^{-ip\cdot x}\theta(p^2)\theta(p_o)\cdot\{\tilde{f}_{(1)}(p^2) + \gamma\cdot p\tilde{f}_{(2)}(p^2)\} \tag{11–433}$$

[8] In quantum electrodynamics, in the Lorentz gauge the situation is somewhat more difficult, since states with time-like photons have negative energy. One must then show that their contribution cancels (by virtue of the indefinite metric) the contribution of the states with the same number of longitudinal photons.

By writing

$$\theta(p^2) = \int_0^\infty da^2 \delta(p^2 - a^2)$$

and introducing the functions $h^{(1)}(m^2)$ and $h^{(2)}(m^2)$ by the relations

$$\tilde{f}_{(1)}(m^2) = (h^{(1)}(m^2) - h^{(2)}(m^2)) \tag{11-434}$$

$$\tilde{f}_{(2)}(m^2) = \frac{1}{m}(h^{(1)}(m^2) + h^{(2)}m^2)) \tag{11-435}$$

Equation (11–433) can be written in the form

$$f(x) = \int_0^\infty da^2 \left\{ h^{(1)}(a^2)\frac{i\gamma\cdot\partial_x + a}{a} + h^{(2)}(a^2)\frac{i\gamma\cdot\partial_x - a}{a} \right\} \cdot \int d^4p e^{-ip\cdot x}\theta(p_o)\delta(p^2 - a^2)$$

$$= i(2\pi)^3 \int_0^\infty \frac{da^2}{a}\{h^{(1)}(a^2)(i\gamma\cdot\partial_x + a) + h^{(2)}(a^2)(i\gamma\cdot\partial_x - a)\} \cdot \Delta^{(+)}(x,a^2) \tag{11-436}$$

Essentially the same arguments as adduced above can be used to derive the following representation of

$$f'(x,x') = \langle 0|\tilde{\psi}(x)\psi(x')|0\rangle \tag{11-437}$$

$$f'(x) = \int d^4p e^{-ip\cdot x}\theta(p^2)\theta(p_o)\{\tilde{f}'_{(1)}(p^2) + \gamma\cdot p\tilde{f}'_{(2)}(p^2)\} \tag{11-438}$$

The invariance of the theory under charge conjugation implies that

$$f_{\alpha\beta}(x,x') = -(C^{-1}f'(x,x')C)_{\alpha\beta} \tag{11-439}$$

from which we infer that

$$\tilde{f}_{(1)} = \tilde{f}'_{(1)} \tag{11-440}$$

and

$$\tilde{f}_{(2)} = \tilde{f}'_{(2)} \tag{11-441}$$

This statement allows us to obtain the following representation

$$(\Psi_o, T(\psi(x)\tilde{\psi}(y))\Psi_o) = \frac{1}{(2\pi)^4}\int e^{-ip\cdot(x-y)}[-\tfrac{1}{2}S'_F(p)]$$

with

$$S'_F(p) = i\int_0^\infty \frac{da^2}{a}\left[\frac{h^{(1)}(a^2)}{\gamma\cdot p - a + i\varepsilon} + \frac{h^{(2)}(a^2)}{\gamma\cdot p + a - i\varepsilon}\right] \tag{11-442}$$

It should be stressed that the weight functions $h^{(1)}$ and $h^{(2)}$ are gauge-dependent.

Similar results can be obtained for the vacuum expectation value of electromagnetic field operators. The spectral representation takes the form

$$\langle 0|A_\mu(x)A_\nu(y)|0\rangle = \int d^4k e^{-ik\cdot(x-y)}\theta(k^2)\theta(k_o)\left[g_{\mu\nu}\beta_{(1)}(k^2) - \frac{k_\mu k_\nu}{k^2}\beta_{(2)}(k^2)\right] \tag{11–443}$$

which in the Lorentz gauge, where $\partial_\mu A^\mu(x) = 0$, assumes the form

$$\langle 0|A_\mu(x)A_\nu(y)|0\rangle = \int d^4k e^{-ik\cdot(x-y)}\theta(k_o)\theta(k^2) \times \left[\left(g_{\mu\nu} - \frac{k_\mu k_\nu}{k^2}\right)\beta_{(1)}(k^2) + bk_\mu k_\nu \delta(k^2)\right] \tag{11–444}$$

The constant b will be determined later. A (noncovariant) spectral representation for the potentials $\mathscr{A}_\mu(x)$ satisfying the gauge condition

$$[\partial_\mu - n_\mu(\partial\cdot n)]\mathscr{A}^\mu(x) = 0$$

can also be written down. It is

$$\langle 0|\mathscr{A}_\mu(x)\mathscr{A}_\nu(y)|0\rangle = \int e^{-ik\cdot(x-y)}\left[g_{\mu\nu} - \frac{k_\mu k_\nu - (n_\mu k_\nu + k_\mu n_\nu)(n\cdot k)}{k^2 - (n\cdot k)^2}\right]\beta(k^2)\cdot\theta(k^2)\theta(k_o) \tag{11–445}$$

REFERENCES

Evans, L., Feldman, G., and Matthews, P. T., *Ann. Phys.*, **13**, 268 (1961).

Gell-Mann, M., and Low, F., *Phys. Rev.*, **95**, 1300 (1954).

Johnson, K., *Phys. Rev.*, **112**, 1367 (1958); *Ann. Phys.*, **10**, 536 (1960); *Nuclear Phys.*, **25**, 435 and 431 (1961).

Johnson, K., and Zumino, B., *Phys. Rev.*, Letters **3**, 351 (1959).

Källén, G., *Helvetia Phys. Acta*, **25**, 417 (1952).

Källén, G., "Quantenelectrodynamik," *Handbuch der Physik*, Band **V**, Teil **1**, Springer Verlag, 1958.

Lehmann, H., *Nuovo Cimento*, **11**, 242 (1954).

Umezawa, H., and Kamefuchi, S., *Prog. Theor. Phys.*, **6**, 543 (1951).

Zumino, B., *J. Math. Phys.*, **1**, 1 (1960).

11.5. Asymptotic Condition.—In Section 11.1, we exhibited the equivalence of the formulation of quantum electrodynamics in the Coulomb and Lorentz gauges in so far as observable quantities were concerned (*i.e.*, scattering amplitudes). We also noted that both of these formulations, when based on a hamiltonian not containing mass renormalization counter terms, suffered from the difficulty that the one-particle states were not steady, *i.e.*, they did not satisfy the condition

$$|1 \text{ particle}\rangle_{\text{in}} = |1 \text{ particle}\rangle_{\text{out}}$$

In the present section we shall make this difficulty apparent in a somewhat different way by showing that it is not possible to satisfy the asymptotic condition when the theory is formulated in terms of an unsubtracted hamiltonian of the form $j_\mu A^\mu(x) - E_0/V$. We shall work in the Lorentz gauge, where the relativistic invariance of the theory is more obvious.

Actually, instead of trying to verify whether the asymptotic condition can be satisfied if the "in" and "out" fields are defined by Eqs. (11–96) and (11–97), we shall inquire as to what must be the source terms which occur on the right-hand side of $(-i\gamma\cdot\partial + m)\psi(x)$ and $\square A_\mu(x)$ in order that $A_{\substack{\text{in}\\\text{out}}}(x)$ and $\psi_{\substack{\text{in}\\\text{out}}}(x)$ be the asymptotic fields to which $A(x)$ and $\psi(x)$ converge (weakly) in the limit as $x_o \to \mp\infty$, *i.e.*, such that for all $|\Psi\rangle$ and $|\Phi\rangle$

$$\lim_{x_o\to\mp\infty} (\Psi,\psi^g(x_o)\Phi) = (\Psi,\psi^g_{\substack{\text{in}\\\text{out}}}\Phi) \tag{11–446}$$

and

$$\lim_{x_o\to\mp\infty} (\Psi,A^h(x_o)\Phi) = (\Psi,A^h_{\substack{\text{in}\\\text{out}}}\Phi) \tag{11–447}$$

In Eqs. (11–446) and (11–447), f is a wave packet solution of the Dirac equation for the mass m (the observed mass of the electron)

$$(-i\gamma\cdot\partial + m)g(x) = 0 \tag{11–448}$$

$$\int d\sigma^\mu(x)\tilde{g}(x)\gamma_\mu g(x) < \infty \tag{11–449}$$

and

$$\psi^g(x_o) = \int_{\sigma=x_o} d\sigma^\mu(x)\tilde{g}(x)\gamma_\mu\psi(x) \tag{11–450}$$

Similarly, if $h_\mu(x)$ is a normalizable positive energy solution of

$$\square h_\mu(x) = 0 \tag{11–451}$$

which satisfies the subsidiary condition

$$\partial^\mu h_\mu(x) = 0 \tag{11–452}$$

and is such that

$$(h,h) = -i\int \overline{h_\nu(x)}\,\frac{\overleftrightarrow{\partial}}{\partial x_\mu}\,h^\nu(x)d\sigma_\mu(x) < \infty \tag{11–453}$$

then the operator A^h is defined as

$$A^h(x_o) = -i \int_{\sigma = x_o} d\sigma_\mu(x) h_\nu(x) \frac{\overleftrightarrow{\partial}}{\partial x_\mu} A^\nu(x) \tag{11-454}$$

Upon making use of the identity

$$\int_{-\infty}^{t} \frac{\partial F(t')}{\partial t'} dt' = F(t) - \lim_{t \to -\infty} F(t) \tag{11-455}$$

and setting $F(t) = \psi^g(t)$, we can rewrite Eq. (11–455) as follows:

$$\psi^g(x_o) - \int_{-\infty}^{x_o} dx_o' \frac{\partial \psi^g(x_o')}{\partial x_o'} = \psi_{\text{in}}^g \tag{11-456}$$

Now for the case of a flat surface $\sigma = x_o$

$$\partial_o \psi^g(x_o) = i \int d^3x \{-i\partial_o \tilde{g}(x)\gamma_o \cdot \psi(x) + \tilde{g}(x)(-i\gamma_o \partial_o \psi(x))\} \tag{11-457}$$

$$= i \int d^3x \tilde{g}(x)(-i\gamma \cdot \partial + m)\psi(x) \tag{11-458}$$

since $g(x)$ obeys the Dirac equation. The (spatial) integration by parts involved in going from Eq. (11–457) to (11–458) is allowed because of the wave packet nature of $g(x)$. Finally, multiplying Eq. (11–456) by $g(x')$, and summing over a complete set of g

$$\sum_g g(x)\tilde{g}(x') = -iS(x - x')$$

we deduce that

$$\psi(x) = \psi_{\text{in}}(x) + \int_{-\infty}^{x_o} d^4x' S(x - x')(-i\gamma \cdot \partial_{x'} + m)\psi(x') \tag{11-459}$$

which equation is equivalent to the asymptotic condition (11–446) and (11–447), and the process is similar for the photon equation. We could, therefore, have proceeded as follows: we could have defined $\psi_{\text{in}}(x)$, $A_{\text{in}\,\mu}(x)$ by the equations

$$\psi(x) = \psi_{\text{in}}(x) + \int S_R(x - x') f(x') d^4x' \tag{11-460}$$

$$A_\mu(x) = A_{\text{in}\,\mu}(x) + \int D_R(x - x') j_\mu(x') d^4x' \tag{11-461}$$

where $\psi_{\text{in}}(x)$ and $A_{\text{in}}(x)$ satisfy free-field equations of motion

$$(-i\gamma\cdot\partial + m)\psi_{\text{in}}(x) = 0 \tag{11–462}$$

$$\Box A_{\text{in}\,\mu}(x) = 0 \tag{11–463}$$

$$\partial^\mu A_{\text{in}\,\mu}(x) = 0 \tag{11–464}$$

and free-field commutation relations

$$\{\psi_{\text{in}}(x),\bar{\psi}_{\text{in}}(x')\} = -iS(x - x'; m) \tag{11–465}$$

$$[A_{\text{in}\,\mu}(x),A_{\text{in}\,\nu}(x')] = -ig_{\mu\nu}D(x - x') \tag{11–466}$$

whose representation is fixed by the requirement that a no-particle state $|0\rangle$ exists, such that

$$\psi_{\text{in}}^{(+)}(x)|0\rangle = \bar{\psi}_{\text{in}}^{(+)}(x)|0\rangle = A_{\text{in}\,\mu}^{(+)}(x)|0\rangle = 0 \tag{11–467}$$

This state $|0\rangle$ is the direct product state formed from the photon no-particle state and the fermion no-particle state.

The commutation rules (11–465) and (11–466), together with the existence of the no-particle states, allow us to formulate an asymptotic particle interpretation for photons and electrons in the remote past, albeit in terms of a formalism involving an indefinite metric.

In Eqs. (11–460) and (11–461), $f(x)$ and $j_\mu(x)$ are defined by the following equation

$$f(x) = (-i\gamma\cdot\partial + m)\psi(x) \tag{11–468}$$

$$j_\mu(x) = \Box A_\mu(x) \tag{11–469}$$

where the *parameter* m, which occurs in Eq. (11–468), in the equation obeyed by $\psi_{\text{in}}(x)$, Eq. (11–462), and in $S_R(x - x'; m)$, is the *observed* (experimental) mass of the electron.

Note that in formulating the theory in this "axiomatic" fashion one does not say anything about the commutation rules satisfied by $\psi(x)$ and $A_\mu(x)$. The $\psi(x)$ and $A_\mu(x)$ field operators can be regarded as functionals of the corresponding "in" fields and defined in terms of them. Their commutation rules are consequences of those satisfied by $A_{\text{in}\,\mu}(x)$ and $\psi_{\text{in}}(x)$.

If $\psi_{\text{in}}(x)$ as defined by Eq. (11–460) is to be the weak asymptotic limit of $\psi(x)$ in the sense of Eqs. (11–446) and (11–447), then clearly

$$\begin{aligned}\lim_{x_0\to-\infty} &\int d\sigma^\mu(x)\tilde{g}(x)\gamma_\mu \int S_R(x - x')\langle\Psi|f(x')|\Phi\rangle d^4x' \\ &= \lim_{x_0\to-\infty} \int_{-\infty}^{x_0} d^4x'\tilde{g}(x')\langle\Psi|f(x')|\Phi\rangle \\ &\to 0\end{aligned} \tag{11–470}$$

for arbitrary but fixed, normalizable states. In particular, suppose we choose $|\Phi\rangle$ to be a one-particle state

$$|\Phi\rangle = \sum_s \int d^4p\theta(p_o)\delta(p^2 - m^2)\phi_s(p)|\mathbf{p},s\rangle \tag{11–471}$$

with the amplitude $\phi_s(p)$ satisfying

$$\sum_s \int d^4p|\phi_s(p)|^2\delta(p^2 - m^2)\theta(p_o) < \infty \tag{11–472}$$

and we choose $|\Psi\rangle$ to be the vacuum state, $|\Psi\rangle = |0\rangle$; furthermore, let

$$g(x) = \sum_s \int d^4q e^{-iq\cdot x}u_s(\mathbf{q})c_s(q)\theta(q_o)\delta(q^2 - m^2)$$
$$q_o = \sqrt{\mathbf{q}^2 + m^2} \tag{11–473}$$

with

$$\sum_s \int d^4q|c_s(q)|^2\delta(q^2 - m^2)\theta(q_o) < \infty \tag{11–474}$$

Then the x' integration can readily be carried out since by virtue of translation invariance

$$\langle 0|f(x)|\mathbf{p},s\rangle = \langle 0|f(0)|\mathbf{p},s\rangle e^{-ip\cdot x} \tag{11–475}$$

(where, since $|\mathbf{p},s\rangle$ is a one-particle state $p_o = \sqrt{\mathbf{p}^2 + m^2}$). Since upon carrying out the $\int d^3x'$ integration the integrand becomes independent of x'_0, one concludes that for this case the condition (11–470) can be satisfied only if $\langle 0|f(x)|\mathbf{p},s\rangle$ vanishes identically, *i.e.*, only if,

$$\langle 0|f(x)|\mathbf{p},s\rangle = \langle 0|f(0)|\mathbf{p},s\rangle e^{-ip\cdot x} = 0 \tag{11–476}$$

A similar argument in the case of the $A_\mu(x)$ equation, Eq. (11–461), taken between the vacuum and one-photon state, yields the result that for the asymptotic condition to be satisfied

$$\langle 0|j_\mu(x)|\mathbf{k},\lambda\rangle = \langle 0|j_\mu(0)|\mathbf{k},\lambda\rangle e^{-ip\cdot x} = 0$$
$$\mu,\lambda = 0,1,2,3 \tag{11–477}$$

Equations (11–477) and (11–476) impose restrictions on the form of $j_\mu(x)$ and $f(x)$. As a consequence of these equations, we also have the result that if $|\mathbf{p},s\rangle$ is a one-electron state

$$\langle 0|\psi(x)|\mathbf{p},s\rangle = \langle 0|\psi_{\text{in}}(x)|\mathbf{p},s\rangle$$
$$= \sqrt{\frac{m}{(2\pi)^3}}\, e^{-ip\cdot x}u_s(\mathbf{p}) \tag{11–478}$$

and similarly, if $|\mathbf{k},\lambda\rangle$ is a one-photon state

$$\begin{aligned}\langle 0|A_\mu(x)|\mathbf{k},\lambda\rangle &= \langle 0|A_{\text{in}\,\mu}(x)|\mathbf{k},\lambda\rangle \\ &= \sqrt{\frac{1}{(2\pi)^3}}\, e_\mu^{(\lambda)}(k)e^{-ik\cdot x} \qquad (11\text{–}479)\end{aligned}$$

for $\lambda = 0,\cdots,3$. These equations can be regarded as normalizing the Heisenberg operators.

A further condition on $j_\mu(x)$ can be obtained as follows: since $j_\mu(x)$ is the source of the electromagnetic fields—it is the conserved ($\partial_\mu j^\mu(x) = 0$) charge-current density—the operator

$$\begin{aligned}Q &= \int d\sigma_\mu(x) j^\mu(x) \\ &= \int d^3x j^0(x) \qquad (11\text{–}480)\end{aligned}$$

is a constant of the motion, and must correspond to the total charge. Hence, for a one-particle state

$$Q|\mathbf{p},s,-e\rangle = -e|\mathbf{p},s,-e\rangle \qquad (11\text{–}481)$$

so that

$$\begin{aligned}\langle \mathbf{p}',s,-e|Q|\mathbf{p},s,-e\rangle &= -e\langle \mathbf{p}',s,-e|\mathbf{p},s,-e\rangle \\ &= -ep_o\delta(\mathbf{p}-\mathbf{p}') \\ &= \int d^3x\langle \mathbf{p}',s,-e|j_o(x)|\mathbf{p},s,-e\rangle \\ &= \int d^3x e^{i(p'-p)\cdot x}\langle \mathbf{p}',s,-e|j_o(0)|\mathbf{p},s,-e\rangle \\ &= (2\pi)^3\delta(\mathbf{p}-\mathbf{p}')\langle \mathbf{p}',s,-e|j_o(0)|\mathbf{p},s,-e\rangle \qquad (11\text{–}482)\end{aligned}$$

whence

$$\langle \mathbf{p},s,-e|j_o(0)|\mathbf{p},s,-e\rangle = \frac{-e}{(2\pi)^3}\, p_o \qquad (11\text{–}483)$$

The next question which arises concerns the explicit forms of $f(x)$ and $j_\mu(x)$. Our previous work in Section 11.1 (correspondence principle arguments) suggests that

$$f(x) = \tfrac{1}{2}e\gamma_\mu(A^\mu(x)\psi(x) + \psi(x)A^\mu(x)) \qquad (11\text{–}484)$$

However, one readily verifies, using invariance techniques similar to those outlined in the last section, that if $f(x)$ is given by Eq. (11–484), it does not satisfy the criterion that $\langle 0|f(x)|\mathbf{p},s\rangle = 0$. It is easy to show that Eq. (11–476) can be satisfied if we add the (mass renormalization) counter term $\Delta m\psi(x)$ to the right side of Eq. (11–484). In fact

Δm is now determined by the requirement that Eq. (11–476) be satisfied. In other words, we take $f(x)$ to be

$$f(x) = -\frac{e}{2}\gamma_\mu\{A^\mu(x),\psi(x)\} + \Delta m\psi(x) \tag{11–485}$$

with

$$\begin{aligned}\Delta m\langle 0|\psi(x)|\mathbf{p},s\rangle &= \Delta m\langle 0|\psi_{\text{in}}(x)|\mathbf{p},s\rangle \\ &= -\frac{e}{2}\langle 0|\gamma_\mu\{A_\mu(x),\psi(x)\}|\mathbf{p},s\rangle\end{aligned} \tag{11–486}$$

Consider next the current operator $j_\mu(x)$. The correspondence principle suggests that its form is $j'_\mu(x) = -(e/2)[\tilde{\psi}(x)\gamma_\mu,\psi(x)]$. Such a form for $j_\mu(x)$ does not satisfy Eq. (11–477). In fact, due to covariance, the spectral representation of the vacuum expectation value of $s_\mu(x)A_\nu(x)$, where $s_\mu(x)$ is an arbitrary four-vector, is given by

$$\langle 0|s_\mu(x)A_\nu(y)|0\rangle = \int d^4k e^{-ik\cdot(x-y)}\left(g_{\mu\nu}\sigma_1(k^2) - \frac{k_\mu k_\nu}{k^2}\sigma_2(k^2)\right) \tag{11–487}$$

The spectral conditions (the positive definiteness of the energy and mass spectrum) assert that $\sigma_i(k^2) = \theta(k_o)\theta(k^2)\sigma_i(k^2)$. If $s_\mu(x)$ is conserved, *i.e.*, it satisfies the continuity equation $\partial_\mu s^\mu(x) = 0$, then

$$\langle 0|s_\mu(x)A_\nu(y)|0\rangle = \int d^4k e^{-ik\cdot(x-y)}\left\{\left(g_{\mu\nu} - \frac{k_\mu k_\nu}{k^2}\right)\sigma(k^2) + Dk_\mu k_\nu\delta(k^2)\right\} \tag{11–488}$$

with $\sigma(0) = 0$. In (11–488) we have explicitly separated the $\delta(k^2)$ part of the spectral weight. Hence, if $|\mathbf{k},\lambda\rangle$ is a one-photon state of momentum $\mathbf{k}$, polarization λ, then

$$\langle 0|s_\mu(x)|\mathbf{k},\lambda\rangle = Dk_\mu k_\nu\varepsilon^{(\lambda)\nu}(\mathbf{k}) \tag{11–489}$$

In order to compensate for the presence of such a term in the matrix element of $[\tilde{\psi}(x)\gamma_\mu,\psi(x)]$ between one-photon states and the vacuum, we could define the current operator $j_\mu(x)$ by stipulating

$$j'_\mu(x) = -\frac{e}{2}[\tilde{\psi}(x)\gamma_\mu,\psi(x)] + L'\partial_\mu\partial^\nu A_\nu(x) \tag{11–490}$$

where the constant L' is to be so determined that Eq. (11–477) is satisfied, in which case L' must be such that

$$\begin{aligned}L'\langle 0|\partial_\mu\partial^\nu A_\nu(x)|\mathbf{k},\lambda\rangle &= L'k_\mu k^\nu\langle 0|A_{\text{in}\,\nu}(0)|\mathbf{k},\lambda\rangle e^{-ik\cdot x} \\ &= +\frac{e}{2}\langle 0|[\tilde{\psi}(x)\gamma_\mu,\psi(x)]|\mathbf{k},\lambda\rangle\end{aligned}$$

or

$$L'k_\mu k_\nu = +\frac{e}{2}(2\pi)^{3/2}\sum_{\lambda=0}^{3}\langle 0|[\tilde{\psi}(0)\gamma_\mu,\psi(0)]|\mathbf{k},\lambda\rangle\varepsilon^{(\lambda)}(k) \quad (11\text{–}491)$$

However, we have no guarantee that the current operator defined by Eq. (11–490) will leave Eq. (11–483) satisfied. Stated differently, we have no guarantee that the charge $-e$, which occurs in the definition (11–490) in the current operator, is the same as the total charge of the one-electron state. In order to be able to satisfy this requirement we shall add another counter term of the form $L''\Box A(x)$ to the expression (11–490) of the current operator. The addition of such a term does not affect Eq. (11–491). Hence, finally, the current operator is defined as

$$j_\mu(x) = -\frac{e}{2}[\tilde{\psi}(x)\gamma_\mu,\psi(x)] + L'\partial_\mu\partial_\nu A^\nu(x) + L''\Box A_\mu(x) \quad (11\text{–}492)$$

where L' is determined by Eq. (11–491) and L'' from the requirement that Eq. (11–483) hold. The set of equations

$$\begin{aligned} f(x) &= (-i\gamma\cdot\partial + m)\psi(x) \\ &= -\frac{e}{2}\gamma_\mu\{A^\mu(x),\psi(x)\} + \Delta m\psi(x) \end{aligned} \quad (11\text{–}493)$$

and

$$\begin{aligned} j_\mu(x) &= \Box A_\mu(x) \\ &= -\frac{e}{2}[\tilde{\psi}(x)\gamma_\mu,\psi(x)] + L'\partial_\mu\partial_\nu A^\nu(x) + L''\Box A_\mu(x) \end{aligned} \quad (11\text{–}494)$$

with the constants Δm, L', L'' determined by Eqs. (11–486), (11–493), and (11–483), constitute the equations of motion of the Heisenberg operators $\psi(x)$ and $A_\mu(x)$. The quantization procedure is defined in terms of Eqs. (11–460)–(11–467), which determine the "in" fields and their properties.

Unfortunately, it is not known whether solutions of these equations exist. It is known that the above set is consistent when the solution is obtained as a perturbation expansion in power of e, but very little can be said about the convergence of such a series.

We close with some remarks concerning the commutation rules obeyed by the field operators $\psi(x)$, and $A_\mu(x)$. As noted in this section, a consistent procedure to obtain these would be to use the equations of motion (11–460) and (11–461), together with the postulated properties of ψ_{in} and A_{in}. The procedure is, however, not without ambiguities because in the equation defining the current operator $j_\mu(x)$, the quantity $-(e/2)[\tilde{\psi}(x)\gamma_\mu,\psi(x)]$ must be supplemented by a rule for handling the singularities that arise in evaluating its matrix elements between certain states due to the confluence of the operators $\psi(x)$ and $\tilde{\psi}(x)$. It turns out that a consistent and useful definition for this quantity is [9]

$$\lim_{\varepsilon\to 0} -\frac{e}{2}\{\psi(x+\varepsilon)\gamma^\mu\psi(x)e^{ie\int_x^{x+\varepsilon}d\xi_\mu A^\mu(\xi)} - \psi(x)\tilde{\psi}(x-\varepsilon)\gamma^\mu e^{-ie\int_{x-\varepsilon}^{x}d\xi_\mu A^\mu(\xi)}$$

where ε_μ is a time-like vector, which, in the limit, goes to zero. One can then iterate Eqs. (11–460) and (11–461) to obtain the explicit form for ψ and A in terms of the "in" field, and proceed to evaluate the various commutators and anticommutators. Here we note only that the spectral conditions (the positiveness of energy and mass spectrum), together with the relativistic invariance of the theory, imply that in the Lorentz gauge

$$\begin{aligned}\langle 0|[A_\mu(x),A_\nu(y)]|0\rangle = \int_0^\infty d\mu^2 \int d^4k e^{-ik\cdot(x-y)}\delta(k^2-\mu^2)\\ \times\, \varepsilon(k)\left[\left(g_{\mu\nu}-\frac{k_\mu k_\nu}{k^2}\right)\beta_1(k^2)\right.\\ \left. + k_\mu k_\nu\left(b\delta(k^2)+\frac{\beta_2(k^2)}{k^2}\right)\right]\end{aligned} \qquad (11\text{–}495)$$

If the equal-time commutator is to vanish, then

$$b = \int_0^\infty \frac{d\mu^2}{\mu^2}\beta_1(\mu^2) \qquad (11\text{–}496)$$

and β_2 must be such that

$$\int_0^\infty \frac{d\mu^2}{\mu^2}\beta_2(\mu^2) = 0$$

From the representation (11–495), it also follows that

$$\begin{aligned}\langle 0|[A_\mu(x),\dot{A}_\nu(y)]|_{x_0=y_0}|0\rangle = i(2\pi)^3\delta^{(3)}(\mathbf{x}-\mathbf{y})\\ \cdot\left[g_{\mu\nu}\int_0^\infty d\mu^2\beta_1(\mu^2) - g_{\mu o}g_{\nu o}\right.\\ \left.\times\int_0^\infty (\beta_1(\mu^2)-\beta_2(\mu^2))d\mu^2\right]\end{aligned} \qquad (11\text{–}497)$$

Hence the radiation operators $A_\mu(x)$, $A_\nu(y)$ do not satisfy the usual canonical commutation rules. Rather, the presence of such factors as $\int_0^\infty d\mu^2\beta_1(\mu^2)$ implies that their commutation rules are more singular than those of the "canonical" (unrenormalized) operators considered

[9] K. Johnson, *Nuclear Phys.*, **25**, 431 (1961).

at the beginning of the present chapter, since at least in any perturbation expansion $\int_0^\infty d\mu^2\beta_1(\mu^2)$ is found to be divergent.

Similar remarks apply to the negaton-positon field operator. From spectral assumptions and relativistic invariance we have previously concluded that

$$\langle 0|\psi(x)\tilde{\psi}(y)|0\rangle = \int d^4q\theta(q)\theta(q^2) \times \{(\gamma\cdot q + \sqrt{q^2})\rho_1(q^2) + \rho_2(q^2)\}d^4q \quad (11\text{–}498)$$

whence, using the invariance under charge conjugation, we deduce that

$$\langle 0|\{\psi(x),\tilde{\psi}(y)\}_{x_0=y_0}|0\rangle = (2\pi)^3\delta(\mathbf{x}-\mathbf{y})\int_0^\infty da^2\rho_1(a^2) \quad (11\text{–}499)$$

Hence, again these ψ operators do not obey canonical commutation rules due to the presence of the factor $\int_0^\infty da^2\rho_1(a^2)$ (which is found to be divergent in perturbation expansion of the theory).

REFERENCES

Evans, L. E., and Fulton, T., *Nuclear Phys.*, **21**, 493 (1960).

Källén, G., *Helv. Phys. Acta*, **25**, 417 (1952); *Handbuch der Physik*, Bd. V/1, Springer Verlag, Berlin-Göttingen.

Karlson, E., *Proc. Roy. Soc.* (*London*), **A230**, 382 (1955).

Lehmann, H., Symanzik, K., and Zimmermann, W., *Nuovo Cimento*, **1**, 205 (1955).

Rollnick, H., Stech, B., and Nunnemann, E., *Z. Physik*, **159**, 482 (1960).

Yang, C. N., and Feldman, D., *Phys. Rev.*, **79**, 972 (1950).

Zimmermann, W., *Nuovo Cimento*, **10**, 597 (1958).

11.6. Radiative Corrections: Negaton in an External Field.— The content of the previous sections of this chapter can be summarized by saying that the essential properties of the vacuum- and one-particle states in the absence of external perturbations are that they are steady:

$$|1 \text{ particle}\rangle_{\text{in}} = |1 \text{ particle}\rangle_{\text{out}} \quad (11\text{–}500)$$

$$|0\rangle_{\text{out}} = |0\rangle_{\text{in}} = |0\rangle \quad (11\text{–}501)$$

and that the one-electron states $|\mathbf{p},s,\pm e\rangle$ have charge $\pm e$ and mass m:

$$Q|\mathbf{p},s,\pm e\rangle = \pm e|\mathbf{p},s,\pm e\rangle \quad (11\text{–}502)$$

$$P^2|\mathbf{p},s,\pm e\rangle = m^2|\mathbf{p},s,\pm e\rangle \quad (11\text{–}503)$$

and that the one-photon states have mass zero:

$$P^2|\mathbf{k},\varepsilon\rangle = 0 \quad (11\text{–}504)$$

In other words, there are no observable consequences of the one-particle systems in the absence of external perturbations besides these: the mass of the one-electron state is m, that of the photon is zero, the electric charge of the negaton is $-e$,[10] and that of the positon, $+e$.

The situation is quite different in the presence of an external (classical) electromagnetic field $A_\mu^e(x)$:

$$\Box A_\mu^e(x) = J_\mu^e(x) \tag{11–505}$$

$$\partial^\mu A_\mu^e(x) = 0 \tag{11–506}$$

in which case the negaton-positon field operator $\psi^e(x)$ satisfies the equation of motion

$$(-i\gamma\cdot\partial + m)\psi^e(x) = (e\gamma\cdot A(x) + e\gamma\cdot A^e(x) - \Delta m)\psi^e(x) \tag{11–507}$$

We can proceed as in our previous discussion, and we can again define "in" and "out" fields[11] by the equation:

$$\psi^e(x) = \psi_{\substack{\text{in}\\\text{out}}}(x) + \int S_{\substack{R\\A}}(x - x',m)(e\gamma\cdot A(x') + e\gamma\cdot A^e(x') - \Delta m)\,\psi^e(x')d^4x' \tag{11–508}$$

These asymptotic fields are required to satisfy free-field commutation rules and free-field equations[12]

$$\{\psi_{\substack{\text{in}\\\text{out}}}(x),\bar{\psi}_{\substack{\text{in}\\\text{out}}}(x')\} = -iS(x - x'; m) \tag{11–509}$$

$$(-i\gamma\cdot\partial + m)\psi_{\substack{\text{in}\\\text{out}}}(x) = 0 \tag{11–510}$$

No-particle states are defined in the usual fashion by

$$\psi_{\text{in}}^{(+)}(x)|0\rangle_{\text{in}} = \bar{\psi}_{\text{in}}^{(+)}(x)|0\rangle_{\text{in}} = 0 \tag{11–511}$$

$$\psi_{\text{out}}^{(+)}(x)|0\rangle_{\text{out}}^e = \bar{\psi}_{\text{out}}^{(+)}(x)|0\rangle_{\text{out}}^e = 0 \tag{11–512}$$

[10] We are clearly bypassing the difficulty of how one measures the charge and mass of a "free" electron.

[11] For an alternate, and physically more satisfying, definition of the "in" and "out" fields in the presence of an external field, see S. S. Schweber and E. C. G. Sudarshan, *Ann. Physics*, **19**, 351 (1962).

[12] Note that we could have defined different "in" and "out" fields by the equation

$$\psi^e(x) = \psi_{\text{in}}^e(x) + \int d^4x' S_R^e(x,x')(e\gamma\cdot A(x') - \Delta m)\psi^e(x')$$

where $\psi_{\text{in}}^e(x)$ obeys the equation

$$(-i\gamma\cdot\partial + m)\psi_{\text{in}}^e(x) = e\gamma\cdot A^e(x)\psi_{\text{in}}^e(x)$$

and $S_R^e(x,x')$ the equation

$$(-i\gamma\cdot\partial + m)S_R^e(x,x') - e\gamma\cdot A^e(x)S_R^e(x,x') = \delta(x - x')$$

It is such "in" fields that must be considered if $A^e(x)$ is such that it admits bound states solutions of the one-particle Dirac equation.

but since an external field is present

$$|0\rangle_{\text{in}} \neq |0\rangle^{\text{e}}_{\text{out}} \tag{11–513}$$

due to the possibility of pair creation by the external field. Note that we have appended a superscript e on the no-particle state $|0\rangle^{\text{e}}_{\text{out}}$ defined by the out operators, to differentiate it from the $|0\rangle_{\text{out}}$ state defined by ${}_{\text{out}}\langle 0| = {}_{\text{in}}\langle 0|S$, where S is the S matrix in the absence of an external electromagnetic field, *i.e.*, the S matrix studied in the last section. We have assumed that the external field is such that it vanishes in the remote past, so that $|0\rangle^{\text{e}}_{\text{in}} = |0\rangle_{\text{in}}$ where $|0\rangle_{\text{in}} = |0\rangle$ is the no-particle state in the absence of an external field.[13] We shall also assume that the external field is adiabatically switched off at time $t = +\infty$. Besides these assumptions of the temporal behavior of A^{e}_{μ}, we shall assume that the external fields vanish at large spatial distances. In other words we shall assume that the external electromagnetic field extends only over a finite region of space-time.

Let us now again consider the scattering of a negaton by the external field A^{e}_{μ}. In the present discussion we, however, include the effects of the interaction of the negaton-positon field with the (quantized) radiation field as well as with the external field. The effect of the external field is taken into account by adding to the hamiltonian[14] describing the interaction of the negaton-positon field with the radiation field a term

$$\delta H^{\text{e}} = \int d^3x j^{\text{e}\mu}(x) A^{\text{e}}_{\mu}(x) \tag{11–514}$$

where $j^{\text{e}}_{\mu}(x)$ is the matter field current whose structure was analyzed in the last section, but is now expressed in terms of the negaton-positon field operators satisfying Eq. (11–507).

The matrix element for the scattering of a negaton by the external field is given by

$${}^{\text{e}}_{\text{out}}\langle \mathbf{p}'s'|\mathbf{p}s\rangle^{\text{e}}_{\text{in}} = {}_{\text{in}}\langle \mathbf{p}'s'|S^{\text{e}}|\mathbf{p}s\rangle_{\text{in}} \tag{11–515}$$

where S^{e} is the S-matrix for the problem at hand, namely, that computed from the interaction hamiltonian

$$\mathscr{H}^{\text{e}}_{\text{in}I}(x) = j^{\mu}_{\text{in}}(x)(A^{\mu}_{\text{in}}(x) + A^{\text{e}\mu}(x)) \tag{11–516}$$

where $j^{\mu}_{\text{in}}(x)$ is assumed to exhibit all the requisite counter terms necessary for the theory under discussion.

[13] All state vectors $|\ \rangle$, such as $|\mathbf{p},s\rangle$, $|\mathbf{k},\varepsilon\rangle$, etc., without the superscript e, refer to the state vector in the *absence* of the external field.

[14] For the structure of the lagrangian in the present situation, see S. N. Gupta, *Proc. Phys. Soc.* (*London*), **A 64**, 426 (1951); G. Källén, *Handbuch der Physik*, Band V, Teil 1, p. 352 ff., Springer Verlag, Berlin-Göttingen, 1958.

By virtue of the asymptotic condition, the scattering matrix can also be written in the form

$$
\begin{aligned}
{}_{\text{out}}^{\ \ \text{e}}\langle \mathbf{p}'s'|\mathbf{p}s\rangle_{\text{in}}^{\text{e}} &= {}_{\text{out}}^{\ \ \text{e}}\langle 0|b_{\text{out}}^{s'}(\mathbf{p}')b_{\text{in}}^{s*}(\mathbf{p})|0\rangle_{\text{in}} \\
&= \lim_{x_o\to-\infty}\ \lim_{x_o'\to-\infty}\ \frac{m}{(2\pi)^3}\int d^3x \int d^3x' \\
&\quad \times \tilde{u}_{s'}(\mathbf{p}')e^{ip'\cdot x'}\gamma^o \cdot \frac{-1}{2}\, S_F'^{\text{e}}(x',x)\gamma^o u_s(\mathbf{p})e^{-ip\cdot x} \qquad (11\text{–}517)
\end{aligned}
$$

where

$$
\begin{aligned}
-\tfrac{1}{2}S_F'^{\text{e}}(x,x') &= {}_{\text{out}}^{\ \ \text{e}}\langle 0|T(\psi^{\text{e}}(x)\tilde{\psi}^{\text{e}}(x')|0\rangle_{\text{in}} \qquad (11\text{–}518)\\
&= {}_{\text{in}}\langle 0|T(S^{\text{e}}\psi_{\text{in}}(x)\tilde{\psi}_{\text{in}}(x'))|0\rangle_{\text{in}} \qquad (11\text{–}519)
\end{aligned}
$$

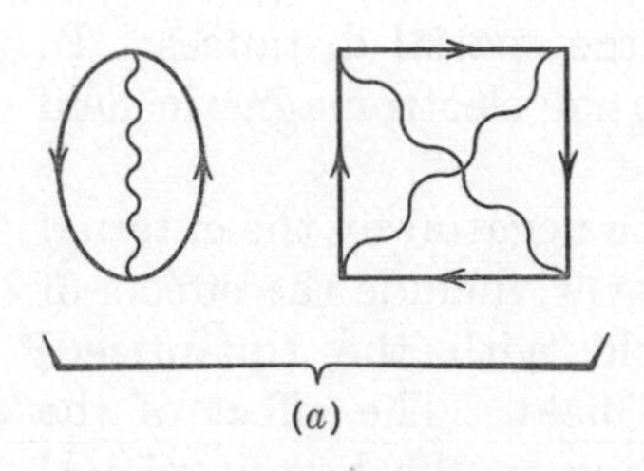

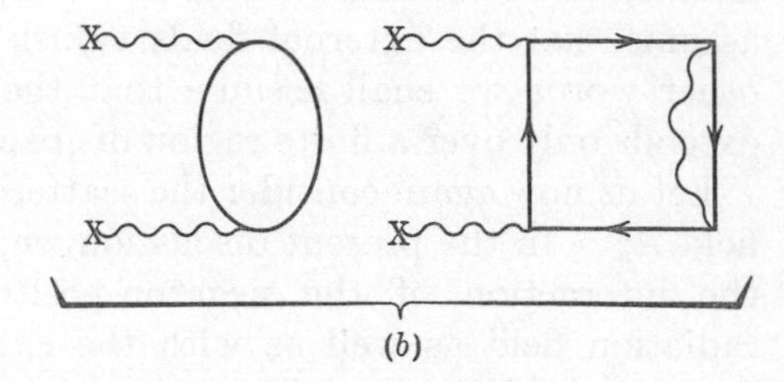

FIG. 11–9.

Substituting into Eq. (11–519), the formal expansion for S^{e}, we obtain that

$$
\begin{aligned}
-\tfrac{1}{2}S_F'^{\text{e}}(x,x') = \sum_{n=0}^{\infty} \frac{(-i)^n}{n!}\int d^4x_1 \cdots \int d^4x_n \\
\times\ {}_{\text{in}}\langle 0|T(j_{\text{in}}^{\mu_1}(x_1)\cdots j_{\text{in}}^{\mu_n}(x_n)\psi_{\text{in}}(x)\tilde{\psi}_{\text{in}}(x'))|0\rangle_{\text{in}} \\
\times\ {}_{\text{in}}\langle 0|T(A_{\text{in}\,\mu_1}(x_1) + A_{\mu_1}^{\text{e}}(x_1))\cdots \\
\times\ (A_{\text{in}\,\mu_n}(x_n) + A_{\mu_n}^{\text{e}}(x_n))|0\rangle_{\text{in}} \qquad (11\text{–}520)
\end{aligned}
$$

Actually we are interested only in the amplitude for scattering relative to the amplitude that the vacuum remain a vacuum, *i.e.*, in the amplitude

$$
K'^A(x,x') = \frac{-\tfrac{1}{2}S_F'^{\text{e}}(x,x')}{{}_{\text{out}}^{\ \ \text{e}}\langle 0|0\rangle_{\text{in}}} \qquad (11\text{–}521)
$$

which is computed from Eq. (11–520) by omitting *all* disconnected vacuum fluctuation diagrams, *i.e.*, diagrams of the form indicated in Fig. 11–9(a) and (b). To first order in the external field, the expression for $S_F'^{\text{e}}$ becomes

$$
\begin{aligned}
-\tfrac{1}{2}S_F'^{e}(x,x') = \sum_{n=0}^{\infty} \frac{(-i)^n}{n!} &\int d^4x_1 \cdots \int d^n x_n \\
&\times {}_{\text{in}}\langle 0|T(j_{\text{in}}^{\mu_1}(x_1)\cdots j_{\text{in}}^{\mu_n}(x_n)\psi_{\text{in}}(x)\tilde{\psi}_{\text{in}}(x'))|0\rangle_{\text{in}} \\
&\times {}_{\text{in}}\langle 0|T(A_{\text{in}\,\mu_1}(x_1)\cdots A_{\text{in}\,\mu_n}(x_n))|0\rangle_{\text{in}} \\
&+ \sum_{n=0}^{\infty} \frac{(-i)^n}{n!}\, n \int d^4x_1 \cdots \int d^4x_{n-1} \int d^4y \\
&\times {}_{\text{in}}\langle 0|T(j_{\text{in}}^{\mu}(y) j_{\text{in}}^{\mu_1}(x_1)\cdots j_{\text{in}}^{\mu_{n-1}}(x_{n-1})\psi_{\text{in}}(x)\tilde{\psi}_{\text{in}}(x'))|0\rangle_{\text{in}} \\
&\times {}_{\text{in}}\langle 0|T(A_{\text{in}\,\mu_1}(x_1)\cdots A_{\text{in}\,\mu_{n-1}}(x_{n-1}))|0\rangle_{\text{in}} A_{\mu}^{e}(y)
\end{aligned}
\tag{11–522}
$$

The first sum corresponds to the contribution from all the diagrams indicated in Fig. 11–10, which will be recognized as being equal to

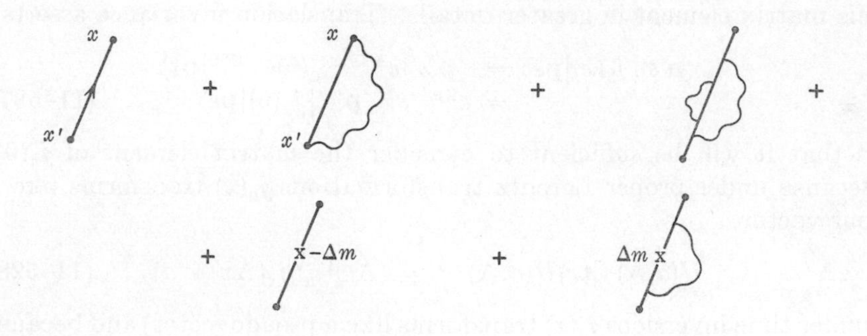

FIG. 11–10.

$-\tfrac{1}{2}S_F'(x - x') = K'_+(x - x') = \langle 0|T(\psi(x)\tilde{\psi}(x'))|0\rangle$. The second term can be written in the form

$$
\begin{aligned}
-i \int d^4y \sum_{m=0}^{\infty} \frac{(-i)^m}{m!} &\int d^4x_1 \cdots \int d^4x_m \\
&\times {}_{\text{in}}\langle 0|T(j_{\text{in}}^{\mu_1}(x_1)\cdots j_{\text{in}}^{\mu_m}(x_m) j_{\text{in}}^{\mu}(y)\psi_{\text{in}}(x)\tilde{\psi}_{\text{in}}(x'))|0\rangle_{\text{in}} \\
&\times {}_{\text{in}}\langle 0|T(A_{\text{in}\,\mu_1}(x_1)\cdots A_{\text{in}\,\mu_m}(x_m))|0\rangle_{\text{in}} A_{\mu}^{e}(y) \\
= -i \int d^4y \; &{}_{\text{in}}\langle 0|T(S j_{\text{in}}^{\mu}(y)\psi_{\text{in}}(x)\tilde{\psi}_{\text{in}}(x'))|0\rangle_{\text{in}} A_{\mu}^{e}(y)
\end{aligned}
\tag{11–523}
$$

where S is the S-matrix in the absence of the external field, *i.e.*, that computed with the interaction hamiltonian $+j_{\text{in}\,\mu}(x)A_{\text{in}}^{\mu}(x)$. Hence, to order A_{μ}^{e}

$$
K_+'^{A}(x,x') = K'_+(x - x') - i \int d^4y \; {}_{\text{out}}\langle 0|T(j^{\mu}(y)\psi(x)\tilde{\psi}(x'))|0\rangle_{\text{in}} A_{\mu}^{e}(y)
\tag{11–524}
$$

so that the original matrix element to order A^{e}_{μ} becomes equal to

$$
\begin{aligned}
&{}_{\text{out}}\langle 0|b^{s'}_{\text{out}}(\mathbf{p}')b^{s*}_{\text{in}}(\mathbf{p})|0\rangle_{\text{in}} \\
&\quad = \delta_{ss'}p_o\delta(\mathbf{p}-\mathbf{p}') - i \lim_{x_o'\to\infty} \lim_{x_o\to-\infty} \frac{m}{(2\pi)^3}\int d^3x \int d^3x'\,\tilde{u}_{s'}(\mathbf{p}')e^{ip'\cdot x'} \\
&\qquad \times \gamma^o \int d^4y\,{}_{\text{out}}\langle 0|T(j^{\mu}(y)\psi(x')\tilde{\psi}(x))|0\rangle_{\text{in}}A^{e}_{\mu}(y)\gamma^o u_s(\mathbf{p})e^{-ip\cdot x}
\end{aligned} \tag{11–525}
$$

$$
= \delta_{ss'}p_o\delta(\mathbf{p}-\mathbf{p}') - i\int d^4y\langle \mathbf{p}'s'|j^{\mu}(y)|\mathbf{p}s\rangle A^{e}_{\mu}(y) \tag{11–526}
$$

To lowest order in the external field, A^{e}_{μ}, the scattering is thus determined by the matrix element of the current operator $j_{\mu}(x)$ between the initial and final one-particle states, $|\mathbf{p},s\rangle$ and $|\mathbf{p}'s'\rangle$. Let us consider this matrix element in greater detail. Translation invariance asserts

$$
\begin{aligned}
\langle \mathbf{p}'s'|j_{\mu}(x)|\mathbf{p}s\rangle &= \langle \mathbf{p}'s'|e^{+iP\cdot x}j_{\mu}(0)e^{-iP\cdot x}|\mathbf{p}s\rangle \\
&= e^{i(p'-p)x}\langle \mathbf{p}'s'|j_{\mu}(0)|\mathbf{p}s\rangle
\end{aligned} \tag{11–527}
$$

so that it will be sufficient to consider the matrix element of $j_{\mu}(0)$. Because under proper Lorentz transformations $j_{\mu}(x)$ transforms like a four vector,

$$
U(a,\Lambda)j_{\mu}(x)U(a,\Lambda)^{-1} = (\Lambda^{-1})_{\mu}{}^{\nu}j_{\nu}(\Lambda x + a) \tag{11–528}
$$

(under time inversions $j_{\mu}(x)$ transforms like a pseudovector) and because of the previously derived transformation properties of the one-particle states,

$$
\begin{aligned}
\langle \mathbf{p}'s'|j_{\mu}(0)|\mathbf{p}s\rangle &= \langle \mathbf{p}'s'|U^*(\Lambda)U(\Lambda)j_{\mu}(0)U(\Lambda)^{-1}U(\Lambda)|\mathbf{p}s\rangle \\
&= \sum_{t't}\sigma_{ts}(p,\Lambda)\overline{\sigma_{t's'}(p',\Lambda)} \\
&\qquad \times (\Lambda^{-1})_{\mu}{}^{\nu}\langle \Lambda p',t'|j_{\nu}(0)|\Lambda p,t\rangle
\end{aligned} \tag{11–529}
$$

where we have denoted $U(a,\Lambda)$ by $U(\Lambda)$. On the right-hand side of Eq. (11–529), we have adopted a four-dimensional notation for the one-particle states $p = (p_o,\mathbf{p})$; $p_o = \sqrt{\mathbf{p}^2 + m^2}$. Equation (11–529) is true for arbitrary Λ. It is possible to make use of this freedom to further reduce the matrix element. Call $\Lambda p = q$ and $\Lambda p' = q'$. It is possible to choose Λ such that

$$
\mathbf{q}' = -\mathbf{q} \tag{11–530}
$$

and, hence, since $q'^2 = q^2 = m^2$ and $q_o,q_o' > 0$

$$
q_o' = q_o \tag{11–531}
$$

(This is the so-called Breit or "brick wall" system.) If we choose the z-axis as the direction of $\mathbf{q}$ then $\mathbf{q}'$ is the vector $\mathbf{q}$ rotated by 180° about the y-axis, hence

$$\langle \mathbf{q}',t'| = \langle \mathbf{q},t'|e^{+i\pi J_2} \tag{11–532}$$

where J_2, the y-component of the total angular momentum, is the generator for rotations about the 2-axis (the y-axis). Hence, the study of the matrix element $\langle \mathbf{p}'s'|J_\mu(0)|\mathbf{p}s\rangle$ can be reduced to the study of the matrix element

$$\langle \mathbf{q},t'|e^{+i\pi J_2}j_\mu(0)|\mathbf{q},t\rangle$$

Now the equation of current conservation

$$\partial^\mu j_\mu(x) = 0 \tag{11–533}$$

implies that

$$(p' - p)^\mu \langle p',s'|j_\mu(0)|p,s\rangle = 0 \tag{11–534}$$

so that in the brick wall system, the continuity equation yields the relation

$$2|\mathbf{q}|\langle q,t'|e^{-i\pi J_2}j^3(0)|q,t\rangle = (q_o - q_o')\langle q,t'|e^{+i\pi J_2}j^o(0)|q,t\rangle \tag{11–535}$$

Hence, since $q_o = q_o'$,

$$\langle q,t'|e^{+i\pi J_2}j_3(0)|q,t\rangle = 0 \tag{11–536}$$

The vanishing of this matrix element is, in fact, independent of the assumption of current conservation, and can be proved using the transformation properties of the current operator and one-particle states under space and time inversion, together with the hermiticity of $j_\mu(0)$. By actually generating the states $|\mathbf{q},t\rangle$, from the states in which the particle is at rest, by a Lorentz transformation along the 3 axis, and the use of the transformation properties of the current operator, essentially the entire kinematical structure of the matrix element of j_o on q can be obtained.[15] We shall, however, not do so here. Rather, we note that the right-hand side of Eq. (11–529) implies that

$$\langle \mathbf{p}'s'|j_\mu(0)|\mathbf{p}s\rangle$$

has the following structure:

$$\langle \mathbf{p}'s'|j_\mu(0)|\mathbf{p}s\rangle = \tilde{u}(\mathbf{p}'s')Q_\mu u(\mathbf{p}s) \tag{11–537}$$

[15] L. Durand, III, P. C. DeCelles, and R. B. Mann, *Phys. Rev.*, **126**, 1882 (1962).

where from invariance, Q_μ must have the following form

$$Q_\mu = (p' - p)_\mu a_1 + (p' + p)_\mu a_2 + \gamma_\mu a_3 + \sigma_{\mu\nu}(p' + p)^\nu a_4 + \sigma_{\mu\nu}(p' - p)^\nu a_5 \tag{11-538}$$

where $a_1, a_2, a_3, \cdots, a_5$ are invariant functions of p'^2, p^2, and $(p' - p)^2$, the three invariants which can be formed from the vectors p and p'. Since p and p' are the four-momenta of a one-particle state of mass m, $p'^2 = p^2 = m^2$. Hence the a_i are only functions of $(p' - p)^2$. Note that actually invariance under homogeneous Lorentz transformation, allows us to consider a more general form for Q_μ, wherein in expression (11–538) the a_i's are replaced by $(a_i + \gamma_5 a_i')$. However, the added terms would transform like pseudovectors under space inversion, and, hence, cannot be present since the left-hand side of (11–537) transforms like a vector under space inversion.

Since the expression (11–538) for Q_μ is to be evaluated between the spinors $\tilde{u}_s(\mathbf{p}')$ and $u_s(\mathbf{p})$, it can be simplified further by using the identities

$$\begin{aligned}\tilde{u}(\mathbf{p}')\sigma_{\mu\nu}(p^\nu + p'^\nu)u(p) &= \frac{1}{2i}\tilde{u}(\mathbf{p}')(\gamma_\mu\gamma_\nu - \gamma_\nu\gamma_\mu)(p^\nu + p'^\nu)u(\mathbf{p}) \\ &= \frac{1}{i}\tilde{u}(\mathbf{p}')(p' - p)_\mu u(\mathbf{p})\end{aligned} \tag{11-539}$$

and

$$\tilde{u}(\mathbf{p}')\sigma_{\mu\nu}(p' - p)^\nu u(\mathbf{p}) = i\tilde{u}(\mathbf{p}')(2m\gamma_\mu - (p_\mu + p_\mu'))u(\mathbf{p}) \tag{11-540}$$

Equation (11–539) is deduced by using the fact $\gamma\cdot p u(\mathbf{p}) = m u(\mathbf{p})$, $\tilde{u}(\mathbf{p}')\gamma\cdot p' = m\tilde{u}(\mathbf{p}')$ and the commutation rules of the γ-matrices. Similar steps are involved in arriving at Eq. (11–540). Hence

$$\langle \mathbf{p}',s'|j_\mu(0)|\mathbf{p},s\rangle = \frac{m}{(2\pi)^3}\tilde{u}(\mathbf{p}',s')[\gamma_\mu F_1(q^2) + i\sigma_{\mu\nu}q^\nu F_2(q^2) + q_\mu F_3(q^2)]u(\mathbf{p},s) \tag{11-541}$$

where

$$q = p' - p \tag{11-542}$$

and the F_i's are linear combinations of the a_i's. The factor $m/(2\pi)^3$ has been introduced for normalization purposes.

We next show that the time reversal properties of $j_\mu(x)$ are such that the matrix element $\langle \mathbf{p}'s|j_\mu(0)|\mathbf{p}s\rangle$ cannot contain a term of the form

$\tilde{u}(\mathbf{p}',s')q_\mu F_3(q^2)u(\mathbf{p},s)$. Under time inversion, the transformation properties of the current density operator are

$$U(i_t)\begin{Bmatrix} j_o(x) \\ j_i(x) \end{Bmatrix} U(i_t)^{-1} = \begin{Bmatrix} j_o(i_t x) \\ -j_i(i_t x) \end{Bmatrix} \tag{11–543}$$

where $U(i_t)$ is anti-unitary. We have previously noted if $|\mathbf{p},s\rangle = |\Psi_{\mathbf{p}s}\rangle$ corresponds to a state of momentum $\mathbf{p}$ and helicity s, then

$$U(i_t)|\mathbf{p},s\rangle = \eta_T|-\mathbf{p},s\rangle; \quad |\eta_T| = 1 \tag{11–544}$$

Hence, the invariance of the theory under time inversion and the hermiticity of $j_\mu(0)$ implies that

$$\begin{aligned}\langle \mathbf{p}',s'|j_\mu(0)|\mathbf{p},s\rangle &= (\Psi_{\mathbf{p}'s'}, j_\mu(0)\Psi_{\mathbf{p}s}) \\ &= (\Psi_{\mathbf{p}'s'}, U^*(i_t)U(i_t)j_\mu(0)U(i_t)^{-1}U(i_t)\Psi_{\mathbf{p}s}) \\ &= -\overline{(U(i_t)\Psi_{\mathbf{p}'s'}, (-1)^{\delta_{\mu o}}j_\mu(0)U(i_t)\Psi_{\mathbf{p}s})} \\ &= -(-1)^{\delta_{\mu o}}\langle -\mathbf{p},s|j_\mu(0)|-\mathbf{p}',s'\rangle \end{aligned} \tag{11–545}$$

It is now easily seen by means of a straightforward evaluation of $\tilde{u}(\mathbf{p}'s')u(\mathbf{p}s)(p' - p)_\mu$ that such a term does not satisfy the condition (11–545), *i.e.*,

$$q_o\tilde{u}(\mathbf{p}'s')u(\mathbf{p}s) \neq q_o\tilde{u}(-\mathbf{p},s)u(-\mathbf{p}',s') \tag{11–546}$$

$$q_i\tilde{u}(\mathbf{p}'s')u(\mathbf{p}s) \neq -q_i\tilde{u}(-\mathbf{p},s)u(-\mathbf{p}',s') \tag{11–547}$$

It is important, however, to note that this result would not obtain if the initial and final state described particles of different mass. Finally, therefore,

$$\langle \mathbf{p}'s'|j_\mu(0)|\mathbf{p}s\rangle = \frac{m}{(2\pi)^3}\,\tilde{u}(\mathbf{p}'s')(\gamma_\mu F_1(q^2) + i\sigma_{\mu\nu}q^\nu F_2(q^2))u(\mathbf{p}s) \tag{11–548}$$

Now from the hermiticity of $j_\mu(0)$, since

$$\overline{\langle \mathbf{p}'s'|j_\mu(0)|\mathbf{p}s\rangle} = \langle \mathbf{p}s|j_\mu(0)|\mathbf{p}'s'\rangle \tag{11–549}$$

it follows that

$$\begin{aligned}&\overline{\tilde{u}(\mathbf{p}',s')(\gamma_\mu F_1(q^2) + i\sigma_{\mu\nu}q^\nu F_2(q^2))u(\mathbf{p},s)} \\ &\qquad = \tilde{u}(\mathbf{p},s)(\gamma_\mu F_1(q^2) - i\sigma_{\mu\nu}q^\nu F_2(q^2))u(\mathbf{p}',s')\end{aligned} \tag{11–550}$$

Since in general, with our choice of γ matrices

$$\overline{\tilde{u}Qw} = \tilde{w}\gamma^o Q\gamma^{*o}u \tag{11–551}$$

the left-hand side of Eq. (11–550) can be rewritten as

$$\tilde{u}(\mathbf{p}s)\gamma_o[\gamma_\mu^* \overline{F_1(q^2)} - i\sigma_{\mu\nu}^* q^\nu \overline{F_2(q^2)}]\gamma_o u(\mathbf{p}'s')$$
$$= \tilde{u}(\mathbf{p}s)(\gamma_\mu \overline{F_1(q^2)} - i\sigma_{\mu\nu}q^\nu \overline{F_2(q^2)})u(\mathbf{p}'s') \quad (11\text{–}552)$$

so that the condition (11–549) implies that the $F_i(q^2)$ are real:

$$F_1(q^2) = \overline{F_1(q^2)} \quad (11\text{–}553)$$

$$F_2(q^2) = \overline{F_2(q^2)} \quad (11\text{–}554)$$

Note that the representation

$$\langle \mathbf{p}'s'|j_\mu(0)|\mathbf{p}s\rangle = \frac{m}{(2\pi)^3}\tilde{u}(\mathbf{p}'s')[\gamma_\mu F_1(q^2) + i\sigma_{\mu\nu}q^\nu F_2(q^2)]u(\mathbf{p}s) \quad (11\text{–}555)$$

automatically guarantees that

$$\langle \mathbf{p}'s'|\partial_\mu j^\mu(x)|\mathbf{p}s\rangle = 0 \quad (11\text{–}556)$$

since

$$(p' - p)^\mu \langle \mathbf{p}'s'|j_\mu(0)|\mathbf{p}s\rangle$$
$$= \frac{m}{(2\pi)^3}\tilde{u}(\mathbf{p}'s')[\gamma\cdot(p' - p)F_1(q^2) + i\sigma_{\mu\nu}q^\mu q^\nu F_2(q^2)]u(\mathbf{p}s) = 0 \quad (11\text{–}557)$$

because

$$\tilde{u}(\mathbf{p}')\gamma\cdot(p' - p)u(\mathbf{p}) = 0 \quad (11\text{–}558)$$

and

$$\sigma_{\mu\nu}q^\mu q^\nu = 0 \quad (11\text{–}559)$$

Stated differently, relativistic invariance (including space and time inversions) automatically insures that Eq. (11–556) is satisfied. We did not have to invoke the continuity equation $\partial_\mu j^\mu(x) = 0$ to arrive at the representation (11–555). (This, however, is a consequence of the fact that the particles in the initial and final state have the *same* mass.) Let us next obtain the physical meaning of the quantities $F_1(q^2)$ and $F_2(q^2)$. Since

$$\int d^3x j_o(x) = Q \quad (11\text{–}560)$$

is the total charge operator, and for a one-negaton state

$$Q|\mathbf{p},s\rangle = -e|\mathbf{p},s\rangle \quad (11\text{–}561)$$

with our normalization of the one-particle states, we deduce that

$$\int d^3x\langle \mathbf{p}'s'|j_o(x)|\mathbf{p}s\rangle = -e\langle \mathbf{p}'s'|\mathbf{p}s\rangle$$
$$= -ep_o\delta(\mathbf{p}-\mathbf{p}')\delta_{ss'} \qquad (11\text{–}562)$$

However, using translation invariance and the representation (11–555), the left-hand side of this last expression is also equal to

$$\int d^3x\langle \mathbf{p}'s'|j_o(x)|\mathbf{p}s\rangle = \int d^3x e^{+i(p'-p)\cdot x}\langle \mathbf{p}'s'|j_o(x)|\mathbf{p}s\rangle$$
$$= (2\pi)^3\delta(\mathbf{p}-\mathbf{p}')\langle \mathbf{p}'s'|j_o(0)|\mathbf{p}s\rangle$$
$$= (2\pi)^3\delta(\mathbf{p}-\mathbf{p}')\frac{m}{(2\pi)^3}\tilde{u}(\mathbf{p}'s')\gamma_o u(\mathbf{p}s)F_1(0)$$
$$= p_o\delta(\mathbf{p}-\mathbf{p}')F_1(0) \qquad (11\text{–}563)$$

Hence

$$F_1(0) = -e \qquad (11\text{–}564)$$

Similarly, if we calculate the expectation value of the operator

$$\tfrac{1}{2}\int d^3x\, \mathbf{r}\times\mathbf{j}(x); \quad (\mathbf{r}=\mathbf{x})$$

in the state in which the negaton is at rest, we obtain the result that

$$\int d^3x\, \mathbf{r}\times\langle \mathbf{p}s'|\mathbf{j}(0)|\mathbf{p}s\rangle|_{\mathbf{p}=0} = \left[\frac{F_1(0)}{2m}+F_2(0)\right]\tilde{u}_{s'}(\mathbf{p})\mathbf{\Sigma}u_s(\mathbf{p})|_{\mathbf{p}=0} \qquad (11\text{–}565)$$

Since $F_1(0)/2m = -e/2m$ is the Dirac moment of the negaton, we deduce that $F_2(0)$ is the static anomalous moment of the electron, *i.e.*, $F_2(0)$ is the static contribution to its magnetic moment over and above its normal Dirac value.

Let us next calculate $F_2(0)$ to lowest order in perturbation theory. Quite generally, if $\mathbf{p}\neq\mathbf{p}'$

$$_{\text{out}}\langle \mathbf{p}'s'|j_\mu(0)|\mathbf{p}s\rangle_{\text{in}} - {}_{\text{in}}\langle \mathbf{p}'s'|T(Sj_{\text{in}\,\mu}(0))|\mathbf{p}s\rangle_{\text{in}}$$
$$= +\frac{(-i)^2}{2!(\hbar c)^2}\int d^4x_1\int d^4x_2$$
$$\times\, {}_{\text{in}}\langle \mathbf{p}'s'|T(j_{\text{in}\,\mu_1}(x_1)j_{\text{in}\,\mu_2}(x_2)j_{\text{in}\,\mu}(0))|\mathbf{p}s\rangle_{\text{in}}$$
$$\times\frac{-\hbar c}{2}D_F(x_1-x_2)g^{\mu_1\mu_2}$$
$$\pm\cdots \qquad (11\text{–}566)$$

where only the lowest order contribution has been written down. Let us, in particular, look at the contribution to the right-hand side of Eq. (11–566), coming from the $-(e/2)[\tilde{\psi}_{\text{in}}(x)\gamma_\mu,\psi_{\text{in}}(x)]$ term in $j_{\text{in}\,\mu}(x)$.

Upon decomposing the T product into normal products, one readily establishes that the contribution from this term is given by

$$\begin{aligned}\langle \mathbf{p}'s'|j_\mu(0)|\mathbf{p}s\rangle = &-\frac{m}{(2\pi)^3}\cdot\frac{-i}{(2\pi)^4}\frac{e^2}{\hbar c}\,e\tilde{u}_{s'}(\mathbf{p}')\\ &\times\int d^4k\gamma_\nu\frac{1}{\gamma\cdot(p'-k)-m+i\varepsilon}\\ &\times\gamma_\mu\frac{1}{\gamma\cdot(p-k)-m+i\varepsilon'}\gamma^\nu\frac{1}{k^2+i\varepsilon''}u_s(\mathbf{p})\end{aligned} \tag{11–567}$$

This expression can be further simplified by noting that $p^2 = p'^2 = m^2$ so that, for example

$$\frac{1}{\gamma\cdot(p'-k)-m} = \frac{\gamma\cdot(p'-k)+m}{-2p'\cdot k+k^2} \tag{11–568}$$

and that by virtue of the commutation rules $[\gamma_\mu,\gamma_\nu]_+ = 2g_{\mu\nu}$ the following relations hold:

$$\gamma_\nu\gamma_\mu\gamma^\nu = -2\gamma_\mu \tag{11–569}$$

$$\gamma_\nu\gamma^{\mu_1}\gamma^{\mu_2}\gamma^\nu = 4g^{\mu_1\mu_2} \tag{11–570}$$

$$\gamma_\nu\gamma^{\mu_1}\gamma^{\mu_2}\gamma^{\mu_3}\gamma^\nu = -2\gamma^{\mu_3}\gamma^{\mu_2}\gamma^{\mu_1} \tag{11–571}$$

The above formulae, together with $\tilde{u}(\mathbf{p}')\gamma\cdot p' = m\tilde{u}(\mathbf{p}')$ and $\gamma\cdot pu(\mathbf{p}) = mu(\mathbf{p})$, allow us to recast the right-hand side of Eq. (11–567) into the form

$$\begin{aligned}&\frac{m}{(2\pi)^3}\frac{ie}{(2\pi)^4}\frac{e^2}{\hbar c}\tilde{u}_{s'}(\mathbf{p}')\int\frac{d^4k}{k^2}\\ &\times\frac{\{2m^2-2k^2+4(p'-k)\cdot(p-k)\}\gamma_\mu - 4mk_\mu + 4\gamma\cdot k(p+p'-k)_\mu}{[-2p'\cdot k+k^2][-2p\cdot k+k^2]}\\ &\times u_s(\mathbf{p})\end{aligned} \tag{11–572}$$

The three denominators in (11–572) can be combined using the Feynman formula [16]

$$\frac{1}{a_1a_2a_3} = 2!\int_0^1 dz_1\int_0^1 dz_2\int_0^1 dz_3\frac{\delta\left(\sum_{i=1}^3 z_i - 1\right)}{\left[\sum_{i=1}^3 a_iz_i\right]^3} \tag{11–573}$$

[16] Feynman's Formula.—One readily verifies by explicitly carrying out the integrations involved that

$$\frac{1}{x_1x_2} = \int_0^1 d\alpha_1 \int_0^1 d\alpha_2 \frac{\delta(\alpha_1 + \alpha_2 - 1)}{(\alpha_1x_1 + \alpha_2x_2)^2} \tag{a}$$

We note further that

$$(-1)^{n-1}\frac{(n-1)!}{x_1^nx_2} = (-1)^{n-1}n! \int_0^1 d\alpha_1 \int_0^1 d\alpha_2 \frac{\alpha_1^{n-1}\delta(\alpha_1 + \alpha_2 - 1)}{(\alpha_1x_1 + \alpha_2x_2)^{n+1}} \tag{b}$$

as is verified by differentiating Eq. (a).

Making use of (a) we can write:

$$\begin{aligned}\frac{1}{x_1x_2x_3} &= \int_0^1 d\alpha_1 \int_0^1 d\alpha_2 \frac{\delta(\alpha_1 + \alpha_2 - 1)}{(\alpha_1x_1 + \alpha_2x_2)^2x_3} \\ &= 2! \int_0^1 d\alpha_1 \int_0^1 d\alpha_2 \int_0^1 d\beta_1 \int_0^1 d\beta_2 \frac{\delta(\alpha_1 + \alpha_2 - 1)\delta(\beta_1 + \beta_2 - 1)\beta_1}{[\beta_1(\alpha_1x_1 + \alpha_2x_2) + \beta_2x_3]^3}\end{aligned} \tag{c}$$

Upon introducing the variables:

$$\begin{aligned}\alpha_1 &= \gamma_1/\beta_1 \\ \alpha_2 &= \gamma_2/\beta_1 \\ \beta_2 &= \gamma_3\end{aligned} \tag{d}$$

and carrying out the integration over β_1 we deduce that

$$\frac{1}{x_1x_2x_3} = 2! \int_0^1 d\gamma_1 \int_0^1 d\gamma_2 \int_0^1 d\gamma_3 \frac{\delta(\gamma_1 + \gamma_2 + \gamma_3 - 1)}{(\gamma_1x_1 + \gamma_2x_2 + \gamma_3x_3)^3} \tag{e}$$

The formula for the general case is proved by induction. Assume that the formula

$$\frac{1}{x_1x_2\cdots x_n} = (n-1)! \int_0^1 d\alpha_1 \int_0^1 d\alpha_2 \cdots \int_0^1 d\alpha_n \frac{\delta(\alpha_1 + \alpha_2 + \cdots + \alpha_n - 1)}{(\alpha_1x_1 + \alpha_2x_2 + \cdots + \alpha_nx_n)^n} \tag{f}$$

is true. Then using (b)

$$\frac{1}{x_1x_2\cdots x_nx_{n+1}} = (n-1)! \int_0^1 d\alpha_1 \int_0^1 d\alpha_2 \cdots \int_0^1 d\alpha_n \frac{\delta\left(\sum_{i=1}^n \alpha_i - 1\right)}{\left(\sum_{i=1}^n \alpha_ix_i\right)^n x_{n+1}} \tag{g}$$

$$= n! \int_0^1 d\alpha_1 \cdots \int_0^1 d\alpha_n \int_0^1 d\beta_1 \int_0^1 d\beta_2 \frac{\delta\left(\sum_{i=1}^n \alpha_i - 1\right)\delta(\beta_1 + \beta_2 - 1)\beta_1^{n-1}}{\left[\beta_1 \sum_{i=1}^n \alpha_ix_i + \beta_2x_{n+1}\right]^{n+1}} \tag{h}$$

Again introduce variables $\gamma_1,\cdots,\gamma_n$ by

$$\begin{aligned}\alpha_1 &= \gamma_1/\beta_1 \\ &\vdots \\ \alpha_n &= \gamma_n/\beta_1\end{aligned} \tag{i}$$

so that

$$d\alpha_1\cdots d\alpha_n = d\gamma_1\cdots d\gamma_n\beta_1^{-n} \tag{j}$$

and

$$\delta(\alpha_1 + \alpha_2 + \cdots + \alpha_n - 1) = \beta_1\delta(\gamma_1 + \gamma_2 + \cdots + \gamma_n - \beta_1) \tag{k}$$

whence, calling $\beta_2 = \gamma_{n+1}$

$$\begin{aligned}\frac{1}{x_1\cdots x_nx_{n+1}} &= n! \int_0^1 d\gamma_1 \cdots \int_0^1 d\gamma_n \int_0^1 d\beta_1 \int_0^1 d\gamma_{n+1} \frac{\delta\left(\sum_{i=1}^n \gamma_i - \beta_1\right)\delta(\beta_1 + \gamma_{n+1} - 1)}{\left[\sum_{i=1}^n \gamma_ix_i + \gamma_{n+1}x_{n+1}\right]^{n+1}} \\ &= n! \int_0^1 d\gamma_1 \cdots \int_0^1 d\gamma_{n+1} \frac{\delta\left(\sum_{i=1}^{n+1} \gamma_i - 1\right)}{\left[\sum_{i=1}^{n+1} \gamma_ix_i\right]^{n+1}}\end{aligned} \tag{l}$$

QED.

to yield, upon carrying out the integration over z_3,

$$\begin{aligned}\frac{1}{k^2(k^2 - 2p'\cdot k)(k^2 - 2p\cdot k)} &= 2! \int_0^1 dz_1 \int_0^1 dz_2 \frac{\theta(z_1 + z_2)\theta(1 - z_1 - z_2)}{[k^2 - 2z_2(p - p')\cdot k - (1 - z_1)2p'\cdot k]^3} \\ &= 2 \int_0^1 dx \int_0^x dy \frac{1}{[k^2 - 2y(p - p')\cdot k - 2p'\cdot kx]^3} \end{aligned} \tag{11–574}$$

The reason for combining the denominators in the manner outlined above is that we can now proceed to carry out the integration over the k variable. We first introduce the variable

$$k' = k - z_2(p - p') \tag{11–575}$$

so that the denominator is a function of k'^2 only. Any contribution of the form $\int d^4k k_\mu f(k^2)$ (we have dropped the prime on the k) now vanishes by symmetry. Recalling that the definitions of the D_F and S_F function entail giving the masses a small negative mass we shall have to evaluate the following kind of integral[17]:

$$I = \int_{-\infty}^{+\infty} d^4k \frac{1}{(k^2 - L + i\varepsilon)^3} \tag{11–576}$$

The path of integration is along the real k_0 axis, the pole having been displaced by the Feynman $i\varepsilon$'s. This path of integration may, however, be rotated by 90° in the complex k_0 plane, so that the integration is up along the imaginary axis from $-i\infty$ to $+i\infty$, because in thus deforming the contour we never cross any singularities. The latter are located above the negative real axis and below the positive real axis. Also, the contribution from the path along the circumference of the large circle in the first and fourth quadrants vanishes since the denominator behaves like $1/k_0^6$.

We may, therefore, introduce a new integration variable $k_o = ik_4$, thus transforming the integral (11–576) into an integral over a *euclidian* four space

$$I = -i \int_{-\infty}^{+\infty} d^3k \int_{-\infty}^{+\infty} dk_4 \frac{1}{(k_4^2 + k_1^2 + k_2^2 + k_3^2 + L)^3} \tag{11–577}$$

which is readily evaluated upon introducing four-dimensional polar

[17] We also have to evaluate integrals of the form $\int k_\mu k_\nu f(k^2) d^4k$. Such integrals can be handled by averaging the integrand over the direction of k_μ which amounts to the substitution

$$k_\mu k_\nu \Rightarrow \tfrac{1}{4} g_{\mu\nu} k^2$$

coordinates. The volume element becomes $2\pi^2 k^3 dk$, and the integral reduces to

$$I = -2\pi^2 i \int_0^\infty \frac{k^3 dk}{(k^2 + L)^3} = -i\pi^2 \int_0^\infty \frac{x dx}{(x + L)^3}$$
$$= -\frac{i\pi^2}{2L} \tag{11–578}$$

It should be noted that the expression (11–572) can be reduced so that it is of the form

$$\frac{m}{(2\pi)^3} \tilde{u}_{s'}(\mathbf{p}')[F_1(q^2)\gamma_\mu + i\sigma_{\mu\nu}q^\nu F_2(q^2)]u_s(\mathbf{p}) \tag{11–579}$$

by using the properties of the γ-matrices and the spinors $\tilde{u}(\mathbf{p}')$ and $u(\mathbf{p})$. We shall here evaluate only the contribution to F_2, so that we are interested only in terms not involving γ^μ. Since, upon integrating over k, the $\gamma \cdot k k_\mu$ term in (11–572) will give rise to a term of the form γ (times a factor), we can also disregard this term. Hence, we need consider only the term

$$+\frac{ie}{(2\pi)^4} \frac{e^2}{\hbar c} 2 \int_0^1 dx \int_0^x dy \int d^4k \frac{\tilde{u}_{s'}(\mathbf{p}')\{4\gamma \cdot k(p + p')_\mu - 4mk_\mu\}u_s(\mathbf{p})}{[k^2 - 2y(p - p') \cdot k - 2p' \cdot kx]^3}$$
$$= 4\pi^2 \frac{e}{(2\pi)^4} \frac{e^2}{\hbar c} \int_0^1 dx \int_0^x dy \tilde{u}_{s'}(\mathbf{p}')$$
$$\times \frac{p'_\mu[x(x - y) - y] + p_\mu[xy - (x - y)]}{[(x - y)^2 m^2 + 2p \cdot p'(x - y)y + y^2 m^2]^2} u_s(\mathbf{p}) \tag{11–580}$$

The right-hand side of Eq. (11–580) can be further reduced, by exploiting the symmetry $x \leftrightarrow (x - y)$, and can then be brought into the form

$$-\frac{e^2}{4\pi\hbar c} \frac{e}{\pi m} \tilde{u}_{s'}(\mathbf{p}')(p' + p)_\mu u_s(\mathbf{p}) \int_0^1 dx(1 - x) \int_0^x \frac{y dy}{x^2 + (q^2/m^2)y(x - y)} \tag{11–581}$$

where

$$q = p' - p \tag{11–582}$$

Relation (11–540) now allows us to infer that to order $\alpha = e^2/4\pi\hbar c$, $F_2(q^2)$ is given by ($\hbar = c = 1$)

$$F_2^{(2)}(q^2) = -\alpha \frac{e}{\pi m} \int_0^1 dx(1 - x) \int_0^x \frac{y dy}{x^2 + (q^2/m^2)y(x - y)} \tag{11–583}$$

The static anomalous magnetic moment of the electron to order α is, therefore, given by

$$F_2^{(2)}(0) = -\frac{e}{2m}\left(\frac{2\alpha}{\pi}\int_0^1 dx(1-x)\int_0^x \frac{y\,dy}{x^2}\right)$$
$$= -\frac{e}{2m}\left(\frac{\alpha}{2\pi}\right) \qquad (11\text{–}584)$$

In other words, due to its interaction with the radiation field, a negaton interacts with a slowly varying external electromagnetic field ($q^2 \ll m^2$) as if its magnetic moment were (approximately to order α) equal to

$$-\frac{e}{2m}\left(1+\frac{\alpha}{2\pi}\right)$$

This result was first obtained by Schwinger.[18] The α^2 contribution to $F_2(0)$ has been calculated by Sommerfield[19] and by Petermann, and the result is that

$$F_2(0) \approx -\frac{e}{2m}\left(\frac{\alpha}{2\pi} - 0.328\,\frac{\alpha^2}{\pi^2} + \cdots\right)$$
$$\approx -0.0011596\,\frac{e}{2m} \qquad (11\text{–}585)$$

in remarkable agreement with the most recent experimental result of Pidd and Crane, who find that the electron magnetic moment anomaly is $(0.0011609 \pm 0.000024)\,e/2mc$. Actually it remains to be shown that none of the other terms in $j_\mu(x)$ contributes to $F_2^{(2)}(0)$. This can indeed be verified explicitly. It is interesting to note that to this order, *i.e.*, to order α, we encounter no divergences in the computation of $F_2^{(2)}$ using the $(e/2)[\bar{\psi}_{\text{in}}(x)\gamma^\mu,\psi_{\text{in}}(x)]A_{\text{in}\,\mu}(x)$ interaction term. On the other hand, we note that the expression (11–572) gives rise to a logarithmically divergent contribution to $F_1^{(2)}$. It is precisely the role of the counter terms in $j_\mu(x)$ to compensate these divergent contributions.

Concluding Remarks.—We have come to the end of our exposition of some aspects of quantum electrodynamics. We have not delved in some of the more technical and difficult facets of the subject matter. Mention should, however, be made of what some of the difficulties are. Foremost at the "technical" level is perhaps the role played by the infrared divergences. The fact that the photon has zero mass not only gives rise to divergences in various matrix elements,[20] but also implies

[18] J. Schwinger, *Phys. Rev.*, **73**, 416 (1948).

[19] C. M. Sommerfield, *Ann. Phys.*, **5**, 26 (1958).

[20] For example, $F_1(q^2)$, if computed in perturbation theory by giving the photon a small mass λ, *i.e.*, a propagator $(k^2 - \lambda^2)^{-1}$, is logarithmically divergent in the limit $\lambda \to 0$ (*i.e.*, $F_1(q^2)$ is proportional to $\log(m/\lambda)$).

that in a rigorous sense, a one-photon or a one-electron state does not exist. Stated differently, in the Lorentz gauge the Lehmann weights investigated in Section 11.4 may not have a δ-function part (the contribution of the one-particle states). These questions are perhaps most easily investigated in the Coulomb gauge.

A second difficulty which has only been alluded to—or rather neglected—in the present outline is the validity of the assumption that "in" and "out" fields exist. The existence of an asymptotic limit might well be rigorously provable for matrix elements of the form $\langle 0|\psi(x)|1 \text{ particle}\rangle$, but not for more general situations without explicitly removing the Coulomb interaction between the particles.

The application of dispersion relations (Chapter 10) to electrodynamic processes has received some attention in recent years. This subject, together with some of the more technical aspects (such as the computation of L', L'', Δm) not covered in these chapters, will be dealt with elsewhere.

Finally, the much deeper and difficult questions concerned with the consistency of commutation rules and of the equations of motion, and the questions concerned with the existence of solutions have not been raised in these chapters. They have also in fact not received even a partial answer in the literature. The question of the limits of quantum electrodynamics may, however, receive an experimental answer in the foreseeable future.

REFERENCES

Computation of Electrodynamic Process:

Akhiezer, A., and Berezetski, V. B., *Quantum Electrodynamics*, State Technics, Theoretical Literature Press, Moscow, 1953.

Heitler, W., *The Quantum Theory of Radiation*, 2nd Ed., Oxford University Press, 1944.

Jauch, J., and Rohrlich, F., *The Theory of Photons and Electrons*, Addison-Wesley, Reading, Mass., 1955.

Källén, G., *Handbuch der Physik*, Band **V**, Teil 1, Springer Verlag, Berlin-Göttingen, 1958.

Petermann, A., *Fortschritte der Physik*, VI, **10**, 505 (1958).

Schwinger, J., Ed., *Quantum Electrodynamics*, Dover Publications, New York, 1958.

Infrared Divergences:

Eriksson, K. E., *Nuovo Cimento*, **19**, 1010 (1961).

Yennie, D. R., Frautschi, S. C., and Suura, H., *Ann. Phys.*, **13**, 379 (1961).

Consistency of Quantum Electrodynamics:

Johnson, K. A., *Phys. Rev.*, **112**, 1367 (1958).

Källén, G., *Kgl. Danske Vidensk Selskab Mat Fys.*, Medd **27**, 12 (1953).

Yennie, D., Gasiorowicz, S., and Suura, H., *Phys. Rev. Letters.*, **2**, 513 (1959).

High Energy Behavior of Quantum Electrodynamics:

Blankenbecler, R., Cook, L. F., and Goldberger, M. L., *Phys. Rev. Letters*, **8**, 463 (1962).
Frautschi, S. C., *Suppl. to Progress Theor. Physics (Japan)*, **8**, 21 (1958).
Gell-Mann, M., and Low, F. E., *Phys. Rev.*, **95**, 1300 (1954).
Johnson, K., *Ann. Phys.*, **10**, 536 (1960).

Application of Dispersion Relation to Quantum Electrodynamics:

Drell, S. D., and Zachariasen, F., *Phys. Rev.*, **111**, 1727 (1958); **119**, 463 (1960).
Fainberg, V. Y., *Soviet Physics JETP*, **35** (10), 968 (1961).
Gell-Mann, M., Goldberger, M., and Thirring, W., *Phys. Rev.*, **95**, 1612 (1954).

CHAPTER 12

SYMMETRY PROPERTIES OF MAGNETIC CRYSTALS

by

J. O. DIMMOCK and R. G. WHEELER

Yale University

12.1. Introduction.—The symmetry properties of a quantum system may be used to simplify greatly the associated eigenvalue problem. If the hamiltonian is invariant under a group of transformations, then the eigenstates may be assigned to specific irreducible representations of the group. Specifically, the problem of determining the eigenstates of a crystal is greatly simplified by the classification of these states according to the irreducible representations of the appropriate crystallographic symmetry group. Such a classification results not only in the determination of the state function symmetries and degeneracies and of the selection rules governing transitions between the states, but also assists further in the determination of matrix elements involving these crystal states. The transformations that one encounters normally when considering a crystalline eigenvalue problem are those rotations, reflections, and translations that leave the time-averaged atomic positions and electronic charge density invariant. In addition, if the crystal has no microscopic time-averaged magnetic moment density, it is also invariant under a reversal of time. If, however, the crystal possesses unpaired electrons, it is possible for the equilibrium state of the crystal to be characterized by a nonvanishing, time-averaged magnetic moment density. Such is the case with ferro-, antiferro-, and ferrimagnetic crystals. These crystals are not invariant under time reversal, since a magnetic moment changes sign under this transformation. It is our purpose here to discuss the symmetry properties and degeneracies of wave functions in these crystals. This discussion is prefaced by a consideration of the symmetry elements peculiar to magnetically ordered systems, the relationship between these elements, and the quantum mechanical operators with which one is concerned in the associated eigenvalue problem. Since the quantum mechanical time reversal operator is anti-unitary, as is shown below, the symmetry groups in question contain both unitary and anti-unitary operators. Such groups are called nonunitary groups. In Section 12.2 then, we shall develop a method that may be used to obtain the co-representations of nonunitary groups. The distinction between these and the representations of unitary groups is indicated below. This method is used to discuss the irreducible representations of the crystallographic point groups. The appropriate method is then developed for space groups and in Section 12.3, the results are illustrated by an application to the antiferromagnetic, one-dimensional Kronig-Penney problem. General space group applications are discussed along with the application to spin wave problems. Finally, the ordering problem in magnetic crystals is discussed.

Symmetry of Magnetic Structures.—As mentioned above, a crystal that does not exhibit magnetic structure is invariant under the reversal of time, in addition to the standard spatial transformations of its crystallographic symmetry group. If a crystal possesses a magnetic structure it is not invariant under a reversal of time.[1] A magnetically ordered crystal will, however, be invariant under a group of spatial transformations, which leave the crystal lattice and the magnetic moment density unchanged. If in addition there exists a transformation that takes the crystal into itself but changes the sign of the magnetic moment density, the crystal and magnetic moment density will be invariant under a combination of this transformation and a reversal of time. This extension of spatial symmetry groups by the inclusion of time reversal increases the number of crystallographic symmetry groups from the 230 classical space groups to 1651 groups, which have been called Shubnikov groups.[2] Of these, 230 correspond to the classical groups without time reversal, 230 to the classical groups augmented by time reversal, and the remaining 1191 to symmetry groups in which time reversal occurs only in combination with other transformations but not by itself. A corresponding increase also occurs in the number of crystallographic point symmetry groups from 32 to 122. Magnetically ordered crystals belong either to the first or third of the above sets, though we are interested here primarily in those that belong to the third set since it is in these that the consideration of time reversal is important.

Relationship Between Physical Transformations and Quantum Mechanical Operators.—In order to obtain information concerning the symmetry

[1] The symmetry of magnetic crystals has been discussed by several authors. See for example: L. D. Landau, and E. M. Lifshitz, *Electrodynamics of Continuous Media*, Addison-Wesley Publishing Company, Reading, Mass., 1960; B. A. Tavger and J. M. Zaitzev, *Soviet Phys.—JETP*, **3**, 430 (1956); Y. LeCorre, *J. phys. radium*, **19**, 750 (1958); G. Donnay, *et al.*, *Phys. Rev.*, **112**, 1917 (1958).

[2] A. V. Shubnikov, *Symmetry and Antisymmetry of Finite Figures*, Acad. Sci. U.S.S.R. Press, Moscow, 1951. See also N. V. Belov, N. N. Neronova, and T. S. Smirnova, *Soviet Physics-Cryst*, **2**, 311 (1957).

properties and degeneracies of the eigenfunctions of a particular hamiltonian, it is necessary to consider the group of quantum mechanical operators that commutes with this hamiltonian. In general one can obtain, through an examination of the system in question, those transformations that leave the system invariant. A correspondence must then be made between these transformations and the quantum mechanical operators that commute with the hamiltonian of the system. Since the state functions are determined to within a phase factor of unit modulus only, there is an ambiguity in the quantum mechanical operators that correspond to the physical transformations.[3] Ignoring the spin of the electron, we can resolve this ambiguity, and make a one-to-one correspondence between each physical transformation and an appropriate quantum mechanical operator. When spin is involved we obtain for every transformation two operators that can be denoted by $\mathbf{Q}$ and $\overline{\mathbf{Q}}$ (Q-bar), where $\overline{\mathbf{Q}}$ is identical to $\mathbf{Q}$, except that it changes the sign of the spin function relative to $\mathbf{Q}$. The number of operators in a quantum mechanical system with spin is thus twice the number of corresponding physical transformations. The groups that these operators form are called "double groups" to indicate that the correspondence between the quantum mechanical operators and the related physical transformations is two-to-one.[4] Since we are ultimately interested in the solutions of the eigenvalue problem, the groups in which we are interested are the double groups of quantum mechanical operators that commute with the hamiltonian of the system. In what follows we deal only with these groups and assume that the appropriate correspondence to groups of physical transformations can be made.

Structure of Nonunitary Groups.—Consider the group G, which contains both unitary and anti-unitary operators. These operators will be denoted by $\mathbf{u}$ and $\mathbf{a}$ respectively. Further it is convenient to write the anti-unitary operators as $\mathbf{a} = \mathbf{v}\boldsymbol{\theta}$ where $\mathbf{v}$ is unitary and $\boldsymbol{\theta}$ is anti-unitary. No loss of generality results from our identification of $\boldsymbol{\theta}$ with the operation of time reversal. It can be shown[5] that the product of two unitary operators is unitary, the product of two anti-unitary operators is also unitary, and the product of an anti-unitary operator and a unitary operator is anti-unitary. Consequently nonunitary groups contain equal numbers of unitary and anti-unitary operators, and

[3] See for example: E. P. Wigner, *Group Theory and its Application to the Quantum Mechanics of Atomic Spectra*, Academic Press Inc., New York, 1959.

[4] See for example: G. F. Koster, *Solid State Physics*, **5**, 173 (1958).

[5] E. P. Wigner, *op. cit.*, Chap. 26. Much of the development in Section 12.2 is based on this chapter.

the unitary operators form an invariant subgroup H of index two. The anti-unitary operators form the coset of H, such that choosing an arbitrary one of these $\mathbf{a}_0$ we can write $G = H + H \cdot \mathbf{a}_0$. The coset is generated by the products of the members of H with $\mathbf{a}_0$, and G can be specified by H and $\mathbf{a}_0$. Since these relations hold not only for the quantum mechanical groups, but also for the crystallographic symmetry groups, we can see how to construct all the 1191 mixed groups containing anti-elements but not time reversal itself. Take each one of the 230 classical space groups and select from it an invariant subgroup of index two. A mixed group can then be constructed from this subgroup and the anti-element coset can be formed from the product of time reversal with the remaining elements of the space group. The groups of quantum mechanical operators can be obtained in a similar manner.

12.2. Representation theory for nonunitary groups.—Before proceeding we should consider what is meant by a unitary and an anti-unitary operator.[5,6] If the hamiltonian of a system commutes with the operators **u** and **a** of the group G, and Ψ and Φ are state functions of the system, **u** is unitary if

$$(\mathbf{u}\Psi,\mathbf{u}\Phi) = (\Psi,\Phi) \tag{12–1}$$

and **a** is anti-unitary if

$$(\mathbf{a}\Psi,\mathbf{a}\Phi) = (\Phi,\Psi) = (\Psi,\Phi)^* \tag{12–2}$$

If Φ is expanded in terms of the eigenstates of the hamiltonian

$$\Phi = \sum_\alpha c_\alpha \mathbf{u}\phi_\alpha$$

one can show[5] that **u** is linear

$$\mathbf{u}\Phi = \sum_\alpha c_\alpha \mathbf{u}\phi_\alpha \tag{12–3}$$

and **a** is antilinear

$$\mathbf{a}\Phi = \sum_\alpha c_\alpha^* \mathbf{a}\phi_\alpha \tag{12–4}$$

That is, unitary operators are linear and anti-unitary operators are antilinear.

The Time Reversal Operator.—In this section we show that spatial operators are linear whereas the time reversal operator is antilinear.[5] This may be seen by examining the eigenfunctions of the time dependent Schrödinger equation

$$H\phi_\alpha = i\hbar \partial\phi_\alpha/\partial t \tag{12–5}$$

[6] E. P. Wigner, *J. Math. Phys.*, **1**, 409, 414 (1960).

The important difference here between spatial operators and the time reversal operator originates in the way each effects the time displacement of the state functions. We have the following schematic multiplication relations.

$$\begin{aligned}&(\text{time displacement by } t) \times (\text{time reversal})\\ &\qquad = (\text{time reversal}) \times (\text{time displacement by } -t)\end{aligned} \tag{12–6}$$

and

$$\begin{aligned}&(\text{time displacement by } t) \times (\text{spatial operator})\\ &\qquad = (\text{spatial operator}) \times (\text{time displacement by } t)\end{aligned} \tag{12–7}$$

Furthermore, under a time displacement ϕ_α goes over to

$$\phi_\alpha(t) = \exp\,(-iE_\alpha t/\hbar)\phi_\alpha$$

whence

$$\Phi(t) = \sum_\alpha c_\alpha \exp\,(-iE_\alpha t/\hbar)\phi_\alpha$$

If the time reversal operator is taken to be linear, the left-hand side of Eq. (12–6) becomes

$$\sum_\alpha c_\alpha \exp\,(-iE_\alpha t/\hbar)\boldsymbol{\theta}\phi_\alpha$$

whereas the right-hand side becomes

$$\sum_\alpha c_\alpha \exp\,(+iE_\alpha t/\hbar)\boldsymbol{\theta}\phi_\alpha$$

and we have achieved a contradiction. On the other hand, if the time reversal operator is taken to be antilinear, both sides of Eq. (12–6) become

$$\sum_\alpha c_\alpha^* \exp\,(-iE_\alpha t/\hbar)\boldsymbol{\theta}\phi_\alpha$$

A similar argument can be used to show that the spatial operators are linear. It can then be shown that spatial operators are unitary whereas the time reversal operator is anti-unitary.

The time reversal operator may now be determined.[5] The simplest anti-unitary operation is the transition to the complex conjugate. This operator **K** is clearly antilinear and anti-unitary.

$$(\mathbf{K}\Psi,\mathbf{K}\Phi) = (\Psi^*,\Phi^*) = (\Psi,\Phi)^*$$

Furthermore, any antilinear operator can be written as the product of a unitary operator and the operator **K**. Specifically, we can write the time reversal operator as $\boldsymbol{\theta} = \mathbf{UK}$, and our problem is now that of determining $\mathbf{U}$. Neglecting the spin coordinates for the moment, we can obtain $\mathbf{U}$ from the commutation relations of $\boldsymbol{\theta}$ with the position and momentum operators. It follows that if $\mathbf{q}$ is a position operator

$$\boldsymbol{\theta}\mathbf{q} = \mathbf{q}\boldsymbol{\theta} \tag{12–8}$$

and if $\mathbf{p}$ is a momentum operator

$$\boldsymbol{\theta}\mathbf{p} = -\mathbf{p}\boldsymbol{\theta} \tag{12–9}$$

therefore

$$\boldsymbol{\theta}\mathbf{q} = \mathbf{UKq} = \mathbf{UqK} = \mathbf{q}\boldsymbol{\theta} = \mathbf{qUK}$$

or

$$\mathbf{Uq} = \mathbf{qU}$$

and, since $\mathbf{p} = -i\hbar\partial/\partial\mathbf{q}$

$$\boldsymbol{\theta}\mathbf{p} = \mathbf{UKp} = -\mathbf{UpK} = -\mathbf{p}\boldsymbol{\theta} = -\mathbf{pUK}$$

or

$$\mathbf{Up} = \mathbf{pU}$$

Hence $\mathbf{U}$ commutes with both position and momentum operators, and must, therefore, depend only on the spin operators. If $\mathbf{s}$ is a spin operator then since $\mathbf{s}$ is similar to an angular momentum operator

$$\boldsymbol{\theta}\mathbf{s} = -\mathbf{s}\boldsymbol{\theta} \tag{12–10}$$

The spin operators may be taken to be the Pauli spin matrices.[7]

$$\mathbf{s}_z = \begin{pmatrix} -1 & 0 \\ 0 & 1 \end{pmatrix}; \qquad \mathbf{s}_y = \begin{pmatrix} 0 & +i \\ -i & 0 \end{pmatrix}; \qquad \mathbf{s}_x = \begin{pmatrix} 0 & 1 \\ 1 & 0 \end{pmatrix} \tag{12–11}$$

From Eq. (12–10) and Eq. (12–11) we see that $\mathbf{U}$ anticommutes with $\mathbf{s}_z$ and $\mathbf{s}_x$, but commutes with $\mathbf{s}_y$. Thus $\mathbf{U}$ may be taken as some multiple of $\mathbf{s}_y$.

A convenient choice is $\mathbf{U} = -i \cdot \mathbf{s}_y$. This is clearly unitary since

$$\mathbf{UU}^\dagger = -i\mathbf{s}_y \cdot (i\mathbf{s}_y^\dagger) = \mathbf{s}_y\mathbf{s}_y^\dagger = \mathbf{E}$$

where $\mathbf{E}$ is the identity operator. The time reversal operator can be written as

$$\boldsymbol{\theta} = (-i)^n \mathbf{s}_{1y}\mathbf{s}_{2y} \cdots \mathbf{s}_{ny}\mathbf{K} \tag{12–12}$$

for a system of n electrons. Since the spin functions are real; we have

$$\begin{aligned} \boldsymbol{\theta}\varphi(\tfrac{1}{2}, -\tfrac{1}{2}) &= \varphi(\tfrac{1}{2}, \tfrac{1}{2}) \\ \boldsymbol{\theta}\varphi(\tfrac{1}{2}, \tfrac{1}{2}) &= -\varphi(\tfrac{1}{2}, -\tfrac{1}{2}) \end{aligned} \tag{12–13}$$

[7] E. P. Wigner, *Group Theory and its Application to the Quantum Mechanics of Atomic Spectra*, p. 232, Academic Press, Inc., New York, 1959.

Equation (12–13) may be generalized to include any eigenfunction of angular momentum $\varphi(j,m)$.[8]

$$\boldsymbol{\theta}\varphi(j,m) = (-1)^{j+m}\varphi(j,-m) \qquad (12\text{–}14)$$

Also

$$\boldsymbol{\theta}^2 = (-1)^n\mathbf{E} = \omega\mathbf{E} = \begin{cases} +\mathbf{E} \text{ for an even number of electrons} \\ -\mathbf{E} \text{ for an odd number of electrons} \end{cases} \qquad (12\text{–}15)$$

We see that the square of the quantum mechanical time reversal operator does not yield the identity for a system consisting of an odd number of electrons, although when one performs the physical transformation of a reversal of time on a system twice, the system returns to its initial state. This is again related to the fact that the state functions are determined only to within a phase factor of unit modulus. However, in this case we do not obtain an ambiguity but the result that the square of the time reversal operator is equal to the identity for a system containing an even number of electrons, whereas it is the negative of this for a system containing an odd number of electrons. Since the anti-unitary operators are constructed from products of unitary operators $\mathbf{v}$ and the time reversal operator $\boldsymbol{\theta}$, $\mathbf{a} = \mathbf{v}\boldsymbol{\theta}$, there are both barred and unbarred $\mathbf{a}$'s corresponding to barred and unbarred $\mathbf{v}$'s and the product of two anti-unitary operators may differ by a sign from the corresponding product of unitary operators depending on the number of electrons in the system. We shall make use of this latter fact later. The fact that there are both barred and unbarred $\mathbf{a}$'s as well as $\mathbf{u}$'s is not troublesome since we can consider an operator and its barred counterpart as independent operators and hence, consider the number of operators in a group to be simply doubled as discussed above.

Multiplication of Co-Representation Matrices.—We have referred above to the representations of nonunitary groups as co-representations. This distinction is made because the co-representation matrices for the group operators do not multiply in the same way as do the operators themselves.[5] As will be seen below, this is a direct result of the fact that some of the operators in the group are antilinear. Consider that ϕ_{α}^{i} is the αth basis function of the ith irreducible co-representation of G. The co-representation matrices $\mathbf{D}^i(\mathbf{u})$ and $\mathbf{D}^i(\mathbf{a})$ may be defined such that

$$\mathbf{u}\psi_{\alpha}^{i} = \sum_{\beta=1}^{k} \mathbf{D}^i(\mathbf{u})_{\beta\alpha}\psi_{\beta}^{i} \qquad (12\text{–}16\text{a})$$

[8] See for example: A. R. Edmonds, *Angular Momentum in Quantum Mechanics*, p. 30, Princeton University Press, Princeton, New Jersey, 1957.

and

$$\mathbf{a}\psi^i_\alpha = \sum_{\beta=1}^{k} \mathbf{D}^i(\mathbf{a})_{\beta\alpha}\psi^i_\beta \tag{12–16b}$$

Then we have from Eqs. (12–3), (12–4), (12–16a), and (12–16b)

$$\mathbf{u}_1\mathbf{u}_2\psi^i_\alpha = \sum_{\beta=1}^{k}\sum_{\gamma=1}^{k} \mathbf{D}^i(\mathbf{u}_1)_{\gamma\beta}\mathbf{D}^i(\mathbf{u}_2)_{\beta\alpha}\psi^i_\gamma$$

$$\mathbf{u}\mathbf{a}\psi^i_\alpha = \sum_{\beta=1}^{k}\sum_{\gamma=1}^{k} \mathbf{D}^i(\mathbf{u})_{\gamma\beta}\mathbf{D}^i(\mathbf{a})_{\beta\alpha}\psi^i_\gamma$$

$$\mathbf{a}\mathbf{u}\psi^i_\alpha = \sum_{\beta=1}^{k}\sum_{\gamma=1}^{k} \mathbf{D}^i(\mathbf{a})_{\gamma\beta}\mathbf{D}^i(\mathbf{u})^*_{\beta\alpha}\psi^i_\gamma$$

and

$$\mathbf{a}_1\mathbf{a}_2\psi^i_\alpha = \sum_{\beta=1}^{k}\sum_{\gamma=1}^{k} \mathbf{D}^i(\mathbf{a}_1)_{\gamma\beta}\mathbf{D}^i(\mathbf{a}_2)^*_{\beta\alpha}\psi^i_\gamma$$

where k is the dimension of the co-representation matrices $\mathbf{D}^i$. These matrices, therefore, multiply as follows

$$\begin{aligned}\mathbf{D}^i(\mathbf{u}_1)\mathbf{D}^i(\mathbf{u}_2) &= \mathbf{D}^i(\mathbf{u}_1\mathbf{u}_2)\\ \mathbf{D}^i(\mathbf{u})\mathbf{D}^i(\mathbf{a}) &= \mathbf{D}^i(\mathbf{u}\mathbf{a})\\ \mathbf{D}^i(\mathbf{a})\mathbf{D}^i(\mathbf{u})^* &= \mathbf{D}^i(\mathbf{a}\mathbf{u})\\ \mathbf{D}^i(\mathbf{a}_1)\mathbf{D}^i(\mathbf{a}_2)^* &= \mathbf{D}^i(\mathbf{a}_1\mathbf{a}_2)\end{aligned} \tag{12–17a}$$

and are called co-representation matrices of the nonunitary group because of the complex conjugate signs in these relations.

Next it is important to see how the **D** matrices transform under a transformation of basis functions. Consider a new set of bases functions $\phi^{(i)}_\alpha$ related to the $\psi^{(i)}_\alpha$ by some transformation matrix **V** such that

$$\phi^{(i)}_\alpha = \mathbf{V}_{\beta\alpha}\psi^{(i)}_\beta$$

Then one can easily show by proceeding as above that the co-matrices **B** taken with respect to the $\phi^{(i)}_\alpha$ are related to the **D** matrices by the transformation

$$\begin{aligned}\mathbf{B}^{(i)}(\mathbf{u}) &= \mathbf{V}^{-1}\mathbf{D}^{(i)}(\mathbf{u})\mathbf{V}\\ \mathbf{B}^{(i)}(\mathbf{a}) &= \mathbf{V}^{-1}\mathbf{D}^{(i)}(\mathbf{a})\mathbf{V}^*\end{aligned} \tag{12–17b}$$

This is, therefore, the form taken by a similarity transformation of co-representation matrices of nonunitary groups, and the two sets of matrices **D** and **B** are considered to be equivalent. It is interesting to note that if one lets $\mathbf{V} = \omega\mathbf{E}$ be a multiple of the unit matrix $\mathbf{B}^{(i)}(\mathbf{u}) =$

$\mathbf{D}^{(i)}(\mathbf{u})$ but $\mathbf{B}^{(i)}(\mathbf{a}) = \omega^{*2}\mathbf{D}^{(i)}(\mathbf{a})$ such that a common arbitrary phase factor remains in the co-representation matrices $\mathbf{D}^{(i)}(\mathbf{a})$ for the anti-unitary elements of nonunitary groups.

Irreducible Co-Representations of Nonunitary Groups.—To determine the co-representation matrices $\mathbf{D}^i$, let us select a set of l functions, which forms a basis for an irreducible representation $\mathbf{\Delta}^i(\mathbf{u})$ of the unitary subgroup H. That is

$$\mathbf{u}\psi^i_\alpha = \sum_{\beta=1}^{l} \mathbf{\Delta}^i(\mathbf{u})_{\beta\alpha}\psi^i_\beta$$

for all $\mathbf{u}$ in H. The dimension of $\mathbf{\Delta}^i(\mathbf{u})$ is l. The nonunitary group G is formed by supplementing H with the coset of operators $\mathbf{ua}_0$. Wigner [5] has shown that the operation of $\mathbf{a}_0$ on the set of functions ψ^i_α yields a set of functions that is related to the initial set in one of three ways. Similarly, the co-representation of G corresponding to $\mathbf{\Delta}^i(\mathbf{u})$ of H is constructed in one of three ways depending on which of the following three cases is realized.

Case (*a*): $\mathbf{a}_0\phi^i_\alpha$ reproduces the set of functions ϕ^i_α. The irreducible co-representation $\mathbf{D}^i$ of G corresponds to a single irreducible representation $\mathbf{\Delta}^i(\mathbf{u})$ of H, and has the same dimension. In this case no new degeneracy is introduced by the coset $\mathbf{ua}_0$.

Case (*b*): $\mathbf{a}_0\phi^i_\alpha$ produces a set of functions ψ^i_α, which is independent of the set ϕ^i_α, but which also forms a basis for $\mathbf{\Delta}^i(\mathbf{u})$ of H. The irreducible co-representation $\mathbf{D}^i$ of G corresponds again to a single irreducible representation of H, but has twice its dimension. In this case the dimension of $\mathbf{\Delta}^i(\mathbf{u})$ is doubled.

Case (*c*): $\mathbf{a}_0\phi^i_\alpha$ produces a set of functions ϕ^j_α, which is independent of the set ϕ^i_α, which forms a basis for the irreducible representation $\mathbf{\Delta}^j(\mathbf{u})$ of H, which is inequivalent to $\mathbf{\Delta}^i(\mathbf{u})$, but which has the same dimension. $\mathbf{D}^i$ corresponds to two inequivalent irreducible representations of H, $\mathbf{\Delta}^i(\mathbf{u})$, and $\mathbf{\Delta}^j(\mathbf{u})$, such that in this case the anti-unitary operators cause $\mathbf{\Delta}^i(\mathbf{u})$ and $\mathbf{\Delta}^j(\mathbf{u})$ to become degenerate.

In order to obtain explicit forms for the co-representation matrices $\mathbf{D}^i$ of the nonunitary group G, in terms of the representation matrices $\mathbf{\Delta}^i(\mathbf{u})$ of the unitary subgroup H, it is necessary to know how the set of functions $\mathbf{a}_0\phi^i_\alpha$ transforms under the operations of H. Let $\mathbf{a}_0\phi^i_\alpha \equiv \psi^i_\alpha$, then

$$\mathbf{u}\psi^i_\alpha = \mathbf{u}\sum_\beta \mathbf{D}^i(\mathbf{a}_0)_{\beta\alpha}\phi^i_\beta = \sum_\gamma [\mathbf{D}^i(\mathbf{u})\mathbf{D}^i(\mathbf{a}_0)]_{\gamma\alpha}\phi^i_\gamma$$

however

$$\mathbf{D}^i(\mathbf{u})\mathbf{D}^i(\mathbf{a}_0) = \mathbf{D}^i(\mathbf{ua}_0) = \mathbf{D}^i(\mathbf{a}_0)\mathbf{D}^i(\mathbf{a}_0^{-1}\mathbf{ua}_0)^*$$

so that

$$\mathbf{u}\psi_\alpha^i = \sum_{\gamma\beta} \mathbf{D}^i(\mathbf{a}_0)_{\gamma\beta}\mathbf{D}^i(\mathbf{a}_0^{-1}\mathbf{ua}_0)^*_{\beta\alpha}\phi_\gamma^i$$

$$= \sum_\beta \mathbf{D}^i(\mathbf{a}_0^{-1}\mathbf{ua}_0)^*_{\beta\alpha}\psi_\beta^i$$

which implies [5] that

$$\mathbf{u}\psi_\alpha^i = \sum_\beta \mathbf{\Delta}^i(\mathbf{a}_0^{-1}\mathbf{ua}_0)^*_{\beta\alpha}\psi_\beta^i \tag{12–18}$$

The explicit forms for the co-representation matrices obtained by Wigner are as follows:

Case (*a*): The representations $\mathbf{\Delta}^i(\mathbf{u})$ and $\mathbf{\Delta}^i(\mathbf{a}_0^{-1}\mathbf{ua}_0)^*$ are equivalent, in which case we can write

$$\mathbf{\Delta}^i(\mathbf{a}_0^{-1}\mathbf{ua}_0)^* = \beta^{-1}\mathbf{\Delta}^i(\mathbf{u})\beta \tag{12–19}$$

which defines β. Two cases are now possible.

In case (a)

$$\beta\beta^* = \mathbf{\Delta}^i(\mathbf{a}_0^2) \tag{12–20}$$

and

$$\mathbf{D}^i(\mathbf{u}) = \mathbf{\Delta}^i(\mathbf{u}); \quad \mathbf{D}^i(\mathbf{a}) = \mathbf{\Delta}^i(\mathbf{aa}_0^{-1})\beta \tag{12–21}$$

Case (*b*): Again the representations $\mathbf{\Delta}^i(\mathbf{u})$ and $\mathbf{\Delta}^i(\mathbf{a}_0^{-1}\mathbf{ua}_0)^*$ are equivalent, but in this case

$$\beta\beta^* = -\mathbf{\Delta}^i(\mathbf{a}_0^2) \tag{12–22}$$

and

$$\mathbf{D}^i(\mathbf{u}) = \begin{pmatrix} \mathbf{\Delta}^i(\mathbf{u}) & 0 \\ 0 & \mathbf{\Delta}^i(\mathbf{u}) \end{pmatrix}; \quad \mathbf{D}^i(\mathbf{a}) = \begin{pmatrix} 0 & \mathbf{\Delta}^i(\mathbf{aa}_0^{-1})\beta \\ -\mathbf{\Delta}^i(\mathbf{aa}_0^{-1})\beta & 0 \end{pmatrix} \tag{12–23}$$

Case (*c*): The representations $\mathbf{\Delta}^i(\mathbf{u})$ and $\mathbf{\Delta}^i(\mathbf{a}_0^{-1}\mathbf{ua}_0)^*$ are not equivalent. In this case

$$\mathbf{D}^i(\mathbf{u}) = \begin{pmatrix} \mathbf{\Delta}^i(\mathbf{u}) & 0 \\ 0 & \mathbf{\Delta}^i(\mathbf{a}_0^{-1}\mathbf{ua}_0)^* \end{pmatrix}$$

and

$$\mathbf{D}^i(\mathbf{a}) = \begin{pmatrix} 0 & \mathbf{\Delta}^i(\mathbf{a}\mathbf{a}_0) \\ \mathbf{\Delta}^i(\mathbf{a}_0^{-1}\mathbf{a})^* & 0 \end{pmatrix} \tag{12–24}$$

We will not be concerned further with the explicit forms of the co-representation matrices. Instead we need ask only to which of the three cases a specific representation $\mathbf{\Delta}^i(\mathbf{u})$ of the group H belongs when H is considered as a subgroup of G. The co-representation matrices can be written down immediately once this is known. The irreducible representations of H can be obtained by standard means since H is unitary. It, therefore, remains to obtain a method by which one can decide between the three cases given the group G and an irreducible representation of H.[9] In order to do this we need the fact that the matrices β and $\mathbf{\Delta}^i(\mathbf{u})$ may be assumed to be unitary,[5] and that the $\mathbf{\Delta}^i(\mathbf{u})$ matrices satisfy the usual orthogonality relation

$$\sum_k \mathbf{\Delta}^i(\mathbf{u}_k)_{rl}\mathbf{\Delta}^j(\mathbf{u}_k)^*_{sm} = \frac{n}{l_i}\,\delta_{ij}\delta_{rs}\delta_{lm} \tag{12–25}$$

where the sum is over all the n elements in H and l_i is the dimension of the irreducible representation $\mathbf{\Delta}^i(\mathbf{u})$. Let us write, adopting the usual convention of an understood summation over repeated indices

$$\begin{aligned}\sum_k \mathbf{\Delta}^i(\mathbf{a}_k^2)_{rr} &= \sum_k \mathbf{\Delta}^i(\mathbf{u}_k\mathbf{a}_0\mathbf{u}_k\mathbf{a}_0)_{rr} \\ &= \sum_k \mathbf{\Delta}^i(\mathbf{u}_k)_{rl}\mathbf{\Delta}^i(\mathbf{a}_0^2)_{lt}\mathbf{\Delta}^i(\mathbf{a}_0^{-1}\mathbf{u}_k\mathbf{a}_0)_{tr}\end{aligned}$$

In cases (a) and (b) this yields using Eqs. (12–19), (12–20), and (12–22)

$$\begin{aligned}\sum_k \mathbf{\Delta}^i(\mathbf{a}_k^2)_{rr} &= \sum_k \mathbf{\Delta}^i(\mathbf{u}_k)_{rl}\mathbf{\Delta}^i(\mathbf{a}_0^2)_{lt}\beta_{ts}^{-1*}\mathbf{\Delta}^i(\mathbf{u}_k)^*_{sm}\beta^*_{mr} \\ &= \frac{n}{l_i}\,\delta_{rs}\delta_{lm}\mathbf{\Delta}^i(\mathbf{a}_0^2)_{lt}\beta_{st}\beta^*_{mr} \\ &= \frac{n}{l_i}\,\mathbf{\Delta}^i(\mathbf{a}_0^2)_{lt}\beta_{rt}\beta^*_{lr} \\ &= \pm\frac{n}{l_i}\,\mathbf{\Delta}^i(\mathbf{a}_0^2)_{lt}\mathbf{\Delta}^i(\mathbf{a}_0^2)^*_{lt}\end{aligned}$$

[9] J. O. Dimmock and R. G. Wheeler, *J. Phys. Chem. Solids*, **23**, 729 (1962). In this paper we obtained a result (Eq. 20 therein) that is different from the result obtained here (Eq. 12–27). Both are correct, although the latter is more convenient.

$$= \pm \frac{n}{l_i} \mathbf{\Delta}^i(\mathbf{a}_0^2)_{lt}\mathbf{\Delta}^i(\mathbf{a}_0^{-1})_{tl}$$

$$= \pm \frac{n}{l_i} \mathbf{\Delta}^i(\mathbf{E})_{ll}$$

$$= \pm n$$

where the plus sign holds in case (a) and the minus holds in case (b). In case (c), $\mathbf{\Delta}^i(\mathbf{a}_0^{-1}\mathbf{u}\mathbf{a}_0)^*$ is inequivalent to $\mathbf{\Delta}^i(\mathbf{u})$ such that from Eq. (12–25),

$$\sum_k \mathbf{\Delta}^i(\mathbf{a}_k^2)_{rr} = \sum_k \mathbf{\Delta}^i(\mathbf{u}_k)_{rl}\mathbf{\Delta}^i(\mathbf{a}_0^2)_{lt}\mathbf{\Delta}^i(\mathbf{a}_0^{-1}\mathbf{u}_k\mathbf{a}_0)_{tr}$$

$$= \sum_k \mathbf{\Delta}^i(\mathbf{u}_k)_{rl}\mathbf{\Delta}^i(\mathbf{a}_0^2)_{lt}\mathbf{\Delta}^j(\mathbf{u}_k)^*_{tr}$$

$$= 0$$

Collecting these results we find that

$$\begin{aligned} \sum_k \chi^i(\mathbf{a}_k^2) &= +n \quad \text{case (a)} \\ &= -n \quad \text{case (b)} \\ &= 0 \quad \text{case (c)} \end{aligned} \qquad (12\text{–}26)$$

where $\chi^i(\mathbf{a}_k^2) = \mathbf{\Delta}^i_{rr}(\mathbf{a}_k^2)$ is the character of the representation matrix for the operator $\mathbf{a}_k^2$. Recall from the properties of nonunitary groups that $\mathbf{a}_k^2$ is a member of the unitary subgroup. We have written above $\mathbf{a}_k = \mathbf{u}_k\mathbf{a}_0$, and it is still more convenient to write $\mathbf{a}_0 = \mathbf{v}_0\boldsymbol{\theta}$ such that using Eq. (12–15), and the fact that $\boldsymbol{\theta}$ commutes with spatial operators, Eq. (12–26) becomes

$$\begin{aligned} \sum_k \chi^i(\mathbf{v}_0\mathbf{u}_k\mathbf{v}_0\mathbf{u}_k) &= +\omega n \quad \text{case (a)} \\ &= -\omega n \quad \text{case (b)} \\ &= 0 \quad \text{case (c)} \end{aligned} \qquad (12\text{–}27)$$

If the group G contains the time reversal operator itself, we can choose $\mathbf{v}_0 = E$, the identity operator, and Eq. (12–27) reduces to

$$\begin{aligned} \sum_k \chi^i(\mathbf{u}_k^2) &= +\omega n \quad \text{case (a)} \\ &= -\omega n \quad \text{case (b)} \\ &= 0 \quad \text{case (c)} \end{aligned} \qquad (12\text{–}28)$$

which was originally found by Frobenius and Schur.[10]

[10] G. Frobenius and J. Schur, *Sitzber. preuss. Akad. Wiss., Physik.-math. Kl.*, **49**, 186 (1906).

Application to Point Groups.—Equations (12–27) and (12–28) may be used directly to obtain the co-representations of nonunitary point groups.[9] It is convenient to consider the 122 point groups in three categories.

(1) The thirty-two point groups without any form of the time reversal operator form a category of magnetic point groups. The representations of these are obtained by standard means and are presented in Section 12.6.

(2) The thirty-two point groups, including the time reversal operator itself, are the groups that apply where the time-averaged magnetic moment is zero; hence, they are associated with paramagnetic and diamagnetic crystals. To find the representations of these we can use Eq. (12–28). The results may be summarized as follows.

Case (*a*). This case includes all real single-group representations, with real character and dimension greater than 1.

Case (*b*). This case includes no single-group representations, and all real one-dimensional, double-group representations. This includes only the following.

Γ_2 of the group C_1
Γ_2^+ and Γ_2^- of the group C_i
Γ_6 of the group C_3
Γ_6^+ and Γ_6^- of the group C_{3i}

Case (*c*). This case includes all single- and double-group representations with complex character.

(3) The remaining fifty-eight magnetic point groups include the time reversal operator only in combination with rotation and rotation-reflection operators. The representations of these groups may be obtained from Eq. (12–27).

We shall not consider the first two categories further. The fifty-eight magnetic point groups are given in Table 12–1 with the Shubnikov, international, and Shoenflies notation.[11] If G' is the full group of unitary and anti-unitary operators, and H is the invariant subgroup of unitary operators, then the Schoenflies notation is $G'(H)$. The fifty-eight magnetic point groups can be found by choosing all possible distinct combinations of G' and H, where G' and H are each one of the thirty-two point groups, H is an invariant subgroup of G', and G'

[11] V. L. Indenbom, *Soviet Phys.—Cryst.*, **5**, 493 (1960); B. A. Tavger and V. M. Zaitsev, *Soviet Phys.—JETP*, **3**, 430 (1956); M. Hammermesh, *Group Theory*, pp. 63–7, Addison-Wesley Publishing Company, Reading, Mass., 1962.

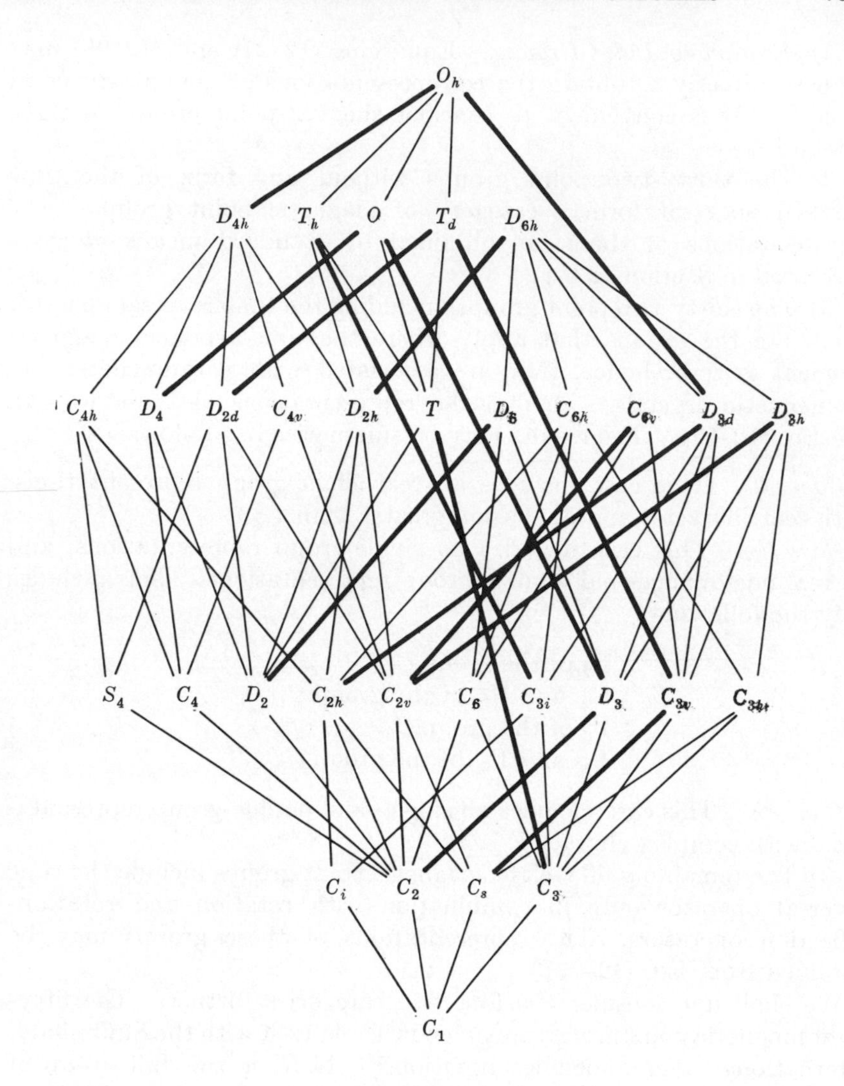

FIG. 12–1. Subgroup Decomposition of the Thirty-Two Point Groups. A heavy line indicates that the subgroup is not invariant.

contains exactly twice as many elements as does H. This can be done by inspection from Fig. 12–1.[12]

It remains to determine to which case each of the representations of H belongs when considered in all fifty-eight possible combinations.

[12] *International Tables for X-Ray Crystallography, Vol. I Symmetry Groups*, pp. 36–7, Henry and Lonsdale, eds., Kynoch Press, Birmingham, England, 1952.

TABLE 12–1. *Magnetic Point Groups (Notation)*

International	Shubnikov	Schoenflies	International	Shubnikov	Schoenflies
$\underline{\bar{1}}$	$\underline{\bar{2}}$	$C_i(C_1)$	$3\underline{2}$	$3:\underline{2}$	$D_3(C_3)$
$\underline{2}$	$\underline{2}$	$C_2(C_1)$	$3\underline{m}$	$3\cdot\underline{m}$	$C_{3v}(C_3)$
$\underline{m}$	$\underline{m}$	$C_s(C_1)$	$\underline{\bar{6}}$	$3:\underline{m}$	$C_{3h}(C_3)$
$\underline{2}/\underline{m}$	$\underline{2}:\underline{m}$	$C_{2h}(C_i)$	$\underline{\bar{3}}$	$\underline{\bar{6}}$	$C_{3i}(C_3)$
$2/\underline{m}$	$2:\underline{m}$	$C_{2h}(C_2)$	$\bar{3}\underline{m}$	$\bar{6}\cdot\underline{m}$	$D_{3d}(C_{3i})$
$\underline{2}/m$	$\underline{2}:m$	$C_{2h}(C_s)$	$\underline{\bar{3}m}$	$\underline{\bar{6}}\cdot\underline{m}$	$D_{3d}(D_3)$
$2\underline{mm}$	$2\cdot\underline{m}$	$C_{2v}(C_2)$	$\underline{\bar{3}}m$	$\underline{\bar{6}}\cdot m$	$D_{3d}(C_{3v})$
$\underline{2m}m$	$\underline{2}\cdot m$	$C_{2v}(C_s)$	$\bar{6}\underline{m2}$	$\underline{m}\cdot 3:m$	$D_{3h}(C_{3h})$
$22\underline{2}$	$2:\underline{2}$	$D_2(C_2)$	$\underline{\bar{6}m}2$	$\underline{m}\cdot 3:\underline{m}$	$D_{3h}(D_3)$
$\underline{mm}m$	$\underline{m}\cdot 2:m$	$D_{2h}(C_{2h})$	$\underline{\bar{6}}m\underline{2}$	$m\cdot 3:\underline{m}$	$D_{3h}(C_{3v})$
$\underline{mmm}$	$\underline{m}\cdot 2:\underline{m}$	$D_{2h}(D_2)$	$\underline{6}$	$\underline{6}$	$C_6(C_3)$
$mm\underline{m}$	$m\cdot 2:\underline{m}$	$D_{2h}(C_{2v})$	$6\underline{2}$	$6:\underline{2}$	$D_6(C_6)$
$\underline{\bar{4}}$	$\underline{4}$	$C_4(C_2)$	$\underline{6}2$	$\underline{6}:2$	$D_6(D_3)$
$\underline{\bar{4}}$	$\underline{\bar{4}}$	$S_4(C_2)$	$6\underline{mm}$	$6\cdot\underline{m}$	$C_{6v}(C_6)$
$\underline{4}/m$	$\underline{4}:m$	$C_{4h}(C_{2h})$	$\underline{6}m\underline{m}$	$\underline{6}\cdot m$	$C_{6v}(C_{3v})$
$4/\underline{m}$	$4:\underline{m}$	$C_{4h}(C_4)$	$\underline{6}/\underline{m}$	$\underline{6}:\underline{m}$	$C_{6h}(C_{3i})$
$\underline{4}/\underline{m}$	$\underline{4}:\underline{m}$	$C_{4h}(S_4)$	$6/\underline{m}$	$6:\underline{m}$	$C_{6h}(C_6)$
$4\underline{2}$	$4:\underline{2}$	$D_4(C_4)$	$\underline{6}/m$	$\underline{6}:m$	$C_{6h}(C_{3h})$
$\underline{4}2$	$\underline{4}:2$	$D_4(D_2)$	$6/m\underline{mm}$	$\underline{m}\cdot 6:m$	$D_{6h}(C_{6h})$
$4\underline{mm}$	$4\cdot\underline{m}$	$C_{4v}(C_4)$	$\underline{6}/\underline{mm}m$	$m\cdot\underline{6}:\underline{m}$	$D_{6h}(D_{3d})$
$\underline{4}m\underline{m}$	$\underline{4}\cdot m$	$C_{4v}(C_{2v})$	$6/\underline{mmm}$	$\underline{m}\cdot 6:\underline{m}$	$D_{6h}(D_6)$
$\bar{4}\underline{2m}$	$\bar{4}\cdot\underline{m}$	$D_{2d}(S_4)$	$6/\underline{m}mm$	$m\cdot 6:\underline{m}$	$D_{6h}(C_{6v})$
$\underline{\bar{4}}2\underline{m}$	$\underline{\bar{4}}\cdot\underline{m}$	$D_{2d}(D_2)$	$\underline{6}/m\underline{m}m$	$m\cdot\underline{6}:m$	$D_{6h}(D_{3h})$
$\underline{\bar{4}2}m$	$\underline{\bar{4}}\cdot m$	$D_{2d}(C_{2v})$	$\underline{m}3$	$\underline{\bar{6}}/2$	$T_h(T)$
$4/m\underline{mm}$	$\underline{m}\cdot 4:m$	$D_{4h}(C_{4h})$	$\underline{\bar{4}}3\underline{m}$	$3/\underline{\bar{4}}$	$T_d(T)$
$\underline{4}/mmm$	$m\cdot\underline{4}:m$	$D_{4h}(D_{2h})$	$\underline{4}3$	$3/\underline{4}$	$0(T)$
$4/\underline{mmm}$	$\underline{m}\cdot 4:\underline{m}$	$D_{4h}(D_4)$	$m3\underline{m}$	$\bar{6}/\underline{4}$	$0_h(T_h)$
$4/\underline{m}mm$	$m\cdot 4:\underline{m}$	$D_{4h}(C_{4v})$	$\underline{m}3\underline{m}$	$\underline{\bar{6}}/4$	$0_h(0)$
$\underline{4}/\underline{mm}m$	$m\cdot\underline{4}:\underline{m}$	$D_{4h}(D_{2d})$	$\underline{m}3m$	$\underline{\bar{6}}/\underline{4}$	$0_h(T_d)$

If it is possible to choose $\mathbf{v}_0 = \mathbf{I}$, the inversion operator, then Eq. (12–27) reduces to Eq. (12–28), and the properties of the representations of H in the group $G'(H)$ are the same as the straight time reversal

TABLE 12–2. *Properties of some Magnetic Groups*

222	Γ_1	Γ_2	Γ_3	Γ_4	Γ_5
$\underline{4}2$	a	a	c	c	a
$\underline{4}\,\underline{2m}$	a	a	c	c	a

$2mm$	Γ_1	Γ_2	Γ_3	Γ_4	Γ_5
$\underline{4}mm$	a	a	c	c	a
$\underline{\bar{4}2}m$	a	a	c	c	a

2	Γ_1	Γ_2	Γ_3	Γ_4
$\bar{4}$	a	b	c	c
$\underline{\bar{4}}$	a	b	c	c

3	Γ_1	Γ_2	Γ_3	Γ_4	Γ_5	Γ_6
$\underline{6}$	a	c	c	c	c	a
$\underline{\bar{6}}$	a	c	c	c	c	a

$2/m$	Γ_1^+	Γ_2^+	Γ_1^-	Γ_2^-	Γ_3^+	Γ_4^+	Γ_3^-	Γ_4^-
$\underline{4}/m$	a	b	a	b	c	c	c	c

mmm	Γ_1^+	Γ_2^+	Γ_3^+	Γ_4^+	Γ_1^-	Γ_2^-	Γ_3^-	Γ_4^-	Γ_5^+	Γ_5^-
$\underline{4}/mmm$	a	a	c	c	a	a	c	c	a	a

$\bar{3}$	Γ_1^+	Γ_2^+	Γ_3^+	Γ_1^-	Γ_2^-	Γ_3^-	Γ_4^+	Γ_5^+	Γ_6^+	Γ_4^-	Γ_5^-	Γ_6^-
$\underline{6}/\underline{m}$	a	c	c	a	c	c	c	c	a	c	c	a

properties of H of category (2) above. Twenty-one of the fifty-eight magnetic groups have this property. They are:

$\underline{\bar{1}}$, $2/\underline{m}$, $\underline{2}/m$, $\underline{mmm}$, $mm\underline{m}$, $4/\underline{m}$, $\underline{4}/\underline{m}$, $4/\underline{mmm}$, $4/\underline{m}mm$, $\underline{4}/\underline{mm}m$, $\underline{\bar{3}}$, $\underline{\bar{3}m}$,

$\underline{\bar{3}}m$, $6/\underline{m}$, $\underline{6}/m$, $6/\underline{mmm}$, $6/\underline{m}mm$, $\underline{6}/m\underline{m}m$, $\underline{m}3$, $\underline{m}3\underline{m}$, $\underline{m}3m$.

If the group H is abelian, and the point group corresponding to the group G' can be reduced to H by the application of an external magnetic field then, in the group $G'(H)$, all the representations of H belong to case (a). Eighteen magnetic groups have this property. They are:

$$\underline{2},\ \underline{m},\ \underline{2}/\underline{m},\ 2\underline{mm},\ \underline{2m}m,\ 2\underline{22},\ \underline{mm}m,\ \underline{4}2,\ 4\underline{mm},\ \bar{4}\underline{2m},\ 4/m\underline{mm},\ 3\underline{2},\ 3\underline{m},$$
$$\bar{3}\underline{m},\ \bar{6}\underline{m2},\ 6\underline{2},\ 6\underline{mm},\ 6/\underline{mmm}.$$

Of the remaining magnetic groups the representations of H in the following all belong to case (a):

$$\underline{\bar{6}m}2,\ \underline{\bar{6}}m\underline{2},\ \underline{6}2,\ \underline{6}m\underline{m},\ \underline{6}/\underline{mm}m,\ \underline{\bar{4}}3\underline{m},\ \underline{4}3,\ m3m.$$

and the results for the rest are given in Table 12–2.

Illustration of the Method.—It appears advantageous to consider a specific example in detail in order to illustrate the method outlined above. Consider a magnetic crystal that has the point symmetry C_{6v}. A possible magnetic point symmetry for this crystal would be $C_{6v}(C_{3v})$. We ask how the energy levels of the point symmetry C_{6v} are perturbed by the presence of the magnetic sublattice. The first step of the solution is the formation of the compatibility table between the groups C_{6v} and C_{3v} (Table 12–3). Next, we determine to what case the irreducible representations of the group C_{3v} belong when considered in the magnetic group $C_{6v}(C_{3v})$. The operator $\mathbf{v}_0$ can be chosen to be the operator $\boldsymbol{\sigma}_d$ of the group C_{6v}. We find the operators

$$\mathbf{v}_0\mathbf{u}\mathbf{v}_0 \cdot \mathbf{u}$$

for all operators $\mathbf{u}$ in the group C_{3v}.

$$\begin{aligned}
\boldsymbol{\sigma}_d\mathbf{E}\boldsymbol{\sigma}_d \cdot \mathbf{E} &= \overline{\mathbf{E}} \\
\boldsymbol{\sigma}_d\mathbf{C}_3\boldsymbol{\sigma}_d \cdot \mathbf{C}_3 &= \overline{\mathbf{E}} \\
\boldsymbol{\sigma}_d\mathbf{C}_3^{-1}\boldsymbol{\sigma}_d \cdot \mathbf{C}_3^{-1} &= \overline{\mathbf{E}} \\
\boldsymbol{\sigma}_d\boldsymbol{\sigma}_v\boldsymbol{\sigma}_d \cdot \boldsymbol{\sigma}_v &= \overline{\mathbf{E}} \\
\boldsymbol{\sigma}_d\boldsymbol{\sigma}_v'\boldsymbol{\sigma}_d \cdot \boldsymbol{\sigma}_v' &= \overline{\boldsymbol{\sigma}}_v'' \cdot \boldsymbol{\sigma}_v' = \mathbf{C}_3 \\
\boldsymbol{\sigma}_d\boldsymbol{\sigma}_v''\boldsymbol{\sigma}_d \cdot \boldsymbol{\sigma}_v'' &= \overline{\boldsymbol{\sigma}}_v' \cdot \boldsymbol{\sigma}_v'' = \mathbf{C}_3^{-1}
\end{aligned}$$

and similarly for the barred operators of C_{3v}.

From the character table of the group C_{3v}, and the operator multiplication relations given above, one finds that all of the representations of the group C_{3v} belong to case (a) when considered in the magnetic group $C_{6v}(C_{3v})$. Note that when the operation of time reversal is allowed, the representations Γ_5 and Γ_6 of the group C_{3v} are degenerate, whereas they are not in the present example.

Finally, from the compatibility table, we observe that as a result of the presence of the magnetic sublattice of the configuration $C_{6v}(C_{3v})$, the representation Γ_9 of the group C_{6v} is split. Thus, if one could observe a state of Γ_9 symmetry in such a crystal (say an antiferromagnetic), one would find that above the Néel point it was doubly degenerate but that the degeneracy would be lifted below the Néel point, presumably by the interaction with the magnetic sublattice.

TABLE 12–3. *Compatibility Between the Groups C_{6v} and C_{3v}*

C_{6v}	Γ_1	Γ_2	Γ_3	Γ_4	Γ_5	Γ_6	Γ_7	Γ_8	Γ_9
C_{3v}	Γ_1	Γ_2	Γ_2	Γ_1	Γ_3	Γ_3	Γ_4	Γ_4	$\Gamma_5 + \Gamma_6$

Application to Space Groups.—The general result derived above may now be applied to space groups.[13] It is always more convenient, however, to deal with a group called the group of the wave vector, which is a subgroup of the space group. Each such group is identified with a point in the Brillouin zone defined by a vector, $\mathbf{k}$. An operator of the space group is a member of the group of the wave vector for a particular point if the operator leaves the corresponding $\mathbf{k}$ vector invariant to within a primitive translation of the reciprocal lattice. Identify the group G with the nonunitary group of the wave vector $G_{\mathbf{k}}$, and H with the unitary group $H_{\mathbf{k}}$ for some point in the Brillouin zone. Then $\mathbf{a}_0$ is a member of $G_{\mathbf{k}}$ and is written as[14]

$$\mathbf{a}_0 = \mathbf{v}_0 \cdot \boldsymbol{\theta} = (\boldsymbol{\rho}_0 | \dot{\boldsymbol{\tau}}_0) \cdot \boldsymbol{\theta} \tag{12–29}$$

where $\boldsymbol{\rho}_0$ is a point operator and $\boldsymbol{\tau}_0$ is the smallest translation operator associated with $\boldsymbol{\rho}_0$, and (since $\boldsymbol{\theta}\mathbf{k} = -\mathbf{k}$)

$$\boldsymbol{\rho}_0 \mathbf{k} = -\mathbf{k} + \mathbf{K}_q \tag{12–30}$$

where $\mathbf{K}_q$ is a primitive translation of the reciprocal lattice. The operators $\mathbf{u}$ are members of H_k and may be written as $\mathbf{u} = (\mathbf{E} \mid \mathbf{R}_n) \cdot (\boldsymbol{\sigma} \mid \boldsymbol{\tau})$, where $\mathbf{R}_n$ is a primitive translation of the direct

[13] J. O. Dimmock and R. G. Wheeler, *op. cit.* Again in this paper we obtained a result appropriate to space groups (Eq. 29 therein) that is different from the result obtained here (Eq. 12–35). Both results are again correct, although the latter is more convenient.

[14] For a review of space group operator rotation, see G. F. Koster, *Solid State Physics*, **5**, 173 (1958).

lattice and $\boldsymbol{\tau}$ is the smallest translation associated with the operation $\boldsymbol{\sigma}$. For all $\boldsymbol{\sigma}$ we have

$$\boldsymbol{\sigma}\mathbf{k} = \mathbf{k} + \mathbf{K}_q \tag{12–31}$$

The sum in Eq. (12–27) is now taken over the operations $(\boldsymbol{\sigma} \mid \boldsymbol{\tau})$ and $(\mathbf{E} \mid \mathbf{R}_n)$ where for each $\boldsymbol{\sigma}$ we associate only one $\boldsymbol{\tau}$.

$$\begin{aligned}\sum_{\mathbf{R}_n,\boldsymbol{\sigma}} \chi^i(\mathbf{v}_0\mathbf{u}\mathbf{v}_0\mathbf{u}) &= \sum_{\mathbf{R}_n,\boldsymbol{\sigma}} \chi^i[(\boldsymbol{\rho}_0 \mid \boldsymbol{\tau}_0)\cdot(\mathbf{E} \mid \mathbf{R}_n)(\boldsymbol{\sigma} \mid \boldsymbol{\tau})(\boldsymbol{\rho}_0 \mid \boldsymbol{\tau}_0)(\mathbf{E} \mid \mathbf{R}_n)(\boldsymbol{\sigma} \mid \boldsymbol{\tau})] \\ &= \sum_{\mathbf{R}_n,\boldsymbol{\sigma}} \chi^i[(\mathbf{E} \mid \boldsymbol{\rho}_0\mathbf{R}_n + \boldsymbol{\rho}_0\boldsymbol{\sigma}\boldsymbol{\rho}_0\mathbf{R}_n)\cdot(\boldsymbol{\rho}_0 \mid \boldsymbol{\tau}_0)(\boldsymbol{\sigma} \mid \boldsymbol{\tau})(\boldsymbol{\rho}_0 \mid \boldsymbol{\tau}_0)(\boldsymbol{\sigma} \mid \boldsymbol{\tau})]\end{aligned} \tag{12–32}$$

However,[4]

$$\boldsymbol{\Delta}^i(\mathbf{E} \mid \mathbf{R}_n') = \boldsymbol{\Delta}^i(\mathbf{E} \mid 0)\cdot\exp(i\mathbf{k}\cdot\mathbf{R}_n') \tag{12–33}$$

and

$$\mathbf{k}\cdot\boldsymbol{\rho}\mathbf{R}_n = \boldsymbol{\rho}^{-1}\mathbf{k}\cdot\mathbf{R}_n \tag{12–34}$$

and

$$\exp(i\mathbf{K}_q\cdot\mathbf{R}_n) = 1$$

Thus, we have, using Eqs. (12–30) and (12–31)

$$\begin{aligned}\boldsymbol{\Delta}^i(\mathbf{E} \mid \boldsymbol{\rho}_0\mathbf{R}_n + \boldsymbol{\rho}_0\boldsymbol{\sigma}\boldsymbol{\rho}_0\mathbf{R}_n) &= \boldsymbol{\Delta}^i(\mathbf{E} \mid 0)\cdot\exp[i\mathbf{k}(\boldsymbol{\rho}_0\mathbf{R}_n + \boldsymbol{\rho}_0\boldsymbol{\sigma}\boldsymbol{\rho}_0\mathbf{R}_n)] \\ &= \boldsymbol{\Delta}^i(\mathbf{E} \mid 0)\cdot\exp[i(\boldsymbol{\rho}_0^{-1}\mathbf{k} + \boldsymbol{\rho}_0^{-1}\boldsymbol{\sigma}^{-1}\boldsymbol{\rho}_0^{-1}\mathbf{k})\cdot\mathbf{R}_n] \\ &= \boldsymbol{\Delta}^i(\mathbf{E} \mid 0)\cdot\exp[i(-\mathbf{k} + \mathbf{K}_q + \mathbf{k} + \mathbf{K}_q'')\cdot\mathbf{R}_n] \\ &= \boldsymbol{\Delta}^i(\mathbf{E} \mid 0)\cdot\exp(i\mathbf{K}_q'''\cdot\mathbf{R}_n) \\ &= \boldsymbol{\Delta}^i(\mathbf{E} \mid 0)\end{aligned}$$

Therefore, Eq. (12–32) becomes

$$\sum_{\mathbf{R}_n,\boldsymbol{\sigma}} \chi^i(\mathbf{v}_0\mathbf{u}\mathbf{v}_0\mathbf{u}) = n'\sum_{\boldsymbol{\sigma}} \chi^i[\mathbf{v}_0(\boldsymbol{\sigma} \mid \boldsymbol{\tau})\mathbf{v}_0(\boldsymbol{\sigma} \mid \boldsymbol{\tau})]$$

where n' is the number of translation operators $(\mathbf{E} \mid \mathbf{R}_n)$ in the group $H_{\mathbf{k}}$. Finally Eq. (12–27) may be written in the form

$$\begin{aligned}\sum_{\boldsymbol{\sigma}} \chi^i\mathbf{v}_0(\boldsymbol{\sigma} \mid \boldsymbol{\tau})\mathbf{v}_0(\boldsymbol{\sigma} \mid \boldsymbol{\tau}) &= \omega m \quad \text{case (a)} \\ &= -\omega m \quad \text{case (b)} \\ &= 0 \quad \text{case (c)}\end{aligned} \tag{12–35}$$

where $m = n/n'$ is equal to the number of distinct point operators $\boldsymbol{\sigma}$ in $H_{\mathbf{k}}$, that is, to the number of terms in the sum. Equation (12–35) is formally the same as the result obtained by Herring,[15] and is identical to it if $\boldsymbol{\theta}$ is a member of the space group.

It might now be appropriate to comment on the principle results of this section. In order to find the irreducible co-representations of a nonunitary space group G, one first determines the irreducible representations of H, or the H_k for all the points and lines of symmetry in the Brillouin zone of the magnetic lattice. Then Eq. (12–35) may be applied to determine the additional degeneracy introduced by the anti-unitary operators of G_k. These operators will exist if the magnetic space group contains operators $\mathbf{a}_0$, of the form of Eq. (12–29), such that Eq. (12–30) is satisfied. If no such operators exist, then the group of the wave vector is unitary, $G_k = H_k$, and need not be considered further. In this case the anti-unitary operators of G take $\mathbf{k}$ into inequivalent wave vectors that are not in the star of $\mathbf{k}$ in the space group H. This results in a doubling of the degeneracy of the corresponding space group representations of H, and would correspond to case (c) if we were considering the full space groups G and H rather than the groups of the wave vector G_k and H_k.

12.3. Wave Functions in Magnetic Crystals.—*Symmetry Properties of Wave Functions in Magnetic Crystals.*—Let us consider a crystal that below some temperature, T_n, the Néel point temperature, exhibits a magnetic structure. That is, it becomes either ferro-, antiferro- or ferrimagnetic. It is our purpose here to discuss the symmetry properties and degeneracies of the wave functions of these crystals in their magnetic state.[16] It is also of interest to determine specifically what role the magnetic ordering has in the selection of these symmetries. The eigenstates of the magnetic lattice are determined partly by the symmetry of the nonmagnetic lattice, that is, by the space group of the crystal above T_n, and partly by magnetic ordering, which occurs when the crystal temperature is lowered through T_n. It is convenient to think of the magnetic ordering as producing a perturbation on the eigenstates of the paramagnetic lattice even though this perturbation may not be small. The group theoretical results, of course, do not depend on its magnitude. Above T_n the crystal is invariant under a group H_0 of unitary spatial operators. This is what is generally considered as the space group of the crystal. In the paramagnetic state the crystal potential is also invariant under the time reversal operator $\boldsymbol{\theta}$, and products of $\boldsymbol{\theta}$ with the members of H_0, since we assume that in this state the crystal possesses a vanishing time-averaged

[15] C. Herring, *Phys. Rev.*, **52**, 361 (1937).
[16] J. O. Dimmock and R. G. Wheeler, *Phys. Rev.*, **127**, 391 (1962).

magnetic moment density. The full symmetry group of the paramagnetic crystal is then G_0, where $G_0 = H_0 + H_0 \cdot \boldsymbol{\theta}$. Below T_n the crystal is no longer invariant under all the operations of G_0. The reduction in symmetry comes about through the magnetic ordering of the lattice. For example, $\boldsymbol{\theta}$ does not leave the magnetic crystal unchanged. The crystal will now be invariant under a group $\mathscr{H}$ of unitary operators that turns out not only the lattice but also the magnetic moment density into itself. In addition, if there exists some spatial operator $\mathbf{v}_0$, which takes the crystal into itself but reverses the sign of the magnetic moment density, then the magnetic crystal will be invariant under the operation $\mathbf{a}_0 = \mathbf{v}_0 \cdot \boldsymbol{\theta}$. Thus, its full magnetic symmetry group will be $\mathscr{G} = \mathscr{H} + \mathscr{H} \cdot \mathbf{a}_0$. Since the time reversal operator $\boldsymbol{\theta}$ is anti-unitary, and thus $\mathbf{a}_0$ is anti-unitary, the groups G and $\mathscr{G}$ are nonunitary. It is seen that H and $\mathscr{H}$ form the invariant unitary subgroups of G and $\mathscr{G}$ respectively. Further $\mathscr{G}$ and $\mathscr{H}$ are subgroups of G and H respectively. The subgroup relations between these four groups, which characterize the crystal in its magnetic and nonmagnetic states, are expressed in the following diagram.

	Nonunitary		Unitary
nonmagnetic	G	$\longrightarrow$	H
	$\downarrow$		$\downarrow$
magnetic	$\mathscr{G}$	$\longrightarrow$	$\mathscr{H}$

The symmetry properties of the eigenstates of the paramagnetic crystal are determined by finding the irreducible representations of the groups of the wave vector $H_{\mathbf{k}}$ for the points and lines of symmetry of the first Brillouin zone of the nonmagnetic lattice for the appropriate space group H.[17] The additional degeneracies of the corresponding representations of $G_{\mathbf{k}}$ may be obtained by the procedure developed by Herring.[15] Similarly the symmetry properties of the eigenstates of the crystal in its magnetic state are determined by finding the irreducible representations of the groups of the wave vector $\mathscr{H}_{\mathbf{k}}$ for the points and lines of symmetry of the first Brillouin zone of the magnetic lattice for the appropriate unitary space group $\mathscr{H}$. The additional degeneracies of the corresponding representations of $\mathscr{G}_{\mathbf{k}}$ may be obtained by the procedure developed in "Application to Space Groups," above.

[17] See L. P. Bouckaert, R. Smoluchowski, and E. P. Wigner, *Phys. Rev.*, **50**, 58 (1936); C. J. Herring, *Franklin Institute*, **233**, 525 (1942); R. J. Elliott, *Phys. Rev.*, **96**, 280 (1954); and F. Seitz, *Z. Krist.*, **88**, 433 (1934), **90**, 289 (1935), **91**, 336 (1935), **94**, 100 (1936), *Ann. Math.*, **37**, 17 (1936).

The effect of the magnetic ordering is now seen by forming the compatibility tables between the representations of $H_{\mathbf{k}}$ and $\mathscr{H}_{\mathbf{k}}$ for corresponding points in the nonmagnetic and magnetic Brillouin zones. When the magnetic and nonmagnetic unit cells of the crystal are the same, *i.e.*, when the translation symmetry is unchanged by the magnetic ordering, the Brillouin zones for H and $\mathscr{H}$ are the same. In this case $\mathscr{H}_{\mathbf{k}}$ will be a subgroup of $H_{\mathbf{k}}$, and $\mathscr{G}_{\mathbf{k}}$ will be a subgroup of $G_{\mathbf{k}}$ for corresponding points. The compatibility tables are thus formed in a straightforward manner. However, when the magnetic unit cell is some multiple of the nonmagnetic unit cell, the Brillouin zones H and $\mathscr{H}$ are not the same. In this case the Brillouin zone of the magnetic lattice is contained within that of the nonmagnetic lattice such that for points common to both, with the exception of those that are on the surface of the magnetic zone, but not on the surface of the nonmagnetic zone, the subgroup relations will hold. The representations for points within or on the nonmagnetic Brillouin zone but outside the magnetic Brillouin zone may be found from the relations $\mathscr{H}_{\mathbf{k}+\mathbf{K}_q} = \mathscr{H}_{\mathbf{k}}$ and $\mathscr{G}_{\mathbf{k}+\mathbf{K}_q} = \mathscr{G}_{\mathbf{k}}$ where $\mathbf{K}_q$ is a primitive translation of the magnetic reciprocal lattice. For these points also the compatibility tables may be immediately formed. The only points for which a difficulty occurs are those that lie on the surface of the magnetic Brillouin zone where this surface does not coincide with that of the nonmagnetic zone. If the group $\mathscr{H}_{\mathbf{k}}$ contains operators $\mathbf{u} = (\boldsymbol{\sigma} \mid \boldsymbol{\tau})$ where, in the usual space group notation $\boldsymbol{\sigma}$ is a point operator and $\boldsymbol{\tau}$ is a translation operator, such that $\boldsymbol{\sigma}\mathbf{k} = \mathbf{k} + \mathbf{K}_q$, where $\mathbf{K}_q \neq 0$, then $\mathscr{H}_{\mathbf{k}}$ and $\mathscr{G}_{\mathbf{k}}$ will not be subgroups of $H_{\mathbf{k}}$ and $G_{\mathbf{k}}$ respectively since $H_{\mathbf{k}}$ and $G_{\mathbf{k}}$ may contain no such operators, as $\mathbf{k}$ is not on the surface of the nonmagnetic Brillouin zone. These points will be clarified in the following section where we will consider an example of this. However, even in these cases one may obtain information concerning the effects of the magnetic sublattice on the energy surfaces by a comparison of the representations of $\mathscr{H}_{\mathbf{k}}$ and $H_{\mathbf{k}}$.

It might be mentioned here that the group theoretical results determine how the introduction of the magnetic sublattice splits the energy bands of the nonmagnetic crystal. They do not indicate how or to what extent the bands may be shifted. Furthermore, in the above case when the magnetic and nonmagnetic lattices are dissimilar, additional discontinuities in the energy surfaces (band gaps) will be introduced. This occurs at the magnetic zone boundary, and it is clear that at this boundary the energy bands of the magnetic and nonmagnetic materials will be quite different.

One-Dimensional Antiferromagnetic Kronig-Penney Problem.—Instead of applying the considerations of the preceding discussion to a three-dimensional space lattice, it may be illuminating if we consider a problem that can be solved exactly. This is the one-dimensional Kronig-Penney problem with a potential that consists of regularly spaced delta functions.[18] It is imagined that this lattice may be ordered ferro-, antiferro- or ferrimagnetically. If the lattice spacing is a, we have the following single particle potentials:

(1) Paramagnetic: $$V = V_0 a \sum_{n=-\infty}^{\infty} \delta(x - na)$$

(2) Ferromagnetic: $$V = (V_0 + V_1 \mathbf{s}_z) a \sum_{n=-\infty}^{\infty} \delta(x - na)$$

(3) Antiferromagnetic: $$V = V_0 a \sum_{n=-\infty}^{\infty} \delta(x - na) + V_1 \mathbf{s}_z a \sum_{n=-\infty}^{\infty} (-1)^n \delta(x - na)$$

(4) Ferrimagnetic: $$V = (V_0 + V_1 \mathbf{s}_z) a \sum_{n=-\infty}^{\infty} \delta(x - na) + V_2 \mathbf{s}_z a \sum_{n=-\infty}^{\infty} (-1)^n \delta(x - na)$$

where $\mathbf{s}_z$ is the usual Pauli spin operator, see Eq. (12–11).

The eigenfunctions of this problem are of the Bloch form, and can be written as

$$\psi_k(x) = e^{ikx} u_k(x)$$

where the function $u_k(x)$ is periodic with the period of the lattice such that

$$u_k(x + na) = u_k(x)$$

The energy of the state is a continuous function of k within the appropriate Brillouin zone. The energy bands for these potentials are given by

(1) $$\cos(ka) = \cos(\alpha a) + \left(\frac{ma^2}{\hbar^2}\right) V_0 \cdot \frac{\sin(\alpha a)}{\alpha a}$$

(2) $$\cos(ka) = \cos(\alpha a) + \left(\frac{ma^2}{\hbar^2}\right) (V_0 \pm V_1) \frac{\sin(\alpha a)}{\alpha a}$$

[18] See for example: H. Jones, *The Theory of Brillouin Zones and Electronic States in Crystals*, Chaps. 1 and 2, North-Holland Publishing Company, Amsterdam, 1960.

$$(3)\ \cos(2ka) = \cos(2\alpha a) + \left(\frac{4ma^2}{\hbar^2}\right) V_0 \frac{\sin(2\alpha a)}{2\alpha a} + 2\left(\frac{ma^2}{\hbar^2}\right)^2 (V_0^2 - V_1^2)\left(\frac{\sin(\alpha a)}{\alpha a}\right)^2$$

$$(4)\ \cos(2ka) = \cos(2\alpha a) + \left(\frac{4ma^2}{\hbar^2}\right)(V_0 \pm V_1)\frac{\sin(2\alpha a)}{2\alpha a} + 2\left(\frac{ma^2}{\hbar^2}\right)^2 [(V_0 \pm V_1)^2 - V_2^2]\left(\frac{\sin(\alpha a)}{\alpha a}\right)^2$$

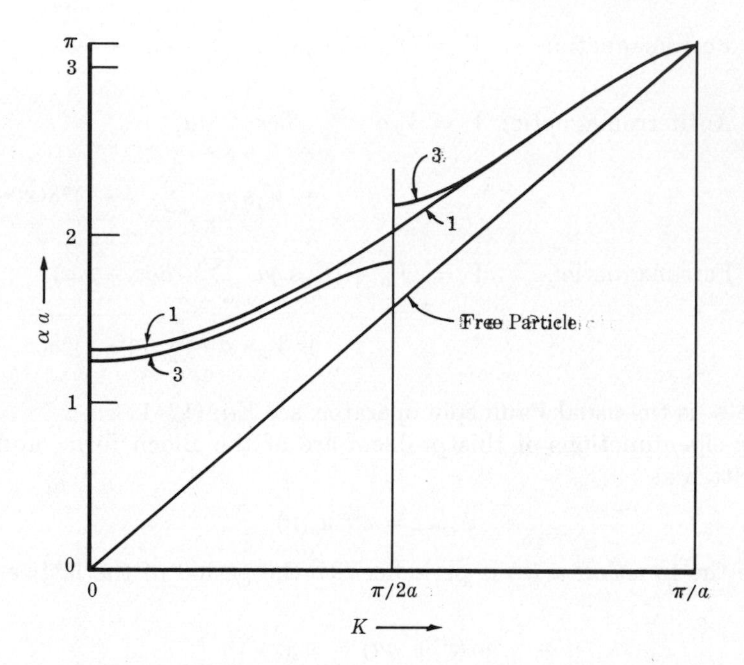

Fig. 12–2. Plot of αa Against K for the Paramagnetic (2) and Antiferromagnetic (3) One-Dimensional Kronig-Penny Potentials. The free particle energy $E = \hbar^2K^2/2m$ is included for the purpose of comparison. Note the discontinuity introduced in the antiferromagnetic band at $\mathbf{K} = \pi/2\mathbf{a}$ due to the reduction in translational symmetry.

where α is related to the energy, $\alpha = (2mE)^{1/2}/\hbar$. The $\pm$ signs refer to spin-up and spin-down states respectively. Notice that the antiferromagnetic energy carries no spin dependence. This is true because the spin-up particle sees the same potential as the spin-down particle only translated one lattice unit. In Fig. 12–2 αa is plotted against k for cases (1) and (3) only since the ferro- and ferrimagnetic cases give no additional information. In Fig. 12–2 we have chosen $V_0 = \hbar^2/ma^2$ and $V_1 = \frac{1}{2}\hbar^2/ma^2$.

We need consider only the symmetry properties of the paramagnetic and antiferromagnetic states since those of the ferromagnetic state may be obtained from the paramagnetic by dropping the additional time reversal degeneracies, and likewise the symmetry properties of the ferrimagnetic state can be obtained similarly from those of the antiferromagnetic state. The basic vector of the paramagnetic lattice is $\mathbf{t}_P = a$, such that the reciprocal lattice vector is $\mathbf{b}_P = 2\pi/a$ and the first Brillouin zone (Fig. 12–3) lies between $\mathbf{k} = \pm\pi/\mathbf{a}$. The basis

C	X	B	X	Γ	X	B	X	C	
$-\pi/a$		$-\pi/2a$		0		$\pi/2a$		π/a	$k \longrightarrow$

Fig. 12–3. The One-Dimensional Brillouin Zone for the Paramagnetic and Antiferromagnetic Structures. The point Γ is at the zone center, the point B is at the edge of the antiferromagnetic zone and the point C is at the edge of the paramagnetic zone. This latter point also corresponds to the edge of the second Brillouin zone of the antiferromagnetic lattice.

vector of the antiferromagnetic lattice is $\mathbf{t}_A = 2\mathbf{a}$, such that the reciprocal lattice vector in this case is $\mathbf{b}_A = \pi/\mathbf{a}$ and the first Brillouin zone lies between $\mathbf{k} = \pm\pi/2\mathbf{a}$.

The space group H of the paramagnetic lattice consists of the elements $(\mathbf{E} \mid 0)$, the identity, and $(\mathbf{I} \mid 0)$, the inversion, and their products with the members $(\mathbf{E} \mid n\mathbf{a})$ and $(\overline{\mathbf{E}} \mid n\mathbf{a})$ of the translation group. $(\overline{\mathbf{E}} \mid n\mathbf{a})$ is the barred operator corresponding to $(\mathbf{E} \mid n\mathbf{a})$ and is identical to it except that it changes the sign of the spin function. In addition to these operators the group G contains their products with the time reversal operator $\boldsymbol{\theta}$. The space group $\mathscr{H}$ of the antiferromagnetic lattice consists of the elements $(\mathbf{E} \mid 0)$ and $(\mathbf{I} \mid 0)$ and their products with the members $(\mathbf{E} \mid 2n\mathbf{a})$ and $(\overline{\mathbf{E}} \mid 2n\mathbf{a})$ of the antiferromagnetic translation group. In addition to these operators the group $\mathscr{G}$ contains their products with the antitranslation $(\mathbf{E} \mid \mathbf{a})\cdot\boldsymbol{\theta}$. Since the groups H and $\mathscr{H}$ are the same except for the translational symmetry the same character tables may be used for $H_{\mathbf{k}}$ and $\mathscr{H}_{\mathbf{k}}$ except for the point B.

Table 12–4 gives the characters, basis functions, and the case a, b, or c to which the irreducible representation of $H_{\mathbf{k}}$ and $\mathscr{H}_{\mathbf{k}}$ belong for the point Γ. The degeneracy in Γ_2^+ and Γ_2^- is the usual Kramers spin degeneracy, which is removed in cases (2) and (4) because of the absence of $\boldsymbol{\theta}$ in these symmetry groups.

TABLE 12–4. *Table for the Point Γ for the Paramagnetic and Antiferromagnetic Lattices*

	(E | 0)	($\bar{E}$ | 0)	(I | 0)	($\bar{I}$ | 0)	(1)	(3)	Bases
Γ_1^+	1	1	1	1	a	a	x^2
Γ_1^-	1	1	−1	−1	a	a	x
Γ_2^+	1	−1	1	−1	b	b	$\varphi(\frac{1}{2},\frac{1}{2})$; $\varphi(\frac{1}{2},-\frac{1}{2})$
Γ_2^-	1	−1	−1	1	b	b	$x\varphi(\frac{1}{2},\frac{1}{2})$; $x\varphi(\frac{1}{2},-\frac{1}{2})$

The situation is the same for point X along the axis for $\mathbf{k} \neq 0$, $\pm\pi/2\mathbf{a}$ or $\pm\pi/\mathbf{a}$. The character table, time reversal properties, and basis functions are given in Table 12–5. The degeneracy in X_2 is again absent in cases (2) and (4).

TABLE 12–5. *Table for the Point X for the Paramagnetic and Antiferromagnetic Lattices*

	(E | 0)	($\bar{E}$ | 0)	(1)	(3)	Bases
X_1	1	1	a	a	x; x^2
X_2	1	−1	b	b	$\varphi(\frac{1}{2},\frac{1}{2})$; $\varphi(\frac{1}{2},-\frac{1}{2})$

times exp (ikx)

Likewise, no degeneracy is removed in the antiferromagnetic case at the point C. The character table, time reversal properties, and basis functions are given in Table 12–6.

TABLE 12–6. *Table for the Point C for the Paramagnetic and Antiferromagnetic Lattices*

	(E | 0)	($\bar{E}$ | 0)	(I | 0)	($\bar{I}$ | 0)	(1)	(3)	Bases
C_1^+	1	1	1	1	a	a	cos $(\pi x/a)$; x sin $(\pi x/a)$
C_1^-	1	1	−1	−1	a	a	x cos $(\pi x/a)$; sin $(\pi x/a)$
C_2^+	1	−1	1	−1	b	b	cos $(\pi x/a)\varphi(\frac{1}{2},\frac{1}{2})$; cos $(\pi x/a)\varphi(\frac{1}{2},-\frac{1}{2})$
C_2^-	1	−1	−1	1	b	b	sin $(\pi x/a)\varphi(\frac{1}{2},\frac{1}{2})$; sin $(\pi x/a)\varphi(\frac{1}{2},-\frac{1}{2})$

Therefore, the only point at which the symmetry properties of the wave functions are changed by the antiferromagnetic ordering is at the point B. Table 12–5 may be used for the characters, time reversal symmetry, and basis functions of the paramagnetic lattice by setting $k = \pi/2a$. In the antiferromagnetic case we use Table 12–7.

TABLE 12–7. *Table for the Point B for the Antiferromagnetic Lattice*

	(**E** | 0)	($\bar{\mathbf{E}}$ | 0)	(**I** | 0)	($\bar{\mathbf{I}}$ | 0)		Bases
B_1^+	1	1	1	1	c	$\cos(\pi x/2a)$; $x \sin(\pi x/2a)$
B_1^-	1	1	−1	−1	c	$x \cos(\pi x/2a)$; $\sin(\pi x/2a)$
B_2^+	1	−1	1	−1	c	$\cos(\pi x/2a)\varphi(\frac{1}{2}, -\frac{1}{2})$; $\cos(\pi x/2a)\varphi(\frac{1}{2}, \frac{1}{2})$
B_2^-	1	−1	−1	1	c	$\sin(\pi x/2a)\varphi(\frac{1}{2}, -\frac{1}{2})$; $\sin(\pi x/2a)\varphi(\frac{1}{2}, \frac{1}{2})$

In this case the anti-unitary operator $\boldsymbol{a}_0$ may be chosen to be $(\mathbf{E} \mid a)\boldsymbol{\theta}$. Consider how this operator transforms the basis functions.

$$(\mathbf{E} \mid a)\boldsymbol{\theta} \cdot \cos(\pi x/2a) = \cos(\pi x/2a + \pi/2) = -\sin(\pi x/2a)$$
$$(\mathbf{E} \mid a)\boldsymbol{\theta} \cdot \sin(\pi x/2a) = \sin(\pi x/2a + \pi/2) = \cos(\pi x/2a)$$
$$(\mathbf{E} \mid a)\boldsymbol{\theta} \cdot \cos(\pi x/2a)\varphi(\tfrac{1}{2}, \pm\tfrac{1}{2}) = \mp \cos(\pi x/2a)\varphi(\tfrac{1}{2}, \mp\tfrac{1}{2})$$
$$(\mathbf{E} \mid a)\boldsymbol{\theta} \cdot \sin(\pi x/2a)\varphi(\tfrac{1}{2}, \pm\tfrac{1}{2}) = \cos(\pi x/2a)\varphi(\tfrac{1}{2}, \mp\tfrac{1}{2})$$

From these transformation properties it is clear that B_1^+ and B_1^- are degenerate as are B_2^+ and $B_{\,2}^-$ as indicated in Table 12–7. From a comparison of Tables 12–5 and 12–7, one sees that the introduction of the antiferromagnetic ordering has increased the degeneracy of the single group representations B_1^+ and B_1^-. This appears strange since the symmetry of the lattice is reduced by the ordering, and we know that a reduction in symmetry can only reduce the eigenfunction degeneracies. Notice, however, that the group of the wave vector for the point B on the surface of the antiferromagnetic Brillouin zone is not reduced by the magnetic ordering, but rather contains the inversion operator in the antiferromagnetic state but not in the paramagnetic state. This occurs because $k = \pi/2a$ is equivalent to $k = -\pi/2a$ in the antiferromagnetic state but not in the paramagnetic state due to the introduction of new Brillouin zone surfaces. This is an example of a case where the symmetry groups $\mathscr{G}_{\mathbf{k}}$ and $\mathscr{H}_{\mathbf{k}}$ of the magnetic structure are not subgroups of $G_{\mathbf{k}}$ and $H_{\mathbf{k}}$ of the nonmagnetic structure, although the full space groups $\mathscr{G}$ and $\mathscr{H}$ are subgroups of G and H respectively. The degeneracies of the full space group are in fact decreased by the magnetic ordering. In the full space group G, each representation at $k = \pi/2a$ is degenerate with its corresponding representation at $k = -\pi/2a$ such that B_1^+ and B_1^- are each doubly degenerate and B_2^+ and B_2^- combine to form a fourfold degenerate representation. The magnetic ordering thus leaves the twofold degeneracy of the space group representations corresponding to B_1^+ and B_1^- unchanged, but splits the fourfold degenerate representation corresponding to B_2^+ and B_2^- into two twofold representations. The increased degeneracy in the group of the wave vector at a Brillouin zone surface is a common occurrence in crystal physics. In the present case the antiferromagnetic ordering of the lattice has introduced a new zone surface at the point B, and, hence, has caused the increased degeneracy. It is also possible for this introduction to create a discontinuity in the energy band. This indeed occurs in the Kronig-Penney problem as is seen in Fig. 12–2. This particularly simple example clearly illustrates the effects of a reduction in translational symmetry, which may accompany the magnetic ordering. This discontinuity in the energy band at the new Brillouin zone surface may be directly calculated. The associated "sticking together" of the energy bands at this surface is seen in Table 12–7.

General Discussion of Band Symmetries and Degeneracies.—The procedure by which one uses the magnetic symmetry of a crystal to determine the symmetry properties of its eigenstates has been described above.[19] The qualitative changes in the band structure due to the magnetic ordering at the Néel point were found to be of two distinct types. The first is simply the splitting of some degenerate states due to the general reduction in symmetry that occurs at the ordering transition. The second is the introduction of new Brillouin zone surfaces and the associated band discontinuities and degeneracies. In addition to these band structure changes the following result may be mentioned. If the group G of the nonmagnetic state contains an operator that takes a given wave vector, $\mathbf{k}_1$, into another wave vector, $\mathbf{k}_2$, then it is generally recognized that if a state of wave vector $\mathbf{k}_1$ with energy $E^i(\mathbf{k}_1)$ exists, then there is a state at $\mathbf{k}_2$ with energy $E^j(\mathbf{k}_2)$ such that $E^i(\mathbf{k}_1) = E^j(\mathbf{k}_2)$, in particular, since $\boldsymbol{\theta}$ is a member of G and $\boldsymbol{\theta}\mathbf{k} = -\mathbf{k}$, $E^i(\mathbf{k}) = E^j(-\mathbf{k})$. This is a general property of energy bands in nonmagnetic crystals and does not depend on the spatial symmetry of the lattice. Since the magnetic group $\mathcal{G}$ is a group of lower order than G, we see that the magnetic ordering may reduce the band symmetry in K-space. For example, in those magnetic crystals lacking inversion symmetry, whose magnetic space group $\mathcal{G}$ contains $\boldsymbol{\theta}$ only in combination with rotation operators, the energy bands do not satisfy the relation $E^i(\mathbf{k}) = E^j(-\mathbf{k})$ for all values of $\mathbf{k}$.

Spin Waves.—In "Application to Point Groups," above, we considered the irreducible representations of magnetic point groups. These would be useful in obtaining the symmetry properties of localized states in magnetic crystals, as impurity or single ion states in the tight

[19] In our work, cited in footnote 16, the method and results are illustrated by a detailed examination of the symmetry properties of wave functions of some magnetic compounds with the rutile structure.

binding approximation. Magnetic space groups, as considered above, are useful, on the other hand, in describing nonlocalized states. Such states would arise in any single particle or band approximations that

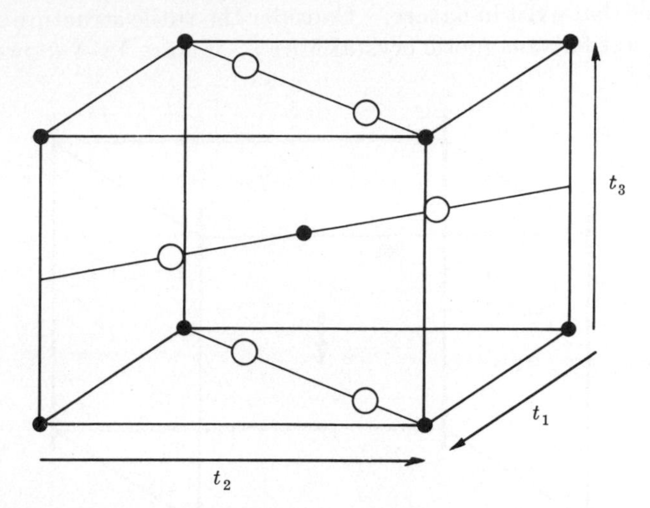

FIG. 12–4. The Nonmagnetic Unit Cell of MnF_2 Showing the Positions of the Ion Sites. The fourfold axis is in the direction t_3. ●, magnetic ion; ○, nonmagnetic ion.

might be attempted. More immediate however, is the application of these magnetic groups to the question of spin-waves and their interactions. Since there is much literature on spin waves,[20] we mention only their transformation properties as these are all that is necessary in our present work. If the crystal under consideration has a sublattice whose direction of magnetization is $\boldsymbol{\lambda}$ then a spin wave traveling through this sublattice with wave vector $\mathbf{k}$ will transform in the group of the wave vector $\mathbf{k}$ as $S_\mu - iS_\nu$ where $\boldsymbol{\lambda}$, $\boldsymbol{\mu}$, and $\boldsymbol{\nu}$ form a right-handed coordinate system ($\boldsymbol{\lambda} - \boldsymbol{\mu} \times \boldsymbol{\nu}$), and S_μ and S_ν transform as pseudovectors in the directions $\boldsymbol{\mu}$ and $\boldsymbol{\nu}$ respectively. That is, the spin wave transforms as a unit of angular momentum directed along $-\boldsymbol{\lambda}$. If the substance in question possesses more than one magnetic sublattice, a wave confined to one will not be an eigenstate of the spin wave hamiltonian since in general there is a coupling between sublattices. However, the transformation properties may be obtained by considering isolated waves, and providing the coupling is nonzero,

[20] See, for example, J. Van Kranendonk and J. H. Van Vleck, *Revs. Modern Phys.*, **30**, 1 (1958).

the selection of eigenstates and the determination of degeneracies results from an application of the group theory.

We shall illustrate this technique by application to two magnetic structures that exist in nature. Consider the rutile structure associated with the antiferromagnetic crystal MnF_2. Figure 12–4 shows the non-

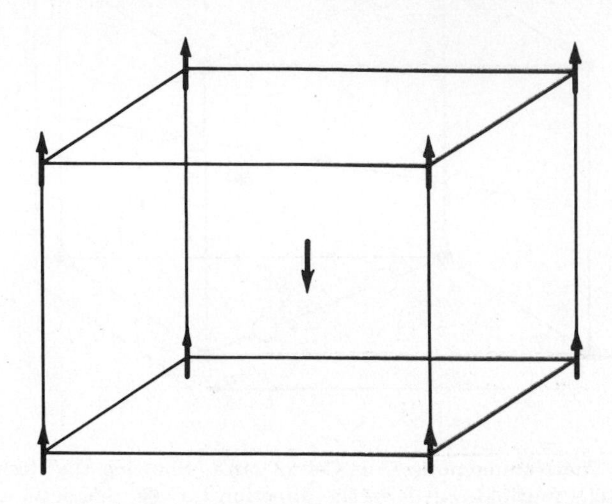

FIG. 12–5. The Magnetic Unit Cell of MnF_2 Showing the Spin Orientation of the Magnetic Ions. The fourfold axis is in the direction of the spin vectors. The nonmagnetic ions are not shown.

magnetic unit cell. The nonmagnetic and magnetic unit cells for this compound are the same. The spins of the magnetic ions are directed along the fourfold axis of the crystal as shown in Fig. 12–5. The subgroup diagram for this case is

	Nonunitary		Unitary
Nonmagnetic	$P4_2/mnm1'$	$\longrightarrow$	$P4_2/mnm$
	$\downarrow$		$\downarrow$
Magnetic	$P4_2'/mnm'$	$\longrightarrow$	$Pnnm$

The notation is that of Belov, Neronova, and Smirova.[2] The primitive translations of the tetragonal lattice are $\mathbf{t}_1 = a\mathbf{i}$, $\mathbf{t}_2 = a\mathbf{j}$, and $\mathbf{t}_3 = c\mathbf{k}$, where $\mathbf{i}$, $\mathbf{j}$, and $\mathbf{k}$ are the unit vectors in the x, y, z directions, respectively. The nonprimitive translation is taken to be $\boldsymbol{\tau} = \frac{1}{2}(\mathbf{t}_1 + \mathbf{t}_2 + \mathbf{t}_3)$. The operators of the space group $Pnnm$ are then

$(\mathbf{E} \mid 0)$, the identity operator;
$(\mathbf{C}_2 \mid 0)$, counterclockwise rotation about the Z axis through 180°;

$(\mathbf{C}_{2x} \mid \boldsymbol{\tau})$, $(\mathbf{C}_{2y} \mid \boldsymbol{\tau})$, counterclockwise rotations through 180° about the x axis (y axis) followed by the translation $\boldsymbol{\tau}$;
$(\mathbf{I} \mid 0)$, the inversion operator;
$(\boldsymbol{\sigma}_n \mid 0) = (\mathbf{C}_2 \mid 0)\cdot(\mathbf{I} \mid 0)$, reflection in the xy plane;
$(\boldsymbol{\sigma}_{v_x} \mid \boldsymbol{\tau}) = (\mathbf{C}_{2x} \mid \boldsymbol{\tau})\cdot(\mathbf{I} \mid 0)$
$(\boldsymbol{\sigma}_{v_y} \mid \boldsymbol{\tau}) = (\mathbf{C}_{2y} \mid \boldsymbol{\tau})\cdot(\mathbf{I} \mid 0)$

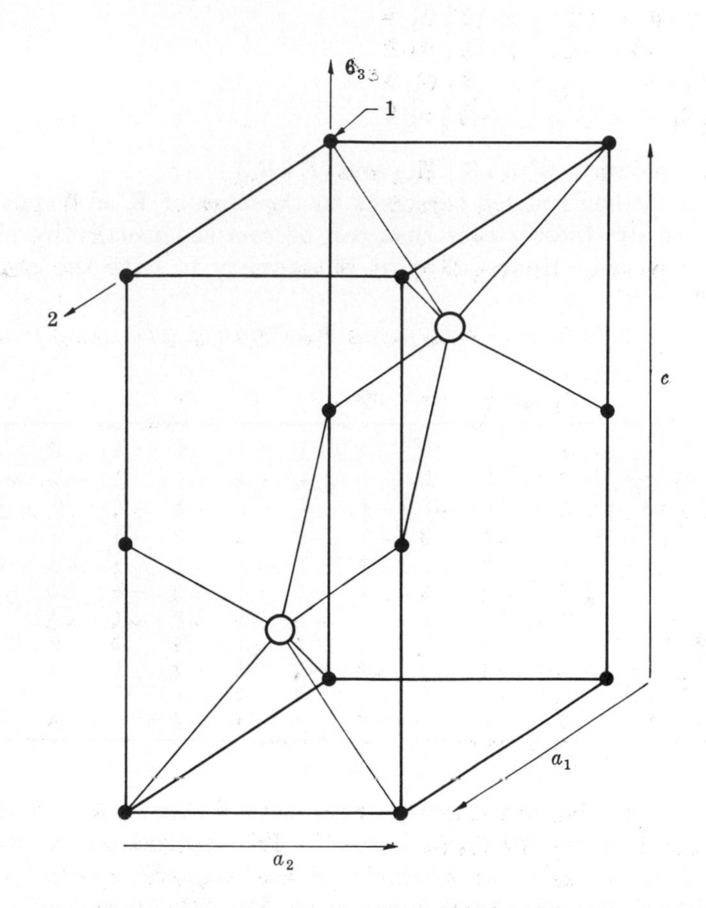

FIG. 12 6. The Nonmagnetic Unit Cell of the NiAs Structure. ●, magnetic ion; ○, nonmagnetic ion.

and products of the above with $(\mathbf{E} \mid \mathbf{R}_n)$ and $(\overline{\mathbf{E}} \mid \mathbf{R}_n)$ where $\mathbf{R}_n = n_1\mathbf{t}_1 + n_2\mathbf{t}_2 + n_3\mathbf{t}_3$.

The nonunitary magnetic space group of MnF_2, $P4_2'/mnm'$ contains, in addition to the elements of $Pnnm$, the following anti-elements

$(\mathbf{C}_4 \mid \boldsymbol{\tau})\cdot\boldsymbol{\theta}$, counterclockwise rotation about the z axis through 90°, followed by the translation $\boldsymbol{\tau}$, followed by time reversal;

$(\mathbf{C}_4^{-1} \mid \boldsymbol{\tau})\cdot\boldsymbol{\theta}$, clockwise rotation about the z axis through 90° followed by the translation $\boldsymbol{\tau}$, followed by time reversal;

$(\mathbf{C}_{2a} \mid 0)\cdot\boldsymbol{\theta}$; $(\mathbf{C}_{2b} \mid 0)\cdot\boldsymbol{\theta}$, clockwise rotations through 180° about the axes $\mathbf{a} = \mathbf{i} + \mathbf{j}$ and $\mathbf{b} = \mathbf{i} - \mathbf{j}$ repectively, each followed by time reversal;

$$(\mathbf{S}_4 \mid \boldsymbol{\tau})\cdot\boldsymbol{\theta} = (\mathbf{C}_4^{-1} \mid \boldsymbol{\tau})\cdot(\mathbf{I} \mid 0)\cdot\boldsymbol{\theta}$$
$$(\mathbf{S}_4^{-1} \mid \boldsymbol{\tau})\cdot\boldsymbol{\theta} = (\mathbf{C}_4 \mid \boldsymbol{\tau})\cdot(\mathbf{I} \mid 0)\cdot\boldsymbol{\theta}$$
$$(\boldsymbol{\sigma}_{da} \mid 0)\cdot\boldsymbol{\theta} = (\mathbf{C}_{2a} \mid 0)\cdot(\mathbf{I} \mid 0)\cdot\boldsymbol{\theta}$$
$$(\boldsymbol{\sigma}_{db} \mid 0)\cdot\boldsymbol{\theta} = (\mathbf{C}_{2b} \mid 0)\cdot(\mathbf{I} \mid 0)\cdot\boldsymbol{\theta}$$

and their products with $(\mathbf{E} \mid \mathbf{R}_n)$ and $(\overline{\mathbf{E}} \mid \mathbf{R}_n)$.

Let us further restrict ourselves to the case of $\mathbf{K} = 0$ spin wave states, namely, those states that can be sampled usually by electromagnetic waves. Hence, then, it is necessary to have the character

TABLE 12–8. *Character Table for the Point* $\Gamma(0,0,0)$ *of the Group Pnnm*

	Γ_1^+	Γ_2^+	Γ_3^+	Γ_4^+	Γ_1^-	Γ_2^-	Γ_3^-	Γ_4^-	Γ_5^+	Γ_5^-
$(\mathbf{E} \mid 0)$	1	1	1	1	1	1	1	1	2	2
$(\overline{\mathbf{E}} \mid 0)$	1	1	1	1	1	1	1	1	−2	−2
$(\mathbf{C}_2,\overline{\mathbf{C}}_2 \mid 0)$	1	1	−1	−1	1	1	−1	−1	0	0
$(\mathbf{C}_{2x},\overline{\mathbf{C}}_{2x} \mid \tau)$	1	−1	1	−1	1	−1	1	−1	0	0
$(\mathbf{C}_{2y},\overline{\mathbf{C}}_{2y} \mid \tau)$	1	−1	−1	1	1	−1	−1	1	0	0
$(\mathbf{I} \mid 0)$	1	1	1	1	−1	−1	−1	−1	2	−2
$(\overline{\mathbf{I}} \mid 0)$	1	1	1	1	−1	−1	−1	−1	−2	2
$(\sigma_h,\bar{\sigma}_h \mid 0)$	1	1	−1	−1	−1	−1	1	1	0	0
$(\sigma_{vx},\bar{\sigma}_{vx} \mid \tau)$	1	−1	1	−1	−1	1	−1	1	0	0
$(\sigma_{vy},\bar{\sigma}_{vy} \mid \tau)$	1	−1	−1	1	−1	1	1	−1	0	0
Time inv.	*a*	*a*	*c* ——	*c*	*a*	*a*	*c* ——	*c*	*a*	*a*

table corresponding to the group of the wave vector for $\mathbf{k} = 0$, namely the Γ point of the Brillouin Zone.[16] This information is given in Table 12–8. In order to determine if the magnetic symmetry $P4_2'/mnm'$ causes any additional degeneracy, Eq. (12–35) is used with $\mathbf{v}_0$ chosen to be equal to $(\mathbf{C}_{2a} \mid 0)$. The result is indicated in the row labeled time inv. The spin waves will transform as $S_x - iS_y$ and $S_x + iS_y$. These functions belong to the representations Γ_3^+ and Γ_4^+ of the group *Pnnm*, which become degenerate in the group $P4_2'/mnm'$. Thus, in MnF_2 at $\mathbf{k} = 0$, we expect the spin wave spectra to be doubly degenerate in the absence of external fields. This has been predicted by direct calculation [21] and indeed has been observed. [22] One can further show that the magnetic dipole operator transforms in the group *Pnnm* as $\Gamma_3^+ + \Gamma_4^+$; hence, observation of these spin waves states is allowed from symmetry considerations.

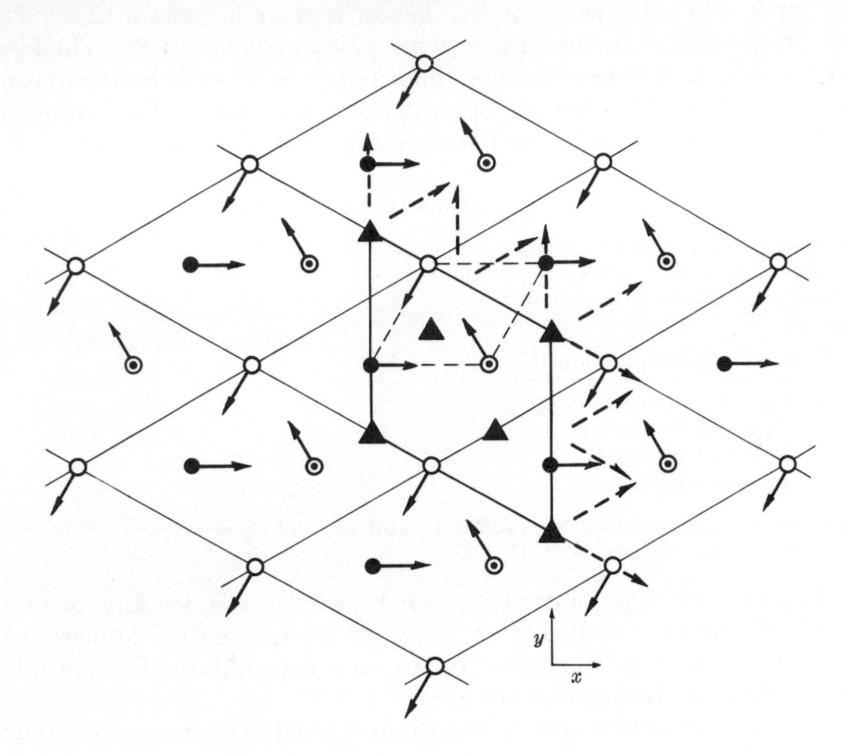

FIG. 12–7. The Magnetic Symmetry Associated with the Group $P\bar{6}2m$. The twofold rotations are relative to $Z = 1/4C$.

Next consider the NiAs crystallographic structure ($P6_3/mmc$) associated with the compound CrSe. This is shown in Fig. 12–6. Neutron diffraction results indicate an antiferromagnetic compound with a magnetic unit cell three times the chemical cell.[23] Further, since there are two inequivalent Cr sites, the magnetic moment arrangement reflects threefold symmetry about the *c* axis, with inequivalent Cr layers having reversed orientations. Although there are several possible alternative arrangements for the spin orientations in the basal plane, we shall consider the case where the spin directions are parallel

[21] F. Keffer and C. Kittel, *Phys. Rev.*, **85**, 329 (1952).
[22] F. M. Johnson and A. H. Nethercot Jr., *Phys. Rev.*, **114**, 705 (1959).
[23] L. M. Corliss, N. Elliot, and J. M. Hastings, *Phys. Rev.*, **122**, 1402 (1961).

to the cell edge and in the basal planes. This is illustrated in Fig. 12–7. With this arrangement there are now six sublattices, where the magnetic space group is $P\bar{6}2m$. Note that there are no anti-elements in this magnetic group. The character tables for the group of the wave vector $\mathbf{k} = 0$ is the same as D_{3h}, hence, appears in Section 12.6. The results for the six modes at $\mathbf{k} = 0$ are given in Table 12–9. The form of the spin deviations corresponding to each irreducible representation can be obtained by the use of projection operators. The numerical subscripts correspond to the two inequivalent Cr layers.

TABLE 12–9.

Magnetic Space Group. $P\bar{6}2m$
Group of $\mathbf{K}$ at $\mathbf{K} = 0$, D_{3h}
Number of modes at $\mathbf{K} = 0$, 6

Irreducible Representation	Basis Functions for Spin Deviation
Γ_6 (twofold degenerate)	$(S_{x_1} - S_{x_2}) \pm i(S_{y_1} - S_{y_2})$
Γ_5 (twofold degenerate)	$(S_{x_1} + S_{x_2}) \pm i(S_{y_1} + S_{y_2})$
Γ_2 (nondegenerate)	$(S_{z_1} + S_{z_2})$
Γ_3 (nondegenerate)	$(S_{z_1} - S_{z_2})$

Magnetic dipole selection rules allow Γ_2 states to be observed with $H \parallel C$, and Γ_5 states to be observed with $H \perp C$.

Finally, this type of analysis can be carried out for any point in the Brillouin zone such that by using the transformation properties of spin waves and the character tables, one may obtain the spin-wave band structure throughout the zone.

12.4. Use of symmetry in the determination of magnetic structures.—Above, under "Symmetry Properties of Wave Functions in Magnetic Crystals" and "One-Dimensional Antiferromagnetic Kronig-Penney Problem," we discussed briefly the changes that may occur in the symmetry properties of wave functions in crystals when the crystal goes from its paramagnetic state to a state that possesses an ordered magnetic structure. These changes are brought about by the change in crystal symmetry, which takes place at the transition point. In this connection it is interesting to mention that one can restrict the symmetry changes in certain cases, which can take place in a given crystal.[24] From the work of Landau and Lifshitz [25, 26] it is found that

[24] J. O. Dimmock, *Phys. Rev.*, **130**, 1337 (1963).

[25] L. D. Landau and E. M. Lifshitz, *Statistical Physics*, Chap. 14, Addison-Wesley Publishing Company, Reading, Mass., 1958.

[26] I. Dzyaloshinsky, *J. Phys. Chem. Solids*, **4**, 241 (1958); *Soviet Phys.—JETP*, **6**, 1120 (1958).

the following restrictions apply to those magnetic structures that can arise when a crystal undergoes a single second-order phase transition from the paramagnetic state to the magnetic state in question. In the immediate vicinity of the transition point the magnetic moment density in the magnetic state transforms as a basis function for a single irreducible representation of the symmetry group of the paramagnetic phase. At lower temperatures the magnetic moment density may change qualitatively from that introduced at the transition point with the restriction that the crystal symmetry remain the same. The theory assumes that the state of the crystal can be described accurately by a single-particle density function, and, hence, involves a Hartree-Fock type approximation neglecting all effects of electron correlations, as is done in the molecular field approximation.

As was originally pointed out by Landau,[27] a second-order phase transition is characterized by a change in crystal symmetry. At the transition point the symmetry group of the crystal changes abruptly from G, the space group of the disordered phase (presumably the high temperature phase) to a group $\mathscr{G}$, which is a subgroup of G. If the transition is truly second order, it is continuous, except for the change in symmetry, and involves no latent heat and no hysteresis.[28] The two phases are identical at the transition point. The disordered phase may be characterized by some function ρ_0, which can be thought of as a general density function, and which is, by definition, invariant under all the operations of G. The ordered phase may be characterized by a function ρ_1, which is invariant under all the operations of $\mathscr{G}$, but not under those operations of G that are not also contained in the group $\mathscr{G}$. ρ_1 is a continuous function of temperature and pressure, and coincides with ρ_0 at the transition point. One can write $\rho_1 = \rho_0 + \rho$, where ρ vanishes continuously at the transition. ρ is that portion of the general crystal density function of the ordered phase that expresses the change in symmetry that takes place at the transition point. In the present discussion we may interpret ρ as a magnetic moment or electron spin density, although it involves the lattice distortion and other effects as well. It is convenient to expand ρ in terms of the basis functions of all the irreducible representations of G.

$$\rho = \sum_n \sum_i c_i^n \phi_i^n \tag{12–36}$$

[27] L. D. Landau, *Physik. Z. Sowjetunion*, **11**, 545 (1937).

[28] An extensive treatment of the thermodynamic properties of second-order phase transitions in magnetic crystals has been given by K. P. Belov, *Magnetic Transitions*, Consultants Bureau, Enterprises, Inc., New York, 1961.

where n is the number of the irreducible representation, and i designates the basis function. Notice that the expansion is unique and completely general since the basis functions ϕ form a complete set. The expansion coefficients are continuous functions of the temperature and pressure, and all vanish at the transition point.

Notice that even though ρ is not invariant under all the operations of G_0, the identity representation has been included in the sum over n in Eq. (12–36). This is true because G_0 is a nonunitary group, containing both unitary and anti-unitary operators, and the co-representation matrices $\mathbf{D}^{(n)}(\mathbf{a})$ for the anti-unitary elements of this group possess a common arbitrary phase factor (see Eq. 12–17a). Therefore, a basis function that transforms according to the identity co-representation of G_0 need not be invariant under this group but could change sign, for example, under the operation of the anti-unitary elements. Such functions may contribute to the spin density, and, consequently, the identity representation must be included in the sum over n in Eq. (12–36).

The thermodynamic potential, or free energy, of the crystal is also continuous at the transition point. Taking A_0 as the free energy of the disordered phase, we can write the free energy of the ordered phase as $A = A_0$ plus an expansion in a set of parameters, which characterize the ordered phase, and which vanish continuously at the transition point. Assuming that the free energy depends only on the density function, one can choose the set of coefficients c_i^n for the expansion parameters. Consider the basis functions fixed such that the c_i^n transform among themselves under the operations of G. The free energy, and thus the terms in its expansion, are invariant under G. There is no invariant linear in c_i^n since ρ is that portion of ρ_1 that is not invariant under G_0. For each representation $\mathbf{D}^n$ of G, we can construct one quadratic invariant of the form $\sum_i (c_i^n)^2$. There are no quadratic terms mixing representations since the direct product of two irreducible representations of a group contains an invariant if and only if the representations are equivalent. In general, cubic and higher order terms in the expansion will mix representations and no general form can be written for them.

Retaining only the quadratic terms the expansion of A has the form

$$A = A_0 + \sum_n a^n \sum_i (c_i^n)^2 + \cdots \qquad (12\text{–}37)$$

The equilibrium state of the system corresponds to that set of values of the c_i^n that minimizes A at a given temperature and pressure. From our definitions the disordered phase is characterized by $c_i^n = 0$. In order for this to correspond to a minimum of A all the a^n in the disordered phase must be positive. In the ordered phase not all the c_i^n vanish such that at least one a^n must be negative, and, hence, we have $a^n(P_N, T_N) = 0$ at the transition point. This gives a relation between P_N and T_N. If two of the a's changed sign we would also have $a^m(P_N, T_N) = 0$ and could then solve for P_N and T_N. In this case the transition would occur at a critical point. Since magnetic transitions are generally not of this type, we can say that only one a^n vanishes at the transition point. Thus, in the equilibrium state immediately below the transition, all expansion parameters vanish except those belonging to a single irreducible representation of the symmetry group of the disordered phase. Therefore, instead of Eq. (12–36) we can write

$$\rho = \sum_i c_i^n \phi_i^n \tag{12–38}$$

and ρ must transform as a basis function of a single irreducible representation of G. Therefore, we have obtained the result that the spin density introduced in a second-order phase transition transforms as a basis function for a single irreducible representation of the symmetry group of the disordered phase. This result, which was originally found by Landau and Lifshitz,[25] is, however, not valid, in general, when higher order terms are included in the expansion of A such that Eq. (12–38) is an approximation that is expected to be good only in the neighborhood of the transition point.

Let us consider how the inclusion of higher order terms in the expansion of the free energy affects the transformation properties of the spin density. If at the transition point $a^n = 0$ corresponding to the irreducible representation $\mathbf{D}^n$ of the symmetry group of the disordered phase, then, as we saw above, in the neighborhood of the transition point ρ transforms as a basis function of $\mathbf{D}^n$. If there is a fourth-order term in the expansion consisting of an invariant formed from the direct product $\mathbf{D}^n \times \mathbf{D}^n \times \mathbf{D}^n \times \mathbf{D}^m$, where $\mathbf{D}^m$ is a different irreducible representation of G, a spin density component that transforms as a basis function of $\mathbf{D}^m$ will contribute to ρ as one moves away from the transition point. A necessary and sufficient condition for such an invariant to exist is that $\mathbf{D}^m$ occur in the decomposition of the direct cube of $\mathbf{D}^n$. $\mathbf{D}^m$ can then be thought of as a third "harmonic" of the "fundamental" representation, $\mathbf{D}^n$. In general, harmonics of all odd orders can contribute to ρ_1 but those of lower order will be more important. From the Landau-Lifshitz theory, the temperature dependence of the fundamental component is $(T_N - T)^{1/2}$ near the transition point. It is easy to show, by including higher terms in the expansion, that the temperature dependence of the jth harmonic is $(T_N - T)^{j/2}$, such that the higher order harmonics do indeed enter more slowly. If the disordered phase of the transition in question is the paramagnetic state, the expansion of the free energy contains only even terms and ρ_1 contains only odd harmonics of the fundamental.

The above discussion of the transformation properties of ρ in terms of the irreducible representations of G is correct as far as it goes but more information can be obtained by considering the basis functions themselves. However, a more complete treatment in terms of the Landau-Lifshitz theory is rather involved. Fortunately, a little insight yields the final result directly. Let us, therefore, reconsider the problem starting at the beginning and using the results obtained thus far. Recall that in the disordered phase the crystal is invariant under a symmetry group G, and that at the transition point the symmetry of the crystal changes. This is brought about by the introduction of a spin density ρ that, in the vicinity of the transition point, transforms as a basis function for a single irreducible representation $\mathbf{D}^n$ of G_0. The particular basis function of $\mathbf{D}^n$ contributing to ρ is selected by the anisotropy terms in the expansion of the free energy. The symmetry group, $\mathscr{G}$, of the ordered phase is the largest subgroup of G that leaves ρ invariant. $\mathscr{G}$ is not determined by G_0 and $\mathbf{D}^n$ alone in the case where the dimension of $\mathbf{D}^n$ is greater than one, since the basis function, as selected by the anisotropy terms, that contributes to ρ may have more symmetry than a general basis function of $\mathbf{D}^n$. As the temperature is lowered further, the symmetry of the crystal remains the same unless it undergoes another transition. Assuming that this does not happen, ρ must remain invariant under $\mathscr{G}$. We saw above that ρ changes through the introduction of components that transform according to "harmonics" of the fundamental representation. We now have the additional restriction that these components must be invariant under $\mathscr{G}$.

In concluding this section, let us summarize the types of information that can be obtained by applying the Landau-Lifshitz theory to specific magnetic structure, assuming that these structures arise from the disordered phase through a single second-order phase transition. First, it is possible to show that some magnetic structures cannot exist in the immediate vicinity of the transition point, but can occur only at lower temperatures. Second, it is sometimes possible to restrict the spin direction in a crystal whose general magnetic structure is known. Third, it is possible to show that some magnetic configurations cannot arise from the disordered phase of the crystal by a single second-order phase transition. Fourth, in those cases where the spin direction or magnitude in a proposed structure is not fixed by the crystal symmetry in the ordered phase, it can be expected, in general, to be temperature-dependent. Therefore, although the Landau-Lifshitz theory is based on rather general considerations, it makes some definite predictions concerning the symmetry of magnetic structures, and should be useful both in connection with the determination of new structures and in considerations of already proposed configurations in magnetic crystals.

12.5. Summary and Conclusions.—Crystals may be classified into two groups according to their transformation properties with respect to the operation of time reversal. If the time-averaged magnetic moment density within the crystal is zero, then the time reversal operator is a member of the crystal symmetry group. If, however, the crystal possesses unpaired spins it is possible for its equilibrium state to exhibit a persistent magnetic moment density. Such is the case in ferro-, antiferro-, and ferrimagnetic crystals. The magnetic phases of these crystals are not invariant with respect to a reversal of time, such that the time reversal transformation is not a member of the crystallographic symmetry group. It can, however, occur in combination with spatial transformations. The inclusion of this additional element increases the number of crystallographic symmetry groups from the 230 classical groups to 1651 groups called Shubnikov groups. A corresponding increase occurs in the number of point groups from 32 to 122.

Since the quantum mechanical time reversal operator is anti-unitary, the groups of operators that commute with the hamiltonian of magnetic systems contain both unitary and anti-unitary operators. Such groups, called nonunitary groups, each consist of a subgroup (of index two) of unitary operators and a coset of anti-unitary operators. The irreducible co-representations of these nonunitary groups can be obtained from the irreducible representations of the unitary subgroup by a procedure discussed in Section 12.2. Using these results, we can compare the symmetry properties and degeneracies of the eigenstates of a magnetic crystal above and below its Néel point. The specific effects of the magnetic ordering are found to be of three types: (1) there is a lifting of some eigenfunction (band) degeneracies because the crystal symmetry is reduced in the magnetic state; (2) if there is a reduction in translational symmetry new Brillouin zone surfaces are introduced, which can cause new band gaps and a "sticking together" of bands at the new surfaces; (3) the symmetry of the energy band in K-space can be reduced.

Furthermore, it has been possible, through the use of general symmetry considerations, to restrict the changes in crystal symmetry, which can occur in a second-order phase transition. It was found that the magnetic moment density introduced at the transition point must transform as a basis function for a single irreducible representation of the symmetry group of the paramagnetic phase of the crystal.

There is much current interest, both experimental and theoretical, in the properties of the magnetic state in crystals. Since the use of group theory has been instrumental in bringing about our present understanding of the eigenstates in nonmagnetic crystals, though this understanding is still far from complete, it is hoped that it may be possible to use the representation theory of nonunitary groups to likewise assist in the understanding of the properties of eigenstates in magnetic crystals.

12.6. Character Tables for the Thirty-Two Point Groups.—Since the present chapter shows how one obtains the irreducible co-representations of nonunitary groups from the irreducible representations of their unitary subgroups, we tabulate here the representations of the thirty-two point groups. In the interest of brevity, we give only one character table for a given set of isomorphic groups, and do not include those groups that may be obtained from those given by taking the direct product with the two element group consisting of the operators **E** and **I**, the inversion. We call this the group I to contrast it with the group C_i, which contains the barred operators. The groups G formed in this way from the group $H(G = H \times I)$ will have twice as many representations as H. To each representation, Γ_i, of H there will correspond two representations of G, Γ_i^+ and Γ_i^-. For Γ_i^+ we will have $\chi^{(i)}(I) = \chi^{(i)}(E)$ and for Γ_i^- we will have $\chi^{(i)}(I) = -\chi^{(i)}(E)$. Specifically the representations of the following groups may be obtained in this way:

$$C_{2h} = C_2 \times I;\ D_{2h} = D_2 \times I;\ C_{4h} = C_4 \times I;\ D_{4h} = D_4 \times I;$$
$$C_{3i} = C_3 \times I;\ D_{3d} = D_3 \times I;\ C_{6h} = C_6 \times I;\ D_{6h} = D_6 \times I;$$
$$T_h = T \times I;\ 0_h = 0 \times I.$$

Character Tables for the Thirty-Two Point Groups

Group C_1

C_1	E	$\bar{E}$
Γ_1	1	1
Γ_2	1	−1

Group C_i

C_i	E	$\bar{E}$	I	$\bar{I}$
Γ_1^+	1	1	1	1
Γ_1^-	1	1	−1	−1
Γ_2^+	1	−1	1	−1
Γ_2^-	1	−1	−1	1

Groups C_2 and C_s

C_2	E	$\bar{E}$	C_2	$\bar{C}_2$
C_s	E	$\bar{E}$	σ	$\bar{\sigma}$
Γ_1	1	1	1	1
Γ_2	1	1	-1	-1
Γ_3	1	-1	i	$-i$
Γ_4	1	-1	$-i$	i

Groups D_2 and C_{2v}

D_2	E	$\bar{E}$	C_2 $\bar{C}_2$	C_2' $\bar{C}_2'$	C_2'' $\bar{C}_2''$
C_{2v}	E	$\bar{E}$	C_2 $\bar{C}_2$	σ_v $\bar{\sigma}_v$	σ_v' $\bar{\sigma}_v'$
Γ_1	1	1	1	1	1
Γ_2	1	1	1	-1	-1
Γ_3	1	1	-1	1	-1
Γ_4	1	1	-1	-1	1
Γ_5	2	-2	0	0	0

Group C_3

C_3	E	$\bar{E}$	C_3	$\bar{C}_3$	C_3^{-1}	$\bar{C}_3^{-1}$
Γ_1	1	1	1	1	1	1
Γ_2	1	1	ω^2	ω^2	$-\omega$	$-\omega$
Γ_3	1	1	$-\omega$	$-\omega$	ω^2	ω^2
Γ_4	1	-1	ω	$-\omega$	$-\omega^2$	ω^2
Γ_5	1	-1	$-\omega^2$	ω^2	ω	$-\omega$
Γ_6	1	-1	-1	1	-1	1

$$\omega = \exp(\pi i/3)$$

Groups D_3 and C_{3v}

D_3	E	$\bar{E}$	$2C_3$	$2\bar{C}_3$	$3C_2'$	$3\bar{C}_2'$
C_{3v}	E	$\bar{E}$	$2C_3$	$2\bar{C}_3$	$3\sigma_v$	$3\bar{\sigma}_v$
Γ_1	1	1	1	1	1	1
Γ_2	1	1	1	1	-1	-1
Γ_3	2	2	-1	-1	0	0
Γ_4	2	-2	1	-1	0	0
Γ_5	1	-1	-1	1	i	$-i$
Γ_6	1	-1	-1	1	$-i$	i

Groups C_4 and S_4

C_4	E	$\overline{E}$	C_4	$\overline{C}_4$	C_2	$\overline{C}_2$	C_4^{-1}	$\overline{C}_4^{-1}$
S_4	E	$\overline{E}$	S_4^{-1}	$\bar{S}_4^{-1}$	C_2	$\overline{C}_2$	S_4	$\bar{S}_4$
Γ_1	1	1	1	1	1	1	1	1
Γ_2	1	1	-1	-1	1	1	-1	-1
Γ_3	1	1	i	i	-1	-1	$-i$	$-i$
Γ_4	1	1	$-i$	$-i$	-1	-1	i	i
Γ_5	1	-1	ω	$-\omega$	i	$-i$	$-\omega^3$	ω^3
Γ_6	1	-1	$-\omega^3$	ω^3	$-i$	i	ω	$-\omega$
Γ_7	1	-1	$-\omega$	ω	i	$-i$	ω^3	$-\omega^3$
Γ_8	1	-1	ω^3	$-\omega^3$	$-i$	i	$-\omega$	ω

$\omega = \exp(\pi i/4)$

Groups D_4, C_{4v}, and D_{2d}

D_4	E	$\overline{E}$	$2C_4$	$2\overline{C}_4$	C_2 $\overline{C}_2$	$2C_2'$ $2\overline{C}_2'$	$2C_2''$ $2\overline{C}_2''$
C_{4v}	E	$\overline{E}$	$2C_4$	$2\overline{C}_4$	C_2 $\overline{C}_2$	$2\sigma_v$ $2\bar{\sigma}_v$	$2\sigma_d$ $2\bar{\sigma}_d$
D_{2d}	E	$\overline{E}$	$2S_4$	$2\bar{S}_4$	C_2 $\overline{C}_2$	$2C_2'$ $2\overline{C}_2'$	$2\sigma_d$ $2\bar{\sigma}_d$
Γ_1	1	1	1	1	1	1	1
Γ_2	1	1	1	1	1	-1	-1
Γ_3	1	1	-1	-1	1	1	-1
Γ_4	1	1	-1	-1	1	-1	1
Γ_5	2	2	0	0	-2	0	0
Γ_6	2	-2	$\sqrt{2}$	$-\sqrt{2}$	0	0	0
Γ_7	2	-2	$-\sqrt{2}$	$\sqrt{2}$	0	0	0

Groups C_6 and C_{3h}

C_6	E	$\overline{E}$	C_6	$\overline{C}_6$	C_3	$\overline{C}_3$	C_2	$\overline{C}_2$	C_3^{-1}	$\overline{C}_3^{-1}$	C_6^{-1}	$\overline{C}_6^{-1}$
C_{3h}	E	$\overline{E}$	S_3^{-1}	$\bar{S}_3^{-1}$	C_3	$\overline{C}_3$	σ_h	$\bar{\sigma}_h$	C_3^{-1}	$\overline{C}_3^{-1}$	S_3	$\bar{S}_3$
Γ_1	1	1	1	1	1	1	1	1	1	1	1	1
Γ_2	1	1	$-\omega^2$	$-\omega^2$	ω^4	ω^4	1	1	$-\omega^2$	$-\omega^2$	ω^4	ω^4
Γ_3	1	1	ω^4	ω^4	$-\omega^2$	$-\omega^2$	1	1	ω^4	ω^4	$-\omega^2$	$-\omega^2$
Γ_4	1	1	-1	-1	1	1	-1	-1	1	1	-1	-1
Γ_5	1	1	ω^2	ω^2	ω^4	ω^4	-1	-1	$-\omega^2$	$-\omega^2$	$-\omega^4$	$-\omega^4$
Γ_6	1	1	$-\omega^4$	$-\omega^4$	$-\omega^2$	$-\omega^2$	-1	-1	ω^4	ω^4	ω^2	ω^2
Γ_7	1	-1	ω	$-\omega$	ω^2	$-\omega^2$	i	$-i$	$-\omega^4$	ω^4	$-\omega^5$	ω^5
Γ_8	1	-1	$-\omega^5$	ω^5	$-\omega^4$	ω^4	$-i$	i	ω^2	$-\omega^2$	ω	$-\omega$
Γ_9	1	-1	$-\omega$	ω	ω^2	$-\omega^2$	$-i$	i	$-\omega^4$	ω^4	ω^5	$-\omega^5$
Γ_{10}	1	-1	ω^5	$-\omega^5$	$-\omega^4$	ω^4	i	$-i$	ω^2	$-\omega^2$	$-\omega$	ω
Γ_{11}	1	-1	$-i$	i	-1	1	i	$-i$	-1	1	i	$-i$
Γ_{12}	1	-1	i	$-i$	-1	1	$-i$	i	-1	1	$-i$	i

$\omega = \exp(\pi i/6)$

Groups D_6, C_{6v}, and D_{3h}

D_6	E	$\bar{E}$	C_2 $\bar{C}_2$	$2C_3$	$2\bar{C}_3$	$2C_6$	$2\bar{C}_6$	$3C_2'$ $3\bar{C}_2'$	$3C_2''$ $3\bar{C}_2''$
C_{6v}	E	$\bar{E}$	C_2 $\bar{C}_2$	$2C_3$	$2\bar{C}_3$	$2C_6$	$2\bar{C}_6$	$3\sigma_d$ $3\bar{\sigma}_d$	$3\sigma_v$ $3\bar{\sigma}_v$
D_{3h}	E	$\bar{E}$	σ_h $\bar{\sigma}_h$	$2C_3$	$2\bar{C}_3$	$2S_3$	$2\bar{S}_3$	$3C_2'$ $3\bar{C}_2'$	$3\sigma_v$ $3\bar{\sigma}_v$
Γ_1	1	1	1	1	1	1	1	1	1
Γ_2	1	1	1	1	1	1	1	−1	−1
Γ_3	1	1	−1	1	1	−1	−1	1	−1
Γ_4	1	1	−1	1	1	−1	−1	−1	1
Γ_5	2	2	−2	−1	−1	1	1	0	0
Γ_6	2	2	2	−1	−1	−1	−1	0	0
Γ_7	2	−2	0	1	−1	$\sqrt{3}$	$-\sqrt{3}$	0	0
Γ_8	2	−2	0	1	−1	$-\sqrt{3}$	$\sqrt{3}$	0	0
Γ_9	2	−2	0	−2	2	0	0	0	0

Group T

T	E	$\bar{E}$	$3C_2$ $3\bar{C}_2$	$4C_3$	$4\bar{C}_3$	$4C_3^{-1}$	$4\bar{C}_3^{-1}$
Γ_1	1	1	1	1	1	1	1
Γ_2	1	1	1	ω	ω	ω^2	ω^2
Γ_3	1	1	1	ω^2	ω^2	ω	ω
Γ_4	3	3	−1	0	0	0	0
Γ_5	2	−2	0	1	−1	1	−1
Γ_6	2	−2	0	ω	$-\omega$	ω^2	$-\omega^2$
Γ_7	2	−2	0	ω^2	$-\omega^2$	ω	$-\omega$

$\omega = \exp(2\pi i/3)$

Groups 0 and T_d

0	E	$\bar{E}$	$8C_3$	$8\bar{C}_3$	$3C_2$ $3\bar{C}_2$	$6C_4$	$6\bar{C}_4$	$6C_2'$ $6\bar{C}_2'$
T_d	E	$\bar{E}$	$8C_3$	$8\bar{C}_3$	$3C_2$ $3\bar{C}_2$	$6S_4$	$6\bar{S}_4$	$6\sigma_d$ $6\bar{\sigma}_d$
Γ_1	1	1	1	1	1	1	1	1
Γ_2	1	1	1	1	1	−1	−1	−1
Γ_3	2	2	−1	−1	2	0	0	0
Γ_4	3	3	0	0	−1	1	1	−1
Γ_5	3	3	0	0	−1	−1	−1	1
Γ_6	2	−2	1	−1	0	$\sqrt{2}$	$-\sqrt{2}$	0
Γ_7	2	−2	1	−1	0	$-\sqrt{2}$	$\sqrt{2}$	0
Γ_8	4	−4	−1	1	0	0	0	0

REFERENCES

1. Hammermesh, M., *Group Theory*, Addison-Wesley Publishing Co., Reading, Mass., 1962.
2. Heine, V., *Group Theory in Quantum Mechanics*, Pergamon Press, New York, 1960.
3. Herzfeld, C. M., and Meijer, P. H. E., "Group Theory and Crystal Field Theory," in F. Seitz and D. Turnbull, eds., *Solid State Physics*, Vol. 12, Academic Press, New York, 1961.
4. Johnson, D. F., "Group Theory in Solid State Physics," *Reports on Progress In Physics*, **23**, 66 (1960).
5. Koster, G. F., "Notes on Group Theory," Technical Report No. 8, Solid State and Molecular Theory Group, M.I.T. (1956) (unpublished).
6. ——, "Space Groups and their Representations," in F. Seitz and D. Turnbull, eds., *Solid State Physics*, Vol. 5, Academic Press, New York, 1957.
7. Lomont, J. S., *Applications of Finite Groups*, Academic Press, New York, 1959.
8. Prather, J. L., *Atomic Energy Levels in Crystals*, Monograph 19, National Bureau of Standards, Washington, D.C., 1961.
9. Sokolov, A. V., and Shirokovski, V. P., "Group Theoretical Methods in the Quantum Physics of Solids (Spatial Symmetry)," *Soviet Physics—Uspekhi*, **3**, 551 (1961).
10. Van der Waerden, B. L., *Die Gruppentheoretische Methode in der Quantenmechanik*, Julius Springer, Berlin, 1932.
11. Weyl, H., *The Theory of Groups and Quantum Mechanics*, Dover Press, New York, 1931.
12. Wigner, E. P., *Group Theory and its Application to the Quantum Mechanics of Atomic Spectra*, Academic Press, New York, 1959.
13. Eyring, H., Walter, J., and Kimball, G. E., *Quantum Chemistry*, John Wiley and Sons, Inc., New York, 1944.
14. Landau, L. D., and Lifshitz, E. M., *Quantum Mechanics, Non-Relativistic Theory*, Addison-Wesley Publishing Co., Reading, Mass., 1958.
15. Eckart, C., "The Application of Group Theory to the Dynamics of Monatomic Systems," *Rev. Mod. Phys.*, **2**, 304 (1930).
16. Margenau, H., and Murphy, G. M., *The Mathematics of Physics and Chemistry*, 2nd Ed., D. Van Nostrand Company, Inc., Princeton, N.J., 1956.

INDEX